THE INVERTEBRATES:

Smaller Coelomate Groups

McGraw-Hill Publications in the Zoological Sciences

E. J. Boell, CONSULTING EDITOR

There are also the related series of McGraw-Hill Publications in the Botanical Sciences' of which Edmund W. Sinnott is Consulting Editor, and in the Agricultural Sciences' of which R. A. Brink is Consulting Editor.

THE INVERTEBRATES:

Smaller Coelomate Groups

Chaetognatha, Hemichordata, Pogonophora
Phoronida, Ectoprocta, Brachiopoda
Sipunculida
The coelomate Bilateria

VOLUME V

LIBBIE HENRIETTA HYMAN

American Museum of Natural History
New York

New York   London   Toronto

McGRAW-HILL BOOK COMPANY, INC.

1959

THE INVERTEBRATES: SMALLER COELOMATE GROUPS

IV

31664

THE MAPLE PRESS COMPANY, YORK, PA.

PREFACE

This volume completes the consideration of the smaller coelomate phyla except Echiurida, which will be considered with Annelida. There then remain three major groups: Mollusca, Annelida, and Arthropoda (broad sense). Volume VI will cover the Mollusca, Volume VII will treat the Annelida, and the Arthropoda would be expected to begin with Volume VIII. However, what with advancing age and unsatisfactory health I do not now expect to deal with the Arthropoda. I do hope to complete Volumes VI and VII and shall make every effort to do so.

The present volume, covering a number of disparate groups, was a laborious task. Especially the Ectoprocta proved exceptionally difficult. Here I gratefully acknowledge expert information from Dr. Mary Rogick, Dr. John Soule, and Prof. Ernst Marcus. To receive direct instruction in the Ectoprocta I spent some time at São Paulo, Brazil, where Professor and Mrs. Marcus showed me unlimited kindness and consideration; but unfortunately illness prevented me from taking advantage of the situation. Dr. G. A. Cooper and Dr. F. G. Stehli have kindly answered inquiries about brachiopods and the latter generously sent preserved specimens of a number of species of brachiopods. Photographs and illustrations kindly provided by others are acknowledged in the legends. Otherwise all illustrations except those reproduced by photography are my own handiwork.

As in the previous volumes the material of this volume is compiled from the literature by the perusal of a vast number of original articles. The great resources of the library of the American Museum of Natural History and the unfailing spirit of helpfulness of its librarians enable an exhaustive study of the literature. I am indebted to William Tavolga for generously translating some Russian articles.

The final chapter, Retrospect, grew out of an address I gave at the scientific meetings at Storrs, Connecticut, in August, 1955. It grew rather longer than I anticipated and even then gives only a fragmentary picture of advances since the publication of the earlier volumes.

I continue to be grateful to the many colleagues who constantly encourage me to persist in this difficult task.

Libbie Henrietta Hyman

CONTENTS

CHAPTER XVI

THE ENTEROCOELOUS COELOMATES—
PHYLUM CHAETOGNATHA

I. HISTORICAL

An extensive account of the history of the phylum is given by Kuhl (1938), according to which the first record of the finding of an arrowworm is that of Slabber (1769), who captured one in the fall of 1768 off the Dutch coast. Slabber gave two figures of the creature, which he called *zee-worm* (sea worm) or *Sagitta* or *pyl* (arrow), and assigned it to Linnaeus's group Intestina, an order of Vermes, but was unable to place it further, recognizing it as distinct from previously known "worms." Two figures of a *Sagitta* appear in a work on whale fishing by Scoresby (1820) on a plate illustrative of the food of whales, but no name is applied to the figures, nor are they mentioned in the text. Quoy and Gaimard (1827) captured some *Sagitta* during a collecting expedition to the Straits of Gibraltar in May, 1826, and gave a brief description without figures, also expressing uncertainty as to the systematic position of the animal. Thereafter, throughout the nineteenth century, numerous articles appeared dealing with the anatomy, embryology, and systematic position of *Sagitta*, including a publication by Darwin in 1844. Darwin begins his article by saying that the species of *Sagitta* are "remarkable for obscurity of their affinities." He found them in abundance in the North Atlantic and off the coasts of Brazil, Argentina, and Chile. He was the first to describe correctly the grasping spines and their action; he also noticed the small teeth near the mouth. In the same year (1844) Wilms published a thesis on *Sagitta* and Krohn gave the best account to date of the anatomy and gametogenesis. Krohn discussed the difficulty of placing *Sagitta* systematically and leaned toward an annelid affinity, opposing the view of molluscan affinity of some of his predecessors. T. H. Huxley (1851) discussed briefly the systematic position of *Sagitta*, rejecting the idea of molluscan affinity and leaning toward relationship with certain arthropods. Gegenbaur (1853) gave a brief report on the embryology of *Sagitta*, which he declared shows not the slightest resemblance to molluscan development, but declined to offer an opinion of the systematic position of the animal. Leuckart (1854), reporting on invertebrate literature for 1848 to 1853, remarked that it had become usual to assign *Sagitta* to the Vermes but in view of the difficulty of allocating it more exactly he proposed to regard the genus as constituting a separate group, Chaetognathi, placed between nematodes and oligochaetes. Gegenbaur (1858), as a result of further study of the embryology, concurred in Leuckart's view, and in 1859 in his famous textbook *Grundzüge der vergleichenden Anatomie* he created for *Sagitta* a class Oestelhelminthes, placed between Nemathelminthes and Annulata, all under Vermes. In later editions (1870, 1874) of this book, Gegenbaur dropped his name Oestelhelminthes and replaced it with Leuckart's name Chaetognathi, while retaining the group in the same systematic position as before. In 1866, A. Schneider allied the chaetognaths with the nematodes in the phylum Nemathelminthes in consequence of his finding certain similarities between the two groups in the arrangement of the body-wall musculature. This view was supported by Metschnikov (1867), who purported to find great sim.-

1

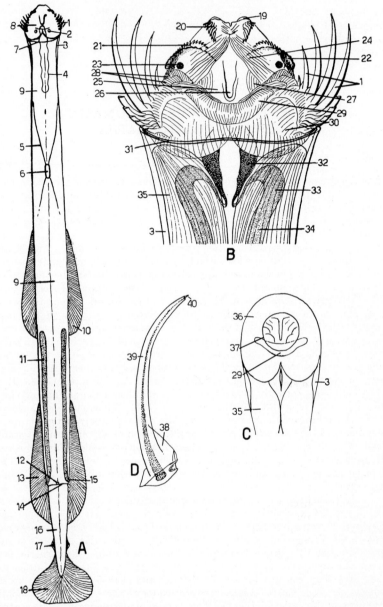

Fig. 1.—External features. *A, Sagitta elegans*, ventral view. *B, Sagitta elegans*, ventral view of anterior end. (*A, B, after Ritter-Zahony*, 1911a.) *C*, ventral view of anterior end of *Sagitta*, showing hood drawn over head (*after Ritter-Zahony*, 1909a). *D*, one of the grasping spines (*after Burfield*, 1927). 1, grasping spines; 2, eyes; 3, collarette; 4, ciliary loop; 5, circumenteric connectives; 6, subenteric ganglion; 7, head-trunk partition; 8, head; 9, trunk; 10, anterior lateral fins; 11, ovary; 12, anus; 13, posterior lateral fins; 14, trunk-tail partition; 15, female gonopores; 16, tail; 17, seminal receptacles; 18, tail fin;

larity between *Sagitta* and the curious draconematid and epsilonematid marine nematodes (III, pages 281–285); he considered the adhesive bristles of the head of these nematodes to correspond to the grasping spines of *Sagitta* and the stilt bristles to the fins of the latter. The alliance of the chaetognaths with the nematodes in a phylum Nemathelminthes has remained extant in textbooks to recent times.

From 1870 onward, more important and extensive studies on the chaetognaths, especially their embryology, were undertaken, primarily with the goal of solving their affinities. Kowalevsky (1871) reported on the development of *Sagitta* and correctly described gastrulation and formation of the definitive mouth and coelomic sacs but was unable to decide between molluscan and vermian affinity. Bütschli (1873) confirmed in the main Kowalevsky's findings and added new information concerning the development of the gonads. The well-known monograph on the chaetognaths by O. Hertwig (1880) gave an excellent account of the anatomy and histology based on original researches and considerably expanded knowledge of the embryology. The question of chaetognath affinity was discussed by Hertwig from the standpoint of the germ-layer theory. Previous opinion was accepted that, as regards anatomical construction, the chaetognaths most nearly resemble nematodes (gordiaceans) and annelids (especially *Polygordius*), but final conclusions as to relationship must be decided on embryological grounds, especially the mode of origin of the coelom, whether enterocoelous or schizocoelous. A few years later there appeared another monograph on the chaetognaths (Grassi, 1883) as part of the *Fauna and Flora of the Gulf of Naples* series. Grassi also had as his goal determination of the systematic position of the group. After recounting the anatomy, histology, and embryology of the chaetognaths, Grassi gave a careful critical comparison with other metazoan groups and concluded that it is impossible to ally the chaetognaths with any of the latter. Grassi was aware that the chaetognaths have in common with brachiopods, echinoderms, and hemichordates the enterocoelous method of origin of coelom and mesoderm but regarded anatomical differences between chaetognaths and these groups as insuperable obstacles to any postulation of affinity. Later works on the embryology are those of Doncaster (1902a), who opposed the idea of molluscan affinity, and Burfield (1927), who, like Grassi, made anatomical comparisons of the chaetognaths with other main invertebrate groups and found no adequate grounds for aligning the former with any of the latter. Burfield was inclined to accept the theory of MacBride (1914) that the chaetognaths are relatively unmodified offshoots of a primitive protocoelomate stock from which all coelomate animals derive.

Meantime anatomical studies with accompanying phylogenetic speculations continued to appear. Gourret (1884) in his monograph of *Spadella* designated the chaetognaths as oligomeric annelids, related to Gephyrea and primitive mollusks, in which the mesoderm had failed to develop as fully as in typical annelids. Günther (1907, 1908) came out strongly for a molluscan affinity; this with equal vigor was denied by Thiele (1907), a specialist on the Mollusca. In his well-known *Vorlesungen über vergleichende Anatomie* (Lectures on Comparative Anatomy) Bütschli (1910) proposed the division of the phylum Vermes into three groups: Amera, corresponding to the acoelomate and pseudocoelomate Bilateria; Polymera, equivalent to Annelida; and Oligomera, comprising groups with two or three coelomic divisions, including the chaetognaths. Bütschli's scheme is followed in the Kükenthal-Krumbach *Handbuch*

19, anterior ends of lateral plates; 20, anterior teeth; 21, posterior teeth; 22, vestibular ridge; 23, vestibular pit; 24, constrictor oris primus; 25, vestibule; 26, mouth; 27, constrictor oris alter; 28, vestibular dilators; 29, bicornuate muscle; 30, lateral complex muscle; 31, line of ventral hood attachment; 32, pharynx bulb; 33, intestinal diverticula; 34, intestine; 35, ventrolateral longitudinal muscle band of trunk; 36, hood; 37, opening left on hood closure; 38, base of spine; 39, shaft of spine; 40, tip of spine.

der Zoologie in which the chaetognaths form a branch (cladus) under the subphylum Oligomera, which also includes Phoronida, Ectoprocta, Brachiopoda, and Branchiotremata. The artificiality of this arrangement is so obvious that it is difficult to understand its adoption by a work of such authority. On the other hand, in the leading German textbook of zoology, the Claus-Grobben-Kühn *Lehrbuch der Zoologie*, the chaetognaths are made an independent branch (cladus) under the phylum Deuterostomia. This viewpoint is similar to that adopted in the present treatise. However, the systematic position and relationships of the chaetognaths, discussed further at the end of this chapter, remain problematical to this day.

The best account of the chaetognaths is that of Kuhl (1938) in Bronn's *Klassen und Ordnungen des Tierreichs.* Other valuable works on the anatomy are the monograph on *Sagitta* by Burfield (1927), Kuhl's (1928) account of the chaetognaths in *Die Tierwelt der Nord- und Ostsee*, and articles by Ritter-Zahony (1909–1911), Kuhl (1929, 1932), and John (1931, 1933). As the chaetognaths are among the most common of planktonic animals, large numbers of them are regularly taken on marine collecting expeditions, and numerous accounts of them have been published in the reports of such expeditions, but these accounts are mostly of a distributional and taxonomic nature.

The phylum is here termed Chaetognatha after Leuckart (1854). The original spelling Chaetognathi is not infrequently employed, but it is usual to alter the spelling to Chaetognatha. There are at the present writing about 50 described species, most of which belong to the genus *Sagitta;* several other genera are recognized. No category higher than genus has been proposed.

II. CHARACTERS OF THE PHYLUM

1. Definition.—The Chaetognatha are small, bilaterally symmetrical enterocoelous marine animals, of mostly planktonic habits, without circulatory or excretory systems and with a slender, transparent torpedo-shaped body, provided with one or two pairs of lateral horizontal fins, and terminating anteriorly in a rounded head armed on each side with a group of grasping spines, posteriorly in a horizontal tail fin.

2. General Characters.—The chaetognaths, or arrowworms, are coelomate animals of relatively small size, with a straight, slender, transparent body displaying perfect bilateral symmetry (Fig. 1). Most conspicuous of the external features are the fins, paired lateral and single caudal thin horizontal extensions supported by rays and serving for flotation and equilibration rather than for locomotion. The anterior end forms a well-delimited head bearing a pair of eyes and on either side the characteristic grasping spines, hard curved spines used in seizing prey and operated by a complex musculature inside the head. The head is also typically armed with arcs of small spines anterior to the mouth. A feature peculiar to the phylum is a fold of body wall that can be drawn over the dorsal and lateral surfaces of the head like a hood. The nervous system consists of ganglia in the head connected by a pair of circumenteric commissures with a large ventral trunk ganglion. The digestive system is a straight tube extending from the mouth located ventrally on the head to the anus found somewhat anterior to the tail fin. Between body wall

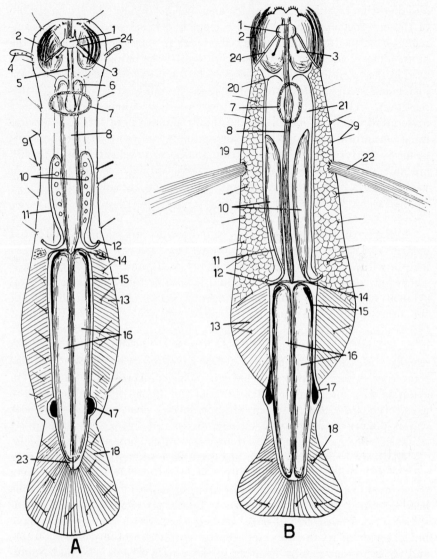

Fig. 2.—Types of chaetognaths. *A, Spadella,* dorsal. *B, Pterosagitta,* dorsal. (*Both after Hertwig,* 1880.) 1, cerebral ganglion; 2, grasping spines; 3, eyes; 4, tentacles; 5, pharynx; 6, intestinal diverticula; 7, ciliary loop; 8, intestine; 9, tangoreceptive bristles; 10, ovaries; 11, oviduct; 12, female gonopores; 13, lateral fins; 14, trunk-tail septum; 15, sperm ducts; 16, testes; 17, seminal receptacles; 18, tail fin; 19, collarette; 20, head-trunk septum; 21, trunk coelom; 22, large tuft of bristles; 23, tail coelom; 24, circumenteric connective.

and digestive tract is found a space usually considered to be a true coelom of the enterocoelous type. This coelom is divided into three compartments by a partition just behind the head and another just behind the anus. The chaetognaths are hermaphroditic; the paired ovaries are situated in the trunk immediately anterior to the postanal coelomic partition just mentioned, and the two testes lie in the tail region posterior to this partition. The eggs are shed free into the sea or attached to objects and undergo direct development of the indeterminate type into a nonswimming vermiform creature that scarcely differs sufficiently from the adult to merit the term larva. The Chaetognatha are exclusively marine and are among the most common of planktonic animals, often occurring in vast numbers in both littoral waters and the open ocean.

III. ANATOMY AND EMBRYOLOGY

1. External Characters.—The chaetognaths are slender, elongated creatures of relatively small size, ranging from a few to over 100 mm. in length, with most members measuring below 40 mm. The body form is somewhat suggestive of a torpedo and is notable for its marked bilateral symmetry (Fig. 1*A*). The common genus *Sagitta* (Fig. 1*A*) and some of the other genera are long and slender, whereas *Spadella* (Fig. 2*A*), *Pterosagitta* (Fig. 2*B*), and *Bathyspadella* (Fig. 15*A*) are somewhat broader in proportion to their length than is *Sagitta*. The chaetognath body is usually stiff, turgid, and capable of but a slight amount of bending, but some species are more or less flaccid. The epipelagic chaetognaths, in common with many other inhabitants of the upper strata of the sea, are usually colorless and transparent, but species characteristic of deeper waters may present the pink, orange, or red tints often seen in deep-sea animals. Parts of the reproductive system often show as denser objects.

The body is regionated into head, trunk, and tail. The rounded or somewhat triangular head is usually well demarcated from the trunk by a constricted neck region as well as by an internal coelomic partition. The head is armed anteriorly with two or four short rows of small teeth or spines termed *anterior* and *posterior teeth* (Fig. 1*B*). Some species have but one pair of tooth rows, apparently representing the posterior teeth, and teeth are completely wanting in the genera *Krohnittella* and *Bathyspadella*. The number of teeth in these rows varies with the species and within each species and increases with age up to sexual maturity, after which senile loss may occur. The anterior teeth consist of a short row of spines, mostly 3 to 10 in number, located to either side of the anterior tip (Fig. 1*B*). The usually larger and more numerous posterior teeth, numbering up to 30 or more, form a pair of rows curving from dorsal to ventral surface of the head, to either side of the vestibule (Fig. 1*B*). The teeth assist in the capture of prey. On the ventral surface of the head,

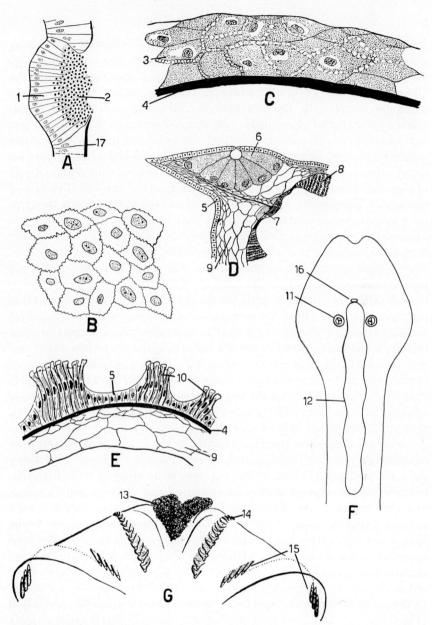

FIG. 3.—Epidermal structures. A, section through the vestibular pit showing glandular epidermis. B, surface view of the epidermis of *Sagitta*. C, section through the collarette of *Sagitta*, showing stratified epithelium. D, mucous gland of *Spadella*. E, adhesive cells of ventral tail epidermis. (D, E, after John, 1933.) F, anterior end of *Sagitta elegans* showing the ciliary loop. (A, B, C, F, after Burfield, 1927.) G, anterior end of *Heterokrohnia mirabilis*, showing mucous reservoir (after Ritter-Zahony, 1911c). 1, vestibular pit; 2, granules of gland cells; 3, cells of collarette; 4, basement membrane; 5, epidermis; 6, mucous gland; 7, nerve; 8, body-wall musculature; 9, mesenchyme; 10, adhesive cells; 11, eyes; 12, ciliary loop; 13, mucous reservoir; 14, anterior teeth; 15, posterior teeth; 16, pore of retrocerebral organ; 17, cuticle.

just behind the posterior teeth, is found a pair of *vestibular organs*, consisting of a transverse row of papillae, or more often of a transverse ridge bearing papillae (Fig. 1*B*), or sometimes simply of a ridge or cushion. Close behind the vestibular organ is found in many chaetognaths a glandular depression, the *vestibular pit*, represented in some species merely by scattered gland cells. At about the center of the dorsal surface of the head, immediately behind the brain, occurs the pore of the *retrocerebral organ* (Fig. 3*F*). In many chaetognaths, the *ciliary loop* (see later) extends onto the posterior part of the head up to this pore. A pair of pigmented eyes is present on the posterior part of the dorsal surface of the head. The central part of the ventral surface of the head is occupied by a large depression termed *vestibule* that leads into the mouth. The sides of the posterior part of the head are occupied by the characteristic food-catching apparatus of the chaetognaths, an arc or chevron-shaped row of hard curved spines, variously called *grasping spines, prehensile spines, seizing jaws*, and similar names. The number of grasping spines in each lateral group varies with the species and within the species, ranging from 4 to 14. Each spine consists of a broadened base to which muscles attach, a curved shaft that is generally wedge-shaped in cross section, widening toward the convex surface, and a tip or point that sets into the shaft end as in a socket (Fig. 1*D*). The powerful muscles that operate the grasping apparatus thicken the posterior part of the head so that when viewed in profile the head is seen to slant obliquely downward toward the neck (Fig. 4*A*). In seizing prey, the spines are spread apart, then suddenly closed inward upon the victim.

A unique feature of the chaetognaths is the *hood*, a fold of body wall containing a coelomic space, that can be drawn over the head. Ventrally the hood is attached about at the junction of head and trunk (Fig. 1*B*); dorsally the attachment curves behind the bases of the grasping spines and then extends forward lateral to the eyes and brain almost to the anterior tip (Fig. 5*D*). When withdrawn, the hood therefore leaves the spines and teeth free, but it can be extended to cover the entire head except for a small area in line with the vestibule (Fig. 1*C*). This strange structure seems to function to protect the food-catching apparatus when not in use and to reduce the resistance of the head in forward swimming. In the genus *Spadella* the hood bears on each side a tentaclelike projection (Fig. 2*A*).

The trunk is more or less slender and slightly fusiform, broadening toward the middle or toward the tail region. It is definitely delimited from the head by the head-trunk septum as well as by the slightly narrowed neck. In most chaetognaths, the epidermis on both sides of this neck region is obviously thickened, forming the *collarette*, composed of a stratified epidermis of large bladdery cells (Fig. 3*C*). The collarette may

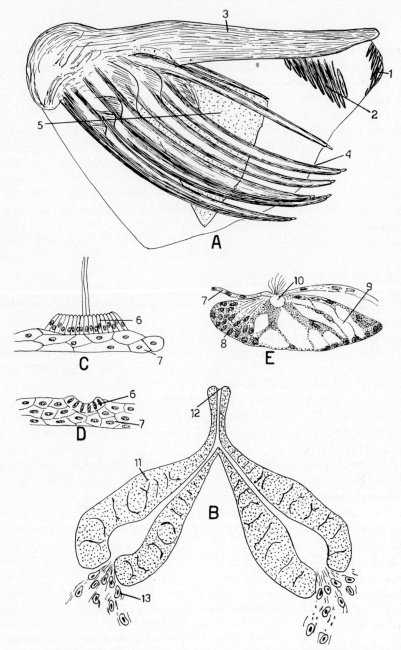

Fig. 4.—Epidermal structures (continued). *A*, side view of the head of *Sagitta*, to show spines and skeletal plates (*after Kuhl*, 1932). *B*, retrocerebral organ of *Sagitta* (*after John*, 1931). *C*, section through the ciliary loop of *Sagitta hexaptera* (*after Hertwig*, 1880). *D*, section through the ciliary loop of *Sagitta enflata* (*after Grassi*, 1883). *E*, section through the ciliary loop of *Spadella cephaloptera* (*after Reisinger*, 1934).   1, anterior teeth; 2, posterior teeth; 3, lateral plate; 4, grasping spines; 5, ventral plate; 6, cells of ciliary loop; 7, epidermis; 8, flagellated cells; 9, gland cells; 10, ring canal; 11, retrocerebral sacs; 12, pore of retrocerebral organ; 13, ganglion cells.

9

extend for some distance along the trunk, and in *Pterosagitta draco* (Fig. 2*B*) the very thick and conspicuous collarette borders both sides of the trunk, finally merging with the lateral fins. Ghirardelli (1950a) described and figured a Mediterranean specimen of *Pterosagitta draco* in which the entire surface of the trunk (not just the sides) and lateral fins was covered with the collarette. In *Bathyspadella* also the collarette extends along the body sides from the neck to the tail fin (Tokioka, 1939b).

The trunk is not definitely demarcated externally from the tail, but a coelomic partition located immediately behind the anus forms the accepted boundary, or in other words the tail is the postanal region as in nematodes. The trunk-tail region is provided with lateral fins, two pairs in *Sagitta, Zahonya,* and some species of *Spadella,* one pair in other chaetognaths (Figs. 13, 14, 18, 19). The position of the lateral fins is unrelated to the trunk-tail regionation, and in fact these fins usually overlap the trunk-tail boundary (Figs. 18, 19). The fins are thin, transparent horizontal epidermal extensions, supported by a double set of delicate fin rays, dorsal and ventral. The fins are generally of somewhat triangular shape but vary in length, form, and body position in different chaetognaths. The tail fin, similar to the lateral fin in structure, is a thin horizontal expansion embracing the posterior end of the body. As the fins contain no muscle fibers they are incapable of swimming movements and act as floating and equilibratory aids.

The body is usually beset with tangoreceptors in the form of pencils of bristles mounted on small eminences. *Pterosagitta draco* has a pair of especially large and long tufts of bristles at about the middle of the trunk region (Fig. 2*B*).

The female gonopores are a pair of small pores situated just anterior to the trunk-tail septum. The seminal vesicles form conspicuous bulges of varying shape located laterally between the lateral and tail fins (Figs. 18, 19). They were formerly considered to open externally by permanent male pores, but recent opinion indicates that such openings are temporary ruptures.

2. Body Wall.—The body is clothed with an extremely thin cuticle, thickened on the sides of the anterior part of the head and wall of the vestibule and wanting on glandular areas. It is secreted by the underlying epidermis, which over most of the body is a low one-layered epithelium with wavy outlines (Fig. 3*B*). The epidermal cells alter to a tall prismatic form on the ventral surface of the head, on the vestibular organ, and in the vestibular lining. In some body regions, especially the dorsal surface of the head and the collarette, the epidermis is stratified and then consists of large bladdery cells (Fig. 3*C*).

In a few areas the epidermis is glandular, then lacking a cuticle. The hood lining consists of a glandular epidermis of the cyanophilous type,

and the vestibular pits are formed of tall, glandular epidermis, also producing a cyanophilous secretion (Fig. 3*A*). In the genera *Eukrohnia* and
Heterokrohnia there are two glandular tracts on the head along the lines of
attachment of the hood that converge to a large glandular reservoir at
the tip of the head (Fig. 3*G*). *Bathyspadella* has a pair of glandular
canals in the neck region. Glandular structures have been described by
John (1933) for *Spadella* that appear to be absent in *Sagitta*. Along the
sides of the tail of *Spadella*, above the level of the tail fin, are found four
parallel rows of mucous glands, lying beneath the epidermis, which is
pierced by their apertures. Each aperture leads into a small cavity to
which the tips of the conical gland cells converge (Fig. 3*D*) and into which
they pour their secretion. In *Spadella* also each female gonopore is
encircled by a large cement gland, consisting of low narrow cylindrical
cells that secrete cement material for fastening the eggs to objects (Fig.
11*A*).

Of uncertain function but possibly glandular is the *retrocerebral organ*
(Kuhl, 1929; John, 1931). This typically consists of a pair of sacs
imbedded in the posterior part of the cerebral ganglion but definitely
separated from the nervous tissue by a membrane. Histologically the
sacs consist of a granular material marked off by partitions into follicles
(Fig. 4*B*), but as nuclei are few or wanting, the cellular nature of the
follicles remains problematical. The narrow lumina of the two sacs
converge dorsally and unite to a common duct that opens behind the
brain by the retrocerebral pore already mentioned. At its inner end each
sac is entered by the processes of a cluster of ganglion cells. In *Spadella*,
according to John (1933), the sacs are reduced to small cell clusters but
the external pore is prominent and bounded by large, deeply staining
cells. The identity of name should not be taken to imply any homology
with the retrocerebral organ of rotifers.

The members of the genus *Spadella*, unlike most other chaetognaths,
have benthonic habits and cling to objects by means of adhesive papillae.
In *Spadella cephaloptera* (John, 1933) these are epidermal projections
located on the ventral surface of the tail and composed of 6 to 10 modified
epidermal cells that are much taller than their fellows and have swollen
tips that act as suckers (Fig. 3*E*). In some other species of *Spadella*
(Mawson, 1944), the adhesive papillae (which have not been figured
histologically) are borne on a number of fingerlike projections situated
just behind the posterior pair of lateral fins (Fig. 13*C*, *D*) and operated by
special muscles.

The hardened structures of the head, including the teeth and grasping
spines and the lateral and ventral plates, are epidermal productions.
The grasping spines are composed of chitin (Hyman, 1958), but this
seems not to be the case with the other epidermal hardenings. The teeth

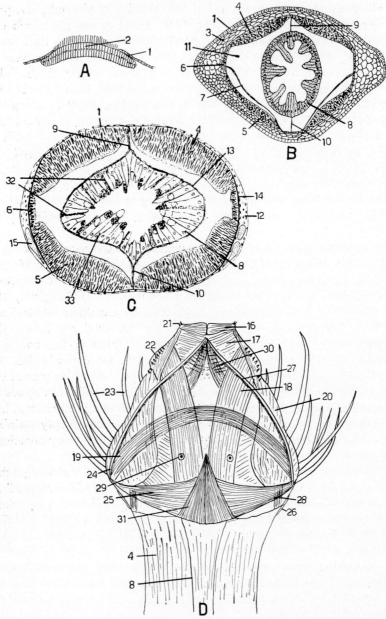

Fig. 5.—Ciliary loop, musculature. *A*, section through the ciliary loop of *Spadella.*
B, section through the trunk of *Spadella.* (*A*, *B*, *after John*, 1933.) *C*, section through the
trunk of *Sagitta.* *D*, dorsal view of head of *Sagitta*, to show head musculature. (*C*, *D*,
after Burfield, 1927.) 1, epidermis; 2, ciliary loop; 3, loose mesenchyme; 4, dorsolateral
longitudinal muscle band; 5, ventrolateral longitudinal muscle band; 6, lateral muscle
band; 7, transverse muscle band; 8, intestine; 9, dorsal mesentery; 10, ventral mesentery;

and spines are secreted by tall epidermal cells at their bases, and these cells extend into their hollow interiors as pulp. The lateral and ventral head plates are stiffenings between the cuticle proper and the epidermis. The lateral plates, acting to support the teeth and grasping spines and as attachment sites for muscles, extend from the anterior end of the head backward along its sides, widening posteriorly (Fig. 4A). The ventral plates, less differentiated than the lateral plates, are somewhat triangular pieces serving for muscle attachment that lie in the sides of the posterior part of the head (Fig. 4A).

The *ciliary loop*, or *corona ciliata*, a structure peculiar to chaetognaths, is a dorsal strip of altered epidermis in the form of a long or short oval, with simple or sinuous contour, that is usually oriented with its long axis parallel to the body axis (Fig. 1A) but is sometimes transverse as in *Spadella* (Fig. 2A). The anterior end of the ciliary loop usually lies immediately behind the retrocerebral pore (Fig. 3F), and the loop extends posteriorly from there to various levels, as far as the neck region or often well back on the trunk. However, in some chaetognaths the ciliary loop is confined to the anterior part of the trunk. The histological construction of the ciliary loop appears to vary considerably in different chaetognaths; at least, divergent descriptions are furnished by different authors. According to Hertwig (1880), the ciliary loop of *Sagitta hexaptera* consists of a strip of tall columnar cells resting upon the regular epidermis, hence forming a ridge, with the central two or three rows of cells provided with long delicate cilia (Fig. 4C). For *Sagitta enflata* Grassi (1883) described the epidermal strip as curved, concave toward the exterior, somewhat sunk into the epidermis, and ciliated along the sides only (Fig. 4D). Burfield (1927), using *Sagitta elegans*, states that in a surface view of stained preparations, the ciliary loop appears double, consisting of two concentric ovals, each three or four cells wide, and both fully ciliated; but in his series of drawings of cross sections, the ciliary loop is depicted simply as a ridge of columnar epidermis. John in his study of *Spadella cephaloptera* (1933) finds the ciliary loop to consist of a strip of columnar ciliated epidermis five or six cells wide, insunk so that the bases of the cilia are flush with the surface (Fig. 5A). But Reisinger in the same species (1934) ascribes an elaborate structure to the ciliary loop. According to his account, adopted by Kuhl (1938), the loop of *Spadella* is an insunk strip of epidermis many cells wide, differentiated

---

11, coelom; 12, stratified epidermis; 13, muscle layer of intestine; 14, basement membrane; 15, circumenteric commissure; 16, obliquus capitis brevis; 17, expansus superior; 18, obliquus capitis longus; 19, hood retractor; 20, spine adductor; 21, anterior teeth; 22, posterior teeth; 23, grasping spines; 24, line of hood attachment; 25, transversus dorsalis; 26, collarette; 27, hood protractor; 28, rectus colli externus; 29, eye; 30, constrictor oris primus; 31, obliquus superficialis; 32, glandular cells of intestine; 33, absorptive cells of intestine.

into an inner zone of gland cells devoid of cilia and an outer zone of tall flagellated cells (Fig. 4E).   The glandular cells take up both acid and basic dyes and eject them into a ring canal located at the periphery of the glandular zone.   Whereas most authors incline to the opinion that the ciliary loop is a sense organ, Reisinger concludes from his experiments with vital dyes that it is a primitive nephridium.   Although the dye experiments may indicate an excretory function for the ciliary loop, they hardly justify Reisinger's conclusion that the loop is a phylogenetic precursor of the solenocytic protonephridium.   As the invertebrate Deuterostomia do not have protonephridia, this would mean that the chaetognaths are looking a long way forward to *Amphioxus!*

The epidermis rests upon a homogeneous basement or basal membrane, very thin over most of the body, thickened to form capsules for the eyes and at the sides of the neck region and sometimes also the adjacent trunk to form so-called *skeletal plates*.   In the head region the basement membrane is of some importance for muscle attachment, and this is also the main function of the skeletal plates.   The basement membrane is also thickened in the region of the fins, and the fin rays seem to be extensions of the membrane into the fins.

Beneath the basement membrane is found the body-wall musculature, of simple arrangement in trunk and tail, where, contrary to what one would expect in a coelomate animal, it consists of a longitudinal layer only and lacks a peritoneal membrane on its inner surface.   In *Spadella* there is a layer of loose mesenchymal tissue, shown by John (1933) to be of ectodermal origin, between the basement membrane and the muscle layer, but this is wanting in *Sagitta* and apparently also in other genera. The body-wall musculature of trunk and tail consists in general of four thick longitudinal bands, two dorsolateral and two ventrolateral (Fig. 5C). There may also be present a pair of small and thin lateral bands.   In some genera there also occurs to the inner side of the ventrolateral bands a thin transverse layer, whose presence is regarded as of considerable taxonomic importance.   This transverse layer is found throughout the trunk and tail in *Heterokrohnia* and *Zahonya*, throughout the trunk in *Spadella* (Fig. 5B), and only in the anterior part of the trunk in *Eukrohnia* and *Bathyspadella*.   Histologically the muscle fibers somewhat resemble those of nematodes, consisting of a fibrillar part next to the basement membrane and a protoplasmic part facing the body cavity.   The fibrillar part seems to consist of longitudinal fibrous plates, or lamellae, set at an oblique angle to each other and to the body surface so that each fiber presents a feathery appearance in cross section (Fig. 6A).   Both the arrangement of the body-wall musculature into longitudinal bands and the general histological structure of the muscle fibers are somewhat reminiscent of nematodes, and it may be recalled that A. Schneider

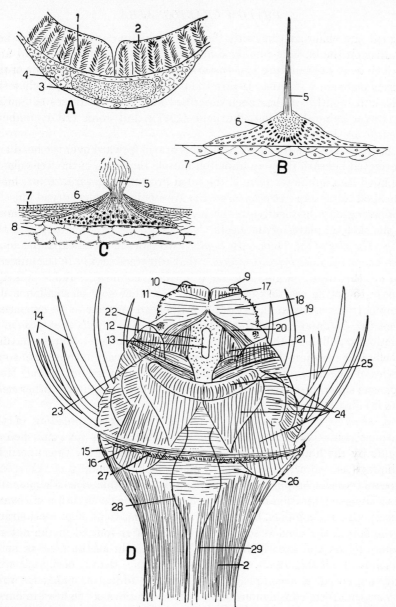

Fig. 6.—Musculature (continued), sense organs. *A*, section through the subenteric ganglion. *B*, tangoreceptor of *Sagitta*. *C*, tangoreceptor (ciliary pit) of *Spadella* (*after John*, 1933). *D*, ventral head musculature of *Sagitta*. (*A, B, D, after Burfield*, 1927.) 1, muscle feathers; 2, ventrolateral longitudinal muscle bands; 3, central granular mass of the subenteric ganglion; 4, ganglion cells of subenteric ganglion; 5, tangoreceptive bristles; 6, sensory hillock; 7, epidermis; 8, mesenchyme; 9, anterior ends of lateral plates; 10, anterior teeth; 11, posterior teeth; 12, vestibule; 13, mouth; 14, grasping spines; 15, collarette; 16, line of hood attachment; 17, obliquus capitis brevis; 18, expansus superior; 19, vestibular organ; 20, constrictor oris primus; 21, constrictor oris alter; 22, vestibular pit; 23, dilator vestibuli externus; 24, complexus lateralis; 25, bicornis; 26, transversus ventralis; 27, hood protractor; 28, pharynx bulb; 29, intestine.

15

aligned the chaetognaths with the nematodes in a phylum Nemathelminthes on the basis of muscle similarity.

The head musculature is necessarily far more complex than the trunk musculature since it must operate the teeth, grasping spines, hood, vestibule, and mouth. It has been described in detail for species of *Sagitta* by Ritter-Zahony (1909a), Burfield (1927), and John (1931) and for *Spadella* by John (1933).

a. Muscles of the Hood.—The hood is drawn forward over the head and contracted beneath it by an unpaired muscle that runs in the free edge of the hood as a sphincter termed the hood protractor (*protractor preputii*). The hood retractors (*retractor preputii*) are a pair of strong curved muscles originating on a connective-tissue layer beneath the brain and inserting on the skeletal plates of the neck.

b. Muscles of the Teeth.—In *Sagitta* two pairs of small expander muscles (*expansus superior* and *inferior*) that run transversely in the anterior end of the head, originating on a median connective-tissue lamella, appear to act as erectors of the teeth. Another pair of small muscles running transversely at the very tip of the head anterior to the expanders (Figs. 5D, 6D) and named short obliques (*obliquus capitis brevis*) seem to function to pull down the anterior teeth; they also originate on the median lamella just mentioned. Expansus inferior is not well developed in some species of *Sagitta*, and it and obliquus capitis brevis are not distinct from expansus superior in *Spadella*, according to John. No doubt other head muscles also act on the teeth.

c. Muscles of the Grasping Spines.—Prior to the spreading of the grasping spines the hood must be retracted; this is accomplished in *Sagitta* by the hood retractors and in *Spadella* mainly by the superficial obliques (see below), according to John. The spreading of the spines appears to be accomplished not so much by the action of particular muscles as by the alteration of head shape through the cooperation of several muscles (lateral complex, bicornuate). At the moment of greatest spread of the spines the head is seen to be somewhat shortened in the anteroposterior axis and greatly broadened transversely at the level of spine attachment (Kuhl, 1932). The closure of the spines, occurring with lightning speed, is accomplished by a pair of adductors (*adductor uncinorum*) that form conspicuous masses along the sides of the head in dorsal view (Fig. 5D). These adductors originate on the posterior parts of the lateral plates of the head and insert on the bases of the grasping spines.

d. General Dorsal Head Musculature.—A dorsal view of the head of *Sagitta* (Fig. 5D) shows the transverse fibers of the short oblique muscles at the very tip of the head followed by the similarly oriented teeth expanders. The central region of the head is occupied by the long oblique muscles (*obliquus capitis longus*) that insert on the anterior ends of the lateral plates and, converging toward the median line, run to their attachments at the posterior end of the head. They act to shorten the head in the anteroposterior direction. The curved hood retractors are seen above the middle portions of the long obliques. The sides of the head are occupied by the considerable masses of the spine adductors. At the rear of the head is noticed a median triangle formed by the two superficial oblique muscles (*obliquus superficialis*), and to either side of this triangle are revealed the transverse fibers of the dorsal transverse muscles (*transversus dorsalis*). The superficial obliques assist in drawing back the hood, and the dorsal transverse muscles, originating on the median lamella and inserting on the posterior ends of the lateral plates, act to pull these ends toward the median line, thus assisting in spreading the grasping spines. Finally, at the sides of the posterior end of the head are seen the dorsal ends of the external neck muscles (*rectus colli externus*), here inserted on the skeletal plates of the sides of the neck; their fibers run dorsoventrally to attach to the lateral plates, and they produce a nodding motion of the head.

e. Muscles of the Mouth and Vestibule.—Some of the muscles seen in ventral view of the head (Fig. 6D) are concerned with the opening and closing of the mouth and vestibule. The teeth expanders appear at the anterior end of the head in ventral view and directly behind them the mouth constrictors, consisting of one pair (*constrictor oris primus*) curving in front of the mouth and another pair (*constrictor oris alter*, wanting in *Spadella*) alongside the mouth opening. Of the three pairs of muscles that dilate the mouth and vestibule (*dilator vestibuli externus, dilator vestibuli internus*, and *dilator oris*, wanting in *Spadella*) only the external dilators are visible externally in ventral view; they lie lateral to the mouth constrictors. The others are to be seen in appropriate transverse sections of the head (Fig. 7B).

f. Other Ventral Muscles.—Running across the head directly behind the vestibule is the conspicuous unpaired bicornuate muscle (*bicornis*), having somewhat the shape of a sausage (Fig. 6D). This muscle is without firm attachments and seemingly acts to alter the shape of the head. The sides of the ventral surface of the posterior part of the head are made of the massive lateral complex muscles (*complexus lateralis*), consisting of several bundles. This muscle mass has dorsal attachments to the spine adductors and lateral attachments to the ventral plates but is free medially except for contacts with the bicornuate muscles which are somewhat imbedded in it. This relative freedom of the complexus lateralis enables it to alter markedly the shape of the head, not only by its expansions and contractions but also by its pull on other muscles. As already intimated, such changes of head shape are of importance in spreading the grasping spines and also no doubt in operating the teeth. Behind the

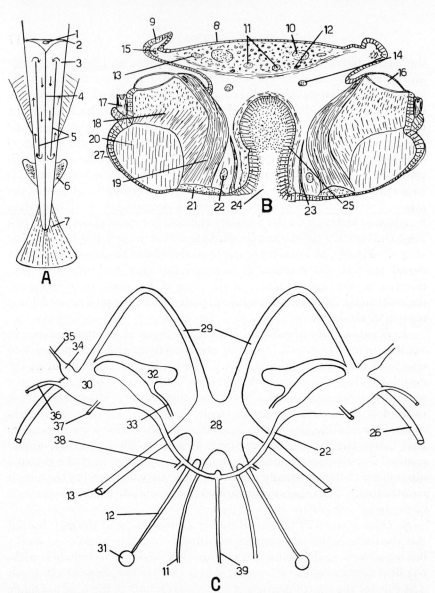

Fig. 7.—Coelom, musculature (concluded), nervous system. *A*, tail region of *Sagitta*, showing coelomic partitions and currents. *B*, section through the mouth level of *Sagitta*, showing nerves and muscles. (*A, B, after Burfield,* 1927.) *C*, main nervous system of *Sagitta*, ventral view (*after Ritter-Zahony,* 1909b). 1, anus; 2, trunk-tail septum; 3, tail coelom; 4, central coelomic partition of tail; 5, incomplete lateral partitions of tail coelom; 6, seminal vesicles; 7, tail fin; 8, epidermis; 9, hood; 10, retrocerebral glands; 11, coronal nerves; 12, optic nerves; 13, circumenteric connectives; 14, obliquus capitis longus; 15, hood protractor; 16, lateral plates; 17, base of grasping spine; 18, dilator vestibuli externus; 19, dilator vestibuli internus; 20, complexus lateralis; 21, constrictor oris alter; 22, sub-pharyngeal commissure; 23, dilator oris; 24, mouth; 25, granular epithelium of pharynx; 26, dorsal nerve; 27, ventral plate; 28, cerebral ganglion; 29, frontal commissure; 30, vestibular ganglion; 31, eye; 32, pharyngeal ganglion; 33, lateral pharyngeal nerve; 34, frontal ganglion; 35, frontal nerve; 36, mandibular nerve; 37, vestibular nerve; 38, labial nerve; 39, ventral pharyngeal nerve.

18

complexus lateralis on each side are seen the posterior ends of the hood protractors (Fig. 6D).

g. *Neck Muscles.*—Nodding movements of the head are controlled by two pairs of neck muscles, the *rectus colli externus* already mentioned and the *rectus colli internus*, located to the inner side of the former but concealed under the dorsal transverse. The internal neck muscle extends from the skeletal plates of the neck to the lateral plates. Situated in the ventral side of the neck is the unpaired ventral transverse muscle (*transversus ventralis*) whose transverse fibers attach to the body wall on either side.

All the body-wall muscles are cross-striated and are histologically similar in this respect to vertebrate muscles.

3. Coelom.—A true coelom is formed by the enterocoelous method during the embryonic stages of chaetognaths, but this is suppressed in the larva and it is impossible to say whether the definitive cavity that later reappears corresponds to the embryonic cavity or not. At any rate the definitive space between body wall and intestine and in the tail is not lined by a peritoneal membrane. The coelomic space of trunk and tail is subdivided as usual in coelomate animals into paired lateral compartments by a median dorsoventral double-walled partition, or mesentery, that in the trunk encloses the intestine between its two walls, forming dorsal and ventral mesenteries for the intestine (Fig. 5C). However, this mesentery also appears not to be composed of peritoneal membrane as is expected in a coelomate animal but, according to Burfield, is a continuation of the basement membrane of the body wall. The mesentery is clothed on each surface with a thin stratum of muscle fibers and contains some perforations so that the lateral compartments of the coelom are in communication. In *Sagitta*, the tail coelom is further subdivided into four compartments by incomplete lateral mesenteries parallel to the median mesentery (Fig. 7A), but this is not the case in *Spadella*. Trunk and tail coeloms are separated by a transverse partition passing behind the anus, but this partition is a secondary formation and cannot be regarded as indicative of primary coelomic divisions. The transverse partition between head and trunk does represent a primary coelomic subdivision, and hence the definitive coelom of chaetognaths consists of three spaces, the head cavity and the paired trunk-tail cavities. The head coelom is considerably reduced by the great development of the head musculature but may be seen in transverse sections to either side of the pharynx (Fig. 7B). It also extends into the hood. The head coelom, like the trunk-tail coelom, appears to lack a definite peritoneal lining. The trunk coeloms also extend into the head for a short distance up to the complexus lateralis muscles.

The coelom contains a colorless fluid in which float very minute spheres and granules, apparently not definite corpuscles.   This fluid circulates in both trunk and tail, moving forward along the inner surface of the body wall and backward along the median mesentery (Fig. 7*A*). The cilia causing this movement were first observed in life by A. Meyer (1927), who saw single, long, widely separated cilia on the inner surface of the trunk wall.   It is not clear what cellular elements that could bear cilia are present in this surface since it has been impossible to demonstrate a definite coelomic epithelium.

4. Nervous System.—The nervous system is fairly complicated, consisting of several ganglia, connecting commissures, and nerves.   The large *cerebral ganglion* forms the main nervous mass of the head, being a single quadrangular or oval body producing a bulge on the dorsal surface of the head just beneath the epidermis.   Anteriorly it gives off a pair of *frontal commissures* that arch outward and downward and enter the *vestibular ganglia* (Fig. 7*C*).   These are a pair of ganglionic masses situated at the sides of the mouth.   They are connected with each other by a *subpharyngeal commissure* passing ventral to the pharynx; hence the nervous system of the head of chaetognaths is a circumenteric ring as in nematodes (Fig. 7*C*).   From the sides of the cerebral ganglion spring the two *circumenteric connectives* that proceed obliquely backward to the *ventral*, or *subenteric, ganglion;* and more posteriorly there arise from the cerebral ganglion a pair of *optic* nerves to the eyes and, medial to these, a pair of *coronal* nerves to the ciliary loop (Fig. 7*C*).   The coronal nerves run posteriorly just beneath the basement membrane of the body wall and finally pierce this, to be distributed along the ciliary loop.   The optic nerves also lie just beneath the basement membrane, which, it will be recalled, forms capsules for the eyes.   Each optic nerve penetrates the anterior wall of this capsule and then divides into two nerves that encircle eye structures.   The vestibular ganglia are also the source of several nerves.   Just at its junction with the vestibular ganglion, each frontal commissure gives off medially a *pharyngeal* nerve; this presents a ganglionic enlargement, the *pharyngeal ganglion*, and then proceeds backward in the pharyngeal wall as the *lateral pharyngeal* nerve.   Anterolaterally the vestibular ganglia give off, in some cases by way of a small frontal ganglion, often indistinct, a *frontal* nerve to the posterior teeth; dorsally there spring from the vestibular ganglia the large *dorsal* nerves that run posteriorly under the lateral plates and appear to supply some of the head muscles.   The vestibular ganglia also give off some small nerves, of which the main ones, according to Burfield, are a pair of *mandibular* nerves to the grasping spines and a pair of *vestibular* nerves to the borders of the vestibule.   The ventral part of the subpharyngeal commissure is the source of a pair of very small *labial* nerves, each provided with a minute

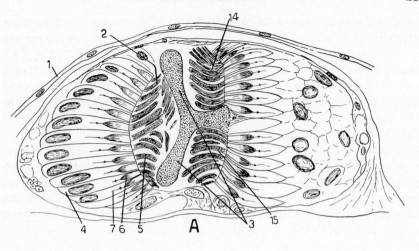

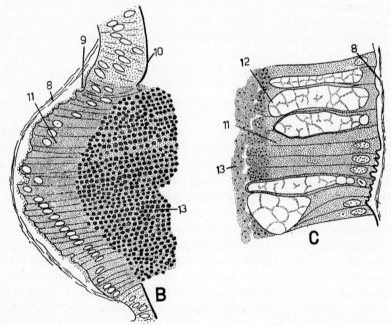

FIG. 8.—Sense organs (concluded), digestive tract. *A*, section through the eye of *Sagitta* (*after Hesse*, 1902). *B*, section through the beginning of the pharynx of *Sagitta*. *C*, section through the pharyngeal bulb of *Spadella*. (*B*, *C*, *after Parry*, 1944.) 1, epidermis; 2, large lateral ocellus; 3, common pigment cup for lateral and two median ocelli; 4, retinal cell; 5, retinal club of retinal cell; 6, refractive body; 7, neurofibril; 8, circular muscle; 9, longitudinal muscle; 10, cuticle; 11, granular cells; 12, vacuolated cells; 13, emitted secretion; 14, one of the upper median ocelli; 15, one of the lower median ocelli.

ganglion, and a midventral unpaired *ventral pharyngeal* nerve to the pharynx.

The circumenteric connectives run obliquely posteriorly and ventrally, at first in the outer wall of the hood, then between the epidermis and the basement membrane. They gradually attain the ventral side and enter the anterior end of the ventral or subenteric ganglion, a large oval mass situated midventrally in the epidermis of the anterior third of the trunk. This ganglion gives off laterally about 12 pairs of small nerves that run in the trunk wall at the base of the epidermis, branching to form a plexus in the sides and dorsal wall of the trunk From the posterior end of the subenteric ganglion arise two large posterior nerves that also branch into a plexus in the wall of the rear part of the trunk and the tail. There is thus an epidermal plexus throughout trunk and tail; it contains numerous ganglion cells and appears to innervate the trunk and tail muscles and tangoreceptors.

The main ganglia are composed of a central mass of fine fibrils, appearing as granules in sections, forming the *punktsubstanz* of German authors, and a peripheral layer of ganglion cells, not of uniform thickness (Fig. 6A). The ganglia are enclosed in a delicate membrane, probably composed of basement membrane.

5. Sense Organs.—There are generally present on the body of chaetognaths a number of bristles or tufts regarded as of tactile nature (Fig. 2). They are more or less arranged in longitudinal rows and may occur also on the fins and on the region enclosed by the ciliary loop. Burfield (1927) reports about 250 such tangoreceptors in *Sagitta elegans,* arranged in six or seven longitudinal rows. In *Sagitta* each tangoreceptor consists of an oval or circular hillock resting on the regular epidermis and composed of a number of elongated cells converging to a center from which springs a bristle made of a number of fine stiff hairs (Fig. 6B). A slightly different histology is seen in *Spadella* where the cluster of elongated cells is imbedded in the epidermis and the projecting hairs undulate like cilia (Fig. 6C) Hence the tangoreceptors of *Spadella* are termed ciliary pits by John (1933) and earlier workers; they are said by the former to be histologically identical with the ciliary loop. John has enumerated nearly 100 such organs on head, trunk, tail, and fins of *Spadella.* A pair of especially large tactile tufts occurs in *Pterosagitta* (Fig. 2B).

The ciliary loop is generally regarded as chemoreceptive, but direct evidence is wanting. In *Spadella* John (1933) found that small jets of water directed at a quiescent animal evoked a response only when aimed at the ciliary loop. According to Parry (1944), prey elicit a feeding response in *Spadella* only when above or behind the head. These observations indicate a tactile function for the loop, or at least the function of detecting water disturbances. John also noticed that during sperm transference pairing *Spadella* would often bring their loops in contact.

A pair of eyes occurs on the rear part of the head of chaetognaths just beneath the epidermis. Each is a rounded, dorsoventrally flattened body enclosed in a capsule penetrated anteriorly by the optic nerve. The investigations of Hesse (1902) and Burfield (1927) have revealed that the eye of *Sagitta* consists of five combined pigment-cup ocelli, one large lateral one and four small median ocelli arranged in two tiers of two each. Hence, transverse or frontal sections of the eyes usually show only three of the five ocelli. The pigment cups of the ocelli are in contact and partially fused in the central region of the eye so that the pigment presents a rayed figure, usually three-rayed (Fig. 8*A*). The cavity of each ocellus is filled with retinal cells that face the pigment cup; hence the ocelli are of the inverse type. Each retinal cell (Fig. 8*A*) is an elongated cell provided basally with a large oval nucleus and terminating distally in a retinal club or rod, marked with striations. Inside the retinal cell between the base of the retinal club and the nucleus is found a clear conical body, apparently of refractive nature, with base in close contact with the inner surface of the retinal club and pointed apex passing into a neurofibril bearing a minute enlargement. Presumably this neurofibril is continuous with the neurofibril proceeding from the base of the retinal cells, but it has not been possible to trace this continuity, nor to trace the basal fibril of the retinal cell into the optic nerve. The structure of the ocelli and retinal cells is very similar to that of the turbellarian eye.

6. Digestive System.—As already noted, the center of the ventral surface of the head is inturned as a vestibule lined by thickened cuticle and leading to the mouth. In the feeding of *Spadella* the mouth is projected forward by muscular action, eliminating the vestibule, which thus appears to owe its existence to the state of the head musculature (John, 1933). No comparable observations are available for *Sagitta*. The mouth, of oval or T-like shape, leads into a muscular tube, the pharynx, usually called esophagus. This expands posteriorly, forming a bulb (Fig. 1*B*). Parry (1944) has given a detailed account of the histology of the digestive tract of both *Sagitta* and *Spadella*, which is here followed. The lining epithelium of the pharynx consists of secretory granular cells at its two ends (Fig. 8*B*) and in between is composed chiefly of vacuolated cells, also of secretory nature, more or less interspersed with granular cells (Fig. 8*C*). *Sagitta* differs in that the lining of the pharyngeal bulb consists chiefly of still a third type of cell, the compound granular cell, in which much of the cell is filled with large granular masses (Fig. 9*A*). In general, the pharyngeal epithelium is tall and columnar dorsally and laterally, often low and cuboidal ventrally. Outside the epithelium is found the usual basement membrane and outside that a layer of longitudinal muscles,

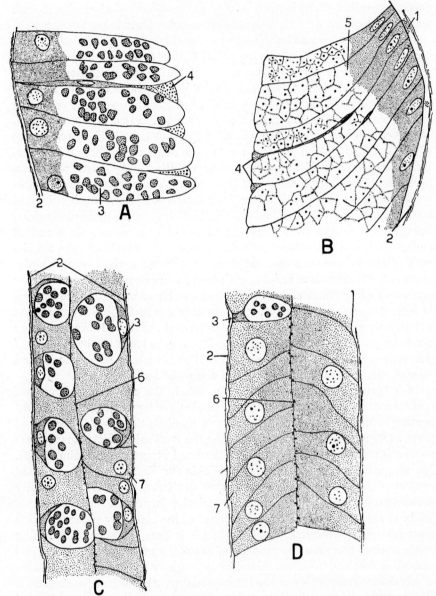

Fig. 9.—Histology of the digestive tract. *A*, section through the pharyngeal bulb
of *Sagitta*, showing compound granular cells. *B*, section through the pharynx of *Sagitta*,
showing vacuolated cells. *C*, longitudinal section through the anterior part of the intestine
of *Sagitta* with compound granular cells. *D*, longitudinal section through the posterior
part of the intestine of *Sagitta* with absorptive cells. (*All after Parry*, 1944.)   1, longitudinal muscles; 2, circular muscle layer; 3, compound granular cells; 4, granular cells;
5, vacuolated cells; 6, location of lumen; 7, absorptive cells.

well developed in *Sagitta* but poorly represented in *Spadella*. This layer encloses the lateral pharyngeal nerves (Fig. 7*B*) and ventrally is interrupted by the ventral pharyngeal nerve. Finally, the outer coat of the pharynx consists of a circular layer, attached dorsally to the superficial oblique muscles and ventrally to the ventral transverse. Laterally the pharynx is bounded by the head coelom, from which it is separated by a thin layer of connective tissue. Just behind the bulb the pharynx passes through the head-trunk septum and narrows to a short tube continuous with the intestine.

The intestine is a long straight tube proceeding to the anus. At its beginning, it may send a pair of lateral diverticula (Fig. 1*B*) forward to the head-trunk septum. These diverticula are said to allow for alterations of head shape, but as they are present in all chaetognaths, this explanation remains dubious. Histologically they are identical with the intestine. The intestine is lined by a cuboidal to columnar epithelium composed of two kinds of cells, glandular and absorptive. The gland cells, most abundant in the anterior part of the intestine, are more or less vacuolated cells, containing in *Sagitta* large granular masses and hence resembling the compound granular cells of the pharyngeal bulb (Fig. 9*C*). The absorptive cells, more abundant posteriorly in the intestine, are finely granular, ciliated, columnar cells (Fig. 9*D*) that in *Spadella* become vacuolated with large inclusions shortly after feeding. In *Spadella*, the epithelium of the anterior part of the intestine is thrown into ridges caused by especially tall cells of either type. The intestine is supported by dorsal and ventral mesenteries (Fig. 5*C*) that do not seem to consist of peritoneal epithelium but rather are continuations of the basement membrane of the intestinal epithelium. Outside this basement membrane is found an exceedingly thin layer of circular fibers continuous with the circular muscle layer of the pharynx. These circular fibers also occur on the outer faces of the mesenteries and are further evidence of the noncoelomic nature of these mesenteries. The terminal part of the intestine is lined by a cuboidal or columnar epithelium of uniform appearance, ciliated in *Spadella;* this is underlain by a thick basement membrane followed by a layer of circular muscles. As it differs histologically from the remainder of the intestine, this terminal part may be called rectum. No special musculature for governing the anal aperture is present.

7. Reproductive System.—The chaetognaths are hermaphroditic with a pair of ovaries situated in the posterior part of the trunk just anterior to the trunk-tail septum and a pair of testes in the tail just behind this septum (Fig. 2). The testes are bandlike bodies in the anterior part of the tail coelom closely applied to its lateral walls and also extending slightly along the posterior face of the trunk-tail septum. They are bounded from the coelom by a delicate covering of connective tissue. As

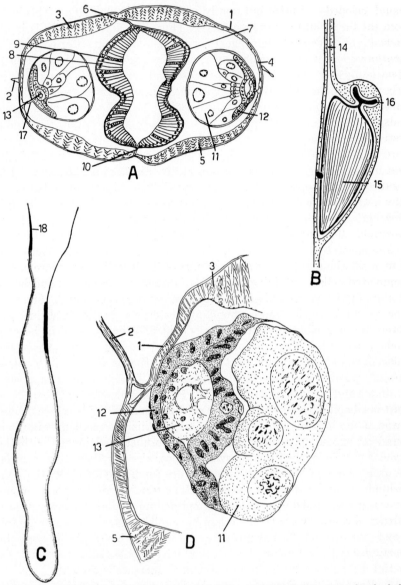

FIG. 10.—Reproductive system. *A*, cross section through *Sagitta* at the level of the ovaries *(after Burfield, 1927)*. *B*, seminal vesicle of *Sagitta (after Jägersten, 1940)*. *C*, sperm of *Sagitta (after Tuzet, 1931)*. *D*, section of ovary of *Sagitta (after Doncaster, 1902a)*. 1, epidermis; 2, anterior lateral fin; 3, dorsolateral longitudinal muscle band; 4, lateral muscle band; 5, ventrolateral muscle band; 6, dorsal mesentery of intestine; 7, intestine; 8, absorptive cells of intestine; 9, granular cells of intestine; 10, ventral mesentery of intestine; 11, ovary; 12, oviduct; 13, inner tube of oviduct; 14, sperm duct; 15, spermatophore; 16, attachment disk; 17, mesentery of ovary; 18, sperm head.

sexual maturity approaches, masses of spermatogonia are budded off from the testes into the tail coelom where they undergo spermatogenesis while at the same time slowly circulating in the coelomic current already mentioned. The tail coelom is divided into two compartments in *Spadella* by the median dorsoventral mesentery, but into four in *Sagitta* (Fig. 11*C*) by two additional secondary mesenteries paralleling the main partition; however, these secondary mesenteries are incomplete at both ends, hence offer no obstruction to the coelomic circulation. From each testis a sperm duct extends posteriorly to the seminal vesicle of that side; anteriorly the sperm duct opens into the tail coelom along the midlateral line by a funnel-shaped opening (ciliated according to Hertwig, 1880), regarded by Goodrich (1945) as a true genital funnel, or coelomostome. The sperm duct proceeds backward imbedded in the lateral body wall (Fig. 11*C*) and opens into the seminal vesicle of that side. This is a variously shaped body (the shape is of taxonomic value, discussion in Tokioka, 1939c) on each side between the lateral and tail fins, projecting conspicuously in most chaetognaths and forming a prominent opaque object when packed with sperm (Fig. 10*B*). The seminal vesicle is clothed externally by the stratified epidermis of the region and lined by a one-layered epithelium, probably glandular, at least in part. It was formerly believed that each vesicle opened externally by a permanent male gonopore, but recent findings (Tokioka, 1939c; Jägersten, 1940; John, 1943) indicate that the spermatophores escape by rupture. The sperm are filiform (Fig. 10*C*).

The ovaries are a pair of solid elongated bodies lying in the posterior part of the trunk coeloms and attached to the lateral body wall by a short mesentery (Fig. 10*A*). They contain eggs in various stages of ripening, and as the ripe eggs are found in the medial part of the ovaries they press upon the intestine, forcing it into a laterally flattened shape. The oviduct of chaetognaths and the manner of escape of the eggs are peculiar. An oviduct of flattened form with crescentic cross section runs along the attached side of the ovary, spreading over its entire lateral surface (Fig. 10*D*). The oviduct is composed of a cuboidal to cylindrical epithelium. *Inside* the oviduct there is another tube with syncytical wall that expands posteriorly into a rounded chamber, the seminal receptacle. This tube-within-tube construction of the oviduct has been described for *Sagitta* by Stevens (1910), Bordas (1920), and Burfield (1927), contrary to John (1943); for *Spadella cephaloptera* by Vasiljev (1925) and Ghirardelli (1954a, 1956), contrary to John (1933); and for *Pterosagitta draco* by Ghirardelli (1953a). The views of John (1933, 1943) that the oviduct is a simple epithelial tube appear to be erroneous. The seminal receptacle is an expanded chamber that stores the sperm received at copulation; from it a short vagina leads to the external female gonopore. The true

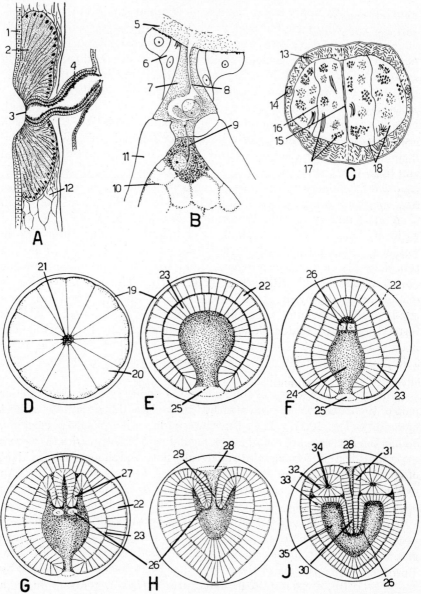

Fig. 11.—Reproductive system (concluded), embryology. *A*, section through the region of the female gonopore of *Spadella*, showing vagina and cement gland (*after John*, 1933). *B*, section through attached end of a ripe ovarian egg of *Sagitta*, showing attachment stalk and passage for sperm (*after Stevens*, 1910). *C*, section through the tail of *Sagitta*. *D–J*, stages of development of *Sagitta*. (*C–J, after Burfield*, 1927.) *D*, blastula. *E*, gastrula. *F*, late gastrula, segregation of primordial germ cells. *G*, beginning of backward progression of coelomic folds. *H*, formation of stomodaeum. *J*, further progress of coelomic folds; division of coelomic sacs into head and trunk parts. 1, epidermis; 2,

oviduct, or outer tube, does not appear to have any connection with the surface, but probably a temporary one forms during egg laying.

Neither outer nor inner tube of the oviduct opens directly into the ovary, but as each egg ripens two cells from the inner wall of the oviduct migrate inward to form an attachment stalk for the egg, and this stalk then hollows centrally to make a fine canal through which the sperm reach the egg (Stevens, 1910, for *Sagitta;* Vasiljev, 1925, Ghirardelli, 1956, for *Spadella;* Fig. 11*B*). The sperm pass up the inner tube from the seminal receptacle. The fertilized eggs then force their way into the oviduct and proceed posteriorly along the latter, squeezing between the outer and inner tubes. It is not clear how they reach the exterior; apparently they do not exit by way of the seminal receptacle and female gonopore. Some sort of temporary duct seems to arise.

8. Breeding Habits.—The chaetognaths are protandric hermaphrodites; the ovaries mature after the tail coeloms are filled with sperm. Very few observations are available on the method of transfer of sperm into the seminal receptacles. The process in *Sagitta* has been described by van Oye (1931) and Jägersten (1940), more fully by the latter. As they circulate in the tail coeloms, the ripe sperm are swept into the sperm ducts by the cilia of the genital funnels and accumulate in the seminal vesicles. Here the sperm mass becomes coated with secretion, forming a spermatophore. According to Jägersten, the filling of a seminal vesicle with sperm requires about 12 hours and is periodic, as considerable time must elapse before enough sperm to fill the vesicle are again ripened. A definite male gonopore is wanting; a disciform cavity distal to the main cavity of the vesicle (Fig. 10*B*) was earlier mistaken for a pore. This cavity is lined by secretory cells and secretes an attachment disk for the spermatophore. As the latter is emitted by rupture this disk adheres to it and serves to attach it to objects, usually in *Sagitta* the fins of the same animal. Clusters of sperm then push out from the spermatophores and eventually gain the seminal receptacles. Self-fertilization is thus apparently the rule in *Sagitta*.

A somewhat different story is related by John (1933) and Ghirardelli (1953c, 1954a) for *Spadella cephaloptera* in which cross-fertilization obtains. According to John, an individual with full seminal vesicles approaches one with an empty seminal receptacle and places a spermato-

cement glands; 3, female gonopore; 4, vagina; 5, seminal receptacle; 6, inner wall of oviduct; 7, stalk cells of egg; 8, passage through stalk cells; 9, sperm; 10, ripe egg; 11, egg envelope; 12, mesenchyme; 13, body-wall musculature; 14, sperm duct; 15, central mesentery of tail; 16, lateral secondary tail mesenteries; 17, sperm in stages of development; 18, coelomic cavities; 19, egg membrane; 20, blastomeres; 21, blastocoel; 22, ectoderm; 23, entoderm; 24, archenteron; 25, blastopore; 26, primordial germ cells; 27, mesodermal folds; 28, definitive mouth; 29, stomodaeum; 30, intestine; 31, pharynx; 32, head coelomic sacs; 33, trunk coelomic sacs; 34, head coelom; 35, trunk coelom.

phore near its female gonopore. The individual thus acting as male then shifts so that the two animals are oriented oppositely; they remain in this attitude, frequently bringing their ciliary loops in contact, while the sperm are wriggling into the seminal receptacle. Reciprocal exchange of sperm was not observed. According to Ghirardelli, two individuals with full seminal vesicles approach and place themselves parallel, facing in opposite directions. Each attaches a spermatophore, containing the entire contents of one seminal vesicle, on the neck of the other, and the sperm escape and travel into the seminal receptacles along the animal's back.

The eggs of *Sagitta* are discharged singly into the sea where they float, mostly near the surface, as round transparent objects 0.2 mm. in diameter. *Spadella* lays a group of 12 to 16 eggs at intervals of 8 to 10 days throughout the year. As the eggs exit the cement glands encircling the vagina (Fig. 11A) secrete an adhesive coat and stalk for each egg. The eggs are held in a cluster by these stalks and attached to seaweeds or some other object on which the *Spadella* rests while ovipositing. The eggs of *Krohnitta* are also stuck together in packets by a gelatinous adhesive secretion (Kuhl, 1928). These packets, attached to the animal's back near the trunk-tail septum, are carried about for some time. Sanzo (1937) found floating in the Straits of Messina gelatinous masses containing 200 to 300 embryos that proved to be those of *Pterosagitta draco;* the habit of this species of laying its eggs in floating gelatinous masses was confirmed by Ghirardelli (1953a). Conant (1896) witnessed the egg laying of *Sagitta hispida* at Beaufort, North Carolina. The eggs remained 20 to 30 minutes in each oviduct while a jelly coat thickened around each and then, pushed on by ovarian contractions, issued in a mass totaling 60 to 70 eggs and adhered to the container.

The breeding cycles of *Sagitta* have been repeatedly studied, by the examination of specimens taken in periodic plankton hauls. These cycles appear to vary with geographical location. Thus Russell (1932, 1933) reported that *Sagitta elegans* produces four or five broods annually from February to September at intervals of 2 or 3 months in the English Channel off Plymouth. But in the North Sea there are two spawning periods during spring and summer with a possible third in October (Wimpenny, 1936); one main breeding period in April and May and a second minor period in autumn on Georges Bank off Cape Cod (Clarke, Pierce, and Bumpus, 1943); and at Woods Hole, at the base of Cape Cod, *S. elegans* appears in December, becomes very abundant by April and May when swarms with ripe eggs are seen, spawns in late April, and disappears by July, thus having but one annual breeding period (Fish, 1925). In several other, more northern, regions, this species also appears to breed but once annually. Thus spawning occurs from January to

May in the Irish Sea off Liverpool (Pierce, 1941); in late spring and summer in the Gulf of Maine (Redfield and Beale, 1940); from February to the middle of June in the fjords of East Greenland (Ussing, 1938); from April or May to August or September off Greenland (Kramp, 1939); from April to October in the Bay of Fundy and from April to the middle of June in the Gulf of St. Lawrence (Huntsman and Reid, 1921); and from June or July to October in the Canadian eastern Arctic (Dunbar, 1941). A similar geographical variation in breeding activities is indicated for *Sagitta setosa*, although fewer data are available. For this species Russell reported six broods annually from February to October in the English Channel, whereas Pierce found only two broods in the Irish Sea, one in April to June, the other in August. The data of Pierce (1951) indicate that all the *Sagitta* species found off the west coast of Florida (*hispida, helenae, tenuis, enflata*) breed continuously throughout the year. In the Mediterranean, *S. enflata* appears to breed twice annually, in spring and fall (Ghirardelli, 1951; Massuti, 1954). An interesting cycle is reported by David (1955) for *S. gazellae*, a species limited to antarctic and subantarctic waters. Mature animals migrate into the deeper, warmer layers to breed, being found mostly at depths of 1000 to 1500 m. Here they spawn over a period of months, beginning in March. The eggs or newly hatched young rise to the surface, being found mostly at a depth of 100 to 150 m. where the young remain for 2 to 3 months, feeding and growing; thereafter they start sinking into the deeper layers.

As regards other genera, *Spadella cephaloptera* is said to spawn throughout the year at short intervals at Plymouth (John, 1933), and Kramp (1939) records that off Greenland *Eukrohnia hamata* breeds in deep water over a long period, probably throughout the year, with maxima in summer and autumn.

9. Development.—The embryology of *Sagitta* has been studied by Kowalevsky (1871), Bütschli (1873), Hertwig (1880), Doncaster (1902a), Elpatievsky (1909, 1910), Buchner (1910), Stevens (1910), and Burfield (1927), but some of these articles are concerned mainly with the germ track. John (1933) has given an excellent account of the embryology of *Spadella*. The *Sagitta* egg contains no evident yolk material, but the *Spadella* egg is provided with minute, uniformly distributed yolk granules. Both undergo equal holoblastic cleavage which results in a spherical coeloblastula of equal pyramidal cells radiating about a small central blastocoel (Fig. 11*D*). At the stage of about 50 blastomeres a typical embolic gastrulation ensues; the invaginating entoderm makes complete contact with the ectoderm, obliterating the blastocoel and producing a two-walled gastrula of classical appearance (Fig. 11*E*). The blastopore marks the future posterior end of the chaetognath. Chaetognaths are notable as an example of early segregation of the germ cells, and there now become evident in the anterior wall of the archenteron (opposite the blastopore) two cells in *Sagitta* (Fig. 11*F*) or one cell in *Spadella* that are the primordial germ cells. These cells are noticeable through their enlarged size and in *Sagitta* also, according to Elpatievsky, Buchner, and Stevens, by the presence in their cytoplasm of a special stainable body of uncertain origin. Ghirardelli (1953d, 1954c) tested this "germinal determinant" in *Spadella* and found that it is osmiophilous and rich in polysaccharides and ribonucleic acid but does not give the Feulgen reaction. The primordial germ cells bulge from the entoderm and soon detach, then lying free in the archenteron, where the single cell of *Spadella* soon divides into two daughter cells. There now ensues the formation of the coelom. In the anterior wall of the archenteron two folds appear (Fig. 11*G*) that progress backward, carrying with them the primordial germ cells, and eventually meet the posterior wall of the archenteron where meanwhile the blastopore has closed completely. These folds mark off a slender central tube, the intestine, from a pair of lateral coelomic sacs. Meantime a stomodaeal invagination has occurred at the anterior end of the embryo; this meets and fuses with the intestine, establishing the definitive mouth and pharynx (Fig. 11*H*). The anterior ends of the ceolomic sacs are cut off as a pair of small head sacs that are hollow at first in *Sagitta* (Fig. 11*J*) but solid at their inception in *Spadella*. The walls of the head coeloms furnish the mesodermal structures of the head, chiefly the head muscles. By the elongation of the embryo the intestine flattens greatly, appearing as a septum between the lateral coelomic sacs, and is left blind at its rear end by the fusion of the coelomic folds with the posterior archenteral wall. The ganglion cells of the main ganglia arise as ectodermal thickenings (Fig. 12*A*) that proliferate the nerve cells into the interior. The hood is also formed by an ectodermal thickening. Sooner or later the primordial germ cells divide to four cells (*Sagitta*) or two binucleate cells (*Spadella*), and as the coelomic folds push posteriorly, two cells or one binucleate cell is left in each lateral coelom. The continued elongation of the embryo within the egg shell causes obliteration of all the coelomic cavities, also of the intestinal lumen (Fig. 12*A*, *D*). Development to hatching requires about 2 days.

The embryo, elongated to a vermiform shape and curved inside the egg shell (Fig. 12*B*), now hatches as a minute creature, about 1 mm. long, usually called larva, but recognizable as a chaetognath (Fig. 12*C*). The extremely transparent *Sagitta* larva floats in the plankton, swimming by sudden darts; but the less transparent *Spadella* larva adheres to the substratum to which the eggs were attached and shows little movement. This adhesion is accomplished by adhesive epidermal cells on the ventral surface of the trunk and by a pair of adhesive projections resembling tentacles that develop on the sides of the head.

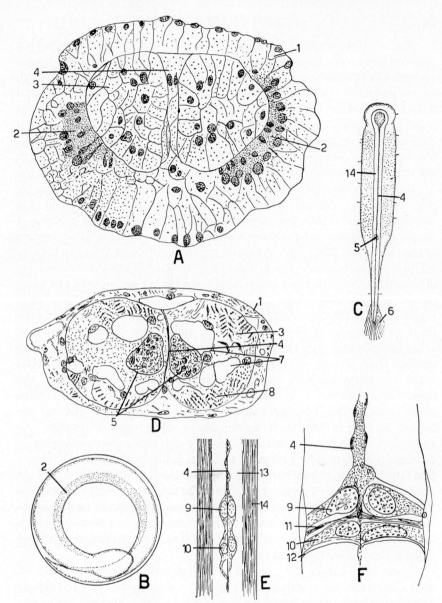

FIG. 12.—Embryology (concluded). *A*, section through an embryo at the level of the subenteric ganglion; coelomic cavities have disappeared. *B*, completed larva in egg membrane. *C*, larva at hatching. *D*, section of larva on the third day after hatching, showing primordial germ cells; coelom is re-forming from scattered spaces, and muscles are differentiating in the mesodermal sacs. *E*, longitudinal section of day-old larva, showing primordial germ cells attached to entodermal septum. *F*, longitudinal view of three-day-old larva; germ cells migrating. (*All of Sagitta; all after Doncaster*, 1902a.) 1, ectoderm; 2, ganglion cells of subenteric ganglion differentiating from ectoderm; 3, meso-dermal sacs; 4, entodermal septum; 5, primordial germ cells; 6, tail fin; 7, spaces to re-form coelom; 8, muscles differentiating; 9, primordial female germ cells; 10, primordial male germ cells; 11, trunk-tail septum; 12, envelope of germ cells; 13, coelom; 14, mesoderm.

The newly hatched chaetognath (Fig. 12*C*) is of slender form, with a rounded head containing the patent pharynx, a trunk on which the tango-receptive bristles are already evident, and a narrowed tail provided with an incipient tail fin. The trunk interior is solid, consisting of a central flattened intestine resembling a partition and called by Burfield the *entodermal septum,* and a pair of lateral mesodermal strands (Fig. 12*A*). The main nerve ganglia appear as epidermal proliferations (Fig. 12*A*). The primordial germ cells are imbedded in the mesoderm in contact with the entodermal septum in the posterior part of the trunk.

During the week after hatching the larval structures develop directly into the adult condition; hence one is hardly justified in speaking of a metamorphosis. Head and trunk become hollow again by a series of spaces that appear and coalesce to become the so-called coelomic cavities of the adult (Fig. 12*D*); but obviously these definitive cavities can bear no relation to the true coeloms of the embryo. In the head the mesoderm differentiates into the head musculature, conferring on the head the adult contours. The two head cavities fuse above the pharynx, producing a single cavity. The ectodermal folds already present in the embryo continue to grow out to produce the hood, and finally the head armature arises as epidermal secretions. In the trunk the mesoderm elongates into strands that become the longitudinal muscle bands (Fig. 12*D*). The trunk entoderm thickens and finally develops a lumen, furnishing the definitive intestine. It would appear that both the dorsal and ventral mesenteries of the intestine and the median mesentery of the tail are formed, at least in part, from the remains of the entodermal septum. In the tail this septum does not undergo any differentiation; consequently the digestive tract ends just prior to the tail, although there is evidence (see later) that originally the chaetognath gut extended into the tail. At the end of about a week after hatching, the intestine bends ventrally to touch the ectoderm, and an anus is then formed without the participation of any proctodaeum. The lateral fins are formed by ectodermal outfolding shortly after hatching. The ciliary loop arises as a thickening of two adjacent rows of ectodermal cells.

About 3 or 4 days after hatching, the primordial germ cells, two on each side in *Sagitta,* multiplied to a group of eight nuclei on each side in *Spadella,* migrate from their position next to the entoderm across the re-formed trunk cavities to the lateral body wall (Fig. 12*E, F*). As they do so the trunk-tail septum appears and half of the germ cells or nuclei are left anterior to the septum and half posterior to it. The manner of origin of the trunk-tail septum has not been definitely ascertained, although Doncaster and John have devoted special attention to the question. Since the septum appears as the germ cells are migrating across the coelom it seems probable that it arises from some mesodermal material

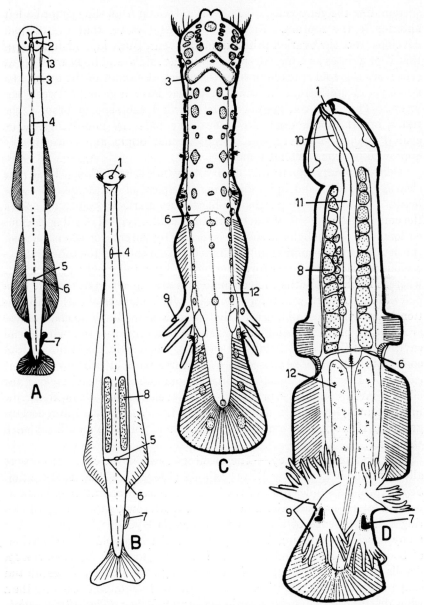

FIG. 13.—Chaetognath genera and species. *A, Sagitta bipunctata (after Ritter-Zahony,* 1911a). *B, Eukrohnia hamata (after Ritter-Zahony,* 1910b). *C, Spadella schizoptera,* dorsal. *D, Spadella sheardi,* ventral. (*C, D, after Mawson,* 1944.) 1, mouth; 2, eyes; 3, ciliary loop; 4, subenteric ganglion; 5, anus; 6, trunk-tail septum; 7, seminal vesicles; 8, ovaries; 9, projections bearing adhesive papillae; 10, pharynx; 11, intestine; 12, tail coeloms; 13, collarette.

surrounding the germ cells. The ovaries develop from the primordia left anterior to the septum. Although Doncaster states that the oviduct develops from the ovarian primordium, Stevens, Burfield, and John agree that it originates as a mesodermal fold in the midlateral body wall. The cells from this fold spread out over the adjacent surface of the ovary as a two-layered epithelium in which a lumen later appears between the layers. The germ-cell rudiments left behind the septum become the testes, but the sperm ducts are formed as ectodermal thickenings. The genital funnels, however, are of mesodermal origin and consequently appear to be true coelomostomes.

Certain points about this embryology merit attention. First, the cleavage is radial and indeterminate, as typical of enterocoelous coelomates. Then in chaetognaths the blastopore marks the posterior end of the embryo and the site of the future anus as also typical of enterocoelous coelomates. Although the coelom is formed by the enterocoelous method, the details of its formation differ markedly from those of the other enterocoelous phyla. The latter form the coelom by entodermal outpouchings, whereas in chaetognaths the coelomic sacs are cut off from the gut by a pair of folds that grow anteroposteriorly. This manner of coelom formation bears some resemblance to that of articulate Brachiopoda. There are but two primary coelomic divisions in chaetognaths, the paired head cavities and the paired trunk-tail cavities, whereas in the enterocoelous coelomates there are supposed to occur three pairs of primary coelomic cavities. Finally the chaetognaths are notable for the total lack of the ciliated larva commonly produced as a developmental stage in marine invertebrates; in this regard also they differ from the typical enterocoelous groups. However, the embryology as a whole points to an affinity with the latter.

10. Systematic Survey.—The chaetognaths known up to 1911 were allocated to six genera by Ritter-Zahony (1909c, d, 1910a, 1911a, b, c). *Sagitta*, which includes most of the known species, is characterized by two pairs of lateral fins, anterior and posterior tooth rows, papillate vestibular ridges, and absence of the transverse muscle layer in the trunk. The many species are distinguished by length and body shape, proportions of body parts, shape and position of the fins, form of the ciliary loop, details of form and number of the grasping spines and the teeth, and shape of the seminal vesicles. Among the more common species with a wide distribution may be mentioned *serratodentata* (Fig. 18*B*), *enflata* (*not inflata*, Fig. 19*C*), *elegans* (Fig. 1*A*), *hexaptera* (Fig. 18*D*), *lyra* (Fig. 18*A*), *bipunctata* (Fig. 13*A*), *minima, maxima, decipiens* (Fig. 19*D*), *bedoti* (Fig. 18*C*), *macrocephala* (Fig. 19*A*), and *planctonis* (Fig. 19*B*). The identification of the many species of *Sagitta* presents difficulties, especially as some species show a high degree of geographical variation,

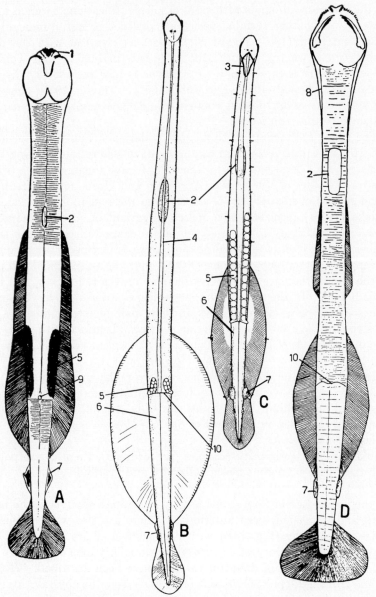

Fig. 14.—Chaetognath genera and species (concluded). A, *Heterokrohnia mirabilis*, ventral (*after Ritter-Zahony*, 1911c). B, *Krohnitta subtilis*. C, *Krohnitta pacifica*. (B, C, after *Tokioka*, 1939c.) D, *Zahonya cestoda* (*after Oye*, 1918). 1, gland reservoir; 2, subenteric ganglion; 3, ciliary loop; 4, intestine; 5, ovaries; 6, tail coeloms; 7, seminal vesicles; 8, collarette; 9, anus; 10, trunk-tail septum.

and the literature abounds with cases of misidentification as well as arguments as to whether certain species are distinct or not. Thus Pierce (1951) and Bieri (1957) regard *S. friderici* as identical with the prior species *tenuis*, whereas Faure (1952), Furnestin (1954), and Tokioka (1955c) consider them distinct. *S. gazellae* is now regarded as distinct from *S. lyra* (David, 1955; Furnestin, 1957). David (1955) considers that three species have been confused under the name *planctonis;* the others are *zetesios* and *marri.*

The genus *Pterosagitta*, with a single widely distributed species *draco* (Fig. 2B), is readily recognized by the massive collarette extending back at least to the lateral fins and by the pair of large tangoreceptive bristle tufts on the sides of the trunk. Vannucci and Hosoe (1952) created a second species of *Pterosagitta*, *besnardi*, from the region of Trinidad, but Tokioka (1955c) regards this as merely a variant of *draco*. The genus *Spadella* of relatively short stocky build is characterized by the small number (two to five) of teeth in the tooth rows, transversely oriented oval or triangular ciliary loop, presence of the transverse muscle band throughout the trunk, presence of adhesive papillae on the tail region, and benthonic habits. In the most common species, *Sp. cephaloptera* (Fig. 2A), there are two pairs of tooth rows and one pair of lateral fins and the adhesive papillae are borne directly on the ventral surface of the tail. In three other species of limited distribution, *schizoptera* (Fig. 13C), *sheardi* (Fig. 13D), and *johnstoni*, only the anterior tooth rows are present, there are two pairs of lateral fins, of which, however, the anterior pair is very small, and the adhesive papillae are located on muscular fingerlike projections found just behind the posterior pair of lateral fins (Mawson, 1944). The pair of tentacles on the hood of *Sp. cephaloptera* is wanting in other species of *Spadella.*

In *Eukrohnia* (originally *Krohnia*, preoccupied), there is one pair of tooth rows with numerous teeth, collarette and vestibular pits are wanting, the transverse muscle bands occur in the anterior part of the trunk, and the single pair of lateral fins is very elongated relative to the body length and much narrowed anteriorly. There are two well-established species, *Eu. hamata* (Fig. 13B) with flask-shaped ciliary loop extending onto the trunk and *Eu. fowleri* with pyriform ciliary loop confined to the head. Other species of doubtful validity have been described. *Heterokrohnia* with single species *mirabilis* (Fig. 14A) from the abyssal Antarctic also has one pair of long lateral fins, but these are not especially narrowed anteriorly; there are two tooth rows with numerous teeth and a transverse muscle layer throughout trunk and tail. Both *Eukrohnia* and *Heterokrohnia* have two glandular tracts on the head along the lines of hood attachment, and these converge to a large glandular reservoir at the head tip (Fig. 3G). *Krohnitta* with two species, *subtilis* (Fig. 14B) and

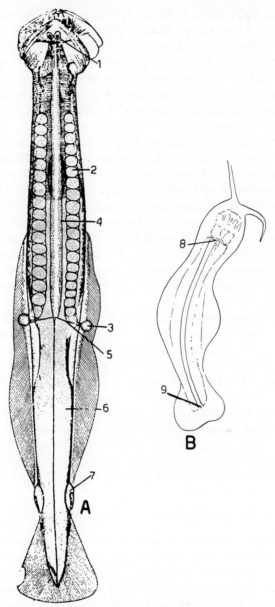

FIG. 15.—Further chaetognaths. *A, Bathyspadella edentata (after Tokioka,* 1939b). *B,* extinct chaetognath, *Amiskwia sagittiformis (after Walcott,* 1911). 1, eyes; 2, ovaries; 3, female gonopores; 4, intestine; 5, trunk-tail septum; 6, tail coeloms; 7, seminal vesicles; 8, head-trunk septum; 9, presumable location of anus.

pacifica (Fig. 14C) from tropical waters, lacks collarette, transverse musculature, and cephalic glandular tracts; it has one pair of lateral fins, short and posteriorly located, and one pair of tooth rows.

In 1912 Germain and Joubin erected two new chaetognath genera, *Pseudosagitta* and *Krohnittella*, each with one species. However, *Pseudosagitta grimaldii* has since been regarded as identical with *Sagitta lyra;* hence the genus *Pseudosagitta* is invalid (Michael, 1919). *Krohnittella boureei*, however, appears to be a valid species; it lacks teeth and collarette and has one pair of lateral fins. Another genus, *Zahonya*, with one species *cestoda*, was created by van Oye in 1918. This has two pairs of lateral fins, one pair of tooth rows, collarette, and transverse musculature throughout trunk and tail (Fig. 14*D*). Tokioka (1952) surmises that *Zahonya cestoda* is only a contracted specimen of *Sagitta robusta*. The most recent chaetognath genus to be proposed, *Bathyspadella*, with one species *edentata* from deep water off Japan (Tokioka, 1939b), is characterized by the short stocky shape (Fig. 15*A*), total absence of teeth, pigmentless eyes, long collarette bordering the trunk and tail, single pair of long narrow lateral fins, and presence of transverse musculature in the anterior part of the trunk.

11. Fossil Chaetognaths.—In 1911 Walcott reported finding in the shales of the middle Cambrian in British Columbia three obviously chaetognath fossil specimens that he named *Amiskwia sagittiformis*. This animal (Fig. 15*B*) was about 20 mm. long with a pair of well-developed tentacles at the tip of the head, a pair of short lateral fins about the middle of the trunk, and a typical tail fin. The intestine shows clearly and runs to the base of the fin rays of the tail fin where presumably the anus was located, much posterior to its present position. There are markings of indeterminable nature in the head region, but the head-trunk septum is sufficiently indicated; apparently the trunk-tail septum was wanting. The absence of any indication of gonads or seminal vesicles in these fossils is rather puzzling.

IV. ECOLOGY AND PHYSIOLOGY

1. Habits and Behavior.—Except *Spadella*, which is benthonic, chaetognaths lead a planktonic existence, being among the most common and characteristic planktonic animals found in all seas and at all latitudes and through a range of depth. Most of the time they float motionless supported by their fins; eventually, however, they begin to sink, whereupon they resort to swimming to maintain their level. Swimming consists of short swift forward darts, each covering a distance of around 5 cm.; this is followed by gliding on the momentum of the darts and a return to floating. The forward dart is so rapid as to be difficult of analysis but is believed to result from the alternate contractions of the dorsal and ventral longitudinal muscle bands of trunk and tail. This would seem to produce up-and-down body waves and tail flirts, but the movement is so rapid that it appears to the naked eye like a trembling. The tail fin lacks musculature and hence is incapable of independent movement, but contractions of the tail musculature would involve the tail fin.

The species of *Spadella* are benthonic, dwelling in shallow water where they adhere to rocks and algae by their adhesive papillae. When undisturbed, they assume a food-catching attitude with tail attached to some object by the adhesive papillae and head and trunk held away from the substrate (Fig. 16*A*) at varying angles, approaching the vertical in species in which the adhesive papillae are borne on projecting processes. When disturbed, *Spadella* also swims by forward jerks but soon takes refuge in the bottom mud.

The chaetognaths are highly predaceous, carnivorous animals, eating any small animal of suitable size with which they come in contact in the plankton. Copepods, euphausiaceans, baby fish, and other chaetognaths constitute the main food items, with an occasional medusa or pelagic tunicate (Lebour, 1922, 1923; Kielhorn, 1952; Massuti, 1954; Caabro, 1955; David, 1955). Copepods, being the commonest element of the macroscopic zooplankton, are naturally the most frequent prey. Lebour (1923) saw *Sagitta bipunctata* swallow whole baby herrings as large as itself. Grey (1930) observed a *Sagitta enflata* grasp a *S. friderici* half its size by the head and swallow it straight down. *Sagitta* captures prey by the lightning action of the head armature following a forward dart upon the victim. It seems to feed mainly at night or in dim light (Parry, 1944). The species of *Spadella* await prey while fastened to the substrate by their adhesive papillae with anterior body elevated. When a suitable prey swims past the head, the *Spadella* captures it by an upward and backward jerk while retaining a firm hold on the substrate. The prey is then manipulated by the grasping spines until either the head or tail end of the victim is worked into the mouth (Parry, 1944).

An elaborate study of the action of the grasping apparatus of *Sagitta* by means of photographs was made by Kuhl (1932). As its main result this study showed that the spreading of the grasping spines is correlated with a marked shortening of the head, presumably accomplished by the contraction of the long oblique muscles. This contraction would bring about the broadening of the rear part of the head—also a factor in spreading the spines—by forcing the rear ends of the lateral plates apart, an action facilitated by the correlated relaxation of the dorsal transverse muscles. The closure of the grasping spines upon the prey is brought about by the contraction of the jaw adductors. The large masses of the lateral complex muscles must also play some role in altering the shape of the head. The teeth assist in holding the prey. A detailed analysis of

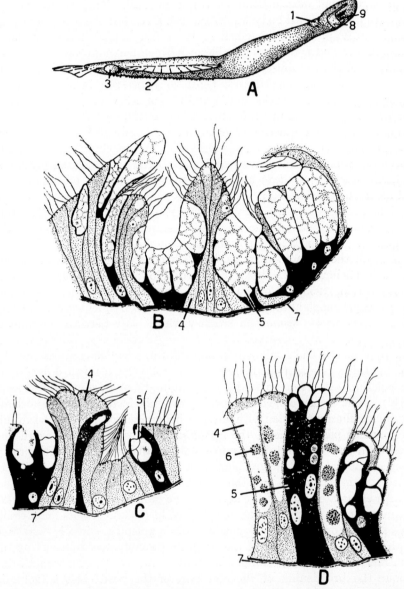

Fig. 16.—Food capture, histology of digestion. *A, Spadella cephaloptera* in food-catching position, attached by its adhesive papillae. *B*, transverse section through the anterior part of the intestine of *Spadella*, before feeding. *C*, same, 10 minutes after feeding; glandular vacuolated cells disrupted. *D*, same, 3 hours after feeding; glandular cells rebuilding; absorptive cells contain vacuoles with large granular masses. (*All after Parry,* 1944.) 1, ciliary loop; 2, adhesive papillae; 3, seminal vesicle; 4, absorptive cells; 5, glandular vacuolated cells; 6, granular masses, presumably digestive products; 7, circular muscle layer; 8, lateral plate; 9, grasping spines.

food capture in *Spadella* was furnished by John (1933). After withdrawal of the hood, the anterior ends of the lateral plates are caused to project forward by the contraction of the superficial obliques, lateral complex, and jaw adductors. At the same time contraction of the mouth constrictors pulls the mouth forward and evaginates the vestibule. The mouth now projects as a short transparent tube supported laterally by the anterior ends of the lateral plates. In this position the external dilators of the vestibule together with the superior expanders act like a sphincter for regulating the mouth aperture. The anterior ends of the lateral plates, the long obliques, and the dorsal transverse also assist in opening and closing the mouth. The contraction of the dorsal transverse diverges the anterior ends of the lateral plates, thus opening the mouth; contraction of the long obliques and superior expanders closes the mouth. The closing of the grasping spines is brought about by the jaw adductors as in *Sagitta*. The bicornuate and lateral complex muscles operate indirectly on the feeding action by altering the head shape and thus the positions of the lateral plates as also in *Sagitta*. The mouth of *Spadella* is returned to its resting position by the contraction of the internal dilators of the vestibule, and the vestibule is thus reestablished.

2. Physiology.—As may be surmised, very little information is available on this topic. With the exception of *Spadella*, chaetognaths cannot be maintained in the laboratory more than a day or two, and this fact, together with their small size, makes them difficult subjects to study. The only physiological information concerns digestion, which was studied by Parry (1944) in both *Sagitta* and *Spadella*. In both, the prey is coated with a sticky secretion from the granular cells lining the anterior portion of the pharynx; this serves to entangle the prey and render it helpless but is not toxic or digestive. It probably also lubricates the prey, which after being swallowed passes to the posterior part of the intestine, where digestion takes place, despite the fact that the main secretory cells are in the anterior intestine. *Spadella* was noticed to gulp sea water after swallowing prey, and this would wash the secretions of the pharyngeal bulb and anterior part of the intestine into the posterior part of the latter. The pH of the *Spadella* intestine when containing prey was 6.4, or slightly on the acid side. In an attempt to identify the enzymes involved in digestion, 1000 *Sagitta* were ground with glycerin and the usual digests set up. Soluble starch and glycogen were hydrolyzed to glucose, but no evidence was found of the presence of proteolytic enzymes. Digestion appears to be wholly extracellular. During digestion in *Spadella* marked changes occur in the secretory vacuolated cells of the anterior part of the intestine, comprising disruption and discharge of most of the vacuoles (Fig. 16*B, C*). The absorptive cells of the intestine also alter during digestion, changing from a finely granular resting state to a highly vacuolated condition with granular masses, presumably digestive products, floating in the vacuoles (Fig. 16*D*). Following digestion the indigestible remains, mostly the exoskeleton of copepods, are ejected through the anus. The entire proc-ess from ingestion to defecation requires about 3 or 4 hours in *Spadella*. In the observations of Grey (1930) on a *Sagitta* swallowed by another *Sagitta* the prey was passed at once to the posterior part of the intestine where it was rotated and moved back and forth until broken down; remains were ejected by the anus 40 minutes after the capture. A euphausiacean offered to a *Sagitta gazellae* was grasped and pushed into the mouth by alternate action of the spines of the two sides; the remains reached the anus in an hour (David, 1955).

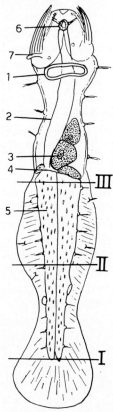

FIG. 17.—Regener-ation. *Spadella cephal-optera*, showing planes of section for regeneration experiments (*after Kul-matycki*, 1918). 1, cili-ary loop; 2, intestine; 3, ovary; 4, trunk-tail sep-tum; 5, tail coeloms with sperm; 6, mouth; 7, tentacle.

3. Regeneration.—Regeneration was studied by Kulmatycki (1918) in *Spadella cephaloptera*, probably the only chaetognath that can be kept in good condition in the laboratory long enough to follow the course of regeneration. Surprising ability to regenerate was found. Following cut I (Fig. 17), in which most of the tail fin was removed, the epidermis grew out, fin rays became visible in 2 days, and the fin regenerated com-pletely in a week, in 4 days in some specimens. The regenerated fin was nearly always larger than the original fin and bore a much larger number of tangoreceptive bristles. Following cut II, in which half of the tail region was amputated, and cut III, in which the entire tail was removed, the wound closed by contraction or clots or both and the tail region regenerated completely. In a study of Florida chaetognaths Pierce (1951) noticed a number of specimens of *Sagitta helenae* and *enflata* that were regenerating the head. The trunk tissues contract to close the wound tightly, and the head forms in the contracted end. "The eyes appear early, followed by the mouth and finally jaws appear."

4. Biological Relations.—Chaetognaths are eaten by other planktonic animals as medusae, ctenophores, and small and young fish. They are much subject to parasitic invasion, and various parasites have been found in them. Grassi (1882) first noticed the occurrence of two kinds of parasitic amoebae, *pigmentifera* and *chaetognathi*, in the tail coeloms and testes of *S. enflata, bipunctata,* and *serratodentata* and in *Spadella.* Janicki (1912, 1928, 1932) took up the study of these amoebae and gave an extended account of them, transferring them to the genus *Paramoeba.* Ramult and Rose (1945) saw *pigmentifera* in the tail coeloms of *S. enflata,* and Ghirardelli (1950a) found both species common in this chaetognath. Hamon (1957) studied *pigmentifera* that she found in the tail coeloms of *S. bipunctata* and determined that the dark inclusion responsible for the placement of these amoebae in the genus *Paramoeba* is in fact an ingested spermatocyte, as the parasites eat stages of spermatogenesis. Chatton (1953) had already transferred these amoebae to the new genus *Janickina,* acknowledged by Hamon. Grassi and Janicki claimed multiple fission of the encysted *pigmentifera* into uniflagellate swarmers, possibly gametes, but this has not been confirmed by later observers. The amoebae seem to flourish only during male sexual maturity and are probably transferred during copulation.

Other protozoan parasites also occur. A flagellate, *Trypanophis sagittae,* parasitic in the intestine of several species of *Sagitta,* was first noticed by Hovasse (1924) and extensively studied by Rose and Hamon (1950) and Hamon (1950, 1951a). This organism has one free flagellum, another that forms the edge of the undulating membrane, and a longitudinal row of little transverse rods along the anterior body half. As the flagellate grows, a large amount of inert material accumulates in the posterior body half that is then cut off and discarded; the remaining anterior portion loses all differentiation and comes to resemble a gregarine. This attaches at one end to the intestinal epithelium and encysts; the further history is unknown. The flagellate was never seen to divide inside the chaetognath host, nor has its manner of entry into the host been ascertained. Gregarines were seen in the gut of chaetognaths by Leuckart (1861), and an acephaline gregarine from the intestine of *Sagitta* was named *Lecudina* (later *Lankesteria*) *leuckarti* by Mingazzini (1891). The finding of *Lankesteria* in the intestine of *S. enflata* was reported by Ramult and Rose (1945). A new cephaline gregarine, *Tricystis planctonis,* was discovered by Hamon (1951b) in the intestine of *S. lyra.* Ikeda (1917) first described an astomatous ciliate, *Metaphrya sagittae,* in the coelom of a *Sagitta,* and this same ciliate has since been observed in the coelom of *S. enflata* (Ramult and Rose, 1945), in the intestine of *S. minima* (Ghirardelli, 1950b, 1952), and in *S. bipunctata* (Massuti, 1954). Oye (1918) often saw peritrichous ciliates, sometimes also flagellate colonies, on the surface of chaetognaths.

Chaetognaths frequently harbor trematodes, mostly in the metacercarial stage, but also as adults. The metacercariae are nonencysting types with fish as definitive hosts. Trematodes in the interior of chaetognaths, in the intestine or coelom or gonads, were noticed by various older authors (Busch, 1851; Leuckart and Pagenstecher, 1858; Claparède, 1863; Gourret, 1884; MacIntosh, 1890; Scott, 1896; Moltschanoff, 1909); some were later identified as belonging to the family Hemiuridae (II, page 272), specifically to *Hemiurus communis* and *rugosus, Derogenes varicus,* and *Aphanurus stossichi;* others as an allocreadiid (II, page 270) *Pharyngora bacillaris* to which belongs the well-known trichocercous cercaria (II, Fig. 103*B*) (Monticelli, 1909; Sinitsin, 1911; Lebour, 1917; Meek, 1928; Steuer, 1928; Ramult and Rose, 1945). Dollfus, Anantaraman, and Nair (1954) found that all examples of *Sagitta enflata* at Madras harbored in their coelom one to three metacercariae of still another digenetic family, the Accacoeliidae, possibly of the genus *Tetrochetus.* Hutton (1954) reported finding several species of larval trematodes, mostly belonging to *Derogenes*, in chaetognaths off Florida and described a new metacercarial species, *owreae*, from *S. enflata, lyra,* and *hexaptera.* *Metacercaria owreae* was also seen in *S. enflata* off Cuba by Caabro (1955). Other records of unidentified larval trematodes in chaetognaths, chiefly in *S. enflata*, include those of Grey (1930), Thomson (1947), Ghirardelli (1948), and Hamon (1956). The foregoing records all concern larval trematodes, but adults have also been found in chaetognaths. Linton (1927) reported finding two adult hemiurids in the intestine of *Sagitta elegans*, and Myers (1956) refound this, identifying it as probably *Hemiurus levinseni*. It is probable that chaetognaths become infected with hemiurid metacercariae by eating copepods, their normal hosts, and act merely as transport hosts.

Larval stages of cestodes are sometimes found in the coelom of *Sagitta.* Grey (1930) saw a cysticercus in the coelom of *S. enflata*, and Dollfus, Anantaraman, and Nair (1954) noticed two tetraphyllid larvae attached to a metacercaria, also in the coelom of *S. enflata.*

Nematodes of some length are not uncommon in the coelom or the intestine of chaetognaths (MacIntosh, 1890; Scott, 1896; Moltschanoff, 1909; Pierantoni, 1913; Lebour, 1917; Meek, 1928; Grey, 1930; Thomson, 1947). A conspicuous juvenile ascaroid was first noticed by Pierantoni in the coelom of Mediterranean chaetognaths and has been often seen since. The possession by this young worm of both a ventricular and an intestinal caecum sufficiently proves it to be an anisakine ascaroid of the genus *Contracaecum* (III, page 326). Gray identified a nematode in *S. friderici* as *Camillanus trispinosus*. Russell (1932) recorded that 7 per cent of *S. setosa* at Plymouth contained nematodes.

Copepods have been rarely reported on chaetognaths. Thomson (1947) saw a copepod attached to the region of the female gonopores of *S. decipiens*, and Ghirardelli (1948) sometimes found a little copepod on *S. hispida* and *bedoti.*

A remarkable ectoparasite was reported by Tregouboff (1949) on

Mediterranean *Sagitta*, later also seen by Ghirardelli (1953*b*). This consists of vesicles without nuclei or definite histological construction, rooted in the chaetognath body. Smaller ones are composed of 1 vesicle, larger ones of up to 3 or 4 concentric vesicles. One *Sagitta* may bear up to 10 such vesicles on its surface. This is probably some sort of obscure protozoan parasite.

5. Ecological Factors in Distribution.—The chaetognaths are among the most common of *planktonic* animals, that is, animals that spend their entire existence floating or swimming in the water without relation to bottom but have such feeble powers of locomotion that they are unable to direct their movements and drift with tides and currents. As planktonic animals they are collected, often in great numbers, on every plankton expedition or investigation and on every collecting trip that makes a point of seining the waters. As a consequence there is available a large literature reporting data on the chaetognaths so collected. These data usually concern the different species taken, the stations at which they were found, the number of individuals of the different species in the various hauls, and the depths from which they came, with usually also accompanying data on temperature and salinity. Some of these reports are devoted chiefly to the study of tides and currents by the use of chaetognaths as indicators and do not appear pertinent here. Among the larger and more important reports from which many of the following statements are abstracted are those of Fowler (1906), Ritter-Zahony (1909c, 1910b, 1911b, c), and Thiel (1938).

Chaetognaths occur in all oceans and at a wide range of depth, but no one species has a universal distribution, although some are practically cosmopolitan in the upper waters. The distribution of each species is limited by its reactions to depth, temperature, salinity, and light penetration or to various combinations of these factors. As regards depth distribution, planktonic animals have been classified by Fowler (1906) as *epiplanktonic*, ranging from the surface to a depth of about 200 m., representing the limit of light penetration, and *mesoplanktonic*, inhabiting depths greater than 200 m. Although not employed by Fowler, the term *bathyplanktonic* (or *bathypelagic*) is convenient for plankton organisms living at depths greater than 1000 m. Recently the term *hadal* has been coined for depths exceeding 6000 m. The great majority of chaetognaths are epi- and mesoplanktonic.

Every chaetognath species lives in a more or less definite region and has a more or less definite depth as its principal habitat. Reaction to temperature is probably the main factor that keeps the species within a certain depth range; hence the optimum depth may vary somewhat with latitude. There is thus also operative a horizontal distribution based on temperature; hence there are warm-, cool-, and cold-water species. The majority of chaetognaths are warm-water, epiplanktonic organisms. There are further coastal, or *neritic*, species that generally occur near shores over the continental shelf and *oceanic* species that avoid coasts and prefer open water. Some species are remarkably sensitive to small changes of salinity, and probably salinity is a decisive factor in keeping oceanic species away from shores since sea water near shores is apt to be diluted by incoming rivers, melting ice, and so on. Thiel (1938) is of the opinion that the amount of available food constitutes the main factor in the distribution of chaetognaths. After an extensive study of the chaetognaths of the South Atlantic he concluded that the areas of greatest abundance of chaetognaths correspond to the areas of greatest abundance of the *nannoplankton* (planktonic animals of small size suitable as food for chaetognaths) and that the deep-water chaetognaths tend to aggregate beneath surface areas of rich nannoplankton. Conversely, areas of minimal abundance of chaetognaths correspond to areas poor in nannoplankton. There are also common and rare species regardless of environmental factors. Finally, it seems to be generally observed that eggs and young occur in more shallow water than adults, or in other words, chaetognaths tend to seek deeper waters as they grow and mature.

The habitat preferences of some of the more common species may now be indicated. *Sagitta serratodentata* (Fig. 18B), easily distinguished by the serrated grasping spines, is one of the commonest epiplanktonic, warm-water chaetognaths. It is found in the surface waters above 50 m. in all tropical and subtropical seas, but does not avoid cooler temperatures and hence is not uncommon in temperate waters and may be carried north in the Gulf Stream. It is therefore frequent in summer in the Gulf of Maine and off Nova Scotia and Newfoundland, disappearing in winter. It is found throughout the Atlantic between 50° north latitude and 40° south latitude and is also common in the Mediterranean, the Red Sea, the Indo-Australian region, and off Japan. *Sagitta enflata* (Fig. 19C) is another warm-water epiplanktonic species common in tropical and subtropical waters between latitudes 40° north and south. Like the preceding species it may be carried into the Gulf of Maine with the Gulf Stream but is less tolerant of colder waters than *serratodentata*. It is reported as very common in the Mediterranean (Joubin, 1928–1934), especially in the Bay of Algiers, where it constituted 40 per cent of the chaetognath population (Ramult and Rose, 1945); as forming 50 per cent of a chaetognath collection in the Red Sea (Ghirardelli, 1948); as extremely common in the Indo–West Pacific area (Burfield and Harvey, 1926; Tokioka, 1954b, 1955a, b, 1956a, b); as the most common chaetognath of the Java Sea (Oye, 1918; Delsman, 1939), of the Philippines (Michael, 1919), and of the Indian Ocean (Ritter-Zahony, 1909d); and as common in the Maldive-Laccadive region (Doncaster, 1902b), off Australia (Johnston and Taylor,

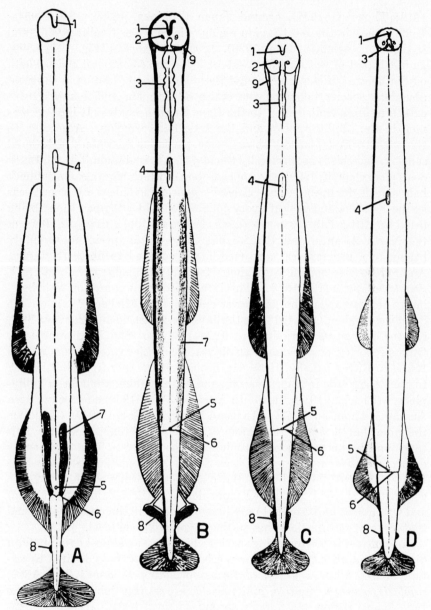

FIG. 18.—Some common species of Sagitta. *A*, *S. lyra*. *B*, *S. serratodentata*. *C*, *S. bedoti*. *D*, *S. hexaptera*. (*All after Ritter-Zahony, 1911c.*) 1, mouth; 2, eyes; 3, ciliary loop; 4, subenteric ganglion; 5, anus; 6, trunk-tail septum; 7, ovaries; 8, seminal vesicles; 9, collarette.

1919; Thomson, 1947), around Japan (Tokioka, 1939c, 1940, 1954a; Kado, 1953), in the West Indian region (Pierce, 1954; Caabro, 1955), and in the South Atlantic (Thiel, 1938). *Sagitta bipunctata* (Fig. 13*A*) is also an inhabitant of warm surface waters, being the commonest chaetognath off San Diego (Michael, 1911) and Bermuda (Moore, 1949) and the most abundant species taken on the cruise of Germain and Joubin (1916) extending from Spitsbergen to the Cape Verde Islands. It is also common in the Mediterranean and the Indo-Pacific region. According to Oye (1918), *S. bipunctata* shows some partiality to waters of lowered salinity, and this is confirmed by the fact that it is abundant in the Black Sea (Moltschanoff, 1909), the upper waters of which have a salinity about half that of the open ocean. *Sagitta bipunctata* avoids the warmest seas as the Red Sea and appears very tolerant of colder temperatures, being listed by Ritter-Zahony in the *Fauna Arctica* (1910b) as a coastal form of the North Atlantic and Pacific; but these arctic specimens probably belong to a geographical race (see later), adapted to northern waters. Another species spread throughout tropical and subtropical waters is *Sagitta hexaptera* (Fig. 18*D*). This is regarded by some authors as belonging to the mesoplankton and lower epiplankton (Michael, 1911, for the San Diego region; Oye, 1918, for the Java Sea; Burfield and Harvey, 1926, for the Indian Ocean; Joubin, 1928–1934, for the Mediterranean). Others report it as a common epiplanktonic species (Mediterranean and Red Sea, Ritter-Zahony, 1909c, d; throughout the area from Spitsbergen to the Cape Verde Islands, Germain and Joubin, 1916; around the Philippines, Michael, 1919; in the South Atlantic, Thiel, 1938; off southwestern Australia, Thomson, 1947; and around Bermuda, Moore, 1949). It seems probable that *S. hexaptera* is more or less epiplanktonic in warmer latitudes and becomes mesoplanktonic in colder waters. This explains its occurrence as far north as the Nova Scotia–Newfoundland region where Huntsman (1919) found it in the outermost warmer stations, off the continental shelf at 200 m. or more depth. Ritter-Zahony (1911b, c) and Oye (1918) indicate that only juveniles occur in the upper waters and that as they mature they sink to the mesoplanktonic level.

In contrast to the foregoing species which have an almost cosmopolitan distribution, other epiplanktonic species of *Sagitta* may be limited to certain areas. Thus a group of forms, including *S. bedoti* (Fig. 18*C*), *regularis, pulchra, neglecta,* and *robusta,* are surface inhabitants of the Indo-Pacific region and apparently are confined to this region by temperature requirements. *Sagitta bedoti* is one of the commonest chaetognaths around Japan (Tokioka, 1939c, 1940, 1942, 1954a; Kado, 1953) and India (Subramaniam, 1940) and is also found throughout the Java Sea (Oye, 1918; Delsman, 1939) and Indonesia (Fowler, 1906) and off Australia as far as 38° south latitude (Thomson, 1947). A similar distribution obtains for the other species of this group, called the *neglecta* group (Tokioka, 1952). Whereas this group of species is limited to western Pacific tropical waters by its avoidance of cooler temperatures, *Sagitta elegans* (Fig. 1A) is an example of a chaetognath confined to northern waters by its avoidance of warmer temperatures. This is an epiplanktonic, neritic, cold-water species, common along the northern shores of the North Atlantic as far as Spitsbergen (81° north latitude, Hardy, 1936). It is the most common and characteristic chaetognath of the northeastern coast of North America, being very common off Cape Cod over the Georges Bank (Clarke, Pierce, and Bumpus, 1943), in the Gulf of Maine, where it constitutes 82 per cent of the chaetognaths present (Redfield and Beale, 1940), and is one of the three dominant planktonic animals (Bigelow, 1926) in the Nova Scotia–Newfoundland region (Huntsman, 1919) and along the west coast of Greenland (Kramp, 1918). Although not usually found south of Nantucket it may extend to Chesapeake Bay during the cooler months of the year (Cowles, 1930). It is further the most common and dominant chaetognath off the western coast of Canada (Lea, 1955). It is lacking in the Southern Hemisphere. As a neritic species, *S. elegans* appears adapted to a wide range of salinity but is not found below 26.5 parts per thousand (Lea, 1955). Surface collections yield mostly juveniles; the adults seem to seek deeper colder water (Huntsman, 1919). Arctic representatives belong to a distinct geographic race. A rather restricted distribution is shown by *S. setosa*, a neritic, epiplanktonic chaetognath limited to the North Sea and the British Isles with possibly some spread into the adjacent Atlantic. Another species of very restricted distribution is *S. helenae*, limited to the shelf water from the eastern Gulf of Mexico to Cape Hatteras (Ritter-Zahony, 1910a; Pierce, 1954; Bumpus and Pierce, 1955).

As common mesoplanktonic species, with their main habitat in cooler waters below 200 m. depth, may be listed *Sagitta lyra, planctonis, decipiens, macrocephala, maxima,* and *minima.* *Sagitta lyra* (Fig. 18A) is a common, widely spread, oceanic, mesoplanktonic chaetognath, found throughout the tropical and temperate Atlantic at depths variously given as 150 to 450 m. or even deeper. It is also common in the Mediterranean (Germain and Joubin, 1916; Joubin, 1928–1934; Ramult and Rose, 1945; Ghirardelli, 1950a, 1952) and is found in the tropical West Pacific but is one of the less common species there. Some authors believe that *S. lyra* may extend into the epiplankton, presumably under suitable conditions of temperature. Bollmann (1934) lists *S. lyra* among the chaetognaths that find their optimum conditions at intermediate temperatures, 17 to 24°C. During the summer *S. lyra* may be carried into the Gulf of Maine from outside deeper waters (Bigelow, 1926) and is also found at the outer stations, off the continental shelf, in the Nova Scotia–Newfoundland region

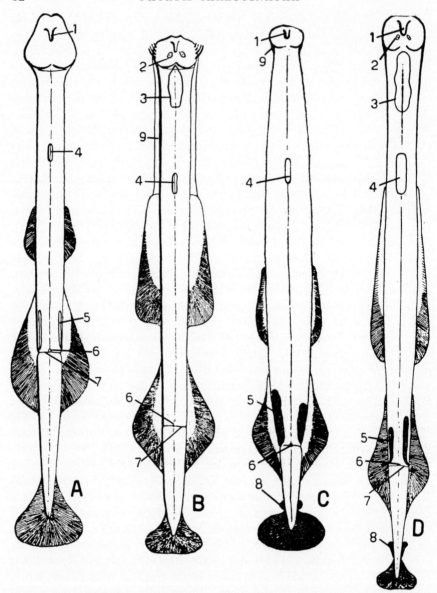

FIG. 19.—Additional common species of chaetognaths. *A, S. macrocephala. B, S. planctonis. C, S. enflata. D, S. decipiens. (All after Ritter-Zahony, 1911c.)* 1, mouth; 2, eyes; 3, ciliary loop; 4, subenteric ganglion; 5, ovaries; 6, anus; 7, trunk-tail septum; 8, seminal vesicles; 9, collarette.

(Huntsman, 1919). Records of *S. planctonis* must be revised in view of the claim of David (1956) that three species have been confused under this name. The true *planctonis* is epipelagic in tropical and subtropical waters and hence belongs with the species considered above. The mesoplanktonic form of cooler waters is called by David *S. zetesios;* this inhabits depths varying from 200 to 600 m. in colder waters, at temperatures not above 10 to 12°C. Presumably it is *zetesios* that is listed by Kramp (1918) from the west coast of Greenland and by Jameson (1914), Johnston and Taylor (1921), and Hardy and Günther (1935) as common in the Antarctic to at least 64° south latitude to depths of 200 to 800 m. *Sagitta decipiens* (includes *sibogae*) (Fig. 19D) is a mesoplanktonic species with a wide distribution (Ritter-Zahony, 1911c) but especially found in the deeper parts of tropical and subtropical waters (Burfield and Harvey, 1926). *Sagitta macrocephala* (Fig. 19A) lives at depths of 800 to 1500 m., between temperature ranges of 4 to 15°C, mostly in the Atlantic between latitudes 45° north and 35° south, according to Thiel (1938); but was found in the Antarctic at 200 m. at 64° south latitude by Johnston and Taylor (1921). *Sagitta maxima*, a large species to 80 mm. in length, belongs to the upper mesoplankton, at depths of 50 to 400 m., in open waters of full salinity, away from shores, at temperatures below 6.5°C. It is a common species in temperate, arctic, and antarctic waters and is particularly characteristic of the northern parts of the North Atlantic. It is reported in north European waters to 80° north latitude (Ritter-Zahony, 1910b) and was found by Kramp (1918) to be the most common chaetognath off the west coast of Greenland at 58 to 60° north latitude. It occurs in spring in the Gulf of Maine (Bigelow, 1926), coming in from outside with cold water, and also occurs in the Nova Scotia–Newfoundland region at stations outside the continental shelf (Huntsman, 1919). Thiel (1938) lists it from the South Atlantic, and it is also regularly found in the Antarctic (Germain, 1913; Jameson, 1914; Mackintosh, 1937). *Sagitta minima*, a very small species under 10 mm. in length, belongs to the lower epiplankton and upper mesoplankton, at depths from 100 to 400 m., mostly around 200 m., and appears limited by temperature requirements to waters neither too warm nor too cold.

Other chaetognath genera, except *Spadella*, are ecologically similar to *Sagitta*. *Eukrohnia hamata* (Fig. 13B) is a widely spread mesoplanktonic or even bathyplanktonic dweller in cold waters of good salinity, mostly at 200 to 600 m., at temperatures below 15°C, but approaches the surface in cold latitudes, being common in both arctic and antarctic waters. It is found throughout the year in the deeper waters of the Gulf of Maine but does not breed there (Bigelow, 1926); in the Nova Scotia–Newfoundland region in boreal water descending from the north (Huntsman, 1919); off the western coast of Canada (Lea, 1955); in abundance in the deeper waters of the west coast of Greenland at 58 to 60° north latitude (Kramp, 1918, 1939); off Labrador (Kielhorn, 1952); and at various far northern points in the Atlantic to 81° north latitude, as Greenland, Baffin's Bay, Lafoten, Spitsbergen, Iceland, and the Barents Sea (Ritter-Zahony, 1910b). It is also common in the Antarctic, being the dominant species around South Georgia at 55° south latitude (Hardy and Gunther, 1935), taken also at 64° by Johnston and Taylor (1921) and from 56 to 77° at temperatures around zero degrees centigrade by Fowler (1907). It is also at home in deeper waters in intermediate regions, being found throughout cruises from Spitsbergen to the Cape Verde Islands (Germain and Joubin, 1916) and from the English Channel to the Antarctic (Bollmann, 1934), also in the Mediterranean (Joubin, 1928–1934) and in the offshore waters of the Gulf of Mexico (Pierce, 1954), and also generally in the South Atlantic (Thiel, 1938) and the Indo-Pacific region (Burfield and Harvey, 1926). Tokioka (1939c) states that it is the most common deep-water chaetognath.

Eukrohnia fowleri is less common than *Eu. hamata* (of which it is regarded as a variant by some) but is also a widely distributed mesoplanktonic species. *Pterosagitta draco* (Fig. 2*B*) classifies as a widely distributed epiplanktonic oceanic species, characteristic of the temperate and tropical Atlantic at depths of 50 to 100 m. and at temperatures of 15 to 25°C (Ritter-Zahony, 1911b; Germain and Joubin, 1916; Bollmann, 1934; Thiel, 1938; Moore, 1949). This species is also widely spread throughout the Indo-Pacific region, being recorded from Australian waters (Johnston and Taylor, 1919; Thomson, 1947), Java (Oye, 1918), Indonesia (Fowler, 1906), the Indo-Pacific in general (Burfield and Harvey, 1926; Tokioka, 1952, 1955a, 1956a), the Maldive-Laccadive Archipelago (Doncaster, 1902b), and Japan (Tokioka, 1939c, 1940; Kado, 1953). It was found very common off Peru by Bieri (1957) but seems infrequent off the Pacific Coast of North America. A somewhat similar distribution obtains for *Krohnitta subtilis* (Fig. 14*B*), a common epiplanktonic to mesoplanktonic species widely found in the central and temperate Atlantic, including the Mediterranean (Ritter-Zahony, 1911b; Germain and Joubin, 1916; Bollmann, 1934; Thiel, 1938). Other records include Australian waters, but not south of 38° (Johnston and Taylor, 1919; Thomson, 1947); Indonesia (Fowler, 1906); the Java Sea (Oye, 1918); the Indo-Pacific in general (Burfield and Harvey, 1926; Tokioka, 1952); Japan (Tokioka, 1939c, 1940; Kado, 1953); the West Indian region (Davis, 1949; Moore, 1949; Vannucci and Hosoe, 1952; Pierce, 1954; Bumpus and Pierce, 1955); and the Panamic region (Michael, 1911; Bieri, 1957).

It may be questioned whether there are any strictly bathypelagic chaetognaths, that is, species confined to abyssal depths. *Heterokrohnia mirabilis* (Fig. 14*A*) was taken on the German Southpolar Expedition, during which specimens were collected in the Antarctic at depths of 2000, 3000, and 3423 m. (Ritter-Zahony, 1911c); but this author surmises that the species is also mesoplanktonic. *Bathyspadella edentata* (Fig. 15*A*) is regarded by its discoverer as a true bathypelagic chaetognath chiefly because of the lack of pigment in its eyes (Tokioka, 1939b); but the depth off Japan from which it came is uncertain because the net was drawn from 1000 m. to the surface. Specimens of a number of common chaetognath species have been taken from great depths. Thus Joubin (1928–1934) states that *S. lyra* has been taken to 2300 m., *S. serratodentata* to 3000 m., and *S. hexaptera* to 4330 m. *Sagitta lyra* is also recorded in Indonesia at 1500 m. (Fowler, 1906), and the German Southpolar Expedition took several hundred specimens in the South Atlantic at 3000 m. (Ritter-Zahony, 1911c). A specimen of *Krohnitta subtilis* was collected off Scotland at 1800 m. by Fraser (1949). *Sagitta planctonis* (really *zetesios?*) is often reported from deep waters, as 1200 to 3000 m. in the Atlantic (Ritter-Zahony, 1911c; Germain and Joubin, 1916; Joubin, 1928–1934), including a record of 2000 m. in the Bay of Biscay (Fowler, 1906). *Sagitta maxima* is recorded at 2660 m. in the Antarctic (Jameson, 1914) and at 1000 to 3000 m. in the material of the German Southpolar Expedition (Ritter-Zahony, 1911c). *Sagitta gazellae*, a species confined to subantarctic and antarctic waters, was supposed to be bathyplanktonic, having been taken by the Scottish Antarctic Expedition at 5500 m. (Jameson, 1914) and by the German Southpolar Expedition at 2500 to 3000 m. (Ritter-Zahony, 1911c); but David (1955) reports its maximum abundance at 50 to 100 m., although it breeds only below 750 m. It is not surprising to find the cold-water species, *Eukrohnia hamata*, often descending to great depths; it was taken by the German Southpolar Expedition at almost all depths to 3423 m. in the Indian, South Atlantic, and Antarctic Oceans, often occurring in swarms at 2500 to 3000 m., further at 4000 m. in the Bay of Biscay (Fowler, 1905). The latter author, dredging in the Bay of Biscay, noted chaetognaths as not uncommon at 2700 to 3600 m., and the German Southpolar Expedition took 14 different species at 3000 m. (Ritter-Zahony, 1911c). Probably almost any mesoplanktonic chaetognath may under proper conditions of temperature descend into bathypelagic levels; this tendency seems more marked in the largest individuals of the species.

Of interest with regard to depth is the collection of chaetognaths from the Kurile-Kamchatka Trench reported by Chindonova (1955). Several common species were taken, mostly at modest depths or within the known depth range, but one specimen was obtained of *Heterokrohnia mirabilis*, at 5000 m. This not only exceeds the known depth range but is the first finding of the species since the record of Ritter-Zahony (1911c).   Three specimens were secured of *S. planctonis* at 1000–2000, 2000–4000, and 4000–8000 m.

As already sufficiently mentioned, the members of the genus *Spadella* contrast with other chaetognaths in their benthonic habits and adaptive development of adhesive papillae.   In consequence, their distribution is somewhat limited.   The best-known species, *Sp. cephaloptera* (Fig. 2*A*), is found chiefly around the British Isles and in the Mediterranean.   *Sp. schizoptera* (Fig. 13*C*) was described by Conant (1895) from the Bahamas but has since been taken on the coast of New South Wales (Mawson, 1944).   The other known species of the genus have so far been found only on Australian coasts (*sheardi*, Fig. 13*D*, and *johnstoni* from New South Wales, Mawson, 1944).

Despite the wealth of collecting data on chaetognaths, it is difficult to ascertain the actual number of chaetognaths per unit of water because in most cases the nets are drawn through considerable vertical or horizontal distances.   It further appears that if the nets are drawn too slowly, many of the chaetognaths escape.   Bigelow (1926) records catches of *S. elegans* off the New England coast of 1000 to 5000 per square meter, but such abundance obtains only for small areas.   The majority of plankton hauls yield relatively few specimens.

It is well known that many planktonic animals exhibit a diurnal migration, rising toward the surface at night and descending at dawn. This migration is usually regarded as a reaction to light, although other factors, especially temperature, could obviously be involved.   Michael (1911) formulated an explanation to the effect that each plankter tends to remain at the level of its optimum light conditions; as the intensity of light diminishes toward sunset the animal follows the waning intensity toward the surface; in darkness it tends to disperse as a light stimulus is wanting; but with the onset of dawn it is again drawn to the surface as its optimum light intensity is reached there but descends as the intensity increases with full daylight.   In his study of the chaetognaths of the San Diego region, Michael found that *Sagitta bipunctata* exhibits a typical diurnal migration, appearing in maximum abundance at or near the surface between 6 and 8 P.M. and 4 and 6 A.M. and descending by noon to depths of 80 to 150 m.   Temperature was also found to play a role as the species reached its greatest abundance at the surface at temperatures between 16 and 17.5°C.   Esterly (1919) in laboratory tests of *S. bipunctata* found that this species is strongly positive to light at a variety of intensities to full daylight and also has a well-defined negative geotropism. This latter reaction causes the animal to come to the surface in darkness and dim light, but in bright light the gravity reaction reverses and a positive geotropism overcomes the light attraction and the animal descends.

An avoidance of cold temperature checks the downward descent. But Rose (1925), testing *S. bipunctata* in the Mediterranean, was unable to detect any response whatever to light. He found the species very sensitive to temperature, choosing the zone of 24 to 28°C in a temperature gradient ranging from 20 to 28°C and avoiding 30° or higher. But a definite diurnal migration was noted for *S. bipunctata*, also *S. hexaptera*, at Bermuda by Moore (1949). As regards the latter species the results of Welsh, Chace, and Minnemacher (1937) indicate retreat to the 400-m. level at midday in the Sargasso Sea and an ascent above this level at night. A marked diurnal migration of *Pterosagitta draco* at Bermuda was noticed by Moore (1949). Joubin (1928–1934) recorded that *S. lyra* rises to the surface at night in the Mediterranean. Hamon (1956) found that the daytime catch of chaetognaths differs from the night catch off Indonesia. On the other hand, a number of authors have failed to find any evidence of a diurnal migration in chaetognaths, and some claim chaetognaths are indifferent to light.

From the frequent prevalence of juveniles in the upper waters it appears that many chaetognaths must undergo an annual vertical migration associated with breeding. This was definitely ascertained for *S. gazellae* in the Antarctic by David (1955). Maturing specimens descend to deeper warmer water, being seldom found in the mature state above 750 m. The young ascend to surface waters at 50 to 100 m. depth and there feed and grow for some months, at a rate of about 5 mm. per month, descending again as they approach sexual maturity. A similar cycle in the Antarctic was indicated for *Eukrohnia hamata* by Mackintosh (1937).

Such data and other data from plankton hauls indicate that chaetognaths live about a year, dying after breeding, since large specimens usually disappear from the catches after young become dominant in them. However, *Sagitta elegans arctica* apparently requires 2 years to attain sexual maturity (Dunbar, 1940). Probably breeding is without relation to longevity in the benthonic *Spadella* species.

6. Geographic Distribution.—As the majority of chaetognaths are warm-water epiplanktonic organisms one may anticipate their greatest abundance in the tropical and subtropical waters of the Indo–West Pacific region, a vast expanse extending from the Red Sea and the central eastern coast of Africa to the Hawaiian Islands and Polynesia and including the coasts of Arabia, India, Siam, and much of Australia and the innumerable islands of the central western Pacific, roughly between the latitudes of 20° north and 20° south. Tokioka (1952) stated that 85 per cent of the known species of chaetognaths occur in this area, and King and Demond (1953) found that chaetognaths constitute 12 per cent of the total plankton catch in the central west Pacific. There exists a large literature on the chaetognaths of this area or of various parts of it of which the following list is not complete: Fowler, 1906; Ritter-Zahony, 1909c; Oye, 1918; Michael, 1919; Burfield and Harvey, 1926; Grey, 1930; Delsman, 1939; Subramaniam, 1937, 1940; Tokioka, 1942, 1954b, 1955a, b, 1956a, b; Thomson, 1947; Ghirardelli, 1948; Burfield, 1950; George, 1952; Hida and King, 1955; King and Demond, 1953; Ganapati and Rao, 1954; Hamon, 1956; Hida, 1957. An exhaustive bibliography of the area together with a tabulation of the findings appears in Thomson (1947). By all accounts *S. enflata* is the most common chaetognath in the area, occurring practically everywhere and constituting 30 to 50 per cent of the chaetognath take in some collections (Burfield and Harvey, 1926; Ghirardelli, 1948; Tokioka, 1955a). Besides *S. enflata*, Tokioka (1955a) considers *S. hexaptera*, *S. serratodentata*, and *Pterosagitta draco* as the most characteristic chaetognaths of the area. Other species commonly taken are *S. bipunctata*, *lyra*, *planctonis*, *robusta*, *decipiens*, *macrocephala*, *minima*, and *Krohnitta subtilis*, together with a group of species limited to the Indo-Pacific area, namely, *S. neglecta*, *bedoti*, *bedfordi*, *crassa*, *regularis*, *neglecta*, *pulchra*, *parva*, *delicata*, *oceanica*, *tropica*, *timida*, *hispida*, and *Krohnitta pacifica*.

Much of Australia (Johnston and Taylor, 1919; Thomson, 1947) participates in the Indo-Pacific fauna, and the same species mentioned above are found off its coasts; 19 species had been recorded by 1947. Peculiar to Australian coasts are species of *Spadella* (page 38). Japan also (Tokioka, 1939c, 1940, 1954a; Kado, 1953) shares in the general Indo–West Pacific chaetognath fauna. Among the most common species are forms mentioned above as peculiar to the general area, namely, *S. crassa*, *bedoti*, *robusta*, *neglecta*, and *regularis*. In northern Japan a northern element is seen in the presence of *S. elegans*.

Proceeding into the boreal North Atlantic (Strodtmann, 1905; Kramp, 1915; Germain and Joubin, 1916; Kuhl, 1928; Meek, 1928; Fraser, 1937, 1939, 1949, 1952; Pierce, 1941) one finds that *S. elegans* and *S. setosa* are the characteristic chaetognaths of the Baltic and North Seas and around the British Isles. Fraser (1952) considers that *S. setosa* is endemic to the North Sea. Others commonly found, especially proceeding southward along the Atlantic coast of Spain and Africa, are *S. hexaptera*, *bipunctata*, *enflata*, *serratodentata*, *macrocephala*, and *hispida*. Furnestin (1957) thinks that a group of species related to *S. friderici* and including also *S. setosa*, *hispida*, *tenuis*, and *helenae* is characteristic of the eastern boreal North Atlantic.

The eastern North Atlantic fauna commonly penetrates into the Mediterranean. Mediterranean chaetognaths have been treated by Joubin (1928–1934), Scaccini and Ghirardelli (1941b), Ramult and Rose (1945), Ghirardelli (1950a, 1952), Faure (1952), Hamon (1952), Furnestin (1953a, b, 1957), Rose and Hamon (1953), Massuti (1954). Common Mediterranean species are *S. hexaptera, lyra, enflata, bipunctata, setosa, serratodentata, minima,* and *friderici* and *Spadella cephaloptera* and *Pterosagitta draco*. Scaccini and Ghirardelli (1941b) found *S. setosa* the most common species in the Adriatic. Furnestin (1953a, b) reported that over half the take off Israel and Morocco consisted of *S. friderici*. The collections of Ramult and Rose in the Bay of Algiers consisted 56 per cent of *S. bipunctata* and 40 per cent of *S. enflata*. Massuti found that on the Mediterranean coast of Spain *S. enflata* dominates in autumn and *S. bipunctata* in spring.

Atlantic arctic chaetognaths have been reported by Ritter-Zahony (1910b), Kramp (1918, 1939), Hardy (1936), and Kielhorn (1952). The typical arctic species are *S. elegans* (arctic variant) and *Eukrohnia hamata;* both are probably circumpolar. Kielhorn listed *Eu. hamata* as the only important chaetognath off Labrador. Ritter-Zahony also reported *S. maxima* and *S. bipunctata,* species common in the northern North Atlantic plankton.

The chaetognath fauna of the Atlantic Coast of North America south of Labrador has been treated by Bigelow (1914a, 1917, 1926), Huntsman (1919), Fish (1925), Cowles (1930), Redfield and Beale (1940), Clarke, Pierce, and Bumpus (1943), Pierce (1953), and Bumpus and Pierce (1955). In the Nova Scotia–Newfoundland region (Huntsman) *S. elegans* is the characteristic species found generally throughout the area in cool shallow waters of low salinity. *Sagitta serratodentata* was also taken inshore and although typically a warm-water form appears to endure lower temperature and more variation of salinity than other chaetognaths of the same category. *Sagitta lyra, S. maxima,* and *Eukrohnia hamata* were found in colder, deeper waters at the outer stations of the region, having descended from the north in boreal currents, whereas *S. hexaptera,* also limited to the deeper outer but warmer stations, had come in from the south via the Gulf Stream. A number of studies have been made of the plankton of the Gulf of Maine (Bigelow, Redfield, and Beale). Of the six species of chaetognaths taken by these authors, *S. elegans* is the most common and characteristic, forming 82 per cent of the chaetognath catch at times. It is most common in the Gulf of Maine and adjacent areas during the warmer parts of the year, although avoiding the warm surface layers at the height of summer, and diminishes inshore in winter. *Sagitta serratodentata* is also general throughout the area, sometimes in numbers equal to or exceeding those of *S. elegans* and varying seasonally with the latter. *Sagitta enflata* is a warm-water epiplanktonic species that may be carried into the Gulf of Maine at times with the Gulf Stream. *Eukrohnia hamata* and *S. lyra* and *maxima* are mesoplanktonic chaetognaths of cool or cold waters that come into the Gulf of Maine from outside waters and may be found there in deeper levels; the first is present at 75 to 250 m. throughout the year, whereas *S. lyra* is a summer visitor found only in July and August and *S. maxima* comes in with boreal water in spring.   In the Massachusetts area *S. elegans* is also the prevalent species. Fish reported it as present in the Cape Cod area from December to July, breeding in spring.   Bigelow found it common in Massachusetts Bay, increasing in numbers in winter, when it formed 50 to 75 per cent of the total plankton catch; *S. serratodentata* was also taken.   In their study of Georges Bank, a flat-topped bottom area east of Cape Cod about 50 miles in diameter and 25 to 100 m. below the surface, Clarke, Pierce, and Bumpus located a permanent population of *S. elegans*, accumulated over the bank because of the relative stability, absence of dislocating currents, and uniformity of temperature and salinity in the water there.   The central water over the bank inhabited by *S. elegans* remains more or less stationary, whereas the outer water circulates with fluctuating conditions, and in this outer water *S. serratodentata* and *S. enflata* may be found.

In short, *S. elegans*, a neritic cold-water form enduring much change of salinity, is the dominant chaetognath of the Atlantic Coast of the northeastern United States as far south as Chesapeake Bay, where Cowles (1930) noted it during the cooler parts of the year with winter breeding as indicated by large catches of young in April and May.   It was the chief chaetognath collected by Bigelow (1915) in a cruise extending from Chesapeake Bay to Nova Scotia; *S. serratodentata* was also taken not infrequently, especially south of New York, and sometimes in abundance.

South of Chesapeake Bay the chaetognath fauna undergoes a decided change.   Cape Hatteras seems to be the dividing point between the colder, less saline coastal waters north of the Cape and the warmer, more saline coastal waters to the south of it.   The chaetognath fauna over the continental shelf off North Carolina was investigated by Pierce (1953) and Bumpus and Pierce (1955).   *Sagitta enflata*, a euryhaline, eurythermal species, is the most common species over the shelf, might constitute 40 to 60 per cent of the chaetognath catch, and occur in quantities as high as 160 in 10 cc. of sea water.   *Sagitta serratodentata* was also abundant, widely distributed over the shelf.   The other species taken off North Carolina are mostly of tropical or subtropical nature, brought in with the Florida current.   They comprised *S. helenae, tenuis, hispida, minima, Krohnitta subtilis* and *pacifica*, and *Pterosagitta draco*, plus two elements from the general North Atlantic plankton, *S. hexaptera* and *bipunctata*.   Chaetognaths were said to be the most common element of the plankton over the Carolina shelf, being taken at all stations without regard to season.

The Carolinian fauna is of course part of the general West Indian fauna. West Indian chaetognaths have been reported by Ritter-Zahony (1910a), Davis (1949), King (1949), Moore (1949), Pierce (1951, 1954), Vannucci and Hosoe (1952), Caabro (1955), and Tokioka (1955c). Most of these investigations concern the waters off the west coast of Florida. Characteristic species, somewhat limited to the West Indian region, are *S. hispida* and *tenuis* from inshore waters, *helenae* from offshore waters. In Pierce's work (1951) *S. helenae* and *tenuis* occurred at all stations and appeared to breed continuously throughout the year; although *S. hispida* was not found throughout the year, it might reach concentrations of 500 per cubic meter of sea water. *S. hispida* was originally described by Conant (1895) from the region of Beaufort, North Carolina, and was later reported by the same author (1896) from Jamaica, Bimini, and other parts of the Bahamas. *Sagitta tenuis* was first described from Jamaica (Conant, 1896) and later reported by Pierce (1951) for both coasts of Florida and for Beaufort. Both *hispida* and *tenuis* were also taken around Cuba (Caabro, 1955) and together with *helenae* extend up the Florida coast to the Carolinas. In addition to these three somewhat endemic species the usual widely spread chaetognaths are present in the West Indian region, namely, *S. enflata, bipunctata, serratodentata, hexaptera, lyra, macrocephala, Krohnitta subtilis* and *pacifica*, and *Pterosagitta draco*, of which the first three or four named are the most common. In a study of Bermudan chaetognaths, Moore (1949) listed *S. hexaptera, bipunctata, serratodentata*, and *lyra* as common species, *hispida* as common inshore, *Pt. draco* and *Kr. subtilis* as fairly common, and *enflata, helenae*, and *planctonis* as uncommon.

For the Pacific Coast of North America there are available the reports of Michael (1911) from the San Diego area and of Lea (1955) from the western coast of Canada. The former found *S. bipunctata* and *serratodentata* the most common and characteristic species of the San Diego area; although *S. enflata* was taken in large numbers, these came from a few collections; hence this species was not regarded as typical of the area. Small numbers were found of *S. maxima* (misidentified as *lyra*), *hexaptera, neglecta, planctonis, Eu. hamata, Kr. subtilis*, and *Pt. draco* (one specimen). Because of the varied currents reaching the western coast of Canada, Lea expected a large variety of chaetognath species, but in fact only four species were taken, *S. elegans, decipiens, lyra*, and *Eu. hamata*, and only the first was at all common. *Sagitta elegans* is thus the dominant species along the colder parts of both North American coasts. Its presence along coasts is generally taken to indicate an influx of oceanic waters.

Thomson (1947), tabulating the available information about Indo-Pacific chaetognaths, stated that eight of the Indo-Pacific species do not occur in the Atlantic and that five Atlantic species are not found in the Indo-Pacific.

Thiel (1938) made an exhaustive study of the chaetognaths of the South Atlantic. The majority of individuals, belonging to *S. serratodentata, enflata, hexaptera,* and *bipunctata,* occur in the upper 50 m. Between 50 and 400 m. are found *S. minima, maxima, planctonis, Pt. draco, Kr. subtilis,* and *Eu. hamata.* Several other species occur in small numbers; unfortunately there is in this article considerable lumping of species now regarded as distinct. At any rate, *S. serratodentata* appears by far the most common species irrespective of depth. Bollmann (1934) also noted that *S. serratodentata* is the most common species in the warm and temperate waters of the Atlantic, constituting one-third of the catch.

Chaetognaths of antarctic and subantarctic waters have been collected by a succession of antarctic expeditions and reported by Fowler (1907), Ritter-Zahony (1911c), Germain (1913), Jameson (1914), Johnston and Taylor (1921), Burfield (1930), Hardy and Gunther (1935), Mackintosh (1937), Ghirardelli (1953b), and David (1955). The most common and characteristic species are *Eu. hamata* and *S. gazellae.* Other species taken in smaller numbers are *S. maxima* and *planctonis* and a few other invaders from the deeper waters of more temperate zones. *Heterokrohnia mirabilis* was known only from the abyssal Antarctic until one specimen was taken at 5000 m. in the Kurile-Kamchatka region (Chindonova, 1955). *Eukrohnia hamata* is definitely the dominant species everywhere in south polar waters. Hardy and Gunther reported that at South Georgia in the subantarctic zone, it dominates at all stations. It was the only species obtained by blasting through the ice at Adelie Land on the edge of the Antarctic Continent south of Australia (Ghirardelli). Mackintosh, making repeated planktonic collections at a series of stations along longitude 80° west from the level of Cape Horn to the level of Graham Land in the true Antarctic, obtained large numbers of *Eu. hamata,* fewer of *S. maxima, gazellae,* and *planctonis* (but see below). This author called attention to an antarctic circulation that carries the cold surface water of lower salinity north to a line known as the Antarctic Convergence, where this water meets warmer, more saline water from the north. At the Convergence this warmer water sinks below the colder surface water and moves toward the pole below this. Planktonic organisms would therefore be moved north to the Convergence, then south again in the deeper warmer waters, hence tend to remain in the Antarctic. Mackintosh's collections showed plankton concentrated in the surface layers in winter, in the deeper water at 500 to 750 m. in summer. *Eukrohnia hamata* was found to be involved in this annual vertical migration, whereas the *Sagitta* species appeared able to remain in the upper layer. David (1955) made a detailed study of *S. gazellae,* previously confused with *lyra,* and decided that it is strictly a subantarctic and antarctic species, probably circumpolar. This auther (1956) also investigated

S. planctonis and concluded that the form listed from the Antarctic under this name is actually a new species, *S. marri,* also restricted to the Antarctic.

The only study of chaetognaths along the Pacific Coast of South America north of the Subantarctic is that of Bieri (1957) for Peru, but this author was interested mainly in chaetognaths as indicators of water movements. Of 15 species found, 8 were considered to have come in from the north or west with an influx of warmer water. The species most frequently taken were *Pt. draco, Kr. pacifica,* and *S. enflata* and *bedoti,* all of which are West Pacific forms, and the other species collected also come mostly from this area.

Chaetognaths, like most other animals, may occur in geographic variants or races, and they also exemplify the general rule of increase in size toward colder latitudes. *Sagitta bipunctata* is stated by Ritter-Zahony (1910b) to increase in size from a length of 12 mm. in the mid-Atlantic with sexual maturity at 5 mm. to a length of 44 mm. in the Arctic with sexual maturity at 30 mm. This size increase involves changes in the relative proportions of trunk and tail, alteration of the position of the posterior pair of lateral fins, formation of intestinal diverticula, and increase in the number of teeth and grasping spines. The number of the last augments from 8 or 9 in the southern limit of the range to 11 and 12, sometimes 13, in the Arctic. Thomson (1947) finds that *S. serratodentata* exists in three geographic subspecies, generally acknowledged by others also, namely, *atlantica,* 12 to 14 mm. long with 11 to 14 posterior teeth; *pacifica,* 14 to 16 mm. long with 19 to 22 posterior teeth; and *tasmanica,* 18 to 20 mm. long with 15 to 19 posterior teeth. These subspecies differ further in the shape of the seminal vesicles. There are two races of *S. gazellae,* a smaller subantarctic race sexually mature at 60 mm., and a larger antarctic race, sexually mature at 75 to 80 mm. (David, 1955). Around Japan Kado (1954) recognizes a small summer type and a large winter type of *S. crassa.* The best known of these geographic variants is the arctic form of *S. elegans,* termed *S. elegans arctica,* common in arctic and subarctic waters of the North Atlantic, chiefly along coasts, and probably circumpolar, being also known from the Bering Strait (Kramp, 1918). It is distinguished from the nominal form by its greater length (to 51 mm., Dunbar, 1941), larger number of grasping spines (10–12, as compared with 9–10 in the nominal form), and relatively shorter tail. There is also a Baltic race, *S. elegans baltica,* generally smaller with still shorter tail.

V. PHYLOGENETIC CONSIDERATIONS

As already indicated, the relationships of the Chaetognatha have remained problematical since their discovery in 1768. Kuhl in 1938 tabulated the various opinions extant in the literature to that date, and from this tabulation it appears that the chaetognaths have been regarded as allied to the mollusks eight times, to the Vermes Oligomera (page 3) six times, to the nematodes five times, to the annelids twice, and once each to the gordian worms, crustaceans, arachnids, hemichordates, and chordates. Two authors incline to the opinion that the chaetognaths belong at the bottom of the Bilateria as primitive "protocoelomates" related to the ancestor of all the bilateral groups. Apparently the chaetognaths have previously been placed among the enterocoelous coelomates, as in the present work, only in the Claus-Grobben-Kühn *Lehrbuch der Zoologie*. It will be recalled that Grobben was the author of the terms Protostomia and Deuterostomia (I, page 30).

The foregoing diversity of opinion is rather puzzling, for it seems obvious to the author that as far as *adult* anatomy is concerned, the chaetognaths resemble only one group, namely, the Aschelminthes. No one studying the adult anatomy of chaetognaths could possibly guess that they are coelomate animals. Their entire construction is of the pseudocoelomate type. The body wall lacks one of the two muscle layers characteristic of coelomate animals and is not lined by a coelomic membrane. Similarly, the intestine altogether lacks the musculature expected in a coelomate form and also is not clothed with a regular coelomic epithelium. The mesentery supporting the intestine is not histologically constructed after the coelomate pattern. The only typical coelomate structures possessed by chaetognaths are the ciliated coelomic funnels of the sperm ducts.

Numerous other resemblances to pseudocoelomate groups can be pointed out. The provision of the head with spines and teeth and of the body with tangoreceptive bristles is common among the aschelminths. The fins can be regarded as corresponding to the alae of nematodes. The division of the body into head and trunk with or without an intervening membrane is seen in priapulids, *Nectonema*, and the gordioid larva. The presence in the body cavity of membranes, sometimes simulating true mesenteries, occurs in gastrotrichs, priapulids, and nematodes. The central nervous system with its group of ganglia in the head region and circumenteric arrangement is obviously reminiscent of nematodes, and the close association of the peripheral nervous system with the epidermis recalls conditions in kinorhynchs and priapulids. The provision of the pharynx with a muscular end bulb reminds at once of nematodes; it also occurs in some nematomorphs. The limitation of the body-wall musculature to a longitudinal layer subdivided into longitudinal bands is again reminiscent of nematodes, and the histological construction of the muscle fibers bears some resemblance to that of nematode muscles.

It must be emphasized that all the foregoing similarities are of a general nature. *None of them is sufficiently specific* to justify an assumption of an aschelminth relationship. Further, the details of the embryology definitely preclude any possibility of relationship to aschelminths. Whereas in the aschelminths the cleavage pattern in general is of the unequal determinate type with resulting eutely and loss of regenerative power, that of the chaetognaths is equal and indeterminate without eutely and with retention of regenerative capability in the adult stage. The embryology also proves that the chaetognaths are true coelomate animals of the enterocoelous category. Nevertheless, the chaetognaths cannot be definitely brought into relationship with other enterocoelous phyla. The manner of formation of the coelomic sacs from the archenteron in chaetognaths by the backward extension of a pair of folds differs decidedly from that seen in other enterocoelous groups where the coelomic sacs are produced by outpouchings of the archenteron. Further, there are but two primary divisions of the coelom in chaetognaths as contrasted with three in echinoderms and hemichordates. These two latter phyla produce free-swimming larvae of the *dipleurula type* (IV, page 691), whereas the chaetognaths are devoid of a larval stage, being hatched as juveniles sufficiently resembling the adults. Finally, it is impossible to see any detailed anatomical resemblances between the chaetognaths and the other enterocoelous phyla.

Discussion of the affinities of the chaetognaths therefore reaches an impasse, in that the adult anatomy shows most resemblance to aschelminths but the embryology indicates a coelomate animal with an enterocoelous mode of formation of the coelom although other resemblances to enterocoelous groups are wanting. Under these circumstances it becomes impossible to ally the chaetognaths with any other existing invertebrate group. MacBride (1914) has attempted to evade these difficulties by passing directly from the gastrula type of structure represented by the Radiata to a *protocoelomate* type at the bottom of the Bilateria. This protocoelomate stage is regarded as surviving today as the Ctenophora and as represented in the ontogeny of the Bilateria by two larval types, the trochophore and the dipleurula. The latter is provided with gastric pouches representing the beginning of an enterocoelous coelom. Chaetognaths are regarded as a very early blind offshoot of the protocoelomate stock. It will be perceived that this theory is a thinly disguised mixture of the ctenophore-trochophore, enterocoel, and gonocoel theories (II, Chap. IX) and that it presents the same difficulties as these, primarily the difficulty of accounting for the acoelomate phyla. Further, as repeatedly stated, the coelomic sacs of the chaetognaths do not arise as enteric outpouchings nor can any definite resemblances be found between chaetognaths and groups genuinely derivable from the dipleurula.

Lameere (1931) considers the chaetognaths as most nearly related to the brachiopods, and this view has found some acceptance among European zoologists. The comparison of the grasping spines with the lophophore of brachiopods is not very convincing, and therefore the postulated relationship rests upon resemblances in embryonic development. In fact, the coelomic sacs of brachiopods are cut off from the archenteron in a manner somewhat similar to their formation in chaetognaths but in a different plane and different part of the body. There are no further striking similarities in the embryology of the two groups. The phylogenetic relationships of the lophophorate phyla (Ectoprocta, Brachiopoda, Phoronida) will be discussed after those groups have been treated.

In view of all the facts it seems probable that the chaetognaths should be regarded as having diverged at an early stage from the primitive ancestor of the Bilateria at the time that the dipleurula ancestor became differentiated. This view perhaps accepts MacBride's idea of a protocoelomate type but rejects the other tenets of this author. The possibility that the chaetognaths are remotely related to the dipleurula ancestor of the other Deuterostomia is the only justification for placing them, as done here, among the Deuterostomia.

Bibliography

Apstein, C. 1911. Résumé des observations sur le plankton des mers explorées pendant les années 1902–1908. Pt. II. Chaetognathes. Conseil Perm. Internation. Explor. Mer, Bull. Trimestriel. **Aurvillius, C.** 1896. Das Plankton des Baffins Bay und Davis St. Festschrift W. Lilljeborg. **Bieri, R.** 1957. The chaetognath fauna off Peru in 1941. Pacific Science 11. **Bigelow, H. B.** 1914a. Explorations in the Gulf of Maine. Bull. Mus. Comp. Zool. Harvard 58. 1914b. Oceanography and plankton of Massachusetts Bay. Bull. Mus. Comp. Zool. Harvard 48. 1915. Exploration of the coast water between Nova Scotia and Chesapeake Bay. Bull. Mus. Comp. Zool. Harvard 59. 1917. Explorations of the coast water between Cape Cod and Halifax. Bull. Mus. Comp. Zool. Harvard 61. 1926. Plankton of the offshore waters of the Gulf of Maine. Bull. U.S. Bur. Fisheries 40, pt. II. **Bollmann, A.** 1934. Die Chaetognathen der deutschen Antarktischen Expedition. Internation. Rev. Ges. Hydrobiol. 30. **Bordas, M.** 1920. Estudio de la ovogenesis en la S. bipunctata. Trabajos Mus. Nacion. Cienc. Natur. Madrid, ser. Zool., Mem. 42. **Buchner, P.** 1910. Die Schicksale des Keimplasma der Sagitten. Festschrift 60 Geburtstag R. Hertwig, vol. I. 1912. Chaetognatha. *Handbuch der Naturwissenschaften.* 1 ed., vol. 2. **Bumpus, D., and E. Pierce.** 1955. The hydrography and the distribution of chaetognaths over the continental shelf off North Carolina. Deep Sea Research, suppl. to 3. **Burfield, S.** 1927. Sagitta. Liverpool Marine Biol. Comm., Mem. 28, in Proc. Trans. Liverpool Biol. Soc. 41. 1930. Chaetognatha. Brit. Antarctic Terra Nova Exped., Zool. 7, pt. 4. 1950. Chaetognatha. Scient. Results Great Barrier Reef Exped., vol. 5, no. 8. **Burfield, S., and E. Harvey.** 1926. The chaetognaths of the Sealark Expedition. Trans. Linnaean Soc. London, Zool. 19. **Busch, W.** 1851. *Beobachtungen über Anatomie und Entwicklungs wirbelloser Thiere.* **Bütschli, O.** 1873. Zur Entwicklung der Sagitta. Ztschr. Wissenschaftl. Zool. 23. 1910. *Vorlesungen über vergleichende Anatomie.* **Caabro, J.** 1955. Quetognatos de los mares cubanos. Mem. Soc. Cubana Hist. Natur. 22. **Chatton, E.** 1953. Ordre des amoebiens nus ou Amoebaea. *In* **P. Grassé** (ed.), *Traité de zoologie*, vol. I, fasc. 2. **Chindonova, I.** 1955. Chaetognatha of the Kurile-Kamchatka Trench. Trudy Inst. Oceanol. Akad. Nauk U.S.S.R. 12. **Claparède, E.** 1863. *Beobachtungen über Anatomie und Entwicklungsgeschichte wirbelloser Thiere.* **Clarke, G., E. Pierce,** and **D. Bumpus.** 1943. Distribution and reproduction of Sagitta elegans on Georges Bank. Biol. Bull. 85. **Conant, F.** 1895. Description of two new chaetognaths. Ann. Mag. Natur. Hist., ser. 6, vol. 16. 1896. Notes on the Chaetognatha. Ann. Mag. Natur. Hist., ser. 6, vol. 18. **Costa, A.** 1869. Di un nuova genere di Chetognati. Annuario Mus. Zool. Univ. Napoli 5, art. 6. **Cowles, R.** 1930. Ecological study of the offshore waters of Chesapeake Bay. Bull. U.S. Bur. Fisheries 46. **Darwin, C.** 1844. Structure and propagation of Sagitta. Ann. Mag. Natur. Hist., ser. 1, vol. 13. **David, P.** 1955. Distribution of Sagitta gazellae. Discovery Repts. 27. 1956. Sagitta planctonis and related forms. Bull. Brit. Mus. (Natur. Hist.), Zool., vol. 4, no. 8. **Davis, C.** 1949. Plankton taken in marine waters off Florida. Quart. Jour. Florida Acad. Sci. 12. **Delsman, H.** 1939. Preliminary plankton investigations in the Java Sea. Treubia 17. **Dollfus, R., M. Anantaraman,** and **R. Nair.** 1954. Metacercarie chez Sagitta enflata. Ann. Parasitol. Hum. Comp. 29. **Doncaster, L.** 1902a. Development of Sagitta. Quart. Jour. Microsc. Sci. 46. 1902b. Chaetognatha. Fauna and Geography of Maldive and Laccadive Archipelagoes, vol. I. **Dunbar, J.** 1940. Size distribution and breeding cycles of four marine plankton animals from the Arctic. Jour. Animal Ecology 9. 1941. The breeding cycle in Sagitta elegans arctica. Canadian Jour. Research, sect. D, 19. **Elpatievsky, W.** 1909. Die Urgeschlechtszellenbildung bei Sagitta. Anat. Anz. 35. 1910. Die Entwicklungsgeschichte der Genitalprodukte bei Sagitta. Biol. Zhurnal 1. **Esterly, C.** 1919. Reactions of various plankton animals with reference to their diurnal migration. Univ. California Publ. Zool. 19. **Faure, Marie-Louise.** 1952. Étude de deux chaetognathes des eaux atlantiques du Maroc. Vie et Milieu 3, fasc. 1. **Fish, C.** 1925. Seasonal distribution of the plankton of the Woods Hole region. Bull. U.S. Bur. Fisheries 41. **Fowler, G.** 1905. Biscayan plankton. The Chaetognatha. Trans. Linnaean Soc. London, ser. 2, Zool. 10. 1906. The Chaetognatha of the Siboga Expedition. Siboga Exped. Monogr. 21. 1907. Chaetognatha. National Antarctic Exped., Natur. Hist. 3. **Fraser, J.** 1937. Distribution of chaetognaths in Scottish waters. Conseil Perm. Internation. Explor. Mer, Jour. de Conseil 12. 1939. Distribution of chaetognaths in Scottish waters. Conseil Perm. Internation. Explor. Mer, Jour. de Conseil 14. 1949. Occurrence of unusual species of Chaetognatha in Scottish plankton. Jour. Marine Biol. Assoc. Unit. Kingd. 28. 1952. Chaetognatha and other zooplankton of the Scottish area. Marine Research Series, Scottish Home Dept. **Furnestin, Marie-Louise.** 1953a. Sur quelques chaetognathes d'Israel. State of Israel, Dept. Fisheries, Sea Fisheries Research Station, Bull. no. 6. 1953b. Étude morphologique, biologique et systematique de Sagitta serratodentata. Bull. Inst. Océanogr. Monaco, no. 1025. 1954. Details anatomiques pour la détermination des chaetognathes. Bull. Soc. Zool. France 79. 1957. Chaetognathes et zooplancton de secteur atlantique marocain. Année Biologique 61. **Ganapati, P.,** and **T. Rao.** 1954. Distribution of the Chaetognatha in the waters off Visakhapatnam Coast. Andhra Univ., Mem. Oceanogr. 1. **Gegenbaur, C.** 1853. Über die Entwicklung von Sagitta. Ztschr. Wissenschaftl. Zool. 5. 1858. Über die Entwicklung der Sagitta. Abhandl. Naturforsch. Gesellsch. Halle 4. 1859. *Grundzüge der vergleichenden Anatomie.* 1870. Same, 2 ed. 1874. *Grundriss der vergleichenden Anatomie.* **George, P.** 1952. Systematic account of the Chaetognatha of Indian coastal waters. Proc. Nation. Inst. Sciences India 18. **Germain, L.** 1913. Chétognathes. Deux. Expéd. Antarctique Française (1908–1910), Sci. Natur., Doc. Scient. Zool. **Germain, L.,** and **L. Joubin.** 1912. Quelques chétognathes nouveaux.

Bull. Inst. Océanogr. Monaco, no. 228. 1916. Chétognathes provenant des campagnes de la Hirondelle et de la Princesse Alice. Résultats Camp. Scient. Monaco 49. **Ghirardelli, E.** 1948. Chetognati raccolti nel Mar Rosso e nell' Oceano Indiano. Boll. Pesca Piscicoltura Idriobiol. 23. 1950a. Osservazioni biologiche e sistematiche sui chetognati della Baia di Villefranche. Boll. Pesca Piscicoltura Idriobiol. 26. 1950b. Morfologia dell'apparecchio digerente in Sagitta minima. Boll. Zool. 17, suppl. 1951. I cicli di maturita sessuale nelle gonadi di Sagitta enflata. Boll. Zool. 18. 1952. Osservazioni biologiche e sistematiche sui chetognati del Golfo di Napoli. Pubbl. Staz. Zool. Napoli 23. 1953a. Apparecchio riproduttore femminile e biologia della reproduzione in Pterosagitta draco. Monitore Zool. Ital. 61. 1953b. Echantillons rapportées des deux expéditions en Terre Adelie. Boll. Zool. 20. 1953c. L'accoppiamento in Spadella. Pubbl. Staz. Zool. Napoli 24. 1953d. Osservazioni sul determinante germinale nelle uova di Spadella. Pubbl. Staz. Zool. Napoli 24. 1954a. Sulla biologia della reproduzione in Spadella. Rendiconti Accad. Scienze Ist. Bologna, Cl. Sci. Fis., ser. 11, vol. 1. 1954b. Osservazioni sul corredo chromosomico di Sagitta. Scientia Genetica 4. 1954c. Determinante germinale e nucleo nelle uova dei Chetognati. Boll. Zool. 21. 1954d. Studi sul determinante germinale nei Chetognati. Pubbl. Staz. Zool. Napoli 25. 1956. L'apparato riproduttore femminile e la deposizione dell'uova in Spadella. Atti Accad. Scienze Ist. Bologna, Cl. Sci. Fis., ser. 11, vol. 3. **Goodrich, E. S.** 1945. Nephridia and genital ducts since 1895. Quart. Jour. Microsc. Sci. 86. **Gourret, P.** 1884. Faune pélagique du Golfe de Marseille. Ann. Mus. Hist. Natur. Marseille, Zool. 2, Mém. 2. **Grassi, G.** 1882. Alcuni protisti endoparassitici. Atti Soc. Ital. Sci. Natur. 24. 1883. I Chetognati. Fauna und Flora des Golfes von Neapel, Monogr. 5. **Grey, B.** 1930. Chaetognatha from the Society Islands. Proc. Roy. Soc. Queensland 42. **Günther, R.** 1907. The Chaetognatha or primitive Mollusca. Quart. Jour. Microsc. Sci. 51. 1908. Die Stellung der Chaetognathen in System. Zool. Anz. 32. **Hamon, Maryvonne.** 1950. Deux nouveaux chétognathes de la Baie d'Alger. Bull. Soc. Hist. Natur. Afrique du Nord 41. 1951a. Trypanophis sagittae. Bull. Biol. France Belgique 85. 1951b. Grégarine parasite du tube digestif de Sagitta. Bull. Soc. Hist. Natur. Afrique du Nord 42. 1952. Note complémentaire sur les chétognathes de la Baie d'Alger. Bull. Soc. Hist. Natur. Afrique du Nord 43. 1956. Chétognathes recuellis dans la Baiae de Nhatrang. Bull. Mus. Nation. Hist. Natur. Paris, ser. 2, vol. 28. 1957. Note sur Janickina pigmentifera. Bull. Soc. Hist. Natur. Afrique du Nord 48. **Hardy, A.** 1936. The arctic plankton collected by the Nautilus, pt. 1. Jour. Linnaean Soc. London, Zool. 39. **Hardy, A., and E. Gunther.** 1935. The plankton of the South Georgia whaling grounds. Discovery Repts. 11. **Hertwig, O.** 1880. Die Chaetognathen. Jena. Ztschr. Naturwiss. 14. **Hesse, R.** 1902. Untersuchungen über die Organe der Lichtempfindung bei niederen Thieren. VIII. Ztschr. Wissenschaftl. Zool. 72. **Hida, T.** 1957. Chaetognaths and pteropods as biological indicators in the North Pacific, U.S. Fish and Wildlife Service, Special Scient. Rept., Fisheries, no. 215. **Hida, T., and J. King.** 1955. Vertical distribution of zooplankton in the central equatorial Pacific. U.S. Fish and Wildlife Service, Special Scient. Rept., Fisheries, no. 144. **Hovasse, R.** 1924. Trypanoplasma sagittae. C. R. Soc. Biol. Paris 91. **Hsu, F.** 1943. Species of Sagitta from China. Sinensia 14. **Huntsman, A.** 1919. Canadian chaetognaths. Rept. Canadian Fisheries Exped. 1914–1915, Dept. Naval Service. **Huntsman, A., and M. Reid.** 1921. The success of reproduction in Sagitta elegans in the Bay of Fundy. Trans. Roy. Canadian Inst. 13, pt. 2. **Hutton, R.** 1954. Metacercaria owreae. Bull. Marine Sci. Gulf Caribbean 4. **Huxley, T. H.** 1851. Observations on the genus Sagitta. Rept. Brit. Assoc. Advanc. Sci. 21. **Hyman, L. H.** 1958. Chitin in lophophorate phyla. Biol. Bull. 114. **Ikeda, I.** 1917. Metaphrya sagittae.

Annot. Zool. Japonenses 9. **Jägersten, G.** 1940. Physiologie der Zeugung bei Sagitta. Zool. Bidrag 18. **Jameson, A.** 1914. Chaetognatha of the Scottish National Antarctic Expedition. Trans. Roy. Soc. Edinburgh 49. **Janicki, C.** 1912. Paramoebenstudien. Ztschr. Wissenschaftl. Zool. 103. 1928, 1932. Studien am Paramoeba. Ztschr. Wissenschaftl. Zool. 131, 142. **John, C.** 1931. Anatomy of the head of Sagitta. Proc. Zool. Soc. London. 1933. Habits, structure and development of Spadella. Quart. Jour. Microsc. Sci. 75. 1943. Structure of the reproductive organs of Sagitta. Proc. Indian Sci. Congress 30. **Johnston, T.,** and **B. Taylor.** 1919. Australian chaetognaths. Proc. Roy. Soc. Queensland 31. 1921. Chaetognatha. Australasian Antarctic Exped., Scient. Repts., ser. C, vol. 6, pt. 2. **Joubin, L.** 1928–1934. Faune et flore de la Méditerranée. Chaetognathes. Comm. Internation. Explor. Scient. Mer Méditerranée. **Kado, Y.** 1953. Chaetognath fauna of the inland sea of Japan. Dobutsugaku Zasshi (Zool. Mag.) 62. 1954. Notes on the seasonal variation of Sagitta crassa. Annot. Zool. Japonenses 27. **Kielhorn, W.** 1952. Biology of the surface zooplankton of boreo-arctic Atlantic Ocean. Jour. Fisheries Research Bd. Canada 9. **King, J.** 1949. Plankton of the west coast of Florida. Quart. Jour. Florida Acad. Sci. 12. **King, J.,** and **J. Demond.** 1953. Zooplankton abundance in the central Pacific. U.S. Fish and Wildlife Service, Fisheries Bull. 54, no. 82. **Kowalevsky, A.** 1871. Entwicklungsgeschichte der Sagitta. Mém. Acad. Sci. St. Pétersbourg, ser. 7, vol. 16, no. 12. **Kramp, P.** 1915. Chaetognathi from the Great Belt and the Kattegat. Meddel. Komm. Havundersog., ser. Plankton 1, no. 12. 1918. Chaetognatha collected by the Tjalfe Expedition to the west coast of Greenland. Vidensk. Meddel. Dansk Naturhist. Foren. 69. 1939. Chaetognatha—the Godthaab Expedition. Meddel. om Grönland 80, no. 5. **Krohn, A.** 1844. Anatomisch-physiologische Beobachtungen über den Sagitta. Ann. Sci. Natur., Zool., ser. 3, vol. 3. **Krumbach, T.** 1903. Die Greifhaken der Chaetognathen. Zool. Jahrb., Abt. System. 18. **Kuhl, W.** 1928. Chaetognatha. *In* **G. Grimpe** and **E. Wagler** (eds.), *Die Tierwelt der Nord- und Ostsee*, Teil VIIb, Lief. 11. 1929. Das Retrocerebralorgan der Chaetognathen. Abhandl. Senckenberg. Naturforsch. Gesellsch. 38, Heft 2. 1932. Untersuchungen über die Bewegungsphysiologie der Fangorgane am Kopf der Chätognathen. Ztschr. Morphol. Ökol. Tiere 24. 1938. Chaetognatha. *In* **H. G. Bronn** (ed.), *Klassen und Ordnungen des Tierreichs*, Bd. IV, Abt. IV, Buch 2, Teil 1. **Kulmatycki, W.** 1918. Regenerationsfähigkeit der Spadella. Zool. Anz. 49. **Lameere, A.** 1931. Précis de zoologie. Recueil Inst. Torley-Rousseau, suppl. tome II. **Langerhaus, P.** 1880. Die Wurmfauna von Maderia III. Ztschr. Wissenschaftl. Zool. 34. **Lea, Helen.** 1955. Chaetognaths of western Canadian coastal waters. Jour. Fisheries Research Bd. Canada 12. **Lebour, Marie.** 1917. Some parasites of Sagitta. Jour. Marine Biol. Assoc. Unit. Kingd. 11. 1922, 1923. The food of plankton organisms. I, II. Jour. Marine Biol. Assoc. Unit. Kingd. 12, 13. **Leuckart, R.** 1854. Bericht über die Leistungen in der Naturgeschichte der niederen Thiere während der Jahre 1848–1853. Arch. Naturgesch. 20, pt. 2. 1861. Bericht über die wissenschaftlichen Leistungen in der Naturgeschichte der niederen Thiere während des Jahres 1859. Arch. Naturgesch. 26, pt. 2. **Leuckart, R.,** and **A. Pagenstecher.** 1858. Untersuchungen über niedere Seetiere. Arch. Anat. Physiol. Wissensch. Medicin. **Linton, E.** 1927. Adult distomes in a Sagitta. Trans. Amer. Microsc. Soc. 46. **MacBride, E. W.** 1914. *Textbook of embryology*. I. *Invertebrata*. **MacIntosh, W.** 1890. Occurrence of chaetognaths in St. Andrew's Bay. Ann. Mag. Natur. Hist., ser. 6, vol. 6. **Mackintosh, N.** 1937. Seasonal circulation of the antarctic macroplankton. Discovery Repts. 16. **Massuti, O.** 1954. Sobre la biologia de las Sagitta del Levante Espanol. Pubbl. Inst. Biol. Aplicada 16. **Mawson, Patricia.** 1944. Some species of Spadella from New South Wales. Trans. Roy. Soc. S. Australia 68. **Meek, A.** 1928. On Sagitta

elegans and setosa from the Northumberland plankton. Proc. Zool. Soc. London.
Metschnikov, E. 1867. Beiträge zur Naturgeschichte der Würmer. Ztschr. Wissenschaftl. Zool. 17. **Meyer, A.** 1927. Cölombewimperung und cölomatische Kreislaufsysteme bei Wirbellosen. Ztschr. Wissenschaftl. Zool. 129. **Michael, E.** 1908. Notes on the identification of the Chaetognatha. Biol. Bull. 15. 1911. Classification and vertical distribution of the Chaetognatha of the San Diego region. Univ. California Publ. Zool. 8. 1919. Chaetognatha collected by the Albatross during the Philippine Expedition. Bull. U.S. Nation. Mus. 100. **Mingazzini, P.** 1891. Gregarine monocistides. Atti R. Accad. Lincei, Rendiconti, ser. 4, vol. 7, semestre 1. **Moltschanoff, L.** 1909. Die Chaetognathen des Schwarzen Meeres. Bull. Acad. Sci. St. Pétersbourg, ser. 6, vol. 3, pt. 2. **Monticelli, F.** 1909. Forma giovane di Aphanurus. Monitore Zool. Italiano 20. **Moore, H.** 1949. Zooplankton of the upper waters of the Bermuda area. Bull. Bingham Oceanogr. Collection 12, art. 2. **Myers, B.** 1956. An adult Hemiurus from Sagitta elegans. Canadian Jour. Zool. 34. **Oye, P. van.** 1918. Die Chaetognathen des Javameeres. Contrib. Faune Indes Néerland. (later Treubia) 1, fasc. 4. 1931. La fécondation chez les Chaetognathes. Bull. Mus. Hist. Natur. Belgique 7, no. 7. **Pagenstecher, H.** 1862. Notes on the anatomy of Sagitta. Ztschr. Wissenschaftl. Zool. 12. **Parry, D.** 1944. Structure and function of the gut in Spadella and Sagitta. Jour. Marine Biol. Assoc. Unit. Kingd. 26. **Pierantoni, U.** 1913. Sopra un nematode parassita della Sagitta. C. R. 9 Congr. Internation. Zool. **Pierce, E.** 1941. Occurrence and breeding of Sagitta in the Irish Sea. Jour. Marine Biol. Assoc. Unit. Kingd. 25. 1951. Chaetognatha of the west coast of Florida. Biol. Bull. 100. 1953. Chaetognatha over the continental shelf of North Carolina. Jour. Marine Science 12. 1954. Notes on the Chaetognatha of the Gulf of Mexico. U.S. Fish and Wildlife Service, Fishery Bull. 89. **Pierce, E., and J. Orton.** 1939. Sagitta as an indicator of water movements. Nature, London, 144. **Quoy, J., and P. Gaimard.** 1827. Observations zoologiques faites dans le detroit de Gibraltar. Ann. Sci. Natur., Zool., ser. 1, vol. 10. **Ramult, M., and M. Rose.** 1945. Recherches sur les chétognathes de la Baie d'Alger. Bull. Soc. Hist. Natur. Afrique du Nord 36. **Redfield, A., and A. Beale.** 1940. Distribution of populations of chaetognaths in the Gulf of Maine. Biol. Bull. 79. **Reisinger, E.** 1934. Zur Exkretionsphysiologie von Spadella. Thalassia 1. **Ritter-Zahony, R. von.** 1909a. Chätognathen. Denkschr. Akad. Wissensch. Wien 84, A, Berichte Komm. Erforsch. Öst. Mittelmeeres, Zool. Ergebn. 14. 1909b. Zur Anatomie des Chaetognathenkopfes. Denkschr. Akad. Wissensch. Wien 84, A, Berichte Komm. Erforsch. Öst. Mittelmeeres, Zool. Ergebn. 16. 1909c. Chaetognathen. Expeditionen in das Rote Meer. Denkschr. Akad. Wissensch. Wien 84, A, Bericht Komm. Oceanogr. Forsch., Zool. Ergebn. 27. 1909d. Die Chaetognathen der Gazelle-Expedition. Zool. Anz. 34. 1910a. Westindische Chätognathen. Zool. Jahrb. Suppl. 11. 1910b. Die Chätognathen. Fauna Arctica 5. 1911a. Chaetognathi. Das Tierreich 29. 1911b. Die Chätognathen der Plankton-Expedition. Ergebn. Plankton-Exped. II, H, e. 1911c. Revision der Chätognathen. Dtsch. Südpolar-Exped. 13, Zool. 5. **Rose, M.** 1925. Biologie du Plankton. Arch. Zool. Exp. Gén. 64. **Rose, M., and M. Hamon.** 1950. Une nouvelle espèce de Trypanophis. Bull. Biol. France Belgique 84. 1953. Chetognathes de la Baie d'Alger. Bull. Soc. Hist. Natur. Afrique du Nord 44. **Russell, F.** 1927. Vertical distribution of plankton in the sea. Biol. Rev. Cambridge Philos. Soc. 2. 1932, 1933. Biology of Sagitta. I–IV. Jour. Marine Biol. Assoc. Unit. Kingd. 18. **Sanzo, L.** 1937. Colonia pelagica di uova di Chetognati. Mem. Com. Talassogr. Ital. 239. **Scaccini, A., and E. Ghirardelli.** 1941a. Chetognati raccolti lungo de coste del Rio de Oro. Note Ist. Italo-Germanica Biol. Marina Rovigno d'Istria 2, no. 21. 1941b. Chetognati del Mare Adriatico. Note Ist. Italo-Germanica Biol.

Marina Rovigno d'Istria 2, no. 22. **Schilp, H.** 1941. The Chaetognatha of the Snellius Expedition. Temminckia 6. **Schmidt, W.** 1940. Zur Morphologie, Polarisationsoptik und Chemie der Greifhaken von Sagitta. Ztschr. Morphol. Ökol. Tiere 37. 1952. Polarisationsoptische Untersuchungen an Sagitta. Ztschr. Zellforsch. Mikro. Anat. 36. **Schneider, A.** 1866. *Monographie der Nematoden.* **Scoresby, W.** 1820. *An account of the arctic regions,* vol. 2. **Scott, T.** 1891, 1893. Food of Sagitta. Ann. Scottish Natur. Hist. 1, 3. 1896. Fauna of the Firth of Forth. Ann. Rept. Fisheries Bd. Scotland 14. Pt. III, Scient. Investigations, art. 4. **Sinitsin, D.** 1911. La génération parthénogénèsique des trématodes de la Mer Noire. Mém. Acad. Sci. St. Pétersbourg, Cl. Sci. Phys. Math., ser. 8, vol. 30, no. 5. **Slabber, M.** 1769. *Natuurkundige Verlustigingen behelzende microscopise Waarnemingen van in- en uitlandse Water- en Land-Dieren.* **Steuer, A.** 1928. Distribution and affinity of the appendiculate trematodes parasitizing marine plankton copepods. Jour. Parasitol. 15. **Stevens, Nettie.** 1903. Oogenesis and spermatogenesis of Sagitta. Zool. Jahrb. Abt. Anat. 18. 1905. Further studies on the oogenesis of Sagitta. Zool. Jahrb. Abt. Anat. 21. 1910. Further studies on reproduction in Sagitta. Jour. Morphol. 21. **Strodtmann, S.** 1905. Die Chaetognathen. Nordisches Plankton, Lief. 3, pt. 10. **Subramaniam, M.** 1937. Distribution of Sagitta in the Indian Seas. Current Science 6. 1940. Sagitta bedoti in Madras plankton. Current Science 9. **Thiel, M.** 1938. Die Chaetognathen-Bevolkerung des Südatlantischen Ozeans. Wissensch. Ergebn. Dtsch. Atlant. Exped. auf dem Meteor 13, Biol. Sonderuntersuchungen, Lief. 1. **Thiele, J.** 1907. Sind die Chaetognathen als Mollusken aufzufassen? Zool. Anz. 32. **Thomson, J.** 1947. The Chaetognatha of southwestern Australia. Bull. Australia Counc. Scient. Indust. Research, no. 222. 1952. The identity of Spadella moretonensis. Proc. Roy. Soc. Queensland 64. **Tokioka, T.** 1939a. New brackish water chaetognath. Annot. Zool. Japonenses 18. 1939b. Three new chaetognaths from Japanese waters. Mem. Imper. Marine Observatory, Kobe, 7, no. 1. 1939c. Chaetognaths from the bays of Sagami and Surrega. Record Oceanogr. Works Japan 10. 1940. Chaetognath fauna of western Japan. Record Oceanogr. Works Japan 12. 1942. Systematic studies of the plankton organisms in Palao. III. Chaetognaths. Studies Palao Tropical Biol. Sta. 2. 1952. Chaetognaths of the Indo-Pacific. Annot. Zool. Japonenses 25. 1954a. Dense patch of chaetognaths. Publ. Seto Marine Biol. Lab. 3, art. 27. 1954b. Chaetognaths from the central Pacific. Publ. Seto Marine Biol. Lab. 4, art. 10. 1955a. Chaetognatha collected by the Syunkotu-Maru. Publ. Seto Marine Biol. Lab. 4, art. 18. 1955b. Chaetognaths from the northeastern part of the Indian Ocean. Publ. Seto Marine Biol. Lab. 5, art. 4. 1955c. Chaetognaths from the Gulf of Mexico. Bull. Marine Sci. Gulf Caribbean 5. 1956a. Chaetognaths collected in the central part of the Indian Ocean. Publ. Seto Marine Biol. Lab. 5. 1956b. Chaetognaths collected in the Arafura Sea. Publ. Seto Marine Biol. Lab. 5. **Tregouboff, G.** 1949. Un parasite nouveau des sagittes. Bull. Inst. Oceanogr. Monaco, no. 953. **Tuzet, Odette.** 1931. Spermatogénèse des Chaetognathes. Arch. Zool. Exp. Gén. 71. **Ussing, H.** 1938. Biology of some important plankton animals in fjords of East Greenland. Meddel. om Grönland 100, no. 7. **Vannucci, M., and K. Hosoe.** 1952. Chaetognatha a Ilha da Trinidade. Boletim Inst. Oceanogr. Sao Paulo 3. **Vasiljev, A.** 1925. La fécondation chez Spadella. Biol. Generalis 1. **Walcott, C.** 1911. Middle Cambrian annelids. Smithson. Miscell. Collections 57, no. 5. **Welsh, J., F. Chace, and R. Minnemacher.** 1937. Diurnal migration of deep-water animals. Biol. Bull. 73. **Wilms, R.** 1844. Observationes de Sagitta. Thesis, Berlin. **Wimpenny, R.** 1936. Distribution, breeding and feeding of some important plankton organisms of the southwest North Sea. Ministry Agricult. Fisheries, Great Britain, Fisheries Invest., ser. 2, vol. 15, no. 3.

CHAPTER XVII

THE ENTEROCOELOUS COELOMATES—
PHYLUM HEMICHORDATA

I. HISTORICAL

A member of the phylum was first recorded by Eschscholtz (1825), who found an enteropneust that he named *Ptychodera flava* buried in sand in shallow water at Odia in the Marshall Islands. He gave a recognizable figure of the animal (reproduced in Van der Horst, 1939) that he thought to be a holothurian. This species is now known to be widely spread throughout the tropical Indo-Pacific. There was next put on record the occurrence of an enteropneust in the Naples region by Delle Chiaje (1829), who gave the animal the name *Balanoglossus clavigerus*, thus creating the most familiar generic name in the phylum. This author states that the animal was locally called ox tongue by the fishermen, whence the *glossus* (*glossa*, tongue, Greek) part of the name, whereas the *balano* part derives not from the Greek *balanos*, meaning an acorn, in reference to the shape of the proboscis, but from the barnacle genus *Balanus*, to which Delle Chiaje seems to have found some resemblance in his specimens. Of course *Balanus* as a barnacle name also derives from the Greek for acorn and barnacles of this type are commonly called acorn barnacles. A third enteropneust was discovered by Stimpson off the Carolina coast and described by Girard (1853), who named it *Stimpsonia aurantiaca* and considered it a nemertean; later this was transferred to the genus *Balanoglossus*. During the next 30 years several other enteropneust species were discovered and described, although the first accurate account of the anatomy was that of Kowalevsky (1866), based on Delle Chiaje's species. It was customary during this period to assign all species to the genus *Balanoglossus*, for Eschscholtz's genus *Ptychodera* had been overlooked. The partition of *Balanoglossus* began with Spengel (1891), who recognized *Ptychodera* and *Balanoglossus* and proposed in addition *Glandiceps* and *Schizocardium;* and in Spengel's monograph (1893) these four genera were considered to contain all the enteropneust species known at that time, comprising 10 previously described species and 9 new ones, one of which, however, is a synonym of *Pt. flava*. In this same monograph Spengel also proposed the name *Dolichoglossus* as a subgenus for those species of *Balanoglossus* having an exceptionally long proboscis, being unaware that Schimkewitsch (1892) had already created the name *Saccoglossus* for enteropneusts of this type. Schimkewitsch's article was written in Russian and thus passed unnoticed, and it was not until 1934 that Van der Horst revived his name *Saccoglossus* and threw *Dolichoglossus* into synonymy with it. In 1901 Spengel recognized as additional enteropneust genera *Spengelia* (Willey, 1898) and *Harrimania* (Ritter, 1900) and himself added two new genera, *Glossobalanus* and *Stereobalanus*. At the time of Van der Horst's comprehensive monograph (1939) in Bronn's *Klassen und Ordnungen des Tierreichs* there were recognized 12 genera and 60 species of enteropneusts; Dawydoff in the *Traité de zoologie* (1948) gave the number of species as 63 distributed among the same 12 genera. New species described since then bring the number up to about 70.

In 1870 Gegenbaur proposed the name Enteropneusti for animals of the type of

Balanoglossus, basing the name (Greek, *enteron*, intestine; *pneumon*, lung) on Kowalevsky's discovery (1866) of the presence of gill slits in *B. clavigerus*. The group has ever since been called by Gegenbaur's name, usually altered to Enteropneusta. In 1885 Bateson, having studied the embryology of some enteropneusts and having noted many resemblances of development and structure to the lower chordates, especially *Amphioxus*, proposed the name Hemichordata to replace Enteropneusta and suggested the inclusion of the hemichordates with the tunicates, cephalochords, and vertebrates in the phylum Chordata. It is unnecessary to remark that this arrangement was extant to recent times, although the inclusion of the enteropneusts in the Chordata has been regularly protested by some students of the Enteropneusta, beginning with Spengel (1893).

The characteristic swimming larva of the Enteropneusta was first seen at Marseilles by Johannes Müller (1850), who mistook it for an echinoderm larva and gave it the name *tornaria* from its habit of rotating in circles. Tornaria larvae were subsequently observed by Krohn (1854) at Messina, Agassiz (1864) off New England, and Fr. Müller (1868) off Brazil. These authors continued to regard the creature as an echinoderm larva, especially an asteroid larva, from its general resemblance to the bipinnaria. It was Metschnikoff (1869, 1870) who discovered that the tornaria is the larva of the Enteropneusta, for at Messina he was able to follow its development into a young acorn worm. This discovery was soon verified by Agassiz (1872, 1873).

The peculiar colonial animal *Rhabdopleura* was first seen by G. O. Sars, who in 1866 dredged up from about 220 m. in the Lofoten Islands off northern Norway some small colonies that he took to be hydroids. He recounts (1874) that his father, Michael Sars, examining the preserved specimens, found them to be very peculiar creatures that seemed allied to Bryozoa. In 1867 G. O. Sars therefore again dredged at Lofoten and, examining the little colonies alive, found them "peculiar in the highest degree," and he and his father decided that they could not be referred to any known group although seemingly related to Bryozoa. The finding of the animal was not recorded, however, until 1869, when M. Sars included it, without description, under the name *Halilophus mirabilis* in a list of deep-water animals from the Norwegian coast. Descriptions of the creature were first published by G. O. Sars (1873, 1874), but in the meantime specimens had been dredged off the Shetland Islands at 160 m. These were described by Allman (1869) under the name *Rhabdopleura normani* and considered by him to be some sort of bryozoan. *Rhabdopleura* was graciously accepted by G. O. Sars (1873) as the name of the genus, although it appears to the author that *Halilophus* has prior right. The species *normani* and *mirabilis* are considered identical. In 1877 Lankester created the term Pterobranchia as a general group name for *Rhabdopleura*, placing the group as a subdivision of Bryozoa.

The equally strange colonial animal *Cephalodiscus* was dredged by the *Challenger* on Jan. 11, 1876, at a depth of 440 m. in the Strait of Magellan and was brought to the attention of zoologists in a preliminary report by McIntosh (1882), who at once recognized it as allied to *Rhabdopleura*. In his final report (1887) McIntosh continued to regard *Rhabdopleura* and *Cephalodiscus* as a type of bryozoan. However, in an appendix to McIntosh's report, Harmer (1887) clearly recognized the relationship of *Cephalodiscus* to *Balanoglossus* and proposed the removal of the former from the Bryozoa into the Hemichordata. Fowler (1892) suggested the inclusion of *Rhabdopleura* also in the Hemichordata and in 1893 arranged the Hemichordata into three groups: Enteropneusta with many gill slits, Cephalodiscida with a pair of gill slits, and Rhabdopleurida without gill slits. It remained for Willey (1899a, b) to divide the Hemichordata into the two classes Enteropneusta and Pterobranchia, an arrangement thereafter generally accepted although at first there was some tendency to include the

Phoronidea as a third class (Harmer, 1905).   Since the original finding, colonies of *Cephalodiscus* have been repeatedly dredged, chiefly in the Antarctic and Subantarctic. Johnston and Muirhead (1951) consider that there were known at that date 16 valid species.   Colonies of *Rhabdopleura* have also been collected a few times since the original finding, notably by the *Challenger* at the island of Tristan da Cunha in the South Atlantic; these specimens, described by Fowler (1892, 1893), belong to the original species, *R. normani.*   Other species have since been erected, of which probably only two are valid.   In 1936 Sato revealed the finding off Japan of a new pterobranch genus, *Atubaria,* with one species *heterolopha.*   Thus the class Pterobranchia consists at the present writing of 3 genera and about 20 species.

In June, 1910, there were fished in the Bay of Biscay at 270 m. by the Norwegian North Atlantic Expedition on the *Michael Sars* two specimens of a pelagic larva recognized by Mortensen as related to the tornaria and hence turned over for study to Spengel, the leading authority on the hemichordates at that time.   Spengel's account, however, was not published until 1932, wherein he gave the organism the name *Planctosphaera pelagica.*   Later additional specimens were taken by the *Dana* expeditions and by Garstang (1939) at Bermuda, but no accounts of these materials were ever published; hence Spengel's account remains the only one.[1]   Spengel concluded that *Planctosphaera* is the larva of a new but unknown type of hemichordate, and in this opinion Van der Horst concurred, proposing (1936) a new class, Planctosphaeroidea, to include the organism.

Thus the Hemichordata as conceived at present comprise three existing classes. In recent years, some invertebrate paleontologists have been strongly inclined to include the extinct group of graptolites in the Hemichordata, rather than in the Cnidaria as is customary (I, page 497).   The question of the affinity of the graptolites with the hemichordates is discussed toward the end of this chapter and answered negatively.

The author follows the opinion of all recent students of the group in removing the Hemichordata from the Chordata and making them an independent phylum of invertebrates.   The author also accepts the opinion of Van der Horst (1939) that Hemichordata is the most suitable and just name of this phylum.   This name does not imply the possession of a notochord by hemichordates; it simply says that hemichordates are "part chordate," that is, related to chordates, something impossible to deny.   In the years from 1895 to 1910 many other names were suggested for the group (historical review in Selys Longchamps, 1904), usually for combinations of the hemichordates with other groups.   In this article, Selys Longchamps, giving a scholarly account of the development of *Phoronis,* effectively demolished the repeated attempts to unite the hemichordates with the phoronids.   Of the various names proposed, only one, Branchiotrema (better, Branchiotremata) of Willey (1899a), has persisted to recent times.   It is used in the Kükenthal-Krumbach *Handbuch der Zoologie* in place of Hemichordata, and for this reason the author employed it now and

---

[1] In the *Traité de zoologie,* vol. XI, p. 434, Dawydoff refers to Stiasny and Damas (1936) with regard to the *Dana* material.   The author, after repeated attempts, was unable to locate any such reference, and letters to Dawydoff remained unanswered. Finally, A. Vedel Täning, editor of the *Dana* reports, kindly informed that the *Dana* material of *Planctosphaera* had in fact been turned over to Stiasny and Damas, both deceased, and that these authors had started to work on it but nothing was ever published and the material cannot be recovered.   However, at the Mar. 25, 1936, session of the Société Zoologique de France, Damas demonstrated and commented upon drawings of *Planctosphaera* made from the *Dana* specimens.

then. However, perusal of Willey's article shows that Willey's name Branchiotrema was proposed, not as a substitute for Hemichordata, but as a substitute for Chordata, and in fact Willey acknowledged Hemichordata (unjustifiably shortened to Hemichorda) for the two classes Pterobranchia and Enteropneusta. Apart from the fact that some hemichordates do not have gill slits, the name Branchiotrema as a substitute for Hemichordata does not therefore appear admissible. The author is unable to perceive any advantage of the recently proposed name Stomochordata (Dawydoff, 1948) over Hemichordata and on principle objects to the invention of new names for groups for which good names, long in use, already exist. An author is entitled to invent a new group name only if he can justify an important rearrangement of taxonomic categories.

The inclusion of the hemichordates in the chordates has been extant in zoological works since it was first proposed by Bateson in 1885. It has been rejected, however, by Van der Horst (1939) and in other recent great treatises on zoology, namely, in the *Handbuch der Zoologie* and the *Traité de zoologie*. The whole organization of hemichordates differs from that of chordates except for the presence of gill slits and their supporting skeleton in enteropneusts, and the structure once supposed to represent the notochord is now regarded as of other nature. Especially, nervous and circulatory systems are of invertebrate type on the whole.

Some European zoologists, mostly of German training, persist in calling the phylum Enteropneusta, whereupon they designate the class usually called Enteropneusta by the strange name of Helminthomorpha. This usage cannot be justified, even on historical grounds, for Gegenbaur (1870) created the name Enteropneusti as a class name for animals of the balanoglossan type and at that time pterobranchs were scarcely known. Using Enteropneusta as a phylum name can only result in confusion and must be strongly condemned.

The outstanding accounts of the phylum are those of Van der Horst (1939) and Dawydoff (1948). Spengel's classical monograph (1893) remains an invaluable source of information and illustrations.

II. CHARACTERS OF THE PHYLUM

1. Definition.—The Hemichordata are solitary or colonial, more or less vermiform enterocoelous coelomates with body and coelom regionated into three successive divisions of unequal length and different structure, with an epidermal nervous system that includes a middorsal center in the second body division and middorsal and midventral cords in the third body division, with a circulatory system that usually includes a contractile sac, without typical nephridia, with a preoral gut diverticulum, with or without gill slits, and with or without tentaculated arms borne on the second body division.

2. General Characters.—The members of the phylum differ so much in general aspect that the inability of early workers to relate them properly is not surprising. Enteropneusts are solitary vermiform animals of moderate to great length with a straight digestive tract and terminal anus, whereas the small or microscopic pterobranchs with a U-shaped digestive tract live enclosed in tubes that are aggregated in great numbers into colonies (except for the solitary, tubeless *Atubaria*). The individuals

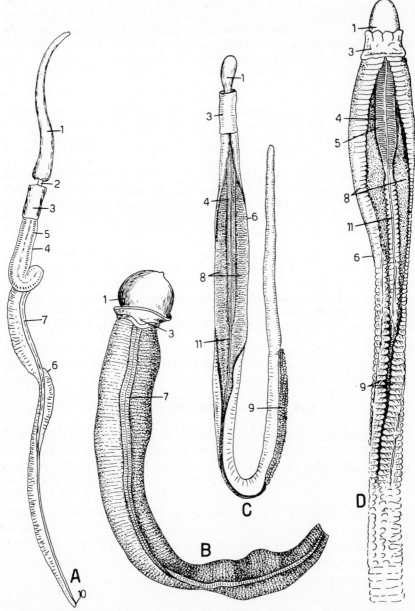

FIG. 20.—Types of enteropneusts. *A, Saccoglossus kowalewskii. B, Glandiceps hacksi,*
Japan *(after Marion,* 1886). *C, Balanoglossus aurantiacus.* (*A, C, from life, Carolina
coast.*) *D, Ptychodera bahamensis,* West Indies, preserved. *B* and *D* incomplete posteriorly. 1, proboscis; 2, proboscis stalk; 3, collar; 4, branchial region; 5, gill pores; 6,
trunk; 7, midventral ridge; 8, genital wings; 9, hepatic region; 10, anus, 11, middorsal ridge.

of a *Cephalodiscus* colony are not organically connected, but *Rhabdopleura* individuals are continuous throughout the colony by way of a cord, or *stolon*. The body in all hemichordates is more or less evidently regionated into three divisions that may be designated by the general terms *protosome, mesosome,* and *metasome*. In pterobranchs the mesosome bears one or more conspicuous pairs of *tentaculated arms*, that is, hollow projections bordered with tentacles. In *Rhabdopleura* there is a pair of these tentaculated arms, which are therefore somewhat suggestive of a lophophore, whereas in *Cephalodiscus* the arms are divided to the base to make a variable number of subdivisions. The tentaculated arms are not to be regarded as a lophophore although no doubt phylogenetically related to that structure.

Numerous pairs of gill slits are present on the dorsal surface of the anterior part of the metasome in enteropneusts; one pair occurs in *Cephalodiscus*, whereas *Rhabdopleura* lacks gill slits. A gill slit is an opening leading from the exterior through the body wall into the lumen of the pharynx. Gill slits occur only in chordates and hemichordates, in the former often in the embryo or larva only. The possible occurrence of gill slits in extinct echinoderms is mentioned in Vol. IV, page 19. The possession of gill slits by an animal may be referred to by the general term *pharyngotremy* (Greek, *trema*, hole). Gill slits seem to have functioned originally for the capture of minute food objects by way of a water current passing in at the mouth and out through the gill slits, obviously a variant of the mucous-ciliary method of feeding; secondarily they became of respiratory nature, as in the lower vertebrates.

The nervous system is primitive, consisting of a plexus in the base of the epidermis, that is, intraepidermal, with middorsal and midventral strands, and a thickening situated middorsally in the mesosome. A circulatory system, mostly of the open type (II, page 42) is present, with main dorsal and ventral channels in the metasome, and a pulsating center, a sort of elementary pericardial sac, in the protosome. In enteropneusts the digestive tract is straight, running from the mouth in the mesosome to the anus at the tip of the metasome, but in pterobranchs makes a U-bend, bringing the anus near the mouth, and is provided with a stomachic enlargement. In both groups a diverticulum extending anteriorly from the buccal cavity acquired fame as a supposed notochord; it is here called *buccal diverticulum*. A structure apparently representing some sort of nephridium is present in enteropneusts and indicated in pterobranchs. The coelom is divided into three compartments corresponding to the body regions, and these compartments are paired in the mesosome and metasome.

Asexual budding resulting in aggregations in *Cephalodiscus* and true colonies in *Rhabdopleura* is a prominent feature of pterobranchs, and cor-

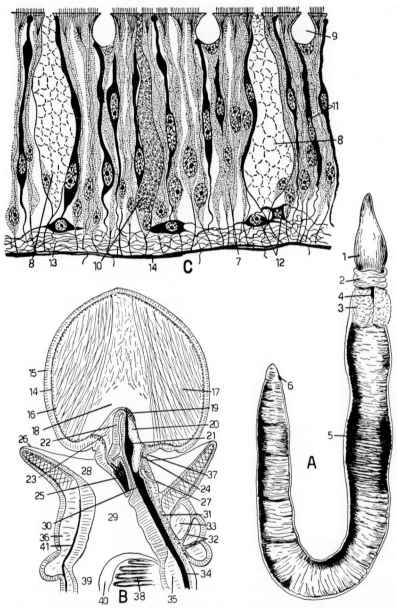

FIG. 21.—General structure. *A, Stereobalanus canadensis,* side view (*after Reinhard,* 1942). *B,* median sagittal section of proboscis and collar of *Glossobalanus minutus* (*after Spengel,* 1893). *C,* scheme of the epidermis of an enteropneust (*after Bullock,* 1945). 1, proboscis; 2, collar; 3, genital ridges and branchial region; 4, common slit for gill pores; 5, hepatic region; 6, anus; 7, ordinary epidermal cell; 8, reticulate gland cell; 9, goblet gland cell; 10, granular gland cell; 11, neurosensory cells; 12, nerve cell bodies of nervous layer; 13, fibrous part of nervous layer; 14, basement membrane; 15, epidermis; 16, circular muscle layer; 17, longitudinal muscle layer; 18, proboscis coelom; 19, glomerulus; 20, heart

respondingly regenerative powers are high in enteropneusts. The sexes are separate, and in the enteropneusts development may involve a characteristic swimming larva known as the *tornaria*, having no resemblance to the adult. The embryology of pterobranchs is poorly known and is usually direct, but a larva remarkably similar to an ectoproct larva occurs in one species.

The hemichordates are exclusively marine and occur at a range of habitats and depths. With the exception of a few enteropneusts the hemichordates are not very common animals and are known mostly from collecting expeditions.

III. CLASSIFICATION OF THE PHYLUM

Because of the small size of the phylum (under 100 species) the classification presents no particular difficulties.

Class I. Enteropneusta, the Acorn Worms. Vermiform solitary hemichordates with numerous gill slits and straight intestine; without tentaculated arms. No subdivisions higher than family have been recognized.

Class II. Pterobranchia. Aggregated or colonial small or minute hemichordates enclosed in a secreted encasement; digestive tract U-shaped; with or without gill slits; with tentaculated arms.

Order 1. Rhabdopleurida. Pterobranchs forming true colonies in which the members are in organic continuity, each enclosed in a secreted tube; with two tentaculated arms; gill slits wanting.

Order 2. Cephalodiscida. Pterobranchs forming aggregations housed in a common secreted encasement; members not organically continuous; with one pair of gill slits; with four to nine pairs of tentaculated arms.

Class III. Planctosphaeroidea. Known only by the transparent, spherical pelagic larva with arborescently branched ciliated bands running over the surface, with a U-shaped digestive tract, and with some coelomic sacs occupying a small part of the gelatinous interior.

IV. CLASS ENTEROPNEUSTA

1. Definition.—The Enteropneusta, or acorn worms, are solitary, vermiform hemichordates with a straight digestive tract and numerous gill slits but without tentaculated arms.

---

vesicle; 21, central sinus; 22, buccal diverticulum; 23, ventral mesentery of proboscis; 24, anterior nerve ring; 25, proboscis skeleton; 26, collarette; 27, proboscis pore; 28, mouth; 29, buccal cavity; 30, venous sinus; 31, collar cord; 32, dorsal strands of collar cord; 33, dorsal mesentery of collar; 34, dorsal longitudinal vessel; 35, dorsal trunk mesentery; 36, ventral collar mesentery; 37, proboscis stalk; 38, skeletal rods of gill slits; 39, pharynx; 40, parabranchial ridge; 41, ventral longitudinal vessel.

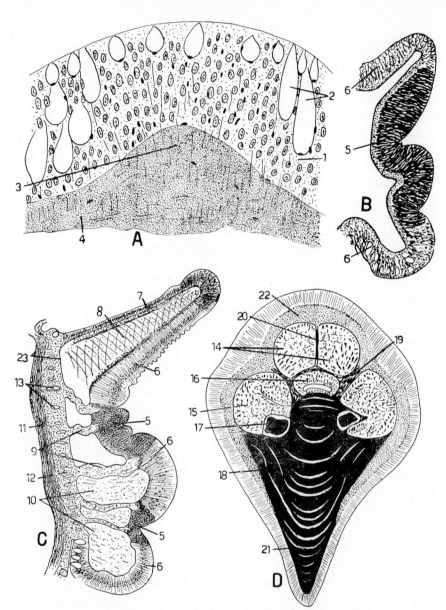

Fig. 22.—Epidermal structure. *A*, transverse section of the epidermis of the trunk, *Glossobalanus minutus*. *B*, longitudinal section of the collar epidermis of *Saccoglossus otagoensis*, showing three zones (*after Van der Horst*, 1929). *C*, longitudinal section of the dorsal side of the collar of *Glossobalanus minutus*, showing five epidermal zones. *D*, cross section through the proboscis stalk of *Balanoglossus clavigerus*, showing proboscis skeleton. (*A*, *C*, *D*, *after Spengel*, 1893.) 1, epidermal cells; 2, goblet gland cells; 3, dorsal trunk nerve cord; 4, general nervous layer; 5, heavily glandular zone; 6, less glandular zone; 7, collarette; 8, diagonal muscles of collarette; 9, dorsal nerve strands; 10, dorsal mesentery of collar; 11, fibrous part of collar cord; 12, epithelial part of collar cord; 13, cavities of collar cord; 14, perihaemal cavities containing longitudinal muscles; 15, anterior extensions of collar coeloms, also containing longitudinal muscles; 16, buccal diverticulum; 17, efferent glomerular blood vessels; 18, main plate of proboscis skeleton; 19, chondroid tissue; 20, dorsal longitudinal vessel; 21, keel of proboscis skeleton; 22, anterior nerve ring; 23, collar cord.

2. External Characters.—The enteropneusts are wormlike animals of considerable size, ranging mostly from 10 to 50 cm. in length; the smallest species, *Saccoglossus pygmaeus*, North Sea, is probably 2 to 3 cm. long when alive, extended (Hinrichs and Jacobs, 1938), and the gigantic *Balanoglossus gigas* from the Brazilian coast attains a length of 1.8 m. (Sawaya, 1951), possibly 2.5 m. (Spengel, 1893). The elongated body is cylindroid without external appendages and of soft consistency, covered in life with mucous secretion and devoid of any form of exoskeleton. It is obviously regionated into three successive parts, *proboscis* (protosome), *collar* (mesosome), and *trunk* (metasome) (Fig. 20), of which the last occupies most of the body length. The enteropneusts are strictly bilateral with definite dorsal and ventral surfaces, but this is not evident without closer study.

The proboscis, or protosome, is generally short, of rounded or conical shape (Figs. 20*B*, *C*, *D*, 21*A*); it is, however, exceptionally elongated in the genus *Saccoglossus* (= *Dolichoglossus*) (Fig. 20*A*). It is generally circular in cross section but in some species bears a deep middorsal groove (Fig. 29*A*), and a midventral depression in the proboscis base was noted in *Glossobalanus ruficollis* by Van der Horst (1929). Posteriorly the proboscis narrows to the slender proboscis stalk, more or less concealed by the collar and continuous with the inner surface of the dorsal part of the collar (Fig. 21*B*).

The collar, or mesosome, is a short cylinder usually about as wide as long and mostly shorter than the proboscis although sometimes longer. The funnellike anterior part of the collar, or *collarette*, embraces the proboscis stalk and usually also the posterior part of the proboscis (Fig. 21*B*). Posteriorly the collar is sharply demarcated from the trunk by a circular indentation. In the genus *Saccoglossus* this posterior fold of the collar slightly overhangs the beginning of the trunk, and this overhang was badly named *operculum* by Bateson; it does not appear to be of morphological importance. The interior of the collarette not occupied by the proboscis stalk houses the mouth that thus defines the ventral side. The surface of the collar is often marked with elevations, depressions, and especially circular grooves.

The trunk bears a middorsal and a midventral ridge for the accommodation of the corresponding median longitudinal nerves and blood vessels. The trunk is not uniformly constructed but varies anatomically along its length, and these anatomically different regions may show externally to an extent varying with different genera. Immediately following the collar is found the gill, or branchial, region, recognized externally by the longitudinal row of gill pores to each side of the middorsal ridge, hence situated on the dorsal side of the body. The gill openings may be sunk into a longitudinal depression or may be mounted on a pronounced elon-

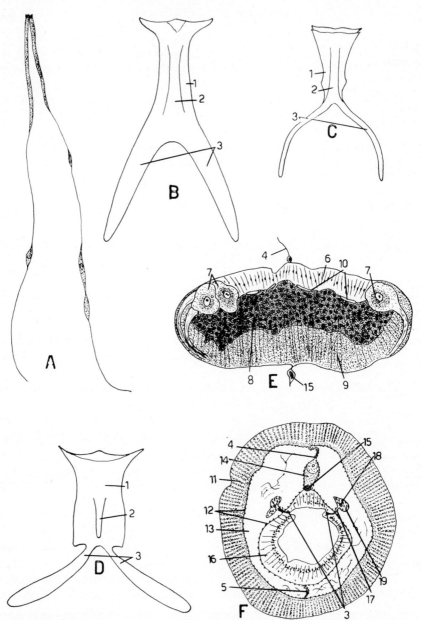

Fig. 23.—Body wall, nervous system. A, two epidermal cells freed by maceration (after Bateson, 1886a). B, proboscis skeleton of Schizocardium peruvianum. C, same of Saccoglossus kowalevskii. D, same of Balanoglossus aurantiacus. E, section of the collar cord of Glandiceps hacksi, with giant cells. (B–E, after Spengel, 1893.) F, section through the collar of Protoglossus, peritoneum retained (after Caullery and Mesnil, 1904). 1, body of proboscis skeleton; 2, keel; 3, horns; 4, dorsal mesentery of collar; 5, ventral mesentery of collar; 6, epithelial part of collar cord; 7, giant cells; 8, cellular part of collar cord; 9, fibrous part of collar cord; 10, lacunae; 11, glandular epidermis; 12, peritoneum; 13, collar coelom; 14, collar cord; 15, dorsal blood vessel; 16, epithelium of buccal tube; 17, peritoneal fold supporting peribuccal vessels; 18, peribuccal vessel; 19, longitudinal muscle bundle.

gated elevation as in *Balanoglossus* and *Ptychodera* (Fig. 20*C*, *D*). The gonads occupy the lateral regions of the anterior part of the trunk and may cause a pronounced swelling on each side, termed a *genital ridge;* or in the genera *Balanoglossus* (Fig. 20*C*) and *Ptychodera* (Fig. 20*D*), the lateral regions containing the gonads are thin and flat, forming two *genital wings* that can be curved dorsally until their margins almost meet. These two genera give the impression that the dorsal side has been split longitudinally and its halves opened out. In *Stereobalanus* (Fig. 21*A*), there are four short, fluffy genital regions, two dorsal and two ventral, and the gill openings are concealed in a groove on each side between the dorsal and ventral genital swellings. When the gonads thus affect the external morphology the whole region containing them may be termed *branchiogenital* region (or, badly, thorax). In many enteropneusts, however, the gonads do not show externally, and hence in such cases the trunk can be differentiated only into branchial and postbranchial regions as in Fig. 20*A*. The gonads may continue, anyway, posteriorly beyond the externally delimited region. The gonopores are so small as not to be detectable on the body surface. Posterior to the region containing the gonads the so-called *hepatic* part of the intestine may express itself externally as obvious sacculations as in *Balanoglossus* (Fig. 20*C*) and *Ptychodera* (Fig. 20*D*), or in other cases by a darker color visible through the body wall in the live specimens (Fig. 21*A*). Thus in some genera the trunk is very obviously regionated into branchiogenital, hepatic, and posthepatic, or caudal, regions, whereas in others no such divisions are externally evident. The caudal region may remain of about the same width throughout or may taper gradually to the terminal anus. The trunk surface is often more or less regularly annulated (Fig. 20*B*, *D*); this is caused by an alternation of low, poorly glandular epidermis at the grooves with tall, highly glandular epidermis on the areas between the grooves.

The coloration of the enteropneusts is mostly on the drab side, a sort of dull buff, but orange or reddish tints may occur on the proboscis or collar, or both, or on the entire body. The hepatic region is usually brown, and the colors of the ripe gonads may show through the body wall.

3. Body Wall.—The body is clothed with a ciliated epidermis, mostly of very tall slender ciliated cells (Fig. 23*A*) that, however, are reduced in height in certain areas, especially over the hepatic sacculations and in the annulations when present. The epithelial cells are interspersed with gland cells, richly so in most of the body, scantily in some areas. The gland cells seem to classify into three general sorts (Fig. 21*C*): mulberry cells filled with coarse granules and extending part or all of the epidermal width, reticulated cells containing a wide-meshed reticulum, and goblet cells with a peripheral flask-shaped expansion having finely granular or clear homogeneous contents and a slender proximal stalk that extends to

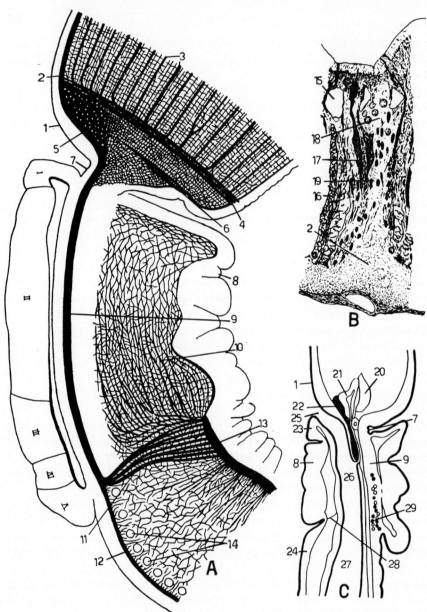

Fig. 24.—Nervous system (continued).   *A*, longitudinal view of the anterior part of the nervous system of *Sac. cambrensis* (*after Knight-Jones*, 1952).   *B*, middorsal sense organ of *Glossobalanus ruficollis* (*after Van der Horst*, 1929).   *C*, sagittal section of the anterior part of a species of *Balanoglossus* (*after Bullock*, 1944), showing distribution of giant cells.   1, proboscis; 2, middorsal nerve cord of proboscis; 3, subsidiary longitudinal cords of proboscis; 4, anterior nerve ring; 5, fanlike nervous expansion; 6, nervous thickening for preoral ciliary organ; 7, proboscis stalk; 8, collar; 9, collar cord; 10, nervous layer of collar epidermis; 11, circumenteric nerve ring; 12, dorsal nerve cord of trunk; 13, ventral nerve cord of trunk; 14, gill pores; 15, goblet cell; 16, reticulate gland cell; 17, granular gland cell; 18, sense organ; 19, nerve tract to sense organ; 20, heart vesicle; 21, buccal diverticulum; 22, proboscis skeleton; 23, collarette; 24, trunk; 25, mouth; 26, buccal tube; 27, pharynx; 28, collar-trunk septum; 29, giant cells.   I–V in *A* indicate histological zones of collar epidermis.

84

the epidermal base. The very glandular collar epidermis is usually
differentiated into three to five histologically different transverse zones
that may be evident to the eye by their differing color and that may or
may not relate to the transverse grooves usually present on the collar surface. In general, these zones consist of transverse bands of epidermis
rich in gland cells alternating with epidermis moderately provided with
gland cells. In *Glossobalanus minutus* and the Ptychoderidae in general,
five zones are present, three lighter bands alternating with two darkly
staining, heavily glandular bands located at the furrows (Spengel, 1893;
Fig. 22C). A similar zonation of the dorsal collar epidermis into five
bands occurs in the primitive genus *Protoglossus* (Burdon-Jones, 1956).
Three zones unrelated to the furrows, a broad median, darkly staining
zone, bordered on each side by a narrower, lightly colored zone, occur in
Saccoglossus otagoensis (Van der Horst, 1929; Fig. 22B); and four zones,
the second and fourth composed of long, thin, heavily staining cells, were
reported by the same author for *Balanoglossus mitsakiensis*. Presumably
other arrangements also occur. The trunk epidermis is in general quite
glandular and productive of mucus (Fig. 22A) but is low and scanty in
glands and cilia in the transverse annulations when present (Barrington,
1940) and over the hepatic sacculations, except at their free ends where a
tall, highly glandular epidermis obtains (Fig. 36A).

The epidermis passes indistinguishably into a thick nervous layer that
occupies its base and is traversed by the filamentous bases of the epidermal
cells (Fig. 21C). Between the main part of the epidermis and the nervous
layer there is sometimes present a very thin connective-tissue mesh or
layer, called the reticulated membrane. The nervous layer is bounded
internally by a strong basement membrane composed of two lamellae
pressed together. In enteropneusts the basement membrane is unusually
developed and of unusual structural importance. In the proboscis stalk
and roof of the buccal cavity it forms the *proboscis skeleton*, consisting of a
median plate and two posterior extensions, or *horns* (Fig. 23B–D). This
skeleton has a lamellate structure and is obviously a thickening of the
basement membrane, being secreted not only by the epidermis but also
by the coelomic tissue to its inner side. The median plate, of varying
shape and usually with a midventral keel, is situated in the proboscis
stalk between the buccal epithelium and the buccal diverticulum (Fig.
27A–C). The horns, of different length in different species, diverge backward in the roof of the buccal cavity, where they usually cause on each
side a longitudinal indentation of the buccal epithelium (Fig. 28A).

The muscular sheath of outer circular and inner longitudinal fibers
that would be expected to the inner side of the basement membrane is not
typically developed in the Enteropneusta. It is usually present in the
proboscis and collarette but is altogether wanting in the main part of the

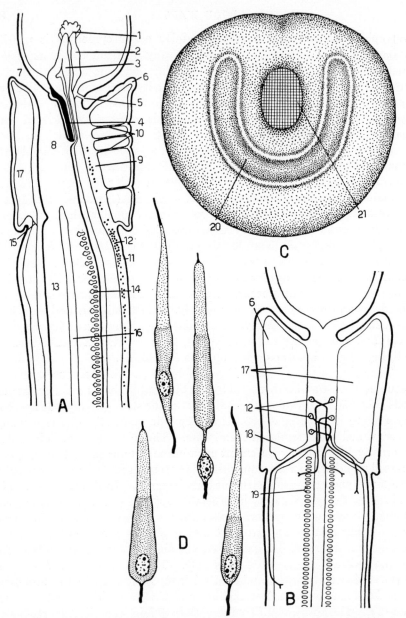

FIG. 25.—Nervous system (concluded), sense organs.   *A*, longitudinal sagittal section of *Sac. pusillus*, showing distribution of giant cells.   *B*, scheme of course of processes of the giant cells, looking down on dorsal side.   (*A*, *B*, *after Bullock*, 1944.)   *C*, proboscis base seen from the rear, showing preoral ciliary organ (*after Brambell and Cole*, 1939a).   *D*, photo-receptive cells of *Sac. kowalevskii* (*after Hess*, 1938).   1, glomerulus; 2, heart vesicle; 3, buccal diverticulum; 4, proboscis skeleton; 5, proboscis pore; 6, collarette; 7, mouth; 8, buccal tube; 9, collar cord; 10, dorsal strands of collar cord; 11, dorsal nerve cord of trunk; 12, giant cells; 13, pharynx; 14, gill slits; 15, collar-trunk septum; 16, parabranchial ridge; 17, collar coelom; 18, circumenteric connective; 19, gill pores; 20, preoral ciliary organ; 21, cutoff proboscis stalk.

collar as a rule, and in the trunk only the longitudinal fibers are generally present, especially ventrally. Details are given in the discussion of the muscular system. Neither is the inner surface of the body wall lined with a definite peritoneum except in the primitive genus *Protoglossus* (see later under coelom). It is a peculiarity of Enteropneusta that the coelomic cavities are mostly filled up with connective tissue and muscle fibers, and hence the peritoneal lining is more or less lost.

4. Nervous System.—In addition to the accounts in Van der Horst (1939) and Dawydoff (1948) an excellent consideration of the enteropneust nervous system is presented by Bullock (1945), and valuable studies of particular species have been published by Silén (1950) and Knight-Jones (1952). The nervous system is in a very primitive condition, consisting mainly of a nervous layer in the base of the epidermis. This layer is intraepidermal, not subepidermal as stated by some writers, for the slender threadlike bases of the epidermal cells pass through it to attach to the basement membrane. These epidermal bases as depicted by Bullock (Fig. 21*C*) remind very strongly of the bases of the epidermal cells of the radial nerve cords of asteroids (IV, page 270) and like the latter are continuations of a strong fibril that traverses the cell interior. The nervous layer is composed mainly of fine fibrils of uniform appearance everywhere, and as these fibrils appear as dots when cut across, the layer gives a punctate impression in sections, and hence is generally so represented in illustrations. Nerve cell bodies are absent from the main mass of nervous fibers, but bipolar and multipolar cells occur along its outer edge (Fig. 21*C*). The nervous layer is well developed in the proboscis, being thickened to form a cord in the middorsal and midventral groove or depression when present. In the *Saccoglossus* proboscis the longitudinal fibers of the nervous layer are aggregated into numerous bundles (Fig. 24*A*) that course along the proboscis toward its tip. The nervous layer also thickens greatly toward the proboscis base where its fibers tend to a circular direction and may form here a more or less definite *anterior nerve ring* from which the longitudinal bundles just mentioned take their departure (Fig. 24*A*). The nervous layer of the proboscis reaches its greatest depth on the dorsal and lateral sides of the proboscis stalk, whereas it is very thin in the ventral epidermis of the stalk. In *Saccoglossus* the dorsal proboscis cord spreads out into a fan-shaped area in the posterior surface of the proboscis (Fig. 24*A*).

In the middorsal and midventral lines of the trunk the nervous layer is thickened to form cords that occupy the median longitudinal ridges previously mentioned; these ridges, however, are often sunk into longitudinal depressions (Fig. 33*C*). The dorsal and ventral nerve cords represent thickenings, mostly in the form of longitudinal fibers, of the nervous layer at the expense of the rest of the epidermis, here sparsely

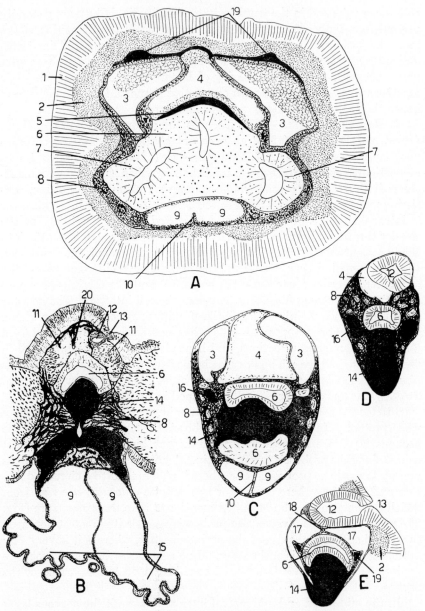

Fig. 26.—Coelom. *A*, section through the proboscis base of *Gloss. hedleyi*, showing the four posterior divisions of the proboscis coelom (*after Hill*, 1897). *B*, section of the posterior end of the proboscis of *Pty. flava* to show formation of racemose organ by ventrolateral pockets of the proboscis coelom (*after Van der Horst*, 1929). *C–E*, three successive sections of proboscis base and stalk of *Sac. kowalevskii* to show proboscis canal and pore (*after Spengel*, 1893). *C*, four posterior proboscis pockets. *D*, left pocket has narrowed to proboscis canal. *E*, proboscis canal opening by proboscis pore. 1, epidermis; 2, anterior

glandular. The dorsal cord is well delimited laterally from the general nervous layer, whereas the ventral cord has a greater lateral spread and a greater total area than the dorsal cord. The ventral trunk cord terminates at the anterior end of the trunk, but the thickening of which it is constituted continues as one or a group of thickenings on each side in the anterior end of the trunk along the line of attachment of the collar-trunk septum, finally joining the dorsal trunk cord where the latter passes into the collar (Fig. 24A). There is thus formed a sort of *circumenteric* nerve ring (*prebranchial* nerve ring of Knight-Jones) that puts the ventral and dorsal nerve cords into direct communication. The dorsal trunk cord continues into the collar but at once leaves the epidermis and runs forward through the collar coelom above the buccal tube and above the perihaemal canals when present as a pronounced longitudinal thickening called the *collar cord* (*neurocord* of Knight-Jones).

The collar cord is the only part of the enteropneust nervous system having an internal position but is continuous at both ends with the general intraepidermal nervous layer, being, as stated by Bullock, "simply a submerged strip of epidermis." It is generally crescentic or semicircular in cross section (Fig. 30C). Its fibers take a general longitudinal direction. The collar cord has a continuous lumen in many members of the family Ptychoderidae (but mostly not in *Balanoglossus*) and in a few Spengelidae but in most enteropneusts contains only small, scattered, isolated cavities, or lacunae, that may number up to several hundred and generally occur in two longitudinal rows, not symmetrically arranged (Fig. 23E). In some of the species in which the collar cord has a continuous lumen this opens to the exterior at each end by the *anterior* and *posterior neuropores*. In other enteropneusts actual neuropores are absent, but their site is indicated by an epidermal pit or depression (Fig. 32B).

The collar cord presumably represents the nervous center of enteropneusts but lacks the usual characteristics of a brain, for it does not contain any especial concentration of nerve cell bodies and does not give off nerves, rather resembling a conduction path. The collar cord is covered externally by a basement membrane derived from that of the surface epidermis. Its thin roof and the lining of the central lumen or of the lacunae consist of ordinary ciliated epidermis (Fig. 23E) that may contain gland cells. The much thicker sides and floor of the collar cord are formed of a deep layer of nerve fibers with a zone of nerve cell bodies to its dorsal side (Fig. 23E). In short, the collar cord represents inturned epidermis of which the nerv-

---

nerve ring; 3, dorsolateral coelomic pockets; 4, heart vesicle; 5, central blood sinus; 6, buccal diverticulum; 7, pockets of 6; 8, chondroid tissue; 9, ventrolateral coelomic pockets; 10, ventral proboscis mesentery; 11, perihaemal spaces; 12, proboscis canal; 13, proboscis pore; 14, proboscis skeleton; 15, racemose sacculations of ventrolateral coelomic pockets; 16, efferent glomerular arteries; 17, anterior ends of collar coeloms; 18, dorsal mesentery of collar; 19, lateral proboscis veins; 20, dorsal vessel.

ous layer is thinned or lacking dorsally and thickened laterally and ventrally. The collar cord does, however, differ histologically from the intraepidermal nervous layer elsewhere in the presence of giant cells. These were discovered by Spengel (1893) but could not be found by subsequent observers until recent years when their presence was verified by Hess (1937), Bullock (1944), Silén (1950), and Knight-Jones (1952). Bullock saw them in nearly all of about 25 species investigated, belonging to three families. They are typically found in the lateralmost areas (Figs. 23*E*, 30*C*) of the posterior part of the collar cord; in two large species of *Balanoglossus* they also occur in the anterior part of the dorsal trunk cord, being more concentrated here than in the collar cord itself (Fig. 25*A*). Spengel (1893) reported finding giant cells in the trunk nerve cords, circumenteric ring, and proboscis stalk in species not available to Bullock. The total number of giant cells varies from about 10 to 30 in the smaller to 160 in the larger species studied. Each giant cell gives off a single conspicuous process that immediately decussates (crosses to the other side) and runs posteriorly in the dorsal trunk cord and by way of the circumenteric ring into the lateral nervous layer of the trunk and into the ventral cord (Fig. 25*B*). Knight-Jones found giant cells in the anterior part of the collar cord in *Saccoglossus*, and the processes from these run anteriorly in the proboscis.

In many enteropneusts the middorsal region of the collar cord is connected with the dorsal collar epidermis. These connections apparently represent remnants of the epidermal invagination by which the collar cord is formed during embryology. They take the form either of a median ridge or crest (Fig. 30*C*) or of a succession of strands extending from the collar cord to the dorsal epidermis, running in the dorsal mesentery of the collar in so far as this is present (Fig. 22*C*). The strands were badly termed "dorsal roots" by Bateson (1886) in his determination to make chordates out of the enteropneusts. They are always present in the Ptychoderidae, also in some Harrimaniidae, and vary from 1 to 18, being mostly less than 6 in number. The strands are frequently hollow. Both crests and strands carry nerve fibers and hence put the collar cord in communication with the dorsal collar epidermis.

The findings of Silén and Knight-Jones indicate the presence of a nervous layer in the base of the epithelium of the digestive tract, best developed in the buccal epithelium and diminishing posteriorly. Silén noted a midventral and a feebler middorsal thickening present in this nervous layer, and these were continuous with a ringlike thickening at the entrance into the buccal tube. In *Glossobalanus* Silén was able to demonstrate interconnected nerve plexi on both surfaces of the ventral (but not the dorsal) trunk mesentery. Fibers from these plexi supply adjacent blood vessels and muscles and pass through the basement membrane into

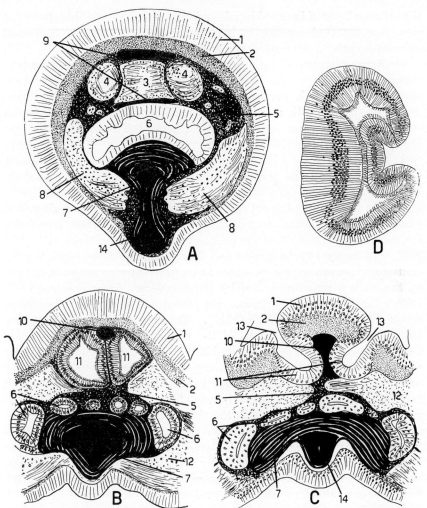

FIG. 27.—Coelom (continued). *A–C*, three successive sections of proboscis base of *Harrimania kupfferi* to show paired proboscis canals and pores (*after Spengel*, 1893). *A*, section through posterior ends of dorsolateral coelomic pockets of proboscis coelom. *B*, more posterior section; pockets have narrowed to proboscis canals. *C*, posterior to *B*, through the proboscis pores. *D*, transverse section of collar canal of *Bal. kowalevskii*, showing crescentic shape (*after Bateson*, 1886). 1, epidermis; 2, anterior nerve ring; 3, heart vesicle; 4, dorsolateral pockets of proboscis coelom; 5, chondroid tissue; 6, buccal diverticulum; 7, proboscis skeleton; 8, anterior ends of collar coeloms; 9, venous sinus; 10, dorsal blood vessel; 11, proboscis canals; 12, collar coeloms; 13, proboscis pores; 14, keel of proboscis skeleton.

the nervous layer of both epidermis and gut epithelium. Fibers have not been demonstrated crossing the basement membrane from the epidermal nervous layer into the adjacent musculature.

5. Sense Organs.—There seem to be very few, if any, sense organs present in enteropneusts. Bullock (1945) showed that the epidermis almost everywhere is permeated with neurosensory cells of the usual invertebrate type with a long process reaching the surface, an interior swelling containing the nucleus, and just below the nucleus a basal fiber that joins the intraepidermal nervous layer (Fig. 21*C*). The presence of such neurosensory cells has been verified by Silén and Knight-Jones, although they find the cells less numerous than thought by Bullock. These neurosensory cells are especially abundant on the proboscis, increasing in numbers toward its base. Van der Horst (1929) described what seems to be a sense organ connected by a strong nervous strand with the middorsal nerve cord of the proboscis of *Glossobalanus ruficollis* (Fig. 24*B*). In many Ptychoderidae and Harrimaniidae there exists on the ventral surface of the proboscis base at its junction with the stalk or even on the stalk a structure called by its discoverers (Brambell and Cole, 1939a) the *preoral ciliary organ*. Its presence in a number of enteropneusts was verified by Bullock (1945). This organ is a U-shaped epidermal depression with the limbs of the U directed dorsally (Fig. 25*C*). The depression is bounded by an epidermal ridge composed of cells taller and with longer cilia than those of the general epidermis and interspersed with gland cells. Knight-Jones has verified the statement of Brambell and Cole that the intraepidermal nervous layer is thickened in the epidermal depression (but not beneath the ridge) (Fig. 24*A*). There seems no reason to doubt that this structure is a sensory organ, probably of chemoreceptive nature. Hess (1938), studying photic response in *Saccoglossus kowalevskii*, investigated histologically areas of highest photosensitivity and found therein cells he designated as photoreceptors (Fig. 25*D*). These appear to be variants of the ordinary neurosensory cells.

6. Coelom.—Ontogenetically the enteropneusts have a spacious coelom lined with peritoneum, but as a peculiarity of this group the coelomic wall itself gives rise to muscular and connective tissue; consequently in the adult the coelom is greatly reduced and mostly devoid of a definite lining.

The proboscis coelom constitutes an unpaired cavity that is more or less occupied by muscle and connective tissue (Figs. 21*B*, 29*A*, 30*A*, *B*). A definite central space that extends to the proboscis tip or nearly so remains in a number of species, but generally speaking the proboscis coelom is confined to the posterior part of the proboscis where there projects into it from behind a complex (Fig. 21*B*) composed of the glomerulus, the central sinus and its associated vesicle, and the buccal

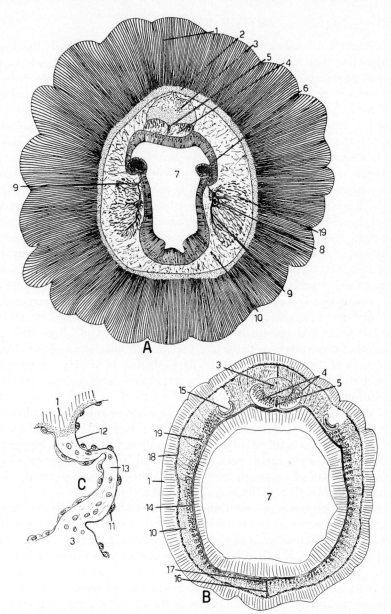

FIG. 28.—Coelom (concluded). *A*, section through the collar of *Sac. mereschkowskii* with exceptionally thick epidermis, has perihaemal but no peribuccal spaces (*after Van der Horst*, 1934a). *B*, section through the collar of *Bal. apertus*, has both perihaemal and peribuccal spaces (*after Spengel*, 1893). *C*, dorsal mesentery of collar of *Protoglossus*, showing peritoneum; mesentery contains a nervous strand (*after Caullery and Mesnil*, 1904). 1, epidermis; 2, nervous layer; 3, collar cord; 4, perihaemal spaces; 5, dorsal blood vessel; 6, horns of proboscis skeleton; 7, buccal tube, in *A* partly subdivided by indentations at horns; 8, peribuccal blood vessels; 9, peritoneal fold for 8; 10, collar coelom; 11, peritoneum; 12, dorsal mesentery; 13, dorsal nerve strand in mesentery; 14, peribuccal space filled with circular muscle fibers; 15, collar canals; 16, ventral mesentery; 17, ventral blood vessel; 18, blood plexus for epidermis; 19, longitudinal muscles.

diverticulum, all discussed later.   The coelom here is generally lined with peritoneum that clothes the complex mentioned and attaches it to the ventral proboscis wall by a median ventral mesentery with free edges at both ends (Fig. 21*B*).   Hence the proboscis coelom is here divided into two ventrolateral compartments that continue posteriorly to a varying extent, ending blindly, usually after reuniting beyond the free posterior edge of the mesentery (Fig. 26).   In *Ptychodera* and some species of *Glossobalanus* these ventrolateral compartments are prolonged into the proboscis stalk where their walls are greatly sacculated.   These sacculations are noticeable in the dorsal wall of the buccal cavity and have been given the name of *cauliflower*, or *racemose*, organ (Fig. 26*B*).   Dorsally the proboscis coelom in the posterior part of the proboscis is also divided into right and left dorsolateral compartments by a middorsal mesentery or by the contact of the central complex with the dorsal proboscis wall (Fig. 26*A*, *C*).   These two dorsolateral compartments also extend posteriorly to either side of the heart vesicle into the proboscis stalk, where the right one typically ends blindly, while the left one, generally larger than the right one, opens to the dorsal surface as a *proboscis pore* by way of a tubular epidermal invagination, called *proboscis canal* (Fig. 26*D*, *E*). Variants of these relations occur in different enteropneusts and in different specimens of the same species.   The proboscis pore may be medially located although still connected to the left dorsolateral coelomic space, or the median pore may connect with both compartments by canals, or the right compartment may open by the pore whereas the left ends blindly, or in some species there are regularly two symmetrical pores and canals, one for each compartment (e.g., in *Harrimania kupfferi* and *maculosus*; Fig. 27*A*–*C*).   Two canals and pores may also occur as an individual variant in *Balanoglossus australiensis* (Hill, 1895).   A sphincter muscle is found at the junction of the canal with the coelomic sac.

There is probably no continuity between the proboscis and collar coeloms, although a definite dividing septum is not present in the adult. The center of the collar is occupied by the buccal part of the digestive tract or buccal tube, and originally the collar coelom extended between the buccal tube and the collar wall as a pair of sacs.   However, this condition is retained only in the primitive genus *Protoglossus*, where the two coelomic sacs of the collar meet in the median sagittal plane to form complete dorsal and ventral mesenteries for the buccal tube (Fig. 23*F*).   In other enteropneusts these mesenteries are more or less incomplete and the two coelomic sacs are more or less occupied by connective tissue and muscle bundles.   The dorsal mesentery is better retained than the ventral one and stretches from the collar cord to the dorsal collar wall enclosing the dorsal nerve strands, or some of them, when present (Fig. 22*C*).   The collar coeloms extend anteriorly into the proboscis stalk, where together

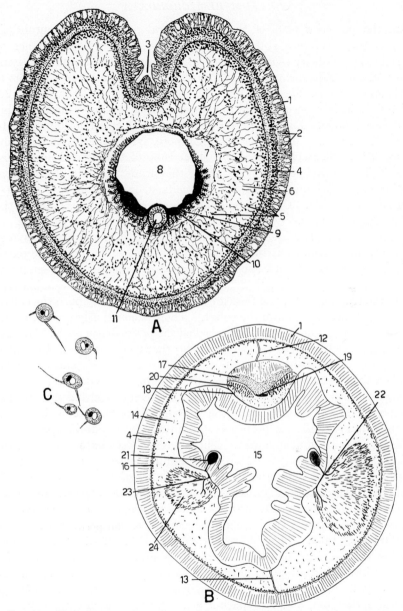

Fig. 29.—Musculature. *A*, section through the proboscis of *Sac. otagoensis* with concentric rings of longitudinal muscles (*after Van der Horst*, 1929).   *B*, section through the collar of *Sac. kowalevskii* with longitudinal bundles attached to the vascular peritoneal folds. *C*, coelomocytes. (*B, C, after Spengel,* 1893.)   1, epidermis; 2, goblet cells of epidermis; 3, middorsal groove; 4, nervous layer of epidermis; 5, rings of longitudinal muscle fibers; 6, connective tissue; 7, proboscis coelom; 8, heart vesicle; 9, glomerulus; 10, central blood sinus; 11, buccal diverticulum; 12, dorsal collar mesentery; 13, ventral collar mesentery; 14, collar coelom; 15, buccal tube; 16, subepidermal longitudinal muscle layer; 17, collar cord; 18, perihaemal spaces; 19, dorsal blood vessel; 20, longitudinal muscles of 18; 21, skeletal horns; 22, peritoneal fold; 23, peribuccal blood vessels supported by 22; 24, longitudinal muscle bundles supported by 22.

with the posterior ends of the ventrolateral pockets of the proboscis coelom they secrete a stiffening tissue called, from its resemblance to vertebrate cartilage, *chondroid tissue*. In forming the chondroid tissue the coelomic walls disintegrate. The chondroid tissue occurs as a sort of reticulum around the main plate of the proboscis skeleton (Figs. 26, 27A–C) and is especially well developed in the families Harrimaniidae and Spengelidae. Like the proboscis coelom, each collar coelom opens to the exterior by way of a collar canal and pore, symmetrical with its fellow (Fig. 28B). The collar canal is a short tube of tall ciliated epidermis, crescentic in cross section (Fig. 27D), that leads from the dorsolateral region of its coelomic sac through the collar-trunk septum into the first gill slit of its side. Collar canals and pores seem to be lacking in the genus *Stereobalanus*.

The collar coelom is separated from the trunk coelom by a transverse collar-trunk septum, but this does not remain a simple transverse partition except in the primitive species *Protoglossus koehleri*. In other enteropneusts the collar coelom is complicated by the invasion of evaginations from the trunk coelom, and these evaginations necessarily push the collar-trunk septum forward into the collar. There is constantly present a pair of digitiform coelomic evaginations called the *periphaemal spaces* (because they enclose a blood vessel between them) that lie in contact as two tubes along the dorsal surface of the buccal tube between this and the collar cord which rests upon them (Fig. 30C). The wall of the perihaemal spaces consists of the collar-trunk septum pushed forward as by a pair of fingers. In most enteropneusts the perihaemal spaces extend the length of the collar and into the proboscis stalk up to the chondroid tissue but in some species are much shorter. They may coalesce anteriorly. In the adult they are generally filled with longitudinal muscle fibers. The other coelomic invasion from the trunk, the *peribuccal fold*, is more or less limited to the families Ptychoderidae and Spengelidae. Here the collar-trunk septum has moved forward along the buccal tube as a very flat fold on each side between the buccal epithelium and the peritoneal covering of the buccal tube. This fold reaches farther forward on the dorsal than on the ventral side; hence its anterior edge gradually curves downward and backward to resume again the horizontal position of the septum. In this way there is produced a very narrow coelomic space around the buccal epithelium, and this space is generally filled with circular muscle fibers (Fig. 28B).

The trunk coelom is paired, and its two halves meet above and below the digestive tract to form dorsal and ventral mesenteries. The short ventral mesentery is generally complete, whereas the dorsal one is usually much interrupted, permitting confluence of the two coelomic cavities above the digestive tube. As just noted, each trunk coelom sends into

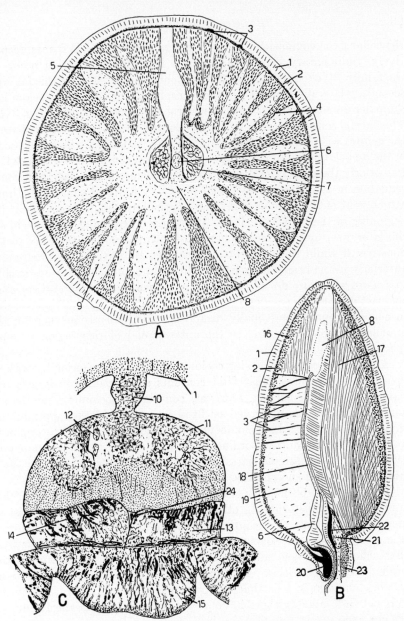

Fig. 30.—Musculature (continued). *A*, section through the proboscis of *Gloss. minutus*, showing radiating longitudinal muscle bundles. *B*, median sagittal section of the proboscis of *Schiz. brasiliense*, showing dorsoventral muscle partition. (*A, B, after Spengel*, 1893.) *C*, cross section of dorsal part of collar of *Sac. mereschkowskii* (*after Van der Horst*, 1934a). 1, epidermis; 2, nervous layer; 3, haemal plexus of basement membrane; 4, radiating longitudinal muscle strands; 5, dorsoventral partition; 6, buccal diverticulum; 7, glomerulus; 8, proboscis coelom; 9, connective tissue; 10, dorsal crest; 11, collar cord; 12, giant cells; 13, perihaemal spaces; 14, longitudinal muscle fibers of 13; 15, wall of buccal tube; 16, circular muscle layer of proboscis; 17, longitudinal muscles; 18, appendix of buccal diverticulum; 19, ventral mesentery; 20, proboscis skeleton; 21, heart vesicle; 22, central sinus; 23, anterior nerve ring; 24, dorsal blood vessel.

the collar two evaginations, the perihaemal and peribuccal spaces, respectively, rudimentary in *Protoglossus*. A further complication occurs in the family Ptychoderidae. In the branchiogenital region of this family a secondary lateral septum is present on each side, dividing the coelom into a smaller dorsolateral and a larger ventrolateral compartment (Fig. 34*H*). This lateral septum extends from the pharynx to the tip or side or base of the genital wing and may subdivide the gonads, part of which then occur in the dorsolateral and part in the ventrolateral compartment (Fig. 34*H*). Posteriorly the dorsolateral compartment declines in size, partly through reduction of the genital region and partly by a dorsal shift of the inner attachment of the septum, and finally opens into the main coelom at the beginning of the hepatic region. Anteriorly on reaching the last gill slit the lateral septum shifts its inner attachment from the pharynx to the dorsal wall while the outer attachment remains fixed. In progressing anteriorly in the branchial region the inner attachment continues to shift to a more and more dorsal position, and hence the dorsolateral coelomic compartment grows smaller and smaller in the anterior direction, ceasing to contain gonads, and finally disappears altogether somewhere in the branchial region, extending to the anterior end of this region in some species.

As the proboscis and collar coeloms open to the exterior by way of their respective pores, their fluid contents are presumably largely sea water. The trunk coelom, however, contains a coelomic fluid that is found coagulated in preserved or fixed material and that contains an abundance of amoeboid coelomocytes (Fig. 29*C*) that seem to originate from the peritoneum. According to Spengel (1893), these coelomocytes gather in numbers around parasites or other foreign bodies and secrete a membrane around such bodies.

It is a strange peculiarity of enteropneusts that their coelomic epithelium tends to transform into other tissues and hence does not persist as such in many areas. When present it is a flattened nucleated membrane (Fig. 28*C*). The peritoneum produces three types of tissue, muscle fibers, chondroid tissue, and connective tissue, and these fill much of the original coelomic cavities. The connective tissue forms a delicate fibrous network containing cells that are presumably the source of the fibrils. This network is everywhere interspersed between the muscle fibers and fills coelomic spaces not occupied by muscles.

7. Musculature.—As just indicated, the muscles of enteropneusts are of coelomic origin, and consequently a definite muscle layer in the body wall between the epidermis and the parietal peritoneum and another muscle layer on the digestive tract between its lining epithelium and the visceral peritoneum, as typical of coelomate animals, are here absent. Instead the muscle fibers usually course in what should be coelomic

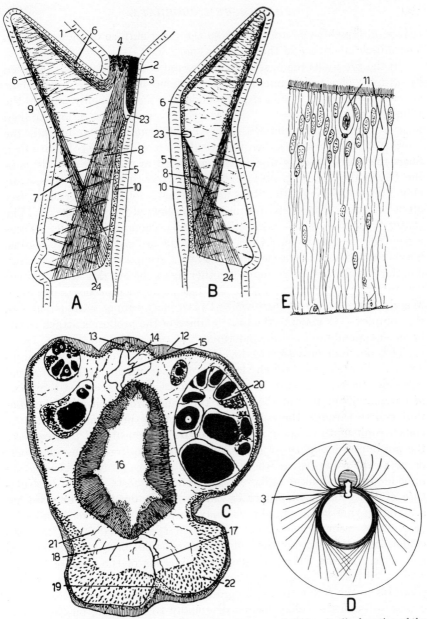

Fig. 31.—Musculature (concluded), digestive system.   A, B, longitudinal section of the ptychoderid collar, showing musculature (*after Van der Horst*, 1939).   A, dorsal side.   B, ventral side.   C, cross section of the esophageal region of *Sac. pusillus* (*after Van der Horst*, 1929).   D, collar muscles of *Gloss. minutus* seen by cutting off the collarette and looking within.   E, histology of the buccal epithelium.   (*D, E, after Spengel*, 1893.)   1, proboscis base; 2, proboscis stalk; 3, proboscis skeleton; 4, chondroid tissue; 5, buccal epithelium; 6, circular muscles of collarette; 7, outer longitudinal bundle; 8, inner longitudinal bundle; 9, diagonal muscles of collarette; 10, peribuccal cavity with circular muscles; 11, goblet cells; 12, epidermis; 13, dorsal nerve cord; 14, dorsal trunk mesentery; 15, dorsal blood vessel; 16, esophagus; 17, ventral trunk mesentery; 18, ventral blood vessel; 19, ventral nerve cord; 20, gonad; 21, trunk coelom; 22, longitudinal muscle layer; 23, peribuccal blood vessel; 24, collar-trunk septum.

spaces, although some are applied to the inner surface of the epidermis. The muscle fibers are of the smooth type.

In the proboscis the basement membrane of the epidermis is followed by a layer of circular muscle fibers, varying in thickness in different genera, being rather thin in the Ptychoderidae and especially weak in the primitive genus *Protoglossus*. There follows a great mass of longitudinal muscle fibers interspersed with connective tissue that almost fills the interior of the proboscis, ontogenetically a coelom. The longitudinal fibers may be uniformly disposed or arranged in radiating strands as in the Ptychoderidae (Fig. 30*A*) or in concentric rings as in *Saccoglossus* (Fig. 29*A*). Although the fibers have a general longitudinal course they often crisscross diagonally, forming a complicated felt (Fig. 30*B*). The center of the proboscis is more or less filled with connective tissue. There is generally present in the posterior part of the proboscis a median sagittal plate of dorsoventral muscle fibers that part around the complex occupying the coelom here and come together again below this to follow the ventral proboscis mesentery to the basement membrane (Fig. 30*B*). Muscle fibers from this dorsoventral plate may supply various parts of the complex. In general, the muscle fibers of the proboscis attach to the basement membrane of the epidermis.

The muscular provision of the collar varies much in different enteropneusts. *Protoglossus*, which lacks both peribuccal and perihaemal coelomic spaces, has scarcely any collar musculature except a thin zone of circular fibers around the buccal tube and two longitudinal bundles that course through the collar coelom from the proboscis stalk to the collar-trunk septum, being attached to the peritoneal fold that encloses the peribuccal blood vessel (Fig. 23*F*). These peritoneal vascular folds occur at the same places where the horns of the proboscis skeleton are imbedded in the buccal wall. In other enteropneusts also the musculature of the collar wall proper is usually feebly developed or wanting, although a thin longitudinal layer may be present as in *Sac. kowalevskii* (Fig. 29*B*), accompanied or not by a circular layer. Generally the subepidermal musculature of the collar is limited to or best developed in the collarette. In the Ptychoderidae the epidermis of the outer collarette wall is subtended by a longitudinal layer followed by a circular layer; posterior to the collarette the longitudinal fibers leave the epidermis and course through the collar coelom diagonally to terminate on the collar-trunk septum at its contact with the buccal tube (Fig. 31*A*, *B*). The inner collarette wall that embraces the proboscis stalk is also muscular with outer circular and inner longitudinal fibers (Fig. 31*A*, *B*). In the ptychoderid *Gloss. minutus*, Spengel (1893) described the muscular arrangement seen by cutting off the rim of the collarette and looking at the cross section. One then sees attached to the main plate of the

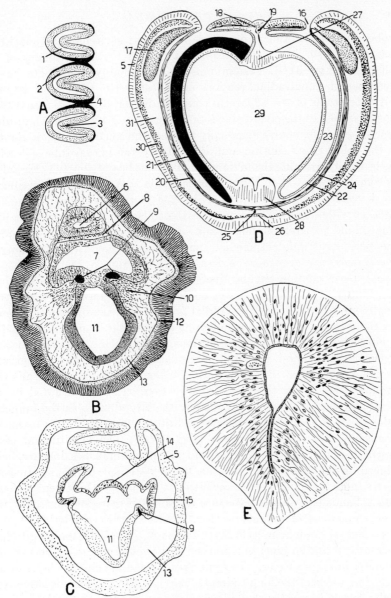

Fig. 32.—Digestive tract (continued). *A*, gill slits and skeletal bars of *Protoglossus* (*after Caullery and Mesnil*, 1904). *B*, cross section of the collar of *Sac. otagoensis*, showing marked indentation of buccal tube by the skeletal horns (*after Van der Horst*, 1929). *C*, cross section of the collar of *Xenopleura* with differentiated buccal roof (*after Gilchrist*, 1925). *D*, cross section through the gill region of *Schizocardium*. *E*, section of the buccal diverticulum. (*D, E, after Spengel*, 1893.) 1, gill slit; 2, gill septum; 3, tongue bar; 4, skeletal rods; 5, epidermis; 6, epidermal depression representing posterior neuropore; 7, dorsal part of buccal tube; 8, perihaemal spaces; 9, skeletal horns; 10, longitudinal muscle bundle; 11, ventral part of buccal tube; 12, nervous layer; 13, collar coelom; 14, median part of buccal roof; 15, lateral part of buccal roof; 16, gill pore; 17, gonad; 18, dorsal nerve cord; 19, dorsal blood vessel; 20, circular muscle layer; 21, skeletal bar of septum; 22, tongue bar; 23, coelom of tongue bar; 24, branchial sac; 25, ventral blood vessel; 26, ventral nerve cord; 27, epibranchial strip; 28, hypobranchial strip; 29, lumen of pharynx; 30, longitudinal muscle layer; 31, trunk coelom.

proboscis skeleton a mass of muscle fibers that encircles the buccal tube near the mouth and also spreads out fanlike to the periphery of the collarette (Fig. 31D). These muscles presumably contribute to the layers seen in longitudinal sections of the collarette. Between the inner and outer walls of the collarette course radial or slightly diagonal fibers that crisscross in the connective tissue (Fig. 31A, B). Inner longitudinal bundles generally course diagonally through the collar coelom, originating on the collar-trunk septum and attaching to the buccal tube at various levels, finally reaching the main plate of the proboscis skeleton (Fig. 31A); they may be related to the peritoneal folds that enclose the peribuccal blood vessels as in *Protoglossus* (Fig. 23F), or these ascending bundles together with those descending from the collarette may form a complete longitudinal coat for the buccal tube as seen in cross section (Fig. 28B). The peribuccal and perihaemal spaces when present (lacking only in *Protoglossus*) are also more or less filled with muscle fibers. The peribuccal spaces contain circular fibers lying just outside the buccal epithelium, and the perihaemal spaces contain longitudinal fibers (Fig. 28B). Finally must be mentioned the radial fibers that, accompanied by connective tissue, cross the coelom penetrating between the longitudinal bundles. It will be seen that muscular conditions in the collar are rather complex.

On the other hand, the trunk musculature is rather simple, consisting throughout the class of a longitudinal layer beneath the epidermis that gradually reduces in the posterior direction. It is interrupted by the dorsal and ventral mesenteries, also by the lateral septa in the branchial region, as well as by other special conditions imposed by the presence of gonads and branchial structures (Fig. 32D). The longitudinal trunk musculature is commonly thicker ventrally and diminishes dorsally, being reduced to the vanishing point on the hepatic sacculations. In some species, notably species of *Saccoglossus*, it forms two thick ventral longitudinal bands (Fig. 31C) that cause the spiral twisting of the trunk often seen in members of this genus (Fig. 20A). The Ptychoderidae have a subepidermal circular muscle layer to the outer side of the longitudinal layer, next to the basement membrane of the epidermis; this forms an anal sphincter in some species. In some Spengelidae the circular layer occurs to the inner side of the longitudinal layer (Fig. 33C). The digestive tract of the trunk is mostly devoid of musculature; longitudinal fibers are always wanting, but in some cases circular fibers encircle the branchial and esophageal regions (Fig. 32D). In all enteropneusts delicate radial muscle fibers cross the trunk coelom between the digestive tube and the trunk wall.

8. Digestive System.—The digestive tract is a straight epithelial tube that in general lacks intrinsic musculature. The large mouth occurs ventrally in the collar between the collarette and the proboscis stalk. It

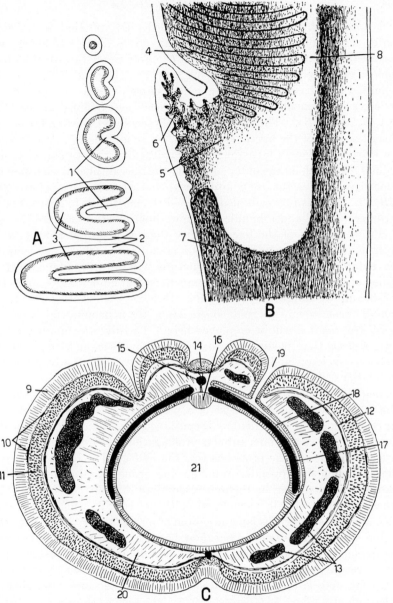

FIG. 33.—Digestive tract (continued). *A*, scheme of subdivision of the gill slit by downgrowth of the tongue bar (*after Bateson*, 1886a). *B*, longitudinal section through the junction of pharynx and esophagus of *Glossobalanus* to show postbranchial canal and caecum (*after Van der Horst*, 1939). *C*, cross section through the pharynx of *Glandiceps talaboti;* pharynx has simple contour (*combined from Marion*, 1886, *and Spengel*, 1893). 1, tongue bar; 2, gill septum; 3, gill slit; 4, skeletal rods of gill apparatus; 5, postbranchial canal; 6, postbranchial caecum; 7, esophagus; 8, parabranchial ridge; 9, epidermis; 10, haemal plexus; 11, longitudinal muscle layer; 12, circular muscle layer; 13, gonads; 14, dorsal nerve cord; 15, dorsal blood vessel; 16, epibranchial strip; 17, skeletal rod of gill septum; 18, branchial sac; 19, gill pore; 20, trunk coelom with radial fibers; 21, pharynx.

103

leads into the buccal tube (formerly called pharynx) that occupies the
center of the collar interior.   The buccal tube is lined with a very tall,
vacuolated, ciliated epithelium (Fig. 31*E*), often richly furnished with the
goblet type of gland cell and having a nervous layer in its base.   It is
delimited by a basement membrane, and outside of this occurs a greater
or lesser investment of longitudinal muscles, as explained above (Figs.
28*A, B,* 29*B,* 32*B*).   The horns of the proboscis skeleton extend backward
along the sides of the buccal epithelium, causing here in *Protoglossus* and
the Harrimaniidae an inbending of the epithelium that produces a longitudinal furrow along the outer surface of the buccal tube on each side and
somewhat divides the tube into dorsal and ventral parts (Figs. 28*A,*
32*B, C*).   At this furrow is also attached the peritoneal fold carrying the
peribuccal vessel and a bundle of longitudinal muscles (Fig. 28*A*).

From the roof of the buccal cavity there is given off anteriorly the
diverticulum made famous by Bateson (1885) as the alleged notochord of
the enteropneusts.   The same structure was termed stomochord by
Willey (1899b), and this name was much used in later works on enteropneusts and was adopted by Dawydoff (1948).   Since words formed from
"chord" seem to imply a solid construction, the noncommittal expression
buccal diverticulum will be employed here.   The diverticulum begins as a
narrow neck that passes anteriorly just above the main plate of the
proboscis skeleton and, expanding considerably and usually presenting
sacculations, continues into the posterior part of the proboscis, where it
participates in the complex projecting into the coelom there (Figs. 26, 27).
The sacculations usually consist of a pair of ventrolateral pockets.   In
the Spengelidae the diverticulum is continued forward in the dorsoventral
muscle septum as a slender tubular prolongation, the *appendix*, that may
extend well toward the proboscis tip (Fig. 30*B*).   The buccal diverticulum, including the appendix, is hollow and opens into the buccal cavity.
Its wall consists of an epithelium resembling that of the buccal cavity,
being composed of tall, vacuolated epithelial cells in which cilia, gland
cells, and a basal nervous layer are often observable (Fig. 32*E*).   In 1900,
Ritter, studying *Harrimania maculosa*, became quite excited on observing
the dorsolateral grooves that constrict off the dorsal part of the buccal
tube here and positively declared this buccal roof to represent a notochord,
as a continuation of the buccal diverticulum.   The same viewpoint was
independently taken by Gilchrist (1925), who seemed unaware of Ritter's
article, for the related *Xenopleura vivipara* in which the constrictions are
very pronounced and the buccal roof differentiated into median and lateral
regions (Fig. 32*C*).   Actually such dorsolateral grooves partly constricting off the buccal roof are common to all members of the families Protoglossidae and Harrimaniidae (Fig. 32*B*) and are caused by or at least
associated with the application of the skeletal horns to the buccal wall.

The condition has no relation to the buccal diverticulum or to an alleged notochord. All recent students of enteropneusts are agreed that the buccal diverticulum does not represent a notochord and probably is just what it appears to be—a preoral extension of the digestive tract (Silén, 1950).

In accordance with the usage of Van der Horst (1939), the first part of the trunk digestive tract beginning at the collar-trunk septum is called *pharynx* because it bears the gill apertures (discussed below). The gill apertures do not occupy the entire circumference of the pharynx in most enteropneusts. Usually the pharynx is regionated into a dorsal half pierced by the gill slits and a ventral part that serves the digestive function. In the Ptychoderidae, but not other enteropneusts, these two parts are separated by a deep lateral constriction on each side (Fig. 34A). In the genus *Schizocardium* the branchial apparatus does occupy most of the circumference of the pharynx and the digestive part is limited to a narrow midventral strip (Fig. 32D), the *hypobranchial ridge*. The digestive part of the pharynx is attached to the ventral trunk wall by the radial muscle strands and the ventral trunk mesentery. Its epithelium may not differ from that of the buccal tube or may be shortened or heightened in comparison with the latter; in general, it is ciliated and provided with numerous small gland cells. In some Ptychoderidae a projecting ridge of especially tall epithelium separates the digestive and branchial regions; these ridges are called *parabranchial ridges* (Fig. 34A). In many enteropneusts the branchial part of the pharynx gradually diminishes and passes smoothly into the esophagus after the last gill slits. In the Ptychoderidae, however, the constriction of the digestive tube into dorsal and ventral parts continues for a short distance behind the last gill slits. The dorsal part, called by Willey (1899b) the *postbranchial canal*, is very deeply constricted from the esophagus (Fig. 33B) and consists of a very thick glandular epithelium, often thrown into folds (Fig. 34H). A further complication is introduced in some species of *Glossobalanus* in which this postbranchial canal sends anteriorly a blind caecum, the *postbranchial caecum*, anteriorly above the rear end of the pharynx, here of diminished diameter (Fig. 33B).

The part of the digestive tract following the pharynx and extending to the hepatic region is called the esophagus. In the Protoglossidae and Ptychoderidae this is histologically similar throughout, presenting a large lumen and a low more or less scalloped epithelium. In the other families, however (Harrimaniidae, Spengelidae), the esophagus is differentiated into an anterior part of varying length with large lumen and thin wall, similar to the digestive part of the pharynx, and a posterior part with reduced lumen and very thick, deeply furrowed epithelium, often with two especially prominent ventral folds (Fig. 34E, F). This section may again

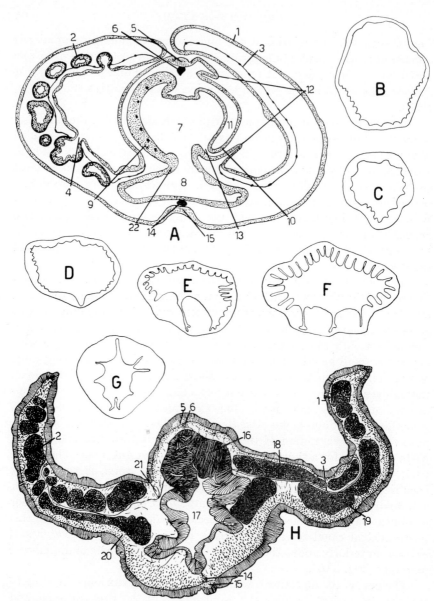

FIG. 34.—Digestive tract (continued). *A*, transverse section through the pharynx of *Ptych. flava (after Willey,* 1899b). *B–G,* successive transverse sections through the esophagus of *Glandiceps (after Spengel,* 1907). *H,* cross section through the genital wings of *Bal. proterogonius* to show postbranchial canal *(after Van der Horst,* 1934a). 1, genital wing; 2, gonad; 3, lateral septum; 4, gonopore; 5, dorsal nerve cord; 6, dorsal blood vessel; 7, branchial part of pharynx; 8, digestive part of pharynx; 9, gill septum with synapticules; 10, tongue bar; 11, coelom of tongue bar; 12, elongated gill pore; 13, gill slit; 14, ventral blood vessel; 15, ventral nerve cord; 16, postbranchial canal; 17, esophagus; 18, medial gonads; 19, lateral gonads; 20, longitudinal muscle layer; 21, lateral longitudinal vessel; 22, parabranchial ridge.

be followed by a region of thin wall similar to the first region (Fig. 35*A*). In the genus *Schizocardium* the pharynx lacks differentiation into branchial and digestive parts (Fig. 32*D*) and passes directly into the thick-walled type of esophagus. A remarkable feature of the esophagus of the Harrimaniidae and Spengelidae, or at least of the better-known genera of these families, is the presence of esophageal canals and pores by which the esophageal lumen communicates dorsally with the exterior (Fig. 35*B*). These usually occur in pairs in the posterior, thinned part of the esophagus, varying from 1 to 15 in number; in *Saccoglossus kowalevskii* there are 4 to 6 pairs. In addition to the paired posterior pores, unpaired or paired irregularly arranged esophageal pores numbering up to 60 are present in *Glandiceps* and *Schizocardium* in the anterior part of the esophagus. Possibly these esophageal connections with the exterior represent aborted gill slits; this view is suggested by the fact that in some cases the canals are furnished with a skeletal support.

The remaining part of the digestive tract is termed intestine. Its anterior part forms a hepatic region distinguished by its dorsal sacculations or at least by a histological differentiation of its dorsal epithelium. Prominent external sacculations marking the hepatic region occur in *Schizocardium* and the Ptychoderidae (Fig. 20*C*). In the absence of these the hepatic region may often be distinguished externally in the living animal by its different brown or greenish color (Fig. 21*A*). Sacculations of the dorsal intestinal wall may be present without their manifesting themselves externally. Whether sacculated or not, the dorsal intestinal epithelium of the hepatic region manifests its hepatic nature by its rich vascular supply and by the dark color of its columnar epithelial cells, caused by brown or green inclusions (Fig. 36*B*, *C*). In a number of enteropneusts the hepatic area of the intestine is divisible by color into anterior and posterior regions. Histological investigation shows that the anterior darker region contains numerous gland cells, wanting in the posterior paler region (Fig. 35*C*, *D*). Otherwise gland cells do not seem to be generally present in the hepatic epithelium. The intestinal epithelium in general consists of columnar ciliated cells that are much taller in the hepatic differentiation.

In *Glandiceps* the hepatic region is accompanied for a short distance by a siphon. This is a middorsal evagination of the hepatic intestine that may or may not separate completely from the intestinal wall to form a small tube distinguished by its low epithelium and lack of cilia.

It is presumably unnecessary to say that the term hepatic applied here is without significance and must not be taken to imply any resemblance to or homology with the vertebrate liver.

Posterior to the hepatic region, from which it is not definitely demarcated, the intestine continues as a tube of low, often sinuous ciliated

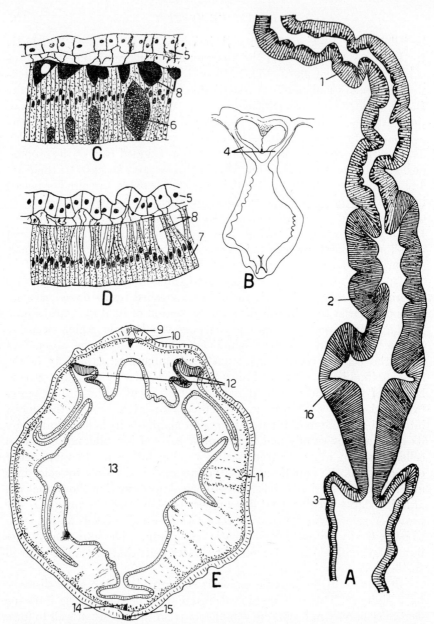

FIG. 35.—Digestive tract (continued). *A*, longitudinal section of the esophagus of *Sac. pusillus*, showing regionation (*after Van der Horst*, 1929). *B*, section after 34*G*, slightly diagonal, to show esophageal canals. *C*, epithelium of anterior part of hepatic sacculations of *Bal. carnosus*. *D*, same as *C* for posterior part of hepatic sacculations. (*A, C, D, after Van der Horst*, 1929.) *E*, cross section of posthepatic intestine of *Bal. australiensis*, showing pair of ciliated grooves (*after Hill*, 1895). 1, anterior region of esophagus; 2, middle thick-walled region; 3, posterior thin-walled region; 4, esophageal canals; 5, epidermis over hepatic sacculation; 6, gland cell; 7, brown inclusions; 8, haemal plexus; 9, dorsal nerve cord; 10, dorsal blood vessel; 11, longitudinal muscle layer; 12, ciliated grooves; 13, intestine; 14, ventral blood vessel; 15, ventral nerve cord; 16, expansion with lightly staining cells.

epithelium with a wide lumen. In the Ptychoderidae a noticeable feature of the intestine is the presence of a ciliated strip or groove in the dorso-lateral region. This consists of an especially tall epithelium provided with extra long cilia. It occurs symmetrically on both sides in *Ptychodera* and *Balanoglossus* but is limited to the left side in most species of *Glossobalanus* (Fig. 35*E*). It may extend the whole length of the intestine or die away posteriorly. In the anterior direction this ciliated structure may extend into or through the whole of the hepatic region situated at the boundary between the hepatic differentiation and the general intestinal wall, and in some ptychoderids even reaches into the branchiogenital region. In *Glossobalanus minutus* the single left-sided ciliated strip and in *G. hedleyi* the paired strips are visible externally as paler stripes of the epidermis overlying them. The posthepatic intestine of the Ptychoderidae is fur-ther distinguished by the presence of a structure badly named *pygochord* by Willey (1899a). This is a longitudinal midventral band of cells extending from the intestinal wall to the body wall enclosed between the two leaves of the ventral mesentery (Fig. 36*D*). The pygochord may be solid or hollow or contain isolated cavities and may be interrupted in its longitudinal course. It usually thickens toward its attachment to the ventral wall. Its cells are often vacuolated, whence Willey's name in allusion to a similar appearance of the notochord. The pygochord gener-ally ceases before reaching the anus.

The terminal part of the intestine may not be differentiated from the rest as in the Harrimaniidae or may be set off as a rectum or end gut by various characters, as increase in diameter, augmented height of its epithelium, appearance of folds in the epithelium, and loss of ciliation. The anus is often provided with a sphincter muscle.

9. Branchial Apparatus.—As already explained, the pharynx is differ-entiated into a dorsal branchial region and a ventral digestive region of about equal extent, except in *Schizocardium* (Fig. 32*D*), where the latter is reduced to a midventral strip (*hypobranchial ridge*). The branchial region is perforated on each side by a longitudinal series of openings, the gill slits, oriented dorsoventrally and leaving a narrow middorsal strip of pharyngeal wall (*epibranchial ridge*) between their dorsal ends (Fig. 38*A*). The gill slits are curved, more or less parallel to the body surface, and when this curvature is considerable as in the Ptychoderidae, a marked lateral constriction of the pharyngeal wall results, strongly demarcating the branchial and digestive portions (Fig. 34*A*). If the curvature is slight, the pharynx maintains a simple tubular contour (Fig. 33*C*). The gill slits begin ontogenetically as oval slits, dorsoventrally elongated, but in all enteropneusts a downgrowth from the dorsal end of the slit, the *tongue bar*, advances ventrally along the center of the slit, thus transform-ing the original oval opening into a U-shaped aperture, with the limbs of

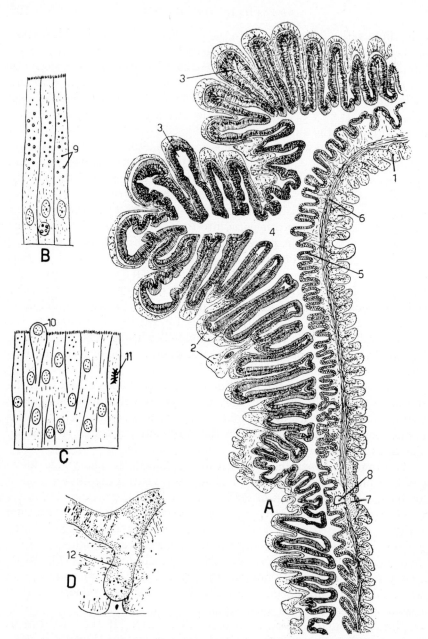

Fig. 36.—Digestive tract (continued). *A*, longitudinal section of hepatic sacculations of *Bal. stephensoni*. *B*, cells of anterior part of hepatic region of *Gloss. minutus*. *C*, cells of posterior part of *B*. (*B, C, after Barrington*, 1940.) *D*, pygochord of *Bal. stephensoni*. (*A, D, after Van der Horst*, 1937.) 1, ventral epidermis; 2, dorsal epidermis (note thickenings at ends of sacculations); 3, hepatic sacculations; 4, intestinal lumen; 5, ventral wall of intestine; 6, longitudinal muscles; 7, ventral nerve; 8, ventral blood vessel; 9, colored granules of hepatic cells; 10, extruding cell; 11, mitotic figure; 12, pygochord.

110

the U directed dorsally (Fig. 33*A*). The tongue bars are hollow, containing a coelomic cavity, but the partitions between successive slits, termed *septa*, are solid. The tongue bar never reaches the ventral end of the gill slit; hence its ventral end remains free and in some enteropneusts may move about extensively. The tongue bars and septa are supported by a system of skeletal rods of the same composition as the proboscis skeleton and formed as a thickening of the basement membrane of the pharyngeal epithelium. Each skeletal piece has somewhat the shape of a hairpin with one prong in the septum and one in the tongue bar (Figs. 37*C*, 38*A*). As a result each septum and each tongue bar contain two prongs coming from two different skeletal pieces. In the septum the two prongs fuse to one, whereas they remain separate in the tongue bar (Fig. 38*A*). Consequently, in their definitive state the skeletal supports appear like trifid structures with their median prong in the septum, their lateral prongs in two adjacent tongue bars, and their dorsal ends forming a sort of arcade. In *Protoglossus* the prongs for the tongue bars are so exceedingly short as scarcely to enter the tongue bar at all (Fig. 32*A*). In the Harrimaniidae, and some Spengelidae, the tongue bars hang freely in the gill slit, as already mentioned, but in other enteropneusts they are bound to the adjacent septa by cross connections, termed *synapticules*, that also contain branches of the skeletal rods (Fig. 38*A*). In consequence the tongue bars are held fixed and immovable.

In enteropneusts the gill slits (which name is here applied to the pharyngeal openings) do not open directly to the exterior, but instead into pouchlike cavities, the *branchial sacs*, that in turn open on the body surface by the gill pores. Usually there is one branchial sac and pore to each gill slit, but in a few species the first two to four sacs on each side unite and open by a single common pore (Fig. 39*A*). In *Stereobalanus canadensis*, according to Reinhard (1942), all the gill pouches on each side are fused and open by a single deep longitudinal slit (Fig. 21*A*); by spreading the edges of this apart it is possible to see the branchial apparatus. Usually the gill pores are small round or oval apertures, much smaller than the branchial sacs that lead to them, but they are large and dorsoventrally elongated in *Ptychodera* (Fig. 34*A*). The gill pores are often provided with a sphincter muscle. Typically the row of pores on each side is sunk into a groove, called the *branchiogenital groove*, since it also receives gonopores. In the Ptychoderidae, however, the long slitlike gill pores are borne along the sides of a pronounced middorsal longitudinal elevation (Fig. 20*D*). The enteropneusts do not have gills in the proper sense of this term, that is, thin-walled projections from the gill septa.

The number of gill pores varies in different species from a few up to several hundred pairs. The number increases with age, and new slits,

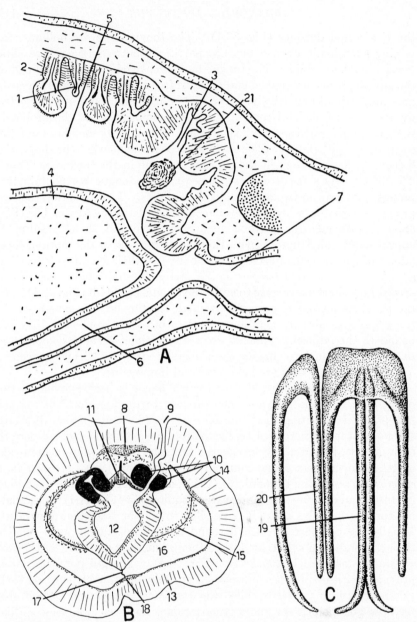

FIG. 37.—Digestive tract (concluded), branchial apparatus. *A*, longitudinal section of *Gloss. minutus*, showing postbranchial canal (*after Barrington*, 1940). *B*, section of the branchial region of *Protoglossus*, simple condition (*after Caullery and Mesnil*, 1904). *C*, branchial skeletal rods of *Sac. kowalevskii* (*after Spengel*, 1893). 1, tongue bar; 2, septum; 3, postbranchial canal; 4, parabranchial ridge; 5, branchial part of pharynx; 6, digestive part of pharynx; 7, esophagus; 8, dorsal nerve cord; 9, gill pore; 10, skeletal rods; 11, epibranchial ridge; 12, pharynx; 13, epidermis; 14, nervous layer; 15, lateral septum; 16, trunk coelom; 17, ventral mesentery; 18, ventral nerve cord; 19, skeletal rods of septum; 20, skeletal rods of tongue bar; 21, mass of food.

sacs, and pores are formed throughout life at the posterior end of the series, thus lengthening the branchial region.

The branchial apparatus usually does not present a smooth surface toward the pharyngeal cavity. In some species the septa project internally more than the tongue bars, and in others the reverse is the case (Figs. 38B, 39A). This is partly caused by differing heights of the epithelium on the surfaces that face the pharyngeal cavity (Fig. 38B). This epithelium is very columnar, ciliated, and often glandular on the pharyngeal faces of the septa or the tongue bars (Fig. 38B) or both (Fig. 39B). The epithelium along the passages leading to the branchial sacs may be reduced in height but is often thick and heavily ciliated (Figs. 38B, C, 39B). The cilia on the pharyngeal surfaces of septa and tongue bars are called *frontal*, those along their sides, *lateral* (Fig. 39B). The branchial sacs are generally lined with a cuboidal or flattened epithelium. The epibranchial ridge consists of very tall slender cells that may be arranged in three to five histologically different longitudinal strips. The parabranchial ridges of the Ptychoderidae are composed of a very high ciliated glandular epithelium.

10. Haemal System.—This system is well developed in enteropneusts, being compounded of definite vessels and lacunar spaces and having a propulsatory center in the proboscis complex. In general, all parts of the system are located between the two lamellae of the basement membrane of the body epithelia or between the two leaves of the mesenteries. Figure 40A gives a general scheme of the system.

There are two main vessels, the *dorsal* and the *ventral longitudinal* vessels. The dorsal vessel runs in the dorsal mesentery below the dorsal nerve cord from the anus into the collar, where it descends slightly to occupy a similar position between the two perihaemal cavities (Fig. 30C). At the anterior end of the collar it expands slightly as the *venous sinus* (Fig. 40A). This receives from in front a *lateral proboscis* vein from each side of the proboscis. The venous sinus then passes by a narrowed connection anteriorly into the *central sinus*, often called heart, an elongated expansion situated in the proboscis base directly above the buccal diverticulum and below the *heart vesicle*. The latter, also called pericardial, or cardiopericardial, sac, is a sac triangular in cross section whose widened base rests directly on the central sinus (Fig. 40C, D). In the Spengelidae the heart vesicle bifurcates anteriorly, and these blind bifurcations are very long in *Schizocardium*, reaching the tip of the appendix of the buccal diverticulum. The central sinus also bifurcates in these cases, and the shape of the glomerulus is correspondingly affected. From the central sinus the blood passes directly into the cavities of the glomerulus. Buccal diverticulum, central sinus, heart vesicle, and glomerulus form the proboscis complex already frequently mentioned as projecting into the

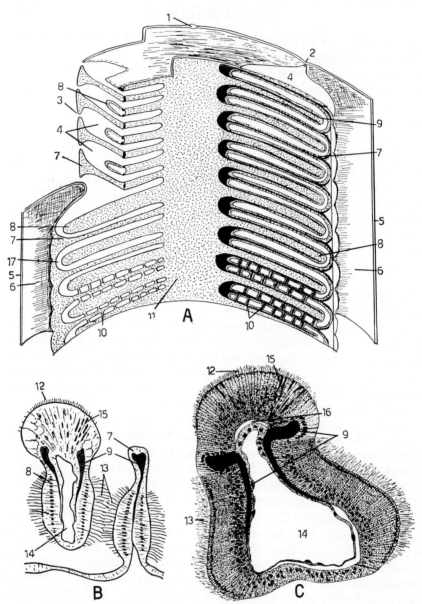

Fig. 38.—Branchial apparatus (continued). *A*, scheme of the branchial apparatus (*after Delage and Hérouard*, 1898); skeletal rods represented on right side only; apparatus partly cut away on upper left; synapticules shown for last two gill slits only. *B*, part of 37*A*, enlarged, showing details; septum lacks frontal cilia. *C*, tongue bar of *Sac. meresch- kowskii* with exceptionally thick epithelium (*after Van der Horst*, 1934a). 1, dorsal nerve cord; 2, branchiogenital groove; 3, gill pore; 4, branchial sac; 5, body wall; 6, coelom (represented as empty); 7, septum; 8, tongue bar; 9, skeletal rods; 10, synapticules; 11, dorsal wall of pharynx (the pharynx is cut open ventrally and viewed looking dorsally); 12, frontal cilia; 13, lateral cilia; 14, coelom of tongue bar; 15, gland cells; 16, blood sinus; 17, branchial sac.

coelom of the proboscis base. This complex is clothed with peritoneum, whose fingerlike outpushings here produce the glomerulus. The latter is thus a mass of coelomic projections covering the sides and anterior end of the proboscis complex or in the Spengelidae extending along the bifurcations of the heart vesicle. The lumina of the glomerular evaginations are filled with blood continuous with the blood in the central sinus. All the body blood therefore passes through the glomerulus.

The blood after leaving the glomerulus is considered to be arterial, although actually it is not aerated but presumably freed of metabolic wastes. The blood leaves the glomerulus by way of four vessels. Two of these supply the proboscis as a *middorsal* and *midventral proboscis* artery. The latter, the larger of the two, descends along the free anterior edge of the ventral mesentery of the proboscis and reaches the ventral proboscis wall, to which it branches richly. The smaller middorsal artery ascends and branches in the dorsal proboscis wall. The other two vessels that leave the glomerulus, called *efferent glomerular* arteries, are important channels that carry most of the blood away from the glomerulus. They run backward, one to each side of the buccal diverticulum, imbedded in the chondroid tissue in some species and sometimes communicating with each other. They then turn ventrally and, supported by the vascular peritoneal folds already noticed on each side of the buccal tube (Fig. 23F), they encircle the buccal tube as the *peribuccal* vessels or arteries and meet ventrally in the collar below the buccal tube to form the ventral longitudinal vessel. The ventral halves of the peribuccal vessels may not be simple channels but may consist of a plexus. The ventral longitudinal vessel in the collar sends forward a ventral collar vessel that runs in the ventral mesentery of the collar when present, otherwise in a ventral fold of the basement membrane of the buccal epithelium. The tissues of the collar are, however, supplied mainly by two extensive lacunar networks, one in the body wall beneath the epidermis, and one in the wall of the buccal tube or in the outer surface of the peribuccal spaces when present. These two networks necessarily communicate at the mouth rim, and they also communicate posteriorly by way of a ring vessel in the collar-trunk septum, from which they appear to obtain their blood. This ring vessel originates from the ventral longitudinal vessel, runs at the collar-trunk boundary beneath the circumenteric nerve connectives, and joins the dorsal longitudinal vessel, generally by way of a number of small vessels. The vascular network in the wall of the buccal tube joins the dorsal longitudinal vessel that here runs between the perihaemal spaces. The dorsal vessel gives rise to a rich lacunar network around the collar cord that may or may not concentrate dorsal to the cord to an epineural longitudinal vessel.

Having passed through the collar-trunk septum the ventral longitudi-

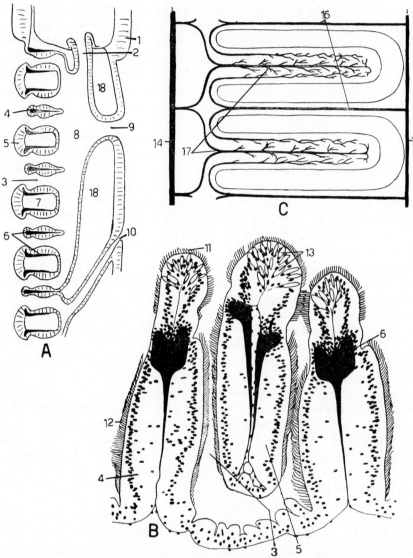

FIG. 39.—Branchial apparatus (concluded), circulatory system. *A*, longitudinal section of anterior part of branchial region of *Bal. misakiensis*, showing collar canal and first four gill slits opening by a common gill pore; note also great difference between septa and tongue bars (*after Van der Horst*, 1929). *B*, section of two septa and one tongue bar of *Sac. cambrensis*, showing similarity of their construction (*after Knight-Jones*, 1953). *C*, haemal system of branchial apparatus (*after Van der Horst*, 1939). 1, collar; 2, collar canal; 3, gill slits; 4, septum; 5, tongue bar; 6, skeletal rods; 7, coelom of tongue bar; 8, branchial sac; 9, first gill pore; 10, second gill pore; 11, frontal cilia; 12, lateral cilia; 13, gland cells; 14, dorsal blood vessel; 15, ventral blood vessel; 16, afferent branchial artery; 17, efferent branchial vein; 18, trunk coelom.

nal vessel continues nearly to the anus in the ventral trunk mesentery, but as this is very narrow, the vessel is practically in contact with both the body wall and the digestive tube and gives off to each of these a rich lacunar network that lies in each case between the two lamellae of the basement membrane. The vascular plexus of the pharynx wall supplies the branchial apparatus; the part of the plexus that lies at the boundary between the digestive and branchial parts of the pharynx or in the parabranchial ridges when present or a *lateral pharyngeal* vessel formed in this location from the plexus gives off a vessel into each branchial septum that runs dorsally in the septum, then gives off a branch that curves ventrally into both adjacent tongue bars (Fig. 39*C*). Thus each tongue bar receives two afferent or arterial vessels. These break up into a plexus, from which an efferent or venous vessel re-forms and runs dorsally up the middle of the tongue bar to join adjacent efferent vessels that open directly into the dorsal longitudinal vessel. In general, the vascular plexus of the trunk digestive tube enters the dorsal longitudinal vessel by way of the dorsal mesentery. The plexus is especially rich in the hepatic differentiation, notably on the hepatic sacculations where its meshes are very small. The gonads are supplied from the subepidermal vascular plexus. In many Ptychoderidae, a *lateral longitudinal* vessel springs from the subepidermal plexus, generally in the branchial region, and runs backward in the lateral septum. It gradually approaches the intestine and finally loses itself in the plexus of the digestive tube. It is, however, also connected by commissural vessels with the dorsal longitudinal vessel, and hence its blood apparently runs posteriorly in its anterior part and anteriorly in its posterior part, to enter the dorsal vessel. Indications of such lateral vessels also occur in other enteropneusts but are absent in the primitive *Protoglossus*.

The dorsal and ventral longitudinal vessels are genuine blood vessels, being lined by an endothelium encircled by a muscle layer (Figs. 40*B*, 41*A*). Both are highly contractile; the blood runs anteriorly in the dorsal vessel, posteriorly in the ventral vessel, and probably ventrodorsally in the connecting subepidermal and digestive plexi. It is presumably aerated in the branchial apparatus. The central sinus is also lined with endothelium but often incompletely so and is not contractile. The heart vesicle contains no blood but is a completely closed sac lined by epithelium, usually taller in its ventral wall (Fig. 40*C*) and clothed externally with peritoneum. Between the two layers is found a layer of circular fibers more or less limited to the ventral wall of the vesicle, although present thinly in some species also in the lateral and dorsal walls. The ventral wall of the vesicle rests upon the central sinus and by its contractions moves the blood in this sinus into the glomerulus. The interior of the heart vesicle is more or less filled with connective tissue and also may

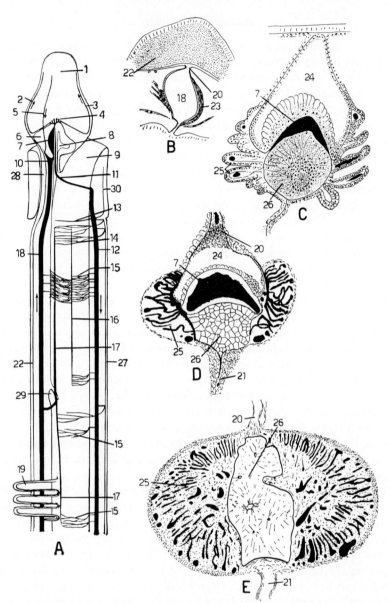

Fig. 40.—Circulatory system (continued), glomerulus. *A*, scheme of the circulatory system (*after Van der Horst*, 1939). *B*, cross section of the dorsal blood vessel of *Sac. kowalevskii* (*after Spengel*, 1893). *C*, heart vesicle and simple type of glomerulus of *Proto-glossus* (*after Caullery and Mesnil*, 1904). *D*, heart vesicle and more complicated glomer-ulus of *Bal. australiensis* (*after Hill*, 1895). *E*, very complicated glomerulus of *Bal. misakiensis* (*after Van der Horst*, 1929). 1, proboscis; 2, dorsal proboscis artery; 3, ventral proboscis artery; 4, glomerulus; 5, lateral proboscis vein; 6, heart vesicle; 7, central sinus; 8, buccal diverticulum; 9, collar; 10, venous sinus; 11, peribuccal artery; 12, ventral vessel; 13, ring vessel of septum; 14, lacunar network to body wall; 15, lacunar network to digestive tube; 16, lateral pharyngeal vessel; 17, lateral longitudinal vessel; 18, dorsal vessel; 19, hepatic sacculations; 20, dorsal mesentery; 21, ventral mesentery; 22, dorsal trunk nerve; 23, circular muscles; 24, heart vesicle; 25, glomerulus; 26, buccal diverticulum; 27, ventral nerve cord; 28, collar cord; 29, postbranchial canal; 30, ventral collar vessel.

contain diagonal muscle fibers, crisscrossing in the interior. Muscle fibers may also be applied to the external wall of the heart vesicle; these belong in some cases to the dorsoventral muscle septum of the proboscis. It appears that all other parts of the circulatory system except those mentioned are mere spaces, and hence classify as lacunae rather than as capillaries, a term used by some authors. The circulatory system is therefore primarily of the open type. The blood is colorless and contains a few cells that seem to be detached endothelial cells.

It will at once occur to any zoologist that the relations of heart vesicle and central sinus are similar to those of the pericardial sac and heart of vertebrates. One may regard the enteropneusts as at a stage in which the pericardial sac has not closed completely around the heart tube. Van der Horst (1939) mentions two species of *Balanoglossus* in which the heart vesicle has closed below around the anterior part of the central sinus, thus reproducing the typical relations of heart and pericardial sac.

11. Excretory Provision.—The glomerulus is generally accepted as an excretory organ, although experimental proof is lacking. An excretory function for this structure was first suggested by Bateson (1885), also independently by Koehler (1886c) and Schimkewitsch (1888). The name glomerulus was then applied to the organ by Spengel (1893) on the ground of a resemblance to the glomeruli of vertebrate kidneys. As already indicated, the glomerulus is a mass of blind tubular evaginations of the peritoneum covering the proboscis complex. It typically forms a thick mass on each side of the heart vesicle, and these two masses are thinly connected dorsal and anterior to the vesicle. In species in which the heart vesicle and central sinus bifurcate, the glomerulus follows the bifurcations. In *Protoglossus* the evaginations are of simple form (Fig. 40C), whereas in many enteropneusts they branch and anastomose into a network (Fig. 40D, E). The peritoneal cells, elsewhere of flattened form, become cuboidal, columnar, or conical in the glomerular evaginations and often proliferate into masses that fill the spaces between the evaginations. The cells are pale, staining poorly, with scanty cytoplasm. In some enteropneusts they give no histological evidence of an excretory function, but in others they contain yellow or brown granulations (Bateson, 1885; Koehler, 1886c; Maser, 1913). The interior cavities of the glomerulus are filled with blood continuous with the blood of the central sinus.

The proboscis peritoneum adjacent to the glomerulus or elsewhere in the proboscis may in some species present an appearance suggestive of excretion, consisting of enlarged tall cells containing yellow or brown granules. Similar cells may occur free in the connective and chondroid tissue of proboscis and collar, and even perhaps elsewhere in the body. Such accessory excretory cells classify as athrocytes or paranephrocytes.

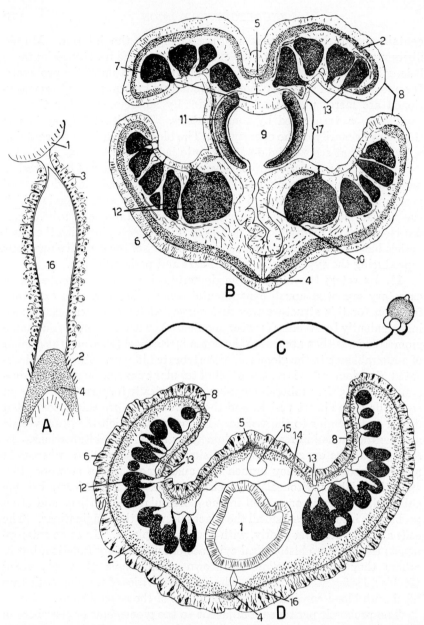

FIG. 41.—Circulatory system (concluded), reproductive system. *A*, section of the ventral vessel of *Sac. kowalevskii*. *B*, section of the pharyngeal region of *Stereobalanus*, with four genital wings. (*A*, *B*, *after Spengel*, 1893.) *C*, spermatozoon of *Sac. horsti* (*after Burdon-Jones*, 1952). *D*, section through the genital wings of *Ptych. bahamensis* (*after Van der Horst*, 1939). 1, intestine; 2, longitudinal muscle fibers; 3, peritoneum; 4, ventral nerve cord; 5, dorsal nerve cord; 6, epidermis; 7, epibranchial ridge; 8, genital wings; 9, branchial part of pharynx; 10, digestive part of pharynx; 11, skeletal rod; 12, gonad; 13, gonopore; 14, lateral septum; 15, dorsal blood vessel; 16, ventral blood vessel; 17, gill pore.

12. Reproductive System and Reproductive Habits.—The sexes are separate and are indistinguishable externally except in case the color of the ripe gonads shows through the body wall in the living animal; but in *Ptychodera flava* males may be distinguished by brown flecks on the genital wings (Rao, 1954). This author also found 1 male to 65 females. The gonads occur in one to several longitudinal rows to the sides of the digestive tube in the anterior part of the trunk. Although lodged in the genital ridges and wings when present, they are not necessarily confined to such areas. They may begin immediately behind the collar-trunk septum as usually in *Ptychodera* but often are absent from the anterior branchial region over an area ranging from the first or second up to the twentieth gill pores. In some species the branchial region lacks gonads, and these begin behind this region. Gonads generally cease at the beginning of the hepatic region but may extend into or through this region and may exceptionally continue into the caudal region. The gonads are generally sacciform bodies but may be elongated or lobulated (Fig. 41*D*), and secondary gonads may arise by subdivision of primary ones through lobulation. The gonads occupy the trunk coelum but actually are retroperitoneal, being enclosed in a membrane continuous with the basement membrane of the epidermis. Each gonad narrows to a neck that opens externally by a pore. These gonopores are generally located to the lateral (external) side of the gill pores in the same branchiogenital groove (also called submedian line, sublateral line). Gonads so opening are called lateral gonads and in the Ptychoderidae are found to the ventral side of the lateral trunk septum (Fig. 41*D*). However, when the gonads are numerous and may have multiplied by secondary constrictions, some of them also occupy a dorsal position, that is, are found to the dorsal side of the lateral septum (Fig. 34*H*) when present, or dorsal to the branchiogenital grooves, and such dorsal gonads open to the dorsal (medial) side of these grooves.

The eggs are relatively large (up to 1 mm. across) and yolky in the Harrimaniidae, in correlation with direct development in this family, small and poor in yolk in the other two families, which develop with a tornaria larva. The sperm may have the usual form, but in many enteropneusts are of odd appearance with four spheres of mitochondria behind the nucleus (Fig. 41*C*).

Natural spawning seems to have been observed only by Burdon-Jones (1951) for *Sacc. horsti* in the Solent (channel between England and the Isle of Wight). Spawning occurred during May and June following suitable rise of temperature (to about 16°C) and was initiated by the females, which begin to discharge eggs from the mouth of the burrow about 30 minutes after the receding tide has exposed the habitat. A mucous cord containing imbedded eggs issues from the burrow and is coiled into a mass

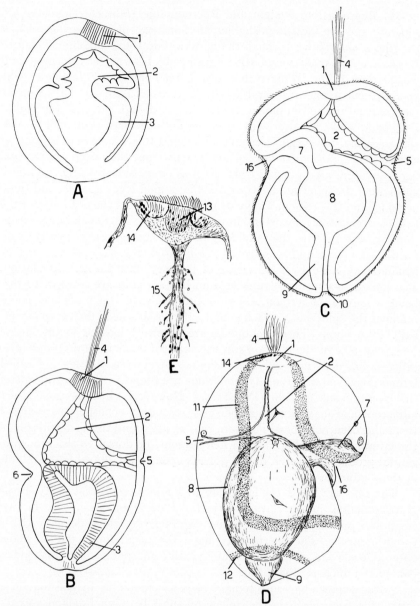

Fig. 42.—Embryology. *A*, formation of protocoel from the archenteron. *B*, formation of the hydropore. *C*, formation of mouth and differentiation of digestive tract. (*A–C, after Heider*, 1909.) *D*, beginning of ciliary bands. *E*, apical organ enlarged. (*D, E, all Bal. clavigerus, after Stiasny*, 1914.) 1, apical thickening; 2, protocoel; 3, archenteron; 4, apical tuft; 5, hydropore; 6, stomodaeal invagination; 7, esophagus; 8, stomach; 9, intestine; 10, blastopore (anus); 11, ciliary band; 12, telotroch; 13, sense center; 14, eye; 15, muscle fibers; 16, mouth.

containing 2000 to 3000 eggs. About 20 minutes after the females began to spawn, clouds of sperm were emitted from the burrows of males. The egg masses soon disintegrate, and the developing embryos are scattered by the returning tide. Similar breeding habits appear to obtain for *S. cambrensis* on the Welsh coast during June and July, whereas in the same area *Protoglossus koehleri* breeds from February to April (Burdon-Jones, 1956). Heider (1909) recorded finding an egg mass at the mouth of the burrow of *Bal. clavigerus* at Trieste in June, and Stiasny (1913, 1914) recorded the breeding period of this species in the Adriatic as May and June, reporting that the eggs are stuck to the wall of the burrow. The same was found for *Sacc. pusillus* in the San Diego region by Ritter and Davis (1904) and Davis (1908) with a breeding period from November to February, at its height in January. Burdon-Jones (1951) suggests that eggs found adhering to the walls of the burrow are only a remnant of a spawning in which the main mass of the eggs is discharged at the burrow mouth as in *Sacc. horsti*. *Glossobalanus minutus*, breeding at Naples from February to May, also emits its eggs in a mucous cord wound into a mass (Dawydoff, 1928). Rao (1954) observed for *Ptych. flava* that both sexes emit clouds of sex cells into the sea water; breeding seemed to occur twice annually, in spring and fall. *Sacc. kowalevskii*, the common enteropneust of the Atlantic Coast of North America, apparently breeds throughout the summer into September, although natural spawning has not been witnessed (Bateson, 1884, 1885; the Colwins, 1953). The female of *Sacc. otagoensis*, New Zealand, is said (Kirk, 1938) to surround itself with a mucous case open at both ends into which the genital ridges containing the eggs are deposited. The ridges are somehow rubbed off, and the embryos develop inside the tissue fragments left in the mucous case while the female departs. Some enteropneusts will spawn in the laboratory when brought in in the ripe state, and most embryological studies are based on eggs so obtained. *Xenopleura vivipara*, Cape of Good Hope, may be viviparous since the one known specimen contained an advanced embryo in the trunk coelom.

13. Development.—Development may be indirect with a tornaria larva or direct without a tornaria. The indirect type has been best followed in *Balanoglossus clavigerus* (Heider, 1909; Stiasny, 1913, 1914a, b), although numerous studies of tornariae are available. Other accounts are those of Payne (1937) for *Ptychodera bahamensis*, Rao (1953) for a species of *Glandiceps*, and Rao (1955a) for *Ptychodera flava;* and Morgan (1891, 1894) gave considerable material on the further development of unidentified tornariae. Main studies of direct development are those of Bateson (1884, 1885) and the Colwins (1953) on *Sacc. kowalevskii*, Davis (1908) on *Sacc. pusillus*, and Burdon-Jones (1952) on *Sacc. horsti;* Kirk (1938) reported briefly on *Sacc. otagoensis*. The early stages are much the same

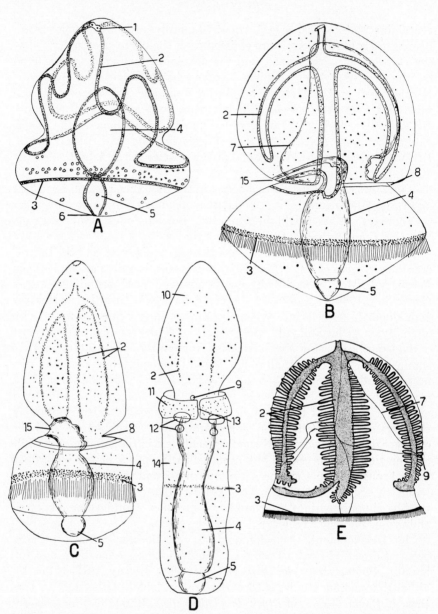

Fig. 43.—Embryology (continued). *A*, fully developed tornaria of *Bal. clavigerus* (*after Stiasny*, 1914). *B–D*, three stages in the development of a Bahama tornaria into a young worm. *B*, size diminished; constriction at future proboscis-collar boundary. *C*, ciliary band disappearing, collar developing. *D*, ciliary band almost gone; collar developed; trunk elongated. *E*, tentaculate type of tornaria, Bahamas. (*B–E, after Morgan*, 1891.) *B–D*, to same scale; *E*, smaller scale. 1, eye; 2, ciliary band; 3, telotroch; 4, stomach; 5, intestine; 6, anus; 7, protocoel; 8, proboscis-collar groove; 9, hydropore; 10, proboscis; 11, collar; 12, first and second gill pores; 13, groove of invagination of collar cord; 14, trunk; 15, mouth.

for all species and for both types of development. Cleavage is holoblastic and approximately equal and mostly of the radial type. There is evidence of micromere formation at the vegetal pole as in echinoids, although the micromeres differ only slightly in size from adjacent blastomeres. A coeloblastula of numerous, subequal cells eventuates in about 6 to 15 hours, and this undergoes typical embolic invagination in 12 to 24 hours. The blastopore soon closes and as in echinoderms marks the future posterior end. The embryo elongates in the future anteroposterior axis, develops cilia, and, after rotating for a time inside the egg membrane, escapes at about 24 to 36 hours and leads a planktonic existence for a time. *S. kowalevskii*, however, does not hatch until the seventh day and at once takes up a benthonic life.

In indirect development the free larva is at first uniformly ciliated except for a long apical tuft of cilia borne on an epidermal thickening evidently of nervous nature (Fig. 42*B, C*). Soon epidermal bands of small cells become evident as forerunners of a sinuous ciliary band similar to that of the asteroid bipinnaria (Fig. 42*D*). As the ciliary band differentiates, the general ciliation disappears and the apical tuft is also lost although the epidermal thickening remains. The larva constantly increases in size, and the ciliary bands become more and more sinuous (Fig. 43*A*) and in some species become edged with a row of small tentacles (Fig. 43*E*). With the appearance of the ciliary bands the larva is termed tornaria but requires some time (3 to 4 weeks in *Balanoglossus clavigerus*) to attain full size and development, being then termed Krohn's stage after the tornaria seen by Krohn (1854). The tornaria then regresses, decreasing in size and developing an equatorial constriction that represents the proboscis-collar boundary (Fig. 43*B*). The ciliary bands gradually disappear, and the larva takes on the same wormlike appearance as in direct development (Fig. 43*B–D*).

As tornariae lead a planktonic life for some days or weeks they are often taken in planktonic towings. Their clear glassy appearance makes them favorite objects for microscopic study. A large number of different ones have been described, but the adults to which they belong have seldom been identified. The first ones seen, those of J. Müller (1850) and Krohn (1854), are said by Stiasny (1913, 1914a, b) to belong to *Bal. clavigerus*. Stiasny-Wijnhoff and Stiasny (1927) summarized the knowledge of all tornariae in the literature to that date, amounting to 62; but a number of others have been described since then. As there are about 70 known species of enteropneusts, many of which do not produce tornariae, one must suppose that there are a number of unknown enteropneust species. Tentaculate tornariae are believed limited to the genus *Ptychodera*.

Tornariae range in size mostly below a millimeter, but some reach 2 or 3 mm. in height and a few especially large ones measure 5 mm. or more in their longest axis. A large tentaculate tornaria from the Bahamas with a height of 4.5 mm. was extensively studied by Morgan (1894; Fig. 43E). The largest known tornaria, also tentaculate, collected in the Cape Verde Islands by Grenacher and described by Spengel (1893), ranged from 5 to 9 mm. in height. In young tornariae the ciliary band is simple, forming a preoral loop passing just above the mouth, then extending along the sides to make another ventral loop (Fig. 42D). There soon forms, independently of the main ciliary band, a ciliated ring around the posterior end of the body (Fig. 42D). This circumanal ring, regarded by some as a telotroch, develops especially long and powerful cilia and is the chief locomotory organ of the tornaria. A ciliary wave passing along this ring causes the larva to rotate constantly in swimming. As the tornaria grows, the ciliary band becomes more or less sinuous, depending on species, sending loops toward the apical pole, where they often meet or fuse at the nervous center (Fig. 43A). In a few cases the loops along the sides put out a fringe of small tentacles that stand away from the surface (Fig. 43E), and such tornariae are termed *tentaculate*. The apical nervous plate is an area of greatly thickened ectoderm composed of tall crowded epithelial cells with a basal layer of nerve fibrils. The central part of the plate forms a rather well defined ciliary organ of slender cells provided with short cilia (not to be confused with the original ciliary tuft, now vanished), and to each side of this is found an eye (Fig. 42E). Accounts of the structure of the eye are not very concordant, and in fact the structure may differ in different species of tornaria. In general, the eye is an epidermal cuplike invagination. According to Stiasny (1914) and Spengel (1893) the concavity of the cup is filled with a clear homogeneous material constituting a lens (Fig. 44A). Morgan, however, in a tornaria off New England, described a bristle projecting from each cell into the cup concavity (1891; Fig. 44B). The eyes are pigmented; Morgan (1891) found pigment granules inside the cells of the cup (Fig. 44C, D), whereas Spengel and Stiasny figured pigment cells adhering to the bases of the cells of the cup (Fig. 44A). From the underside of the apical plate a muscle strand extends to the protocoel (Fig. 42E). The interior of the tornaria contains a complete digestive tract like that of echinoderm larvae and one or more coelomic vesicles. The heart vesicle develops in the later stages of the tornaria, and its pulsations were noticed by early observers.

Direct development also usually includes a free-swimming larval stage (Fig. 47B). The embryo hatches as a completely ciliated oval larva provided with an apical tuft and a circumanal or teletrochal girdle of especially long cilia. These larvae swim about only for a day or so. They soon develop an equatorial constriction marking the proboscis-collar boundary (Fig. 47C) and a little later a second constriction repre-

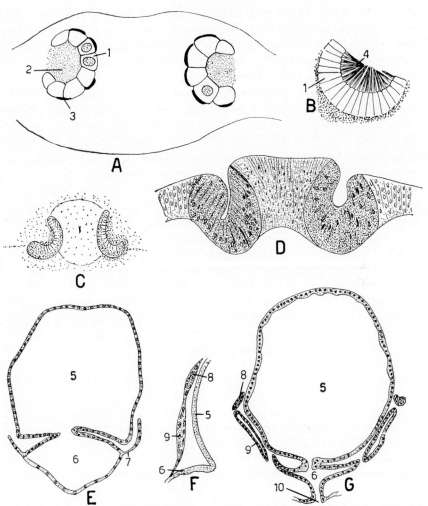

FIG. 44.—Embryology (continued). *A*, eyes of the tornaria of *Bal. clavigerus* (*after Stiasny*, 1914). *B*, eye of New England tornaria (*after Morgan*, 1891). *C*, eyes of Bahama tornaria. *D*, section through *C*. (*C, D, after Morgan*, 1894.) *E*, origin of collar and trunk coeloms by sprout from intestine in *Bal. clavigerus*. *F*, later stage of the outgrowth (*after Spengel*, 1893). *G*, outgrowth separated from intestine and constricted into collar and trunk coeloms. (*E, G, after Stiasny*, 1913.) 1, cells of cup; 2, lens; 3, pigment; 4, bristles of retinal cells; 5, stomach; 6, intestine; 7, outgrowth to form coeloms; 8, collar coelom; 9, trunk coelom; 10, anus.

senting the collar-trunk boundary (Fig. 48*A*). During these changes the larva has gradually elongated and taken on a wormlike appearance. It gradually assumes a benthonic life, losing its apical tuft and telotroch, and by continued growth and elongation (Fig. 48) alters into a young enteropneust without undergoing any marked transformation. *Sacc.*

otagoensis (Kirk, 1938) and *Glossobalanus minutus* (Dawydoff, 1928) never develop an apical tuft or telotroch, and hence lack a swimming phase; the latter larva is also devoid of mouth and anus.   *Sacc. kowalevskii* hatches in the wormlike state and very soon takes to creeping, although provided with apical tuft and telotroch.

The internal development follows much the same course in all species investigated.   At an early stage the inner end of the archenteron is cut off as a coelomic vesicle (Fig. 42*A*).   This rapidly alters to an angular shape with a wall of flattened epithelium.   One angle attaches to the underside of the apical nervous plate and is later drawn out into a muscular strand.   Another angle grows toward the dorsal side of the larva and there establishes an opening (Fig. 42*B*, *C*).   This coelomic vesicle is the proboscis coelom, and the pore is the proboscis pore.   The resemblance to events in echinoderm embryology is amazing, and therefore the vesicle is usually called in the literature hydrocoel and the pore hydropore.   The vesicle is not, however, homologous with the hydrocoel but with the axocoel; to avoid confusion it is better referred to as protocoel.   The wall of the protocoel begins to give off mesenchyme, much of which transforms into muscle fibers.   Shortly after giving off the protocoel the inner end of the archenteron bends toward the ventral surface, opposite the hydropore, and there unites with the ectoderm by way of a very shallow stomodaeum to produce the definitive mouth (Fig. 42*C*).   The archenteron then rapidly differentiates into the same three divisions made familiar in echinoderm development, esophagus or foregut, stomach, and intestine or hind gut, and the latter establishes an anal opening at the site of the closed blastopore.   Mesenchyme cells from the protocoel gather around the esophagus and transform into circular muscle fibers.   There is surprising diversity in the accounts of the mode of origin of the collar and trunk coeloms in different species.   Only in *Saccoglossus pustllus* (Davis, 1908) is the process similar to what occurs in echinoderms.   Here the protocoel sends back an extension on each side of the archenteron, and these extensions constrict into an anterior mesocoel, or collar coelom, and a posterior metacoel, or trunk coelom (Fig. 45*A–C*).   In *Bal. clavigerus* (Stiasny, 1914a, b), also *Glandiceps* (Rao, 1953), a solid outgrowth extends forward from the hind gut along each side of the stomach, and the anterior part of this constricts off as the mesocoel while the posterior part is the metacoel (Fig. 44*E–G*).   Spengel (1893), studying various unidentified tornariae, supports this account, which is reasonably similar to events in echinoderms.   According to Bateson (1884), the mesocoels and metacoels in *Sacc. kowalevskii* arise independently (Fig. 45*D*) as solid outgrowths or evaginations of the wall of the stomach and hind gut, respectively, and Morgan (1891) supported this account for some of the forms he studied but maintained (1894) that in the tentaculate tornaria of the Bahamas

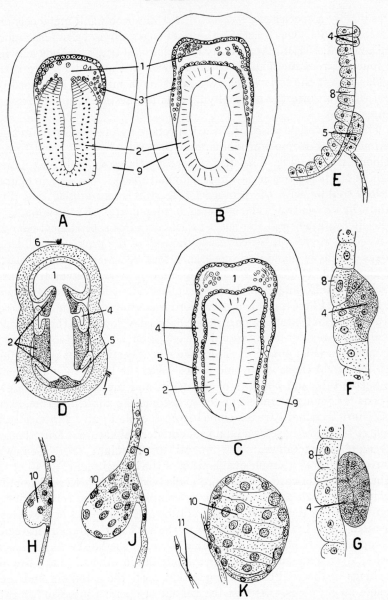

Fig. 45.—Embryology (continued). *A–C*, method of formation of collar and trunk coeloms in *Sac. pusillus* (*after Davis, 1908*). *D*, scheme of formation of the coeloms in *Sac. kowalevskii* (*after Bateson, 1884*). *E*, formation of collar and trunk coeloms in New England tornaria. *F, G*, further stages of mesocoel of *E*. (*E–G, after Morgan, 1891.*) *H, J*, origin of heart vesicle from ectoderm in *Bal. clavigerus*. *K*, further stage with heart vesicle free and developing muscle fibers. (*H–K, after Stiasny, 1914.*) 1, protocoel; 2, archenteron; 3, backward extension of protocoel; 4, mesocoel; 5, metacoel; 6, apical tuft; 7, telotroch; 8, wall of stomach; 9, ectoderm; 10, heart vesicle; 11, proboscis canal (hydroporic canal).

(presumably a species of *Ptychodera*), the mesocoels and metacoels originate independently as spaces in groups of mesenchyme cells (also reported by Dawydoff, 1944). Apparently the collar and trunk coeloms may form by four different methods in enteropneusts, but all of these are enterocoelous except the last, which by some stretch may also be regarded as enterocoelous since the mesenchyme cells in question originate from the protocoel.

The heart vesicle arises near the hydropore as an ectodermal invagination, according to most accounts, and therefore does not seem to be of coelomic nature (Fig. 45*H–K*). Morgan, Bateson, and Rao indicate origin of the heart vesicle as a mesenchymal space. The vesicle migrates to close contact with the protocoel (Fig. 46*A*), and muscle cells differentiate in its ventral wall, enabling it to pulsate. By pushing in the adjacent protocoel wall the heart vesicle acquires a peritoneal covering. At its contact with the heart vesicle the wall of the protocoel proliferates masses of cells of glandular appearance that become the cellular part of the glomerulus (Fig. 46*B, C*). The general nervous system arises as an ectodermal thickening, which is especially evident in the median lines of the larva. At first the dorsal nerve cord is continuous to the anterior end of the collar, but later the part in the collar develops into the collar cord either by a regular longitudinal invagination as in vertebrates or by delamination (Fig. 46*D–F*). The definitive digestive tract is continuous with the larval tract. It would appear that the larval foregut becomes the buccal tube and pharynx of the adult, and the larval stomach elongates as the young worm elongates to become the adult intestine, except for a short terminal part developed from the hind gut. Practically the whole of the digestive epithelium is of entodermal nature. Larval mouth and anus are retained. The buccal diverticulum arises somewhat belatedly either as a simple evagination of the buccal roof (Fig. 47*A*) that pushes its way forward into the proboscis below the heart vesicle, or after beginning as such an evagination, is completed by the constricting off longitudinally of the roof of the buccal tube and then grows in the anterior direction. The branchial sacs arise in the wall of the foregut in regular anteroposterior sequence at a variable stage, in the late tornaria in some species, after the assumption of benthonic life in others. They are outpouchings of the wall of the foregut that meet the ectoderm and break through as gill pores. At first the gill slit or opening into the foregut is rounded or oval and becomes U-shaped by the downgrowth of the tongue bar from the dorsal border of the slit. The coelomic sacs expand and fill the available space between the digestive tube and the epidermis. Their walls give rise to all the musculature and connective tissue of the body. The protocoel persists as the proboscis coelom, and the hydropore persists as the proboscis pore. The perihaemal spaces may be seen originating as

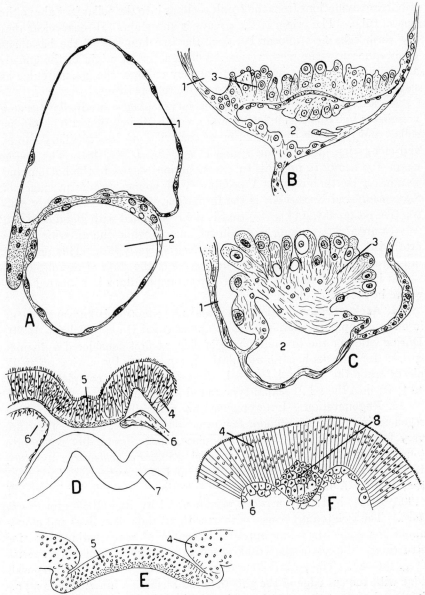

Fig. 46.—Embryology (continued). *A*, heart vesicle in contact with the protocoel. *B*, wall of protocoel in contact with heart vesicle developing into the glomerulus. *C*, further development of the glomerulus. (*A–C, all Bal. clavigerus, after Stiasny*, 1914.) *D*, formation of the collar cord by epidermal invagination, *Glandiceps (after Rao*, 1953). *E*, same for New England tornaria (*after Morgan*, 1891). *F*, collar cord forming by delamination in *Sac. kowalevskii (after Bateson*, 1885). 1, protocoel; 2, heart vesicle; 3, primordium of glomerulus; 4, epidermis; 5, neural invagination; 6, collar coelom; 7, entoderm; 8, delaminated group of cells to form collar cord.

tubular evaginations from the trunk coeloms into the collar just above the buccal tube.   The origin of the gonads is uncertain.   It seems clear that the germ cells first appear between the two lamellae of the basement membrane or of the mesenteries.   A mesenchymal origin of the gonads and germ cells is thus indicated.   As they enlarge, the gonads bulge as sacs into the coelom, remaining, however, retroperitoneal.

As already indicated, swimming larval stages gradually become vermiform by reduction in length and breadth, regionation into proboscis, collar, and trunk by the formation of constrictions, loss of ciliary bands, and elongation of the trunk region (Figs. 43*B–D*, 47, 48).   The young worm, too heavy to progress by ciliary action, settles to the bottom and assumes a benthonic life.   A peculiarity of young vermiform stages of *Sacc. horsti* and *kowalevskii* is the formation of an adhesive, highly contractile, postanal tail (Fig. 48) that is richly supplied with gland cells and acts to anchor the young worm in its burrow while the anterior end is protruded to engage in respiratory or feeding activities.   This postanal tail is resorbed later; it is highly suggestive of the stalk of pterobranchs.

As in echinoderms no trace of a protonephridium is indicated anywhere in the embryology.

14. Asexual Reproduction.—Asexual reproduction is known to occur in one enteropneust, *Bal. capensis*, Cape of Good Hope (Gilchrist, 1923). During summer the juvenile phase of this, at first considered a distinct species, for it lacks hepatic sacculations, reproduces by cutting off small pieces from the tail end forward.   These regenerate completely (Fig. 49*A, B*) into the adult sexual type found in winter.

15. Regeneration.—Enteropneusts are generally stated to have high regenerative powers, although few exact data are available.   They are very fragile and apt to break into pieces that presumably regenerate (observed in *Gloss. minutus* by Spengel, 1893, *Bal. clavigerus* by Cori, 1902, *Bal. misakiensis* by Kuwano, 1902, and *Sacc. serpentinus* by Assheton, 1908).   A detailed study of regeneration was made by Dawydoff (1902, 1907a, b, 1909) for *Gloss. minutus* and by Rao (1955e) for *Ptych. flava*.   The isolated proboscis, with or without the collar, lives and moves about for some time but appears incapable of regenerating posterior structures.   Pieces of the trunk regenerate completely in both species (Fig. 49*C–E*).   The posterior cut closes by the fusion of the cut body-wall edge with the cut edge of the gut, thus establishing a functional anus; no further change at the posterior end took place during the period of observation.   The anterior cut surface closes in the same way, and the proboscis and collar usually arise from a regeneration bud formed at this closed surface.   This bud differentiates first into the proboscis, and later the collar is constricted from the posterior part of this.   According to Dawydoff, proboscis and collar may also form by dedifferentiation and

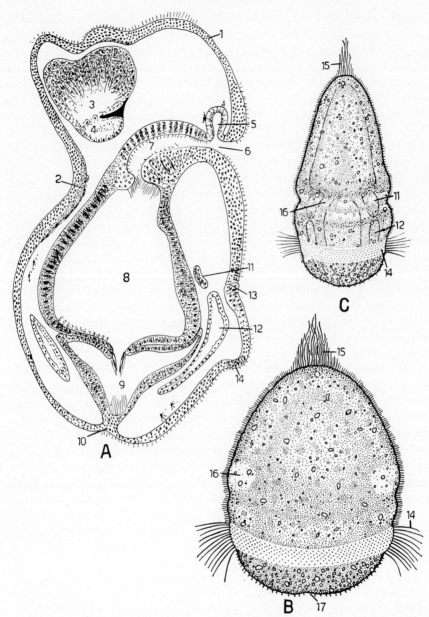

Fig. 47.—Embryology (continued). *A*, median longitudinal section of New England tornaria, showing buccal diverticulum (*after Morgan*, 1891). *B*, newly hatched larva of *Sac. horsti*. *C*, later stage of *B*. (*B*, *C*, *after Burdon-Jones*, 1952.) 1, epidermis; 2, nervous layer; 3, protocoel with wall developing muscle fibers; 4, heart vesicle; 5, buccal diverticulum; 6, mouth; 7, foregut; 8, stomach; 9, intestine; 10, anus; 11, mesocoel; 12, metacoel; 13, beginning groove at proboscis-collar boundary; 14, telotroch; 15, apical tuft; 16, location of future collar; 17, anal indentation.

redifferentiation of the anterior part of the original piece, and this seems usually to occur in pieces from posterior levels. When the anterior cut surface closes over, the mouth may arise by union of the cut edge of the digestive epithelium with the cut epidermal edge; or the anterior end of the digestive tube in the piece may differentiate into buccal epithelium that makes contact with the epidermis to form a mouth opening. The coelom of the regenerated proboscis and collar originate by evagination from the trunk coelom of the piece. Rao describes in this process much degeneration and engulfment by coelomocytes of muscle fibers and connective tissue of the coelomic evagination; new tissues are then formed by the rearrangement of coelomic elements. The heart vesicle in both species is definitely of coelomic origin, being pinched off from the posterior part of the proboscis coelom; its wall then differentiates muscle fibers and connective tissue. The buccal diverticulum originates as a forward evagination of the digestive epithelium that has transformed into buccal epithelium. The collar cord arises from a thickening of the nervous layer of the collar that then invaginates as in embryology. The gill apparatus arises much as in embryology after the part of the digestive tube concerned has transformed histologically into a pharynx. Other processes occur as in embryonic development. It appears that there is a general transformation by processes of dedifferentiation and redifferentiation of the tissues of the old piece to fit the new morphology.

16. Systematic Account.—Enteropneusts do not differ sufficiently among themselves to warrant the erection of categories higher than families, of which three are recognized. The primitive species *Protoglossus* (= *Protobalanus*) *koehleri* was made the basis of a family Protoglossidae by its discoverers (Caullery and Mesnil, 1904), but Burdon-Jones (1956), having refound the species on British coasts and having given an excellent and well-illustrated description, concludes that it fits well enough into the family Harrimaniidae. *Protoglossus koehleri* lacks perihaemal and peribuccal prolongations of the trunk coelom into the collar coelom and retains an unaltered condition of the coelomic cavities and mesenteries (Fig. 23F). The skeletal provision of the gill apparatus scarcely extends into the tongue bars (Fig. 32A), and consequently there are no synapticules.

The Harrimaniidae, including *Protoglossus*, lack hepatic sacculations, and genital ridges are mostly not in evidence. Peribuccal spaces and lateral trunk septa are absent, but perihaemal spaces may be present. Despite the presence of skeletal rods in the tongue bars in most species, synapticules are wanting. The main genus *Saccoglossus* (= *Dolichoglossus*) is characterized by the exceptionally long proboscis (Fig. 20A). *Sacc. kowalevskii*, found on both sides of the North Atlantic, is probably the most familiar and best-studied enteropneust. Other genera are

Harrimania with paired proboscis pores (Fig. 27*B*, *C*), *Stereobalanus* (Fig. 41*B*) with short, fluffy dorsal and ventral genital ridges, and gill pores fused to a common slit, and *Xenopleura*, with a single, poorly described species, possibly viviparous (Gilchrist, 1925).

Characteristic features of the Spengelidae are the very long horns of the proboscis skeleton and the extension of the buccal diverticulum as an appendix (Fig. 30*B*). Lateral septa are absent, and hepatic sacculations are mostly wanting. Main genera are *Spengelia* and *Schizocardium* with synapticules and peribuccal spaces and *Glandiceps* without either; in *Schizocardium* with hepatic sacculations the gill apparatus embraces practically the whole pharynx circumference (Fig. 32*D*). A fourth genus, *Willeyia*, was imperfectly known by one spècies from Zanzibar until 1940 when Van der Horst described another species from nearby. *Willeyia* is intermediate between *Spengelia* and *Glandiceps*, having peribuccal spaces but no synapticules.

The third and most highly evolved family, the Ptychoderidae, is readily recognized by the pronounced regionation of the trunk, expressed in the genital ridges or wings and the hepatic sacculations. Other characters are short horns of the proboscis skeleton (Fig. 23*D*), presence of peri-haemal and peribuccal coelomic cavities in the collar (Fig. 28*B*) and of lateral septa in the trunk, presence of synapticules and parabranchial ridges in the branchial region, and of a pygochord and ciliary grooves in the postbranchial part of the digestive tube. The parabranchial ridges strongly constrict the pharynx into a dorsal branchial and a ventral digestive part (Fig. 34*A*). *Balanoglossus* (Fig. 20*C*) and *Ptychodera* (Fig. 20*D*) have pronounced genital wings, and the branchial region forms a sort of ridge between them. Differences in the form of the hepatic sacculations in these two genera appear in the figures. *Ptychodera* further has large gill pores, a racemose organ (Fig. 26*B*), a continuous canal in the collar cord, and lateral septa that attach in the tips of the genital wings (Fig. 41*D*), whereas in *Balanoglossus* the gill pores are small, the collar cord contains numerous discontinuous lacunae, there is no racemose organ, and the lateral septa extend only halfway into the genital wings (Fig. 34*H*). *Ptychodera flava* is spread throughout the Indo-Pacific, and *Ptych. bahamensis* in the West Indies (Fig. 20*D*) is scarcely distinguishable from it. *Balanoglossus* contains about 20 species, of which the best known are *Bal. clavigerus* from the Mediterranean and *Bal. aurantiacus* (Fig. 20*C*) from the Carolina coast. The third genus, *Glossobalanus*, is distinguished chiefly by the presence of genital ridges rather than wings; the hepatic sacculations are arranged in two longitudinal rows. There are about 10 species, of which *Gloss. minutus* from the Mediterranean furnished the chief material of Spengel's monograph (1893). The Ptychoderidae in general probably develop by way of a tornaria larva, although connec-

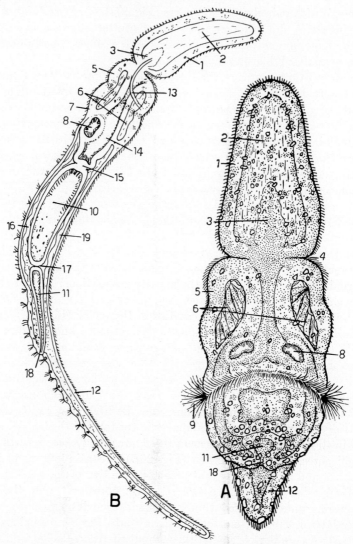

Fig. 48.—Embryology (concluded). *A*, creeping stage of young *Sac. horsti*, dorsal view, 6 days old. *B*, burrowing juvenile of *Sac. horsti*, 8 days old. (*A*, *B*, *after Burdon-Jones*, 1952.) 1, proboscis; 2, proboscis coelom; 3, complex projecting into proboscis; 4, proboscis-collar groove; 5, collar; 6, collar coelom; 7, collar-trunk boundary; 8, first gill pore; 9, telotroch; 10, hepatic region of intestine; 11, terminal part of intestine from larval intestine; 12, postanal adhesive tail; 13, horn of proboscis skeleton; 14, pharynx; 15, valve at entrance of pharynx into esophagus; 16, dorsal vessel; 17, valve at original stomach-intestine boundary; 18, anus; 19, ventral vessel.

tion between the tornaria and the adult has been made for only a few species.

It may be added that most species of enteropneusts are known only by the original description based on one or a few, often imperfect, specimens. A projected monograph of the enteropneusts of the Pacific Coast of North America by Ritter was never published, and the names therein, although sometimes employed by California zoologists, are without validity. There are apparently several undescribed species in this area, possibly a new genus, belonging to the Harrimaniidae.

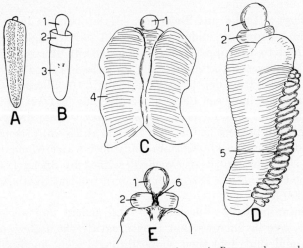

Fig. 49.—Asexual reproduction and regeneration. *A, B*, asexual reproduction in *Bal. capensis (after Gilchrist,* 1923). *A*, regenerating tail end after 14 days. *B*, same, after 25 days. *C–E*, regeneration of cut pieces of *Gloss. minutus (after Dawydoff,* 1909). *C*, piece through genital wings regenerating. *D*, piece through hepatic sacculations regenerating. *E*, dorsal view of regenerating proboscis and collar, showing groove of invagination for collar cord. 1, proboscis; 2, collar; 3, trunk; 4, genital wing; 5, hepatic sacculations; 6, groove of nervous invagination.

17. Metamerism in Enteropneusts.—It cannot be too strongly emphasized that the regionation of the enteropneust body into three successive parts is *not* metamerism and has no relation to metamerism. The essence of metamerism is the serial repetition of body parts along the anteroposterior axis. There is no repetition of parts in the three body regions of enteropneusts since each of these regions is differently constructed and contains different organs. The concept of *oligomery*, that is, of animal groups composed of three "segments" as first proposed by Bütschli and adopted in the *Handbuch der Zoologie* and by various, mostly Germanic, authors, must be rejected as false and artificial. One might as well talk about a mammal with body regionation into head, thorax, and abdomen as "oligomerous." There are, however, some indications of metamerism in enteropneusts, notably in the serial repetition of the gill apparatuses.

These also arise in typical anteroposterior sequence, with the newest one at the posterior end of the series. Although in general the gonads are irregularly distributed, they are known in a few species to alternate regularly with the branchial sacs (Van der Horst, 1930). One may further mention the surface annulation of the trunk, although Spengel (1893) states that this is not as regular as appears on superficial examination; it is usually not related to the gill pores. One may conclude that enteropneusts give evidence of incipient segmentation. It must be noted that there is no evidence of metamerism in the muscular, nervous, and circulatory systems.

18. Ecology: Habits and Behavior.—Enteropneusts in general live concealed in burrows or under stones or in plant tangles. They are mostly limited to the upper littoral zone, chiefly the intertidal zone, although a few descend to 100 m. and a tornaria described by Ritter and Davis (1904) came from depths of 45 to 180 m. *Glandiceps talaboti* from the Mediterranean has been taken at depths ranging from 30 to 350 m., and three imperfect specimens of *Spengelia sibogae* were dredged by the *Siboga* from coral bottom in the Sulu Islands at 275 m. (Spengel, 1907). Only one enteropneust is known from really deep water, *Gland. abyssicola*, of which a single imperfect specimen (described by Spengel, 1893) was taken by the *Challenger* in 1873 in the eastern tropical North Atlantic off Africa at 4500 m.

Some enteropneusts, especially of the genera *Balanoglossus* and *Saccoglossus*, live in burrows that they excavate themselves in sand or sandy mud and that hold their shape through being lined with mucus acting to cement the sand grains together. The best account of such a burrow is that of Stiasny (1910) for *Bal. clavigerus* on Italian coasts. The burrow is U-shaped with two openings 10 to 30 cm. apart, a round one for the posterior end, a funnellike one for the anterior end (Fig. 50*B*). The horizontal part of the U lies 50 to 75 cm. below the surface and seems less permanent and stable than the vertical parts. The vertical part housing the anterior end may branch. The animal moves back and forth in the burrow, depending on the state of the tide, and the ends are most apt to protrude when the tide is ebbing. Then the proboscis tends to reach out of the burrow and explore the surface of the sand, and the anal end may protrude about 2 cm. and emit a coil of feces (Fig. 50*B*). These coils are conspicuous on the surface of the sand when the tide is out and betray the presence of the animals (Fig. 50*C*). Any jarring or disturbance causes prompt withdrawal into the burrow. A similar account is given of the burrows and castings of an undescribed species of *Balanoglossus* in Japan by Hatai and Mii (1955), who also present a photograph of the sand flat dotted with the spiral castings of the worms. Apparently *Sacc. kowalevskii*, well known to emit coiled castings, also inhabits a U bur-

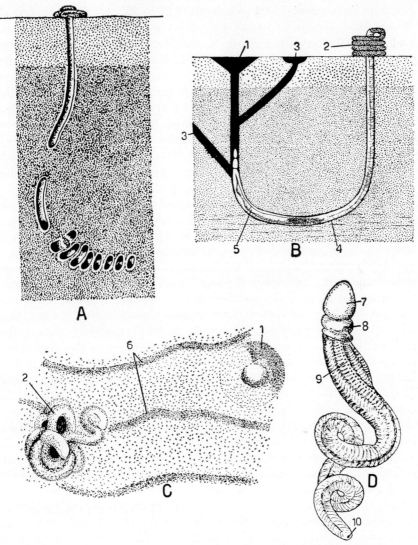

Fig. 50.—Ecology. *A*, spiral burrow of *Sacc. inhacensis*, Delagoa Bay, South Africa (*after Van der Horst*, 1940). *B*, scheme of U-burrow of *Bal. clavigerus*, Mediterranean (*after Stiasny*, 1910). *C*, exposed fecal coil and funnel of *Bal. clavigerus* at low tide (*sketched after a photograph by Stiasny*, 1912). *D*, *Harrimania kupfferi*, characteristic enteropneust of the Baltic (*after Spengel*, 1893). 1, funnel opening for anterior end; 2, fecal coil or casting; 3, accessory anterior openings; 4, main U of burrow; 5, worm in burrow; 6, sand ripples; 7, proboscis; 8, collar; 9, gill pores; 10, anus.

row with its horizontal part at a depth of 20 to 35 cm. *Sacc. cambrensis*, Welsh coast, makes U-shaped, irregularly spiral burrows in clean sand and fine shelly gravel to a depth of 5 to 20 cm. and also throws up small castings (Brambell and Cole, 1939b). *Sacc. serpentinus* on Scottish coasts forms sinuous burrows in the sand, from which the attenuated proboscis often protrudes at night (Assheton, 1908). The habitation of *Sacc. inhacensis*, Mozambique, is a spirally coiled, more or less vertical burrow (Fig. 50A) in muddy sand, lined by clear sand cemented with mucus (Van der Horst, 1934b). *Sacc. pusillus*, California, lives in horizontal cavities close to the surface (Davis, 1908). *Bal. misakiensis*, Japan, also occupies horizontal burrows, at depths to 60 m. (Kuwano, 1902).

The method of burrowing was described for *Sacc. cambrensis* by Knight-Jones (1952) and for *Ptych. flava* by Rao (1954). Burrowing is accomplished entirely by the proboscis, which is elongated and thrust forward, then contracts by its longitudinal musculature, forming a peristaltic bulge that travels posteriorly at a speed of about 1 mm. per second and with a frequency of about 12 per minute. Meantime, before the bulge has reached the proboscis base, the tip is thrust onward again and another bulge follows. These bulges serve to anchor the proboscis while the tip moves onward; the body is drawn passively along. Rao further noted that when the proboscis tip is applied to the sand strong ciliary action causes the sand to stream backward over the collar, hollowing out a depression into which the proboscis tip is easily driven. Ritter (1902) found that *Sacc. pusillus* burrows by alternate elongations and contractions of both proboscis and collar, anchoring the proboscis in the sand by a peristaltic bulge while the body is drawn onward. He also saw this species cover itself with sand by ciliary action. Cilia drive the sand grains back over the proboscis to the collar where a sand girdle forms, and this is gradually pushed back by concomitant additions from in front until the whole animal is covered.

Many enteropneusts, especially members of the genera *Ptychodera*, *Spengelia*, *Glandiceps*, and *Harrimania*, do not make definite burrows but live buried in sandy, gravelly, or shelly bottom or in substrates more or less permeated with decaying organic material or under stones or among corals or in seaweeds or their root tangles. Presumably in such cases the animal is separated from its surroundings by a mucous lining. A predilection for the vicinity of seaweeds has been noticed by many observers. On favorable sites as sand or mud flats specimens may be fairly abundant and often members of two or three species occur in the same locality.

In view of the benthonic habits of enteropneusts it is surprising to find that they sometimes take to the surface. Ikeda (1908) records seeing on three successive mornings in September myriads of a species of *Glandiceps* at the surface; fishermen informed him this was a not unusual occurrence in August and September. In 1899 Spengel (1909) observed hordes of *Gland. malayanus* at the surface in the harbor of Surabaja, Java. Neither author states the method of swimming nor the function of the swarms, although they determined that there was no relation to spawning.

Enteropneusts are generally described as sluggish and inactive animals. The most active part is the proboscis, constantly engaged in exploring the surroundings. Extension of a part is normally brought about by contraction of a circular muscle layer; although this is weak in the proboscis of many enteropneusts, it is nevertheless usually present. One may note further the presence of a dorsoventral muscle sheet and the diagonal course of many of the fibers of the longitudinal muscle masses, and these may aid proboscis extension. There is no proof that intake and outgo of water by way of the proboscis pore (or pores) play any role in locomotion, but it would seem that the pore must close during digging if the proboscis is to maintain the necessary turgidity.

Probably enteropneusts usually do not crawl about on the surface, but if placed on the surface may progress by extending the proboscis, attaching its tip, and pulling the body passively along, or by such proboscis attachment aided by peristaltic waves along the body in an anteroposterior direction (Benham, 1899; Crozier, 1917; Bullock, 1940; Knight-Jones, 1952). The last author described retreat behavior accomplished by reverse peristalsis, beginning at the posterior end of the trunk and progressing forward. Probably movements up and down the burrow are accomplished by peristaltic waves. However, Bullock (1940) and Knight-Jones (1952) ascribe undisturbed progression and movements in the burrow to ciliary action alone. Rao (1954), however, found that ciliary action only augments surface progression in *Ptych. flava*, caused chiefly by peristaltic waves arising at the proboscis tip and passing posteriorly. A main function of ciliary currents is probably to move the mucus copiously secreted by these animals. Bullock, commenting on the paucity of responses of enteropneusts, stated (1940) that burrowing and advance and retreat in the burrows "comprise the sum total of muscular exertions of most of these animals." He found but one clear-cut and dependable piece of behavior, the shortening reflex, that is, relatively rapid shortening and coiling of the trunk by way of its layer of longitudinal muscles, elicited by poking the proboscis. This reaction is presumably mediated by way of the giant cells and their long processes.

The general sluggishness of enteropneusts makes them poor objects for study of response to particular stimuli. The proboscis is evidently the most sensitive part of the animal and tends to engage in constant exploratory movements. In natural conditions explorations by the proboscis may correlate with darkness or the ebbing of the tide. Crozier (1915) for *Ptychodera* intimates without clear description local response, presumably muscular contraction, to mechanical stimulation, with the following order of sensitivity: proboscis, posterior end, genital wings, abdominal surface, collar. In *Sacc. cambrensis* (Knight-Jones, 1952), jarring or a light touch on the proboscis evokes its retraction, and strong stimulation of the posterior end may initiate burrowing movements of the proboscis. A definite response to light is given by all enteropneusts tested (Crozier, 1917; Hess, 1936, 1938; Bullock, 1940; Knight-Jones, 1952). The animals are negative to ordinary light intensities, turning the proboscis away from the light and moving in a direction opposite the source of light. *Sacc. cambrensis*, on sudden exposure to a bright light, contracted the proboscis, then burrowed or gave retreat movements. Experiments with beams of light show that all parts of the surface are photosensitive but the proboscis is the most sensitive area, followed by the collar. A beam of light may evoke an orientation away from the light or only local muscular movements or aimless squirming. Removal of the collar cord is without effect upon the photic response. Isolated proboscides show negative phototaxis as in the intact animal, but an animal minus the proboscis or minus the proboscis and stalk, depending on species, is incapable of photic orientation, and of course the same is true of trunk pieces. Neurosensory cells thought to be photoreceptors (Fig. 25*D*) were described by Hess (1938).

There was little definite information on food and feeding until the recent studies by Barrington (1940) and Knight-Jones (1953). Enteropneusts are generally thought to eat sand, and this is certainly true of the burrowers that emit castings, for these consist of sand. In *Sacc. cambrensis*, object of Knight-Jones's study, the gut swollen with sand is visible through the stretched body wall. However, many enteropneusts neither dig burrows nor emit castings. For species of *Glandiceps* ingestion of diatoms and protozoans is claimed (Ikeda, 1908), and the same type of food is taken by *Bal. capensis* (Gilchrist, 1925). According to the studies first mentioned, made on *Gloss. minutus* and *Sacc. cambrensis*, feeding is primarily of the mucous-ciliary type. Sand grains or other particles that touch the proboscis become entangled in mucous secretion, and such mucous strands are passed back along the proboscis to the collarette, which may reject them if the animal is not feeding or deflect them to the mouth. Particles are also carried directly into the mouth by the strong ciliary currents operative there. The cilia on the ridges of the preoral ciliary organ beat so as to direct particles into the groove of this organ, which probably has a chemoreceptive function; such particles then also eventually pass into the mouth. The usual statement that the mouth is held permanently open is apparently erroneous, for Knight-Jones states that the mouth is opened by radial fibers and closed by a sphincter underlain by a nervous thickening. The gill apparatus plays a role in feeding, for its cilia help maintain a powerful ciliary current entering the mouth and exiting by the gill pores; however, this apparatus does not act to capture food particles.

Cilia are of great importance in the activities of enteropneusts. The whole body surface (except the trunk annulations when present) is ciliated. The cilia of the proboscis beat steadily backward and probably never reverse, and in the preoral ciliary organ they beat from the dorsal ends of the U toward its midventral part, where their current joins the general posteriorly directed stream. On collar and trunk ciliary currents normally beat backward, aiding in forward progression (Bullock, 1940; Knight-Jones, 1952; Rao, 1954); Knight-Jones finds the strong cilia of the trunk ridges between the annulations effective in forward locomotion. On disturbance, causing general contraction and retreat peristalsis, these cilia also reverse, beating forward. The coordination between the direction of ciliary beat and the direction of peristalsis suggests nervous control of the former.

Mucous secretion is also fundamental to the activities of enteropneusts. These animals are constantly covered with mucous secretion, which, together with any imbedded particles, is moved by ciliary action, mostly in a posterior direction. Cavities and burrows occupied by enteropneusts are kept lined with mucus that hardens and forms a smooth and more or less permanent surface. Use of mucus in feeding and covering the animal with sand was already described.

A number of enteropneusts, but not all, give off an offensive odor, usually stated as reminiscent of iodoform and sufficiently strong in some species as to betray the presence of the animals. Probably the odoriferous substance is emitted in the slime.

Luminescence in enteropneusts has been known since its discovery in *Gloss. minutus* by Panceri (1875). It is confined to members of the family Ptychoderidae. Delage and Hérouard (1898) reported luminescence in a ptychoderid of the Breton coast, apparently *Bal. clavigerus*, and Kuwano (1902) mentioned its occurrence in *Bal. misakiensis*, Japan. Rao (1954) observed a bright green luminescence, inhibited by light, of the entire body except the branchial region, of *Ptych. flava*, seemingly caused by emission of a luminescent slime. Two Bermuda species of uncertain identity, one probably *Ptych. bahamensis*, are luminescent (Crozier, 1917, 1920). The luminescent response of these Bermudan species is diminished by day or in the presence of light and augments at night when a sharp blow on the aquarium will cause all the worms to luminesce with a greenish light. This rhythmic diurnal variation in luminescent response continued for 8 days in specimens kept in continuous darkness. However, these species will luminesce during daylight hours if the stimulation is strong enough, as also verified by Harvey (1926a). For *Gloss. minutus* at Naples Harvey (1926a, b) reported luminescence during daylight hours and inhibition of luminescence in the absence of oxygen. This author was unable to throw any light on the mechanism of luminescence in enteropneusts. As already indicated, the

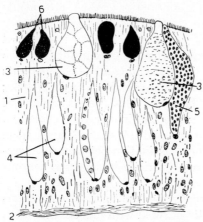

luminescence is vested in a slime that is emitted on stimulation from all parts of the body. Dahlgren (1917) made histological preparations of *Ptych. bahamensis* and identified as photogenic cells epidermal gland cells of goblet type whose contents did not take mucous stains but stained black with iron haematoxylin (Fig. 51), which fails to stain mucous cells. Such goblets blackened by iron haematoxylin are abundant in the epidermis throughout the body of this species, and their contents is presumed to discharge to produce the luminescent slime.

FIG. 51.—Luminescence. Section of the trunk epidermis of *Ptych. bahamensis*, showing supposed luminous cells (*after Dahlgren*, 1917). 1, epidermal cells; 2, nervous layer; 3, reticular gland cells; 4, mucous gland cells; 5, granular gland cell; 6, luminous cells.

Interesting observations have been made on the habits and behavior of enteropneust larvae. Tornariae are typical planktonic organisms that probably swim continuously. Their very large blastocoel, containing scarcely any organs except the digestive tract, confers on them a low specific gravity (1.033 at their maximum development, according to Ritter and Davis, 1904) which, nevertheless, is higher than that of sea water; hence they will sink unless they swim continuously. In swimming the tornaria takes a spiral upward course, rotating constantly. The cilia of the telotroch constitute the chief locomotory mechanism; a wave runs around this band of cilia in a counterclockwise direction, and hence the tornaria rotates in a clockwise direction as seen from above (Ritter and Davis, 1904). These authors gave the rate of swimming as 6 mm. per second, or about 20 m. per hour. They could find no reaction to light to account for the upward course, but other authors have reported high positivity to light (Stiasny, 1935) and it may be recalled that tornariae are provided with a pair of ocelli. Russell (1925), studying plankton movements in the English Channel during July and August, found that a large tornaria present rises to the surface at midnight when on one occasion 14,480 were taken in one 10-minute haul of a net 6 m. long with an aperture 2 m. in diameter. They began to leave the surface before dawn, and during the daytime most were located at a level between 7 and 20 m.; by 9 P.M. the majority had again risen above 7 m. depth. The movements of this tornaria indicate a negative response to light. Whereas most tornariae probably haunt the upper waters, some seem to dwell at considerable depths. The tornaria studied by Ritter and Davis (1904) was taken by towing at 45 to 180 m. off California, and a tornaria of the Naples region, probably that of *Gland. talaboti*, lives at 60 to 100 m. (Stiasny, 1935). Presumably tornariae produced by species living at some depth would remain at this depth since their feeble powers of swimming would hardly suffice to carry them to the surface. However, most authors have supposedly overlooked the possibility of a nocturnal rise toward the surface. Tornariae feed on minute planktonic organisms that are swept into the mouth by the action of the cilia of the preoral loop and especially those of the esophagus (Masterman, 1908). As the tornaria ages and reduces in size with the onset of metamorphosis, its specific gravity rises (Ritter and Davis, 1904) and it tends to remain near the bottom, finally digging in, after it has begun to take on a vermiform appearance. In digging a burrow (described by Morgan, 1894), the proboscis tip is thrust obliquely or vertically into the sand, the proboscis then swells and shortens, drawing the body up, and these processes are repeated until the larva disappears into the sand, in one-half to several minutes. As the proboscis enters the sand it throws out a thick coat of mucus that cements the surrounding sand into a tube. The young worm is here stated to move by peristalsis "like the adult."

The behavior of the more directly developing type of larva was well related by Burdon-Jones (1952) for *Sacc. horsti*. This larva also takes a spiral upward course to the surface, being positively phototactic, and rotates as described for the tornaria; but intervals of rest during which the telotroch ceases beating and the larva sinks alternate with swimming periods. The anal end develops an adhesive patch by which the larva may attach tenaciously. As the larva elongates it tends more and more to creep over the bottom, exploring it with the proboscis, and finally settles on sand of a certain fineness. By this time the adhesive postanal tail has grown out and the larva inhabits a mucus-lined burrow of fine sand grains; it will not thrive in coarse substrates. In the absence of sand the larvae construct tubes of hardened mucus. By the time the first pair of gill pores has appeared the juvenile worms begin to feed by the mucus-ciliary method with tail anchored in the burrow and anterior end protruding (Fig. 52). Particles caught in the mucus of the proboscis are passed back to the collarette, where they are deflected into the mouth. The respiratory current, in at the mouth and out of the gill pores, is of great aid in drawing the food strands into the mouth.   The young worms may also feed by standing erect with gaping mouth and drawing in particles directly with the respiratory current.   Laboratory cultures throve well on diatoms.   The young worm tends to remain permanently

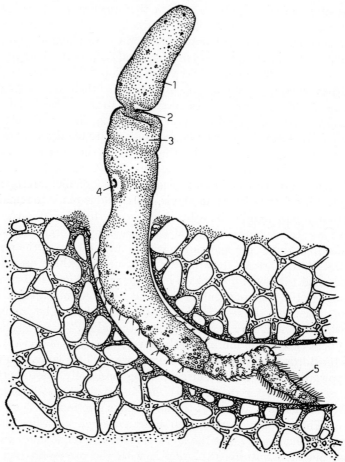

Fig. 52.—Behavior.   Juvenile *Sacc. horsti* attached in its burrow, in feeding attitude (*after Burdon-Jones*, 1952).   1, proboscis; 2, proboscis stalk; 3, collar; 4, first gill pore; 5, postanal adhesive tail.

in the same burrow, gliding inside it, apparently by ciliary action, or creeping in a leechlike fashion, attaching the tail, extending the body forward, then attaching the proboscis, releasing the tail, and drawing the body forward.   The retreat reaction is also given.   Coordination of ciliary action with muscular contraction again suggests nervous control of the former.

19. Physiology.—Enteropneusts are poor objects for laboratory experiments because of their sluggish responses and tendency to break into pieces on handling. Most of the experimental work concerns the functioning of the nervous system (Bullock, 1940, 1945; Knight-Jones, 1952). According to Bullock, the general intraepidermal plexus conducts diffusely after the manner of a nerve net, and body portions show a high degree of autonomy. The isolated proboscis exhibits negative phototaxis, moves about in the usual exploratory manner, and is able to burrow; and such behavior is also given by pieces of the proboscis, especially more anterior pieces. Digging waves are not altered in *Sacc. cambrensis* by cuts in the proboscis, except a cut across the main dorsal proboscis nerve of this species (Fig. 24*A*); this interrupts the wave, which, however, may begin again independently posterior to the cut, but at a lowered frequency. Thus conduction in this dorsal proboscis nerve cord is polarized, and the cord is also responsible for the propagation of the peristaltic digging waves. The general proboscis plexus is also involved in this propagation, for lengthwise cuts produce some interference if close to the middorsal cord. In *Sacc. pusillus*, which lacks a definite middorsal proboscis cord, propagation over the proboscis is not polarized but diffuse in all directions, although with a decrement, and various cuts do not affect the behavior of the proboscis as a whole. In this species stimulation of the free end of a tongue of proboscis tissue cut in any plane (Fig. 53*A*) will evoke the usual shortening reflex, proof that the stimulus was propagated anteriorly in the tongue to the proboscis tip, then backward along the body. The proboscis appears to be the controlling center of the animal, for, following its removal, the animals show decreased activity and tend to remain quiescent.

The collar cord acts primarily as a conducting pathway rather than as a coordinating center. Cuts through the collar cord greatly impair response and activity of the animal by interrupting pathways, but initiation of activities appears centered in the proboscis. The giant cells of the collar cord are believed to function for rapid propagation of impulses affecting the body as a whole, namely, the shortening reflex by which the trunk is suddenly shortened. The conduction of this impulse is far more rapid than the conduction of the usual peristaltic waves. Bullock found that this reflex is not affected by cutting through the dorsal trunk cord but is impaired by cutting either the ventral trunk cord or the circumenteric connectives and is abolished behind the cuts if both dorsal and ventral trunk cords are sectioned. This experimental result agrees with the pathways of the axones of the giant cells (Fig. 25*B*). Isolated collars of *Sacc. pusillus* respond to touch and light but die rapidly.

The dorsal and ventral trunk cords, especially the latter, are important pathways for impulse conduction, but conduction may take place through the general intraepidermal plexus. Crozier (1915) states that in *Ptychodera* the integrity of dorsal and ventral trunk cords is necessary for the propagation of peristalis, but Bullock found that conduction may occur although with difficulty despite cuts through these cords. Stimulation of lateral areas isolated from both trunk cords by longitudinal incisions will evoke contractions of regions posterior to the cuts. In Bullock's material, conduction in the general trunk plexus appeared easier in the transverse than in the longitudinal direction. Isolated trunks or parts of trunks remain inactive but respond to stimuli by localized contraction, even if only 1 mm. square, and mostly do not give a general contraction. Such response is inhibited by light narcosis, hence is of nervous, not muscular, nature. The general intraepidermal plexus is thus present and active by conduction in all directions in all trunk pieces. Small trunk pieces move about by ciliary action and may often alter or reverse direction; larger pieces do not move. Retreat peristalsis, initiated by stimulation of the proboscis and propagated from the posterior end forward, is dependent on the integrity of the ventral trunk cord and begins only anterior to a cut through this cord (Knight-Jones); similarly stimulation of the posterior end in *Sacc. cambrensis* is not propagated anterior to a cut through the ventral trunk cord, but response might begin at this cut and travel posteriorly.

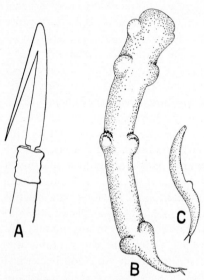

Fig. 53.—Physiology, ecology. *A*, diagram showing tongue of proboscis tissue (*after Bullock*, 1940). *B*, female parasitic copepod, *Ive balanoglossi. C*, male of *B*. (*B, C, after Mayer*, 1879.)

Information concerning digestive processes is limited to the articles of Barrington (1940) on *Gloss. minutus* and Knight-Jones (1952) on *Sacc. horsti* and *cambrensis;* the latter, however, devotes himself mainly to the histology and ciliary currents of the digestive tract. In general, the entire digestive tract is ciliated and the ciliary currents are mostly directed backward, moving the food cord along. *Saccoglossus* belongs to those enteropneusts in which the esophagus is regionated into three histologically different sections. Knight-Jones observed peristalsis in the first section, and a local contraction could be induced by touching the epithelium of the opened esophagus. The second section, with narrowed lumen and esophageal pores, is also characterized by the very thick, highly glandular epithelium; this is the most glandular part of the *Saccoglossus* digestive tube and probably the site of enzyme secretion. Here begin the middorsal and midventral grooves found throughout the rest of the digestive tract; cilia adjacent to these grooves beat so as to drive particles into the grooves, where they are transported posteriorly. No currents were seen through the esophageal pores, and no function for these openings is apparent, except possibly the emission of excess water as the food rope concentrates. In the intestine of *Saccoglossus* the gut contents were usually stationary but would be carried posteriorly by spasmodic outbursts of ciliary activity. Knight-Jones made no study of the digestive enzymes of *Saccoglossus*.

Barrington discovered that the slime emitted by the proboscis of *Gloss. minutus* contains a potent amylase that would be swallowed with the food strands. In this species the pharynx is well constricted into dorsal branchial and ventral digestive regions, but Barrington found food in both regions, although the heavier material, mainly sand, tended to accumulate in the digestive part, which, however, has a low epithelium without glands and seems to play little role in digestion. This species possesses a postbranchial canal in which food gathers and which seems to produce digestive secretions, as probably does also the esophagus. Barrington surmises that the golden-brown inclusions in the cells of the hepatic sacculations are of enzymatic nature, although food does not enter these sacculations. Extracts of the entire body or of parts of the body contained an amylase, active between pH 5.5 and 8.0, and extracts of the hepatic region (including the body wall) contained an amylase that would digest glycogen and saccharose, also a maltase, a weak protease, and a weak lipase, most active at pH 6.5. No enzyme other than amylase was found in the proboscis slime.

Bullock (1940) states that "not even a plausible guess has been offered concerning the function of the gill slits in balanoglossids."[1] However, the British workers have clearly shown that the gill apparatus functions as in tunicates and cephalochordates; that is, its cilia (together with the cilia of the buccal cavity) maintain a powerful water current that enters at the mouth and exits by the gill pores. A main function of this current is the sucking in of the food-laden mucous strands produced by the proboscis, but a concomitant respiratory function is scarcely to be doubted. This current is readily seen in juveniles that have set themselves up in burrows (Burdon-Jones, 1952), and its presence in adults has been attested by Barrington (1940) and Knight-Jones (1953). However,

---

[1] The expression "balanoglossid" in referring to enteropneusts should be discontinued. There is no family Balanoglossidae for which the adjective balanoglossid would be appropriate, and *Balanoglossus* is now only one of the genera of the Enteropneusta.

the gill apparatus of enteropneusts does not function to capture food particles, as is the case with lower chordates.   The main motive force for the current in the branchial region is furnished by the long "lateral" cilia found on the sides of the septa and tongue bars, that is, along the anterior and posterior margins of these structures.   It has been noticed (Knight-Jones and Millar, 1949; Knight-Jones, 1952) that waves pass along the lateral cilia in a clockwise direction (as seen from the lumen) on both sides of the pharynx, that is, asymmetrically on the two sides, as in tunicates and cephalochordates.   Cilia on the inner surface of the gill apparatus, that is, the surface facing the pharyngeal lumen, are called frontal and may occur on either septa or tongue bars or on both.   The central part of the epithelium bearing the frontal cilia is provided with mucous glands, the lateral parts are nonglandular, and this division into three dorsoventral strips is said by Knight-Jones (1953) to obtain also in cephalochordates.   In some enteropneusts the gill pores are encircled by a sphincter of circular fibers, and from the gill pores fibers belonging to the radial system radiate fanlike in the walls of the branchial sacs.   In most enteropneusts the gill pores are only partly closable by fibers from the longitudinal trunk muscles that pass in bundles between them. Muscle fibers are wanting in the septa and tongue bars, and hence the water current would seem to be regulated by the branchial sacs and gill pores.

What is known about the circulation was already indicated.   The heart vesicle begins to beat shortly after being formed during larval development and continues throughout life.   The blood runs forward in the dorsal vessel, is forced through the glomerulus, and runs backward in the peribuccal and ventral vessels.   It probably runs from ventral to dorsal in the lacunae of the body wall, digestive wall, and gill apparatus, but this is not definitely demonstrated.   What is surmised about excretion was stated on page 119.

Cary (1933) successfully cultivated the tissues of *Ptych. bahamensis* in balanced salt medium of half the concentration of sea water plus nutrition in the form of a peptic digest of the animal.   Small bits from the hepatic region would start expanding in a few minutes, putting out slender processes.   First nerve processes elongated, followed by connective-tissue cells, and in about 30 minutes by the hepatic epithelial cells.   Migration of cells, accompanied by division, continued for some hours, after which the whole mass became covered by epidermal migration.   Following this event growth, migration, and mitotic activity ceased, although such cultures would live for at least 3 weeks and could be successfully subcultured repeatedly.   In cultures of hepatic epithelium alone, the cells migrate by amoeboid activity, putting out slender pseudopodia, but remaining connected to the remnant of the original piece by slender strands. After being dispersed by migration the cells undergo active mitosis that often results in one daughter receiving most of the brown granules. Daughters without the brown granules become especially active and multiply rapidly. Muscle cells were found to be very loosely bound together and often separated from the main piece during the making of the culture. Others dispersed by migration, but migration soon ceased and the muscle cells would remain stationary as slender strands or as short contracted objects of irregular outline. Muscle cells may continue rhythmical contraction in cultures for at least 4 weeks.

20. Ecology: Biological Relations.—Enteropneusts tend to live in aggregations of the same or different species, but this may be the mere consequence of the settling of larval stages in favorable sites and their avoidance of other places. However, *Gloss. ruficollis* apparently lives only in the burrows of the much larger *Bal. carnosus* (Willey, 1899b; Okuda, 1939), and Willey indicates that *Speng. porosa* and *Gloss. hedleyi* are always found in company with *Ptych. flava*. All these species belong to the Indo-Pacific region.

Enteropneusts appear infected with many kinds of protozoan parasites, but little information is available about them beyond the remarks in Spengel (1893). This author noted what he thought to be flagellates in the branchial sacs and around the gill pores of *Harr. kupfferi*, and similar parasites were recorded by Marion (1886) in the gill apparatus of *Gland. hacksi*. Spengler also found gregarines in the hepatic sacculations of *Bal. clavigerus* and *Harr. kupfferi* and other sporozoans in the ciliated furrows of the intestine of *Gloss. sarniensis* and in the esophageal epithelium of *Gland. hacksi*. No doubt some of these are identical with the sporozoans described and named by Leger and Duboscq (1917) from *Gloss. minutus*. They identified a schizogregarine (I, page 147), *Selenidium metchnikovi*, in the intestine, and two coccidians, doubtfully assigned to *Eimeria*—*beauchampi* in the hepatic sacculations and *epidermica* in the proboscis epidermis. A haplosporidian (I, page 164) from the muscles, gonads, and coelomic cavities of *Gloss. minutus* was studied by Sun (1910), who named the organism *Protoenterospora ptychoderae*. This occurs as oval bodies, mostly in groups. When about to sporulate these bodies migrate to the gut epithelium, also the epidermis, and are discharged to the exterior.

Trematode metacercariae were found by Spengel (1893) in the coelom of proboscis and collar of *Harr. kupfferi* and fragments of nematodes in the proboscis musculature of *Schiz. brasiliense*. Polychaete annelids have twice been discovered making a home in the dorsal trough between the genital wings in species of *Balanoglossus* (Giard, 1882; Gravier, 1905). The inevitable copepod parasites occur on enteropneusts. Hill (1895) reported that most specimens of *Bal. australiensis* had enlargements on the edge of the genital wings, and these contained a large female copepod with attendant small males. Willey (1899b) observed tumors or galls containing copepods in the genital wings of *Ptych. flava*. A parasitic copepod found by Spengel (1893) in the coelom of *Gloss. minutus* was described by Mayer (1879) under the name of *Ive balanoglossi* (Fig. 53*B*, *C*). Other crustacean associates of enteropneusts include little crabs found by Kuwano (1902) as regular inhabitants of the burrows of *Bal. misakiensis* and an amphipod *Corophium volutator* commensal with *Sac. cambrensis* (Brambell and Cole, 1939a).

If enteropneusts did not live concealed, they would probably be eaten freely by fish. Devanescen and Chacko (1942) reported that local Indian enteropneusts had been eaten by two kinds of fish that consequently smelled of iodoform. It would seem that the fish must have learned to dig the enteropneusts out of their burrows.

21. Ecology: Geographic Distribution.—The Enteropneusta are probably very imperfectly known. Many species have been described from a single specimen or a single collecting, and therefore one cannot say whether they are actually rare or not. Because they live buried in the bottom, enteropneusts are difficult to collect except in the intertidal zone and many undiscovered species may exist at moderate depths. They are further fragile and tend to break into fragments; hence it is difficult to secure complete specimens, especially in the case of the larger species. The frequent finding of new kinds of tornariae certainly indicates the existence of many undiscovered species. According to present knowledge enteropneusts favor warm and temperate waters. The majority of the known species inhabit tropical and subtropical waters, and especially the genus *Ptychodera* is limited to such waters. *Ptychodera flava*, probably the most widely distributed enteropneust, is found throughout the Indo-Pacific area from the Red Sea and Mozambique to the Galapagos Islands. All the species of *Spengelia* and *Willeyia* are also Indo-Pacific, but each of the species has been taken but once or twice. Species of *Glandiceps*, *Saccoglossus*, *Glossobalanus*, and *Balanoglossus* also occur in the Indo-Pacific; of these *Bal. carnosus* and *Gloss. ruficollis*, which inhabit the same burrows, are the better-known forms. From Australia (Thomas, 1956) there are known two endemic species (*Bal. australiensis* and *Sacc. apantesis*) and three Indo-Pacific forms (*Ptych. flava*, *Bal. carnosus*, and *Gloss. hedleyi*). Of the six species known from Japan (Okuda and Yamada, 1955a), five are endemic (*Bal. misakiensis* and *borealis*, *Gland. eximius* and *hacksi*, and *Sacc. sulcatus*) and one (*Bal. carnosus*) has come in from the general Indo-Pacific area. Rao (1955b, c, d) lists eight species as known from Madras and the Gulf of Manaar, of which five are not found elsewhere.

In the tropical and subtropical Atlantic there are known from the

West Indies (Van der Horst, 1924) *Ptych. bahamensis*, distinguishable from *Ptych. flava* only by its tornaria, *Bal. biminiensis* and *jamaicensis*, and *Sacc. carabiacus*. An additional species, *Gloss. crozieri*, occurs at Bermuda, where West Indian species are also found. *Schiz. brasiliense* and *Bal. apertus* and *gigas* appear limited to the coast of Brazil, where an imperfect specimen of the first was recently refound (Sawaya and Forneris, 1953). These authors also described three new species of *Balanoglossus* from Brazilian coasts, and Björnberg (1953, 1955) reported a number of new tornariae from the general West Indian region.

In southern temperate and colder waters, several enteropneusts are recorded locally from and appear limited to South Africa (Gilchrist, 1908a, b, 1925; Kapelus, 1936) as *Sacc. inhacensis*, *Bal. capensis* and *natalensis*, and the only known species of the genus *Xenopleura*. *Sacc. otagoensis* is endemic to New Zealand (Van der Horst, 1929), the most southerly record for enteropneusts. No species are known from the Subantarctic or Antarctic.

Apparently a number of enteropneust species are endemic to the Pacific Coast of North America, but the promised monograph about them by Ritter was never published. Published forms include *Sacc. pusillus* from California, often mentioned in the preceding pages, *Gloss. berkeleyi* from British Columbia (Willey, 1931), and *Harrimania maculosa* from Alaska (Ritter, 1900). A species of *Schizocardium* (*S. peruvianum* Spengel, 1893) occurs on the coast of Peru.

On the Atlantic Coast of North America the common species is the well-known *Sacc. kowalevskii*, found in sand flats from Massachusetts to the Carolinas, also occurring on European coasts. On the Carolina coast there is also present another species, *Bal. aurantiacus* (Fig. 20*C*), apparently restricted to this area. The interesting *Stereobalanus canadensis* (Fig. 21*A*) is a northern species, endemic to the coasts of Maine and Nova Scotia.

Western Europe harbors a number of enteropneust species. In the Mediterranean are found *Bal. clavigerus*, *Gland. talaboti*, and *Gloss. minutus* and *elongatus*. French and British coasts form the home of the primitive species *Protoglossus koehleri*, refound and redescribed by Burdon-Jones (1956); there further occur in this area in places *Gloss. sarniensis* and *marginatus* and *Sacc. ruber*, *serpentinus*, *horsti*, and *cambrensis*. Burdon-Jones (1956) lists a total of seven species found around the British Isles, including some of the foregoing, plus *Bal. clavigerus*, *Harr. kupfferi*, and *Sacc. pygmaeus*. The characteristic species of the North and Baltic Seas is *Harr. kupfferi* (Fig. 50*D*), also found on the coast of Greenland. *Sacc. mereschkowskii* inhabits arctic seas, having been taken in the Bering Sea and the waters north of Russia and Siberia, and very likely is circumpolar. It is to be noticed that nearly all

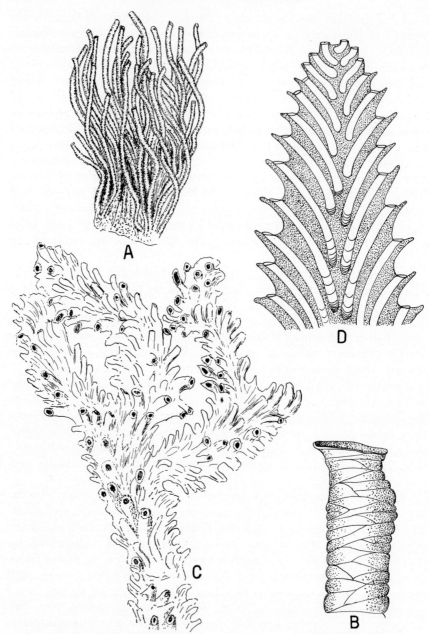

Fig. 54.—Coenecium of *Cephalodiscus*. *A*, coenecium of *Cephalodiscus densus*, illustrating *Orthoecus* type. *B*, one tube of *A*, showing method of deposition of secretion. (*A*, *B*, *after Andersson*, 1907.) *C*, coenecium of *C. nigrescens*, illustrating *Idiothecia* type (*after Ridewood*, 1918). *D*, scheme of arrangement of zooid tubes in branch end of *C. nigrescens* (*after Ridewood*, 1907).

enteropneusts of the cold waters of both hemispheres belong to the Harrimaniidae, although this family also contains tropical members.

V. CLASS PTEROBRANCHIA

1. Definition.—The Pterobranchia are small hemichordates with or without gill slits, with two or more tentaculated arms borne by the mesosome, and with recurved digestive tract, that live as aggregations or colonies housed in an externally secreted encasement. The class includes three genera, *Cephalodiscus*, *Rhabdopleura*, and *Atubaria*, best treated separately.

A. Cephalodiscus

1. Coenecium.—*Cephalodiscus* occurs in aggregations of some size, composed of many unconnected individuals that have arisen by budding from an original single, sexually produced progenitor. This aggregation inhabits a secreted encasement, the *coenecium*, of unknown chemical nature (but *not* chitinous), that also includes adherent foreign objects as sand grains, sponge spicules, worm tubes, fragments of mollusk shells, echinoid spicules, and so on. The form of the coenecium varies greatly in different species and is the basis for assembling the species into four subgenera. In the simplest type (subgenus *Orthoecus*), exemplified by *C. densus* (Fig. 54*A*), the coenecium consists of upright tubes, each occupied by an individual *Cephalodiscus*. These tubes are permanently fixed to a substrate and are more or less adherent to each other or partly imbedded in a common secretion or basally united by anastomoses of the tubes. The first complication is shown by the *Idiothecia* group of species, illustrated by *C. nigrescens* (Fig. 54*C*), in which the coenecium takes the form of a branching growth studded with little projections open at their tip. Each such opening leads into a tubular cavity in the coenecium that houses an individual (Fig. 54*D*). Next (*Demiothecia* group of species) individual tubes are eliminated from the branching coenecium, which then contains large cavities opening now and then by wide apertures. The first species described, the one taken by the *Challenger*, *C. dodecalophus*, belongs to this category, consisting of a branching coenecium with many anastomoses among the branches (Fig. 55*A*). Finally a fourth subgenus (*Acoelothecia*) was created by John (1931) for *C. kempi*, in which the coenecium consists of a spongy mass in the interstices of which the members dwell (Fig. 57*B*).

The coenecium is often ornamented with filamentous projections that give it the appearance of a seaweed (Fig. 55*A*). Often such projections are supported by spinelike depositions of especially hard secretion (Fig. 57*A*), and the spongy mass of the *Acoelothecia* type of coenecium is composed of such spines crisscrossing to form somewhat regular meshes that

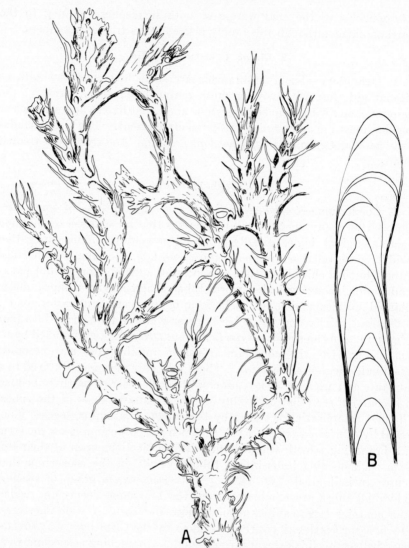

Fig. 55.—Coenecium (continued). *A*, part of a coenecium of *C. dodecalophus*, illustrating *Desmiothecia* type (*after McIntosh*, 1887). *B*, one of the filaments of the *Desmiotheca* type, built up of overlapping layers of secretion (*after Andersson*, 1907).

house the animals (Fig. 57*B*). The material of the individual tubes when present is also firmer and of darker coloration than the intermediate secretion, which is soft and gelatinous. The coenecium is secreted by the protosome of the animals, and tubes and spines are built up by successive overlapping depositions as shown by the markings left on them (Figs. 54*B*, 55*B*, 56*A*).

The coenecium is often of a drab or yellowish-brown color, but some species are reported as orange, red, or brown. The color is generally lost on preservation in alcohol. Tubes when present are more strongly colored than the intermediate substance, which is mostly pale, and young secretion is paler than older parts of the coenecium.

2. External Features of Cephalodiscus.—The individuals, conveniently termed *zooids*, that occupy the coenecium are minute creatures of strange aspect, mostly below 5 mm. in length (omitting the stalk), although in one species, *C. densus* (John, 1931), the zooids, normally 4 to 7 mm. long, may exceptionally reach a length of 14 mm. They consist of a plump body bearing feathery arms on the dorsal side of its neck (Fig. 56B, C) and a long stalk of attachment that gives off buds near its end (Fig. 64B). Despite the differing appearance of the coenecium the zooids of the various species are practically identical.

The body is regionated into three parts, although these are not as evident as in enteropneusts. The first part, or protosome, is a flexible shield-shaped, or disciform, structure that is tilted toward the ventral side so as to conceal the mouth. It is variously called proboscis, buccal shield, or cephalic shield in the literature. Viewed ventrally, the cephalic shield is flat with a more or less circular outline, indented laterally with a pair of notches (Fig. 56C); a curved red pigment band runs from one notch to the other, parallel to the posterior edge of the shield. Dorsally the central part of the shield is directly continuous with the mesosome or collar without the intervention of a stalk, and as the shield is tilted ventrally, it follows that the dorsal side of the collar is much longer than its ventral side, part of which is further taken up with the mouth opening. On its dorsal side the collar bears the arms, bilaterally arranged in two curved rows, composed of five to nine arms each, depending on species (Fig. 56B). All the arms of one row are fused basally. Each arm consists of a central stem bearing a groove on its ventral surface and provided on each side with a fringe of 25 to 50 tentacles. In some species the stem of the arm terminates in a glandular knob (Fig. 59C). The number of tentacles is variable and may increase with age. A fold of body wall, the *oral lamella* (Fig. 58D), partly encircles the collar, extending from the base of the most posterior arms around the ventral side behind the mouth. This serves to direct the food caught by the arms into the mouth. The trunk is divisible into an anterior plump sacciform part, containing the recurved digestive tract and the gonads, and a posterior slender stalk of attachment. The former bears the transversely elongated anus and the two gonopores dorsally near the collar; a single pair of gill slits is found laterally on the trunk just behind the posterior border of the collar. The hollow muscular stalk may continue from the rear end of the trunk sac or from its side and is usually much displaced and

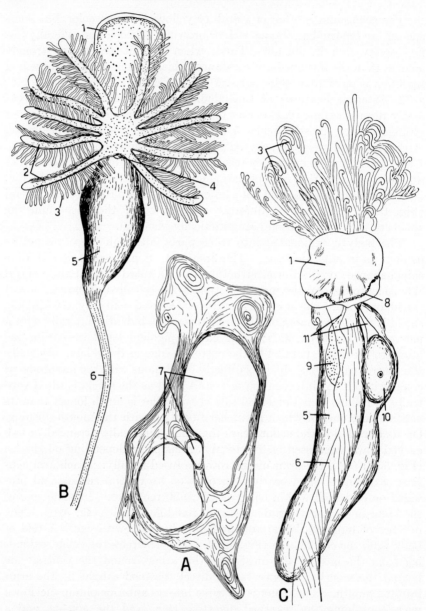

Fig. 56.—Coenecium (continued), zooids. A, section across coenecium of *C. hodgsoni*, *Desmiothecia* type. B, a zooid of *C. hodgsoni*, seen from the dorsal side. (A, B, after *Andersson*, 1907.) C, a hermaphroditic zooid of *C. australiensis*, seen from the ventral side (*after Johnston and Muirhead*, 1951). 1, cephalic shield; 2, arms; 3, tentacles; 4, anus; 5, trunk sac; 6, stalk; 7, cavities for zooids; 8, pigment stripe; 9, testis; 10, ovary; 11, gonoduct.

contracted in preserved specimens. Its length varies with the species and in the living state probably much exceeds that of the rest of the animal; lengths up to 4 cm. have been recorded. The end of the stalk is adhesive and acts to attach the animal to the coenecium or while moving about. As already indicated, the zooids of *Cephalodiscus* are unconnected with each other and can move about freely. Near the adhesive end of the stalk is a budding zone from which new zooids are constantly budded (Fig. 64*B*).

3. **Body Wall.**—The body wall consists of epidermis, nervous layer, basement membrane, subepidermal musculature, and peritoneum. The epidermis (best described by Andersson, 1907) varies in height in different regions and is generally ciliated and often glandular (Fig. 57*D*). The ciliation is especially well developed on the ventral (grooved) surface of the arms and tentacles, on the surface of the oral lamella that faces the mouth, and on the dorsal surface of the trunk sac in the vicinity of the anus. Andersson (1907) surmises that the entire body surface is ciliated, although in preserved material the cilia are often not demonstrable on the more scantily ciliated areas. The main glandular area occupies the central part of the ventral surface of the cephalic shield (Fig. 59*A*). Here the very tall epidermal cells are heavily loaded with eosinophilous spherules and ovals of secretion (Fig. 58*A*). This glandular area of the cephalic shield (Fig. 59*A*) is believed to secrete the coenecium. Peripherally the ventral epidermis of the cephalic shield diminishes in height and contains gland cells of the goblet type. A red or reddish-yellow curved pigment stripe bounds the posterior border of the central glandular area of the shield (Fig. 59*A*). This consists of a strip two to four cells wide of tall, attenuated cells filled with colored granules, thought by Andersson to be of a secretory, rather than of a pigmentary, nature. The function of the pigment band, present in all species of *Cephalodiscus*, remains problematical. The dorsal epidermis of the cephalic shield is low but well provided with mucous goblets.

The concave ventral surface of the arms and tentacles is clothed with a rather low, nonglandular, heavily ciliated epidermis (Fig. 57*C*), whereas the dorsal, convex side is generally much thickened and highly glandular, being thickly provided with plump mucous cells (Fig. 57*C*). In the *Demiothecia* group of species, the arm tips are swollen into terminal knobs, shown by Andersson (1907) to be of glandular nature, consisting of mucous glands interspersed with more slender gland cells filled with fine fibrils (Fig. 58*B*). These terminal knobs as well as the general dorsal surfaces of the arms no doubt serve to capture prey by way of sticky secretions.

The epidermis of the trunk sac is columnar, sparsely ciliated except for the better ciliation in the anal region, and more or less provided with

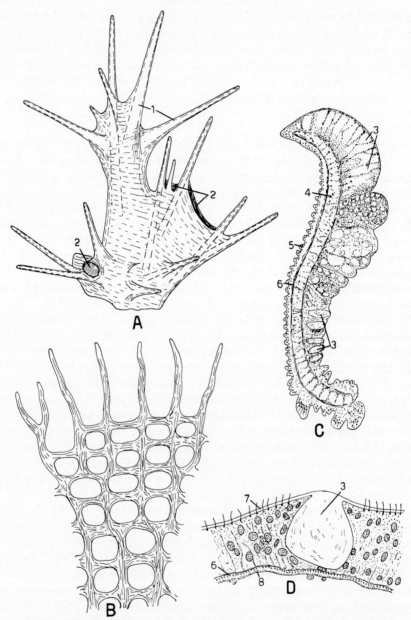

Fig. 57.—Coenecium (concluded), epidermis. *A*, bit of coenecium of *C. hodgsoni*, showing spicules (*after Ridewood*, 1918a). *B*, bit of coenecium of *C. kempi, Acoelothecia* type (*after John*, 1931). *C*, longitudinal section of an arm, showing glandular dorsal epidermis. *D*, epidermis of trunk near anus. (*C, D, after Andersson*, 1907.) 1, spicules; 2, openings; 3, gland cells of dorsal epidermis; 4, coelom of arm; 5, ventral epidermis of arm; 6, longitudinal muscle fibers; 7, cuticle; 8, peritoneum.

mucous gland cells (Fig. 57*D*), also to a lesser extent with granular glands. In the stalk epidermis gland cells are limited to the dorsal surface; cilia are probably absent.   According to Schepotieff (1907) the concavity of the end of the stalk contains gland cells like those of the ventral side of the cephalic shield (Fig. 58*D*), whereas Andersson (1907) denied the presence of gland cells here and attributed the adhesive action of the stalk end to the formation of a vacuum cup.

The base of the epidermis is occupied by a nervous layer (see below), and this is subtended by a strong basement membrane that does not give rise to definite skeletal structures, although it is markedly thickened in the dorsal wall of the tentacles, where it probably acts as a stiffening. To the inner side of the basement membrane is found throughout much of the body a subepidermal layer of longitudinal muscle fibers (Fig. 57*D*). As in enteropneusts the peritoneum is partly transformed into muscle and connective tissue but remains intact in places.

4. Nervous System.—The nervous system consists of a fibrillar plexus in the base of the epidermis to the outer side of the basement membrane. The delicate, filamentous bases of the epidermal cells pass through the plexus to attach to the basement membrane.   Probably this plexus is present throughout the body but is difficult to demonstrate wherever the epidermis is much reduced in thickness.   In the dorsal wall of the collar, between the bases of the arm rows, is found the central part of the nervous system, or *collar ganglion*, in the form of an extensive thickening of the general intraepidermal plexus, from which it is not definitely delimited (Fig. 59*A*).   Unlike the collar cord of enteropneusts, the collar ganglion here retains the primitive intraepidermal position.   It consists of a fibrous mass containing ganglion cells in its centrodorsal part (Fig. 59*D*). Ganglion cells are generally absent in other parts of the plexus except the midventral trunk nerve.   From the collar ganglion, several so-called nerves extend that are merely thickenings of the plexus.   Into each arm is given off an arm nerve that runs along the dorsal side of the arm (Fig. 60*A*).   Anteriorly the collar ganglion is continuous with a median dorsal and a pair of laterodorsal thickenings of the general plexus of the cephalic shield, which latter is very well developed on both sides of the shield. From the posterior end of the collar ganglion a short and rather weak middorsal trunk nerve proceeds posteriorly as far as the anus.   Posteriorly the ganglion also gives off a prominent pair of circumenteric connectives (Fig. 60*A*) that proceed ventrally, approximately along the collar-trunk boundary behind the gill pores, to the ventral side of the trunk sac, where they unite to form a midventral trunk nerve, which, however, is not well delimited from the general plexus.   It gives off one or two pairs of lateral thickenings.   These midventral and lateral trunk nerves become more definite posteriorly and continue into the ventral side

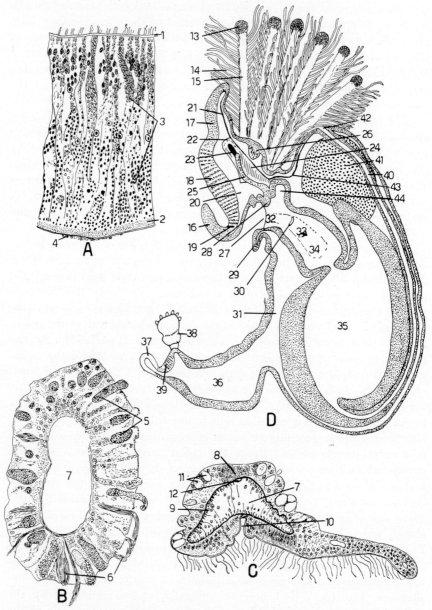

FIG. 58.—Epidermis (concluded), general structure. *A*, cross section of epidermis of glandular center of cephalic shield. *B*, cross section through the terminal glandular knob of an arm of *C. dodecalophus*. *C*, cross section through an arm and one tentacle. (*A–C, after Andersson,* 1907.) *D*, schematic median sagittal section of *Cephalodiscus* (*after Schepotieff,* 1907c). 1, cuticle; 2, nervous layer; 3, glandular epidermis; 4, peritoneum; 5, granular gland cells; 6, fibrous gland cells; 7, arm coelom; 8, dorsal arm nerve; 9, longi-

of the stalk as one or three rather pronounced thickenings of the nerve plexus here (Fig. 59*B*). The midventral nerve of the stalk may continue around the end of the stalk to the dorsal side of the latter, where it runs forward. A general resemblance of the nervous system to that of the enteropneusts is evident, but the system is in a still more primitive condition than in the latter. There is no sign of any lumen in any part of the pterobranch nervous system.

5. Coelom.—As in enteropneusts, the coelom is divided into three successive compartments, of which the first, or protocoel, is unpaired, whereas the other two, the meso- and metacoels, are subdivided by a median dorsoventral mesentery. The protocoel occupies the interior of the cephalic shield, which is therefore hollow, except posteriorly behind the red pigment stripe where its dorsal and ventral walls are fused, eliminating the coelom (Fig. 59*A*). Dorsally the projection of the heart vesicle and associated structures into the protocoel somewhat separates off a pair of dorsolateral pockets from the main cavity, and there is further a median dorsal pocket above the heart vesicle (Fig. 61*C*). Each dorsolateral pocket leads into a canal lined by a columnar, heavily ciliated epithelium and opening to the exterior by a small pore (Fig. 61*C*). These structures obviously correspond to the proboscis canals and pores of enteropneusts but are here always symmetrically paired. The pair of pores is found just anterior to the base of the first pair of arms, and the canals pass through the anterior part of the collar ganglion, for they slant somewhat posteriorly. The protocoel is separated from the mesocoel by a septum that is transverse in some species, more or less slanted in others.

The mesocoel, or collar coelom, embraces the buccal tube and is subdivided into right and left halves by a dorsal and ventral mesentery (Fig. 60*C*). The dorsal mesentery is very thick and strongly developed, serving as a site of muscle attachment. The thinner ventral mesentery is practically complete. The arms and tentacles are hollow, containing extensions of the collar coelom of their side (Fig. 60*B*), and there is also a coelomic extension from each side into the oral lamella (Fig. 60*C*). The collar coelom is also evaginated into the protocoel as a pair of blind pockets lying to either side of the heart vesicle and the protocoel canals (Fig. 61*C*). As in enteropneusts there is a collar canal and pore for each half of the mesocoel. The collar canal is here circular in cross section, not crescentic as in enteropneusts (Fig. 28*B*), but a similarity is indicated by

tudinal muscle fibers; 10, ventral groove of arm; 11, mucous gland cells; 12, arm blood sinus; 13, terminal knob; 14, tentacles; 15, arms; 16, part of cephalic shield without coelom; 17, cephalic shield; 18, glandular center of cephalic shield; 19, pigment stripe; 20, shield coelom; 21, shield-collar septum; 22, heart vesicle; 23, central sinus; 24, dorsal collar mesentery; 25, buccal diverticulum; 26, collar ganglion; 27, mouth; 28, upper lip; 29, oral lamella; 30, gill slit; 31, trunk coelom; 32, buccal tube; 33, pharynx; 34, esophagus; 35, stomach; 36, stalk; 37, young bud; 38, older bud; 39, glandular center of stalk end; 40, intestine; 41, ovary; 42, anus; 43, collar-trunk septum; 44, dorsal recess of pharynx.

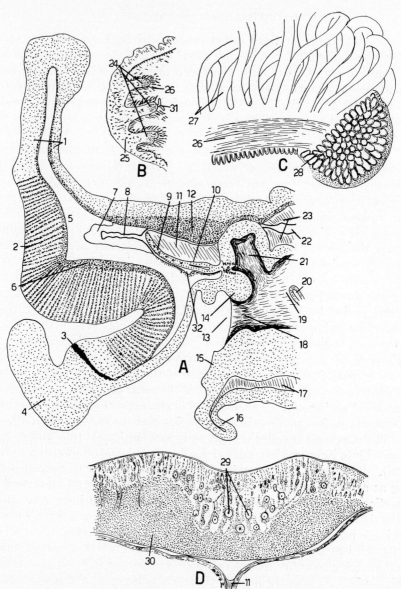

Fig. 59.—General structure (continued), nervous system. *A*, sagittal section through anterior end (*after Schepotieff*, 1907c). *B*, cross section of ventral wall of stalk base, showing three nerves. *C*, end of arm of *C. dodecalophus*, showing knob filled with mucous glands (*after McIntosh*, 1887). *D*, cross section of collar ganglion. (*B, D, after Andersson*, 1907.) 1, cephalic shield; 2, glandular center of cephalic shield; 3, pigment stripe; 4, part of shield without coelom; 5, shield coelom; 6, nervous layer; 7, heart vesicle; 8, central sinus; 9, buccal diverticulum; 10, shield-collar septum; 11, dorsal collar mesentery; 12, collar ganglion; 13, mouth; 14, dorsal lip; 15, ventral lip; 16, oral lamella; 17, ventral trunk mesentery; 18, buccal tube; 19, pharynx; 20, gill slit; 21, dorsal recess of pharynx; 22, blood sinus; 23, dorsal trunk mesentery; 24, ventral nerves of stalk; 25, epidermis; 26, longitudinal muscle fibers; 27, tentacles; 28, mucous glands of terminal knob; 29, ganglion cells; 30, fibrous part of collar cord; 31, ventral stalk sinus; 32, ventral shield sinus.

the much greater thickness of one wall of the canal (Fig. 61*D*). The collar canal consists of altered, inturned epidermis, heavily ciliated, especially on the thickened side. The collar pores are located on the sides of the neck just in front of the gill pores, therefore not opening in common with the gill pores as in enteropneusts; however, relationship to the gill pores is shown by a groove of altered epidermis extending from the collar pore to the corresponding gill pore. The mesocoel is separated from the metacoel by a definite septum (Fig. 58*D*), which is much slanted with its dorsal attachment much anterior to its ventral one.

The metacoel, or trunk coelom, is divided into right and left halves by dorsal and ventral mesenteries (Fig. 60*C*). It is almost completely filled by the digestive tract and gonads, but less occupied with muscles and connective tissue than the other coelomic divisions. It sends a pair of ventral evaginations into the collar coelom, and these extend up to the collar canals (Fig. 62*A*). The trunk coelom also possesses a pair of lateral septa as in the Ptychoderidae, although these are reduced in some species. They are found in the gonadal region and typically extend from the gonoduct to the dorsal mesentery, being free posteriorly and attached to the body wall anteriorly (Fig. 61*F*). The trunk coelom extends into the stalk, which lacks mesenteries; but its central lumen is almost completely filled with muscles and connective tissue (Fig. 61*A*).

6. Musculature.—As already indicated, a thin layer of longitudinal muscle fibers underlies the epidermis over much of the body; very likely these fibers are also of peritoneal origin like the musculature in general. This layer is lacking in the ventral part of the cephalic shield, which, however, is highly muscular and labile; muscle fibers radiate through the protocoel from the shield-collar septum to the ventral wall of the shield, with some fibers reaching its dorsal wall (Fig. 60*B*). In addition, the dorsal shield wall is provided with fibers that radiate over its inner surface from the septum and probably belong to the general subepidermal musculature. In the collar the oral musculature is prominent. This originates on the collar-trunk septum and as paired oral muscles (Fig. 60*C*) sweeps around the sides of the buccal tube and inserts on the shield-collar septum, also on the dorsal collar mesentery. This oral musculature can narrow the mouth and buccal tube, but closure of the mouth is effected by bringing the cephalic shield against it. The trunk and stalk possess a strong system of longitudinal fibers by which these parts can be contracted. In the stalk the longitudinal fibers form a thick layer (Fig. 61*A*) under the epidermis, slightly thicker ventrally than dorsally; they originate on the basement membrane of the distal end of the stalk. The contraction of these muscles is responsible for the fact that the stalk in preserved specimens seems to spring from the side of the trunk sac whereas in life it is in line with the latter. Continuing into the trunk sac these fibers spread

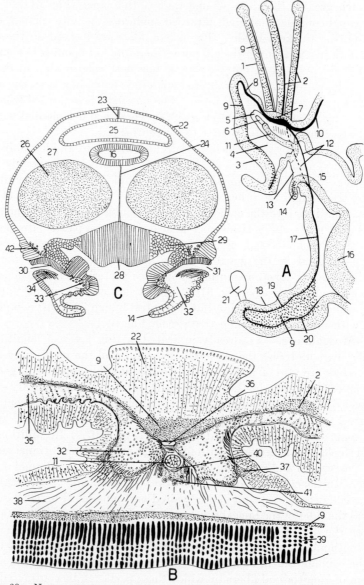

Fig. 60.—Nervous system (concluded), coelom. A, scheme of the nervous system of
Cephalodiscus. B, transverse section through anterior part of *Cephalodiscus*, showing
collar coeloms. (*A, B, after Schepotieff*, 1907c.) C, scheme of section through the collar
canals (*after Ridewood*, 1907a). 1, arm; 2, dorsal arm nerve; 3, cephalic shield; 4, protocoel;
5, heart vesicle; 6, central sinus; 7, collar ganglion; 8, main nerve to cephalic shield; 9,
especially thick parts of nervous layer; 10, dorsal trunk nerve; 11, buccal diverticulum; 12,
circumbuccal connectives; 13, mouth; 14, oral lamella; 15, pharynx; 16, stomach; 17,
ventral trunk nerve; 18, stalk; 19, ventral stalk nerve; 20, dorsal stalk nerve; 21, bud;
22, epidermis; 23, dorsal trunk mesentery; 24, ventral trunk mesentery; 25, intestine; 26,

out in the trunk wall, but the majority form two ventral bundles that extend forward as far as the gill slits, terminating in a pair of coelomic pockets mentioned above as evaginated from the trunk coelom into the collar (Fig. 62*A*).

A peculiarity of the musculature is the presence of a heavy bundle of muscles extending from the collar canal to the adjacent body wall (Fig. 61*D*). This bundle, which also exists in *Atubaria*, was thought by some early investigators to be a bunch of solenocytes, but its muscular nature has been sufficiently proved, for example, by Ridewood (1907a), who even finds these fibers to be cross-striated, in contrast to the other muscles of *Cephalodiscus;* but this is very doubtful.

7. Digestive System.—The transversely elongated mouth, more or less concealed by the posterior part of the cephalic shield, is bounded above and below by a thickened epidermis forming weak upper and lower lips. Behind the lower lip occurs the oral lamella as a projecting flap (Fig. 58*D*). The mouth leads into the buccal tube, very short ventrally, longer dorsally, where its surface is increased by a dorsal recess in contact with the undersurface of the collar ganglion (Fig. 59*A*). Much of the buccal epithelium is provided with mucous gland cells. From the buccal roof, just in front of the dorsal recess, springs the buccal diverticulum, a tubular evagination that extends forward along the shield-collar septum and is attached to the dorsal epidermis by the dorsal collar mesentery (Fig. 59*A*). The buccal diverticulum may contain a single continuous lumen or a succession of cavities; its opening into the buccal roof may or may not be evident. The diverticulum is lined by a low epithelium, probably often ciliated, and mostly showing only a weak vacuolation (Fig. 61*B*).

The buccal tube passes into the pharynx through the collar-trunk septum. The pharynx is in general lined with a tall, heavily ciliated epithelium, more or less glandular. The single pair of gill passages opens through the dorsolateral walls of the pharynx (Fig. 58*D*). They are somewhat elongated passages lined by highly vacuolated cells (Fig. 62*A*) and extend from the external slitlike gill pore to the oval gill slit, opening widely into the pharynx lumen. In continuity with the gill passages and lined by the same highly vacuolated cells are a pair of dorsolateral pharyngeal pockets (Fig. 60*C*). These are regarded by Van der Horst (1939) as representing branchial sacs. The whole gill apparatus is very much simpler than in enteropneusts, for there are no tongue bars and no skeletal supports. The pharynx continues as the esophagus, differ-

---

gonad; 27, trunk coelom; 28, roof of pharynx; 29, vacuolated pockets of pharynx; 30, collar canal; 31, collar pore; 32, collar coelom; 33, oral muscles; 34, muscles of collar canal; 35, arm coelom; 36, dorsal blood sinus; 37, lateral nerves to cephalic shield; 38, muscles of protocoel; 39, gland cells of center of cephalic shield; 40, ventral shield sinus; 41, cells of glomerular type; 42, ventral trunk muscles.

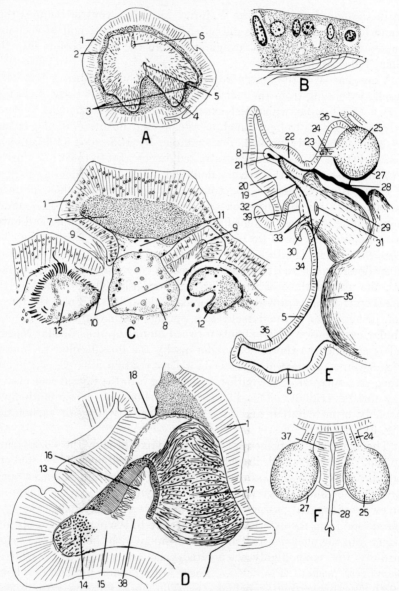

Fig. 61.—General structure (continued). *A*, section through the stalk (*after Harmer*, 1905). *B*, histological appearance of buccal diverticulum. *C*, section through anterior part of heart vesicle, showing the shield canals. *D*, section through left collar coelom, showing muscle of collar canal. (*B*, *D*, *after Andersson*, 1907.) *E*, scheme of the circulatory system. *F*, mesenteries of gonads. (*C*, *E*, *F*, *after Schepotieff*, 1907c.) 1, epidermis; 2, nervous layer; 3, nervous thickenings of stalk; 4, longitudinal muscles; 5, ventral stalk sinus; 6, dorsal stalk sinus; 7, median dorsal nerve to shield; 8, heart vesicle; 9, shield canal; 10, pockets of protocoel leading to shield canals; 11, dorsal pocket of protocoel; 12, extensions of collar coeloms into protocoel; 13, pharynx wall; 14, longitudinal trunk muscle; 15,

entiated from it only by a less ridged wall and a paucity of gland cells. The esophagus opens into the stomach.

The stomach is sharply demarcated from the preceding tubular parts of the digestive tract by its expanded saclike form; it fills the greater part of the interior of the trunk sac (Fig. 58D). The stomach wall is well differentiated histologically from the preceding parts of the digestive tract by its very tall epithelium provided with a rod border and filled with secretion granules. The tubular intestine continues from the stomach, curves at once dorsally, and continues forward to the anus with its ventral wall in contact with the stomach and its dorsal wall lying beneath the dorsal trunk epidermis. The intestinal epithelium is much lower than that of the stomach and contains secretory cells only for a short distance beyond the stomach. The terminal part of the intestine is expanded as a rectum.

8. Circulatory System.—Because of the small size of the animals, this system is imperfectly known in *Cephalodiscus*. It is apparently wholly lacunar, for the main channels are said to lack definite walls. The dorsal sinus appears to originate from lacunae in the stomach wall. It runs forward above the esophagus and pharynx as a considerable channel that connects with a sinus surrounding each gonad (Fig. 61E). The dorsal sinus then continues forward beneath the collar ganglion and terminates in the central sinus. This as in enteropneusts is associated with a contractile heart vesicle, but positional relations differ in the two groups. Whereas in enteropneusts the central sinus and heart vesicle lie above the buccal diverticulum, they are here located in front of it. The central sinus is long and tubular and almost completely embraced by the heart vesicle (Fig. 59A). Muscle fibers occur not only on the inner surface of the heart vesicle but also on the outer surface of the central sinus, and the space between the two structures is also crossed by radial muscle fibers (Fig. 62D). From the caudal end of the central sinus a large ventral shield sinus runs backward beneath the buccal diverticulum and parts around the buccal tube as a pair of peribuccal channels, apparently present in some forms only as a system of lacunae (Fig. 61E). From the peribuccal channels or lacunae the main ventral sinus originates at the collar-trunk septum and proceeds posteriorly along the ventral side of the stalk. At the end of the stalk it turns dorsally and continues forward along the dorsal side of the stalk and along the dorsal side of the intestine, gradually disappearing. Cells are said to be scantily present in the fluid in the blood channels.

---

collar coelom; 16, collar canal; 17, muscle mass of collar canal; 18, collar-trunk septum; 19, cephalic shield; 20, protocoel; 21, central sinus; 22, collar ganglion; 23, gonopore; 24, gonoduct; 25, gonad; 26, anus; 27, genital sinus; 28, main dorsal sinus; 29, buccal diverticulum; 30, oral lamella; 31, gill slit; 32, ventral shield vessel; 33, peribuccal channels; 34, pharynx; 35, stomach; 36, stalk; 37, lateral septum; 38, opening of collar canal into collar coelom; 39, mouth.

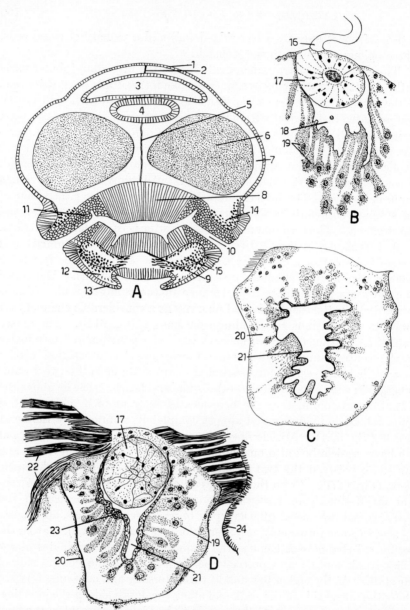

Fig. 62.—General structure (concluded). *A*, schematic section through the gill slits (*after Ridewood*, 1907a). *B*, section through the ventral shield sinus, showing glomerulus. *C*, section through the anterior part of the heart vesicle. *D*, section through the posterior part of the heart vesicle. (*B–D, after Schepotieff*, 1907c.) 1, epidermis; 2, dorsal trunk mesentery; 3, intestine; 4, stomach; 5, ventral mesentery; 6, gonad; 7, trunk coelom; 8, roof of pharynx; 9, floor of pharynx; 10, gill passage; 11, vacuolated cells of gill passage; 12, collar coelom; 13, oral lamella; 14, oral muscles; 15, projections of trunk coeloms into collar; 16, dorsal collar mesentery; 17, buccal diverticulum; 18, ventral shield sinus; 19, glomerular type of cell; 20, heart vesicle; 21, central sinus; 22, muscles of heart vesicle; 23, muscles of central sinus; 24, shield-collar septum.

9. Glomerulus.—A structure probably corresponding to the glomerulus of enteropneusts is present in *Cephalodiscus*. The wall of the ventral shield sinus as it passes beneath the buccal diverticulum is much folded, and these folds are surrounded by altered peritoneal cells (Fig. 62*B*, *D*) of elongated pyriform shape with granular contents. Similar altered peritoneal cells also occur scantily in other sites and possibly are of excretory nature. Some authors think such cells may detach and be emitted by way of the canals and pores of the cephalic shield and collar.

10. Reproduction.—Each zooid of *Cephalodiscus* is provided with a pair of gonads symmetrically located in the anterodorsal part of the trunk in front of the stomach (Fig. 61*E*). Each gonad is an oval or sacciform body that opens by a short gonoduct on the adjacent surface. The two gonopores occur on the dorsal side of the trunk just behind the collar-trunk boundary. The oviducts are commonly colored red or reddish, and this color appears to be of the same nature as the red stripe across the cephalic shield of the zooids. The two gonads are separated (Fig. 60*C*) by the median dorsal trunk mesentery, and each is supported by the corresponding lateral septum (Fig. 61*F*). The posterior part of the gonad, however, projects into the trunk coelom, although retroperitoneal. Between the gonad tissue and its covering peritoneum is located the genital blood sinus mentioned above.

The sexes are generally separate but not distinguishable externally. All the members of a coenecium may be of one sex, or a mixture of the two sexes may be present. Further, hermaphrodites are not uncommon; in these one gonad is female and the other male (Fig. 56*C*). It is stated for *C. hodgsoni* (= *inequatus*) that the female zooids are red with 12 arms and the male zooids pale brown with 10 or 11 arms (John, 1931). A strange sexual condition is reported for *C. sibogae*, of which one coenecium is known, taken by the *Siboga* near Celebes at a depth of 75 to 94 m. (Harmer, 1905). This coenecium contains neuter and male zooids, but no females. The neuter zooids have four pairs of tentaculate arms and are typically constructed but lack gonads, whereas the males, although of the same size as the neuters, differ from all other known *Cephalodiscus* zooids. They have only two arms, which are devoid of tentacles, and their digestive tract is vestigial; the space thus left in the trunk sac is filled with two large testes (Fig. 63*A*).

Breeding is probably seasonal. The Magellanic species, *C. dodecalophus*, appears to breed during the milder season of the year, from October to January, according to Andersson (1907), and this author surmises breeding during the same season for other subantarctic species. Developing eggs were found in specimens of *C. gilchristi*, Cape of Good Hope, collected in July and October. The eggs are shed into the cavities of the coenecium, where they undergo development.

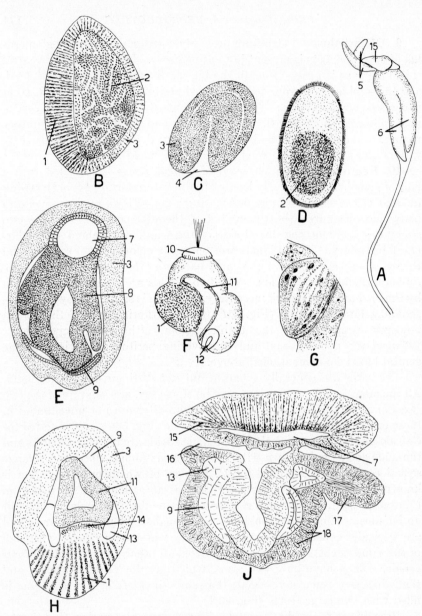

FIG. 63.—Reproduction. *A*, male of *C. sibogae* (*after Harmer*, 1905). *B*, section of blastula. *C*, section of gastrula (*after Andersson*, 1907). *D*, free-swimming larva. *E*, longitudinal section of more advanced larva showing origin of protocoel. *F*, ectoproct type of larva of *C. indicus*. *G*, apical sense organ of *F*. *H*, cross section through *F*. (*D–H, after Schepotieff*, 1909.) *J*, longitudinal section of a larva of *C. nigrescens*. (*B, J, after John*, 1932.) 1, thickened epidermis of future ventral surface of cephalic shield; 2, inner yolk mass; 3, epidermis; 4, blastopore; 5, arms; 6, testes; 7, protocoel; 8, yolk-filled archenteron; 9, metacoel; 10, apical sense organ; 11, archenteron; 12, sucker; 13, mesocoel; 14, nervous tissue; 15, cephalic shield; 16, mouth; 17, arm base; 18, mucous glands.

11. Development.—Accounts of the development are based chiefly on the fortunate finding of embryos in preserved specimens obtained on collecting expeditions, although living larvae were seen by Andersson (1903) and Gilchrist (1917). The development is therefore imperfectly known, and the various accounts show considerable disagreement, possibly because based on different species. Main accounts of the embryology are those of Harmer (1905), Andersson (1907), Schepotieff (1909), Gilchrist (1917), and John (1932). The account of Gilchrist is so unclear and so much at variance with that of others that it is ignored here.

The eggs are relatively large and very yolky but nevertheless undergo holoblastic, nearly equal segmentation. The blastula (Fig. 63*B*) is said by some to be hollow, by others solid. Various accounts are also given of the origin of the entoderm, but most probably there is a regular embolic invagination (Fig. 63*C*). Very soon the embryo develops a complete coat of cilia, escapes from the egg membrane, and swims about, probably only for a brief period (Fig. 63*D*). The larva develops an apical sense organ, bearing in some species a tuft of long cilia, and continuous below with a nervous layer. This apical organ is very similar to the central part of the apical organ of the tornaria (Fig. 63*G*). The ectoderm of part of the ventral surface of the larva thickens and becomes highly glandular (Fig. 63*F*). It is admitted by all observers that this is the primordium of the central glandular area of the future cephalic shield and that it develops precociously to enable early formation of the coenecium. The interior of the larva contains the archenteron and five coelomic cavities, but the manner of origin of the latter has not been definitely ascertained. Probably the protocoel is cut off from the anterior end of the archenteron as in enteropneusts (Fig. 63*E*). A figure of John's (1932) indicates one elongated evagination from the archenteron that subsequently divides into mesocoel and metacoel on each side (Fig. 63*J*). Other accounts indicate a separate origin of mesocoels and metacoels by evagination from the archenteron as described by Bateson for enteropneusts. Schepotieff (1909) figures for *C. indicus* a larval stage so remarkably similar to the larva of ectoprocts (Fig. 63*F*) that the author suspects some sort of mistake or mixup with adjacent ectoprocts. Following the swimming stage the larva elongates, much resembling a young enteropneust (Fig. 64*A*), having a straight intestine that has now formed an anus at the site of the blastopore, also a mouth. The arms originate as dorsal bulges, and the buccal diverticulum develops as an evagination of the buccal tube as in enteropneusts. Andersson (1907) regards the heart vesicle as of coelomic origin. After the main parts have appeared the intestine begins to bend dorsally, establishing the U-shape.

There has been much argumentation in the literature as to the orientation of the cephalodiscid body. The majority maintain that the apparent

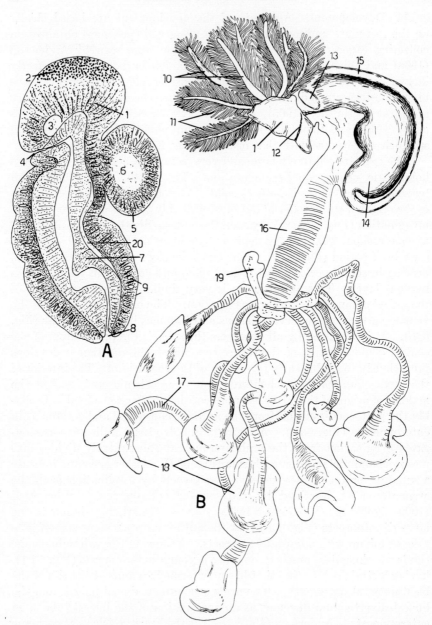

Fig. 64.—Reproduction (continued). *A*, longitudinal section of late larva, showing enteropneust-like appearance (*after John*, 1932). *B, C, fumosus* with numerous buds (*after John*, 1931). 1, cephalic shield; 2, glandular area of shield; 3, protocoel; 4, mouth; 5, arm bud; 6, coelom of arm; 7, digestive tube; 8, anus; 9, mucous glands of epidermis; 10, arms; 11, tentacles; 12, pigment stripe; 13, gonad; 14, stomach; 15, intestine; 16, stalk; 17, stalks of buds; 18, shields of buds; 19, young bud; 20, metacoel,

dorsal surface of the trunk sac is the true dorsal surface. The author, however, must side with the minority opinion that the trunk sac is largely ventral and the true dorsal surface is limited to the area from the cephalic shield to the anal aperture. The embryology sufficiently establishes that the original dorsal surface is greatly shortened when the originally straight digestive tube takes on a U-bend. However, it is convenient to employ the terms dorsal and ventral with reference to the adult morphology.

12. Asexual Reproduction.—An outstanding feature of *Cephalodiscus* is the formation of buds from a zone near the end of the stalk (Fig. 64*B*). Each zooid of a coenecium is usually found bearing one or two up to 14 buds, depending on species. All the zooids of a coenecium originate by budding from an original sexually produced individual, and hence under favorable conditions a coenecium constantly increases in size and in number of zooids. Apparently buds do not leave the parent coenecium to found new coenecia.

Main accounts of the development of buds are those of Masterman (1898), Harmer (1905), Ridewood (1907b), and Schepotieff (1908), summarized by Van der Horst (1939). The bud begins as a clavate or pyriform outgrowth of the stalk epidermis containing an extension of the stalk coelom that from the start is subdivided by a dorsoventral mesentery. Soon the distal end of the bud flattens and broadens to become the cephalic shield that is soon delimited posteriorly by a groove and that soon shows the characteristic curved red pigment stripe (Fig. 65*E*). Proximal to the shield the bud enlarges as the trunk sac, and thus the main parts of the zooid are delineated. For some time, however, the cephalic shield is disproportionately large (Fig. 64*B*); later this disproportion is eliminated and the stalk also lengthens greatly, often bringing the bud on a level with the parent zooid. On the dorsal surface the first pair of arms appears as a pair of buds (Fig. 65*A, B, C*), followed by the other arms in anteroposterior order. About this time the collar region becomes delineated from the trunk sac (Fig. 65*C*) and the arms are found to be hollow extensions of the collar region. In the interior of the bud the coelom is early subdivided by cross partitions into an anterior protocoel and paired mesocoel and metacoel. According to some authors the digestive tract arises entirely as an ectodermal invagination that pushes between the two leaves of the dorsoventral mesentery and soon undergoes the characteristic U-bend (Fig. 65*F, G*); other authors indicate a participation of an internal mass as described later for *Rhabdopleura* (page 188). The heart vesicle seems to originate as a coelomic sac cut off from the protocoel. The buccal diverticulum arises as in embryology as a foregut evagination (Fig. 65*G*). The gill passages are formed by evaginations of the intestinal wall that meet the epidermis. The canals and pores of the protocoel and mesocoel arise by epidermal invagination. The gonads probably originate from peritoneal cells.

13. Ecology.—As may be surmised, there is little to report on this subject. Living zooids were seen by Andersson (1907) and Gilchrist

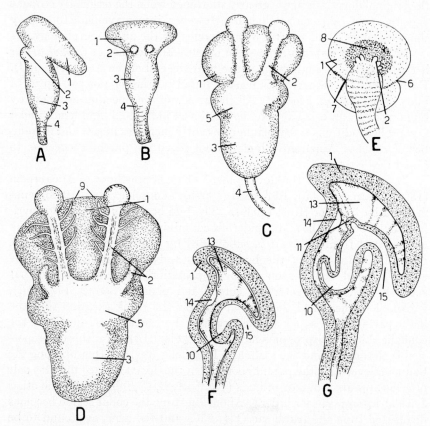

FIG. 65.—Development of buds of *Cephalodiscus*. *A*, young bud of *C. dodecalophus* from side. *B*, same as *A* from dorsal view, showing buds of first pair of arms. *C*, later stage of same from dorsal side showing differentiation of collar. *D*, later stage of same with two pairs of arms. *E*, bud of *C. densus* from dorsal side (*after Ridewood*, 1918a). *F*, sagittal section of bud of *C. dodecalophus* showing formation of digestive tract by epidermal invagination. *G*, sagittal section of later stage of *F* showing buccal diverticulum. (*All but E after Masterman*, 1898.) 1, cephalic shield; 2, arm bud; 3, trunk sac; 4, stalk; 5, collar; 6, notch; 7, pigment stripe; 8, glandular area of shield center; 9, tentacles; 10, digestive tract; 11, buccal diverticulum; 12, epidermis; 13, coelom; 14, main dorsal sinus; 15, mouth.

(1915). By stretching the stalk the zooids may reach out of the openings of the coenecium and wind about the coenecial projections, using the adhesive surface of the cephalic shield as a holdfast (Fig. 66*E*, *F*); or they may emerge altogether to the exterior, holding on by the shields of the buds. *Cephalodiscus* probably feeds on minute organisms and particles that are captured by the adhesive secretions of the arms and conveyed by ciliary action along the grooves of the arms to the oral lamella that directs them into the mouth.

Coenecia have been dredged from various types of bottom, muddy, sandy, gravelly, or rocky. They are sometimes found growing on other sessile animals as sponges or bryozoans, and colonial forms such as hydroids and bryozoans may use the coenecia as substrates. Coenecia are limited to the sublittoral and archibenthal zones, having been taken between 50 and 650 m. The data of collection of all the known species are summarized by Johnston and Muirhead (1951). Most of the species inhabit the Subantarctic and Antarctic. The characteristic species of the Subantarctic is *C. dodecalophus*, taken in the Strait of Magellan and off the Falkland Islands. In the true Antarctic the following species have been repeatedly collected and are probably circumpolar: *C. nigrescens, hodgsoni* (includes *aequatus* and *inaequatus*), *densus* (includes *rarus* and *anderssoni*), and *solidus*. Some of these also extend into the Subantarctic. Records for south temperate regions comprise *C. evansi*, New Zealand, *australiensis*, southwestern Australia, and *gilchristi*, South Africa. *Cephalodiscus* is not, however, limited to cold waters, for species are known from tropical seas: *C. gracilis* and *sibogae*, secured by the *Siboga* at Borneo and Celebes, respectively (Harmer, 1905), *C. indicus*, from Ceylon and India (Schepotieff, 1909), and unnamed material from the coast of Indo-China (Dawydoff, 1944). The sole finding in the north temperate zone is that of *C. levenseni*, taken by the *Siboga* off Japan (Harmer, 1905).

A few parasites have been found in preserved specimens of *Cephalodiscus*. Ridewood and Fantham (1907) gave an extended account of a sporozoan, *Neurosporidium cephalodisci*, doubtfully assignable to the Haplosporidia, that they found in some abundance in the thicker parts of the intraepidermal nervous layer of *C. nigrescens*. The spore develops directly into a rounded cell that by multiple fission produces a multi-nucleated mass; in this each nucleus with accompanying cytoplasm gives rise to a ball of spores. The parasitic copepod, *Zanclopus cephalodisci*, was reported from the stomach of *C. gilchristi* by Ridewood (1906) and Calman (1908), and a related species, *Z. antarcticus*, occurs in the stomach of *C. densus* (Gravier, 1912a).

B. Atubaria

In a dredging made at 200 to 300 m. in Sagami Bay, Japan, in August, 1935, there were noticed some curious tiny animals clinging to colonies of the athecate hydroid, *Dicoryne conferta*, and waving the anterior end about. A total of 43 specimens were secured and preserved. Examination of these showed a pterobranch closely related to *Cephalodiscus*. Sato (1936) gave a preliminary description of the creature under the name

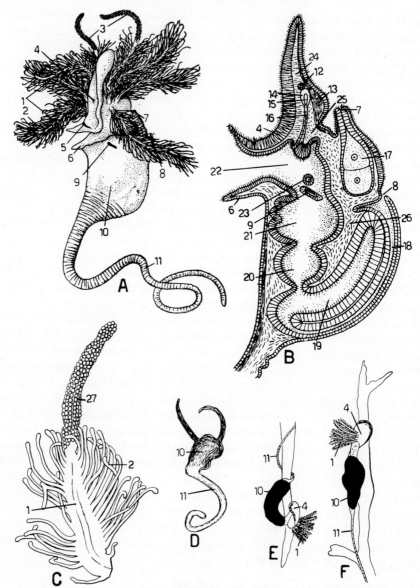

Fig. 66.—*Atubaria, Cephalodiscus* (concluded). *A,* entire individual of *Atubaria,* seen from the side. *B,* median sagittal section of *Atubaria.* (*A, B, after Komai,* 1949.) *C,* arm of *Atubaria.* *D,* young *Atubaria;* arms lack tentacles. (*C, D, after Sato,* 1936.) *E, F,* living zooids of *Cephalodiscus* climbing on projecting filaments of the coenecium (*after Andersson,* 1907); stalk remains attached inside coenecium. 1, arms; 2, tentacles; 3, rod termination of two of the tentacles; 4, cephalic shield; 5, pigment stripe; 6, oral lamella; 7, gonopore; 8, anus; 9, gill slit; 10, trunk sac; 11, stalk; 12, shield canal; 13, collar ganglion; 14, heart vesicle; 15, central sinus; 16, buccal diverticulum; 17, ovary; 18, intestine; 19, stomach; 20, esophagus; 21, pharynx; 22, buccal tube; 23, collar canal; 24, protocoel; 25, collar coelom; 26, trunk coelom; 27, terminal glandular rod.

Atubaria heterolopha, and Komai (1949) later added further information based on a study of Sato's microscopic preparations.

Atubaria differs from *Cephalodiscus* chiefly in the absence of a coenecium. The possibility that in the dredging process the animals were shaken out of their coenecium is very remote. It seems quite certain that *Atubaria* lives in a naked state with its stalk twined about the much larger hydroids. The general anatomy is almost identical with that of *Cephalodiscus.* The body is regionated into cephalic shield, marked with the usual red pigment stripe, collar bearing the eight tentaculated arms or plumes, plump trunk sac, and long flexible and muscular stalk (Fig. 66A). A conspicuous point of difference from *Cephalodiscus* concerns the second pair of arms, which have a long rodlike distal part devoid of tentacles (Fig. 66C). This pair of terminal rods is obviously glandular and evidently corresponds to the terminal glandular knobs of the arms of some species of *Cephalodiscus.* The stalk apparently lacks an adhesive tip.

A median sagittal section (Fig. 66B) shows great similarity of internal structure to that of *Cephalodiscus.* The digestive tube is better demarcated by constrictions into buccal tube, pharynx, esophagus, stomach, and intestine, and the stomach is more elongated and less saclike than in *Cephalodiscus.* The anus is located more posteriorly on the dorsal side of the trunk sac than in *Cephalodiscus* and is preceded by a slight rectal diverticulum. The pharynx wall is pierced by a pair of gill slits that are approached by an area of vacuolated cells as in *Cephalodiscus.* Appearance and relations of buccal diverticulum, central sinus, heart vesicle, and collar ganglion are the same as in *Cephalodiscus* (Fig. 66B).

All the specimens obtained were either mature females or juveniles. The juveniles are peculiar in bearing only two arms which lack tentacles (Fig. 66D). There was no evidence whatever of budding in the material obtained.

C. Rhabdopleura

1. Coenecium.—This consists of a branching tube creeping over and cemented to a substratum and giving off at frequent intervals short free erect tubes, each of which houses a zooid (Fig. 67A). The colony usually grows on a hard substratum as rocks, mollusk shells, bryozoans, tunicates, and the like, but has been taken on sandy bottom. It does not exceed dimensions of around 10 cm. and often is only 1 to a few centimeters across. The entire colony is formed by budding from a single progenitor and continues to grow and bud new zooids at some of the branch ends. The colony is mostly of a pale brownish coloration.

The creeping tube of the colony is flattened on its side of contact and often incorporates foreign particles as sand grains, bits of shell, and the

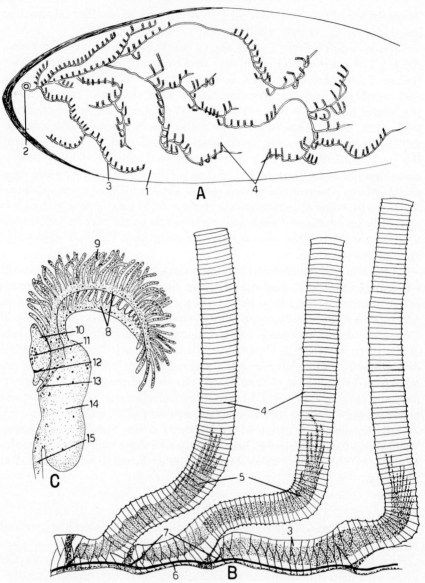

Fig. 67.—*Rhabdopleura.*   A, colony of *Rhabdopleura* on a clam shell.   B, creeping tube and three erect tubes with enclosed retracted zooid (*after Schepotieff*, 1907b).   C, zooid of *Rhabdopleura.*   (*A, C, after Schepotieff*, 1907a.)   1, clam shell; 2, start of colony as ring; 3, creeping tube; 4, erect tubes; 5, retracted zooid; 6, black stolon; 7, branch of black stolon attached to base of zooid stalk; 8, arms; 9, tentacles; 10, cephalic shield; 11, gland center of cephalic shield; 12, pigment stripe; 13, oral lamella; 14, trunk sac; 15, stalk.

like, whereas the erect tubes are cylindrical, clean, and translucent, at least distally. The creeping tube is divided into chambers by transverse partitions, and each such chamber typically leads into an erect tube; hence the zooid, which is attached at the partition, is housed partly in a horizontal section of the creeping tube and partly in the free erect tube (Fig. 67*B*). In the growing ends of branches the chambers are closed until the bud has grown sufficiently to break through the unattached side of the chamber. The zooid developed from the bud then secretes the free tube as very regular, successive rings with flared ends (Fig. 67*B*), eventually to a height of 6 to 7 mm. The creeping tube is also made of successive secretions, mostly not deposited as regular rings but as diagonal pieces (Fig. 67*B*). The secretion emanates as in *Cephalodiscus* from the glandular center of the cephalic shield of the zooid. Its chemical nature is not known. It is definitely not chitinous (Rudall, 1955).

In the attached wall of the creeping tube, imbedded in the secretion, runs a black cord known as the *black stolon* that connects all the zooids of the colony (Fig. 67*B*). At each transverse partition it gives off a short branch to the base of the zooid occupying the chamber. The stolon consists of a hard black hull enclosing living tissue (Fig. 68*A*, *B*). The latter is composed of outer, much vacuolated tissue enclosing groups of granules and a central denser syncytial core. The side branch of the stolon that passes through the partition to the zooid base is similarly constructed except that it contains a number of transverse partitions (up to 10) of the same black material as the hull of the stolon (Fig. 68*C*). The last of these separates the peripheral tissue of the stolon from the epidermis of the zooid stalk, but the central core continues into the zooid base and terminates as a knob in the coelom of the zooid stalk (Fig. 68*C*). From the observations of Schepotieff (1907b) it appears that the progenitor of a colony secretes a hemispherical house encircled by a ring tube enclosing a thick ring-shaped black stolon; and from this center a creeping tube enclosing a branch of the black stolon grows out in one direction or two opposite directions, establishing a colony (Fig. 68*D*). The transverse partitions appear in the creeping tube, and into each chamber so established the black stolon gives off a bud.

2. External Features of the Zooids.—The zooids (best described by Lankester, 1884, and Schepotieff, 1904, 1907a, b, 1908) much resemble those of *Cephalodiscus*. They are extremely small, mostly below a millimeter in length (exclusive of the stalk), although they are capable of considerable extension. They are mostly dark brown in color. The body is regionated into cephalic shield, collar with a pair of arms, trunk sac, and stalk, as in *Cephalodiscus* (Fig. 67*C*). The cephalic shield is of oval form with a central glandular area bounded posteriorly by the usual pigment stripe but lacks lateral notches. The collar is very short ventrally, being

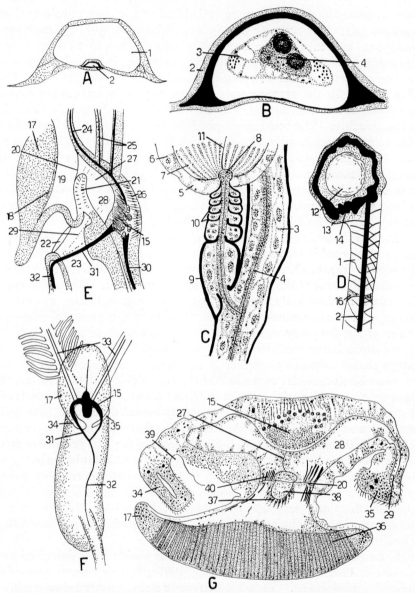

Fig. 68.—*Rhabdopleura* (continued). *A*, cross section of the creeping tube. *B*, cross section of the black stolon. *C*, creeping tube and zooid base, showing relation to black stolon. *D*, start of colony (*after Schepotieff*, 1907b). *E*, view of nervous system in sagittal section. *F*, scheme of nervous system from ventral side. *G*, cross section through anterior part showing coelomic cavities. (*All but D after Schepotieff*, 1907a.) 1, creeping tube; 2, black stolon; 3, vacuolated layer of living enclosure of black stolon; 4, central core of living enclosure of black stolon; 5, zooid base; 6, epidermis of zooid stalk; 7, muscles of stalk; 8, terminal knob of central core of black stolon fastened in zooid base; 9, black hull; 10, partitions of black hull; 11, dorsoventral mesentery; 12, hemispherical house of pro-

there almost entirely occupied by the mouth, longer dorsally where it bears one pair of arms or plumes, bordered as usual by a row of tentacles on each side. The arms are held curved gracefully backward when the zooid is extended from its tube; when retreated into the tube, they are held straight forward (Fig. 67*B*).

From the base of the arms, the oral lamella extends ventrally on each side as a pronounced fold; the two folds meet behind the mouth without, however, any fusion of their contained coelomic cavity. It is a remarkable peculiarity of *Rhabdopleura* that the right oral lamella is constantly much larger and longer than the left one (Fig. 68*F*). The trunk sac is of elongated oval form (Fig. 68*F*); it bears the anus just behind the arm bases on the right side, and the single gonopore is also located on the right just in front of the anus (Fig. 69*E*). It will be noticed that *Rhabdopleura* exhibits a pronounced asymmetry in favor of the right side. The stalk springs from the ventral side of the trunk sac and is attached at its basal end to a branch of the black stolon as explained above (Fig. 67*B*). Thus *Rhabdopleura* forms a true colony in which all the zooids are in organic continuity and are permanently fastened in their tubes.

3. Internal Structure.—This is similar to that of *Cephalodiscus* but is less known. The epidermis varies much in height and is ciliated, at least where of some thickness. The ciliation is strongly developed on the tentacles, on the ventral surface of the arms, and in the groove to the oral side of the oral lamella.

The cephalic shield resembles that of *Cephalodiscus* in the details of its structure. The central area of its thick ventral epidermis is composed of thickly placed, elongated glandular elements that secrete the tube (Fig. 69*C*). The interior of the cephalic shield constitutes the protocoel and is crossed by radiating muscle fibers that extend from the shield-collar septum to the ventral wall of the shield. The protocoel opens to the exterior by a pair of canals and pores; the latter are situated just anterior to the arm bases.

The collar encloses a pair of coelomic cavities, separated by a median dorsal mesentery. Each leads dorsally into the arm coelom of that side, which is almost filled with connective tissue (Fig. 68*G*), extends ventrally into the corresponding oral lamella, and connects to the exterior by the usual collar canal and pore. The collar pores are so minute as usually

genitor zooid; 13, primary ring; 14, primary ring of black stolon; 15, collar ganglion; 16, first partition; 17, cephalic shield; 18, nervous layer of 17; 19, protocoel; 20, shield-collar septum; 21, buccal diverticulum; 22, mouth; 23, buccal tube; 24, main anterior shield nerve; 25, branches of 24 into arms; 26, epidermis over collar ganglion; 27, dorsal collar mesentery; 28, collar coelom; 29, extension of collar coelom into oral lamella; 30, posterior dorsal trunk nerve; 31, circumenteric connective; 32, ventral trunk nerve; 33, ventral arm nerves; 34, right oral lamella; 35, left oral lamella; 36, glandular center of cephalic shield; 37, glomerular type of cells; 38, ventral shield sinus; 39, deep groove to oral side of oral lamella; 40, muscle fibers.

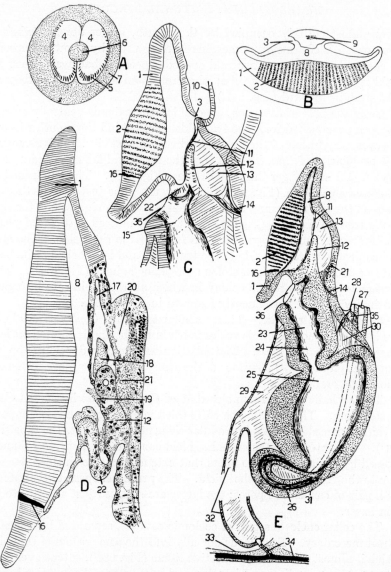

Fig. 69.—Structure of *Rhabdopleura* (continued). *A*, cross section through the zooid base. *B*, cross section through the cephalic shield, showing shield canals and pores (*after Schepotieff*, 1905). *C*, median longitudinal section through the anterior part of *Rhabdopleura*, showing coelomic relations. *D*, median longitudinal section of anterior part of body (*after Andersson*, 1907). *E*, scheme of the digestive tract in sagittal view. (*A, C, E, after Schepotieff*, 1907a.) 1, cephalic shield; 2, glandular center of shield; 3, shield canal and pore; 4, trunk coeloms; 5, longitudinal muscle fibers; 6, stolon knob in zooid base; 7, epidermis; 8, protocoel; 9, anterior shield nerve; 10, arm base; 11, shield-collar septum; 12, buccal diverticulum; 13, dorsal collar mesentery; 14, collar canal and pore; 15, extension of collar coelom into oral lamella; 16, pigment stripe; 17, heart vesicle; 18, central sinus; 19, ventral shield sinus; 20, collar coelom; 21, collar ganglion; 22, upper lip; 23, pharynx; 24, esophagus; 25, stomach; 26, intestine; 27, anus; 28, gonopore; 29, ventral trunk mesentery; 30, dorsal trunk mesentery; 31, trunk sac; 32, stalk; 33, creeping tube; 34, black stolon; 35, gonad; 36, mouth.

to be demonstrable only on microscopic sections. In the base of the dorsal collar epidermis is found the collar ganglion, just behind the arm bases (Fig. 68E). It gives off about the same nervous thickenings as in *Cephalodiscus:* a median anterior thickening to the cephalic shield, a posterior dorsal trunk nerve, and a pair of circumenteric connectives that meet ventrally to form a midventral trunk nerve that probably continues weakly along the ventral side of the stalk (Fig. 68E). There are, further, a nerve from the ganglion along the dorsal side of each arm and also two weaker nerves along the ventral side (Fig. 68F). A general intraepidermal plexus is probably present but has been demonstrated only in a few places. Ganglion cells occur in the anterior and posterior dorsal nerves and in the circumenteric connectives.

The trunk sac contains the usual pair of coelomic cavities, occupied by the digestive tract and gonad. The digestive tract has the same U-form as in *Cephalodiscus* (Fig. 69E). The mouth occupies the ventral side of the collar and is overhung by the posterior part of the cephalic shield. The thickened epidermis of the dorsal wall of the mouth forms a slight bulge that may be regarded as an upper lip, while just below the mouth the right and left sides of the oral lamella establish a boundary; as the right oral lamella is larger than the left one, the mouth is somewhat displaced toward the left side. The short buccal tube gives off anteriorly into the cephalic shield a well-developed buccal diverticulum that lies in the shield-collar septum and is supported by the dorsal collar mesentery. The diverticulum has no definite lumen in the common species, *Rhab. normani*, but is said to have a continuous lumen opening into the buccal cavity in *Rhab. striata* (Schepotieff, 1909). The buccal tube is followed by the pharynx distinguished by the presence of a pair of deep dorsolateral grooves formed of vacuolated cells (Fig. 70A). These grooves are believed to represent gill pouches, which in *Rhabdopleura* do not break through to the exterior. Posterior to the gill pouches the pharynx passes into the esophagus, and this in turn passes through the collar-trunk septum into the large sacciform stomach, lined by a tall epithelium. The stomach almost fills the trunk sac, and hence the intestine, leaving the posterior end of the stomach and making a forward curve, runs anteriorly to the right side of the stomach (Fig. 69E). The anus occupies an elevation behind the arm bases.

Coelomic relations are simpler than in *Cephalodiscus* since there are no forwardly projecting blind pockets, or in other words the shield-collar and collar-trunk septa are simple membranes. The ventral trunk mesentery is poorly expressed in the trunk sac but continues into the stalk, dividing this into right and left halves (Fig. 69A).

A general subepidermal layer of longitudinal muscle fibers is, according to Schepotieff (1907a), very weakly developed and scarcely distinguishable from the peritoneum.   The strongest musculature in the body is that of the stalk where two ventral longitudinal bundles extend forward, diminishing after entering the trunk sac, in which they continue to the esophagus.   A part of this musculature passes along the side of the esophagus into the corresponding arm as the dorsal arm musculature. Another part encircles the buccal tube, acting to alter the mouth opening, and also supplies the oral lamella.   The main mass of the esophageal musculature extends forward to either side of the buccal diverticulum, attached to the shield-collar septum, and on reaching the dorsal wall of the cephalic shield sprays out in a fanlike manner to terminate on the ventral wall of the shield.

The circulatory system, so far as known, resembles closely that of *Cephalodiscus*.   The heart vesicle crowns the anterior tip of the buccal diverticulum and encloses the central sinus (Fig. 69*D*).   From the latter the ventral shield sinus runs posteriorly beneath the buccal diverticulum and bifurcates around the buccal tube, presumably reuniting in the ventral trunk wall to form a ventral trunk sinus that continues into the stalk. There appears to be a dorsal trunk sinus that presumably enters the central sinus from behind.

Glomerular tissue composed of stalked peritoneal cells is present around the central sinus and ventral shield sinus (Fig. 70*B*) but is less developed than in *Cephalodiscus*.

4. Reproduction.—Most of the colonies that have been found are sterile, although some colonies with males and females are known. Schepotieff (1907a) records that of 300 colonies examined, about 25 contained male individuals and three contained female individuals, both mixed in with many neuters.   In colonies with males these amount to about one-third of the zooids present, whereas females are very scarce. The single gonad occupies the right metacoel and is of elongated form in males, rounded in females; its short duct opens on the adjacent trunk surface by a gonopore situated to the right of and behind the anus (Fig. 70*C–E*).   In the testis only the proximal part produces the sperm and the distal part forms a seminal vesicle packed with ripe sperm; in some individuals these two parts are found separated by a constriction, and this possibly represents the ultimate ripe state of the testis (Fig. 70*E*).   The ovary contains but one very large, yolky egg at a time.   The eggs are discharged to the exterior and were once found by Schepotieff adherent to the arms, but nothing is known of the embryonic development.   Burdon-Jones (1956) declares that *Rhabdopleura* is known to have a free-swimming larva, but the author found nothing to this effect in the literature.

A colony presumably originates from a single, sexually produced individual from which one or more stolons grow out.   Subsequent increase in the zooid number resulting in colony formation takes place

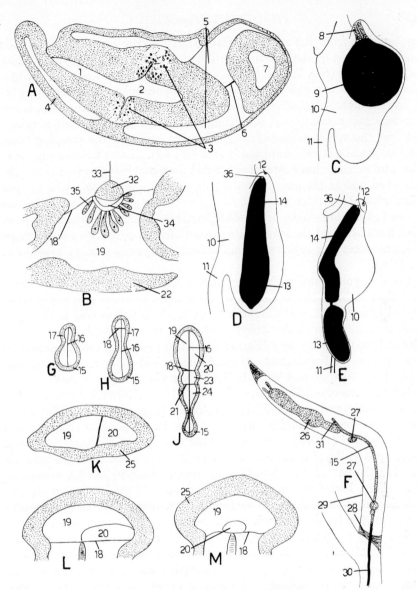

FIG. 70.—Structure of *Rhabdopleura* (concluded), budding. *A*, transverse section through anterior part of the trunk sac, showing the gill pouches. *B*, section through collar region showing glomerular type of cells (*after Schepotieff*, 1905). *C*, ovary. *D*, testis. *E*, riper state of testis. (*A*, *C–E*, *after Schepotieff*, 1907a.) *F*, growing stolon end with buds. *G–J*, stages of young buds. *K–M*, development of the heart vesicle from the protocoel. (*F–M*, *after Schepotieff*, 1907b.) 1, buccal cavity; 2, pharynx; 3, gill pouches; 4, oral lamella; 5, trunk coeloms; 6, ventral trunk mesentery; 7, intestine; 8, oviduct; 9, ovary; 10, trunk sac; 11, stalk; 12, anus; 13, testis; 14, seminal vesicle; 15, stolon; 16, median mesentery; 17, bud; 18, shield-collar septum; 19, protocoel; 20, heart vesicle; 21, collar-trunk septum; 22, cephalic shield; 23, collar; 24, trunk; 25, epidermis; 26, terminal bud; 27, lateral buds; 28, partition; 29, creeping tube; 30, black stolon; 31, growing continuation of stolon; 32, buccal diverticulum; 33, dorsal collar mesentery; 34, ventral shield sinus; 35, glomerular-type cells; 36, gonopore.

by budding from the stolons.   Only actively growing stolon ends bud;
such ends arise by outgrowth from the base of the preceding young zooid
of the branch (Fig. 70F).   These young stolons consist of an outer epidermis enclosing a pair of cavities lined by peritoneum and separated by
a median mesentery, all directly continuous with the epidermis and trunk
coeloms and mesentery of the young zooid from which the stolon arises.
At first the stolon extends freely along the cavity of the creeping tube,
and only while in this state can it give off buds.   Later the older parts of
the stolon that have already budded become incorporated into the
attached wall of the creeping tube (Fig. 68A) by secreting a wall around
themselves that later turns black.   The living part of the stolon also
alters to the state shown in Fig. 68B, losing its coelomic cavities.   Stolons
that have attained the black state cannot bud but probably under certain
circumstances can rejuvenate and sprout out young stolons capable of
budding.

    Active young stolons bud at the end and along the sides (Fig. 70F),
and the end bud after becoming a young zooid gives off a new stolon, as
stated above, that continues the process.   The young bud is simply a
hollow evagination of the stolon, containing the same two coelomic cavities and median mesentery (Fig. 70G).   Soon peritoneal cells produce two
cross partitions that constitute the future shield-collar and collar-trunk
septa (Fig. 70H, J) and indicate the body regions.   The protosome soon
enlarges as the cephalic shield, and a subdivision of its cavity produces the
heart vesicle and the definitive protocoel (Fig. 70K–M).   The collar
region is set off later, and the arms bud from it.   A peculiar story is given
by Schepotieff (1907b) as to the manner of origin of the digestive tract.
Cells apparently of peritoneal origin gather into a rod that lies between
the two leaves of the dorsoventral trunk mesentery.   An epidermal
stomodaeal invagination meets this rod and divides it into a shorter
anterior part, which becomes the buccal diverticulum, and a longer posterior part, the future stomach that fuses with the stomodaeum and also
with a long proctodaeal invagination, which becomes the intestine (Fig.
71A–D).   After the buds have undergone considerable development partitions form in the creeping tube, separating each young zooid into its
own chamber.   According to Lankester (1884), the young zooid then
breaks through the upper wall of the creeping tube and begins to build up
the free part of its tube by successive secretion of rings.

    Buds may fail to develop beyond the initial stage and hence remain in
closed chambers which are interpolated between chambers that lead to a
free tube.   Such sterile buds and closed chambers are quite common in
some colonies.   The bud becomes encapsulated in a secreted hull, and the
stolon from which it springs transforms to the black stage.   The function
of such sterile buds is problematical, but it has been suggested that they

are dormant buds since they are particularly common in colonies collected in autumn. Hence one may suppose that they are an overwintering device and will resume growth with temperature rise in spring.

From the remarks of Vaney and Conte (1906) and Schepotieff (1907b), it appears that zooids may degenerate from the arms basally and regenerate again from the stalk by way of a regeneration bud that develops much like regular buds.

5. Ecology.—Observations on living *Rhabdopleura* have been recorded by G. Sars (1874), Schepotieff (1907a), and Burdon-Jones (1954). When undisturbed, the arms and shield project from the tube with the arms curved back (Fig. 67C); but the arms are capable of much change of position. When touched or disturbed, the zooids retreat into their tubes by contraction of the stalk, and the arms then extend straight in the tube (Fig. 67B). Extension after such retraction is very slow and seems to be accomplished by application of the cephalic shield to the wall of the tube. The older observers considered the animals very sensitive to changes of environment since they found most dead when brought up in the dredge; the survivors might be kept alive an hour or two in cold running sea water. However, Burdon-Jones kept colonies in healthy condition for 2 months in running sea water at a temperature of about 7°C. Slow temperature change from 5 to 12°C appeared without immediate effect, although survival at 12° was limited to several days. The favorable salinity range was 33 to 35 parts per thousand. No response to light was noted. Colonies kept in the dark gave no response when bright light was suddenly shone upon them.

Rhabdopleura no doubt feeds in the same manner as *Cephalodiscus*, by trapping minute organisms in the mucus of the tentacles and passing such food along the ventral surface of the arms and the deep ciliated groove that runs along the oral side of the oral lamellae. Schepotieff (1907a) found remains of diatoms, radiolarians, and crustacean larvae in the stomach.

Most of the colonies that have been collected belong to the original species, *Rhab. normani*. This occurs at depths ranging from 5 to 550 m. but is most typical of depths of 100 to 300 m. It is not uncommon throughout the European boreal region, from Lofoten to the Azores, and has also been taken off West Greenland. Burdon-Jones (1954) found colonies easily obtainable by dredging along the Norwegian coast at a variety of places. The colonies usually grow on or in the vicinity of the boreal oculinid corals *Lophelia* (formerly *Lophohelia*) and *Amphihelia*. They usually grow on the old dead parts of the corals but might also occur on stones, shells, and echinoderm tests as well as on living sessile animals as bivalves, tunicates, sponges, ectoprocts, and barnacles. *Rhab. normani* has also been collected in high southern latitudes. The *Chal-*

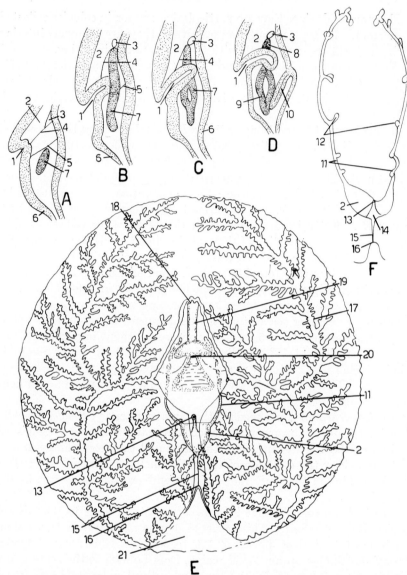

FIG. 71.—*Rhabdopleura, Planctosphaera.* *A–D*, stages in the formation of the digestive tube in buds of *Rhabdopleura (after Schepotieff,* 1907b). *A,* beginning stomodaeal invagination; inner mass forming. *B,* continued invagination; inner mass elongated. *C,* stomodaeum divides inner mass into buccal diverticulum and stomach. *D,* proctodaeal invagination meets stomach. *E, Planctosphaera,* viewed from the ventral surface. *F,* protocoel of *Planctosphaera,* showing horns. (*E, F, after Spengel,* 1932.) 1, stomodaeal invagination; 2, protocoel; 3, heart vesicle; 4, shield-collar septum; 5, collar-trunk septum; 6, trunk; 7, internal mass; 8, buccal diverticulum; 9, stomach; 10, proctodaeal invagination; 11, horns of protocoel; 12, diverticula; 13, hydropore; 14, hydroporic canal (= shield canal); 15, strand to point representing apical plate; 16, site representing apical plate; 17, ciliary band; 18, mouth; 19, esophagus; 20, anus; 21, posterior depression.

190

lenger took it at Tristan da Cunha (Fowler, 1904), and the German South Polar Expedition on the *Gauss* found some empty coenecia off Kaiser Wilhelm II Land at 66° south latitude (Broch, 1927), at a temperature of −1.84°C and at a depth of 350 m.

Other specific names have been applied, two of which appear valid. *Rhab. annulata*, of which only the empty coenecium is known, has been collected near Celebes (Harmer, 1905), off New Zealand (Norman, 1921), and off Tasmania and southern Australia (Johnston, 1937b), at depths ranging from 75 to 549 m. The Australian specimen came from scrapings from the underside of a rock just below low-tide mark but is surmised to have been washed up from deeper water. *Rhab. annulata* differs from *Rhab. normani* in the greater flare at the ends of the rings of the zooid tube and the absence, or nearly so, of a horizontal attached section of the zooid tube, for this erects itself freely shortly beyond the partition. A third, apparently valid species, *Rhab. striata*, was described by Schepotieff (1909) from material collected on coral reefs at Ceylon at 2 to 15 m. of depth. This species differs from *Rhab. normani* primarily in that the stolon is hollow (Fig. 72*A*) and the buccal diverticulum contains a continuous lumen opening into the buccal cavity.

VI. CLASS PLANCTOSPHAEROIDEA

Knowledge of this class is based upon the descriptions by Spengel (1932) and Van der Horst (1936) of the better of the two specimens taken by the *Michael Sars* (see historical account). Although other specimens have since been collected, they have not been described in print. *Planctosphaera pelagica* is a transparent spherical larva about 10 mm. in diameter. The interior is almost filled with a glassy jelly that permits such viscera as are present to be clearly seen. These viscera are concentrated into one area occupying about one-fourth of the interior. Despite the spherical form of the creature its structure is strictly bilateral, as may be seen from the ventral view (Fig. 71*E*).

Over the surface of the sphere runs the very sinuous and highly branched ciliary band whose branches return from a central point in the middle of the anterior surface, paralleling their course so as to appear double (Fig. 72*B*). The posterior part of the ventral surface is occupied by an extensive but shallow depression that receives the anus and leads by a long tubular invagination to the mouth. Shortly behind the anus is found the hydropore (pore of the protocoel), and still further posterior around the curve of the sphere to about the center of the posterior surface occurs what corresponds to the apical nervous plate of the tornaria. This structure may be considered to have been displaced downward from an apical to a posterior position.

The digestive tract is L-shaped as in the tornaria but is less clearly

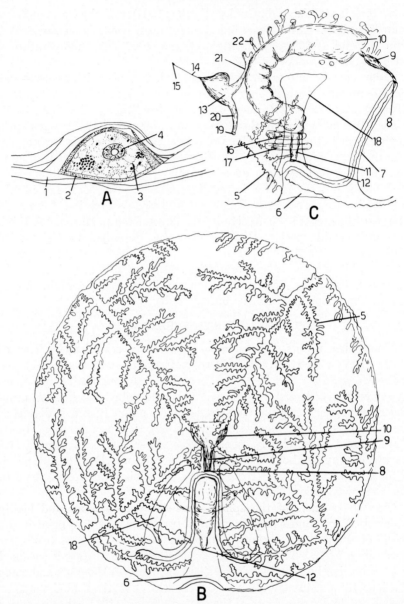

Fig. 72.—*Rhabdopleura, Planctosphaera* (concluded).   *A*, section of the stolon of *Rhab.
striata (after Schepotieff*, 1909).   *B*, *Planctosphaera*, seen from the anterior surface.   *C*,
viscera of *Planctosphaera*, seen from the right side.   (*B*, *C*, *after Spengel*, 1932.)   1, attached
wall of creeping tube; 2, hull of stolon; 3, vacuolated layer of stolon; 4, core of stolon with
lumen; 5, ciliated band; 6, depression; 7, deep tubular depression leading to mouth; 8,
mouth; 9, esophagus; 10, stomach; 11, intestine; 12, anus; 13, protocoel; 14, strand to 15;
15, point representing apical plate; 16, mesocoel; 17, metacoel; 18, boot-shaped invagination;
19, hydropore; 20, hydroporic canal; 21, horns of protocoel; 22, diverticula of 21.

differentiated into three sections (Fig. 72C). The mouth, at the inner end of a deep tubular invagination into the jelly, leads into a short slender esophagus or foregut, and this is followed by the broader but long and tubular stomach that narrows to a short intestine.

The remaining interior structures are coelomic cavities. The protocoel, situated behind the stomach, has a triangular form; from its side it gives off the hydroporic, or protocoel, canal to the adjacent surface; from its tip arises a strand that connects to the surface, thus identifying the position of the apical plate; and from each of its other angles a horn proceeds anteriorly along the stomach, giving off little diverticula in its course (Figs. 71F, 72C). The two mesocoels are present as transversely elongated cavities, one to each side of the intestine, and slightly posterior to them are a similar pair of metacoels (Fig. 72C). A small vesicle, possibly representing a heart vesicle, is found in close proximity to the protocoel. All these parts correspond to those found in the tornaria; but there is also present a pair of blind sacs not represented in the tornaria. Each of these is a boot-shaped invagination from the ventral depression and extends inward along the intestine to the stomach (Fig. 72B).

Planctosphaera is clearly the larva of an unknown type of hemichordate. As the tornaria bears no resemblance to the adult enteropneust, so also it may be assumed that the planctosphaera does not resemble the adult to which it belongs. Hence it is impossible to deduce the appearance of the adult from the larva.

VII. ALLEGED AFFINITY OF GRAPTOLITES WITH HEMICHORDATES

The graptolites (Class Graptolithina) are extinct colonial marine animals known only by the exoskeleton of branches bearing a series of cups (thecae) each of which housed a zooid. The graptolites lived from the upper Cambrian into the Carboniferous but were most abundant during the Ordovician and Silurian eras. They were briefly described and illustrated in the first volume of this series (I, page 497), where they were placed among the hydrozoan Cnidaria. Excellent recent accounts of them are those of Bulman (1938, 1955) and Waterlot (1948, 1953).

Some resemblance of graptolites to *Rhabdopleura* was already noticed by Allman (1872), who, however, devoted most of his article to expounding the hydrozoan affinities of the graptolites. Relationship of graptolites to *Rhabdopleura* was definitely advocated by Schepotieff (1905), on unconvincing grounds, however, based on a lack of understanding of the structure of graptolites. In recent years Kozlowski (1938, 1947, 1948) has strongly urged the inclusion of graptolites in the hemichordates on the basis of Polish material of the former found in an unusually good state of preservation; and this conclusion has been accepted in recent treatises on invertebrate paleontology (Waterlot, 1953; Bulman, 1955). Kozlowski's argument begins by stating that the graptolites, like the ptero-branchs, secrete chitinous tubes that enclose the soft parts.   In fact, the nature of the tubes of graptolites is not known.   In a letter to the author Kozlowski has admitted using the term "chitinous" in a meaningless sense, and Bulman (1955) also admits that there is no exact knowledge of the chemical composition of the graptolite periderm.   But there *is* exact knowledge about the coenecium of *Rhabdopleura*.   Rudall (1955) has shown that this coenecium is definitely *not* chitinous.   Further, the coenecium of pterobranchs is secreted by the glandular center of the cephalic shield and is laid down in successive emissions, whereas in graptolites the tubes of periderm appear to be formed in place by the underlying epidermis as in hydroids.   These discrepancies were already mentioned by Bohlin (1952).   Hence the first argument of Kozlowski is worthless.

Kozlowski places most importance on the structure of the tubes, which in graptolites are said by him to consist of successive half rings dovetailed together along opposite lines (Fig. 73*A*, *B*).   No such struc-ture pertains to the coenecium of *Cephalodiscus*, which is composed, as reported above, of irregular overlapping outflows of secretion.   In *Rhabdopleura* such zigzag sutures occur only in the creeping tube (and then along one line only), whereas in the erect tubes the secretion is laid down as successive whole rings, although oblique sutures sometimes occur. Kozlowski admits that such whole rings are very rare in graptolites, although they sometimes occur.   Kozlowski further found that the tubes of graptolites consist of two layers, an inner layer composed of the dove-tailed hardened half rings and an outer layer of quite different nature (Fig. 73*A*, *B*).   Obviously such structure is without counterpart in *Rhabdopleura*, in which the tubes consist of a single layer (Fig. 68*A*). Fossil tubes of *Rhabdopleura*, dating from the upper Cretaceous and the Eocene, hence far removed from graptolites in geological time, have been figured and described by Thomas and Davis (1949) and Kozlowski (1956).   These have essentially the same tubal structure as present specimens, with the tube definitely consisting of a single layer.

Other graptolite features that do not find counterparts in *Rhabdopleura* are the sicula and the nema or virgula (I, page 497).   The mode of growth of graptolite stems appears to be of the sympodial type (I, page 405) in which the temporary terminal structure buds off the succeeding one, whereas *Rhabdopleura* buds after the monopodial type, producing a termi-nal zooid behind which younger lateral ones develop (Fig. 70*F*).   There is, further, no representation in *Rhabdopleura* of the polymorphism of the dendroid graptolites, believed to be the most primitive graptolite group. Here at each terminal budding three types of thecae are produced simul-

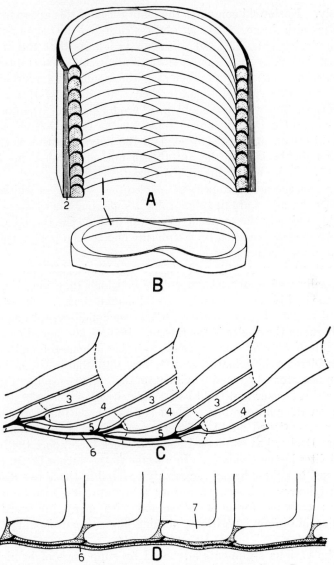

Fig. 73.—Graptolites and *Rhabdopleura*. *A*, tube of a graptolite. *B*, one pair of half rings of *A*. *C*, scheme of a dendroid graptolite showing thecae in groups of three. *D*, scheme of *Rhabdopleura*, for comparison with *C*. (*All after Kozlowski*, 1948.) 1, half ring; 2, outer layer of tube; 3, 4, 5, the three thecae of each group; 6, stolon; 7, base of tube of *Rhabdopleura*.

taneously.   Kozlowski compares the main theca of this group of three in graptolites with the zooid tube of *Rhabdopleura,* but the comparison is not very convincing (Fig. 73C, D).   Kozlowski admits that the manner of growth of the colony constitutes a chief difference between graptolites and *Rhabdopleura.*   The former branch after the manner of a hydroid colony, producing a succession of separate thecae in groups of three, whereas *Rhabdopleura* grows in a straight line, producing buds that only later become separated into their own tubes by the formation of partitions. Kozlowski (1948) attempted to explain the polymorphism of graptolite thecae on the basis that the autothecae housed females, the bithecae males.   No such sexual dimorphism exists in *Rhabdopleura.*   Bulman (1955) recalls the peculiar species *Cephalodiscus sibogae,* of which the one small piece known contained dimorphic zooids; but the *coenecium* is not dimorphic and only the coenecium is comparable to the thecae of grapto- lites.   Arguments based on tube structure and zooidal polymorphism are not, hence, very convincing.

Recently Decker (1956) and Decker and Gold (1957) have reported on unusually well-preserved graptolites in which they identify, besides autothecae and bithecae, gonothecae and nematothecae.   The structures identified as gonothecae appear clearly in their photographs as fusiform bodies borne in the angles of the thecae.   If these are indeed gonothecae, they negate Kozlowski's idea that the autothecae housed females.   Little cups considered to be nematothecae (I, page 409), that is, thecae housing a bunch of nematocysts, are also evident on their photographs.   Structures identified by Decker and Gold as a single circlet of tentacles are also to be seen on the photographs.   These authors have found the different structures mentioned on 14 different species from 8 formations.   Over the years Decker has supported and continues to support the inclusion of graptolites in the Cnidaria.   In a letter to the author he summarized his reasons, but these have been mostly covered in the above discussion. One point, however, deserves mention: "On graptolites with thousands of apertures available for observation and with many preserved polyps protruding in different positions, nothing like an anal opening has been seen."

Of the various arguments advanced by supporters of hemichordate affinity of graptolites there remains only one having a genuine claim to validity.   This is the presence in both graptolites and rhabdopleurid pterobranchs of a stolon connecting the zooids (Fig. 73C, D).   The similarity schematically expressed in these figures appears to be real, but no great weight can be placed upon it because stolons are of common occurrence throughout the animal kingdom.

The inclusion of graptolites in the Hemichordata is therefore here rejected as insufficiently grounded.

VIII. PHYLOGENETIC CONSIDERATIONS

1. Hemichordates and Echinoderms.—The adult echinoderm and the adult hemichordate are so completely different that no one could suspect any relationship between them on the basis of adult anatomy. Consequently, the argument for their affinity rests wholly on the embryological evidence, which, however, is very convincing. The fact that for several years after its discovery the tornaria larva was considered the larva of an echinoderm, especially an asteroid, sufficiently indicates the strong resemblance between the larval forms of the two groups. This resemblance is not superficial but extends to many details. The ciliated band takes a similar course in the tornaria and the bipinnaria or auricularia, although the telotroch is lacking from all echinoderm larvae. The digestive tract has the same shape and the same subdivisions into foregut, stomach, and intestine in echinoderm and hemichordate larvae, and in both the blastopore becomes the larval anus. The greatest and most convincing resemblances, however, concern the coelomic sacs, which in both are, in general, of enterocoelous origin. In both, the coelom may be considered to divide itself into three successive anteroposterior parts, the protocoel (axocoel), the mesocoel (hydrocoel), and the metacoel (somatocoel). Although the separation of axocoel and hydrocoel is not too clear in many echinoderms, the existence of these two parts on at least a theoretical basis has been accepted for echinoderms by embryologists. The manner of formation of the coelomic sacs is variable in the two groups, but counterparts of the different modes can be found among particular echinoderms and particular enteropneusts. For instance, the formation of the coeloms in *Saccoglossus pusillus* (Fig. 45*A–C*) is very like that in many echinoderms. It is especially the manner of formation and behavior of the protocoel, sending out a hydroporic canal to meet a surface hydropore, that is the most remarkable of the many resemblances in the embryology of echinoderms and enteropneusts. To be sure, this behavior of the protocoel in enteropneusts resembles that of the hydrocoel (mesocoel) rather than that of the axocoel (protocoel) in echinoderms, but in the latter the axocoels are often not clearly separated from the hydrocoels and the two may behave as one unit. Further, in enteropneusts the mesocoels (collar coeloms) also put out a canal and pore to the surface. The association of the protocoel canal and pore with the left side is also notable in the two groups. The protocoel is paired in echinoderms and appears unpaired in enteropneusts, although this point has been the subject of arguments; thus Schepotieff (1908) maintains that the protocoel was primitively paired in enteropneusts and pterobranchs and that one part becomes the definitive protocoel and the other the heart vesicle. As seen above, varied accounts are given of the origin of the

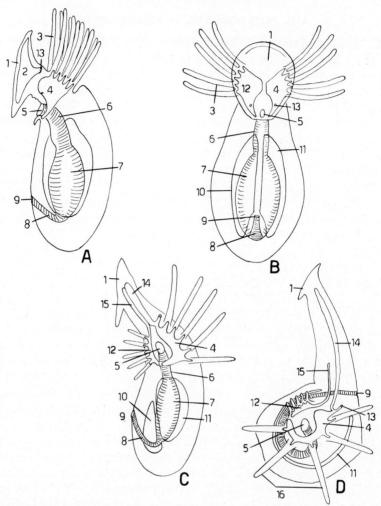

Fig. 74.—Theoretical derivation of echinoderms from pterobranchs.   *A, Cephalodiscus*-like ancestor, seen from the left side.   *B*, same as *A*, ventral view.   *C*, stage in transformation to echinoderm, seen from ventral view, right hydrocoel and tentacles diminishing. *D*, beginning stalked echinoderm.   (*All after Grobben, 1923.*)   1, cephalic shield; 2, protocoel (axocoel); 3, tentacles; 4, left hydrocoel; 5, mouth; 6, esophagus; 7, stomach; 8, intestine; 9, anus; 10, right somatocoel; 11, left somatocoel; 12, right hydrocoel; 13, hydropore; 14, left axocoel; 15, right axocoel; 16, primary podia.

heart vesicle in enteropneusts, but in any case this vesicle is related to the protocoel and is probably homologous with the dorsal sac (madreporic vesicle) of echinoderm larvae, also reported as of somewhat variable origin, but probably theoretically derivable from the right axocoel.   It seems likely that the madreporic vesicle of echinoderm larvae is the homologue of the heart vesicle of hemichordates.   Both are closely related to a structure that seems to have combined vascular and excretory functions—the glomerulus of enteropneusts and the axial gland of echinoderms. Dawydoff (1948) calls attention to the fact that the horns of the protocoel seen in *Planctosphaera* also occur in an auricularia from Bermuda.

It is not reasonable to suppose that the many resemblances in embryonic events between hemichordates and echinoderms can be accidental or the result of convergence. There appears no escape from the conclusion that hemichordates and echinoderms stem from a common ancestor. The metamorphosis of echinoderms indicates that they have deviated greatly from the ancestral type; hence it must be supposed that hemichordates are nearer the ancestral type than are echinoderms. In other words, the common ancestral stock gave off the echinoderms as a blind branch, then continued along its main line of evolution to hemichordates and chordates.

The common ancestor of hemichordates and echinoderms is generally visualized as the dipleurula larva ever since Bather expounded this theory in 1900 (IV, page 691). The author already indicated a considerable dissatisfaction with the dipleurula theory (IV, page 693). A main failing of this theory is the lack of an explanation of the ambulacral system. If, as just indicated, hemichordates are to be regarded as nearer the ancestral stock than are echinoderms, a homology of the ambulacral system with the tentaculated arms suggests itself. Both are derivatives of the mesocoel (hydrocoel), and both take the form of tentacular outgrowths of this coelomic division. To the discussion of this matter already given (IV, page 694) may be added the arguments brought forward by Grobben (1923), whose figures are reproduced here (Fig. 74). Grobben visualizes the common ancestor as an unattached creature somewhat like *Cephalodiscus* with a tentacular apparatus of five arms on each side. The cephalic shield appears to be in the same location as the attachment pit of crinoid and asteroid larvae and conceivably was drawn out to become an attachment stalk. By reduction of the right group of tentacles and overgrowth in a curvature of the left side, a pelmatozoan type can then be derived as shown in the figures. That pterobranchs are more primitive than enteropneusts is generally admitted. The more primitive condition of their nervous system, still in continuity with the epidermis, is a main argument for this supposition. Presumably the enteropneusts have lost the tentaculated arms. The postanal tail seen in juveniles of some enteropneusts (Fig. 48*B*) is obviously a reminiscence of the stalk of a pterobranch ancestor.

2. Hemichordates and Chordates.—A close relationship of hemichordates to chordates has been generally acknowledged by zoologists ever since Bateson (1885) included the Hemichordata in the phylum Chordata as a subphylum of the latter. This arrangement is still extant in elementary works on zoology, although it has been abandoned in the larger French and German treatises and is unequivocally rejected in the present volume. Evidence for the affinity of hemichordates and chordates is generally stated to comprise resemblance in three structures—the notochord, the central nervous system, and the gill slits.

The question of the presence of a notochord in enteropneusts and pterobranchs was already considered in the foregoing pages. Modern students of these groups do not accept the idea of the notochord nature of the buccal diverticulum. This diverticulum is an evagination of the anterior wall of the buccal cavity and cannot be definitely assigned to the entoderm since the boundary between ectoderm and entoderm in the buccal wall has not been clearly established. The formation of the buccal diverticulum as a hollow forward evagination of the buccal wall appears radically different from the mode of formation of the notochord as a solid rodlike elevation from the roof of the archenteron along its length. Much has been made of histological resemblance between the structures in question. The notochord of vertebrates consists of large vacuolated cells; although a similar appearance often obtains in the buccal diverticulum, this structure almost as frequently consists of ordinary epithelial cells. Newell (1952) has mentioned several other features in which the buccal diverticulum differs from the notochord, such as lack of a sheath, lack of relation to the blastopore, absence of supporting function, and different relation to the main dorsal blood channel. In vertebrates the notochord is always dorsal to the main dorsal blood vessel, whereas the buccal diverticulum is ventral to the middorsal blood channel. It may be concluded that hemichordates do not have any representative of the notochord. Komai (1951) suggested that the buccal diverticulum by its manner of formation more nearly resembles the anterior lobe of the vertebrate hypophysis than it does the notochord. The surmise of Silén (1954) that the buccal diverticulum represents ancestrally some sort of preoral gut appears at present the best interpretation of this problematical structure. The claim of Mookerjee, Ganguly, and Gupta (1955) that the buccal diverticulum is of nervous nature can only be considered as preposterous. No real evidence is presented in support of this assertion. Their labeling of the proboscis skeleton as notochord is an incredible misunderstanding of the structure of enteropneusts. Rudall (1955) has examined the proboscis skeleton of enteropneusts and found that it is typically collagenous, like the connective tissue of vertebrates.

Resemblance between the nervous systems of hemichordates and chordates rests on a better basis. In its dorsal position, its occasionally hollow construction, its mode of formation from the dorsal epidermis, and the occasional presence of a neuropore, the collar cord of enteropneusts is comparable with the neural cord of vertebrates. But this comparison fails as regards the rest of the nervous system. In its intraepidermal position, and in the presence of circumenteric connectives and of a main ventral nerve cord, the nervous system of enteropneusts is distinctly invertebrate. The invertebrate features of the nervous system of hemichordates outweigh the chordate features.

Pharyngotremy then remains as the chief link between hemichordates and chordates. They are the only animal groups with pharyngotremy (if one excepts the doubtful case of the extinct echinoderm *Cothurnocystis*, IV, page 19). Not only is pharyngotremy a main structural feature of both enteropneusts and lower chordates but the accord in the details of the gill apparatus between enteropneusts and amphioxus is truly astonishing. Although an endostyle and epibranchial groove are wanting in enteropneusts, the branchial apparatus in both groups has the same general construction with tongue bars, synapticules, and an arcade of trifid skeletal supports. Such identity is inconceivable except on the basis of a common ancestry. Hence a phylogenetic relationship between hemichordates and chordates is not open to question.

This relationship does not, however, justify the inclusion of the hemichordates in the phylum Chordata. The few similarities just mentioned are far outweighed by important differences. Main among these is the absence in chordates of body and coelomic regionation corresponding to that of hemichordates. Segmentation underlies the whole structure of chordates and is clearly expressed in the plan of the muscular, nervous, circulatory, and excretory systems, whereas in hemichordates these systems totally lack any traces of segmentation. Segmentation is at best very faintly expressed in hemichordates (page 137) and may be considered at an incipient stage in them. Hemichordates are definitely invertebrate in general morphology and in most details of their construction, and these facts are concealed if they are included in the Chordata. Further, they are closer to the echinoderms than they are to the chordates, and if they are to be united with any other phylum would more justifiably be included with echinoderms. The best solution of this situation is to regard them as an independent phylum of invertebrates stemming from an ancestral type that led, on the one hand, to echinoderms and, on the other hand, to hemichordates and chordates.

This conclusion negates any possibility of a direct origin of vertebrates from echinoderms, an idea that seems to be widely spread. Caster (1952a, b) intimated, without ever presenting any detailed account or giving a thorough discussion, a direct relationship between carpoid echinoderms (IV, page 17) and ostracoderms, apparently based on a similarity of pattern between the plates of a carpoid and the skull bones of ostracoderms. The author regards any comparison between calcareous echinoderm plates and vertebrate skull bones as inadmissible. The evidence does not appear to admit any other conclusion than the origin of chordates from a line of which echinoderms are a side branch.

Bibliography

GENERAL

Dawydoff, C. 1948. Embranchement des Stomocordés. *In* **P. Grassé** (ed.), *Traité de zoologie*, vol. XI. **Delage, Y.,** and **E. Hérouard.** 1898. *Traité de zoologie concrète*, vol. VIII. Les procordés. **Harmer, S. F.** 1910. Hemichordata. *Cambridge natural history*, vol. 7. **Selys Longchamps, M. de.** 1904. Développement postembryonnaire et affinités des Phoronis. Acad. Roy. Belgique, Class. Sci., Mém. in quarto, ser. 2, vol. 1. **Van der Horst, C. J.** 1939. Hemichordata. *In* **H. G. Bronn** (ed.), *Klassen und Ordnungen des Tierreichs*, vol. 4, Abt. 4, Buch 2, Teil 2.

ENTEROPNEUSTA

Agassiz, A. 1864. Notes on the embryology of starfishes (Tornaria). Ann. Lyceum Natur. Hist. New York 8. 1872. Tornaria, the young stage of Balanoglossus. Amer. Natural. 6. 1873. The history of Balanoglossus and Tornaria. Mem. Amer. Acad. Arts Sci. 9, pt. 2. **Asshetcn, R.** 1908. New species of Dolichoglossus. Zool. Anz. 33. **Barrington, E.** 1940. Observations on feeding and digestion in Glossobalanus. Quart. Jour. Microsc. Sci. 82. **Bateson, W.** 1884. Early stages in the development of Balanoglossus. Quart. Jour. Microsc. Sci. 24. 1885. Later stages in the development of Balanoglossus. Quart. Jour. Microsc. Sci. 25, suppl. 1886a. Continued account of the later stages in the development of Balanoglossus. Quart. Jour. Microsc. Sci. 26. 1886b. The ancestry of the Chordata. Quart. Jour. Microsc. Sci. 26. **Björnberg, T.** 1953. Tres novas tornarias das costas Brasil. Boletim Inst. Oceanogr. Sao Paulo, Brazil, 4. 1955. Sobre quatro tornarias. Boletim Inst. Oceanogr. Sao Paulo, Brazil, 6. **Brambell, F.,** and **H. Cole.** 1939a. Preoral ciliary organ of Enteropneusta. Proc. Zool. Soc. London 109B. 1939b. Saccoglossus cambrensis. Proc. Zool. Soc. London 109B. **Brambell, F.,** and **C. Goodhard.** 1941. Saccoglossus horsti. Jour. Marine Biol. Assoc. Unit. Kingd. 25. **Bullock, T.** 1940. Functional organization of the nervous system of Enteropneusta. Biol. Bull. 79. 1944. Giant nerve fiber system in balanoglossids. Jour. Comp. Neurol. 80. 1945. Anatomical organization of nervous system of Enteropneusta. Quart. Jour. Microsc. Sci. 86. **Burdon-Jones, C.** 1950a. Enteropneust genus new to British Isles. Nature, London, 165. 1950b. Records of British enteropneusts. Nature, London, 165. 1951. Observations on the spawning of Saccoglossus. Jour. Marine Biol. Assoc. Unit. Kingd. 29. 1952. Development and biology of the larva of Saccoglossus. Philos. Trans. Roy. Soc. London 236B. 1953. Records of British Ptychoderidae. Nature, London, 172. 1956. On Protoglossus koehleri. Proc. Zool. Soc. London 127. **Cary, L.** 1933. Tissues of Ptychodera in vitro. Carnegie Inst. Washington, Papers Tortugas Lab. 28, no. 13. **Caullery, M.,** and **F. Mesnil.** 1904. Protobalanus. Zool. Jahrb. Abt. Anat. 20. 1916. Sur Dolichoglossus kowalevskii. Bull. Soc. Zool. France 41. **Colwin, A.,** and **L. Colwin.** 1953. Embryology of Saccoglossus kowalevskii. Jour. Morphol. 92. **Cori, C.** 1902. Vorkommen des Balanoglossus in Triester Golfe. Zool. Anz. 25. **Crozier, W.** 1915. Behavior of an enteropneust. Science 41. 1917. Photic sensitivity of Balanoglossus. Jour. Exptl. Zool. 24. 1920. Rhythm of light production in balanoglossids. Anat. Record 20. **Dahlgren, U.** 1917. Production of light by Enteropneusta. Jour. Franklin Inst. 183, pt. 5. **Davis, B.** 1908. The early life history of Dolichoglossus pusillus. Univ. California Publ. Zool. 4. **Dawydoff, C.** 1902. Über die Regeneration der Eichel bei den Enteropneusten. Zool. Anz. 25.

1907a. Sur la embryologie des formations cardio-péricardiques des entéropneustes. Zool. Anz. 31. 1907b. Sur le développement des nephridium de la trompe chez les entéropneustes. Zool. Anz. 31. 1909. Regenerationsprozess bei den Enteropneusten. Ztschr. Wiss. Zool. 93. 1928. Quelques observations sur le développement des entéropneustes. C. R. Acad. Sci. Paris 186. 1944. Formation des cavités coelomiques chez les Tornaria du plancton indochinois. C. R. Acad. Sci. Paris 218. **Delle Chiaje, S.** 1829. *Memorie sulla storia e notomia degli animali senza vertebre del regno di Napoli*, vol. 4. **Devanescen, D.**, and **P. Chacko.** 1942. Balanoglossids as food for fish. Proc. Indian Sci. Congr. 29. **Edwards, C.** 1953. Occurrence of Glossobalanus sarniensis in northern Ireland. Nature, London, 172. **Elmhirst, R.** 1934. Enteropneusta of the Clyde sea area. Nature, London, 134. **Eschscholtz, F.** 1825. Bericht über die zoologische Ausbeute der Reise von Kronstadt bis St. Peter und Paul. Oken's Isis for 1825, Heft 6. **Garstang, W.** 1939. Spolia Bermudiana II. The ciliary feeding mechanism of Tornaria. Quart. Jour. Microsc. Sci. 81. **Gegenbaur, C.** 1870. *Grundzüge der vergleichenden Anatomie.* 2 ed. **Giard, A.** 1882. Sur un type synthétique d'annélide commensal du Balanoglossus. C. R. Acad. Sci. Paris 95. **Gilchrist, J.** 1908a. On two new species of Ptychodera. Ann. South African Mus. 6. 1908b. New forms of Hemichordata from South Africa. Trans. South African Philos. Soc. 17. 1923. Dimorphism and asexual reproduction in Ptychodera capensis. Jour. Linnaean Soc. London 35. 1925. Xenopleura vivipara. Quart. Jour. Microsc. Sci. 69. **Girard, C.** 1853. New nemerteans from the coast of the Carolinas. Proc. Acad. Natur. Sci. Philadelphia 6. **Gravier, C.** 1905. Polynoidien commensale des Balanoglossus. C. R. Acad. Sci. Paris 140. **Harvey, E.** 1926a. Inhibition of animal luminescence by light. Biol. Bull. 51. 1926b. Oxygen and luminescence. Biol. Bull. 51. **Hatai, K.**, and **H. Mii.** 1955. Markings on a tidal flat. Records Oceanogr. Works Japan, new ser. 2. **Heider, K.** 1909. Entwicklung von Balanoglossus clavigerus. Zool. Anz. 34. **Hess, W.** 1936. Reaction to light in Ptychodera. Carnegie Inst. Washington, Papers Tortugas Lab. 31. 1937. Nervous system of Dolichoglossus kowalevskii. Jour. Comp. Neurol. 68. 1938. Reactions to light and the photoreceptors of Dolichoglossus kowalevskii. Jour. Exptl. Zool. 79. **Hill, J.** 1895. New enteropneust from New South Wales. Proc. Linnaean Soc. New South Wales, ser. 2, vol. 10. 1897. Enteropneusta of Funafuti. Pts. I, II. Mem. Australian Mus. 3. **Hinrichs** and **L. Jacobi.** 1938. Saccoglossus pygmaeus. Zool. Anz. 121. **Ikeda, I.** 1908. Swimming habit of a Japanese enteropneust. Annot. Zool. Japon. 6. **Kapelus, Freda.** 1936. Anatomy of Saccoglossus inhacensis. Ann. Natal Mus. 8. **Kirk, H.** 1938. Breeding habits and early development of Dolichoglossus otagoensis. Trans. Proc. Roy. Soc. New Zealand 68. **Knight-Jones, E.** 1952. Nervous system of Saccoglossus cambrensis. Philos. Trans. Roy. Soc. London 236B. 1953. Feeding in Saccoglossus. Proc. Zool. Soc. London 123. **Knight-Jones, E.**, and **R. Millar.** 1949. Bilateral asymmetry shown by the metachronal waves in protochordate gill slits. Nature, London, 163. **Koehler, R.** 1886a. Observations zoologiques et anatomiques sur une nouvelle espèce de Balanoglossus. C. R. Acad. Sci. Paris 102. 1886b. Balanoglossus sarniensis. Internation. Monatsschr. Anat. Histol. 3. 1886c. Recherches anatomiques sur une nouvelle espèce de Balanoglossus. Bull. Soc. Sci. Nancy, ser. 2, vol. 8. 1886d. Sur le Balanoglossus sarniensis. C. R. Acad. Sci. Paris 102. **Komai, T.** 1951. The homology of the notochord in pterobranchs and enteropneusts. Amer. Natural. 85. **Kowalevsky, A.** 1866. Anatomie des Balanoglossus. Mém. Acad. Impér. Sci. St. Pétersbourg, ser. 7, vol. 10, no. 3. **Krohn, A.** 1854. Beobachtungen über Echinodermenlarven. Arch. Anat. Physiol. Wissensch. Med. **Kuwano, H.** 1902. New enteropneust from Misaki. Annot. Zool. Japon. 4. **Leger, L.**, and **O. Duboscq.** 1917. Sporozoaires de Glossobalanus. Ann. Inst.

Pasteur 31. **MacBride, E.** 1920. Larvae of Echinoderma and Enteropneusta. Brit. Antarctic ("Terra Nova") Exped. 1910, Natur. Hist. Repts., Zool. 4, no. 3. **Marion, A.** 1885. Sur deux espèces de Balanoglossus. C. R. Acad. Sci. Paris 101. 1886. Études zoologiques sur deux espèces d'entéropneustes. Arch. Zool. Exp. Gén., ser. 2, vol. 4. **Maser, O.** 1913. Über Balanoglossus carnosus. Zool. Jahrb. Abt. Anat. 33. **Masterman, A.** 1908. Certain points of the structure of Tornaria. Quart. Jour. Microsc. Sci. 52. **Mayer, P.** 1879. Ein neuer parasitischer Copepode. Mitt. Zool. Stat. Neapel 1. **Meek, A.** 1922. Glossobalanus marginatus. Quart. Jour. Microsc. Sci. 66. **Metschnikoff, E.** 1865. Entwicklung von Balanoglossus. Ber. Forsch. Anat. Physiol. 1866. Über eine Larve von Balanoglossus. Arch. Anat. Physiol. Wissensch. Med. 1869. Über Tornaria. Nachtrichten Gesellsch. Wissensch. Univ. Göttingen, no. 15. **Morgan, T.** 1891. Growth and metamorphosis of Tornaria. Jour. Morphol. 5. 1894. Development of Balanoglossus. Jour. Morphol. 9. **Morton, J.** 1950. Occurrence in New Zealand of Balanoglossus australiensis. Trans. Proc. Roy. Soc. New Zealand 78. **Müller, Fr.** 1868. Über das Herz der Tornaria. Ber. Fortschr. Anat. Physiol. in 1867. 1898. Observacoes sobre a fauna marinha. Rev. Mus. Paulista 3. **Müller, Joh.** 1850. Über die Larven und die Metamorphose der Echinodermen. Abhandl. Akad. Wissensch. Berlin, für 1848. **Okuda, S.** 1939. Enteropneusta from the Palau Islands. Jour. Fac. Sci. Hokkaido Univ., ser. 6, Zool. 7. **Okuda, S.,** and **M. Yamada.** 1955a. Enteropneusta of Akkeshi Bay. Publ. Akkeshi Marine Biol. Sta., no. 6. 1955b. Tornaria larvae from Akkeshi Bay. Annot. Zool. Japon. 28. **Panceri, P.** 1875. La luce e gli organi luminosi di alcuni annellidi. Rendiconto Accad. Sci. Fis. Matem. Napoli 14. **Payne, F.** 1937. Early development of Ptychodera. Carnegie Inst. Washington, Papers Tortugas Lab. 31. **Punnett, R.** 1903. The Enteropneusta. *Fauna and Geography of the Maldive and Laccadive Archipelago,* vol. 2, pt. 2. **Rao, K.** 1953. Development of Glandiceps. Jour. Morphol. 93. 1954. Bionomics of Ptychodera flava. Jour. Madras Univ., sect. B, vol. 24. 1955a. Early development of Ptychodera flava. Jour. Zool. Soc. India 6. 1955b. Enteropneusta from Madras and the Gulf of Manaar. Proc. Indian Sci. Congr. 42, pt. III, sect. 7. 1955c. Two new species of enteropneusts from Madras. Proc. Indian Sci. Congr. 42, pt. III, sect. 7. 1955d. Tornaria from Madras. Hydrobiologia 7. 1955e. Morphogenesis during regeneration in an enteropneust. Jour. Animal Morphol. Physiol. 1, no. 2. **Reinhard, E.** 1942. Stereobalanus canadensis. Jour. Washington Acad. Sci. 32. **Ritter, W.** 1900. Papers from the Harriman Alaska expedition. II. Harrimania maculosa. Proc. Washington Acad. Sci. 2. 1902. The movements of the Enteropneusta. Biol. Bull. 3. **Ritter, W.,** and **B. Davis.** 1904. Studies on the ecology, morphology, and speciology of the young of some Enteropneusta of western North America. Univ. California Publ. Zool. 1. **Russell, F.** 1925. Vertical distribution of marine macroplankton. Jour. Marine Biol. Assoc. Unit. Kingd. 13. **Sawaya, P.** 1951. Balanoglossus gigas on the Brazilian coast. Nature, London, 167. **Sawaya, P.,** and **L. Forneris.** 1953. Enteropneustos brasileiros. Zoologia, Sao Paulo, Brazil, no. 18. **Schimkewitsch, W.** 1888. Über Balanoglossus mereschkovskii. Zool. Anz. 11. 1892. Über die Beziehung zwischen den Enteropneusta und Acrania. Revue Sci. Natur. St. Pétersbourg (Viestnik Estestvoznaniia) 3. **Silén, L.** 1950. On the nervous system of Glossobalanus marginatus. Acta Zoologica 31. **Spengel, J. W.** 1884. Zur Anatomie des Balanoglossus. Mitt. Zool. Stat. Neapel 5. 1891. Über die Gattungen der Enteropneusten. Verhandl. Dtsch. Zool. Gesellsch. 1. 1893. Die Enteropneusten des Golfes von Neapel. Fauna und Flora des Golfes von Neapel, Monogr. 18. 1901. Die Benennung der Enteropneusten-Gattungen. Zool. Jahrb. Abt. System. 15. 1904. Neue Beiträge zur Kenntnis der Enteropneusta. Zool. Jahrb. Abt. Anat. 20. 1907. Studien über die Enteropneusten der Siboga

Expedition. Siboga Exped. Monogr. 26. 1909. Pelagisches Vorkommen von Enteropneusten. Zool. Anz. 34. **Stiasny, G.** 1910. Zur Kenntnis der Lebensweise von Balanoglossus clavigerus. Zool. Anz. 35. 1912. Die Sandwirbel des Balanoglossus clavigerus. Zool. Anz. 39. 1913. Studien über die Entwicklung von Balanoglossus clavigerus. Zool. Anz. 42. 1914a. Studien über die Entwicklung von Balanoglossus clavigerus. I. Die Entwicklung der Tornaria. Ztschr. Wiss. Zool. 110. 1914b. Studien, etc. II. Darstellung der weiteren Entwicklung. Mitt. Zool. Stat. Neapel 22. 1920. Über Westindische Tornarien. Proc. Kong. Akad. Wetensch. Amsterdam 29. 1921. Die Tornaria-Sammlung von Mortensen. Vidensk. Meddel. Dansk Naturhist. Foren. 73. 1928. Tornarien von Japan. Zool. Jahrb. Abt. System. 56. 1935. Beiträge zur Kenntnis der Enteropneusten des Golfes von Neapel. Pubbl. Staz. Zool. Napoli 15. **Stiasny-Wijnhoff, G.,** and **G. Stiasny.** 1926. Über Tornarien-typen. Zool. Anz. 68. 1927. Die Tornarien. Ergebn. Fortsch. Zool. 7. **Sun, A.** 1910. Ueber einen Parasit aus der Körperhöhle von Ptychodera. Arch. Protistenk. 20. **Thomas, A.** 1956. Saccoglossus apantesis, a new enteropneust from South Australia. Trans. Roy. Soc. South Australia 79. **Tokioka, T.** 1937. Tornaria susakiensis. Annot. Zool. Japon. 16. **Trewavas, E.** 1931. Enteropneusta. Scient. Repts. Great Barrier Reef Exped., vol. 4, no. 2. **Van der Horst, C. J.** 1924. West Indische Enteropneusten. Bijdragen Dierkunde Afl. 23. 1925. Enteropneusta. *Die Tierwelt der Nord- und Ostsee*, Teil VIIa. 1929. Observations on the Enteropneusta. Vidensk. Meddel. Dansk Naturhist. Foren. 87. 1930. Metamerism in Enteropneusta. Quart. Jour. Microsc. Sci. 73. 1932a. Enteropneusta. *In* **W. Kükenthal** and **T. Krumbach** (eds.), *Handbuch der Zoologie,* vol. 3, pt. 2. 1932b. Die Enteropneusten-Gattung Ptychodera. Zool. Anz. 99. 1934a. Die Enteropneusten aus den Meeren der USSR. Zool. Jahrb. Abt. Anat. 58. 1934b. The burrow of an enteropneust. Nature, London, 134. 1937. On a new South African species of Balanoglossus. Ann. South African Mus. 32. 1940. The Enteropneusta from Delagoa Bay. Ann. South African Mus. 32. **Willey, A.** 1897. On Ptychodera flava. Quart. Jour. Microsc. Sci. 40. 1898. Spengelia. Quart. Jour. Microsc. Sci. 40. 1899a. Remarks on some recent work on the Protochorda. Quart. Jour. Microsc. Sci. 42. 1899b. Enteropneusta from the South Pacific. *In* **A. Willey,** *Zoological results based on material collected in New Britain, New Guinea, Loyalty Islands and elsewhere,* pt. 3. 1931. Glossobalanus berkeleyi. Trans. Roy. Soc. Canada, ser. 3, vol. 25.

PTEROBRANCHIA

Allman, G. 1869. On Rhabdopleura. Quart. Jour. Microsc. Sci. 9. **Andersson, K.** 1903. Ein Weiterentdeckung von Cephalodiscus. Zool. Anz. 26. 1907. Die Pterobranchier der schwedischen Südpolar-Expedition. Wissensch. Ergebn. Schwed. Südpolar Exped. 5. **Bergersen, B.,** and **H. Broch.** 1932. Rhabdopleuridae. *In* **W. Kükenthal** and **H. Krumbach** (eds.), *Handbuch der Zoologie,* vol. 3, pt. 2. **Broch, H.** 1927. Die Pterobranchier. Rhabdopleura. Dtsch. Südpolar Exped. 19, Zool. 11. **Burdon-Jones, C.** 1954. Habitat and distribution of Rhabdopleura. Univ. Bergen Arbok, Naturvit. Rekke, no. 11. **Calman, W.** 1908. Parasitic copepod from Cephalodiscus. Trans. South African Philos. Soc. 17, Marine Invertebrates South Africa 5. **Dawydoff, C.** 1944. Rhabdopleura et Cephalodiscus dans le mer de Chine méridionale. C. R. Acad. Sci. Paris 218. **Fowler, G.** 1892. Structure of Rhabdopleura. Proc. Roy. Soc. London 52. 1893. The morphology of Rhabdopleura. Festschrift 70 Geburtstag Rud. Leuckart. 1904. Notes on Rhabdopleura. Quart. Jour. Microsc. Sci. 48. **Gilchrist, J.** 1915. Observations on the Cape Cephalodiscus. Ann. Mag. Natur. Hist., ser. 8, vol. 16. 1917. Development of the Cape Cephalodiscus. Quart. Jour. Microsc. Sci. 62. **Gravier, C.** 1912a.

Sur un copépode nouveau parasite d'un Cephalodiscus. Bull. Mus. Nation. Hist. Natur. Paris 18. 1912b. Sur les Ptérobranches. C. R. Acad. Sci. Paris 154. 1912c. Répartition géographique des espèces du Cephalodiscus. Bull. Mus. Nation. Hist. Natur. Paris 18. 1912d. Ptérobranches. Deux. Exped. Antarctiques Franç. (1908–1910), Sci. Natur. Doc. Scient. **Harmer, S.** 1887. Cephalodiscus. Rept. Scient. Results Voyage Challenger, Zool. 20, pt. 62, appendix. 1897. Notochord of Cephalodiscus. Zool. Anz. 20. 1905. The Pterobranchia of the Siboga Expedition. Siboga Exped., Monogr. 26. **Harmer, S.,** and **W. Ridewood.** 1913. The Pterobranchia of the Scottish National Antarctic Expedition. Trans. Roy. Soc. Edinburgh 49. **John, C.** 1931. Cephalodiscus. Discovery Repts. 3. 1932. Development of Cephalodiscus. Discovery Repts. 6. **Johnston, T.** 1937a. Rhabdopleura. Austral. Antarctic Exped. Sci. Repts., ser. C, vol. 3, pt. 4. 1937b. Occurrence of Rhabdopleura annulata in South Australian waters. Records South Australian Mus. 6. **Johnston, T.,** and **Nancy Muirhead.** 1951. Cephalodiscus. Brit. Austral. New Zealand Antarctic Research Exped. Repts., ser. B, vol. 1, pt. 3. **Komai, T.** 1949. Internal structure of Atubaria. Proc. Japan. Acad. 26. **Kozlowski, R.** 1949. Découverte du ptérobranche Rhabdopleura à l'état fossile. C. R. Acad. Sci. Paris 228. **Krumbach, T.** 1927. Cephalodiscus. Dtsch. Südpolar Exped. 19, Zool. 11. **Lankester, E.** 1874. Remarks on the affinities of Rhabdopleura. Quart. Jour. Microsc. Sci. 14. 1884. Contribution to the knowledge of Rhabdopleura. Quart. Jour. Microsc. Sci. 24. 1905. New species of Cephalodiscus. Proc. Roy. Soc. London 76B. **Masterman, A.** 1897. On the Diplochorda, I, II. Quart. Jour. Microsc. Sci. 40. 1898. Anatomy and budding process of Cephalodiscus. Trans. Roy. Soc. Edinburgh 39. 1903. On the Diplochorda, IV. Quart. Jour. Microsc. Sci. 46. **McIntosh, W.** 1882. Cephalodiscus. Ann. Mag. Natur. Hist., ser. 5, vol. 10. 1887. Report on Cephalodiscus. Rept. Scient. Results Voyage Challenger 20, pt. 62. **Norman, J.** 1921. Rhabdopleura. Brit. Antarctic ("Terra Nova") Exped., Natur. Hist. Repts., Zool. 4. **Ridewood, W.** 1906. Cephalodiscus gilchristi. Marine Investigations South Africa 4. 1907a. Pterobranchia: Cephalodiscus. Nation. Antarctic Exped., Natur. Hist. Repts. 2. 1907b. Development of plumes in buds of Cephalodiscus. Quart. Jour. Microsc. Sci. 51. 1908a. New species of Cephalodiscus from the Cape seas. Marine Investigations South Africa 4. 1912. On specimens of Cephalodiscus. Ann. Mag. Natur. Hist., ser. 8, vol. 10. 1918a. Cephalodiscus. British Antarctic ("Terra Nova") Exped., Zool. 4, pt. 2. 1918b. Pterobranchia. Austral. Antarctic Exped., Sci. Repts., ser. C, vol. 3, pt. 2. **Ridewood, W.,** and **H. Fantham.** 1907. On Neurosporidium cephalodisci. Quart. Jour. Microsc. Sci. 51. **Sars, G.** 1873. Formes remarquables de la vie animale dans les grandes profondeurs de la côte norvégienne. Arch. Sci. Phys. Natur. Geneva 47. 1874. On Rhabdopleura mirabilis. Quart. Jour. Microsc. Sci. 14. **Sars, M.** 1869. Fortsatte Bemerkninger over det dyriske livs Udbredning i Havets Dybder. Forhandl. Vidensk. Selsk. Christiania, for 1868. **Sato, T.** 1936. Über Atubaria heterolopha. Zool. Anz. 115. **Schepotieff, A.** 1904. Zur Organisation von Rhabdopleura. Bergens Mus. Aarbog, no. 2. 1905. Über Organisation und Knospung von Rhabdopleura. Zool. Anz. 28. 1907a. Die Anatomie von Rhabdopleura. Zool. Jahrb. Abt. Anat. 23. 1907b. Knospungsprozess und Gehäuse von Rhabdopleura. Zool. Jahrb. Abt. Anat. 24. 1907c. Cephalodiscus. Zool. Jahrb. Abt. Anat. 24. 1908. Knospungsprozess von Cephalodiscus. Zool. Jahrb. Abt. Anat. 25. 1909. Die Pterobranchier der indischen Ozean. Zool. Jahrb. Abt. System. 28. **Thomas, H.,** and **A. Davis.** 1949. Rhabdopleura in the English Eocene. Bull. Brit. Mus. (Natur. Hist.), Geol. 1. **Vaney, A.,** and **A. Conte.** 1906. Recherches sur la Rhabdopleura. Rev. Suisse Zool. 14.

PLANCTOSPHAEROIDEA

Garstang, W. 1939. Spolia bermudiana I. Quart. Jour. Microsc. Sci. 81 (footnote only). **Spengel, J.** 1932. Planctosphaera pelagica. Scient. Results Michael Sars North Atlantic Deep Sea Exped., vol. 5, no. 5. **Van der Horst, C. J.** 1936. Planctosphaera and Tornaria. Quart. Jour. Microsc. Sci. 78.

GRAPTOLITHINA

Allman, G. 1872. Morphology and affinities of graptolites. Ann. Mag. Natur. Hist., ser. 4, vol. 9. **Bohlin, B.** 1952. The affinities of the graptolites. Bull. Geol. Inst. Univ. Uppsala 34. **Bulman, O.** 1925–1932. Monograph of British dendroid graptolites. Palaeontograph. Soc. London. 1932–1936. On the graptolites prepared by Holm. Arkiv Zool. 24A, 26A, 28A. 1938. Graptolithina. *In* O. **Schindewolf** (ed.), *Handbuch der Palaeozoologie*, Bd. 2D, Lief. 2. 1954. Status of invertebrate paleontology 1953. VII. Graptolithina. Bull. Mus. Comp. Zool. Harvard 112. 1955. Graptolithina. *In* R. C. **Moore** (ed.), *Treatise on invertebrate paleontology*, pt. V. **Decker, C.** 1956. Place of graptolites in the animal kingdom. Bull. Amer. Assoc. Petroleum Geol. 40. **Decker, C., and I. Gold.** 1957. Bithecae, gonothecae, and nematothecae on Graptoloidea. Jour. Paleontol. 31. **Hundt, R.** 1941. Lebensweise der Graptolithen. Der Biologe 10. **Kozlowski, R.** 1938. Informations préliminaires sur les graptolithes du Tremadoc de la Pologne. Ann. Mus. Zool. Polonici 13, no. 16. 1947. Les affinités des graptolithes. Biol. Rev. Cambridge Philos. Soc. 22. 1948. Les graptolithes du Tremadoc de la Pologne. Palaeontologica Polonica 3. 1956. Sur Rhabdopleura du Danien de Pologne. Acta Palaeontologica Polonica 1. **Rudall, K.** 1955. Distribution of collagen and chitin. Symposia Soc. Exptl. Biol., no. 9. **Ruedemann, R.** 1904, 1908. Graptolites of New York. Mem. New York State Mus. 7, 11. 1947. Graptolites of North America. Mem. Geol. Soc. America 19. **Schepotieff, A.** 1905. Über die Stellung der Graptolithen in zoologischen System. Neues Jahrb. Mineral. 2. **Sinclair, G.** 1948. The affinities of the graptolites. Amer. Jour. Sci. 246. **Thomas, H., and A. Davis.** 1949. Rhabdopleura in the English Eocene. Bull. British Mus. (Natur. Hist.), Geol. 1, no. 1. **Waterlot, G.** 1948. Classe des graptolites. *In* P. **Grassé** (ed.), *Traité de zoologie*, vol. XI. 1953. Classe des graptolites. *In* J. **Piveteau** (ed.), *Traité de paléontologie*, vol. III.

PHYLOGENY

Baldwin, E. 1952. *Dynamic aspects of biochemistry.* 2 ed. **Caster, K.** 1952a. Relationships of the carpoid echinoderms in the light of Enopleura. Bull. Geol. Soc. America 63. 1952b. Concerning Enopleura. Bull. Amer. Paleontol. 34, no. 141. **Dawydoff, C.** 1948. Les affinités des Stomocordés. *In* P. **Grassé** (ed.), *Traité de zoologie*, vol. XI. **Gislen, T.** 1930. Affinities between the Echinodermata, Enteropneusta, and Chordonia. Zool. Bidrag 12. **Grobben, K.** 1923. Theoretische Erörterungen betreffend die phylogenetische Ableitung der Echinodermen. Sitzungsber. Akad. Wissensch. Wien, Math. Naturwiss. Kl. 132, Abt. 1. **Komai, T.** 1951. The homology of the "notochord" found in pterobranchs and enteropneusts. Amer. Natural. 85. **Mookerjee, H., D. Ganguly, and G. Gupta.** 1955. Central nervous system, axial skeleton and anterior metamerism of Ptychodera. Anat. Anz. 102. **Newell, G.** 1952. The homology of the stomochord of the Enteropneusta. Proc. Zool. Soc. London 121. **Schepotieff, A.** 1908. Die Pterobranchier. Pt. 3. Vergleichend-anatomische Teil. Zool. Jahrb. Abt. Anat. 25. **Silén, L.** 1954. Reflections concerning the stomochord. Proc. Zool. Soc. London 124.

CHAPTER XVIII

THE ENTEROCOELOUS COELOMATES—
PHYLUM POGONOPHORA

I. HISTORICAL

The Dutch ship *Siboga*, collecting in Indonesia in 1899–1900, dredged up at several different stations and from depths ranging from 462 to 2060 m. a total of about 25 specimens and a number of empty tubes of a strange animal that was turned over for study to the eminent French zoologist Maurice Caullery. Caullery published several thorough accounts of the material (1914, 1944, 1948) but was unable to place the animal, which he named *Siboglinum weberi*, with certainty in the zoological system. Naturally puzzled by the total lack of a digestive system, Caullery suspected that part of the animal was missing. In 1948 another eminent French zoologist, C. Dawydoff, suggested with remarkable perspicuity an affinity of *Siboglinum* with hemichordates. However, the systematic position of the animal remained enigmatical until 1951, when Ivanov announced that *Siboglinum* is a pogonophore.

Still another problematical animal was described by Uschakov (1933) from specimens dredged at 3500 m. in the Okhotsk Sea. This is a vermiform animal with a crown of tentacles and was considered by its describer to be a polychaete annelid of the family Sabellidae; therefore he named it *Lamellisabella zachsi*, despite the fact that it lacks segments, setae, regularly repeated transverse coelomic partitions, and a ventral nerve cord. Johannson, a specialist on the Sabellidae, reexamined the specimens (1937, 1939), pointed out these deficiencies, and rightly concluded that *Lamellisabella* cannot be an annelid but must represent a new, hitherto unknown class for which he proposed the name Pogonofora, later altering this to the more correct form, Pogonophora. He was at first inclined to relate the Pogonophora to the Phoronida, but subsequently withdrew this suggestion. Ulrich (1949) made an analysis of the Pogonophora from the available facts about *Lamellisabella* and placed the group in a *Tierkreis* (literally, animal circle) that included echinoderms, hemichordates, and lophophorates (Phoronida, Ectoprocta, Brachiopoda). He considered the Pogonophora to constitute a separate phylum fitting between the lophophorates and the hemichordates, a conclusion already reached by Reisinger in 1938. In recent years a number of new pogonophores have been obtained from deep dredgings in the Bering and Okhotsk Seas and adjacent areas and have been described by Ivanov (1949, 1952, 1957a). These outstanding studies by Ivanov have shown that the pogonophores are closely related to the hemichordates and belong among the Deuterostomia. At first Ivanov was inclined to make Pogonophora a class of Hemichordata, but later rightly concluded that they constitute an independent phylum. He gave this phylum (1955) the name Brachiata, but the author feels that the familiar name Pogonophora should be retained. It is true that Pogonophora was first proposed as a class, but there can be no objection to raising the rank to that of phylum since such raising of ranks is prevalent in zoology today.

In addition to the Russian findings from the dredgings of their deep-sea research vessel *Vitjaz*, two specimens, each a representative of a new genus, were obtained by

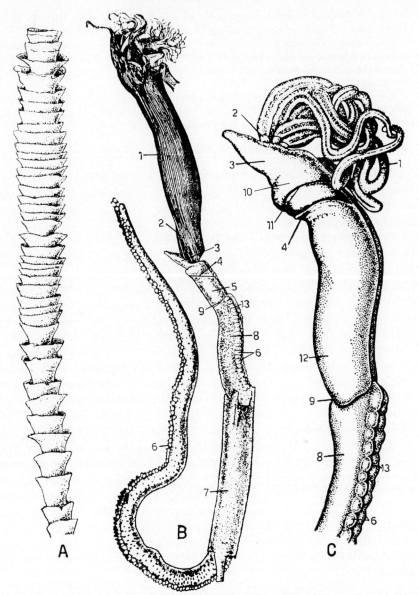

FIG. 75.—Pogonophora. *A*, tube of *Lamellisabella gorbunovi* (*after Ivanov*, 1949).
B, *Spirobrachia grandis*, with short piece of tube, only preannular part of trunk present.
C, anterior part of *Birsteinia vitjasi*. (*B*, *C*, after *Ivanov*, 1952.)   1, tentacles; 2, fused
base; 3, cephalic lobe; 4, bridle; 5, protomesosome; 6, adhesive papillae; 7, piece of tube;
8, trunk; 9, location of mesosome-trunk septum; 10, protosome; 11, protosome-mesosome
boundary; 12, mesosome; 13, midventral groove.

the Danish deep-sea expedition on the *Galathea* (Kirkegaard, 1956a, b).   No doubt many additional species will be discovered by further deep-sea dredgings.

The finding of an entire new phylum of animals in the twentieth century is certainly astounding and ranks in zoological importance with the finding of the coelacanth fish and the archaic gastropod, both belonging to groups believed extinct for hundreds of millions of years.

The citations in the foregoing account comprise the whole of our knowledge of the Pogonophora.   Ivanov has kindly informed the author that he is engaged in writing an account of the Pogonophora for the *Traité de zoologie.*

II. CHARACTERS OF THE PHYLUM

1. Definition.—The Pogonophora are solitary, tubicolous, very vermiform deuterostomes, with body regionation as in hemichordates, without a digestive tract or gill slits, and with one to many fringed tentacles borne on the protosome.

2. General Characters.—The Pogonophora, or beard worms (Greek, *pogon*, beard), are excessively long, slender worms that inhabit a closely fitting tube of their own secretion.   The body regionation is similar to that of hemichordates except that the division between protosome and mesosome is often not expressed externally.   A single tentacle or bunch of tentacles, having a fringe of pinnules along one or both sides, is borne on the protosome.   Mouth, anus, and digestive tract are totally wanting, without trace even in sections.   The nervous system is intraepidermal; a nervous center occurs in a dorsal lobe of the protosome.   A closed circulatory system is present with main middorsal and midventral vessels and a muscular enlargement of the ventral vessel in the protosome that constitutes a heart and may be accompanied by a pericardial sac.   The protosome has a pair of coelomoducts that constitute the nephridia.   The sexes are separate, but not externally distinguishable except by the position of the gonopores.   The pair of gonads is located in the metasome. In males there is a pair of gonopores on the ventral surface just behind the trunk septum, whereas in females the gonopores occur at about the middle of the trunk.   Pogonophores appear to brood their young in their tubes; at least embryos have been found there in some species.

Pogonophores are exclusively marine and are mostly limited to abyssal depths, although a few species range into archibenthal or even littoral waters.

III. CLASSIFICATION OF THE PHYLUM

Ivanov (1955, 1957a) arranges the pogonophores into two orders, as follows:

Order 1. Athecanephria.   Protosome externally delimited from mesosome; coelomoducts divergent with lateral nephridiopores; with one tentacle or a number of separate tentacles; pericardial sac present;

postannular part of trunk without transverse ventral rows of adhesive papillae; spermatophores fusiform.

Order 2. Thecanephria. Protosome often not externally delimited from mesosome; coelomoducts convergent, with medial pores; tentacles numerous, separate or basally fused; without pericardial sac; postannular trunk with ventral transverse rows of adhesive papillae; spermatophores flattened.

At the present writing (1958) there are known 22 species in 9 genera arranged into 5 families (Ivanov, 1957a).

IV. ANATOMY AND EMBRYOLOGY

1. External Characters.—The pogonophores are cylindrical worms with straight bodies of long and exceedingly slender dimensions. In length the known species range from below 10 to 35 cm. with a diameter of generally less than 1 mm., even less than 0.5 mm., but the larger species attain diameters of 1 to 2.5 mm. Each worm lives enclosed in a secreted tube fitted rather closely to its body and of smooth contour (Fig. 75*B*) or composed of successive rings (Fig. 77*F*) or of funnellike pieces (Figs. 75*A*, 80*B*). Often the tubes show alternating bands of dark and light color. The oral end of the tube is commonly of thinner and less opaque consistency than the remainder and may terminate in a funnel expansion. The tubes are longer than the contained worm, often much so. Thus one of the longest species, *Zenkevitchiana longissima*, about 35 cm. long, including the tentacles, inhabits tubes that may reach a length of 1.5 m., nearly 5 feet. These tubes apparently have an erect position in the bottom ooze.

The body is definitely regionated into a short anterior section and a very long trunk (Figs. 75*B*, 76*A*), clearly separated by a constriction that represents the location of the mesosome-metasome septum. In the order Athecanephria the anterior section is definitely divided into protosome and mesosome by a constriction (Fig. 75*C*), but this constriction is wanting in some members of the order Thecanephria, where the anterior region may be termed, if necessary, protomesosome (Fig. 76*A*). The protosome or its representative terminates anteriorly in a rounded or triangular lobe, the *cephalic lobe*, that contains the central nervous ganglion (Fig. 75*C*). In accord with Ivanov, the cephalic lobe is here considered to mark the dorsal side, although some regard it as ventral (Jägersten, 1956). On the mesosome or the corresponding region is found a structure called *girdle* by Caullery (1944) or *bridle* by Ivanov (1952). This consists of a pair of ridges that begin weakly on the dorsal side and slant obliquely backward, increasing in height, to the midventral line, where they may or may not fuse (Fig. 75*B*, *C*). Caullery found that

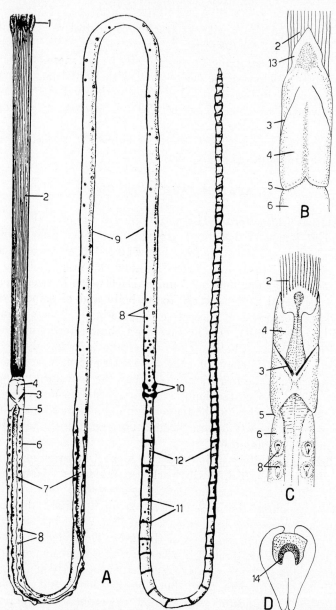

Fig. 76.—Pogonophora (continued). *A*, scheme of the structure of *Lamellisabella*, seen ventrally (*after Ivanov*, 1952). *B*, dorsal view of anterior end of *Lamell. zachsi*. *C*, ventral view of anterior end of *Lamell. zachsi*. *D*, adhesive papilla of *Lamell. zachsi* with horseshoe hardening. (*B–D*, *after Johansson*, 1939.) 1, fringe (shown at tentacular ends only); 2, tentacles; 3, bridle; 4, protomesosome; 5, location of mesosome-trunk septum; 6, trunk; 7, midventral groove; 8, adhesive papillae; 9, preannular part of trunk; 10, belts; 11, rows of adhesive papillae; 12, postannular part of trunk; 13, cephalic lobe; 14, horseshoe hardening.

the ridges of the bridle consist of thickened cuticle. Ivanov surmises that the bridle catches on the oral edge of the tube when the worm is protruded, thus holding it in place.

From the ventral side of the protosome at the base of the cephalic lobe spring the tentacles, a characteristic feature of the phylum. The genus *Siboglinum*, of which eight species are now known, has but a single tentacle, often found thrown into coils (Fig. 77*F*). Most other genera have 5 up to 80 tentacles; *Galathealinum* has over 100, and *Spirobrachia* may have over 200. The tentacles may be free to the base as in *Birsteinia* (Fig. 75*C*) and *Polybrachia* (Fig. 80*A*), or basally fused into a sort of cylinder as in *Lamellisabella* (Fig. 76*A*). In some genera as *Polybrachia*, the tentacles spring from a horseshoe-shaped base, and this is regarded by Ivanov (1957a) as the primitive arrangement. Finally in *Spirobrachia* the fused basal part of the numerous tentacles is wound into an ascending spiral (Fig. 79*E*). The tentacles of all species are provided on one or both sides with short lateral projections, the *pinnules* (Fig. 77*G*), omitted for simplicity from many figures.

The very long, slender trunk shows a certain amount of regionation, mostly with regard to the arrangement and type of the numerous adhesive structures that seem to serve to anchor the worm in its tube. A landmark for this regionation is constituted by the *belts*, which are two adjacent oblique raised girdles (Figs. 76*A*, 78*D*), bearing hardened platelets armed with microscopic denticles. Ivanov terms the trunk anterior to the belts the preannular region, that posterior to the belts the postannular region. The first part of the preannular region generally has a midventral groove, or trough (Fig. 76*A*), that begins immediately behind the mesosome-metasome septum and extends for some distance but not to the belts. The edges of this groove bear a row of conspicuous papillae, also seen in Fig. 75*B*, *C*. In *Siboglinum* these papillae contain a flask-shaped multicellular gland (Fig. 79*C*) that presumably emits an adhesive secretion or perhaps a secretion contributing to the tube. In other pogonophores these papillae may be topped with hardened platelets or, in *Lamellisabella* (Fig. 76*C*, *D*), with a tiny horseshoe of hardened material. Dorsally the preannular part of the trunk bears a median longitudinal ciliated strip that extends posteriorly to varying lengths (Fig. 79*C*). Behind the groove the papillae of the remaining preannular portion of the trunk are reduced in number and are very irregularly arranged (Fig. 76*A*). In the Thecanephria the papillae increase in number again behind the belts and are arranged on the postannular region in ventral transverse rows (Fig. 76*A*) more or less regularly repeated, hence giving a false impression of metamerism. Such postannular transverse rows of papillae are wanting in *Siboglinum* and other Athecanephria where the postannular trunk commonly bears only irregular scattered papillae.

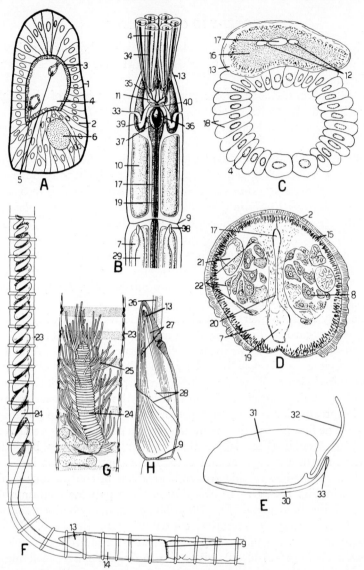

FIG. 77.—Pogonophora (continued). *A*, cross section through a tentacle of *L. zachsi*. *B*, scheme of the anterior end of pogonophores (*after Ivanov*, 1955). *C*, section through the tentacle bases of *L. zachsi*. *D*, section through the trunk of *L. zachsi*. *E*, nephridium of *L. zachsi*. (*A, C–E, after Johansson*, 1939.) *F*, anterior end of *Siboglinum* in its tube. *G*, tip of the tentacle of *Siboglinum*. *H*, side view of protomesosome of *Siboglinum*. (*F–H, after Caullery*, 1944.) 1, cuticle; 2, epidermis; 3, peritoneum; 4, tentacular coelom; 5, blood channels; 6, tentacular nerve; 7, trunk coelom; 8, gonad; 9, septum between mesosome and trunk; 10, mesocoel; 11, protocoel; 12, coelomic spaces in cephalic lobe; 13, cephalic lobe; 14, protomesosome; 15, longitudinal muscle fibers; 16, brain; 17, middorsal blood vessel; 18, tentacle bases; 19, ventral blood vessel; 20, median dorsoventral mesentery; 21, mucous glands; 22, blood channels of gonad; 23, tube; 24, tentacle; 25, tentacular fringe; 26, tentacle base; 27, longitudinal muscle bundles; 28, bridle; 29, sperm duct; 30, nephridial duct; 31, nephridial sac; 32, tube from sac; 33, nephridiopore; 34, afferent tentacular vessel; 35, lateral cephalic vessel; 36, heart; 37, pericardium; 38, male gonopores; 39, coelomoducts (= nephridia); 40, transverse connection of coelomoducts.

2. Internal Anatomy.—This unfortunately is imperfectly known since it must be studied by means of sections and the available material is mostly in poor histological condition. Ivanov's important 1952 article was limited to external morphology, and although he gave a summary of the internal structure in 1955, information about internal anatomy must be obtained chiefly from Johansson's article (1939) on *Lamellisabella*, Caullery's article (1944) on *Siboglinum weberi*, and Jägersten's article (1956) on *Siboglinum ekmani*. The body is clothed with an epidermis, mostly columnar but varying in height in different regions, and provided with a cuticle whose special thickenings were noted above. The epidermis of *Siboglinum* is mentioned as generally glandular, and that of *Lamellisabella* is liberally provided, except on the protosome, with large flask-shaped gland cells that project into the coelom (Fig. 77*D*). The ciliated dorsal strip and the very large multicellular glands that occupy the ridges bounding the midventral groove of the preannular part of the trunk are shown in Fig. 79*C*. The epidermis is generally subtended by a thin layer of circular muscle fibers followed by a much thicker and more evident layer of longitudinal fibers (Fig. 77*D*), especially thick in the mesosome where it almost fills the coelom (Fig. 78*B*). More anteriorly in the protosome of *Siboglinum* are found additional longitudinal muscles in the form of two bundles (Fig. 78*A*) that contribute to the muscles of the tentacle (Fig. 78*C*). The strong septum between mesosome and metasome is heavily muscularized.

In *Lamellisabella* the tentacles are clothed with a columnar epidermis covered with cuticle and lined with peritoneum and containing a nerve in its outer side (Fig. 77*A*). Two bands of longitudinal muscles are described in the tentacle of *Siboglinum* (Fig. 78*C*), of which the more conspicuous one courses along the line of attachment of the fringe of pinnules. In all pogonophores the tentacles are hollow, containing a coelomic extension which in the described cases houses blood sinuses, usually two (Fig. 77*A*). The pinnules are of remarkable construction (Ivanov, 1955). Each is a long slender extension of one of the epidermal cells of the tentacle (Fig. 81*A*). The epidermal cells adjacent to those that produce the pinnules are ciliated; hence each tentacle has two longitudinal tracts of cilia.

The nervous system so far as known is intraepidermal as in hemichordates (Fig. 78*A*). According to Caullery and Jägersten the brain, situated in the cephalic lobe, is ring-shaped in *Siboglinum* (Fig. 78*A*), whereas Ivanov represents it as an elongated mass giving off lateral arcs from which spring the tentacular nerves. Perhaps these lateral arcs are simply the ventral part of the nerve ring. There are indications that the brain gives off posteriorly a middorsal nerve that supplies the middorsal ciliated band of the trunk. A midventral trunk nerve seems not

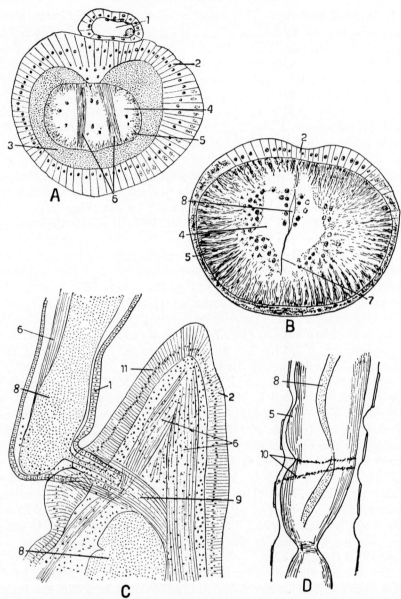

FIG. 78.—Pogonophora (continued).   *A*, section through the protosome of *Siboglinum*.
B, section through the mesosome of *Siboglinum*.   *C*, longitudinal section of anterior end of
Siboglinum, showing tentacle attachment.   *D*, small part of trunk of *Siboglinum*, showing
the belts.   (*All after Caullery*, 1944.)   1, tentacle base; 2, epidermis; 3, nerve ring; 4, protocoel; 5, longitudinal muscle layer; 6, muscle bands; 7, dorsoventral mesentery; 8, blood
vessel; 9, muscle band into tentacle; 10, belts; 11, cephalic lobe.

to have been discerned. Jägersten indicates a diffuse nervous ring in the mesosome-metasome septum.

The interior is occupied by a coelom, mostly not lined by definite peritoneum. According to Ivanov (1955), the protosome contains a single sacciform or crescentic protocoel from which a pair of coelomoducts proceed to the exterior. In *Siboglinum* the protocoel is confusingly subdivided by dorsoventral muscle bands (Fig. 78*A*), but Jägersten concedes the probability of an unpaired protocoel here. The coelomic lumina of the tentacles arise from the protocoel. The coelom of the mesosome is paired without coelomoducts. The trunk coelom also consists of right and left cavities that meet medially to establish a dorsoventral mesentery (Fig. 79*D*). Ivanov considers the gonoducts to constitute the coelomoducts of the trunk coelom.

A circulatory system of the closed type is well developed and often found distended with blood. A middorsal and a midventral blood vessel are evident throughout trunk and mesosome, running between the leaves of the mesentery (Figs. 77*D*, 79*D*). Jägersten has observed in addition two pairs of lateral vessels in the trunk. According to Ivanov the ventral vessel is enlarged in the protosome to a muscular heart (not seen by others) from whose anterior end branches continue into the tentacles (Fig. 77*B*). In the Athecanephria a small sac, considered a pericardium, is applied to the dorsal wall of the heart enlargement. Each tentacle contains two vessels, an afferent and an efferent, and both contribute to a loop into each pinnule (Fig. 81*A*). The efferent tentacular vessels connect with the dorsal vessel in which the blood runs backward. It is stated by Ivanov that in the ventral vessel the blood runs forward. This reversal of the usual direction of flow in the main median vessels seems to support the contention of Jägersten that the cephalic lobe is ventral. In fact, it may be conceded that the orientation of the pogonophore body is not yet definitely settled. In *Siboglinum* the vessel wall consists of a thin membrane with longitudinal fibers on its inner side, whereas in *Lamellisabella* the vessels are said to have the usual muscular coat. No blood cells have been observed.

The coelomoducts of the protosome are regarded as nephridia, although they lack a definite nephrostome, having merely a simple opening into the protocoel. Their form in *Lamellisabella* is shown in Fig. 77*E*, where a sacciform enlargement of uncertain histological construction is present. Ivanov (1955) states that the nephridia are ciliated and are connected near the coelomostomes by a transverse canal (Fig. 77*B*). In the Athecanephria the nephridia diverge and open to the exterior laterally. In the Thecanephria they are stated to be long and coiled and to converge to a medial position in which they bulge into the dorsal blood vessel.

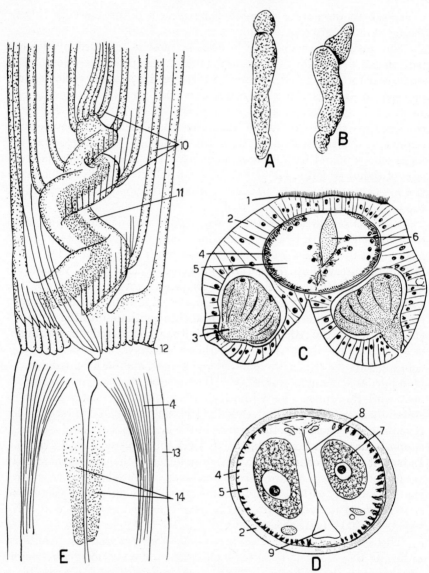

Fig. 79.—Pogonophora (continued). *A, B*, embryos of *Siboglinum*, found in its tube. *C*, cross section through the anterior part of the trunk of *Siboglinum*. *D*, cross section through the posterior part of the trunk of Siboglinum. (*A–D, after Caullery*, 1944.) *E*, anterior end of *Spirobrachia grandis*, to show spirally coiled fused tentacular bases (*after Ivanov*, 1952). 1, dorsal ciliated strip; 2, epidermis; 3, multicellular mucous gland; 4, longitudinal muscle layer; 5, trunk coelom; 6, blood vessel; 7, ovary; 8, dorsal blood vessel; 9, ventral blood vessel; 10, fused tentacle bases; 11, spiral coil; 12, tentacular attachments at base of cephalic lobe; 13, protomesosome; 14, coelomic sacs (protocoels).

The sexes are separate but are distinguishable externally only by the position of the gonopores. Observers other than Ivanov have had females only, but Ivanov has had males of both *Siboglinum* and *Lamellisabella*. Little detail has been furnished about the reproductive system, and observers other than Ivanov could not find any gonoducts. The gonads occur as a pair of elongated bodies occupying the metacoel, one in each half of the latter, and are said to be separated from the coelom by their own cellular walls. The testes, according to Ivanov, are long bodies occupying the posterior half of the trunk, with long, ciliated, glandular sperm ducts that open by ventral gonopores just behind the mesosome-metasome septum (Fig. 77*B*). The sperm ducts are filled with spermatophores, fusiform or flattened bodies containing the sperm and continuing at one end into a long filament of attachment. Definite formed ovaries could not be found by others, but Ivanov states that the ovaries occupy the anterior half of the trunk with short posterior oviducts that open in the middle region of the trunk. The eggs are relatively large and rich in yolk, an indication of brooded development.

3. Development.—Caullery (1944) already found in one specimen of *Siboglinum* in the part of the tube occupied by the tentacle six developing young (Fig. 79*A*, *B*) that strikingly resemble young stages of the buds of *Cephalodiscus* (Fig. 65*A*). Jägersten (1957) has also found young in the tube of *Siboglinum*, at a slightly more advanced stage. And now Ivanov (1957b) has had the good fortune to find a series of stages of development of *Siboglinum*, as well as some of *Oligobrachia*. In *Siboglinum caulleryi* the egg batch consists of 10 to 30 elongated eggs lying in a row in the tube above the female, all oriented alike. The pole of the egg facing the orifice of the tube becomes the anterior end of the worm, the opposite pole the posterior end. Cleavage is holoblastic but unequal and results in a fusiform embryo (stereoblastula?) of many small blastomeres in the animal half, few larger blastomeres in the vegetal half (Fig. 81*B*, *C*). The blastomeres are also larger on the ventral than on the dorsal surface, with two especially large ones near the animal pole (Fig. 81*C*). The embryo is markedly bilateral. There is no formation of a blastopore, and gastrulation appears to occur by delamination. At the stage of 130 to 140 blastomeres, three inner cells represent the rudiment of an archenteron; there are further found in the interior two groups of small cells assumed to be mesenchyme. The coeloms are formed by the enterocoelous method, similar to the method in *Saccoglossus pusillus;* that is, the protocoel sends out posterior extensions that divide into mesocoel and metacoel on each side (Fig. 81*D–F*). The embryo elongates, and constrictions appear, marking the body regionation (Fig. 81*F*). In *Oligobrachia* a definite yolky entoderm appears (Fig. 81*G*), but this soon breaks down to furnish food material. Later

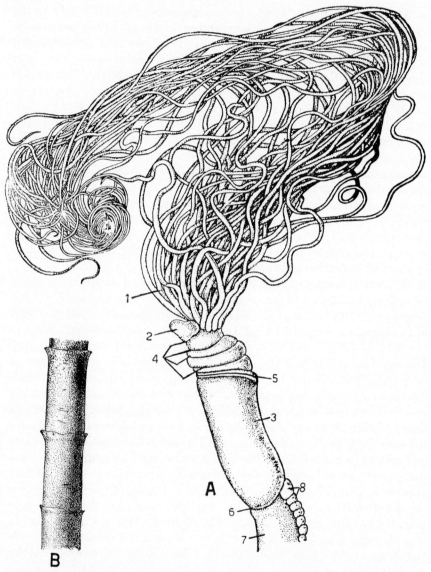

FIG. 80.—Pogonophora (continued). *A*, anterior end of *Polybrachia*. *B*, tube of *Polybrachia*. (*Both after Ivanov*, 1952.)   1, tentacles; 2, cephalic lobe; 3, protomesosome; 4, grooves; 5, bridle; 6, trunk septum; 7, trunk; 8, adhesive papillae.

stages of the *Sibognlinum* larva were reported by Jägersten (1957).   These are little worms with body constricted into short protomesosome and much longer metasome, each provided with a girdle of cilia (Fig. 81*H*). Setae are present, further the ciliated band of the metasome retained in the adult.   A small indentation at the anterior tip may be reminiscent of an ancestral mouth. The interior contains a tract of spongy tissue that seems to represent a digestive tract but is without lumen or delimited wall or terminal openings. The larva probably leads a brief free existence.

It is clear from the above findings that a digestive tract is indicated in the embryology of pogonophores but is used up as a nutritive supply for the embryo since it contains the yolk.

4. Systematic Account.—Ivanov (1957a) has arranged the known pogonophores into two orders and five families. In the Athecanephria, the protosome is definitely demarcated from the mesosome, the nephridia diverge to lateral nephridiopores, the tentacles are free, and the postannular part of the trunk lacks ventral transverse rows of adhesive papillae. This order contains two families, Oligobrachiidae with 6 to 12 tentacles and Siboglinidae with 1 tentacle. The former includes the genera *Oligobrachia* with buried glands instead of the usual papillae along the borders of the midventral groove of the first part of the trunk and *Birsteinia* (Fig. 75C) with the usual papillae. Each genus has at present one species. The Siboglinidae with the single genus *Siboglinum* (Fig. 77F) with now eight species are known by the single tentacle.

In the Thecanephria with three families the nephridia converge to a medial position, a pericardial sac is wanting, and the postannular trunk bears regularly repeated transverse ventral rows of adhesive papillae. The Polybrachiidae with free tentacles include *Heptabrachia* and *Polybrachia* with protosome distinct from the mesosome and *Galathealinum* and *Zenkevitchiana* with protomesosome. *Heptabrachia* with 5 to 8 tentacles and ringed tube comprises three species, and *Polybrachia* with 18 to 73 tentacles and tube with repeated flares (Fig. 80A, B) also includes three species. *Galathealinum bruuni*, one of the finds of the *Galathea* deep-sea expedition, possesses over 100 tentacles and has a pair of wing-like folds just in front of the bridle (Kirkegaard, 1956a). Probably belonging to this family is another find of the *Galathea, Krampolinum galatheae* (Kirkegaard, 1956b), based on the peculiarities of the tube of the poorly preserved specimen.

The family Lamellisabellidae with single genus *Lamellisabella*, comprising two species at present, is characterized by the fusion of the tentacles (18 to 31 in number) to a cylinder (Fig. 76A). Proto- and mesosome are fused and the adhesive papillae are topped with a little horseshoe of hardened material (Fig. 76D). The Spirobrachiidae, also with protomesosome and with numerous tentacles (39 to 223 in the two known species of *Spirobrachia*), are distinguished by the spiral coiling of the fused base of the tentacles (Fig. 79E). *Spirobrachia grandis* (Fig. 75B) has the largest number of tentacles, over 200, known in the phylum.

In view of the current interest in deep-sea dredging, constant additions to the foregoing list may be expected.

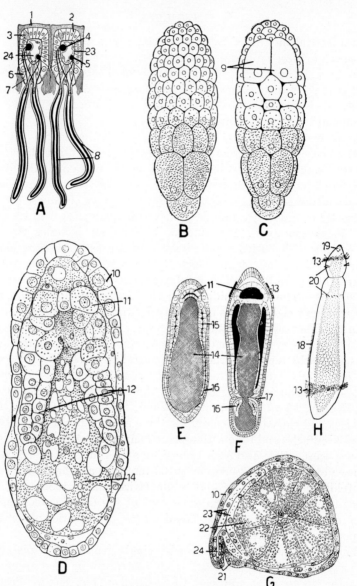

Fig. 81.—Pogonophora (concluded). *A*, cross section through two tentacles of *L. zachsi* (after *Ivanov*, 1955). *B*, late cleavage stage of *Siboglinum*, dorsal view. *C*, same as *B*, ventral view. *D*, *Siboglinum*, formation of coeloms. *E*, *F*, scheme of coelom formation in *Siboglinum*, two stages. *G*, cross section of embryo of *Oligobrachia*, showing entoderm. (*B–G*, after *Ivanov*, 1957b.) *H*, larva of *Siboglinum* (after *Jägersten*, 1957). 1, cuticle; 2, epidermis; 3, nerve; 4, efferent vessel; 5, afferent vessel; 6, ciliated cell; 7, gland cell; 8, fringes; 9, large cells; 10, ectoderm; 11, protocoel; 12, extensions to make meso- and metacoels; 13, girdle of cilia; 14, entodermal mesh; 15, mesocoel; 16, metacoel; 17, trunk septum; 18, dorsal ciliary strip; 19, slight indentation, may be reminiscent of ancestral mouth; 20, setae; 21, primordia of tentacles; 22, cellular entoderm; 23, peritoneum; 24, tentacular coelom.

V. BIOLOGY

As the pogonophores are obtained only by dredging, mostly at abyssal depths, little is known of their habits. They are benthonic animals, leading a sedentary life in the bottom ooze, enclosed in a long cylindrical tube in which they are not fastened but which they never leave. The tubes apparently have an upright position, with their lower ends buried in the ooze. As the tubes are much longer than the worms, the latter presumably move up and down in the tubes and must protrude at the top for respiratory and food-gathering purposes.

As a digestive tract is completely wanting, the matter of nutrition has naturally excited the attention of zoologists. It is clear that animals of such size and capable of producing yolky eggs and masses of sperm must take in food somehow. Further, it is now known that young stages also lack a digestive tract and do not feed, hence there is no storage of food in young stages for adult consumption. Ivanov (1955) outlines the matter of nutrition as follows, but one must realize that this account is pure surmise. He considers that, in feeding, the worm protrudes from the tube and holds the tentacles bunched to form a cylinder (the tentacles are already fused into this condition in *Lamellisabella* and *Spirobrachia*). A similar effect is produced in *Siboglinum* by the corkscrew coiling of the single tentacle (Fig. 77*F*). When the tentacles are thus arranged to enclose a central cylindrical space the pinnules are intermeshed in this space to produce a food-catching net. It has been noted that there are ciliary tracts alongside the pinnule bases, and these presumably produce a current along the intertentacular cylindrical space, bringing minute food organisms in contact with the pinnules. Ivanov believes not only that the food is digested outside the worm in this pinnular mesh but that the products of digestion are absorbed through the pinnules. The latter supposition is credible because of the thin walls and abundant blood supply of the pinnules (Fig. 81*A*); but the matter of digestion meets the difficulty that the tentacular epidermis does not seem to be glandular or to contain enzymatic cells. Ivanov states that such are present between the pinnule bases and the ciliary tracts, but they are not mentioned in descriptions of tentacular histology by others and Jägersten (1957) definitely failed to find them. It must be realized, however, that available material is not in good histological condition. Jägersten suggests that perhaps pogonophores absorb decomposition products produced by the activities of bacteria, known to be present in ocean abysses. Ivanov thinks the worm, having gathered a load of food in the pinnular mesh, retreats into the tube for processes of digestion and absorption.

The author, having determined that the tubes of phoronids and the noncalcareous part of the exoskeleton of ectoprocts are composed of chitin, became curious as to the composition of pogonophore tubes. Ivanov kindly informed that pogonophore tubes had been examined chemically and found to consist of condensed tunicin, that is, the same type of cellulose that comprises the tunic of tunicates. This is certainly an astonishing finding. Further, the cuticle and the various cuticular hardenings are also of polysaccharide nature.

Pogonophores often live in associations of the same or of mixed species. Ivanov (1957a) mentions that in two places in the Kurile-Kamchatka Trench *Zenkevitchiana longissima* occurred in such abundance that myriads of their long white tubes were wound around the frame of the dredge. From the same Trench and from the same depth (8000 to 9000 m.), large numbers of *Spirobrachia beklemischevi* were brought up.

Of the 22 known species of Pogonophora 17 are limited, so far as known, to the Bering and Okhotsk Seas and general Kurile-Kamchatka area and 13 of these have been taken only at abyssal and hadal depths ranging from 1440 to 9700 m. Three, notably all Athecanephria, range into archibenthal and littoral waters: *Siboglinum plumosum* recorded at 124 to 318 m., *Siboglinum caulleryi*, 23 to 8100 m., and *Oligobrachia dogieli*, 124 to 2850 m. The last was also taken in the adjacent Sea of Japan at 2850 m. *Lamellisabella zachsi*, of which the original specimens came from the Okhotsk Sea at 3500 m., has since been found, astonishingly enough, in the Gulf of Panama at about 3000 m., along with *Krampolinum galatheae*, not known elsewhere (Kirkegaard, 1956b). *Siboglinum weberi* and *Galathealinum bruuni* are known only from the tropical West Pacific (Caullery, 1944; Kirkegaard, 1956a). *Siboglinum ekmani* inhabits the Skagerak at modest depths, 180 to 650 m. (Jägersten, 1956, 1957). As the Skagerak, off the southern tip of Norway, is one of the most collected places in the world, it is rather surprising that the presence of a pogonophore there was not realized sooner. The material in fact had been collected in 1933, and the tubes were seen and recognized as containing an unknown wormlike animal but were not subjected to close study at the time. It seems probable that pogonophore tubes have been repeatedly collected in deep-sea dredgings but not recognized as of particular significance.

VI. RELATIONSHIPS

It is not open to doubt that the Pogonophora belong to the Deuterostomia. This is sufficiently evidenced by the body regionation into three parts accompanied by the typical subdivisions of the coelom, further by the enterocoelous mode of formation of the coelom. Among the deuterostomes, the Pogonophora appear most closely related to the Hemichordata. Similarities are the single protocoel with a pair of coelomoducts and pores to the exterior, the presence of a pericardial sac in at least some pogonophores, the location of the gonads in the trunk, the intra-epidermal position of the nervous system, the strong septum between mesosome and trunk, a general similarity in cross sections of the trunk region, an encroachment of muscle fibers and connective tissue on the coelom with loss of a definite peritoneum, and indications of incipient metamerism in the trunk region although there seems to be no counterpart in hemichordates of the adhesive papillae of pogonophores with their armature. However, the inclusion of Pogonophora in Hemichordata is not admissible. Primary and important differences are that in pogono-phores the main nervous mass is located in the protosome and the tentacular apparatus springs from the protosome and contains coelomic exten-sions of the protocoel, whereas in hemichordates the main nervous mass is situated in the mesosome and the tentaculated arms of ptero-branchs are borne by the mesosome and contain coelomic extensions of the mesocoels. It is very doubtful that there is any homology at all between the tentacles of pogonophores and the tentaculated arms of pterobranchs. The point mentioned by Ivanov (1955) that the heart is dorsal in hemichordates and ventral in pogonophores lacks force because it is not certain which is the dorsal and which the ventral side of pogono-phores. The position of the gonopores is not decisive, either, as the gonopores are dorsal in pterobranchs. The lack of gill slits in pogono-phores is irrelevant since they have no digestive tract, anyway. Another main difference is that the coelomoducts of the protocoel in pogonophores appear to be differentiated as nephridia. Pogonophores lack mesocoelic coelomoducts, and hemichordates lack metacoelic coelomoducts, repre-sented in pogonophores by the gonoducts.

One must agree with Ivanov that the Pogonophora constitute a dis-tinct phylum of animals. They are unique among free-living Metazoa in the total absence of a digestive tract.

VII. CONCLUDING REMARKS ON THE DEUTEROSTOMIA

The present chapter concludes the consideration of the enterocoelous coelomates which was begun with Vol. IV. The evidence is convincing that the phyla Echinodermata, Hemichordata, Pogonophora, and Chor-data constitute an assemblage of related forms that can justifiably be united under one concept, that of Deuterostomia, here regarded as synonymous with the expression enterocoelous coelomates. Main char-acters of the invertebrate Deuterostomia are the retention of the blasto-pore or its site as anus, the origin of the coelom as archenteral outpouch-ings, and the division of the coelom into protocoel, mesocoel, and metacoel, all probably paired primitively. Chemically the phyla are characterized by a total want of chitin and the occurrence of creatine phosphagen in at least some members of each phylum (not tested in Pogonophora at present writing).

The inclusion of Chaetognatha in this assemblage remains doubtful and rests mainly on the enterocoelous mode of formation of their coelom and the retention of the blastopore site as the location of the future anus. But the chaetognaths have but two pairs of coelomic subdivisions, and the grasping spines consist of chitin. Chaetognatha may perhaps be regarded as an early offshoot of the main deuterostomatous line.

Although the Deuterostomia constitute a phylogenetic unit, the author vigorously opposes regarding this unit as a phylum and reducing its member phyla to the rank of subphyla. Each of the member groups is constructed on a definite plan that differs sufficiently from the plans of the other groups and warrants ranking each group as a phylum. The author is not favorable to the concept of superphylum applied by some to the concept Deuterostomia. Marcus (1958) divides the Deuterostomia into two superphyla, one to include Echinodermata and Hemichordata, also now no doubt Pogonophora, and one to comprise the Chordata.

The remaining chapters of this book and the future volumes will deal with the protostomatous coelomates, which the author previously assembled under the category Schizocoela. In view of the varying modes of coelom formation in the lophophorate phyla it now appears difficult to maintain this category and it will be called instead protostomatous coelomates, in contrast with deuterostomatous coelomates. The author positively rejects the concepts, of which more at the end of this volume, that all Bilateria are coelomate and that all coeloms are of the enterocoelous category.

Bibliography

Caullery, M. 1914. Sur les Siboglinidae. C. R. Acad. Sci. Paris 158; Bull. Soc. Zool. France 39. 1944. Siboglinum. Siboga Exped. Monogr. 25 bis, livr. 138. 1948. Le genre Siboglinum. *In* **P. Grassé** (ed.), *Traité de zoologie*, vol. XI. **Dawydoff, C.** 1948. Contribution à la connaissance de Siboglinum. Bull. Biol. France Belgique 82. **De Beer, G.** 1955. The Pogonophora. Nature, London, 176. **Ivanov, A. V.** 1949. A new representative of the class Pogonophora. Zool. Zhurn. 28. 1951. On the affiliation of the genus Siboglinum with the class Pogonophora. C. R. (Doklady) Acad. Sci. U.S.S.R. 76. 1952. New Pogonophora from far eastern seas. Zool. Zhurn. 31. Translation, 1954, by **A. Petrunkevitch** in System. Zool. 3. 1955. The main features of the organisation of the Pogonophora. On external digestion in Pogonophora. On the assignment of the class Pogonophora to a separate phylum of Deuterostomata—Brachiata. C. S. (Doklady) Acad. Sci. U.S.S.R. 100; translation by **A. Petrunkevitch** in System. Zool. 4. 1956. On the systematic position of Pogonophora. System. Zool. 5. 1957a. Neue Pogonophora aus dem nordwestlichen Teil des Stillen Ozeans. Zool. Jahrb. Abt. System. 85. 1957b. Materials on the embryology of Pogonophora. Zool. Zhurn. 36. **Jägersten, G.** 1956. Investigations on Siboglinum ekmani encountered in Skagerak. Zool. Bidrag 31. 1957. On the larva of Siboglinum. Zool. Bidrag 32. **Johannson, K.** 1937.

Über Lamellisabella zachsi. Zool. Anz. 117. 1939. Lamellisabella zachsi. Zool. Bidrag 18. **Kirkegaard, J.** 1956a. Pogonophora, Galathealinum. Galathea Repts. 2. 1956b. Pogonophora, first records from the eastern Pacific. Galathea Repts. 2. **Marcus, E.** 1958. On the evolution of the animal phyla. Quart. Rev. Biol. 33. **Reisinger, E.** 1938. Pogonofora. Fortschritte Zool. 3, for 1937. **Ulrich, W.** 1949. Über die systematische Stellung einer neuen Tierklasse. Sitzungsber. Dtsch. Akad. Wissensch. Berlin, Math. Natur. Kl., no. 2. **Uschakav, P.** 1933. Eine neue Form der Familie Sabellidae. Zool. Anz. 104.

CHAPTER XIX

THE LOPHOPHORATE COELOMATES—PHYLUM PHORONIDA

I. HISTORICAL

The first scientific notice of the phylum was the finding by Joh. Müller (1846, 1847) in the autumn of 1845 of the characteristic larva swimming in numbers at the surface of the sea near Helgoland. Müller named the creature, which he thought to be an adult animal, *Actinotrocha branchiata*, and gave some good figures of it. Further illustrations were furnished by Wagener (1847), a student of Müller's who had accompanied him on his collecting excursions at Helgoland. *Actinotrocha* was next seen at Messina by Gegenbaur (1854), who correctly placed it as a larval stage. The adult phoronid was discovered on English coasts by Wright (1856a, b), who first found an aggregation of the worms in their tubes on a stone occupied by the solitary coral *Caryophyllia*, and later another species on an oyster shell permeated with the boring sponge *Cliona*. Wright created for the worms the name *Phoronis* (from Greek mythology)[1] but of course had no idea of their relation to the actinotroch larva. Transformation of actinotrochs into a tentaculate vermiform adult was seen at Messina by Krohn (1857, 1858) and at Helgoland by Schneider (1862), who considered the resulting worm to be a sipunculoid, but it remained for Kowalevsky (1867), who also followed the metamorphosis, to realize that the actinotroch is the larval stage of Wright's worm *Phoronis*. Kowalevsky's work was followed by the classical study of . Metschnikoff (1871) on the metamorphosis of the actinotroch. Thereafter through the rest of the nineteenth century and into the first decade of the twentieth numerous studies were published on the anatomy and embryology of phoronids, but there is very little in the way of recent literature on the group.

The name Phoronida for the group dates from Hatschek (1888), and the alternative spelling, often used, Phoronidea, from Lang (1888). The former is here adopted as more suitable for the rank of phylum.

Main works on the Phoronida are the classical monograph of Selys Longchamps (1907) and the somewhat unsatisfactory accounts of Cori in the *Handbuch der Zoologie* (1937) and in Bronn's *Klassen und Ordnungen des Tierreichs* (1939).

II. INTRODUCTION TO THE LOPHOPHORATE PHYLA

With the Phoronida we begin the study of three groups of coelomates— Phoronida, Ectoprocta, and Brachiopoda—that have in common the possession of a lophophore. A relationship of these three groups was

---

[1] According to the International Rules of Zoological Nomenclature the name of a larva proposed before the discovery of the adult animal to which it belongs has valid priority. It is therefore self-evident that *Actinotrocha* is the valid name of the genus usually called *Phoronis*, as Poche (1903) early insisted. Application has been made to the International Commission of Zoological Nomenclature for a ruling validating *Phoronis* (Silén, 1952).

first surmised by Caldwell (1882), but it remained for Hatschek (1888) to express this relationship by making them classes of a phylum Tentaculata, which excluded Entoprocta as well as other groups with which varied arrangements had been made by a succession of preceding authors.   However, the name Tentaculata is unfortunate, for tentacles occur in many unrelated animal groups; further, this name had already been used by Lankester in an entirely different sense.   The name Lophophorata would have been far more appropriate, and here the three groups in question will be referred to as the lophophorate phyla, or lophophorates.   The common possession by these three phyla of a lophophore of similar construction and similar relationship to the body morphology leaves no doubt of their close affinity.

A lophophore is defined as a tentaculated extension of the mesosome that embraces the mouth but not the anus and has a coelomic lumen. This definition automatically excludes the Entoprocta, whose tentacular provision is not regarded as a lophophore by the author, and it also excludes the tentaculated arms of pterobranchs and the tentacles of pogonophores.   By some the term lophophore is limited to the basal ridge that bears the tentacles, but this appears an artificial distinction and the whole structure will be called lophophore or tentacular crown. The shape of the lophophore varies.   Probably the horseshoe shape is the original one; it is retained in Phoronida, phylactolaematous Ectoprocta, and some Brachiopoda.   The circular shape of the gymnolaematous lophophore is known from ontogeny to derive from a crescentic condition. The greatest variation in shape occurs among brachiopods, in which the primitive shape of the lophophore is alleged to be a circular disk.

Theoretically the body of lophophorates is regionated, as in deuterostomes, into three parts, protosome, mesosome, and metasome, and each part contains a coelomic division, protocoel, mesocoel, and metacoel; but these assumptions are poorly supported by embryology and by adult morphology.   The lophophore appears to be borne by the mesosome, and its coelomic lumen is part of the mesocoel, but the protosome and protocoel are scarcely present and the main nervous system is situated in the mesosome.

Presumably the ancestral type of the Lophophorata was a vermiform animal with body regionated into head, lophophoral region, and trunk, but the head appears to have undergone practically complete degeneration, probably as a consequence of a sessile or sedentary mode of life. The regionation is now mainly indicated by the presence of a coelomic septum located just behind the lophophoral base and separating the mesocoel from the metacoel fairly well, except in brachiopods, in which this septum is very imperfect.   The author rejects altogether the idea that the body regions of tentaculates and deuterostomes are directly related to annelid segmentation. They are not segments in any valid sense of this term.

It is characteristic of lophophorates that the digestive tract is recurved, bringing the anus near the mouth and shortening the true dorsal surface. A median posterior position of the anus is seen only in the brachiopod genus *Crania*, where it may be primitive since this genus has other generalized features.

Metanephridia are present in Phoronida and Brachiopoda but are wanting without trace in Ectoprocta, and the same is true of a circulatory system.

Lophophorates generally produce free-swimming larvae that are interpreted as trochophores. This ranges the lophophorates in the Protostomia despite the fact that the Brachiopoda are enterocoelous. The Lophophorata thus seem to form some sort of link between the Protostomia and the Deuterostomia.

III. CHARACTERS OF THE PHYLUM

1. Definition.—The Phoronida are tubicolous, vermiform coelomates with a terminal lophophore in the form of a horseshoe that embraces the mouth, with a recurved digestive tract having the anal opening near the mouth, with a closed circulatory system containing red blood corpuscles, and with a pair of metanephridia that also act as gonoducts.

2. General Characters.—The Phoronida are slender solitary worms that inhabit a tube of their own secretion. The body, not obviously regionated, presents as its most conspicuous feature the terminal crown of tentacles or *lophophore*, consisting of a single row of tentacles borne on a double ridge of the body wall, curved into a crescentic shape. The mouth, situated between the two ridges of the lophophore, leads into a long tubular digestive tract that, after presenting a stomachic enlargement, recurves at the posterior end of the worm and then runs anteriorly, paralleling its former course, to terminate with the anus, located dorsal to the mouth outside the lophophore. There is a diffuse intraepidermal nervous layer that is concentrated into a main nervous field located between mouth and anus and continuous with a nerve ring in the base of the outer ridge of the lophophore. The trunk is supplied by a lateral nerve, actually a giant fiber, usually present on the left side only. The trunk interior is occupied by a coelom corresponding to the metacoel of hemichordates and separated from anterior coelomic cavities by a transverse septum at the level of the lophophoral base. The circulatory system, containing red corpuscles, is mainly of the closed type and is constituted of two longitudinal trunk vessels continuous posteriorly and opening anteriorly into ring vessels in the lophophoral coelom. A pair of metanephridia is present in the anterior end of the trunk, opening by a

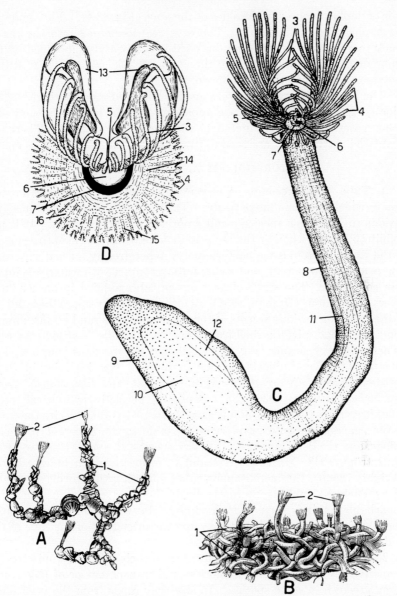

FIG. 82.—Phoronida, external features. *A*, some specimens of *Phoronis psammophila*, with tubes coated with rock grains and shells. *B*, aggregation of *P. hippocrepia*. (*A, B, after Shipley*, 1910.) *C*, *Phoronis architecta*, young adult (*after Wilson*, 1881). *D, P. architecta*, looking into the tentacular crown, only bases of outer tentacles shown; mature adult with fully developed lophophoral organs (*after Brooks* and *Cowles*, 1905). 1, tube; 2, tentacular crown; 3, inner tentacles; 4, outer tentacles; 5, gap in inner tentacles where new ones form; 6, epistome; 7, mouth; 8, trunk; 9, end bulb; 10, stomach; 11, prestomach; 12, intestine; 13, lophophoral organs; 14, haemal ring in lophophore; 15, blood vessels to tentacles; 16, fused tentacle bases.

pair of nephridiopores to the sides of the anus (Fig. 83*A*).   Phoronids are hermaphroditic or dioecious.   The eggs are discharged into the sea or stuck to objects or, most often, brooded in a concavity embraced by the lophophore.   They develop into the characteristic *actinotroch* larva that metamorphoses into the juvenile worm.

The Phoronida are exclusively marine and are found sparingly over a wide geographical range but are apparently absent from polar and sub-polar waters.   They are limited to the upper littoral zone.   There are about 15 known species assigned to two genera, *Phoronis* and *Phoronopsis*.

IV. MORPHOLOGY AND DEVELOPMENT

1. Tube.—All phoronids occupy a cylindrical tube of their own secre-tion in which they can move freely.   These tubes usually occur in aggre-gations that in some species result from asexual propagation.   It is not definitely known whether the secretion emanates from the entire surface of the worm or from some part thereof.   When freshly formed the secre-tion is fluid, transparent, and sticky but on contact with water sets into a firm condition.   The secreted part of the tube, applied in one or more layers, is chitinous (Hyman, 1958).   During the sticky phase there adhere to the secretion various objects of the environment as sand grains, minute pebbles, sponge spicules, shell fragments, and the like, that give the tube its definitive appearance (Fig. 82*A*), although often a short length of clear tube free of adhered objects remains at the top.   Species living in sandy bottom, as *Phoronis architecta* (Andrews, 1890) and *Phoronopsis viridis* and *striata* (Hilton, 1930), have separate, perfectly cylindrical, erect tubes, covered with a layer of fine sand grains.   In other species the tubes of the aggregation may form an inextricable tangle adherent to shells, pilings, and the like (Fig. 82*B*).   In two species, *P. ovalis* (Harmer, 1917; Brattström, 1943; Marcus, 1949) and *P. hippocrepia* (includes *gracilis*) (Wright, 1856b), the membranous tubes enclosing the worms are them-selves enclosed in burrows in mollusk shells or calcareous rock.   A remarkable habit is seen in *P. australis* (Haswell, 1893; Ikeda, 1902), whose delicate transparent tubes occupy the interstices of the tube of the cnidarian *Cerianthus*.

2. External Characters.—Removed from their tubes phoronids reveal themselves as slender worms, colorless and transparent or of pale color-ation, greenish in some species.   In size they range from the very small *P. ovalis*, about 6 mm. long with 18 to 25 tentacles, to *Phoronopsis viridis*, about 200 mm. long with around 300 tentacles.   The length of most species lies below 100 mm.   Main parts of the body are the tentacular crown at the anterior end and the long, slender trunk (Fig. 82*C*).

The tentacles are borne in a single row along both ridges of a double ridge of the body wall, curved into the shape of a crescent or horseshoe

(Fig. 82C). Tentacles and ridges will here be considered to constitute the *lophophore*, or *tentacular crown*, although many authors limit the term lophophore to the ridges. This appears an artificial distinction since tentacles and ridges form one unit of continuous tissue. The convexly curved ridge of the lophophore runs ventral to the mouth and is termed *external* or *outer;* the concavely curved ridge passes dorsal to the mouth and is called *internal* or *inner*. The limbs of the crescent or horseshoe are therefore directed dorsally and in some species are spirally rolled (Fig. 83A, B), thus providing space for a great increase in the number of tentacles, which varies in different species from about 20 to over 500, possibly even to a thousand. The spiral coils are double like the rest of the lophophore.

In the median line of the inner row of tentacles occurs a break (Fig. 83A), to each side of which new tentacles arise; hence the youngest and shortest tentacles are found in the middle of the inner row. In *P. mülleri* (but not in any other species), a site of tentacle formation (without any gap) occurs in the middle of the outer row also. The number of tentacles thus increases with age and is somewhat variable within a given species. Apart from the growing zone or zones the tentacles are of about the same length throughout the crown. They are hollow, slender, ciliated extensions of the body wall, laterally flattened, hence oval in cross section (Fig. 83C). They are basally fused, forming a membrane bordering the mouth and buccal grooves (Fig. 82D) and continuous with the lophophoral ridges.

The mouth, located midventrally between the two lophophoral ridges, is a large, dorsoventrally flattened, crescentic aperture, continuous at its angles with the *buccal grooves* found between the lophophoral ridges throughout their length, including the spiral coils when present. The mouth is overhung dorsally by a rounded to crescentic fold of body wall, the *epistome* or upper lip (Fig. 82D), situated ventral to the median part of the inner lophophoral ridge. The anterior surface of the animal forms a concavity, used as a brood chamber, bounded laterally by the limbs (arms) of the lophophore and dorsally by a projection bearing three pores, medially the anus and laterally the two nephridiopores (Fig. 83A). A plane bisecting the mouth and epistome and passing through the anus constitutes the medial sagittal plane of the animal, which is thus bilaterally symmetrical, at least anteriorly.

The concavity of the lophophore may be provided with a pair of *lophophoral organs* that vary greatly with species and season and appear definitely absent in some phoronids. In others they take the form of a pair of glandular depressions partly covered by a flap of body wall (Figs. 83A, B, 85B, C). In still others or at seasons they form conspicuous white earlike thickenings of the dorsal epidermis of the bases of the inner tentacles (Figs. 82D, 85A). Each lophophoral organ is connected with

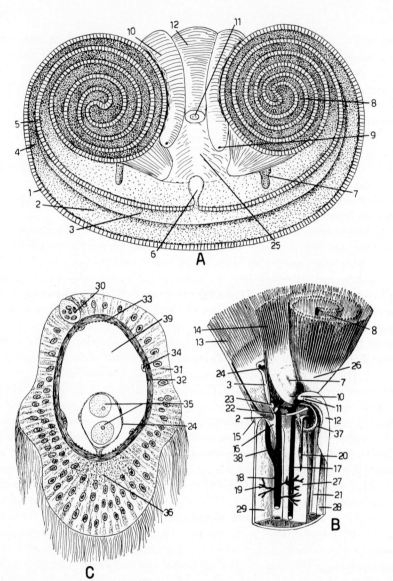

Fig. 83.—Lophophore. *A*, view looking into anterior end of *P. australis*, showing spirally rolled type of lophophore; tentacles cut off at base (*after Benham, 1889*). *B*, anterior end of *P. australis*, cut vertically (*after Shipley, 1910, altered from Benham, 1889*). *C*, cross section of a phoronid tentacle (*after Selys Longchamps, 1907*). 1, outer ridge of lophophore; 2, mouth; 3, epistome; 4, buccal groove; 5, inner ridge of lophophore; 6, gap in inner ridge where new tentacles form; 7, lophophoral organ in the form of a glandular depression; 8, spiral coil of lophophore; 9, nephridiopore; 10, nephridial ridge; 11, anus; 12, rectal ridge; 13, outer tentacles; 14, inner tentacles; 15, nerve ring; 16, esophagus; 17, median vessel; 18, lateral vessel; 19, capillary caeca of lateral vessel; 20, nephridial funnel; 21, intestine; 22, septum; 23, lophophoral ring vessel; 24, tentacular vessel; 25, lophophoral concavity; 26, fused tentacular bases; 27, lateral mesentery; 28, dorsal mesentery; 29, ventral mesentery; 30, gland cell; 31, epidermis; 32, basement membrane; 33, longitudinal muscle fibers; 34, peritoneum; 35, red blood corpuscles; 36, main tentacular nerve; 37, nephridium; 38, forking of lateral vessel; 39, tentacular coelom.

the nephridiopore of its side by a ciliated groove. The possible function of the lophophoral organs is discussed later under reproduction.

In the genus *Phoronis* the tentacular crown is demarcated from the trunk by a slight groove, whereas in *Phoronopsis* a high, anteriorly directed, collarlike fold occurs here, widest laterally and diminishing toward the median lines (Fig. 84*C*).

The trunk is slender and cylindrical, without appendages of any kind, and of uniform diameter except for the posterior end, which is enlarged into an *end bulb* (Fig. 82*C*), badly called *ampulla* by most authors. The trunk is usually faintly annulated.

3. Body Wall.—This consists of epidermis, basement membrane, layer of circular muscles, layer of longitudinal muscles, and peritoneum (Fig. 84*B*). The epidermal epithelium varies in height from flattened to columnar in various body regions and contains neurosensory cells and gland cells (Fig. 84*A*). A thin cuticle appears generally present, best developed on the outer surface of the lophophore (Fig. 84*B*) and diminishing from there to the vanishing point along the trunk. The tentacular epidermis is heavily ciliated, at least along its inner side (Fig. 83*C*), but ciliation is sparse elsewhere and probably limited to the anterior part of the trunk. The gland cells are plump cells filled with coarse granules or spherules of varying sizes (Fig. 84*A*) or with homogeneous masses of secretion (Figs. 84*A*, 89*C*). Gland cells are numerous on the outer surfaces of the tentacles (Fig. 83*C*), very abundant on the outer surfaces of the lophophore (Fig. 84*B*), and fairly abundant on the anterior part of the trunk (Figs. 84*B*, 89*C*); from there the gland cells diminish in number posteriorly but are thickly present on the tip of the end bulb. In *P. ovalis* Marcus (1949) noted two sorts of granular gland cells, acidophilous and basiphilous, and ascribed the secretion of the chitinous tube to the former. However, Silén (1952), studying several species, attributed the secretion of the tube to the type of gland cell filled with a homogeneous mass of secretion. This type occurs abundantly on the anterior part of the trunk (Figs. 84*B*, 89*C*), also at the tip of the end bulb. Possibly the latter area begins the formation of the tube as a thin film, and the much more extensive secretion from the anterior trunk is added layer by layer to increase the thickness of the tube. The lophophoral organs when present are also sites of glandular epidermis. When these organs take the form of glandular depressions beneath an overhanging flap of body wall (Fig. 85*B*), the epidermis of the depression is composed almost solidly of gland cells (Fig. 85*C*). Gland cells are also abundantly present on the more highly developed types of lophophoral organs. A nervous layer occurs throughout the body in the base of the epidermis, and this everywhere gives off to the surface groups of neurosensory cells (Figs. 84*A*, 87) located between the ordinary epidermal cells. The epidermis is underlain by a strong base-

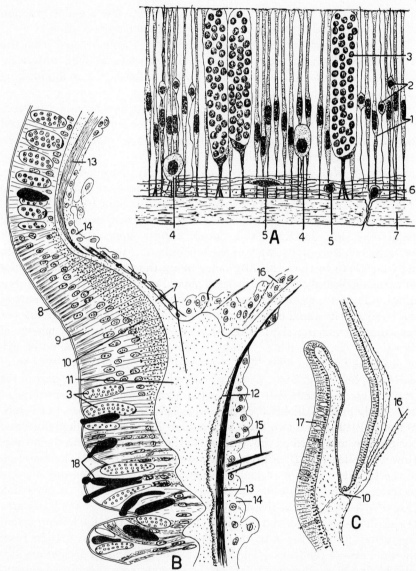

FIG. 84.—Structure of the body wall.   A, scheme of the epidermis (*after Silén*, 1954a).
B, longitudinal section of the body wall just below the lophophore (*after Selys Longchamps*,
1907).   C, vertical section, one side only, of anterior part of *Phoronopsis harmeri*, to show
collar fold (*after Pixell*, 1912).   1, ordinary epidermal cells; 2, neurosensory cells; 3, granular gland cell; 4, unipolar nerve cells; 5, bipolar nerve cells; 6, motor cell with axone passing
through basement membrane; 7, basement membrane; 8, cuticle; 9, epidermis; 10, nerve
ring; 11, thickening of basement membrane; 12, circular muscle layer; 13, longitudinal
muscle layer; 14, peritoneum; 15, radial muscles for esophagus; 16, septum; 17, collar
fold; 18, gland cells with homogeneous contents.

ment membrane, very thick in the base of the lophophore (Fig. 84B) and in the tentacles (Fig. 83C).

To the inner side of the basement membrane is found the muscular layer of the body wall, typically developed in the trunk region. Here an outer thin layer of circular fibers is followed by a more strongly developed longitudinal layer. The latter occurs as a simple layer only at the two ends of the trunk; toward the trunk middle the fibers become more and more aggregated into bundles, and these project more and more into the coelom as folds, often very high (Fig. 86A, B). These muscle folds were formerly conceived as composed of fibers arranged featherlike along both sides of a central plasmatic material, but Silén (1952) finds the folds formed by increasing heights of the fibers (Fig. 86C) and also notes groups of low fibers between the bases of the tall ones (Fig. 86C). By means of these folds the number of muscle fibers possible in a given area is thus increased, and understandably the middle part of the phoronid trunk is extremely muscular and contractile. The number of muscle folds in a cross section varies with species in known cases from 18 to 129 and may not be constant in different individuals of the same species. There are 18 bundles in P. pallida (Fig. 86B), 5 in the ventrolateral coelomic chambers and 4 in the dorsolateral ones. Very numerous bundles occur in Phoronopsis harmeri, about 126 (Fig. 86A). The muscle bundles are stated to be often taller and more numerous on the left side, but published figures show them as often taller ventrally than dorsally. In Fig. 86A, they are tallest in the ventrolateral coelomic compartment. In the end bulb, the longitudinal layer reduces to a simple, weakly developed condition, and in the rear part of the end bulb the muscle layers are reversed, with the circular fibers to the inner side (Fig. 86D). The muscle fibers are of the smooth type. The longitudinal trunk fibers are said by Silén to be syncytial with their nuclei relegated to their bases since no nuclei are seen in the folds.

An unusual arrangement of the trunk musculature obtains in P. pallidus (Silén, 1952). The trunk anterior to the end bulb can be constricted into three regions by the formation of sphincters, produced by increase of height of the circular fibers into a platelike shape (Fig. 86D). The degree of development of the muscle folds and of the low fibers between their bases varies in these three regions.

The body wall is lined by peritoneum, mostly evident as a nucleated syncytial layer. In the region of the muscle folds, the peritoneum bulges between the bases of the folds but is greatly thinned over their surface, where in fact it is represented chiefly by a few nuclei.

The tentacles, being protrusions of the body wall, consist of the same layers as the latter. They are oval in cross section, clothed with a columnar ciliated epithelium, much taller and more heavily ciliated on the

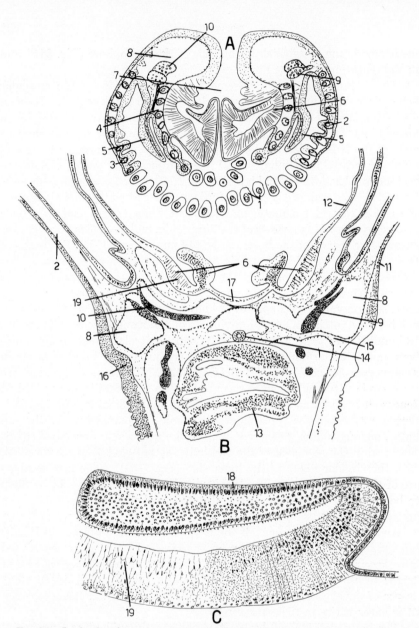

FIG. 85.—Lophophoral organs. *A*, section through the base of the tentacular crown of *P. psammophila* with highly developed lophophoral organs. *B*, vertical section through anterior end of *P. hippocrepia*. (*A, B, after Selys Longchamps*, 1907.) *C*, section through lophophoral organ of *P. australis;* organ here is glandular depression (*after Benham*, 1889). 1, sections of tentacle bases; 2, coelom of tentacle; 3, outer tentacles; 4, inner tentacles; 5, epistome; 6, lophophoral organ; 7, concavity of lophophore; 8, lophophoral coelom; 9, afferent ring vessel; 10, efferent ring vessel; 11, outer ridge of lophophore; 12, inner ridge of lophophore; 13, esophagus; 14, rectum; 15, septum; 16, location of nerve ring; 17, location of main nervous field; 18, overhanging flap of body wall; 19, glandular area.

inner than the outer surface (Fig. 83*C*), and provided with gland cells and groups of neurosensory cells. The nervous layer is greatly thickened in the inner side of the tentacle, forming there a tentacular nerve (Fig. 83*C*): and a similar but less developed nerve courses in the outer side of the tentacle (Silén, 1954a). The tentacles are provided with an especially strong and thick basement membrane that acts as a supporting skeleton; they are therefore rather stiff with but slight powers of movement. The circular muscle layer appears wanting, but a few longitudinal fibers occur to the inner side of the basement membrane at each end of the oval (Fig. 83*C*). Finally, the lumen is lined by peritoneum and encloses a conspicuous blood vessel adherent to the peritoneum.

The outer surface of the lophophore is richly furnished with gland cells, and in the interior the basement membrane is especially thickened as a skeletal support, consisting of two slightly different layers. The lophophore in general lacks muscularity, being provided with only a few longitudinal fibers.

4. Nervous System.—The classical account of the nervous system found in the monographs of Selys Longchamps and Cori requires alteration in the light of the fresh and extensive researches on this system by Silén (1954a). The entire body wall is provided with a nervous layer situated in the base of the epidermis and consisting of horizontal fibers and bipolar and unipolar nerve cell bodies (Fig. 84*A*). From the nervous layer numerous sensory nerve cells, typically in groups, ascend in the epidermis to the surface (Figs. 84*A*, 87); they are the usual filamentous cells with a terminal bristle and a central bulge containing the nucleus. Axones from motor cells near the basement membrane penetrate the latter into the muscle layers of the trunk.

At the anterior end of the body the general nervous layer is continuous with a nervous center in the form of a ring, located intraepidermally along the outer ridge of the lophophore, at the level of the septum. This ring is broadest and thickest middorsally in the lophophore concavity between the epistome and the anal papilla, and this middorsal part of the nerve ring may be regarded as the main nervous center (*preoral nervous field* of Silén), although it is not as definitely delimited as a brain as supposed by earlier authors. The nerve ring gives off a nerve to each of the outer tentacles. In species with a simple crescentic lophophore, the inner lophophoral ridge and tentacles are supplied directly from the preoral nervous field since this is already in contact with the concavity of the inner ridge. Where the lophophoral arms are spirally coiled a tract from the preoral nervous field accompanies each spiral. A tract is similarly given off into each of the lophophoral organs. Motor fibers from the nerve ring pass through the basement membrane into the anterior ends of the longitudinal muscle bundles of the trunk.

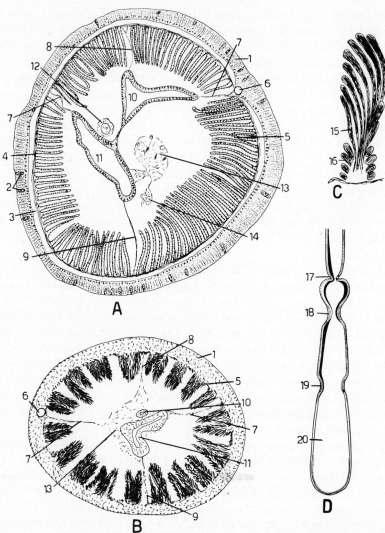

Fig. 86.—Muscular system. *A*, section through muscular part of trunk of *Phoronopsis harmeri*, showing muscle ridges (*after Pixell*, 1912). *B*, section through muscular part of trunk of *P. pallida*. *C*, one muscle bundle of *P. pallida*. *D*, scheme of muscles of *P. pallida;* dots indicate circular muscles, black relative thickness of longitudinal muscles. (*B–D, after Silén*, 1952.) 1, epidermis; 2, gland cells; 3, basement membrane; 4, circular muscle layer; 5, longitudinal muscle ridges; 6, lateral nerve; 7, lateral mesentery; 8, dorsal mesentery; 9, ventral mesentery; 10, intestine; 11, prestomach; 12, median vessel; 13, vasoperitoneal tissue; 14, lateral vessel; 15, high fibers of bundle; 16, low or marginal fibers of bundle; 17–19, three successive sphincters; 20, end bulb, circular fibers inside.

There is present in phoronids but one so-called nerve, the *lateral* nerve, actually a giant fiber. This is generally present on the left side only, but in a few species a right lateral nerve, equal to or smaller than the left one, also exists; lateral nerves are altogether absent from the very small *P. ovalis*. The single left lateral nerve originates in one or more motor cells (Figs. 87, 88*B*) in the right side of the middorsal part of the nerve ring, passes in the nerve ring to the left side, leaves its epidermal position to run along the left nephridium, and then reenters the epidermis, where it remains throughout the rest of its course, in the left dorsolateral trunk wall at the site of attachment of the left lateral mesentery, disappearing at the beginning of the end bulb. When a right lateral nerve is present, this originates in the left side of the middorsal part of the nerve ring and crosses to the right side, continuing along the trunk at the site of attachment of the right lateral mesentery. Thus the lateral nerves decussate in the nervous center, as appears typical of giant fibers generally. In general, the lateral nerve is a cylindrical fiber enclosed in a thick sheath. In some species, however, notably *P. hippocrepia*, the nerve and its sheath constantly subdivide and reunite again, forming a succession of irregular links (Fig. 88*B*). The lateral nerves give off transverse branches through the basement membrane into the trunk musculature and function to bring about quick, synchronous contraction of the latter.

The sensory equipment of phoronids is limited to the neurosensory cells mentioned above that occur abundantly in groups on the muscular part of the trunk and on the tentacles (Hilton, 1922; Silén, 1954a) but are sparse on the end bulb and over the nerve ring. A special cluster of these neurosensory cells occurs in connection with the glandular type of lophophoral organ, on the outer medial side of the covering flap (Fig. 88*A*). Silén (1954a), who discovered this group of sense cells, terms it *lophophoral sense organ*.

5. Coelom.—The coelom is separated into two main parts, the trunk coelom or metacoel, and the coelom of the tentacular crown, by a slightly oblique septum or diaphragm attached to the body wall at about the level of the nerve ring and embracing the esophagus (Fig. 85*B*). The metacoel is embryologically provided only with a midventral mesentery since a middorsal mesentery is never formed; but a secondary dorsal mesentery supporting the intestine is usually present in adult worms. There are also typically present in the adult other secondary mesenteries, especially a right and left lateral mesentery (Fig. 86*A*, *B*). Thus the metacoel is usually divided into four longitudinal compartments, two ventrolateral and two dorsolateral ones; but as the lateral mesenteries are much displaced dorsally, the ventrolateral compartments are much the larger (Fig. 86*A*). The typical arrangement obtains chiefly in the middle muscular part of the trunk, being less perfect at the two ends, where the

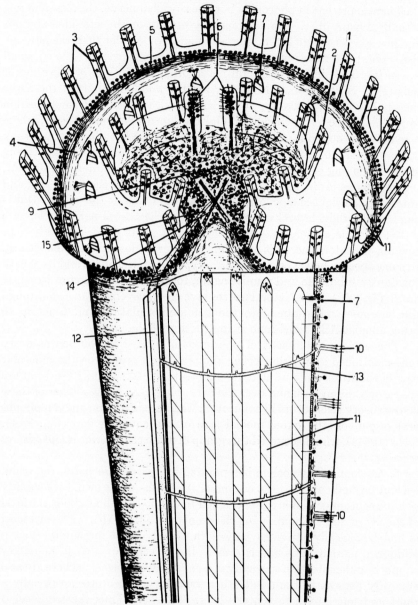

Fig. 87.—Scheme of the nervous system of phoronids (*after Silén*, 1954a). 1, outer tentacles; 2, inner tentacles; 3, neurosensory cells of tentacles; 4, nerve ring; 5, unipolar cells of nerve ring; 6, lophophoral sense organs; 7, motor neurones for upper ends of muscle bundles; 8, tentacular nerve; 9, main nervous field; 10, groups of neurosensory cells of trunk; 11, longitudinal muscle bundles of trunk; 12, lateral nerve (giant fiber); 13, transverse branch of giant fiber; 14, decussating tracts for anal region; 15, decussation of giant fiber.

various compartments may run together. The mesenteries are thin membranes composed of two layers of peritoneum, sometimes enclosing radial muscle fibers. The metacoel opens to the exterior by way of the nephridia, which therefore constitute coelomoducts.

Anterior to the septum the coelom consists of the cavities of the epistome, lophophore, and tentacles, all in communication with each other (Fig. 85*B*). The cavity of the epistome, crossed by numerous strands of connective and muscle fibers, communicates at its sides with the coelom of the lophophore, and the latter is continuous with the coelomic canals of the tentacles. The parts of the coelom anterior to the septum lack openings to the exterior.

The coelom contains a colorless fluid, probably slightly albuminous, since it throws down a granular precipitate with fixatives. In the coelomic fluid are found red blood corpuscles, spindle bodies (Fig. 91*B*) of unknown purpose, and four kinds of coelomocytes (Ohuye, 1942): hyaline phagocytic amoebocytes that put out broad, thin pseudopods, eosinophilous granulocytes, basophilous granulocytes, and nonmotile rounded cells with large eosinophilous inclusions (Fig. 88*C–E*). In species with a colored tentacular crown, motile pigmented cells are generally present in the lophophoral coelom.

6. Nephridia.—Phoronids are provided with a pair of nephridia that classify as metanephridia (II, page 46) and constitute the ducts of the metacoel. They are situated in a retroperitoneal position in the anterior end of the metacoel close to the posterior face of the septum. Where the lateral mesenteries extend anteriorly to the septum the proximal parts of the nephridia are found between the two layers of these mesenteries (Fig. 88*G*). Each nephridium is a U-shaped tube composed entirely of ciliated epithelium, covered with peritoneum on the side toward the metacoel. In most species the nephridium begins with a simple oval opening into the metacoel near the median dorsal wall of the esophagus. However, in several species each nephridium opens into the metacoel by two funnels, a small median one opening into the ventrolateral chamber of the metacoel and a much larger one opening into the dorsolateral chamber. The rim of the larger aperture is drawn out posteriorly into a long appendage (Fig. 88*F*) supported in the lateral mesentery.

As it leaves its coelomic opening or openings, the nephridial tube is narrowed for a short distance but soon widens into the descending part of the tube that reaches the dorsal body wall by way of the lateral mesentery or other parts of the peritoneum. The tube then makes a U-turn and ascends in the dorsal body wall just outside the peritoneum to the nephridiopore on the sides of the anal papilla. These two ascending limbs of the nephridia are more or less clearly demarcated externally from

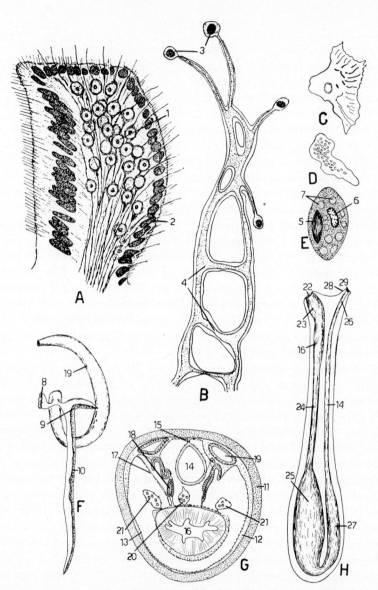

Fig. 88.—Various systems. *A*, lophophoral sense organ. *B*, cells of origin and initial part of giant fiber of *P. hippocrepia*. (*A, B, after Silén*, 1954a.) *C–E*, coelomocytes of phoronids (*after Ohuye*, 1942). *C*, phagocytic amoebocyte. *D*, granulocyte. *E*, round cell with large inclusions. *F*, nephridium of *P. australis* (*after Benham*, 1889), has two nephrostomes. *G*, section through anterior part of trunk of *P. psammophila*, showing relation of nephridia to lateral mesenteries (*after Selys Longchamps*, 1907). *H*, scheme of the digestive tract of phoronids. 1, neurosensory cells; 2, ordinary epidermal cells; 3, motor cells of origin; 4, giant fiber in links; 5, spindle body; 6, nucleus; 7, inclusions; 8, small nephrostome; 9, large nephrostome; 10, funnel appendage; 11, epidermis; 12, basement membrane; 13, peritoneum; 14, intestine; 15, dorsal mesentery; 16, esophagus; 17, lateral mesentery; 18, nephrostome; 19, nephridial tubule; 20, median vessel; 21, the two branches of the lateral vessel; 22, mouth; 23, buccal tube; 24, prestomach; 25, stomach; 26, rectum; 27, initial wide part of intestine; 28, anal papilla; 29, anus.

the rectum (Fig. 83*A*). The nephridial ducts and the rectum belong to the trunk, being situated posterior to the septum.

The nephridia presumably have excretory functions, for they are said to contain brown, refringent granules and material has been observed emerging from the nephridiopores. The nephridia also serve for the emission of sex cells.

7. Digestive System.—The digestive tract extends throughout the trunk, recurving on itself at the posterior end of the end bulb, hence having the general shape of a hairpin (Fig. 88*H*). The crescentic mouth, receiving into its angles the buccal grooves found between the two ridges of the lophophore, is overhung dorsally by the epistome and can be closed by the bending of the latter over the opening. The ciliated beginning of the digestive tract bounded dorsally by the epistome may perhaps be regarded as a buccal tube (Fig. 89*A*). It passes at once into the esophagus, characterized by its thick, folded wall and yellowish color. Its wall consists of a very tall, heavily ciliated epithelium containing some gland cells and basally a continuation of the nervous layer of the epidermis. The epithelium is supported on a well-developed basement membrane, followed externally by a layer of circular fibers. The esophagus is further attached to the body wall by radial muscle fibers continuous with the muscle layers of the latter (Fig. 89*C*). The esophagus passes insensibly into a region called *prestomach* or *proventriculus*, which is the longest part of the descending limb of the digestive tract and is distinguished from the esophagus by its cuboidal epithelium, mostly weakly ciliated (Fig. 89*F*), and by the presence of a middorsal strip of taller, strongly ciliated cells. The nervous layer apparently ceases at the posterior end of the esophagus. The prestomach appears to lack muscular investment. The prestomach extends to the end bulb where the digestive tube widens into the ovoid stomach, occupying the ventral part of the bulb. The middorsal ciliated strip continues as a ciliated groove from the prestomach along the stomach. Elsewhere the stomach wall consists of very tall, slender, poorly ciliated epithelial cells except along the sides where the epithelium bulges inward as a spongy syncytium, especially during digestion (Fig. 90*C*). External to the epithelium is found a haemal network (Fig. 90*B*) followed by a thin investment of connective tissue and muscle fibers. The stomach continues to the end of the end bulb where it constricts and passes into the intestine; this makes a forward curve and ascends along the dorsal side of the entire trunk. The part of the intestine enclosed in the end bulb differs from the rest of the intestine in its greater diameter, taller epithelium, and investment with longitudinal muscle fibers (Fig. 90*D*). The remainder of the intestine is a long, slender tube suspended from the dorsal body wall and composed of a cuboidal, slightly ciliated epithelium scarcely underlain by muscle fibers (Fig. 90*E*).

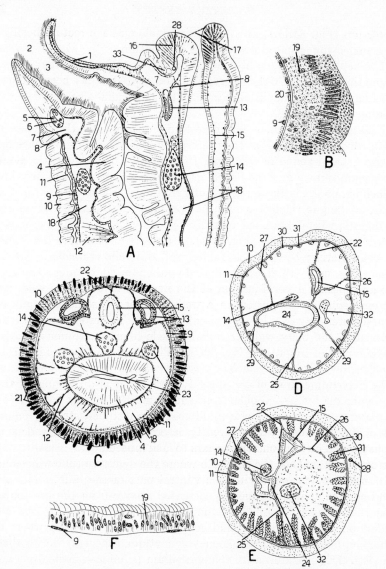

Fig. 89.—Digestive system. *A*, median sagittal section through anterior end. *B*, histology of esophagus. *C*, cross section of body through esophagus (*after Selys Longchamps*, 1904a). *D*, cross section of body through upper part of prestomach. *E*, cross section through lower part of prestomach. (*B, D, E, after Cori*, 1890.) *F*, histology of prestomach. (*A, F, after Selys Longchamps*, 1907.) 1, epistome; 2, mouth; 3, buccal tube; 4, esophagus; 5, afferent lophophoral ring vessel; 6, efferent lophophoral ring vessel; 7, lophophoral coelom; 8, septum; 9, peritoneum; 10, epidermis; 11, basement membrane; 12, radial muscles of esophagus; 13, nephridium; 14, dorsal vessel; 15, intestine; 16, anal papilla with tall epithelium; 17, anus; 18, trunk coelom; 19, epithelium; 20, muscle layer; 21, homogeneous gland cells; 22, dorsal mesentery; 23, branches of lateral vessel; 24, prestomach; 25, ventral mesentery; 26, left lateral mesentery; 27, right lateral mesentery; 28, lateral nerve; 29, accessory mesenteries; 30, circular muscle layer; 31, longitudinal muscle bundles; 32, lateral vessel; 33, main nervous field.

Gland cells have been reported only for the esophagus, possibly also the prestomach, but are shown in Ohuye's figures of the intestine of *P. australis* (Fig. 97*A*). The intestine passes without change into the rectum lodged in the anal papilla. The anus is encircled by an extremely tall, probably glandular, epidermis (Fig. 89*A*).

Rounded cells with granular contents were noted by Silén (1952) between the bases of the epithelial cells in the intestine of several species and in the esophagus of at least one species. He regarded them as elements of the epithelium, but the work of Ohuye (1942) indicates that they are coelomocytes (Fig. 97*A*). The entire digestive tract is of course clothed externally with peritoneum and is suspended by mesenteries continuous with and composed of peritoneum. In addition to the median, lateral, and accessory mesenteries already noted, a mesentery is present between the two limbs of the digestive tract (Fig. 89*D, E*).

8. Circulatory System.—The circulatory system is for the most part of the closed type. There are two longitudinal trunk vessels, a *median* or *dorsal* or *afferent* vessel in which the blood runs anteriorly, and a *lateral* or *ventral* or *efferent* vessel in which it runs posteriorly. These two vessels communicate in the extensive haemal plexus found on the stomach wall just beneath its covering peritoneum. The median vessel originates from this plexus (Fig. 90*A*) and ascends the trunk without giving off any branches, being situated between the two limbs of the digestive tract but slightly to the right, enclosed in the right dorsolateral coelomic chamber (Fig. 89*D, E*). More anteriorly it lies directly dorsal to the esophagus (Fig. 89*C*) and then passes through the septum into the lophophoral coelom, where it forks in T-fashion to become a ring vessel (actually horseshoe-shaped like the lophophore) in the lophophoral coelom. From this afferent ring vessel a vessel ascends each tentacle, situated in the inner side of the tentacular coelom (Fig. 83*C*). There is but one vessel in each tentacle, and in this the blood surges back and forth. At the tentacular base, the tentacular vessel gives off a branch that enters the efferent lophophoral ring vessel (actually horseshoe-shaped) that lies in the lophophoral coelom closely applied to the afferent ring (Fig. 85*A, B*) and collects from the tentacles. From the efferent ring a pair of branches pierce the septum and, proceeding posteriorly, dorsolateral to the esophagus (Fig. 83*B*, 89*C*), unite at about the level of the posterior end of the esophagus to form the lateral or efferent vessel. This proceeds posteriorly along the left side of the descending digestive tube, enclosed in the left ventrolateral coelomic chamber (Fig. 89*D, E*). Along most of its course but especially posteriorly it gives off numerous short lateral diverticula, also called *capillary caeca*, generally simple, but branched in *P. australis* (Benham, 1889; Fig. 91*A*) and *Phoronopsis harmeri* (Pixell, 1912), and terminates in the haemal plexus of the stomach wall (Fig. 90*A*).

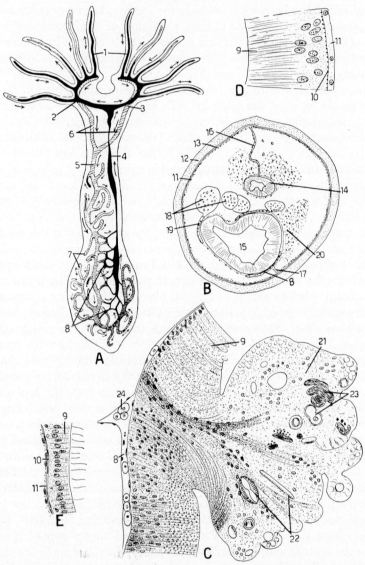

Fig. 90.—Circulatory and digestive systems. *A*, scheme of the phoronid circulatory system (*after Bethe*, 1927). *B*, cross section through the stomach (follows Fig. 89*E*). *C*, section through stomach wall, showing syncytial bulge with food vacuoles. *D*, section through lower part of the intestine. (*C, D, after Selys Longchamps*, 1907.) *E*, section of upper part of the intestine. (*B, E, after Cori*, 1890.) 1, tentacular vessel; 2, afferent lophophoral ring; 3, efferent lophophoral ring; 4, dorsal or afferent vessel; 5, lateral or efferent vessel; 6, two branches that form lateral vessel; 7, capillary caeca; 8, plexus in stomach wall; 9, epithelium; 10, muscle layer; 11, peritoneum; 12, epidermis; 13, basement membrane; 14, intestine; 15, stomach; 16, dorsal mesentery; 17, ventral mesentery; 18, parts of lateral vessel; 19, capillary caecum; 20, vasoperitoneal tissue; 21, syncytial bulge of stomach wall; 22, diatoms; 23, other food bodies; 24, erythrocytes in stomach plexus.

The main blood vessels are lined with a flattened epithelium and clothed with peritoneum continuous with that of the adjacent parts of the digestive tract, either directly or by way of a mesentery. Between these two epithelia occurs a layer of mainly circular muscle fibers (Fig. 97C). The capillary caeca are highly contractile and have both circular and longitudinal muscle fibers in their wall. The plexus of the stomach wall consists merely of spaces beneath the peritoneum, hence constitutes a part of the circulatory system that is not closed.

The blood is composed of a colorless fluid containing red corpuscles that owe their color to haemoglobin. These erythrocytes are disks of circular outline, about 10 microns in diameter.

9. Reproduction.—The gonads are intimately associated with the peritoneum of the capillary caeca and in some species with that of the lateral vessel also (Fig. 91A). Following spawning, the small flat peritoneal cells of these vessels enlarge enormously to a pyramidal or conical shape so as to form a radiating halo around the vessel (Fig. 91B, C) and acquire a variety of inclusions, chiefly spindle bodies of unknown nature and spheres of various sizes that appear composed of nutritive substances, mainly fat (Cori, 1890; Ikeda, 1903; Selys Longchamps, 1907; Rattenbury, 1953). This vasoperitoneal tissue apparently functions to nourish the developing gonads. The sex cells themselves originate from untransformed peritoneal cells on the surfaces of the capillary caeca (Fig. 91C). As they enlarge and mature they spread throughout the vasoperitoneal tissue that correspondingly diminishes, being reduced to mere strands at the time of spawning. Thus gonads and vasoperitoneal tissue undergo an annual cycle of change.

Most phoronids are hermaphroditic, but some are dioecious. The sexes of dioecious species cannot be distinguished externally except by the color of the ripe gonads visible through the body wall. The gonads are loose, indefinite masses closely applied to the lateral vessel and the capillary caeca, hence posteriorly located. Usually in hermaphroditic species the ovary occurs to the dorsal side of the lateral vessel, the testis to its ventral side (Fig. 91A), but the relation is reversed in *P. pallida* (Silén, 1952). It is improbable that supposed dioecious species are actually protandric hermaphrodites.

In the Northern Hemisphere most phoronids breed in spring or summer over a period of two or three to several months as *P. architecta*, Carolina coast, March or April to November or December (Brooks and Cowles, 1905), *P. pallida*, Sweden, June to August (Silén, 1952), and *Phoronopsis viridis*, California, March and April (Rattenbury, 1953). Winter breeding obtains for *P. ijimai* (probably identical with *P. hippocrepia*), Japan, November to June or July (Ikeda, 1901). In the Southern Hemisphere, summer breeding from November to May was reported for

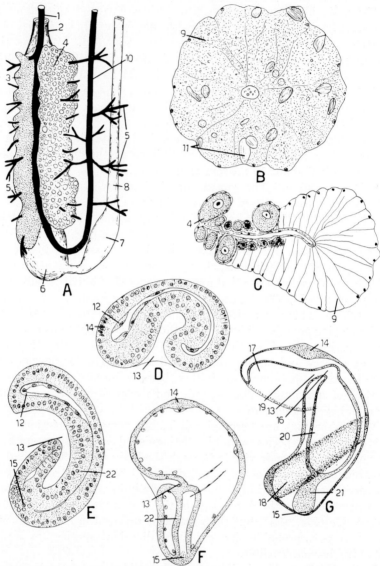

FIG. 91.—Reproduction, embryology. *A*, rear part of *P. australis*, showing gonads (*after Benham*, 1889). *B*, capillary caecum with peritoneum developed into vasoperitoneal tissue (*after Cori*, 1890). *C*, ovary developing around capillary caecum (*after Ikeda*, 1903). *D*, gastrula stage. *E*, late gastrula, with axiation altered as blastopore closes forward. *F*, early larva, intestine making contact with ectoderm. *G*, later larva with ciliated ring established. (*D–G*, *after Selys Longchamps*, 1902, 1907.) 1, lateral vessel; 2, prestomach; 3, testis; 4, ovary; 5, capillary caeca; 6, stomach; 7, beginning part of intestine; 8, intestine; 9. vasoperitoneal tissue; 10, dorsal vessel; 11, spindle bodies; 12, mesenchyme; 13, blastopore; 14, apical nervous thickening; 15, site of future anus; 16, esophagus; 17, preoral lobe; 18, ciliary ring; 19, vestibule; 20, stomach; 21, intestine; 22, archenteron.

P. capensis, South Africa, by Gilchrist (1907). The ripe sex cells are shed into the coelom, where fertilization occurs in some species as *P. mülleri* and *hippocrepia* (Selys Longchamps, 1907) and *Phoronopsis viridis* (Rattenbury, 1953); but in others the eggs are fertilized after being shed to the exterior. Brooks and Cowles (1905) found that ripe specimens of the dioecious *P. architecta* brought into the laboratory would spawn in about 24 hours, mostly at night. The sex cells are spawned by way of the nephridia, directly into the sea water in some species, whereas in others the eggs accumulate and undergo development on the concavity of the lophophore, being held in place by the inner tentacles, also probably by adhesive secretion from the glandular area of the lophophoral organs. As spawning continues intermittently over weeks or months, the lophophoral concavity, acting as a brood chamber, contains eggs and embryos in all stages of development. A different breeding habit obtains for *Phoronopsis albomaculata*, which plasters its eggs to the inside of its tube (Gilchrist, 1907) or to an adjacent rock (Gilchrist, 1919), evidently by means of adhesive secretion from the lophophoral organs.

However, the role of the lophophoral organs in reproduction is difficult to assess because of the total want of these organs in some species and their seasonal changes in others. The lack of lophophoral organs is not necessarily associated with the absence of the brooding habit, for the organs occur in species that spawn directly into the sea, as *P. pallida*, *mülleri*, and *architecta*. In *P. architecta* (Brooks and Cowles, 1905) and *P. psammophila* (Selys Longchamps, 1907), the lophophoral organs are present only in ripe males, retrogressing after spawning and never developing in females. However, well-developed lophophoral organs occur in the hermaphroditic *P. pallida* and *hippocrepia* simultaneously with a ripe ovary and in the latter species also with embryos in the brood chamber (Silén, 1952). Attachment of the eggs (see above) is apparently at least one function of these organs. The ciliated furrow that extends from the nephridiopore to the corresponding lophophoral organ must surely serve to direct the eggs toward the latter, whose glandular secretion probably sticks them to the lophophoral concavity. In *P. capensis* (Gilchrist, 1907) the flap overhanging the glandular depression of the lophophoral organ acts to guide the eggs from the nephridiopore to the brood chamber. Sperm were seen in the concavities of the lophophoral organs by Brooks and Cowles (1905) and Cori (1939), and the supposition of the former that the organs act as seminal receptacles, presumably trapping sperm of other individuals on their mucous surfaces, appears plausible.

10. Embryology.—Main articles on the development are those of Metschnikoff (1871), Wilson (1881), Roule (1890, 1896, 1899a, b, 1900), Ikeda (1901), Selys Longchamps (1902, 1904b, 1907), Brooks and Cowles (1905), and Rattenbury (1954). Cleavage in all species studied is holo-

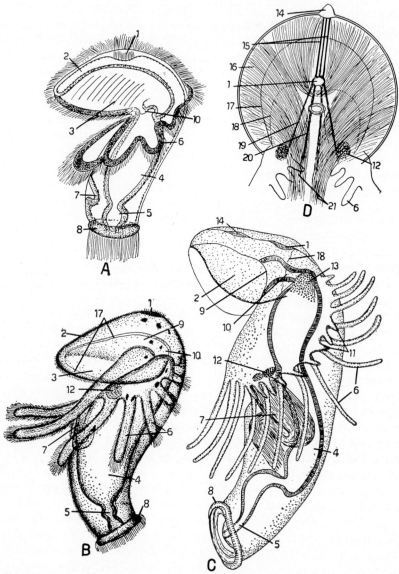

FIG. 92.—Embryology (continued). *A*, young actinotroch, with developing tentacles (*after Selys Longchamps*, 1907). *B*, later actinotroch, tentacles and trunk elongating (*after Wilson*, 1881). *C*, mature actinotroch with buds of definitive tentacles (*after Selys Longchamps*, 1902). *D*, preoral lobe seen from behind to show nervous structures and muscle fibers (*after Brooks and Cowles*, 1905). 1, apical nervous thickening; 2, preoral lobe; 3, vestibule; 4, stomach; 5, intestine; 6, larval tentacles; 7, metasome pouch; 8, telotroch; 9, mouth; 10, esophagus; 11, definitive tentacles; 12, mass of blood corpuscles; 13, stomach diverticulum; 14, sensory papilla; 15, three nerves to 14; 16, muscle fibers; 17, edge of preoral lobe; 18, preoral septum; 19, retractor muscles; 20, posterior nervous tracts; 21, dorsal trunk retractors.

blastic and more or less equal but varies in pattern with species, being irregular or radial or spiral. The most careful study of cleavage is that of Rattenbury, who found definite indications of a spiral pattern in *Phoronopsis viridis*. Cleavage eventuates in a coeloblastula having at its apical pole an apical sensory plate provided with exceptionally long cilia (flagella?); the cells of this plate have previously evidenced differentiation from the rest of the ectoderm by assuming a longer, narrower shape. The vegetal surface of the blastula flattens and invaginates in typical embolic fashion, at the same time giving off mesoderm cells into the blastocoel. The very large blastopore gradually narrows in such a way that the small remaining opening occupies a ventral position and is displaced inward by the enlargement of the anterior part of the larva into an overhanging preoral lobe that bears the apical plate of thickened ectoderm (Fig. 91*D–G*). A mouth is thus established, and the blastopore remains as the connection between this and the original archenteron. There does not seem to be a true stomodaeal invagination but rather the formation of a passage (*vestibule*) by the overgrowth of the preoral lobe. The posterior part of the larva and the contained archenteron elongate, and the latter fuses with the ectoderm to establish an anus without any proctodaeum. The archenteron differentiates into stomach and intestine and has the usual L-shape (Fig. 92*B*). An ectodermal thickening close in front of the anus invaginates as a nephridial pit (Fig. 93*A*) that later gives rise to the larval protonephridia. At about this time or a little later the larva, completely ciliated, takes up a planktonic existence, escaping from the brood chamber in brooding species. It has an oval form with the expanded preoral lobe bent forward (Fig. 92*A–C*). In the interior the digestive tract, differentiated into esophagus, stomach, and intestine, is separated by a considerable space from the ectoderm; this space, quite large in the preoral lobe, is irregularly lined with mesoderm, some of which may have differentiated into delicate muscle fibers. The mesoderm continues to be given off from the archenteron as it invaginates and from the digestive tube for some time.

The larva before or after taking up a planktonic life develops a postoral ciliated ridge that slants obliquely downward from an anterodorsal to a posteroventral position (Fig. 91*G*), and this quickly begins to put out hollow ciliated projections that become the larval tentacles (Fig. 92*A–C*). The tentacles form in pairs from the midventral region in the dorsal direction. The number of pairs eventually produced is definite for each species and varies with species from about 6 to 24. As the tentacles continue to appear in sequence and to elongate into a definitive slender shape, the posterior part of the larva lengthens and a telotroch forms around the anus. The fully developed larva, termed *actinotroch*, has a characteristic appearance (Fig. 92*C*). It swims at the surface of the sea

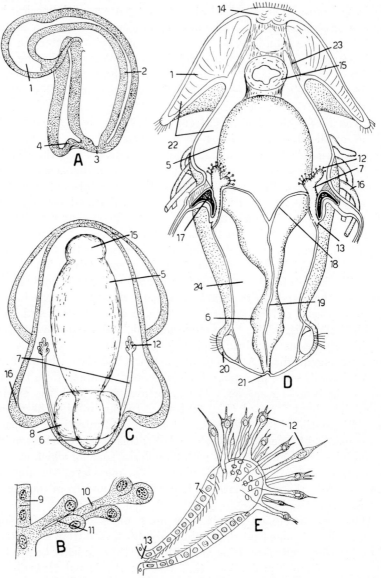

FIG. 93.—Embryology (continued), development of the nephridia. *A*, early actino-troch, showing nephridial pit (*after Ikeda*, 1901). *B*, developing nephridium. *C*, frontal section of later actinotroch with advancing nephridia. (*B*, *C*, *after Shearer*, 1906.) *D*, frontal section of mature actinotroch. *E*, completed protonephridium. (*D*, *E*, *after Goodrich*, 1903.) 1, preoral lobe; 2, archenteron; 3, site of future anus; 4, nephridial pit; 5, stomach; 6, intestine; 7, nephridium; 8, trunk coelomic sac; 9, ectoderm; 10, primordium of nephridium; 11, beginning lumen; 12, solenocytes; 13, nephridiopore; 14, nervous thick-ening; 15, esophagus; 16, larval tentacles; 17, lophophoral coelom; 18, septum; 19, ventral mesentery; 20, telotroch; 21, anus; 22, preseptal space; 23, retractors; 24, trunk coelom.

and is a common and familiar constituent of the plankton during summer in the North Temperate Zone.

The fully developed actinotroch (Fig. 92*C*) is an elongated creature, varying with species from less than 1 to 4 or 5 mm. in length, with a large hollow preoral lobe bent forward above the mouth like a hood. The preoral hood is edged with thickened and strongly ciliated ectoderm, and in the center of its anterior surface occurs the nervous thickening bearing especially long cilia. In some species a sensory papilla is found somewhat anterior to the nervous center (Fig. 92*C*, *D*). From the back of the preoral lobe a girdle of slender tentacles encircles the anterior part of the body, slanting ventrally to a position below the mouth. The tentacles are longest midventrally and decrease in length progressively toward the middorsal line. In the midventral line just behind the tentacular girdle occurs an ectodermal invagination (Fig. 92*A*) that will become the ectoderm of the definitive trunk. The tentacular girdle is followed by the long larval trunk provided with a terminal telotroch of strongly ciliated, thickened ectoderm encircling the terminal anus. Although the larva is completely ciliated, it appears that the telotroch is the chief locomotory organ. Close to the anus is found the nephridial pit.

The larva is probably provided with a complete intraectodermal nervous plexus, but this and its thickenings to form nervous tracts are demonstrable to different degrees in different species of actinotrochs. This nerve plexus is continuous with the nervous thickening, also called ganglion, in the center of the dorsal surface of the preoral lobe. The ganglion contains nerve cells and fibers, and Ikeda (1901) has shown with methylene blue staining that nerve fibers radiate from it throughout the preoral lobe, which further is provided with a nervous tract along its edge. Three longitudinal tracts proceed anteriorly from the ganglion along the middorsal region of the preoral lobe (Ikeda, 1901; Brooks and Cowles, 1905), supplying the sensory papilla when present (Fig. 92*D*), and longitudinal tracts run posteriorly from the ganglion down the back of the preoral lobe, contributing to a tract along the base of the tentacular girdle.

Concomitant with the elongation of the larval trunk, the digestive tube also lengthens. The large mouth, changeable in size and shape with movements of the preoral lobe, opens into the curved esophagus formed of ciliated, glandular ectoderm, and this leads into the stomach enlargement, now also much elongated. In many species the anterior end of the stomach presents a ventral expansion or diverticulum, more or less biparted, situated just beneath the esophagus (Fig. 92*C*). The epithelium of this diverticulum is more or less vacuolated and contains colored inclusions, hence apparently serving a glandular function. The intestine, also much elongated, consists of a cylindrical ciliated epithelium.

Both stomach and intestine are of entodermal origin, derived from the original archenteral invagination.

The mesenchyme occupying the interior cavity (blastocoel) has given rise to a considerable musculature, also varying in detail in different species. The trunk ectoderm is underlain by delicate outer circular and inner longitudinal fibers. The preoral lobe is provided with radiating and concentric muscle fibers, forming a sort of lattice, and its cavity is crossed by numerous delicate muscle fibers (Fig. 92D). There appears generally present a pair of retractor muscles extending from the region of the ganglion and passing to each side of the esophagus to insert on the ventral wall at the level of the tentacular girdle. A pair of longitudinal trunk retractors is also usually present, proceeding along the ventral side of the trunk from the tentacular to the anal region, acting to shorten the trunk. Brooks and Cowles (1905) describe a pair of dorsal trunk retractors that supply muscle fibers to the tentacular girdle, forming a ring musculature there from which fibers enter the tentacles. The digestive tract also has a muscular investment, best developed in the esophagus, dorsal stomach wall, and wall of the stomach diverticulum.

The origin of the coelomic cavities is of the greatest theoretical importance, but unfortunately the available knowledge is not decisive. Cowles (1904a) and Selys Longchamps (1907) imply that the trunk coelom arises by rearrangement of mesenchyme cells along the inner surface of the ectoderm. Shearer (1906) states that a group of mesenchyme cells closely applied to the dorsal wall of the intestine near the anus acquires a cavity and begins to spread as a sac (Fig. 93C). This sac folds around the intestine, and its ends meet midventrally to establish the definitive ventral mesentery of the digestive tube. Hence it appears that ontogenetically the trunk coelom is unpaired and a dorsal mesentery is wanting. Anteriorly the expanding coelomic sac reaches the level of the tentacular girdle where it establishes the definitive *trunk septum* (Fig. 93D). This is very oblique, slanting from a dorsal position at the level of the junction of esophagus and stomach to a ventral position at about the middle of the stomach. It completely separates the trunk coelom from the anterior, or *preseptal*, space, which retains its embryonic status, that of surviving blastocoel, until late in embryonic development. The lumina of the larval tentacles are continuous with the preseptal space. The latter is somewhat subdivided by a *preoral septum*, formed apparently by rearrangement of mesenchyme cells, extending from a point behind the ganglion to the esophagus (Fig. 92D). Although this membrane is very imperfect and hence does not shut off the cavity of the front part of the preoral lobe from the rest of the preseptal space (this remainder is called collar cavity by several authors), it seems to be a definite coelomic partition. Consequently the actinotroch coelom may perhaps be regarded as divided by two septa into three compartments, but none of these is paired. Reports of earlier authors of an enterocoelous origin of the coelomic cavities of phoronids have not been verified and must be considered erroneous.

The origin, development, and relations of the larval nephridia have been clearly elucidated by Ikeda (1901), Goodrich (1903), and Shearer (1906). The nephridia begin as an ectodermal invagination near the anus that soon bifurcates. With the rapid elongation of the trunk region, the two openings with their attached strands are displaced to lateral positons, one to each side of the intestine (Fig. 93C). When the trunk coelomic sac begins to expand, the nephridia, lying between the coelomic lining and the ectoderm, are pushed anteriorly along the dorsal trunk wall until eventually the nephridiopores reach a position just behind the tentacular girdle and the nephridia project into the preseptal space (Fig. 93D). Thus from the start the nephridia retain a retroperitoneal position. During the displacement the nephridial strands elongate and develop lumina, thus becoming tubes. These tubes, very long for a time, later shorten, and the cells at their closed proximal ends develop into solenocytes (II, page 46). Thus the nephridia of the actinotroch belong to the category of protonephridia with solenocytes (Fig. 93E), as do also the nephridia of the trochophore (II, page 14). The proximal end of the actinotroch nephridium may subdivide into two or three branches, each topped with a cluster of solenocytes, and thus the nephridium may reach an appearance very similar to the nephridia of certain polychaetes.

The definitive circulatory system is already laid down in the larva. In the early larva, masses of mesenchyme cells in the preseptal cavity begin to differentiate into red blood corpuscles. There are one to four such masses, usually four, conspicuous in the living larva by reason of their reddish color. In case of four masses, one pair lies ventrally just above the stomach diverticulum and the other pair is found more dorsally at the sides of the stomach (Fig. 92C, D). Both main longitudinal vessels are usually present in the actinotroch, but in some species only the dorsal vessel. Both vessels originate as a cord of cells that later hollows to a tube situated in the stomach wall between its epithelium and covering peritoneum. From the beginning both vessels are continuous with similar spaces in the stomach wall that become the haemal plexus. Capillary caeca appear early as peritoneal evaginations. Anteriorly the main vessels open into the preseptal space, which is thus indicated as a sort of haemocoel. Since the masses of forming red corpuscles also lie in this space it is readily understood that corpuscles may easily enter the vessels. The part of the preseptal space just above the tentacular girdle is more or

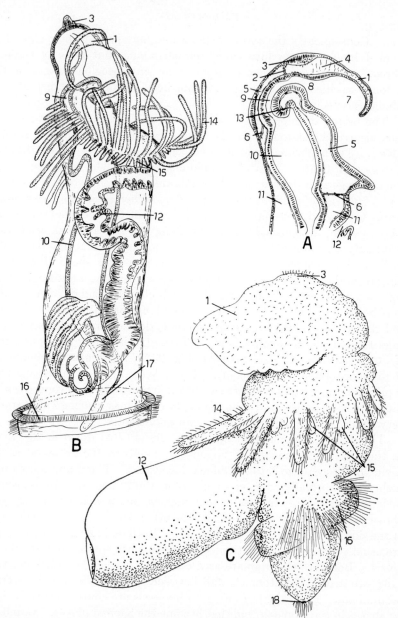

Fig. 94.—Embryology (continued). *A*, median sagittal section of anterior part of late actinotroch, showing coelomic membranes (*after Ikeda*, 1901). *B*, actinotroch about to metamorphose, with fully developed metasome pouch (*after Selys Longchamps*, 1907). *C*, metamorphosing actinotroch with metasome pouch everted (*after Roule*, 1900). 1, preoral lobe; 2, preoral septum; 3, nervous thickening; 4, anterior part of preseptal space; 5, posterior part of preseptal space ("collar cavity"); 6, septum; 7, vestibule; 8, mouth; 9, esophagus; 10, stomach; 11, trunk coelom; 12, metasome pouch; 13, stomach diverticulum; 14, larval tentacles; 15, definitive tentacles; 16, telotroch; 17, intestine; 18, anus.

less separated by the preoral septum from the rest of the preseptal space, and hence forms a ring blood sinus continuous with the lumina of the larval tentacles.

The actinotroch stage endures for some time, probably several weeks, during which the larva feeds on microscopic organisms gathered by ciliary currents. Along with the foregoing changes the ectodermal invagination, or *metasome pouch*, early evident in the midventral line just below the tentacular girdle, steadily deepens, becoming a long tube in the trunk, eventually so long that it is thrown into folds (Fig. 94*B*). It has acquired a strong muscular investment that represents the body-wall musculature of the definitive trunk. The definitive tentacles have begun to appear as buds (Fig. 92*C*) at the bases of the larval tentacles, and their lumina are continuous with the definitive lophophore coelom which forms in the late larva as a horseshoe-shaped tubular cavity immediately anterior to the trunk septum (Fig. 93*D*). Concerning the origin of the lophophore coelom the literature contains only the statement of Goodrich (1903) that this cavity appears somewhat late in larval life "as a split between two layers of a narrow band of mesoblast." The lophophore cavity is never completed dorsally, hence the horseshoe shape of the adult lophophore.

When the metasome pouch has completed its development, the larvae become sluggish and opaque and sink to the bottom. Metamorphosis ensues and is a very rapid process, occupying but 15 to 25 minutes according to Ikeda (1901). Through convulsive body contractions, the metasome pouch (which may previously have protruded to some extent) is suddenly fully everted (Fig. 94*C*) to the exterior, carrying with it the digestive tract, which thus is thrown into the hairpin loop typical of the adult. The metasome pouch is thus the definitive body wall of the trunk. The preoral lobe shrinks and is cast off (Fig. 95*A*) and ingested; hence the epistome is not a remnant of the preoral lobe, since it is wanting in the newly metamorphosed worm, but forms later simply as a fold on the anal side of the mouth. The ganglion is included with the castoff preoral lobe and thus bears no relation to the adult nervous center, which seems to arise *in situ* as an epidermal thickening. The ectodermal parts of the larval tentacles are cast off (Fig. 95*A*) and ingested, and the definitive tentacles, already present as buds and hence short at first (Fig. 94*B*), rapidly increase in length and number.

Internal changes may be briefly considered. The larval digestive tube is retained as that of the adult but undergoes considerable elongation when the metasome everts. The anterior part of the stomach is drawn out to become the adult prestomach, and the intestine is also greatly stretched. The stomach diverticulum, located after metamorphosis at the boundary of prestomach and stomach, disappears. The metasome

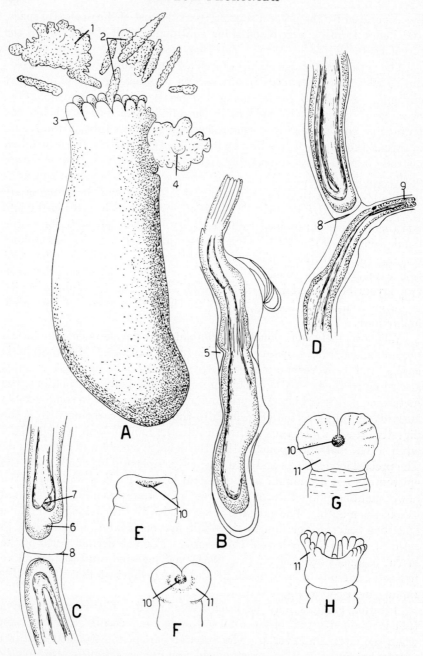

FIG. 95.—Embryology (concluded), fission and regeneration. *A*, young phoronid immediately after metamorphosis (*after Roule*, 1900). *B*, beginning stage of transverse fission of *P. ovalis*, with tube thickened at fission place. *C*, partition of tube formed, ends

eversion brings the anus with its telotroch to an anterior position, where it forms a protuberance immediately after metamorphosis; later it is carried inward by an ectodermal depression that probably becomes the distal part of the rectum, and the telotroch disintegrates. The larval metacoel, septum, and ventral mesentery are retained in the adult, and the lophophoral coelom, already present in the late larva, becomes the coelom of all parts anterior to the trunk septum. Preseptal cavities of the larva are retained in part as definitive blood vessels, for, as already mentioned, the preseptal space is in reality a haemocoel. The tubular linings of the larval tentacles become the tentacular vessels of the definitive tentacles, and the part of the preseptal space that forms a ring cavity (collar cavity in much of the literature) along the base of the larval tentacular girdle remains as the ring vessel of the lophophoral coelom. The main longitudinal vessels are already present in the late actinotroch and already open into that part of the preseptal space that becomes the lophophoral ring vessel. There is but one ring vessel in the newly metamorphosed worm, and this probably becomes the two superimposed ring vessels of the adult by a simple horizontal division (Brooks and Cowles, 1905). The convulsive movements involved in metasome eversion break up the masses of red corpuscles and set them in motion. As they are already located in the preseptal space that becomes the ring vessel, they find easy access into the circulatory system.

Probably the most interesting question involved in the metamorphosis of the actinotroch is the relation of the larval to the adult nephridia. It has been seen that the actinotroch has protonephridia whereas the adult nephridia are of the metanephridial category. Phoronids would therefore seem to furnish ideal material for the solution of the difficult question of the relation of metanephridia to protonephridia (II, page 46). Unfortunately, the literature on phoronid development contains no decisive observations on this question. At metamorphosis the terminal clusters of solenocytes detach, fall into the preseptal space, and there disintegrate. The nephridiopores and protonephridial tubes appear to be retained as such in the adult, and seemingly the metanephridial nephrostome of the adult is a new formation (Goodrich, 1903; Selys Longchamps, 1907). The metanephridia of phoronids therefore probably classify as nephromixia (II, page 47), that is, as ducts combining nephridial and gonadial functions, formed by the grafting of a nephrostome (true coelomostome) onto a protonephridial tubule.

---

regenerating. *D*, posterior fission product growing out at right angles to old tube. (*B–D*, after Harmer, 1917.) *E–H*, four stages in regeneration of new tentacular crown after old one has been cast off in autotomy (after Selys Longchamps, 1907). 1, castoff preoral lobe; 2, castoff larval tentacles; 3, definitive tentacles; 4, remains of telotroch region; 5, thickening of tube at site of fission; 6, new end bulb forming; 7, digestive tube ends united; 8, tube partition; 9, new anterior end of posterior fission product; 10, mouth; 11, new lophophore.

Following metamorphosis the young worm immediately adopts a sedentary existence and begins to secrete a tube.

11. Asexual Reproduction.—Reproduction by transverse fission is known to occur in *P. ovalis* (Harmer, 1917; Brattström, 1943; Marcus, 1949; Lönöy, 1954). According to Harmer, fission occurs only in the nonmuscular part of the trunk, typically prior to the end bulb, and is initiated by a ring thickening of the tube, followed by constriction of the body (Fig. 95*B*). The anterior part simply completes its posterior end within the old tube, but the regenerating posterior part, having no space within the old tube for the regenerating anterior end, secretes a new anterior part for its tube, bent at right angles to the old tube and continuous with it. Tubes with such right-angled bends (Fig. 95*D*) are said by Harmer to be common in the aggregation. Fission is frequent, and many specimens in an aggregation are found without lophophores or with regenerating small ones. Marcus, on the other hand, states that the epidermis and tube may form septa at any level, dividing the animal in two, and that *P. ovalis* also reproduces by budding. Buds are said to arise on the ventral side in the nonmuscular region as epidermal projections that soon secrete a tube and into which the descending limb of the digestive tract sends a branch. The buds of Marcus (Fig. 96*A*) appear to correspond to Harmer's cases of fission, and further study is required to elucidate the contradictions in these two accounts.

The fission reported for *P. hippocrepia* and *Phoronopsis albomaculata* appears rather of the nature of autotomy.

12. Autotomy and Regeneration.—It has been noticed by several observers (first by Van Beneden, 1858) that phoronids when kept in laboratory aquaria often cast off their tentacular crowns and regenerate new ones. Specimens without crowns and in process of regenerating new ones are often found in nature; possibly the crowns have been bitten off by small fish. The act of casting off the crown is accomplished by a strong constriction of the circular muscle (Cori, 1890), which also closes both wounds. The part cast off includes, besides the lophophore, the septum, nephridia, and initial and terminal parts of the digestive tract, at about the level of junction of esophagus and prestomach or through the beginning of the prestomach. According to Selys Longchamps (1907), autotomized anterior ends are incapable of regenerating posteriorly and eventually disintegrate but posterior regeneration will occur if the cut lies through the muscular region of the trunk. However, in the very small species, *P. ovalis*, castoff tentacular crowns do regenerate (Silén, 1955). The very short stump elongates, soon begins to adhere to the substrate, and starts secreting a tube; internal changes are similar to those described by Schultz (see below). Gilchrist (1919) observed in *Phoronopsis albomaculata* that the part of the autotomized anterior end below the lophophore might later constrict off and, although very small, regenerate into a complete worm. In all cases the decapitated trunk regenerates a new anterior end, often in a relatively short time, and trunk pieces also regenerate into complete worms. Selys Longchamps (1907) cut the muscular part of the trunk of *P. psammophila* into six pieces and obtained complete regeneration of all six. Even pieces only 1 mm. long regenerate, but in this species the end bulb apparently lacks regenerative capacity. *P. mülleri* regenerates a new anterior end at all trunk levels, according to Schultz (1903), and this is also true of *Phoronis vancouverensis* (Marsden, 1957). Distal pieces of this species will not regenerate posteriorly unless the posterior cut is through the end bulb, which houses the gonads and vasoperitoneal tissue. Distal pieces tend to cast off the tentacular crown, and sometimes the regenerated tentacular crown is discarded and a new one regenerated. Posterior pieces including whole or part of the end bulb regenerate the missing anterior parts and form complete individuals. Such pieces may first divide and each fragment then regenerates completely.

Details of the regeneration process were furnished by Schultz (1903). Anterior ends complete themselves posteriorly by closure of the wound and fusion of the cut ends of the two main blood vessels and of the two parts of the digestive tube. Regeneration of a new anterior end at a cut trunk surface is more complicated. The wound closes, and mouth and esophagus originate by an epidermal invagination that fuses with the stump of the descending limb of the digestive tract; but if the esophagus is retained in the decapitated trunk, it simply fuses with the surface to re-form a mouth. Around the mouth appears a crescentic ridge that increases in height (Fig. 95E, F) and becomes subdivided into tentacles that form bilaterally in the dorsoventral direction (Fig. 95G, H). The lophophore is thus restored. In the interior the two main longitudinal vessels fuse at once, thus promptly reestablishing the circulation; subsequently a forking at the site of junction restores the lophophoral ring vessel. The cut end of the intestine closes and re-forms an anus by simple fusion with the surface without a proctodaeal invagination. The septum and coelomic cavities are reestablished by rearrangement of peritoneal cells. According to Schultz, the nephridia regenerate entirely from the peritoneum; a peritoneal proliferation produces the nephrostome and then grows to the surface to reestablish the nephridial tube.

V. ECOLOGY AND PHYSIOLOGY

1. Habits and Behavior.—All phoronids lead a sedentary, benthonic existence in the upper littoral zone (above 50 m.), enclosed in a secreted tube in which they are not fastened. The tubes may occur singly, imbedded vertically in sandy or muddy bottom; or as tangled aggregations fastened to pilings, rocks, or other objects; or as intricate associations permeating mollusk shells or other calcareous shells or calcareous rock. Species dwelling singly in separated tubes, when removed from their tubes, promptly burrow into the bottom again, rear end first, concomitantly secreting a tube (Selys Longchamps, 1904a). Such newly secreted tubes are delicate and membranous but thicken by successive outflows of secretion over a period of 2 or 3 weeks. The habit of burrowing in calcareous shells and rocks is seen in *P. ovalis* (Harmer, 1917; Brattström, 1943; Marcus, 1949; Silén, 1956), *P. capensis* (Gilchrist, 1907), and races of *P. hippocrepia*, including one called *gracilis* (Selys Longchamps, 1904a). The worms inhabiting these burrows are themselves enclosed in the usual closely fitting tube of their own secretion. The burrows generally parallel the shell surface, hence lie beneath the periostracum; but their upper ends open to the exterior by a right-angled bend. Most of such openings occur on the outer, that is, the convex, surface of the shell, but some are found on the inner, or concave, surface. As many as 150 burrows per square centimeter of shell surface were noted by Marcus for the very small species, *P. ovalis*. Although the pieces of bivalve and gastropod shells inhabited by such phoronid colonies are often eroded and permeated with burrows of boring sponges and other animals, observers are agreed that the worms excavate their burrows by their own activities and need not take advantage of preexisting weaknesses in the shells. The mechanism of boring is not, however, known, and apparently secretion of acid is not involved. Marcus has noted that advancing tips of *P. ovalis* are clothed with a tall epidermis of secretory appearance. The unique habitat of *P. australis* with its tubes entwined in the material of the tube of *Cerianthus* was mentioned above. Ikeda (1902) reported that the upper end of every *Cerianthus* tube is tenanted by the phoronid, which at low tide when the cnidarian is withdrawn into its tube is seen radiating in the expanded state from the aperture.

It is known for *P. hippocrepia* (or races thereof) that during winter at Naples (Cerfontaine, 1902) or summer at Japan (Ikeda, 1901) the colonies degenerate, leaving only some body fragments in the tubes, and that such fragments regenerate the colonies at the onset of more favorable weather.

The movements of phoronids are mostly limited to emergence of the anterior end from the tube and expansion of the tentacular crown under undisturbed conditions and folding of the crown and withdrawal into the tube on disturbance. Such movements are obviously mediated by the body-wall musculature. A light touch on the tentacles may elicit no response, a second touch evokes partial contraction, and repeated cautious stimuli or a strong stimulus is followed by retraction into the tube (Silén, 1954a). A light touch just below the lophophore is more effective in evoking a marked contractile response than light stimulation of the tentacles, according to Hilton (1922). Jarring or other strong disturbance elicits rapid folding of the tentacular crown and withdrawal into the tube. In general, the tentacular crown reacts as a whole and individual tentacles show little independent movement. In *P. ovalis*, which lacks a giant fiber, retreat into the tube occurs by jerks at first followed by a smooth even contraction, whereas in species with a giant fiber disturbance results in a sudden and complete withdrawal caused by instantaneous contraction of the entire muscular region of the trunk (Silén, 1954a). Such sudden trunk contraction is mediated by the giant fiber (lateral nerve), for if the latter is cut across just below the septum, the trunk does not contract on adequate stimulation of the tentacles; if cut lower down, the trunk contracts as far as the cut (Silén, 1954a). Probably during retraction into the tube the animal is anchored posteriorly by way of the end bulb. After retraction into the tube emergence and expansion of the tentacular crown occur rather slowly.

It is evident from their construction and behavior that phoronids are ciliary-mucus feeders, gathering in small items by way of tentacular ciliary currents. These currents have been described for *P. capensis* by Gilchrist (1907). The main current operates to a distance about equal to the length of the tentacles and is directed to the space between the two ridges of the lophophore, hence into the buccal grooves and mouth. This current exits between the tentacular bases and flows over the anal and nephridial openings, thus also carrying away wastes. Particles, however, are often rejected at the mouth angles and by the tentacles, some cilia of which beat toward the tentacular tips; these tips on the arrival of rejected particles bend outward, causing such particles to fall off. All particles become coated with mucus. Individual tentacles were sometimes seen bending suddenly to the mouth, perhaps depositing food. The cilia cease beating on disturbance that evokes retraction into the tube.

Hilton (1922) noted no response of California phoronids to shadows or to sudden illumination. No information was found on response to other external factors.

2. Physiology.—Experiments by the author (Hyman, 1958) have shown that the phoronid animal contains no chitin but that the secreted tubes consist of chitin.

The performance of the intraepidermal nerve net was studied by Silén (1954a) on the isolated muscular part of the trunk of *P. mülleri*, cut anteriorly below the lophophore, hence deprived of the nerve ring, and posteriorly just anterior to the end bulb. Such trunks respond everywhere to light mechanical stimulation by a local contraction and to stronger stimulation by a ring contraction that is propagated slowly, with decrement, in both directions. Stimulation of a tongue of the body wall evokes contraction of the main piece, and vice versa. The isolated end

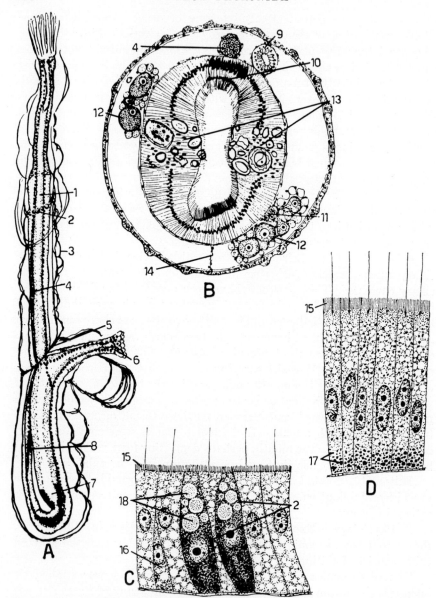

Fig. 96.—Asexual reproduction (concluded); physiology. *A*, lateral budding in *P. ovalis*. *B*, cross section of stomach of *P. ovalis*, showing paired areas of intracellular digestion. (*A*, *B*, *after Marcus*, 1949.) *C*, upper part of stomach of the actinotroch. *D*, lower part of stomach of actinotroch. (*C*, *D*, *after Becker*, 1937.) 1, prestomach; 2, gland cells; 3, tube; 4, dorsal vessel; 5, tube partition; 6, anterior end of bud; 7, stomach of bud; 8, intestine of bud; 9, intestine; 10, middorsal ciliated groove; 11, lateral vessel; 12, ovary developing in vasoperitoneal tissue; 13, areas of intracellular digestion; 14, ventral mesentery; 15, brush border; 16, replacement cell; 17, fat spherules; 18, enzymatic spherules.

bulb reacts like the trunk, although feebly and with a slower rate of transmission. Such experiments prove conduction in the nerve net equally in all directions. The result of section of the giant fiber was indicated above, but impulses can still reach the trunk muscles and induce a slowly propagated contraction by way of the nervous tracts that pass directly from the nerve ring into the anterior ends of the muscle bundles.

Digestion has been studied in the actinotroch of *P. mülleri* by Becker (1937), who considers that the results apply to the adult phoronid also. The larval esophagus is lined by tall ciliated cells, some of which are altered into vacuolated gland cells probably of enzymatic nature. The stomach epithelium consists mainly of tall vacuolated cells provided with flagella and a brush border and containing fat spherules and protein granules, hence evidently acting to absorb and store products of digestion (Fig. 96D). Intermingled with these cells are broader cells of glandular nature with heavily staining basal region and vacuolated periphery (Fig. 96C). In the lateral wall at about the middle of the stomach is found on each side an area of very different appearance, composed of a bulging, vacuolated syncytium containing large vacuoles surrounding recognizable remains of diatoms and other unicellular organisms. Small fat and protein spherules and granules of excretion are also present in the digestive syncytium. A similar paired area of stomach wall has been generally noticed in the adult phoronid (Selys Longchamps, 1907; Marcus, 1949; Lönöy, 1954; Fig. 96B); hence digestion in both larval and adult phoronids is largely intracellular and the products of digestion are stored in the stomach epithelium. The stomach diverticulum present in the larva only was found by Becker to consist of a uniform epithelium containing basally large and small fat spheres and distally vacuoles with excretion granules. The larval intestine is formed of a low epithelium interspersed with cells apparently glandular, whereas the adult intestine is usually said to be lacking in glandular elements; however, Ohuye (1942) depicts intestinal gland cells in *P. australis* (Fig. 97A).

An active circulation of the blood has been witnessed by many observers of living phoronids, notably by Gilchrist (1907); the most detailed study of the circulation was made by Bethe (1927). Each tentacular vessel and capillary caecum is autonomically contractile, acting independently of the two main longitudinal vessels and of adjacent tentacular vessels and caeca. The tentacular vessels fill from the afferent lophophoral ring vessel and empty by a contraction from their tips basally. Such contractions occur every 3 to 10 seconds. The caeca empty by a sudden general contraction and shortening that lasts 5 to 10 seconds, followed by a longer period of relaxation during which the caecum fills again. The circulation is maintained by contraction waves in the two longitudinal vessels, especially the median one, which shows regular rhythmic contraction waves several times a minute in a posteroanterior direction. Contractions in the lophophoral ring vessels and in the lateral vessel are weaker and less regular, but eventually the blood descends in the lateral vessel to the sinuses in the stomach wall from which the median vessel originates.

According to Ohuye (1942), the blood corpuscles and coelomocytes arise from the endothelial lining of the blood vessels (Fig. 97*B, C*). The ordinarily flat cells of this lining bulge into the lumen and are cut off as corpuscles that gradually acquire haemoglobin. Similarly, the peritoneal covering of the blood vessels may give rise to red blood corpuscles and coelomocytes, as also the lining of the tentacles and the vasoperitoneal tissue. The last further serves to dispose of outworn corpuscles and coelomocytes.

On the subject of excretion it may be recalled that granules presumably of excretory nature occur in the nephridia and in the digestive epithelium. Ohuye (1942) found that injected dyes and colored particles are vigorously taken up by the endothelium of the circulatory system, the peritoneum everywhere, including the vasoperitoneal tissue, the nephridial tubes, and the coelomocytes. The last accumulate in the base of the digestive epithelium (Fig. 97*A*) through which the injected material is eliminated. Pixell (1912) reported for *P. vancouverensis* the presence in the vasoperitoneal tissue of quantities of refringent granules that apparently traverse the body wall and accumulate on the external surface as obvious white spots. These accumulations can be scraped off and were subjected to chemical tests that indicated some uric acid derivative, possibly guanine. Similar excretory granules were noticed by Pixell in *Phoronopsis harmeri*.

3. Geographic Distribution.—Phoronids so far as known are limited to shallow waters of tropical and temperate zones. They are not uncommon in favorable localities. The majority of the known species have been found along European coasts, but this circumstance no doubt results from the better knowledge of the marine littoral fauna there than elsewhere in the world. Phoronids extend along European coasts from Scandinavia into the Mediterranean. From Scandinavian coasts there are reported *P. hippocrepia* (includes *gracilis, kowalevskii*), *mülleri, ovalis*, and *pallida* (Silén, 1952), and these, except the last, and with the addition of *P. psammophila* (includes *sabatieri*), extend westward along the North Sea and around the British Isles. *P. hippocrepia, mülleri*, and *psammophila* also occur in the Mediterranean. A species *P. euxinicola* found at Sebastopol on the Black Sea (Selys Longchamps, 1907) is of doubtful status but at least indicates that phoronids may live in brackish water. On the Atlantic Coast of the United States *P. architecta* occurs in Chesapeake Bay and in the vicinity of Beaufort, North Carolina (Wilson,

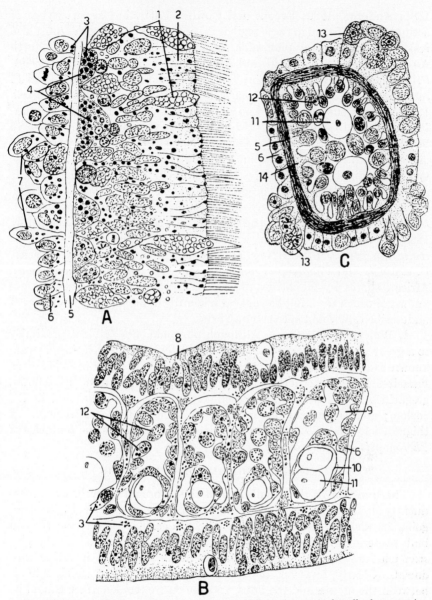

Fig. 97.—Physiology (concluded). *A*, cross section of intestinal wall after carmine staining, showing carmine grains passing through the wall. *B*, cross section through a tentacle base after carmine staining. *C*, cross section through a main blood vessel, showing proliferation of corpuscles and coelomocytes. (*All after Ohuye*, 1942.) 1, gland cells; 2, ordinary epithelial cells; 3, carmine granules; 4, granulocytes in epithelial base; 5, muscle layer; 6, peritoneum; 7, peritoneal proliferations; 8, epidermis; 9, tentacular coelom; 10, tentacular blood vessel; 11, red blood corpuscles; 12, proliferation of red blood corpuscles; 13, proliferation of coelomocytes; 14, lining endothelium of blood vessel.

1881; Andrews, 1890; Brooks and Cowles, 1905), but as two types of actinotroch are found in these regions, a second unknown species must also reside there.   Several phoronids inhabit the Pacific Coast of North America: *Phoronopsis viridis* and *striata* along California (Hilton, 1930), *P. pacifica* along California and in Puget Sound (Torrey, 1901), and *P. vancouverensis* and *Phoronopsis harmeri* around Vancouver Island (Pixell, 1912).   Only one species is known from the whole of South America, *P. ovalis* from Brazilian shores (Marcus, 1949), shown by Lönöy (1954) to be identical with Swedish specimens.   *P. ijimai*, Japan, is very likely identical with *P. hippocrepia*, but as Ikeda (1901) reported four Japanese types of actinotroch, other species must occur there.   Among these is *P. australis* (Ikeda, 1902), originally found at Port Jackson, Australia (Benham, 1889), and recently taken off India (Nair and Shaw, 1956). *Phoronis buskii*, obtained by the *Challenger* at the Philippines (McIntosh, 1888), is very likely identical with *P. australis*.   The widely spread *P. ovalis* was reported from New Zealand by Silén (1956).   Two species, *P. capensis* and *Phoronopsis albomaculata*, were discovered along South African shores by Gilchrist (1907).   As a number of actinotrochs are known of which the adult has not been identified, presumably a number of undescribed phoronid species must exist.

   4. Biological Relations.—Although phoronids live in close proximity to a great variety of other invertebrates, no definite interrelationships are known except the occupancy by *P. australis* of the tubes of *Cerianthus*. Parasites have been noticed by Selys Longchamps (1907) as follows: gregarines in the intestinal epithelium and their cysts floating in the coelom; and trematode metacercariae in the lophophoral coelom.   A thigmotrich ciliate, *Heterocineta phoronopsidis*, occurs on the tentacles of *Phoronopsis viridis* (Kozloff, 1945).

VI. MORPHOLOGICAL CONSIDERATIONS

   The question of the orientation of the phoronid body has been frequently discussed, lengthily by Selys Longchamps (1907).   In the foregoing account the tentacular crown has been considered anterior, the end bulb posterior, the surface bearing the mouth and along which the prestomach runs ventral, and the surface along which the intestine runs dorsal.   Clearly, however, the true dorsal surface is that which extends between the mouth and the anus, and the entire trunk surface should be considered ventral.   During the process of metamorphosis the evagination of the metasome pouch brings the original and true posterior end bearing the anus into close proximity with the mouth, and the original dorsal surface is thereby greatly shortened.

   The anterior end of the phoronid is bilaterally symmetrical, but various asymmetries of the internal structures of the trunk have been noticed in the foregoing account. The lateral vessel and lateral nerve are typically found on the left side only, although a small right lateral nerve is sometimes present. The muscle bundles are often asymmetrical in height and number with reference to the secondary trunk axes, although the statement in the literature that in case of such asymmetry height and number are greater on the left side is not borne out by published figures, which generally show a preponderance of the ventral side in these regards. However, a general tendency toward left dominance in the trunk of phoronids must be admitted and of course recalls the dominance of the left side in echinoderms. Selys Longchamps (1907) ascribes the trunk asymmetry of the adult phoronid to the asymmetry of the metasome pouch, which is pushed to the left side in the actinotroch.

Various early authors (review in Selys Longchamps, 1907) have conceived the phoronid body as "trimetamerous," and this concept has been promulgated by Cori in his monographs (1937, 1939) and thereby widely spread. Obviously a comparison with hemichordates is intended. The author has already indicated the utter falsity of regarding the body regions of hemichordates as segments, and the same analysis applies to phoronids. The phoronid body is not segmented in any proper sense of this term. However, the question whether phoronids are regionated into three parts corresponding to the regionation of hemichordates requires consideration. According to the Cori concept, the epistome represents the protosome, the lophophoral region the mesosome, and the trunk the metasome. This interpretation is not well substantiated by the facts of embryology and adult anatomy. The epistome is not a body region, does not contain a separate coelom, and its coelom is not connected to the exterior by a canal and pore, as is the case with the hemichordate protocoel. In cold fact the phoronid body is subdivided into only two regions by means of the septum. The coelom of these two regions is not paired, not even embryonically. The trunk region of adult phoronids is connected to the exterior by a pair of metanephridia, something that is not the case in hemichordates. As discussed under embryology the coelom of the actinotroch may possibly be regarded as divided into three compartments, of which none is paired; and the anteriormost compartment, possibly representing a protocoel, although it lacks connection with the exterior, is lost at metamorphosis. Resemblance to hemichordates is therefore practically limited to the presence of a strong septum separating the trunk from more anterior regions and the location of the lophophore on the same body region as bears the tentaculated arms of pterobranchs. These resemblances are sufficient to suggest some underlying plan common to the two groups inherited from the remote past.

That the actinotroch is an altered trochophore does not appear open to doubt. At its summit is seen the typical sensory tuft underlain by a thickened nervous plate. The girdle of larval tentacles develops from a ciliary band that passes below the mouth, and hence represents the metatroch of the trochophore. Possibly the cilia edging the preoral lobe correspond to the prototroch. A telotroch (or paratroch) around the anal end occurs in some trochophores. As in the trochophore the interior of the actinotroch is the blastocoel and communicates with the exterior by a pair of solenocytic protonephridia. The similarity of the digestive tract in the two types of larvae is probably not significant since this form of digestive tract is common among the larvae of coelomates. In the actinotroch the anterior part of the blastopore is retained as the mouth, although the blastopore does not appear to contribute to the anus also as in some Protostomia. A main difference between the actinotroch and the trochophore is that in the former the mesoderm is not arranged in teloblastic bands (II, page 14) as in the trochophore. The mesoderm of the actinotroch occurs as mesenchyme only, but all of it appears to belong to the entomesodermal category.

The Phoronida are therefore to be placed among the coelomate Protostomia. As their mode of coelom formation does not fit very well into any category the author now considers it best to abandon the category Schizocoela and replace it by the expression protostomatous coelomates. The Phoronida agree with other protostomatous coelomates in having a trochophore type of larva. The relationship of the Phoronida to other coelomate phyla is discussed later in this volume.

Bibliography

Andrews, E. A. 1890. On a new American species of Phoronis. Ann. Mag. Natur. Hist., ser. 6, vol. 5. **Becker, G.** 1937. Untersuchungen über den Darm und die Verdauung von Phoroniden. Ztschr. Morphol. Ökol. Tiere 33. **Beneden, P. van.** 1858. Note sur un annélide cephalobranche sans soies. Ann. Sci. Natur., ser. 4, vol. 10. **Benham, W. B.** 1889. The anatomy of Phoronis australis. Quart. Jour. Microsc. Sci. 30. **Bethe, A.** 1927. Eigenthümliche Formen und Mittel der Blutbewegung. Ztschr. Vergl. Physiol. 5. **Brattström, H.** 1943. Phoronis ovalis. Lunds Univ. Aarskrift, Avd. 2, vol. 39, no. 2. **Brooks, W.,** and **R. Cowles.** 1905. Phoronis architecta: its life history, anatomy, and breeding habits. Mem. Nation. Acad. Sci. U.S.A. 10. **Caldwell, W.** 1882. Structure, development, and affinities of Phoronis. Proc. Roy. Soc. London 34; Quart. Jour. Microsc. Sci. 25. **Cerfontaine, P.** 1902. Recherches expérimentales sur le régénération et l'hétéromorphose. Arch. Biol. 19. **Cobbold, S.** 1858. On a probably new species of Actinotrocha. Quart. Jour. Microsc. Sci. 6. **Cori, C. J.** 1890. Anatomie und Histologie der Gattung Phoronis. Ztschr. Wissensch. Zool. 51. 1932. Phoronidea. *In* G. Grimpe and E. Wagler (eds.), *Die Tierwelt der Nord- und Ostsee*, Teil VII, C2. 1937. Phoronidea. *In* W. Kükenthal and T. Krumbach (eds.), *Handbuch der Zoologie*, Bd. III, Hälfte 2, Lief. 10. 1939. Phoronidea. *In* H. G. Bronn (ed.), *Klassen und Ordnungen des Tierreichs*, Bd. IV, Abt. 4, Buch 1. **Cowles, R. P.** 1904a. Origin and fate of body cavities and the nephridia of the Actinotrocha. Johns Hopkins Univ. Circulars, ser. 2, no. 2. 1904b. Origin and fate of the blood vessels and blood corpuscles of the Actinotrocha. Zool. Anz. 27. **Dyster, F.** 1858. Notes on Phoronis hippocrepia. Trans. Linnaean Soc. London 22. **Garstang, W.** 1891. Phoronis at Plymouth. Jour. Marine Biol. Assoc. 2. **Gegenbaur, C.** 1854. Bemerkungen über Actinotrocha. Ztschr. Wissensch. Zool. 5. **Gilchrist, J.** 1907. New forms of the Hemichorda from South Africa. Trans. South African Philos. Soc. 17. 1919. Reproduction by transverse fission in Phoronopsis. Quart. Jour. Microsc. Sci. 63. **Goodrich, E. S.** 1903. On the body cavities and nephridia of the Actinotrocha larva. Quart. Jour. Microsc. Sci. 47. **Gravely, F.** 1927. Gephyrea and Phoronis. Bull. Madras Mus., new ser. 1. **Gustafson, G.** 1936. Distribution of Phoronis mülleri on the Swedish west coast. Arkiv Zoologi 28B, no. 1. **Harmer, S. F.** 1917. On Phoronis ovalis. Quart. Jour. Microsc. Sci. 62. **Haswell, W. A.** 1882. Note on an Australian species of Phoronis. Proc. Linn. Soc. New South Wales 7. 1893. Occurrence of a second species of Phoronis in Port Jackson. Proc. Linnaean Soc. New South Wales, ser. 2, vol. 7. **Hatschek, B.** 1888. *Lehrbuch der Zoologie.* **Hedgpeth, J.** 1954. Phoronida, Gulf of Mexico. U.S. Fish and Wildlife Service, Fishery Bull. 89. **Hilton, A. W.** 1922. Nervous system of Phoronida. Jour. Comp. Neurol. 34. 1930. Phoronida from the coast of southern California. Jour. Entomol. Zool. 22. **Hyman, L.** 1958. Occurrence of chitin in lophophorates. Biol. Bull. 114. **Ikeda, I.** 1901. Development, structure and metamorphosis of Actinotrocha. Jour. College Sci. Tokyo Univ. 13. 1902. Occurrence of Phoronis australis near Misaki. Annot. Zool. Japon. 4. 1903. Development of sexual organs and their products in Phoronis. Annot. Zool. Japon. 4. **Judges, Eve.** 1933. Phoronis mülleri in the Irish Sea. Nature, London, 172. **Kowalewsky, A.** 1867. Anatomie und Entwicklung von Phoronis. Mém. Acad. Impér. St. Pétersbourg 10, no. 15. **Kozloff, E.** 1945. Heterocineta phoronopsidis. Biol. Bull. 89. **Krohn, A.** 1857. Metamorphose de l'actinotroque. Tageblatt Bonner Naturforsch. Versammlung; Arch. Naturgesch. 24, pt. 2. 1858. Über Pilidium und Actinotrocha. Arch. Anat. Physiol. **Lang, A.** 1888. *Lehrbuch der vergleichenden Anatomie*, Abt. 1. **Ledig, Ruth.** 1919. General structure of Phoronis pacifica. Jour. Entomol. Zool. 11. **Lönöy, N.** 1954. Comparative study on Phoronis ovalis from Norwegian, Swedish, and Brazilian waters. Univ. Bergen Arbok for 1953, Naturvit. Rekke, art. 2. **Marcus, Eveline.** 1949. Phoronis ovalis from Brazil. Zoologica, Sao Paulo, Brazil, no. 14. **Marsden, Joan.** 1957. Regeneration in Phoronis. Jour. Morphol. 101. **Masterman, A.** 1896. On the structure of Actinotrocha. Proc. Roy. Soc. Edinburgh 21. 1897. On the Diplochorda. 1. The structure of Actinotrocha. Quart. Jour. Microsc. Sci. 40. 1900. On the Diplochorda. 3. The early development and anatomy of Phoronis buskii. Quart. Jour. Microsc. Sci. 43. **McIntosh, W. C.** 1888. Phoronis buskii. Rept. Scient. Results Voyage Challenger, Zool. 27. **Meek, A.** 1917. On the Phoronidea. Rept. Dove Marine Lab. Cullercoats, new ser. 6. 1924. Plankton investigations. Rept. Dove Marine Lab. Cullercoats, new ser. 13. **Menon, K.** 1902. Notes on Actinotrocha. Quart. Jour. Microsc. Sci. 45. **Metschnikoff, E.** 1871. Über die Metamorphose einiger Seetiere. 3. Über Actinotrocha. Ztschr. Wissensch. Zool. 21. **Müller, J.** 1846. Bericht über einige neue Thierformen der Nordsee. Arch. Anat. Physiol. 1847. Fortsetzung über einige neue Thierform der Nordsee. Arch. Anat. Physiol. **Nair, K.,** and **J. Shaw.** 1956. Occurrence of Phoronis ovalis off India. Jour. Univ. Bombay 25. **Ohuye, F.** 1942. Blood corpuscles and the blood formation in Phoronis. Sci. Repts. Tohoku Univ., ser. 4, Biol. 17. **Oka, A.** 1897. Sur une nouvelle espèce japonaise du genre Phoronis. Annot. Zool. Japon. 1. **Pixell, H.** 1912. Two new species of Phoronidea from Vancouver Island. Quart. Jour. Microsc. Sci. 58. **Poche, F.** 1903. Über den richtigen Namen der Gattung Phoronis. Zool. Anz. 26. **Rat-**

tenbury, Joan. 1953. Reproduction in Phoronopsis viridis. Biol. Bull. 104. 1954. The embryology of Phoronopsis viridis. Jour. Morphol. 95. **Roule, L.** 1890. Sur le développement des feuillets blastodermiques chez Phoronis. C. R. Acad. Sci. Paris 110. 1896. Sur les métamorphoses larvaires du Phoronis. C. R. Acad. Sci. Paris 122. 1898. Sur la place des phoronidiens dans la classification des animaux. C. R. Acad. Sci. Paris 127. 1899a. La structure de la larve actinotroque. Proc. 4 Internation. Congr. Zool. 1899b. Considérations sur le développement embryonnaire des phoronidiens. Bull. Acad. Sci. Toulouse 2. 1900. Étude sur le développement embryonnaire des phoronidiens. Ann. Sci. Natur., Zool., ser. 8, vol. 11. **Schepotieff, A.** 1906. Über einige Actinotrochen der Norwegeschen Fjorde. Ztschr. Wissensch. Zool. 84. **Schneider, A.** 1862. Ueber die Metamorphose der Actinotrocha branchiata. Arch. Anat. Physiol. **Schultz, E.** 1897. Über Mesodermbildung bei Phoronis. Trav. Soc. Natural. St. Pétersbourg 28. 1903. Über die Regenerationserscheinungen bei Phoronis. Ztschr. Wissensch. Zool. 75. **Selys Longchamps, M. de.** 1902. Recherches sur le développement des Phoronis. Arch. Biol. 18. 1904a. Über Phoronis und Actinotroch bei Helgoland. Wissensch. Meeresunters, Abt. Helgoland, new ser. 6. 1904b. Développement postembryonnaire et affinités des Phoronis. Mém. Acad. Roy. Belgique, Collect. in quarto, Cl. Sci., ser. 2, vol. 1. 1907. Phoronis. Fauna und Flora des Golfes von Neapel, Monogr. 30. **Shearer, C.** 1906. Studies on the development of larval nephridia. Pt. 1. Phoronis. Mitt. Zool. Stat. Neapel 17. **Shipley, A.** 1910. Gephyrea and Phoronis. Cambridge Natural History, vol. II. **Shrubsole, W.** 1886. Actinotrocha of the British coasts. Nature, London, 34. **Silén, L.** 1952. Researches on Phoronidea of the Gullmar Fiord area. Arkiv Zoologi, new ser. 4. 1954a. On the nervous system of Phoronis. Arkiv Zoologi, new ser. 6. 1954b. Developmental biology of Phoronidea of the Gullmar Fiord area. Acta Zoologica 35. 1955. Autotomized tentacle crowns in Phoronis. Acta Zoologica 36. 1956. On shell-burrowing Phoronis from New Zealand. Trans. Roy. Soc. New Zealand 84. **Skramlik, E. von.** 1954. Die Regelung der Strömungsrichtung des Blutes. Experientia 10. **Spaulding, M.** 1906. Note on the occurrence of Phoronis larvae at Monterey Bay, California. Zool. Anz. 30. **Steuer, A.** 1933. Zur Fauna des Canale di Lerne bei Rovigno. Thalassia 1. **Torrey, H. B.** 1901. On Phoronis pacifica. Biol. Bull. 2. **Veillet, A.** 1941. Description et mécanisme de la métamorphose de la larve actinotroque. Bull. Inst. Océanogr. Monaco, no. 810. **Wagener, R.** 1847. Über den Bau der Actinotrocha. Arch. Anat. Physiol. **Wilson, E. B.** 1881. Origin and significance of the metamorphosis of Actinotrocha. Quart. Jour. Microsc. Sci. 21. **Wright, S.** 1856a. Description of two tubicolar animals. Edinburgh New Philos. Jour. 4. 1856b. Phoronis hippocrepia. Proc. Roy. Phys. Soc. Edinburgh 1.

CHAPTER XX

THE LOPHOPHORATE COELOMATES—PHYLUM ECTOPROCTA

I. HISTORICAL

Sessile colonial animals as cnidarians and ectoprocts were confused by early naturalists under the name of zoophytes that were regarded as of the nature of plants. Perhaps the earliest recognizable figure of a member of the phylum is that of Rondelet (1558; Fig. 98), who illustrated a frondose ectoproct, found growing on rocks or floating pieces of wood, regarded by him as a zoophyte or sea plant (*giroflade de mer*). Imperato (1599) is generally credited with first having asserted the animal nature of zoophytes but actually made only a few casual remarks on this matter, such as that madrepores have degenerated into animals and that the organ-pipe coral is formed of animal concretions. He regarded most zoophytes as plants, rating the red coral as a stony plant. He called attention to the "pores," meaning thereby incrusting ectoprocts which he had noticed often in association with corals. The pattern of their cases reminded him of snake skin. His name "pore" for ectoprocts survives in many generic names of the phylum as *Retepora*, *Membranipora*, etc. Imperato's remarks made little impression, and the plant nature of the red coral was strongly asserted by Marsigli (1711, 1725; also spelled Marsilli), who saw the expanded polyps of this alcyonarian, mistaking them for flowers with eight "petals" (tentacles). It is Peyssonel (1729, 1753) who deserves credit for establishing the animal nature of zoophytes. In 1723 he had gone to sea with the fishers of red coral and also saw the "flowers" described by Marsigli when pieces of red coral are placed in sea water; but he declared them to be "insects" inhabiting the coral and responsible for its formation. He further asserted that madrepores and other forms previously considered to be stony sea plants are produced by the labor of animals. Although his views were received with skepticism, they were confirmed by de Jussieu (1742), who studied zoophytes on the coast of Normandy and concluded that the so-called plants are the lodges of animals. He gave excellent figures of various cnidarians and ectoprocts and noticed that when such organisms are placed in sea water, the polyps with "horns" (tentacles) emerge and on disturbance retire into their tubes. It was he who created the name polyps for the animals, previously called insects, that inhabit these formations. At about this time also Trembley (1744) published his famous researches on hydra, proving its animal nature by its movements, feeding, budding, and regeneration. Trembley also saw and figured accurately the fresh-water ectoproct *Lophopus*, which he called the *polyp with the plume;* this animal was also seen and figured by Baker (1753), who named it *bellflower* animal. Ellis (1754, 1755a, b, c) was strongly and independently convinced of the animal nature of organisms previously considered to be marine vegetables. He examined various hydroids and incrusting ectoprocts, terming the latter celliferous corallines, first as preserved specimens, then alive at the seashore. He stated that these apparent plants are ramified animals.

Despite these proofs of the animal nature of cnidarians and ectoprocts the great classifiers of the latter part of the eighteenth century (e.g., Linnaeus, 1758; Pallas, 1766; Cuvier, 1798) continued to use the categories Zoophyta and Lithophyta for a conglomeration of sessile animals and continued to believe that such forms were at least partly of plant nature. Ectoprocts were lumped with cnidarians as polyps under Zoophyta. Cuvier in 1817 began replacing the category Zoophyta with Radiata but included under this heading in addition to the true radiates (echinoderms and polyps) a variety of animals. Incrusting ectoprocts were placed under polyps as polyps with cells.

Not until nearly a quarter of the nineteenth century had passed did zoologists begin to realize that the category of polyps comprised two quite different types of animal structure. Blainville (1820) first recorded the presence in ectoprocts of two openings to the digestive tract and stated that ectoprocts should be placed in a higher category than true polyps, near ascidians. Grant (1827) also noticed differences

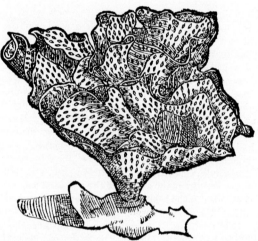

Fig. 98.—Oldest known figure of an ectoproct, by Rondelet (1558); probably one of the Reteporidae.

between ectoprocts and hydroid polyps, as the ciliated tentacles and recurved digestive tract of the former, although he failed to see the anus. Audouin and Milne Edwards (1828) definitely verified the presence of two openings to the digestive tract in some polyps and divided polyps into four categories of which the last included polyps with an anus. These authors compared ectoprocts with compound ascidians and thus began the unfortunate association of ectoprocts and tunicates that was promulgated by Milne Edwards for years and that culminated in his creation (1843) of the name Molluscoidea for the combination of these two groups.

In the meantime the English naturalist Thompson had made independent observations on various zoophytes, and in 1830 he published to the effect that zoophytes include two very different types, ordinary polyps and another type that he called Polyzoa, distinguished by ciliated tentacles and a separate digestive tract. Independently Ehrenberg (1831, 1833) noticed that some coral animals have two openings to the digestive tract and proposed the names Anthozoa for those with one opening and Bryozoa for those with two.

Thus the two names Polyzoa and Bryozoa were independently created for the same group of animals. The endless controversy as to which of these two names should properly be employed reminded Stebbing (1911a) of Dickens's endless suit of Jarndyce versus Jarndyce. There cannot be any doubt that Thompson's name Polyzoa was published prior to Ehrenberg's name Bryozoa, but rules of priority do not apply to the higher systematic categories. In general, English workers (Allman, 1856; Busk, 1859; Hincks, 1880; Harmer, 1911; Herdman, 1911) have favored the name Polyzoa partly on grounds of priority, partly on the basis that Thompson intended by his name to indicate a group of "zoophytes" distinct from hydroids. On the other hand, some English workers, notably Waters (1880) and Stebbing (1911a, b), have rejected Polyzoa, arguing that Thompson used Polyzoa rather as a generic name, not as the name of an animal group, whereas Ehrenberg definitely designated Bryozoa as a group name. Continental and American workers early accepted Bryozoa, have continued to use this name, and are overwhelmingly in favor of calling the phylum Bryozoa (Bassler, 1953). Harmer (1947) reviewed the relative merits of the names Bryozoa and Polyzoa and concluded that Thompson did use the name Polyzoa as a group name but failed to make a definite statement to that effect. The author, having read Thompson's article in the original, must concur with Harmer's opinion. Thompson used the name Polyzoa in something more than a generic sense, as a name for zoophytes that he had noticed differed essentially from the hydroids among which they grew. However, he failed to state definitely and clearly that he was proposing Polyzoa as a group name, whereas Ehrenberg did definitely and clearly state that he was creating Bryozoa as a group name for zoophytes with two openings to the digestive tract. In these circumstances one may perhaps award the palm to Ehrenberg.

However, the entire argument becomes unnecessary and futile if one accepts, as does the author, the view that the old phylum Bryozoa (or Polyzoa) comprised two groups of quite different grades of structure, Entoprocta and Ectoprocta, and that these should be given phylum status, with the elimination of the concept Bryozoa. Nitsche (1869) first divided Bryozoa into these two groups, and they have been accepted ever since as justifiable major subdivisions of Bryozoa. Hatschek (1888) raised these subdivisions to phylum rank, and this usage was followed in the *Handbuch der Zoologie* and by the author (III, page 521), although it has not yet been accepted by many students of Bryozoa. Many zoologists will no doubt prefer, on mere grounds of familiarity, to retain the name Bryozoa in place of and as identical with Ectoprocta, but such usage seems apt to lead to confusion. There is a natural and understandable reluctance to abandon an old and familiar name, but as such reluctance must eventually be overcome, why not now? The term bryozoans may perhaps be retained as a common or popular name for the ectoprocts.

In fairness, it must be stated that some eminent students of the old phylum Bryozoa do not admit the necessity or desirability of splitting this phylum into the separate phyla Entoprocta[1] and Ectoprocta. Although E. Marcus in 1926 stated that Entoprocta and Ectoprocta are two completely separate groups of Protostomia he continued in his taxonomic works to unite them under the name Bryozoa, later (1938a, 1939a) argued against the separation, and is still of the latter opinion. The question has recently been carefully reviewed by Brien and Papyn (1954), who conclude that the entoprocts differ decidedly from the ectoprocts in their embryology, metamorphosis, and adult anatomy and who therefore support their separation into two distinct phyla. The main point of resemblance is the possession by both groups of a trochophore type of larva, but of course this type of larva is common to a number of protostomatous phyla. Brien and Papyn agree with the present author that the tentacles of the Entoprocta do not constitute a lophophore. They regard the Entoprocta as an early offshoot of the protostomatous line leading to the Annelida, whereas

---

[1] It appears necessary to point out that Entoprocta, *not* Endoprocta, is the correct spelling, as originally given by Nitsche.

the Ectoprocta are later derivatives of the same line; in this way they explain embryological similarities between the two groups.

The most extensive general account of the Ectoprocta is that of Cori (1941), somewhat unsatisfactory. Valuable references are those of Hincks (1880), Busk (1884,
1886), Prouho (1892), Calvet (1900), Levinsen (1909), Harmer (1915, 1926, 1930, 1931,
1934), Borg (1926a, 1944), and Marcus (1926a, 1926b, 1937a, 1938a, 1939a, 1941a,
1942a). Extinct members are treated by Buge (1952) and Bassler (1953), and the
latter gives a very useful complete classificatory arrangement to genera.

II. CHARACTERS OF THE PHYLUM

1. Definition.—The Ectoprocta are microscopic sessile colonial coelomates that are permanently fastened in exoskeletal cases or gelatinous
material of their own secretion, that are provided with a circular or
crescentic lophophore and a recurved digestive tract bringing the anus
near the mouth, and that lack nephridia and a circulatory system.

2. General Characters.—The Ectoprocta, or moss animals, exist as
colonies that are typically derived by asexual reproduction from a single
progenitor (*ancestrula*), originating by the metamorphosis of a sexually
produced larva. The colony (called *zoarium* in ectoproct terminology) is
nearly always immovably attached to a substrate as shells, seaweeds,
pilings, bodies of other animals, and so on, although a few colonies are
motile, and manifests a great variety of form. It may be arborescent
(Fig. 101*A*) or frondose (Fig. 101*E*) or very often forms flat spreading
incrustations on objects (Fig. 102*A*, *B*), or sometimes is composed of
adherent or erect stolons bearing the zooids (Fig. 99). The colony is
composed of individuals (zooids), each of which is typically enclosed in a
secreted exoskeletal case of varied contour (Figs. 103–106) and has some
degree of organic continuity with fellow zooids of the colony. The case is
termed *zoecium;* the zoecia of a colony may be separate (Fig. 99) but
usually are contiguous with walls in contact or in common (Fig. 102).
The case has an opening to the exterior here called *orifice* (to avoid the
term *aperture* used in several confusing senses by ectoproctologists),
provided in many ectoprocts with a closing apparatus.

The ectoproct individual or zooid consists of two main parts, the
tentacular crown or lophophore, protrusible through the orifice, and the
trunk, permanently fastened in the zoecium, which in fact constitutes
part of the body wall. The lophophore is identical with that of phoronids,
consisting of a body-wall extension subdivided distally into a single row of
ciliated tentacles; all parts of the lophophore are hollow, containing a
continuous coelomic cavity. In the marine or gymnolaemate ectoprocts
the lophophore is circular but has the shape of a horseshoe (one exception)
in the fresh-water or phylactolaemate forms. As in phoronids it always
embraces the mouth but never the anus. The trunk interior is occupied
by a coelom lined by peritoneum and containing the digestive tract,

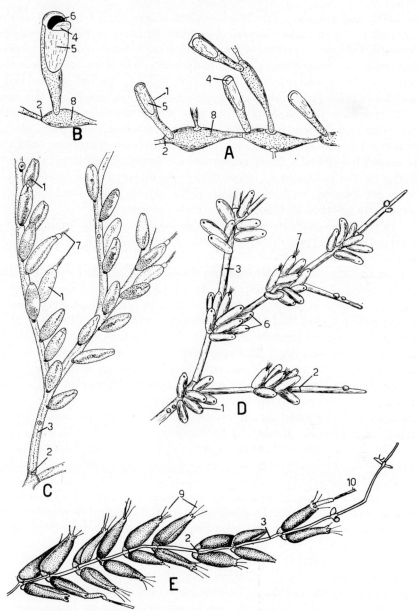

Fig. 99.—Forms of ectoproct colonies. *A, Aetea,* zooids with attached expanded base. *B,* one zooid of *Aetea,* showing operculum. *C, Vesicularia,* zooids borne irregularly along erect branching stolons (*after Busk,* 1886). *D, Bowerbankia,* zooids in clusters along erect branching stolons. (*A, B, D, after Marcus,* 1938a.) *E, Aeverrillia,* zooids in pairs along creeping stolon (*after Rogick* and *Croasdale,* 1949). 1, zooids; 2, septum; 3, internode of stolon; 4, operculum; 5, frontal membrane of zooid; 6, orifice; 7, protruding tentacles; 8, expanded zooid base; 9, spines around orifice; 10, pleated collar.

muscles, and gonads. The trunk coelom is separated from that of the lophophore by a rather imperfect septum situated at the level of the lophophoral base. The recurved digestive tract hangs freely in the coelom with few attachments to the body wall. The anus opens near the mouth. The nervous system consists of a plexus throughout the body wall and a main ganglionic mass situated between the mouth and the anus and encircling the pharynx; from this center nerves ascend into the tentacles and descend along the digestive tract and other parts of the trunk. The side of the zooid containing the nervous center and the anus is considered dorsal. Most ectoprocts are hermaphroditic with gonads borne on the peritoneum. Circulatory, respiratory, and excretory systems are wanting, no doubt because of the minute size of the zooids, and gonoducts or other coelomic ducts are also absent.

In the gymnolaemate ectoprocts, the zooids are polymorphic, that is, exist as several types, explained later. Polymorphism is best expressed in cheilostomes.

Asexual reproduction by budding obtains throughout the phylum and is the means of colony formation. An additional mode of asexual reproduction is seen in phylactolaemates, which in autumn produce special reproductive bodies that are able to survive winter conditions and that hatch in spring to reestablish the colonies. Mature ectoproct colonies also reproduce sexually. The eggs may be shed into the water but in marine ectoprocts are usually brooded to a larval stage in the zooid or in special brood chambers of which a variety occur. Free-swimming larvae usually regarded as altered trochophores eventuate, and these settle on suitable substrates and metamorphose into the progenitor zooid (ancestrula) that generates the colony by budding.

The Ectoprocta are chiefly marine and among the most common animals found in collecting along ocean shores. They are mostly limited to the littoral zone, although known to descend to depths of nearly 6000 m. They are widely distributed in the oceans of the world in all latitudes. The group Phylactolaemata is limited to fresh water, and its members are sparingly found under stones or on twigs and other objects in clear lakes, reservoirs, ponds, and streams. Ectoprocts are often mistaken by beginners for hydroids but are easily distinguished from them on microscopic examination by the ciliation of the tentacles and as regards marine species also by the boxlike or vaselike cases each provided with an orifice.

Ectoprocts with calcareous zoecia preserve well as fossils, and a bewildering array of extinct members of the phylum is known, treated by Buge (1952) and Bassler (1953). There are about 4000 described existing species and, according to Buge, 15,000 extinct ones. Bassler (in correspondence) considers the latter figure too high but is not able to give a figure of his own.

III. CLASSIFICATION OF THE PHYLUM

The classification of the Ectoprocta seems to have reached a reasonably stable condition although there are arguments as to the relative ranks of the different groups. The arrangement here presented follows mostly Osburn (1950–1953) and Bassler (1953), with the omission of wholly extinct suborders. Bassler gives a complete synopsis of the families and genera of Ectoprocta which is very useful despite the frequent contradictions in the diagnoses.

Class I. Gymnolaemata or Stelmatopoda. Ectoprocta with circular lophophore and without epistome, body-wall musculature, or direct coelomic communications between zooids; marine with very few exceptions.

Order 1. Ctenostomata. Zoecia not calcified, membranous; orifice terminal or subterminal, with a closing apparatus in the form of a pleated collar; without ovicells or avicularia. Silén (1942a) and Soule (1954) have given grounds for reducing the usual four suborders to two.

Suborder 1. Stolonifera. Zooids separate, vaselike, budded only from creeping or erect stolons, not from each other; ancestrula originates the colony by giving off stolons.

Suborder 2. Carnosa. Zooids separate or contiguous, usually budded from each other; ancestrula originates the colony by budding off zooids.

Order 2. Cheilostomata. Colonies branching, lamellate, or incrusting; zooids more or less contiguous but with separate walls; zoecia boxlike with small subterminal orifice provided with a hinged lid (operculum); brood chambers frequently in the form of ovicells; polymorphic, often with avicularia or vibracula or both.

Suborder 1. Anasca. Zooids without compensation sac.

Division 1. Inovicellata. Zooids separate, with tubular adherent bases, simulating stolons; uncalcified; with external brood sac.

Division 2. Scrupariina. Uncalcified; plantlike with uniserial or biserial branches; zooids separate.

Division 3. Malacostega. Generally calcified except for the frontal membrane; zooids more or less contiguous; with or without ovicells and avicularia.

Division 4. Coilostega. With cryptocyst extending to the orifice, leaving opesiules; ovicells hyperstomial or endozoecial.

Division 5. Pseudostega. With complete cryptocyst and polypide tube; ovicells endotoichal.

Division 6. Cellularina. Branching colonies with uncalcified or moderately calcified zoecia; with hyperstomial ovicells and typical avicularia.

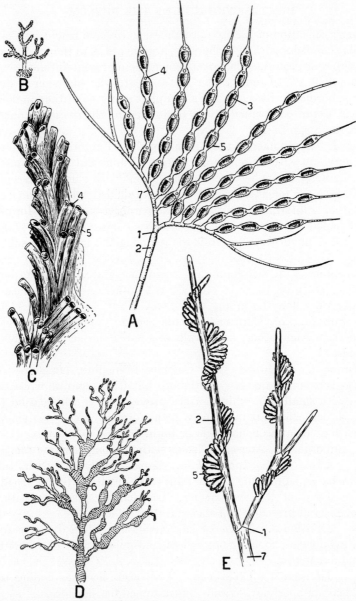

Fig. 100.—Colony forms (continued).   A, *Cothurnicella*, each internode gives rise to a branch composed of a single file of zooids (*after Levinsen*, 1909).   B, tubuliporid colony. C, branch of B, with multiserial zooids.   (B, C, after Busk, 1886.)   D, colony of *Amathia*, partly covered with an incrusting ectoproct.   E, *Amathia*, from life, Brazil, showing double rows of zooids arranged in spirals.   1, node; 2, internode; 3, opesium; 4, orifice; 5, zooid; 6, incrusting ectoproct; 7, stolon.

Division 7. Cribrimorpha. With calcareous ventral shield formed by fusion of spines outside frontal membrane.

Suborder 2. Ascophora. With compensation sac.

Order 3. Cyclostomata or Stenostomata. Zooids tubular, more or less fused, completely calcified; orifice terminal, more or less circular; without operculum or avicularia; brood chambers in the form of gonozooids or compounded of a gonozooid and other zooids, development polyembryonic.

Suborder 1. Articulata. Colony with joints, branching; gonozooids simple expansions of ordinary zooids.

Suborder 2. Tubuliporina. Colony without joints, gonozooid spreading and lobulate.

Suborder 3. Cancellata. Colony without joints; zoecial wall double; spaces between autozooids filled with coelomic chambers; kenozooids limited to basal disk; brood chamber an expanded gonozooid.

Suborder 4. Cerioporina. Colony without joints and with double zoecial wall; composed of intermingled autozooids and kenozooids fused up to the orifice; brood chamber compounded.

Suborder 5. Rectangulata. Without joints; colony discoidal or wartlike, with tubular radiating zooids separated by coelomic chambers; brood chamber compounded.

Four wholly extinct suborders.

Order 4. Trepostomata. Wholly extinct; colonies massive, well calcified; zoecia long and tubular crossed by horizontal septa.

Order 5. Cryptostomata. Wholly extinct, colonies frondose or branching; zoecia tubular, short, with orifice concealed at the bottom of a long vestibule.

Class II. Phylactolaemata or Lophopoda. Ectoprocta with a horseshoe-shaped (circular in one genus) lophophore; epistome present; body wall with a muscular layer; coeloms of zooids continuous; colony branching or a gelatinous mass; not calcified, monomorphic; exclusively in fresh water.

The class names Gymnolaemata and Phylactolaemata were created in 1856 by Allman, who seemed to be unaware that the latter group had already been named Lophopoda by Dumortier in 1835 and the former Stelmatopoda by Van der Hoeven in his *Handbook of Zoology*, which came out in parts in the second Dutch edition between 1846 and 1855 (English translation by G. Clark in 1856). One must therefore agree with Cori (1941) that Stelmatopoda and Lophopoda are the just names of these classes, but they have not been generally adopted. The name Cyclostomata is identical with the name of the group of round-mouthed fishes and should therefore be altered to avoid confusion. Marcus (1938a) has suggested Stenostomata in place of Cyclostomata.

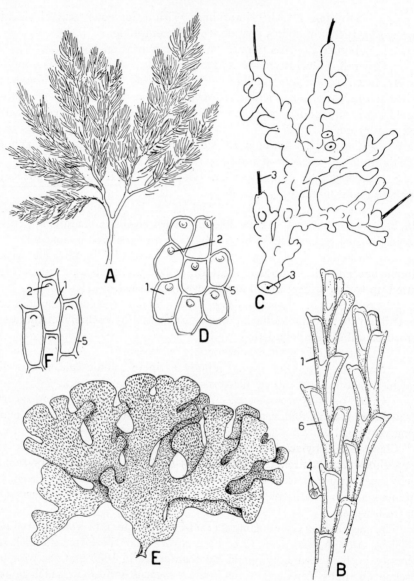

Fig. 101.—Colony forms (continued). *A, Bugula,* example of a much-branched colony. *B,* branch of *Bugula,* showing biserial zooids. *C, Alcyonidium,* forming a gelatinous crust on gorgonian stems. *D,* bit of *C,* showing zooids. *E,* colony of *Flustra,* calcified, resembling a millepore. *F,* bit of *D,* showing zooids. (*All from preserved specimens.*) 1, zooid; 2, operculum; 3, gorgonian stem; 4, avicularium; 5, zoecium; 6, frontal membrane.

Some prominent students of ectoprocts (Marcus, 1938a; Silén, 1942a) favor the union of the Ctenostomata and Cheilostomata into one group. Marcus has proposed the following arrangement of the Gymnolaemata:

Order Stenostomata (= Cyclostomata)

Order Eurystomata

    Suborder Ctenostomata

    Suborder Cheilostomata

Bassler (1953) opposes the idea of a close relationship between cteno-stomes and cheilostomes on the grounds of the great time interval that has elapsed between the first appearances of members of these groups as fossils. Silén (1954) counters that this argument rather supports the view that the ctenostomes represent ancient lateral twigs from the main line of ascent of cheilostomes. The present author is of the opinion that the work of Soule (1953, 1954) has shown great divergence of the stolon-iferous ctenostomes from other gymnolaemates and that therefore Cteno-stomata should be retained as a distinct order; or perhaps the carnose ctenostomes should be united with the cheilostomes and the stoloniferous members separated as an independent order. Borg (1926b, 1944) main-tains that the cyclostomes differ so much from other ectoprocts that they should constitute a separate class that he terms Stenolaemata, coordinate with Gymnolaemata and Phylactolaemata. This concept has not met much acceptance.

As the two classes of Ectoprocta differ considerably they are treated separately below. In discussing the gymnolaemates it will be necessary to refer constantly to the three existing gymnolaemate types—cteno-stomes, cheilostomes, cyclostomes; hence the reader should early acquire some understanding of the characteristics of these three groups. The following accounts are limited to the existing members; consideration of extinct ectoprocts will be confined to the systematic survey.

IV. CLASS GYMNOLAEMATA

1. Definition.—The Gymnolaemata are ectoprocts with a circular lophophore and without epistome, body-wall musculature, or open coelomic communications between zooids.

2. Remarks on Terminology.—The study of ectoprocts is burdened with a large and fantastic terminology, much of it dating from a period when the structure of the animals was not understood. Hence the terminology lacks relation to terms employed for other groups of animals. Frequently the ectoproctologists seem to get themselves entangled in their own terminology, using the same word (e.g., aperture) in several different senses. A useful glossary of the terminology is given by Bassler (1953), who suggested many eliminations but is not sufficiently drastic in this regard. In the following accounts the special terms invented for

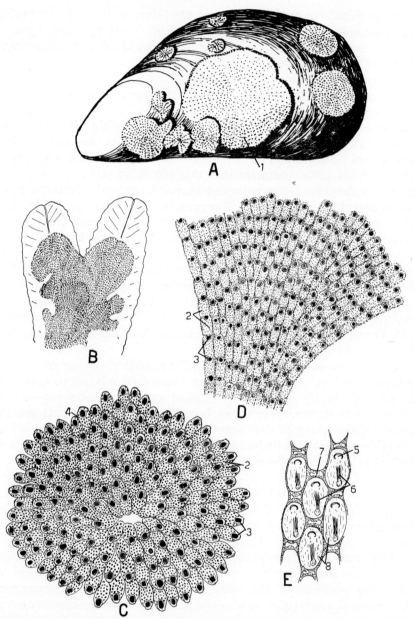

Fig. 102.—Colony forms (concluded), incrusting types.   *A*, bivalve shell with several incrusting colonies (*after Rogick*, 1945b).   *B*, algal frond with incrustation of *Acanthodesia*. *C*, colony of *Cryptosula*, radiating type of growth.   *D*, *Schizoporella unicornis*, fanlike growth.   *E*, bit of *B*, showing zooids.   (*B–E*, from specimens.)   1, colony of *Cryptosula;* 2, calcified zoecium; 3, orifice; 4, pseudopores; 5, operculum; 6, contracted polypide; 7, calcareous area; 8, frontal membrane.

ectoprocts will be avoided as far as possible and replaced by terms applicable to invertebrates in general.

The expression *zoarium* for the ectoproct colony appears superfluous and will not be employed. *Zooid* means a complete unit of the colony, that is, the living parts of an individual animal plus the lifeless secreted exoskeleton. The latter is termed *zoecium*, and this word, confused in the literature of ectoprocts, will here be used strictly to refer to the exoskeletal case. The zoecium is part of the body wall, and for the layers of the body wall the usual names (cuticle, epidermis, peritoneum) will be employed, replacing the fantastic terms (ectocyst, endocyst) found in ectoproct literature. The old workers had the grotesque idea that the zooid consists of two animals, the boxlike body wall which they called *cystid* and the internal contents which they called *polypide*. Although these names are objectionable because of the idea behind them, it appears impossible to avoid using them. The expression cystid will therefore be used to indicate the vaselike or boxlike fixed part of the body wall, including the exoskeletal layer (zoecium) and the living layers adherent to its underside; the term polypide will designate the internal living movable parts of the zooid, that is, the lophophore, the digestive tract, and the nervous and muscular systems. As in phoronids lophophore will mean the entire tentacular crown, both the tentacles and their supporting base. The opening of the zoecium to the exterior will be called *orifice*, and the confused term aperture will be avoided altogether. An extension of the rim of the orifice into a collar will be called *orificial collar*, whether short or long, to avoid the bad terms (*peristome, peristomie*) found in ectoproct literature. The term peristome usually means a smooth membranous area around the mouth and hence is out of place here, not to mention the fact that the orifice is not the mouth. The orifice of the orificial collar will be called secondary orifice. Other necessary terms will be explained in their appropriate connections.

3. Form of the Colony.—The gymnolaemate colony occurs in a variety of shapes that depend on the mode of budding and are also somewhat variable within the same species. A very simple colony type is seen in the cheilostome *Aetea*, where the minute colony consists of a succession of single zooids (Fig. 99A) partly erect, partly adherent to the substrate. Other simple types of colonies, seen in the stoloniferous ctenostomes, consist of separate zooids borne on erect or creeping stolons in pairs as in *Aeverrillia* (Fig. 99E) or in clusters as in *Bowerbankia* (Fig. 99D) and *Amathia* (Fig. 100D, E) or in irregular rows as in *Vesicularia* (Fig. 99C); peculiar to *Amathia* is the spiral curve of the zooid groups. Stolons, which are simply tubes of body wall, are divided by perforated partitions or *nodes* (also called septa) into lengths termed *internodes* that are regarded as highly altered zooids. An unusual colony form is seen in

Cothurnicella (old name, *Chlidonia*), a stoloniferous cheilostome in which each internode of the branches gives rise to a single file of zooids (Fig. 100*A*).

Nonstoloniferous colonies, which comprise the vast majority of gymnolaemates, consist of a continuous succession of zooids more or less fused to each other. When not calcified such colonies may form branching, plantlike growths of some size, as in the familiar *Bugula* (Fig. 101*A*). The branches (Fig. 101*B*) consist of a succession of zooids in uniserial, biserial, or multiserial arrangement, with zooids facing in any direction or all in one direction. Sometimes, notably in *Alcyonidium*, the zooids are imbedded in a gelatinous secretion and may incrust other animals (Fig. 101*C*, *D*) or form upright cylindrical growths. The majority of gymnolaemate colonies, however, are more or less calcified. With increasing calcification, colonies become compact and shorter, taking shapes that simulate millepores and corals, or form flat incrustations. Among calcified gymnolaemates branching upright growths with multiserial zooids are seen in tubuliporids (Fig. 100*B*, *C*) and frondose or foliaceous shapes in *Flustra* (Fig. 101*E*, *F*) and other Flustridae, and in the Reteporidae; in such types the zooids may occur on both surfaces or on one surface only. The colonies of the Reteporidae are generally reticulate, that is, the branches anastomose, leaving openings (fenestrae) through the colony that hence has a lacelike appearance (Fig. 145*C*). The great majority of calcified gymnolaemates are incrusting, occurring as thin flat sheets on shells, algal fronds, pilings, other animals, or almost any object. These sheets are usually made of one layer of zooids with their dorsal surfaces ("backs") cemented to the substrate and their orifices facing in one direction, away from the substrate (Fig. 102). Incrusting colonies may radiate from a central point (*Cryptosula*, Fig. 102*C*) or may spread fanlike (*Schizoporella*, Fig. 102*D*) or often adjust their expansion to the shape of the substrate (*Acanthodesia*, Fig. 102*B*, *E*).

Remane (1936, 1938) discovered what he considered to be a solitary ctenostome, *Monobryozoon ambulans* (Fig. 103*A*), dwelling in the sand near Helgoland. This has a vaselike form with a number of short stolons, each tipped with a cluster of adhesive cells, borne on its basal part. These stolons adhere to the sand grains, anchoring the animal or enabling it to move slowly; each stolon is capable of developing into a new zooid that then constricts off. Since such stolons are regarded as highly modified zooids, *Monobryozoon* is in effect a small colony, not solitary as supposed by Remane. Hence all known ectoprocts are colonial.

When not directly adherent to the substrate, colonies are anchored by some form of stolon, then called *radicular fiber* or *rhizoid*. These may occur as rootlike clusters at the colony base (Fig. 103*B*) or as a rounded or irregularly contoured holdfast (Fig. 103*E*); or often long single stolons

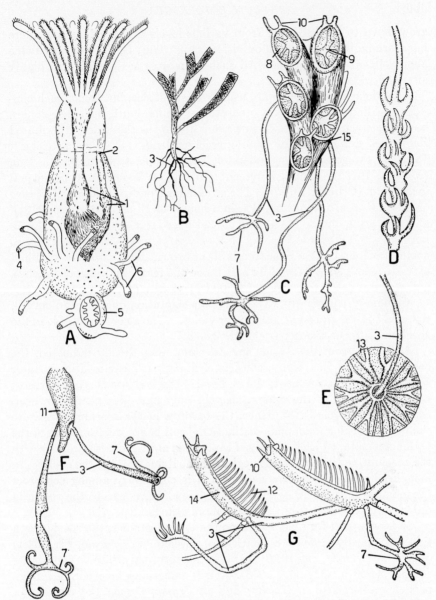

FIG. 103.—Attachment devices. *A, Monobryozoon* with basal stolons (*after Remane,* 1936). *B, Flustra* with rhizoids (*after Busk,* 1884). *C, Scrupocellaria* with three rhizoids ending in claws (*after Peach,* 1878). *D,* anchoring rhizoid of *Scrupocellaria,* with hooks. *E,* terminal holdfast of *Scrupocellaria. F,* primary zooid of a species of *Bugula* with clawed rhizoids. (*D–F, after Hincks,* 1880.) *G,* part of a colony of *Beania,* with anchoring rhizoids with clawed ends (*after Marcus,* 1937a). 1, digestive tract; 2, anus; 3, rhizoids; 4, adhesive tips of stolons; 5, stolon developing into zooid; 6, stolons; 7, clawed ends of rhizoids; 8, frontal membrane; 9, branched spine protecting frontal membrane; 10, spines of zoecium; 11, ancestrula (primary zooid); 12, row of spines along edge of frontal membrane; 13, holdfast; 14, thickened cuticle of zoecium; 15, calcified part of zoecium (gymnocyst).

grow down to the substrate from various levels of the colony and there may terminate in clawlike subdivisions (Fig. 103*C, D, F, G*) or may twine about objects like tendrils. All such structures are regarded as highly altered zooids.

Gymnolaemate colonies are usually of small size, but some reach considerable dimensions. Many ctenostomes form minute, delicate colonies, but some erect themselves to surprising heights as the widely distributed *Zoobotryon pellucidum* (Fig. 139*A*), reaching lengths of 45 cm. (Reichert, 1870), or the gelatinous cylinders of *Alcyonidium*, to 60 to 90 cm. long (Marcus, 1926a). The arborescent growths of *Bugula* may be several inches high (Osburn, 1912a). The calcareous frondose colonies of *Flustra* (Fig. 101*E*) not infrequently attain a height of 15 cm. (Marcus, 1926a), and incrusting cheilostomes may spread over large areas. Thus Landsborough (1852) records a colony of *Membranipora membranacea*, a species commonly found on the huge fronds of the brown kelp *Laminaria*, that had extended along such a frond for a distance of 5 feet, at a width of 8 inches, and was estimated to consist of 2,300,000 zooids.

Colonies are generally white or of pale coloration but range to orange, red, and brown, and some are blue or violet. The color may reside in the zoecium or in the living parts of the zooid.

4. Structure of the Zooid : the Zoecium.—As already indicated, the zooid, or unit of the colony, consists of living parts enclosed in an outer secreted lifeless encasement, the *zoecium*. The zoecium is often the most conspicuous part of the colony, also the only part that persists in dead colonies and in fossils. Further, the features of the zoecium constitute the main basis for taxonomic distinctions, and hence the literature of the Gymnolaemata, which is mainly of taxonomic nature, deals primarily with the zoecium, to the deplorable neglect of the living parts of the zooid. In fact, in the case of calcareous zoecia it is customary among ectoproct taxonomists to burn away with a blowpipe all parts except the zoecia in order to see the details of the latter more clearly.

In its simplest form, as seen among the ctenostomes, the zoecium is a thin case, hardly more than a cuticle, of vaselike (*Vesicularia*, Fig. 104*A*) or tubular (*Nolella*, Fig. 104*B*) shape, with a terminal orifice. These cases consist of chitin (Hyman, 1958). They sometimes incorporate foreign particles as usually in *Nolella;* and in *Cryptopolyzoon* the clusters of zoecia are covered with a mass of sand grains (Dendy, 1888). As a variant the ctenostome zoecium may form spinous projections as around the orifice in *Aeverrillia* (Fig. 104*C*) or along the sides in *Buskia*, in which genus the species *B. nitens* growing on a hydroid stem gives a ludicrous effect of creeping insects (Fig. 104*D*). In *Farrella* and *Flustrellidra* (= *Flustrella*) the chitinous rim of the orifice is altered into two lips, of which the lower one is closable by way of attached muscles (Fig. 104*E*).

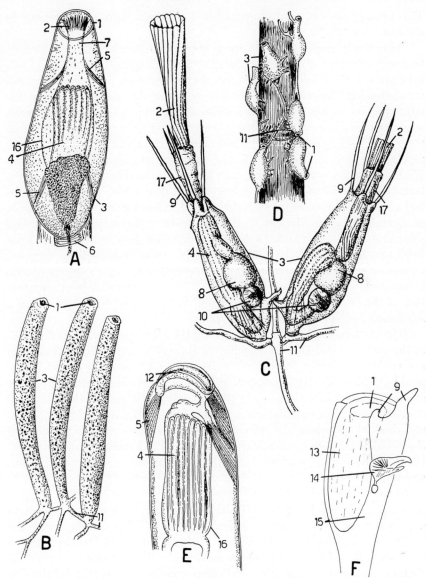

Fig. 104.—Zoecium. A, single zooid of *Vesicularia* (*after Busk*, 1886). B, three zoecia of *Nolella*. C, two zooids of *Aeverrillia* with spiny zoecia. (B, C, *after Marcus*, 1937a.) D, *Buskia nitens*, with lateral spines, growing on a hydroid stem (*after Alder*, 1857). E, anterior end of zooid of *Farrella*, with closing lips (*after Van Beneden*, 1845a). F, one zoecium of *Bugula*, with frontal membrane. 1, orifice; 2, pleated collar closing orifice; 3, zoecium; 4, retracted tentacles; 5, muscles; 6, short internode of attachment; 7, vestibule; 8, digestive tract; 9, spines; 10, gizzard; 11, stolon; 12, movable lip; 13, frontal membrane; 14, avicularium; 15, thickened chitin of zoecium; 16, tentacle sheath; 17, vestibular membrane.

This arrangement seems to foreshadow the formation of an operculum in cheilostomes.

Apparently such simple chitinous zoecia do not offer sufficient protection and support for the development of large colonies, for colonies of this type are usually small and in the minority in the class. Various means of strengthening the zoecia are seen among gymnolaemates. Colonies are strengthened by abandoning the stoloniferous type of growth with weak separated zoecia and assuming more compact shapes with contiguous zoecia. This has occurred especially among the cheilostomes, where the zoecia then become boxlike, of oval, rectangular, or polygonal contour. With contiguity of the zoecia the orifice necessarily migrates from a terminal to a subterminal position on one surface, which thereby is identified as ventral, also called *frontal*. Such boxlike zoecia also have a back or dorsal surface, adherent to the substrate in incrusting colonies, and sides and ends. In cheilostomes the orifice becomes closable by a little chitinous hinged lid, the *operculum* (Fig. 105), operated by muscles. Curiously enough, in the most familiar cheilostome, *Bugula*, an operculum is wanting in most species (Fig. 104*F*); this is also the case in other members of the family Bicellariellidae (Silén, 1941) and is to be regarded as a secondary loss, not a primitive condition.

The obvious method of strengthening the colony is to thicken the walls of the zoecia. But this meets with the difficulty that volume changes of the zooid necessarily accompany extension and retraction of the lophophore. This difficulty is not encountered in phoronids because the latter are not fastened in their tubes. The living layers of part of the body wall of ectoprocts are permanently attached to the undersurface of the zoecium, and the lophophore can be retracted only by withdrawal into the body of the zooid that thereby necessarily expands. The demands of this situation have been met by gymnolaemates in several ways, some very curious and unpredictable.

Strengthening the thin chitinous zoecium by the secretion of some pliant material to its outer side has been rarely utilized. It is found among carnose ctenostomes, chiefly in the genus *Alcyonidium*, where the boxlike zoecia with ventral orifice (Fig. 101*D*) are imbedded in a gelatinous secretion of unknown chemical nature. By this means colonies of *Alcyonidium* may form erect cylinders nearly a meter in height. A common device in cheilostomes is the thickening of all walls of the zoecium, except the ventral wall, which remains a thin pliant chitinous cuticle. This ventral area of thin cuticle plus the underlying living layers of the body wall is called the *frontal membrane*. The operculum is to be regarded as a small bit of the frontal membrane that has become hinged to the rest of it. The other walls of the zoecium may also remain chitinous, but are generally much thickened as in *Bugula* (Fig. 104*F*) and

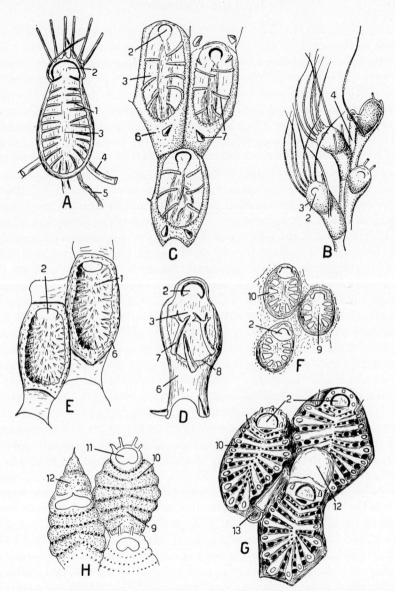

Fig. 105.—Zoecium (continued). *A*, a zooid of *Beania*, seen from the front, with a row of spines around the edge of the frontal membrane. *B, Bicellariella*, with exceptionally long spines (some broken off in the specimen) and reduced opesium (*after Hincks*, 1880). *C, Electra*, with calcified border (gymnocyst) to the frontal membrane and calcified spines protecting the latter. *D*, another species of *Electra* with large spines and beginning cryptocyst. *E, Conopeum*, with chitinous spines on the frontal membrane. *F–H*, types of cribriform cheilostomes. *F, Membraniporella*, with wide openings in the frontal shield. *G, Colletosia*, with ribs and rows of holes between the ribs. *H, Cribrilina*, with rows of small holes. (*A, C–E, G, after Marcus*, 1937a; *F, H, after Osburn*, 1950.) 1, chitinous spines; 2, operculum; 3, frontal membrane; 4, stolon; 5, rhizoid; 6, gymnocyst; 7, calcareous spines; 8, cryptocyst; 9, calcareous shield; 10, holes through shield; 11, orifice; 12, ovicell; 13, avicularium.

Beania (Fig. 105*A*). The large opening left in the ventral wall of the zooid by removal of the frontal membrane is termed *opesium*. The frontal membrane, hence also the opesium, may occupy the entire ventral surface of the zooid as in *Beania* (Fig. 105*A*), or the thickened chitin may encroach considerably on this surface (*Bugula*, Fig. 104*F*; *Bicellariella*, Fig. 105*B*; *Aetea*, Fig. 99*A*, *B*), leaving a rather small, oval frontal membrane. But even when reduced to the minimum area compatible with its function of permitting expansion of the interior, the frontal membrane remains the most vulnerable part of the colony and protective spines are often developed around it. A row of spines along each edge may arch over the membrane as in *Beania* (Figs. 103*G*, 105*A*). Extremely long spines bordering the edge of the frontal membrane, especially anteriorly, occur in *Bicellariella* (formerly *Bicellaria*, Fig. 105*B*).

Calcification of the zoecium is the most prevalent means of fortifying the colony and is common among cheilostomes, universal in cyclostomes. The deposition of calcium carbonate occurs to the inner side of the chitinous cuticle, between this and the epidermis. A chitinous cuticle is always present on the outer surface of the zoecium throughout the gymnolaemates. As with heavy chitinization of the zoecial wall, so also with calcification some device must be adopted to permit expansion and contraction of the interior with withdrawal and extension of the lophophore. This device among cheilostomes may be the same as discussed above; that is, more or less of the ventral zoecial wall remains uncalcified as a frontal membrane covering the opesium (Figs. 103*C*, 105*C–E*). Here also the frontal membrane may be protected by spines springing from the bordering calcareous edge and arching over the membrane. A row of spines on each side may arch over the membrane as in some species of *Electra* (Fig. 105*C*), or the membrane may be guarded by a few large spines as in another species of *Electra* (Fig. 105*D*). In *Scrupocellaria* and other genera of the Scrupocellariidae, a spine (*scutum*) of bizarre shape partly shields the frontal membrane (Fig. 103*C*). Rarely the membrane itself produces small chitinous spines (*Conopeum*, Fig. 105*E*). The calcified part of the frontal wall bordering the frontal membrane is called *gymnocyst* in the antiquated terminology of ectoproctologists, and the spines leaning over the membrane are part of the gymnocyst and also calcified. In Fig. 106*A* is shown the calcified part, resembling a coffin or bathtub, of the zoecium of an incrusting cheilostome (*Membranipora membranacea*), after removal of all chitinous and living parts; here practically the whole frontal surface has remained uncalcified.

The foregoing arrangements are relatively simple and easily understood, but more complicated devices, less easily understood, are also found among cheilostomes. In a group of forms known as cribriform cheilostomes, belonging to the family Cribrilinidae, the rows of calcified

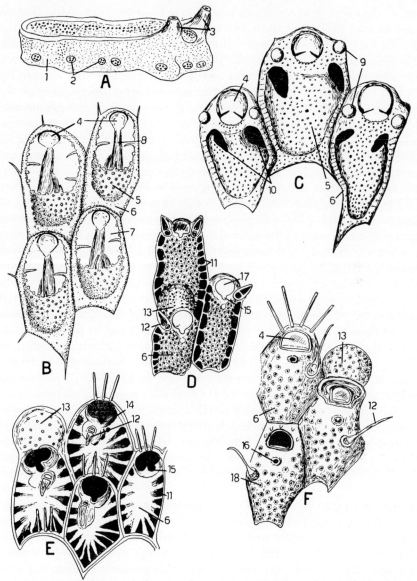

FIG. 106.—Zoecium (continued). *A*, calcareous zoecium of *Membranipora* after removal of all organic parts (*slightly altered after Nitsche*, 1871). *B*, *Acanthodesia*, with cryptocyst advanced about halfway. *C*, *Thalamoporella*, with completed cryptocyst. *D–F*, ascophoran cheilostomes. *D*, *Schizoporella*, with areoles. *E*, *Smittina*, with collar extending the orifice. *F*, *Microporella*, with ascopore. (*B–F*, *after Marcus*, 1937a.) 1, calcareous zoecium; 2, rosette plates; 3, calcareous part of spines; 4, operculum; 5, cryptocyst; 6, gymnocyst; 7, frontal membrane; 8, tentacle sheath; 9, knobs; 10, opesiules; 11, areoles; 12, avicularia; 13, ovicell; 14, orificial collar; 15, notch for opening of ascus; 16, ascopore; 17, orifice; 18, pseudopores.

spines that arch over the frontal membrane from the edge of the gymnocyst on each side fuse together to form a calcareous shield ventral to the
frontal membrane.   Stages of this process are illustrated in Fig. 105*F–H*.
The original spines appear as ribs in the shield, and the holes left between
the ribs permit the necessary in-and-out movements of the underlying
frontal membrane.   As the calcified spines are part of the gymnocyst, the
calcareous shield is to be regarded as a development of the gymnocyst.
In still other cheilostomes a calcareous shelf termed the *cryptocyst*
advances from the rear edge of the gymnocyst forward beneath (that is,
dorsal to) the frontal membrane, finally reaching the anterior edge of the
gymnocyst.   A beginning stage of this process is illustrated in Fig. 105*D*;
the cryptocyst has advanced about halfway in Fig. 106*B*, and is complete
in Fig. 106*C*, leaving two large holes known as *opesiules*.   It is to be
understood that in life the frontal membrane attached to the margin of the
gymnocyst is present to the outer side of the cryptocyst but is not shown in
the figures.   It must also be understood that all calcareous formations are
covered externally by cuticle and lined by the epidermis that secretes
them.   The cryptocyst is never complete because holes through it are
necessary for the passage of the muscles that operate the overlying frontal
membrane.   Thus in such a form as that in Fig. 106*C*, a large muscle
passes through each opesiule to the frontal membrane, as indicated schematically in Fig. 107*E*.   As a further complication the calcareous wall of
the cryptocyst may dip down at the opesiules to join the dorsal or lateral
walls of the zoecium, as shown schematically in Fig. 107*F*, thus leaving
only a narrow tubular passage for the extrusion of the lophophore.

Still another arrangement occurs in a large group of cheilostomes, the
Ascophora, in which the zoecium is completely calcified.   This is accomplished by the calcification of the frontal membrane, that is, the deposition of a layer of calcium carbonate between its cuticle and its epidermis.
As the zooid can now no longer expand or contract, a new type of
mechanism is necessary to permit volume changes of the interior.   This
mechanism takes the form of a thin-walled sac, the *compensation sac* or
ascus, found in the interior immediately beneath (dorsal to) the calcified
front.   The ascus opens to the exterior either by a notch (also called
sinus, vanna) in the proximal rim of the orifice (Fig. 106*D*) or by a separate pore, the *ascopore* (Fig. 106*F*).   When the orifice is extended by way
of an orificial collar (see below), the notch in the collar is termed *rimule*
(Fig. 106*E*) and a hole formed by closure of the rimule is called *spiramen*
(Fig. 145*G*).   In case of a sinus, the operculum has a small backward
extension or tab, the *poster*, that fits into it (Fig. 107*N, S, T*), or else the
poster is hinged to the main anterior part or *anter* of the operculum
(Fig. 107*Q*).   The operation of the ascus is described later.

The operculum is generally semicircular or crescentic but occurs in a

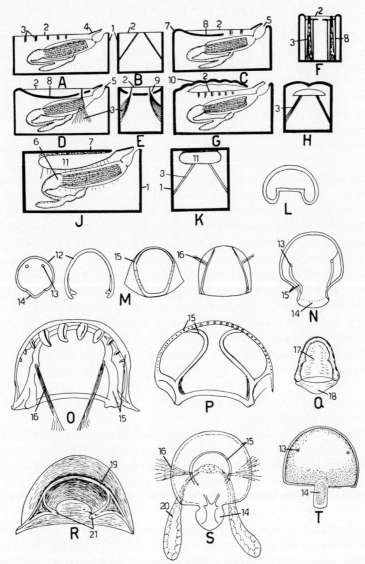

Fig. 107.—Zoecium (continued). *A–K*, schemes of the zoecium of various cheilostomes (*combined from Harmer*, 1930, *and Silén*, 1942a). *A*, simple zoecium with frontal membrane. *B*, cross section of *A*. *C*, zoecium with partial cryptocyst. *D*, cryptocyst completed. *E*, cross section of *D*, through the opesiules. *F*, cross section of same type as *E*, but cryptocyst dipping down at the opesiules. *G*, cribriform cheilostome. *H*, cross section of *G*. *J*, ascophoran type with ascus. *K*, cross section of *J*. *L, M, N*, types of operculum (*after Marcus*, 1937a). *O, P*, opercula of *Steginoporella* (*after Marcus*, 1949). *Q*, operculum of an ascophoran, subdivided (*after Marcus*, 1926a). *R*, operculum of *Hemiseptella*, seen from the inner side (*after Busk*, 1884). *S*, operculum of *Schizoporella* with attached vestibular glands (*after Marcus*, 1939a). *T*, operculum of *Arthropoma* (*after Osburn*, 1952). 1, calcified wall; 2, frontal membrane; 3, parietal muscles; 4, operculum; 5, orifice; 6, retracted polypide; 7, gymnocyst; 8, cryptocyst; 9, opesiule; 10, cribriform gymnocyst; 11, ascus; 12, thickened rim; 13, muscle dots, site of attachment of occlusor muscles; 14, tab to cover entrance into ascus; 15, thickenings; 16, occlusor muscles; 17, anter; 18, poster; 19, ridge; 20, vestibular glands; 21, points for muscle attachment.

wide range of shape variants (Fig. 107*L–T*) and is often stiffened by thickenings (sclerites) along its rim or as arches on its inner surface. Especially fancy opercula with arched thickenings and a toothed margin occur in the anascan genus *Steginoporella* (Fig. 107*O, P*). The thickenings on the inner surface serve for muscle attachments and may be developed into a collarlike ridge as in *Hemiseptella* (Fig. 107*R*); but often the muscles attach in a pair of depressions known as *muscle dots* (Fig. 107*N*). The operculum generally consists of two layers of chitinous cuticle with a cavity ("lucida") between (Fig. 123*E*) but may be more or less calcified.

The orifice in cheilostomes may present various diversities as a median tooth, the *lyrule*, in its posterior rim and a pair of lateral teeth, the *condyles* or *cardelles*, acting as pivots for the operculum (Fig. 108*A*). A pronounced median eminence below the orifice is termed *mucro*. The orificial rim may be extended in a collarlike manner, and this extension is here called *orificial collar* to replace the bad term peristome used by ectoproctologists. The one term orificial collar will be used whether the collar is short (Fig. 106*E*) or long and tubular (Fig. 108*B*), and the special name ("peristomie") for the long ones will be eliminated. The terminal opening in case of an orificial collar then becomes the secondary orifice ("peristomice"); the operculum remains at the bottom of the orificial collar, covering the true orifice. As indicated above, the orificial collar when present in ascophoran cheilostomes may bear a notch for entrance into the ascus, and this notch may close over or nearly so to form a hole, the spiramen, that opens into the orifice, whereas the ascopore opens directly into the ascus.

The calcified front of the cheilostome zoecium often appears porous (Fig. 106*D, F*), but these are not true pores, being merely fenestrations in the calcification. They are filled in life with tissue and covered externally and internally by the layers of the body wall. They are therefore best termed *pseudopores;* especially large pseudopores along the borders of the front (Fig. 106*D, E*) are known as *areoles.* There are, however, true pores through the side walls of the zoecia (see later). In ascophoran cheilostomes the calcified front may consist of up to three layers, an innermost smooth *olocyst*, a middle granular *pleurocyst*, and an outer *tremocyst* that contains the pseudopores.

The zoecia of cyclostomes are generally of simple tubular shape with a circular terminal orifice. In case of upright colonies the zoecia occur in uniserial to multiserial branches (Figs. 100*C*, 108*C*), but round incrustations with radiating zoecia also obtain in the group (Fig. 109*D*). The zoecia may be almost completely separate as in *Crisia* (Fig. 108*D*) or partially fused as in *Tubulipora* (Fig. 100*C*) or free only distally (*Stomatopora*, Fig. 108*C*), or the orifices may be flush with the colony surface. Whereas in cheilostomes zoecia generally retain their own walls as shown

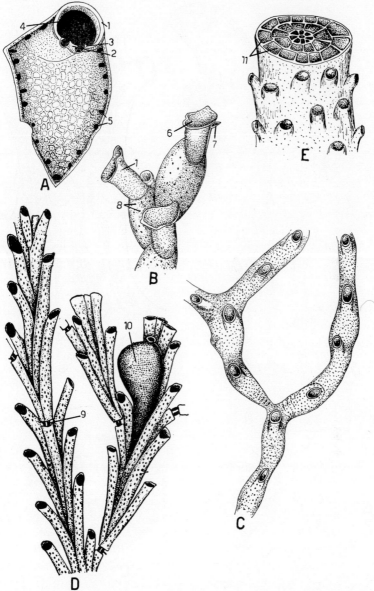

Fig. 108.—Zoecium (continued). *A*, zoecium of cheilostome *Rhamphostomella*, showing details of orifice. *B*, zoecia of cheilostome *Lagenipora* with very high orificial collar. (*A, B, after Osburn*, 1952.) *C*, cyclostome *Stomatopora* with uniserial zoecia (*after Hincks*, 1880). *D*, cyclostome *Crisia* with nearly separate tubular zoecia (*after Rogick* and *Croasdale*, 1949). *E*, cyclostome *Entalophora* with zoecia fused (*after Calvet*, 1931). 1, orificial collar; 2, lyrule; 3, cardelles; 4, orifice; 5, areoles; 6, secondary orifice; 7, avicularium; 8, pseudopores; 9, joint; 10, gonozooid; 11, sections of zoecia.

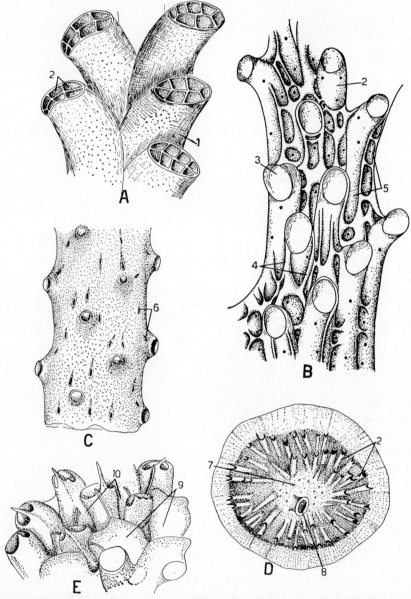

Fig. 109.—Zoecium (continued). *A, Tubulipora*, with zoecia fused in bundles. *B, Hornera*, with ridges and depressions forming between the zoecia (*after Borg*, 1926a). *C*, later stage of *Hornera*, depressions narrowed to slits. (*A, C, after Calvet*, 1931.) *D*, colony of *Lichenopora* (*after Hincks*, 1880). *E*, part of a colony of *Lichenopora*, showing alveoli (*after Harmer*, 1896). 1, fascicle of zoecia; 2, zoecium; 3, orifice; 4, calcareous walls; 5, depressions; 6, slits; 7, brood chamber; 8, orifice of brood chamber; 9, completed, closed alveoli; 10, beginning, widely open alveoli.

in Fig. 106*C*, *E*, in cyclostomes the walls of contiguous zoecia are fused to form a common wall and such fused zoecia may occur in bundles called *fascicles* (Figs. 108*E*, 109*A*). Cyclostome zoecia are completely calcified, with pseudopores, and as no opening or flexible area exists except the orifice, evidently still another device, explained later, must be present to allow lophophore extension and retraction.

More complicated conditions obtain in the cyclostome suborders Cancellata, represented by the family Horneridae, and Rectangulata, represented by the Lichenoporidae. In these two families, as shown by Borg (1926a), the free zoecial walls are double. The outer wall corresponds in structure to the wall of a ctenostome zoecium, being usually uncalcified; the inner wall, similar to a cryptocyst, is heavily calcified and thickens markedly with age. Further, the zoecia in these families diverge as the colony grows and the spaces between them become filled with more or less hollow calcifications. In the Horneridae longitudinal calcareous ridges form between the zoecia, and these become united by transverse ridges, with a resulting calcareous network (Fig. 109*B*) of which the depressions gradually narrow with continued calcification, becoming reduced to slits (Fig. 109*C*). In the Lichenoporidae, which form small round incrusting colonies with the zoecia radiating from a central point (Fig. 109*D*), the spaces between the zoecia become subdivided by calcareous partitions erected at right angles to the substrate into chambers (*alveoli*) that at first are roofed over in life only by the outer thin noncalcified wall mentioned above, hence appear open in dead specimens. Gradually, however, the calcification advances from the side walls beneath this outer wall after the manner of a cryptocyst until the chambers close over completely in most species (Fig. 109*E*). There then remains a space (actually coelomic) between the two walls, and this, like the original space, can be subdivided by calcareous septa forming secondary alveoli ventral to the original ones (Fig. 110*A*). The inner walls of the alveoli may be denticulate. The alveolar cavities are of coelomic nature and communicate by true pores through the walls.

The foregoing account applies to the zoecia of typical, fully formed zooids (*autozooids*). The zoecia of other types of zooids and the morphology of brood chambers are described later.

Zoecia are generally of microscopic dimensions, below 0.5 mm. in length. The longest zoecia occur in the ctenostome genus *Nolella* (old name, *Cylindroecium*), in which the tubular zoecia (Fig. 104*B*) are often 1 to 2 mm. in length and may reach a length of 4 mm. in some species.

5. Structure of the Zooid: Living Parts.—The living parts of the zooid comprise the protrusible, free movable anterior end and the main body immovably attached inside the zoecium. The protrusible part is composed of the lophophore and the necklike region between the lophophoral base and the attachment at the diaphragm.

  a. Lophophore.—The lophophore, closely resembling that of phoronids, is circular in gymnolaemates, encircling the central mouth, and consisting of a basal ridge continuous with a single row of ciliated tentacles.   In the expanded state the tentacles diverge, forming a food-catching funnel (Fig. 110*B*); on retraction they close to a bundle that is drawn down into the zoecium (Fig. 104*A*, *E*).   The number of tentacles varies in different species from 8 to about 34 and is not entirely constant in individuals of the same species.   The tentacles are hollow, containing a coelomic lumen continuous with a ring coelom in the lophophoral base.   They are composed of an epidermal epithelium covered externally with a cuticle and underlain by a thick basement membrane, acting as a support, followed by the lining peritoneum (Fig. 110*C*).   Cross sections (best study by Lutaud, 1955) show that the tentacles are broader on the external side, narrowing to the internal side, and that their epidermis consists of nine longitudinal rows of cells with somewhat indistinct boundaries (Fig. 110*C*).   The outer surface and the tentacular tips are devoid of cilia but provided, according to some authors, with the projecting tactile hairs of neurosensory cells.   The cilia occur as a pair of lateral longitudinal tracts (Fig. 110*C*).   The median cell along the inner surface also usually bears short cilia, said by most authors to lack motility.   The two cells to the sides of this median cell differ histologically from the other cells of the tentacular epidermis, being granular, with elongate, heavily staining nuclei; according to Lutaud (1955) each of these cells bears a sensory bristle and contains a fusiform body related to the bristle (Fig. 110*C*). The tentacles are independently movable by way of longitudinal muscle fibers situated along the inner and outer sides just beneath the peritoneum (Fig. 110*C*).   Each tentacle is provided with two motor and two sensory nerves (Graupner, 1930).

  The lophophoral base contains a ring coelom and houses the main nervous center.

  b. Body Wall.—The body wall includes the zoecium, which is an exoskeletal secretion of the epidermis.   In the simplest gymnolaemates, the ctenostomes, the body wall consists of the chitinous zoecium, of varying thickness, the underlying epidermis, and the lining peritoneum (Fig. 110*D*).   The epidermis is generally a thin, flat epithelium with a nuclear bulge at intervals but may attain some thickness in places, especially around the orifice or in regions of rapid growth (Borg, 1926a), where the cells have a columnar shape narrowing to taillike bases (Fig. 112*B*).   The typical flat epidermis appears syncytial, but polygonal cells may be demonstrated by silver nitrate staining (Calvet, 1900; Fig. 112*A*).   In carnose ctenostomes, a gelatinous or leathery layer may be present to

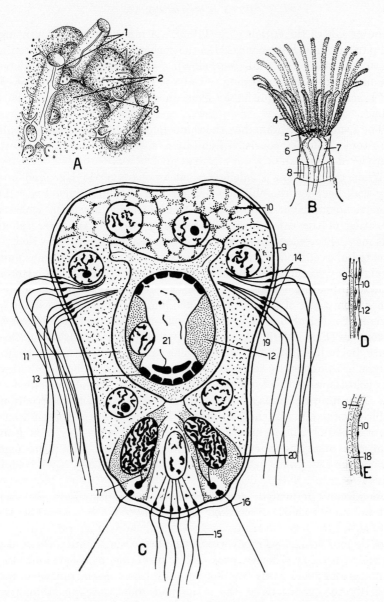

Fig. 110.—Zoecium (concluded), lophophore, body wall. *A*, alveoli between zoecia of *Lichenopora* (*after Harmer*, 1896). *B*, *Alcyonidium*, with lophophore expanded (*after Prouho*, 1892). *C*, section through a tentacle (*after Lutaud*, 1955). *D*, scheme of body wall of a ctenostome. *E*, body wall of *Alcyonidium* with gelatinous layer (*after Calvet*, 1900). 1, distal ends of zoecia; 2, primary alveoli; 3, secondary alveoli; 4, crown of tentacles; 5, mouth; 6, tentacle sheath; 7, pharynx; 8, pleated collar; 9, cuticle; 10, epidermis; 11, basement membrane; 12, peritoneum; 13, longitudinal muscle fibers; 14, lateral bunches of cilia; 15, median cilia; 16, sensory bristle; 17, fusiform body associated with sensory bristle; 18, gelatinous layer; 19, basal bodies of cilia; 20, epidermal cells supporting sensory bristles; 21, coelom of tentacle.

the outer side of the cuticle (Fig. 110*E*).   A muscular layer is wanting in
that part of the body wall incased in the zoecium but occurs in the tentacle
sheath and vestibular wall (see below).   The lining peritoneum is very
thin and tenuous and according to Calvet (1900) exists as a network (Fig.
112*F*) scarcely distinguishable from mesenchyme cells found in the
coelom.

The frontal membrane has the same construction as the body wall of
ctenostomes, that is, consists of chitinous cuticle, epidermis, and peritoneum, as in Fig. 110*D*.

When the zoecium is calcified a calcareous layer is deposited in the
body wall between the chitinous cuticle and the epidermis (Fig. 112*C*).
This calcareous layer is permeated with chitinous fibrils on which the
deposition of the calcareous salts seems to occur.   All outer calcified
walls may be presumed to have the construction shown in Fig. 112*C*.   As
indicated above, double frontal walls occur in many cheilostomes and in
the higher cyclostomes.   The structure of double walls in the latter was
elucidated by Borg (1926a).   The outer wall is similar to that of ctenostomes, composed of cuticle, epidermis, and peritoneum; the inner wall
consists of a calcareous layer clothed on both sides with epidermis and
peritoneum (Fig. 112*D*).   The space between the two walls is of coelomic
nature, being lined by peritoneum.   The calcareous wall may constantly
increase in thickness by secretion from the epidermis on both its surfaces,
and cyclostomes of this type may therefore become heavily calcified with
age.   Less information is available about the histological construction of
double frontal walls in cheilostomes, although some was contributed by
Calvet (1900).   The structure of a double wall consisting of a frontal
membrane overlying a cryptocyst appears in Fig. 112*E*; the cavity
between the two walls (*hypostege* in ectoproct terminology) is of coelomic
nature.

As already indicated, communication pores, the *interzoidal pores*,
exist between zooids.   According to the analysis of Silén (1944a) these
are of two sorts, those in transverse walls and those in lateral walls in case
of contiguous zooids.   Transverse walls, always single, are present at the
two ends (distal or anterior, proximal or posterior) of zooids and also at
the nodes and zooid bases of stoloniferous forms.   Such transverse walls,
especially the partitions at the nodes and zooid bases of stoloniferous
types, are generally formed by a circular fold of epidermis and peritoneum
that grows inward across the stolon or across the zooid from all sides; the
epidermis secretes a chitinous layer except for a central hole (or holes)
that remains plugged with a rosette of altered epidermal cells (Fig. 113*A*,
F, *G*).   Figure 113*A*, *F* illustrates a transverse partition at a stolonal
node with one central hole; and Fig. 113*G* illustrates the formation of a
similar partition with four holes.   Another type of pore arrangement in a

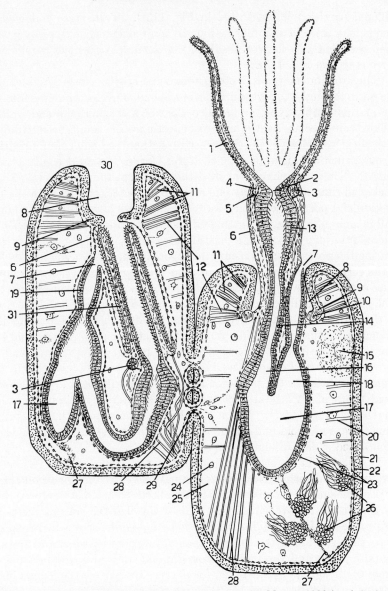

FIG. 111.—Scheme of retracted and extended zooid (*after Marcus*, 1926a).   1, tentacles;
2, mouth; 3, ganglion; 4, ring coelom of lophophore base; 5, coelomic septum; 6, tentacle
sheath; 7, anus; 8, vestibule; 9, diaphragm; 10, sphincter; 11, dilators of vestibule; 12,
dilators of diaphragm; 13, pharynx; 14, esophagus; 15, ovary; 16, cardia; 17, stomach;
18, pylorus; 19, intestine; 20, parietal muscles; 21, cuticle; 22, epidermis; 23, peritoneum;
24, coelomocytes; 25, coelom; 26, testes; 27, funiculus; 28, retractors of lophophore; 29,
pore plates; 30, orifice; 31, retracted tentacles.

stolonal partition is illustrated in Fig. 113C.   Transverse end walls of zooids may arise in a similar fashion by a circular ingrowth or by growth from the frontal to the dorsal side of the zooid, leaving holes, as shown in three stages in Fig. 113E.

The interzooidal pores of ctenostomes and of all cyclostomes, including the pores through the alveolar walls of the higher cyclostomatous families, are of this simple type, as are also the pores through the end walls of cheilostome zoecia.   But in many cheilostomes the zooids are contiguous with their lateral walls closely pressed together, and the communications through such lateral walls take the form of *pore plates* (also called *rosette plates*).   These are circular or oval thin places in the wall encircled by a thickened rim and pierced by one or more pores (Fig. 114G).   In the production of a pore plate a body-wall fold advances inward from the lateral wall in a circular manner, cutting off a small portion (*pore chamber*) of the zooidal interior and leaving a pore or pores as described above.   The part bearing the pores then thins out and in some unknown way induces a hole in the corresponding wall of the adjacent zooid (Fig. 113H).   Thus a pore plate consists of two parts, the plate with holes and a thickened rim (Fig. 114G) in the lateral wall of one zooid and a corresponding hole in the wall of the adjacent zooid.   As contiguous zooids generally alternate in a quincunx arrangement, it follows that the anterior part of one zooid is in contact with the posterior parts of adjacent zooids.   It is the rule that the pore plates are in the lateral wall of the anterior halves of zooids, the corresponding holes in the posterior parts of adjacent zooids.   Hence each zooid bears in its lateral walls pore plates anteriorly, simple openings posteriorly (Fig. 114A).   The mode of formation of pore chambers is the same as that of zooid buds; hence pore chambers and the resulting plates are aborted zooids (Silén, 1944a).

In no case in Gymnolaemata are the pores open holes.   They are always plugged with a rosette of epidermal cells, presumably accompanied by peritoneal cells.   The communication between zooids therefore probably consists of a slow percolation of fluid through the cells at the pores. This process is further aided by mesenchymal cords, also called *funicular cords*, that run along the sides of zooidal interiors between and through the pore plates and through the pores in end walls and nodal partitions. These cords, originally mistaken for nerves, are quite conspicuous in life in transparent species (Fig. 113B) and in stoloniferous forms run along the center of the stolons branching freely in the interior (Fig. 113B).   Funicular cords are for the most part wanting in cyclostomes.

The body wall is generally inturned at the orifice for a varying distance, very long in cyclostomes (Fig. 112D), to a constriction termed the *diaphragm*, operated by muscles.   The passage between the orifice and the diaphragm is called the *vestibule* and is also alterable by attached

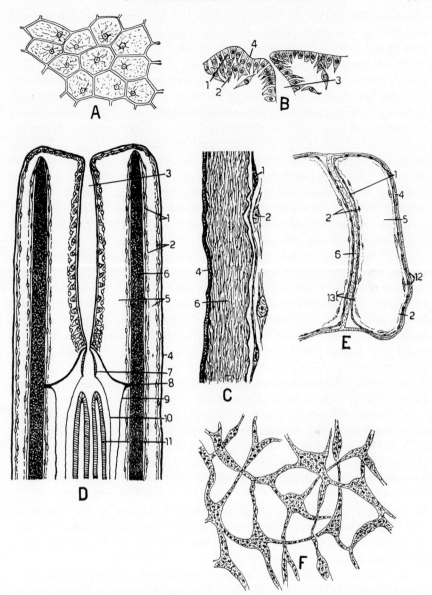

Fig. 112.—Body wall. *A*, surface view of epidermis after silver nitrate staining. *B*, epidermis at orifice of cyclostome *Crisia* (*after Borg*, 1926a). *C*, scheme of a calcified body wall. *D*, distal part of zooid of a higher cyclostome with double wall. (*C*, *D*, *after Borg*, 1926b.) *E*, scheme of a cheilostome double wall with cryptocyst. *F*, parietal peritoneum. (*A*, *E*, *F*, *after Calvet*, 1900.) 1, epidermis; 2, peritoneum; 3, vestibule; 4, cuticle; 5, coelom; 6, calcareous layer; 7, diaphragm with sphincter; 8, fixator ligaments of membranous sac; 9, membranous sac dividing coelom; 10, tentacle sheath; 11, retracted tentacles; 12, frontal membrane; 13, cryptocyst.

muscles (Fig. 111). At the diaphragm the fixed part of the body wall attached to the inner surface of the zoecium is continuous with the free part of the body wall, called *tentacle sheath*.

In ctenostomes the diaphragm bears a circular collar, here called *pleated collar* (usual names collare, setigerous collar), that projects freely into the vestibule. It consists of an inner and outer wall of chitinous cuticle and is pleated after the manner of a fan. In at least some species the pleats are supported by riblike thickenings of the cuticle. When the zooid is retracted the pleats fold together into a cone that blocks the vestibule; hence the pleated collar acts as a closing apparatus for ctenostomes. The pleats were mistaken by early workers for bristles or setae and may in fact end distally in little projecting points. When the zooid extends through the orifice the pleats spread open and the collar may be seen around the base of the tentacle sheath (Fig. 110B). An unusually long pleated collar is present in *Aeverrillia* (Fig. 104C).

In a number of cheilostomes a pair of *vestibular glands* (also called oral glands, opercular glands) opens into the vestibule close to the diaphragm; they are often adherent to the operculum (Fig. 107S). These glands have been especially studied by Waters (1909), who found that they vary much in size and shape in different species. They may be globular or flask-shaped (Fig. 114D) or long and tubular, and in *Lepralia occlusa* the single gland with paired ducts is a large, multilobular mass of at least 30 lobes (Waters, 1909). The glands are definitely secretory, but their function is unknown. Waters inclines to the view that they are excretory, but Calvet (1900) reported that they do not store dyes.

c. Tentacle Sheath.—Tentacle sheath is the name applied to that part of the body wall that extends from the lophophoral base to the diaphragm (Fig. 111), covering the necklike region of the protruded animal. It consists of a thin cuticle underlain by a flattened, tenuous epidermis, followed by a delicate layer of outer longitudinal and inner circular muscle fibers and the lining peritoneum. The tentacle sheath bears the anal opening and encloses the anterior part of the digestive tract (Fig. 111) but is not attached to the latter; hence when the lophophore is retracted the tentacle sheath introverts and surrounds the bunched tentacles (Fig. 111, left), whence its name.

d. Digestive Tract.—The digestive tract has the U-form characteristic of sessile animals (Figs. 111, 114E). The mouth, a simple, round opening encircled by the lophophoral base, is closable by circular fibers and may also be provided with radial fibers. The mouth leads into the foregut, generally provided with longitudinal furrows and often clearly divisible into pharynx and esophagus; but these two regions may not be definitely delimited. The pharynx, broadest just beyond the mouth, is lined by a columnar ciliated epithelium continuous with the inner epidermis of the

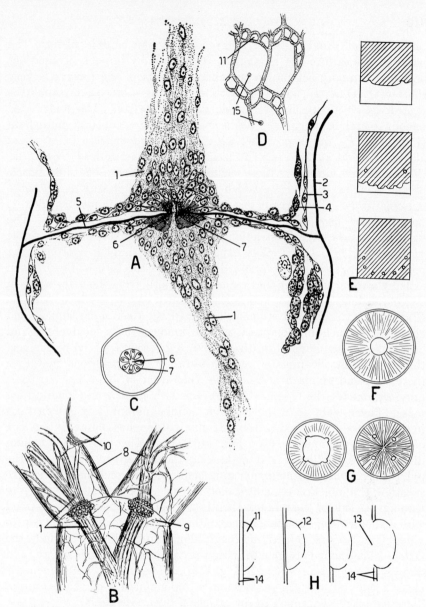

Fig. 113.—Interzooidal communications. *A*, transverse partition at zooid base of *Bowerbankia* (*after Brien and Huysmans, 1937*). *B*, stolons of *Zoobotryon* with funicular cords (*after Reichert, 1870*). *C*, one of the stolonal partitions of *B* (*after Waters, 1914*). *D*, zoecia of *Microporella* from the dorsal side, with pore chambers (*after Levinsen, 1909*). *E*, three stages in formation of a transverse wall with holes, from frontal to dorsal side. *F*, transverse wall in *Paludicella* with central hole. *G*, two stages in formation of a transverse wall in *Beania*, leaving four holes. *H*, four stages in the formation of a pore plate. (*E–H, after Silén, 1944a.*) 1, funicular cord; 2, cuticle; 3, epidermis; 4, peritoneum; 5, chitinized part of transverse partition; 6, central hole of 5; 7, rosette plug of epidermal cells; 8, stolons; 9, stolonal partition; 10, zooid base; 11, pore chamber; 12, pore plate formed; 13, corresponding hole in contiguous zooid; 14, double wall of two contiguous zooids; 15, ascopore.

tentacles and provided with a layer of circular muscle fibers. The pharynx passes into the esophagus, recognized by its lack of ciliation; however, in many ectoprocts the ciliated region of the foregut is very short (Fig. 114*E*, *F*), and it is not clear if this short region should be regarded as constituting the whole of the pharynx. The nonciliated region, sometimes very long, has a characteristic vacuolated epithelium (Fig. 114*E*, *F*) and is provided with circular and delicate longitudinal fibers. Several authors (e.g., Marcus, 1939a) have noticed cross striations along the surfaces of these vacuolated cells; these seem to be muscle fibers belonging to the cells, which therefore would classify as epithelio-muscular cells. The foregut terminates with a constriction at which its posterior end may project into the lumen as a valve (Fig. 114*F*). The stomach begins at the constriction as a short to long tubular section, the *cardia* (Figs. 111, 114*E*), then expands to a sac having a pronounced posterior elongation, the *caecum*, that occupies the turn of the U, then exits by a tubular *pylorus* that extends anteriorly from the main stomach sac, paralleling the cardia, and is also bounded distally by a constriction (Fig. 111). Cardia and stomach are lined by a columnar, nonciliated glandular epithelium, composed of two kinds of cells, acidophilic and basophilic, some bulging into the lumen (Fig. 115*C*, *D*). As zooids age, this epithelium accumulates reddish-brown waste inclusions that give the cardia and stomach a distinctive coloration in life. The cardia is provided outside the basement membrane with circular and longitudinal muscle fibers, whereas in the stomach the fibers are mainly circular and in the caecum are especially heavy and united by anastomoses into a sort of network (Graupner, 1930; Fig. 115*B*, *G*). The pyloric epithelium differs in being ciliated and in lacking the red-brown inclusions; the pylorus is provided with circular muscle fibers. Beyond the pyloric constriction, the intestine (usually called rectum) leads to the anal opening through the side of the tentacle sheath (Fig. 111). The intestine is lined with a glandular epithelium similar to that of the stomach sac and is provided with delicate circular and longitudinal muscle fibers, especially the latter. The main muscular provision of vestibule, tentacle sheath, and digestive tract is represented in Fig. 115*B*. The entire digestive tract is clothed externally with peritoneum. Understanding of the ectoproct digestive tract owes much to the article of Silén (1944b).

In some ctenostomes, especially the family Vesiculariidae, the proximal part of the cardia is altered into a gizzard (Fig. 114*E*). This is a rounded body provided with a thick layer of circular muscle fibers and lined by epithelial cells capped with hard, heavy denticulations. The gizzard was especially studied in the vesiculariid genus *Bowerbankia* by Bobin and Prenant (1952), who followed in developing zooid buds stages in the formation of the teeth by secretion at the periphery of the epithelial

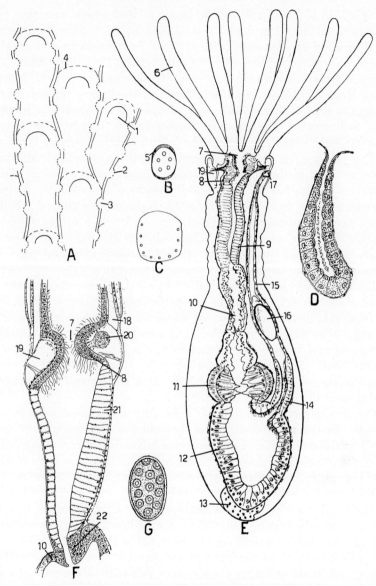

Fig. 114.—Interzooidal communications (concluded); digestive tract. *A*, several zooids of *Flustra*, showing positions of pore plates and corresponding holes. *B*, pore plate of *A*. *C*, transverse end wall of *A*. (*A–C, after Silén,* 1944a.) *D*, vestibular gland (*after Calvet,* 1900). *E, Zoobotryon,* showing digestive tract (*after Ries,* 1936). *F*, longitudinal section of foregut of *Bugula* (*after Braem,* 1940a). *G*, multiporous pore plate of *Smittina* (*after Levinsen,* 1909). 1, operculum; 2, pore plate; 3, hole corresponding to 2; 4, transverse end wall; 5, pore ring; 6, tentacles; 7, mouth; 8, pharynx; 9, esophagus; 10, cardia; 11, gizzard; 12, stomach sac; 13, funiculus; 14, pylorus; 15, intestine; 16, ball of feces; 17, anus; 18, lumen of tentacle; 19, ring coelom; 20, ganglion; 21, vacuolated epithelium of esophagus; 22, cardiac valve.

cells (Fig. 116*A*, *B*).   In *Bowerbankia* and related genera numerous teeth
are present, arranged in dorsal and ventral areas of large denticles and
lateral areas of smaller ones (Fig. 116*A*).   In these cases each tooth or
denticle is secreted and borne by one cell (Fig. 116*B*), but a different type
of gizzard armature occurs in *Aeverrillia* (Osburn and Veth, 1922; Marcus,
1941a; Rogick, 1945a); here the gizzard epithelium is capped by four
denticulate shields (Fig. 115*E*), each of which is secreted by a group of
cells.   Still another type is seen in *Cryptopolyzoon* (Dendy, 1888; Waters,
1910; Marcus, 1941a), in which the very muscular gizzard bears two
grinding plates (Fig. 115*F*).   Annandale (1916) has pointed out that a
beginning stage of the gizzard occurs in *Hislopia*, also a vesiculariid, in
which the proximal part of the cardia shows a thick hardened lining.
Although referred to in the literature as chitinous, the gizzard armature
has not been chemically investigated.

  e. Coelom and Coelomocytes.—The coelom is divided by an imperfect
septum into a small ring coelom occupying the lophophoral base with
extensions into the tentacles and the large general body cavity between
the digestive tract and the body wall.   This septum extends from the distal end of the tentacle sheath just below the tentacle bases to the pharynx
wall (Fig. 111, right); hence the ring coelom encircles the beginning of the
pharynx.   The ring coelom is crossed by a number of radiating strands of
peritoneum and muscle fibers extending from the pharynx wall to the
tentacle sheath (Fig. 116*C*).   Anteriorly it is continuous with the coelomic
lumina of the tentacles and posteriorly with the general coelom by an
opening near the ganglion.

  The general or trunk coelom is a considerable space crossed by muscle fibers (see below) and containing the funicular cords mentioned above,
as well as mesenchyme and coelomocytes.   The lining peritoneum of the
coelom forms a syncytial network rather than a continuous sheet (Calvet,
1900; Fig. 112*F*).   The funicular cords, often extensively branched (Fig.
115*A*), have a fibrillar appearance (Fig. 117*B*) and seem to consist of
connective tissue clothed with peritoneum.   A conspicuous funicular
cord, usually called simply *the* funiculus, attaches the stomach caecum to
the posterior zooidal wall in all ectoprocts (Fig. 111, right).   Funicular
cords other than the funiculus appear wanting in cyclostomes (Borg,
1926a), and in stoloniferous ctenostomes this funiculus is also the only
funicular cord in the zooid, passing through the pores in the transverse
partition at the zooid base to become continuous with the cord in the
stolon (Fig. 113*B*).   The coelom contains free connective-tissue cells,
mostly of fusiform shape, and an abundance of coelomocytes, usually
described as of two sorts (Calvet, 1900; Borg, 1926a): an amoeboid
phagocytic type and a fusiform type filled with granules (Fig. 117*A*).
The amoeboid type is frequently of rounded shape, capable of putting out

short pointed pseudopods, but also often takes on various appearances, especially through forming one to several vesicles (Fig. 117*A*). The coelom is filled with a fluid that contains a considerable amount of protein.

Minor coelomic cavities continuous with the main coelom directly or by true pores include the space between double walls and the cavities of the alveoli in the cyclostomatous family Lichenoporidae. A special subdivision of the main coelom in cyclostomes concerned with the protrusion and retraction of the lophophore was elucidated by Borg (1923, 1926a). Here the proximal and major part of the coelom is completely subdivided by a longitudinal cylindrical partition (*membranous sac* of Borg) into an inner sac that embraces the tentacle sheath and digestive tract and an outer sac continuous anteriorly with the undivided distal part of the coelom (Fig. 112*D*). Further details about this mechanism and its mode of operation are given later.

In the anascan family Thalamoporellidae free calcareous spicules, mostly shaped like the toxas and sigmas of sponges (I, Fig. 83), occur in the main coelom and in the coelomic space between the frontal membrane and the cryptocyst. Possibly they serve as a reserve supply of calcium carbonate.

The coelom has no permanent opening to the exterior, but it is known for some ectoprocts, mostly ctenostomes, that at breeding time an exit for the eggs forms on the lophophore. This may be a simple pore, the *supraneural pore*, between the mouth and the base of the dorsal tentacles, or the outer side of the base of the two most dorsal tentacles may fuse to form a ciliated tube, known as the *intertentacular organ*, from which eggs have been seen to emerge (Fig. 116*D*). The pore or tube opens from the ring coelom, but this, as already stated, is connected to the main coelom by an aperture near the ganglion. It is possible but improbable that this pore or tube represents a reminiscence of an original coelomic opening of the lophophoral coelom to the exterior. It will be recalled that in phoronids the lophophoral coelom lacks connection with the exterior.

f. Muscular System.—Various muscles associated with the protrusion and retraction of the anterior end course through the coelom and probably are to be regarded as displaced body-wall musculature. The *parietal* muscles, wanting in cyclostomes (Borg, 1926a), are a longitudinal series of short transverse muscles in the sides of the zooid that extend obliquely downward from their origin on the lateral walls to their insertion on the frontal membrane (Figs. 116*D*, 117*E*). They consist of single strands or small bundles of strands and vary in number in different ectoprocts and in different individuals of the same species. In *Bugula* 20 to 40 pairs have been recorded (Calvet, 1900), 10 to 30 pairs in *Farrella* (Marcus, 1926b), 6 pairs in *Victorella* (Braem, 1939), and 5 to 6 pairs in *Flustra* (Silén, 1938). Parietal muscles are generally absent from the posterior part of

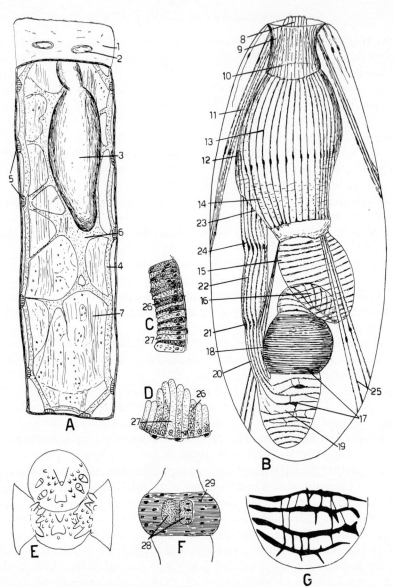

FIG. 115.—Funicular cords, digestive tract (continued). *A*, zooid of *Membranipora* to show funicular tissue (*after Nitsche*, 1871). *B*, digestive tract of *Zoobotryon*, with main muscle layers indicated (*after Gerwerzhagen*, 1913). *C*, cells of stomach wall of *Thalamoporella*. *D*, cells of stomach wall of *Bugula* (*after Calvet*, 1900). *E*, the four denticulated shields of the gizzard of *Aeverrillia*. *F*, gizzard of *Cryptopolyzoon*. (*C, E, F, after Marcus*, 1941a.) *G*, muscle net of stomach caecum (*after Graupner*, 1930). 1, transverse end wall of zoecium; 2, communication pores of 1; 3, stomach; 4, lateral funicular cords; 5, pore plates; 6, funiculus; 7, strands of connective tissue; 8, pleated collar; 9, vestibule; 10, diaphragm; 11, dilators of vestibule; 12, tentacle sheath; 13, longitudinal fibers of 12; 14, transverse fibers of 12; 15, pharynx; 16, esophagus; 17, ring muscles; 18, gizzard; 19, stomach; 20, pylorus; 21, pyloric sphincter; 22, intestine; 23, location of anus; 24, longitudinal fibers of 20 and 22; 25, retractors of the lophophore; 26, basophilic cells; 27, acidophilic cells; 28, grinding plates; 29, nuclei of ring muscles.

314

the zooid and with the development of a cryptocyst become more and more limited to the distal region, finally in species with a complete cryptocyst reducing to a pair of bundles each of which converges to a tendon passing through an opesiule to the frontal membrane outside the cryptocyst (Fig. 107E). In the Ascophora the parietal muscles are inserted on the inner (dorsal) wall of the ascus (Fig. 107J).

The muscles that operate the operculum are probably derived from the parietal series. There is always present a pair of *occlusor* muscles to close the operculum; these originate from the adjacent lateral or dorsal zooidal walls as a bundle of fibers that converge to a tendon inserted on the inner surface of the operculum, usually on a ridge or thickening (Fig. 107O, P, R, S) but sometimes into a pair of pits known as *muscle dots* (Fig. 107M, N). The operculum is usually opened by pressure from the advancing lophophore, but a pair of opening, or *divaricator*, muscles may be present, originating on the zooidal wall behind the origin of the occlusor muscles and inserting by tendon on the frontal membrane just behind the hinge line of the operculum. Sometimes another pair of opening muscles, the *depressor* muscles, is present behind the divaricators (Fig. 123B).

The most important muscles of the zooid interior are the powerful retractors of the lophophore (Figs. 111, 117E). These are a group of muscle fibers on each side that usually insert on the lophophoral base, generally on the coelomic septum; but some fibers may attach to the basement membrane of the foregut at various levels. The retractors usually originate on the posterior wall of the zooid or near there but are short in cyclostomes, originating somewhat more distally on the side walls. Their contraction pulls in the extruded lophophore.

In a few ctenostomes in which the zooids are movable on the stolons, this is accomplished by longitudinal fibers that extend from the nodal partition into the zooid base (Fig. 117E), or more often by muscles enclosed in the basal part of the zooid (page 398).

The remaining muscles are concerned with the operation of the vestibule, diaphragm, and tentacle sheath. The diaphragm contains circular fibers continuous with those of the tentacle sheath but here concentrated into a definite sphincter (Fig. 118D), strongly developed in cyclostomes, that can occlude the opening. In the cyclostomatous family Crisiidae an additional sphincter is present at the distal end of the vestibule. Dilation of vestibule, diaphragm, and distal end of the tentacle sheath is accomplished by radiating muscle bands that probably all belong to one series but are customarily divided into parietovestibular, parietodiaphragmatic, and parietovaginal groups, here called simply dilators of the vestibule, diaphragm, and tentacle sheath, respectively. The vestibular wall contains a layer of circular fibers and is attached to the zooid wall by dilator

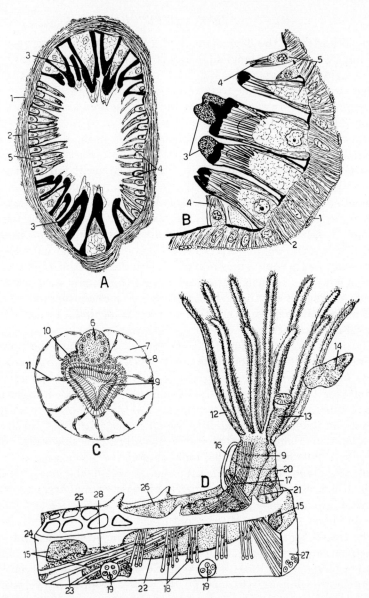

FIG. 116.—Digestive tract (concluded), muscular system. *A*, cross section through the gizzard of *Bowerbankia*. *B*, late stage in development of gizzard teeth. (*A, B, after Bobin and Prenant*, 1952.) *C*, cross section through the pharynx of *Bugula* (*after Calvet*, 1900). *D*, zooid of incrusting cheilostome, *Electra*, in natural position, to show muscles (*after Marcus*, 1926a). 1, peritoneum; 2, circular musculature; 3, large dorsal and ventral teeth; 4, small lateral teeth; 5, cells that secrete teeth; 6, ganglion; 7, ring coelom; 8, body wall; 9, pharynx; 10, ring nerve; 11, muscular strands crossing ring coelom; 12, tentacular crown; 13, intertentacular organ; 14, egg just discharged through 13; 15, other eggs; 16, operculum; 17, occlusor of operculum; 18, parietal muscles; 19, pore plates; 20, anus; 21, intestine; 22, stomach; 23, retractors of lophophore; 24, calcareous zoecium; 25, gymnocyst with pseudopores; 26, frontal membrane; 27, transverse end wall with simple pores; 28, funiculus.

fibers, often arranged, especially in ctenostomes, in four groups (Fig. 117*C*, *D*, *F*, *G*), five in *Pottsiella erecta* (Braem, 1940b), usually in two opposite groups in cheilostomes (Fig. 117*H*). The pull of the four dilator muscles often confers a quadrangular shape on the vestibule and orifice of ctenostomes. In cyclostomes the vestibular dilators are represented by muscle strands that parallel the long vestibule and spray into its lining epidermis (Fig. 121*A*). The diaphragmatic dilators, wanting in cyclostomes, extend from the diaphragm to the zooid wall (Fig. 117*C*, *D*), sometimes also in four equidistant groups, and often not definitely separable from the vestibular dilators. Dilators of the tentacle sheath are also often present. These, according to Calvet (1900), are continuations of the longitudinal fibers of the sheath that leave the sheath near the diaphragm as eight bundles that curve to their attachment on the zooid wall (Figs. 117*H*, 118*C*).

Stolons and kenozooids are typically devoid of muscle fibers, but transverse fibers are sometimes present (review in Silén, 1950) and longitudinal fibers occur in the stolons of *Monobryozoon* (page 288).

There is some dispute about the histological nature of the muscle fibers of gymnolaemates. It is usually stated that the lophophore retractors are cross-striated (Fig. 118*F*), but Marcus (1939a) reported that retractor fibers appear smooth when examined in polarized light. Cross-striation is also claimed for the longitudinal muscles of the tentacles (Silbermann, 1906) and for the circular fibers of the pharynx (Bronstein, 1938a; Braem, 1940a), but Marcus attributes many of these claims to contraction folds in the basement membrane or staining effects. However, the fibers that cover the vacuolated cells of the foregut appear genuinely striated (Marcus, 1939a). Striated muscles undoubtedly occur in the avicularia and vibracula (see later).

g. Nervous System.—Main studies on the nervous system are those of Gerwerzhagen (1913) on *Zoobotryon*, Marcus (1926b) on *Farrella*, Graupner (1930) on *Flustrellidra*, and Bronstein (1937) on *Alcyonidium*, all ctenostomes, most suitable because of their transparency. The most successful results were obtained with methylene blue staining of living specimens, but methylene blue fails in many cases. The nervous center, called the ganglion, a small mass of nerve cells and fibrous tissue, is situated in the ring coelom resting against the dorsal wall of the pharynx (Fig. 116*C*). The ganglion is continuous with a nerve ring around the pharynx, which is thick laterally, there containing nerve cells, but reduced to a thin fibrous strand without cells ventrally. From the nerve cells of the nerve ring two ganglionated motor fibers and two sensory fibers ascend each tentacle in an arrangement shown in Fig. 119*A*. An anastomosis of the tentacular nerves by a ring fiber at the tentacle bases was reported for *Bugula* by Bronstein. The tentacle sheath is well sup-

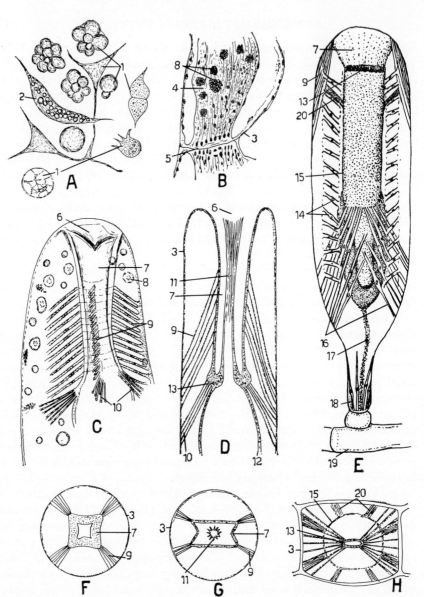

Fɪɢ. 117.—Coelom, muscular system (continued). *A*, coelomocytes. *B*, funicular cord. *C*, anterior end of *Bowerbankia*, with muscles. *D*, anterior end of *Sundanella sibogae*, ctenostome, with muscles. *E*, ctenostome *Farrella*, showing muscles (*after Marcus*, 1926b). *F*, schematic section through the vestibular base of a ctenostome. *G*, another type of dilator arrangement found in ctenostomes. *H*, scheme of dilator arrangement in *Bugula*. (*A–C, H, after Calvet*, 1900; *D, F, G, after Braem*, 1939.) 1, various forms of vesicular type of coelomocyte; 2, granular coelomocyte; 3, body wall; 4, funicular cord; 5, stolonal partition; 6, orifice; 7, vestibule; 8, coelomocytes; 9, dilators of vestibule; 10, dilators of diaphragm; 11, pleated collar; 12, pharynx; 13, diaphragm; 14, parietal muscles; 15, tentacle sheath; 16, retractor of lophophore; 17, funiculus; 18, stalk muscles; 19, stolon; 20, dilators of tentacle sheath.

plied by a pair of sensory and a pair of motor nerves coming from the ganglion (Fig. 119B) or by a single pair that soon forks into a motor and a sensory branch on each side (Fig. 119A). These nerves ramify in the tentacle sheath and probably connect with a subepithelial plexus present in the sheath. The sensory nerves extend to the attachment of the tentacle sheath at the diaphragm, where they join a ring strand that includes numerous sensory nerve cells and that also innervates the pleated collar (Fig. 119B, C). Another ring strand is also reported at the other end of the tentacle sheath near the tentacle bases (Fig. 119B). The motor nerves of the tentacle sheath may also supply the diaphragm dilators and may contribute fibers to the lophophore retractors, but the latter are usually innervated by a pair of strong nerves emanating directly from the ganglion (Fig. 119C). The digestive tract receives innervation by a pair of nerves or a nerve bundle proceeding into it from the posterior part of the ganglion (Figs. 118A, 119A) and also, according to Bronstein, is supplied by a branch on each side from the nerves of the tentacle sheath.

There is a general subepithelial nervous network, discovered by Marcus, throughout the wall of the zooid (Fig. 119C), except in walls cemented to a substrate. Stellate nerve cells occur at the nodes of the network. The network is concentrated at the orifice, where it continues down the vestibule to join the nervous ring at the diaphragm, and no doubt is also continuous with the plexus in the tentacle sheath mentioned above.

Although Marcus failed to find any nervous connections between zooids, Bronstein reported that the nervous plexus continues along the stolons in *Bowerbankia*, and Hiller (1939) saw nerve fibers passing between zooids by way of the pores in the pore plates in *Membranipora*.

The Gymnolaemata are devoid of special sensory organs, but neurosensory cells of the usual tangoreceptive type with an externally projecting bristle (Fig. 118E) have been reported on the tentacles by Silbermann (1906) and Graupner (1930).

h. Reproductive System.—This system consists simply of the gonads since gonoducts are wanting. The germ cells, recognizable by their rounded shape and large nuclei, differentiate from the peritoneum during early stages of budding and become incorporated into the developing zooid, producing gonads on the peritoneum of body wall, digestive tract, or funiculus. The majority of gymnolaemates are hermaphroditic, with one ovary, sometimes two, and one or more testes in the same zooid. The ovary, consisting of a cluster of ovocytes enclosed in a thin peritoneum (Fig. 119D), is generally borne distally in the zooid. The testis, generally subdivided into groups showing all stages of spermatogenesis (Fig. 119E) and often giving off balls of sperm into the coelom, is usually located proximally in the zooid (Fig. 111).

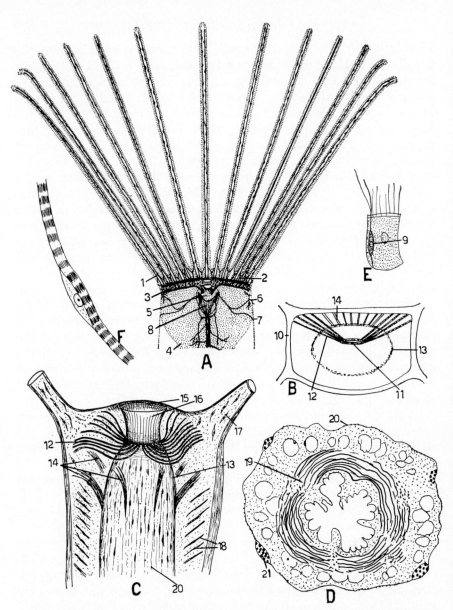

Fig. 118.—Muscular system (concluded), nervous system. *A*, nervous system of anterior end of ctenostome *Flustrellidra*, stained with methylene blue (*after Graupner*, 1930). *B*, arrangement of dilators of *Alcyonidium*. *C*, anterior end of *Bugula* with dilator muscles. (*B*, *C*, *after Calvet*, 1900.) *D*, section through the diaphragm of ctenostome *Victorella* (*after Braem*, 1939). *E*, epidermal cell of tentacle with neurosensory cell (*after Silbermann*, 1906). *F*, striated muscle cell of lophophore retractor (*after Nitsche*, 1871). 1, motor nerves of tentacle; 2, sensory nerves of tentacle; 3, nerve ring around pharynx; 4, pharynx; 5, ganglion; 6, motor branch to tentacle sheath; 7, sensory branch to tentacle sheath; 8, nerves to digestive tract; 9, neurosensory cell; 10, zoecium; 11, diaphragm; 12, dilators of diaphragm; 13, tentacle sheath; 14, dilators of tentacle sheath; 15, orifice; 16, vestibule; 17, spine; 18, parietal muscles; 19, sphincter of diaphragm; 20, longitudinal fibers of tentacle sheath; 21, dilators of vestibule.

A dioecious or monoecious condition may be simulated by protandry or protogyny, and in fact it appears that often the two sorts of gonads do not ripen simultaneously. A curious type of protandry obtains in *Alcyonidium duplex* (Prouho, 1892), in which the male zooids degenerate after producing and setting free testes and a female zooid that develops one ovary regenerates in the same zoecia previously occupied by males. A true separation of the sexes is known for several cheilostomes. In *Flustra membranacea-truncata* a few hermaphroditic individuals occur, but most of the zooids of the colony are either male or female (Vigelius, 1884), with a preponderance of females; and in the related *Carbasea indivisa* the colonies are monoecious with male and female zooids (Stach, 1938b). The colonies of *Hippothoa hyalina* consist of normal sterile autozooids and reduced male and female zooids with greatly aborted polypides and sexually distinct opercula (Jullien, 1888b; Marcus, 1938a; Fig. 120A, B); here, too, female zooids outnumber the males. Similar facts obtain for *Hippothoa bougainvillei* (Rogick, 1956b). Colonies of *Thalmoporella evelinae* (Marcus, 1941a) are also composed of sterile, male, and female zooids, with the males five to six times as numerous as the females; the sexual zooids have normal, feeding polypides, but the tentacle number in females is only 14 as compared with the 17 much longer tentacles of sterile and male individuals. The biserial branches of the monoecious *Synnotum aegyptiacum* (Marcus, 1941b) consist of successive pairs of zooids, one male and one female in each pair (Fig. 120C). A monoecious condition appears quite common in cyclostome colonies (Borg, 1926a); usually the male zooids mature first, the females later. According to Robertson (1903), some species of the genus *Crisia* are dioecious, occurring as male and female colonies; other members of the family Crisiidae are probably monoecious. Colonies of species of *Lichenopora* contain simultaneously male, female, and hermaphroditic zooids (Borg, 1926a).

6. Mechanism of Protrusion and Retraction of the Lophophore.— The essential feature of the protrusion of the lophophore is the evagination of the tentacle sheath which, being attached at the lophophoral base, pushes the tentacular crown before it as it everts and becomes the body wall of the protruded necklike region (Fig. 111). As already indicated, eversion of the tentacle sheath is accomplished by several different mechanisms among the gymnolaemates. The simplest mechanism is seen in ctenostomes where the contraction of the parietal muscles pulls the ventral and dorsal walls of the flexible chitinous zoecium closer together, thus exerting pressure on the interior and forcing the lophophore out. At the same time diaphragm and vestibule are expanded by the contraction of their dilator muscles, and the pleated collar opens. In some ctenostomes vestibular dilators are wanting and the vestibule also evaginates carrying the pleated collar to the exterior (Fig. 104C). Retraction is accomplished

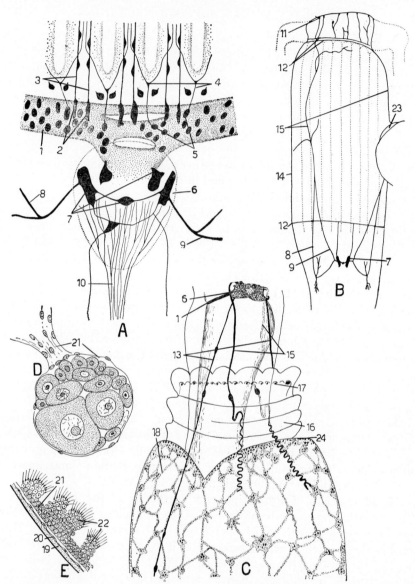

Fig. 119.—Nervous system (concluded), reproductive system. *A*, enlarged view of nervous supply to the tentacles, *Flustrellidra*. *B*, nervous supply of tentacle sheath, *Flustrellidra*. (*A, B, after Graupner*, 1930.) *C*, nervous system of anterior part of *Farrella* (*after Marcus*, 1926b). (*A–C*, after methylene blue staining.) *D*, ovary. *E*, testis. (*D, E, after Prouho*, 1892.) 1, nerve ring; 2, motor cells; 3, motor nerves to tentacles; 4, sensory nerves to tentacles; 5, sensory nerve cells; 6, ganglion; 7, main nerve cell masses of ganglion; 8, motor branch to tentacle sheath; 9, sensory branch to tentacle sheath; 10, bundle of nerves to digestive tract; 11, sensory nerve cells around orifice; 12, ring nerves of tentacle sheath; 13, nerves to retractors of lophophore; 14, tentacle sheath; 15, nerves to tentacle sheath; 16, pleated collar; 17, sensory cells of pleated collar; 18, subepidermal nerve net of body wall; 19, cuticle; 20, epidermis; 21, peritoneum; 22, testes; 23, anus; 24, sensory cells at orifice rim.

primarily by contraction of the retractors of the lophophore with concomitant relaxation of the muscles concerned in protrusion and with the folding of the pleated collar into a cone that blocks the vestibule (Fig. 115*B*). Contraction of the lophophoral retractors throws the digestive tract into loops since this is not otherwise attached to the zooidal wall except by the funiculus.

A similar mechanism obtains in cheilostomes that retain a flexible frontal wall (frontal membrane). Contraction of the parietal muscles pulls this wall in, forcing the opening of the operculum (assisted by the divaricator muscles when present) and the protrusion of the lophophore; at the same time the diaphragm and vestibule are expanded by the contraction of their dilators. The vestibule in cheilostomes, also cyclostomes, is permanently invaginated. Retraction is accomplished as in ctenostomes with the additional feature of the closure of the operculum by its occlusor muscles. The mechanism remains the same in the cribriform cheilostomes, for here the frontal membrane with attached parietal muscles persists beneath the calcified outer frontal wall, and is also similar in cheilostomes with a cryptocyst, for even when the latter is complete parietal muscles concentrated into a single pair pass through the opesiules to the frontal membrane outside the cryptocyst (Fig. 107*E, F*).

When, however, the frontal wall of the zoecium becomes completely calcified, some other mechanism is clearly necessary. In ascophoran cheilostomes this takes the form of the compensation sac or ascus. This is a large elongated sac situated immediately beneath the frontal wall, to the underside of which its floor is adherent (Fig. 107*J*). The parietal muscles have altered their insertions to attach to the roof of the ascus. Their contraction expands the ascus, causing intake of water, thus compressing the interior of the zooid and forcing the extrusion of the lophophore. Simultaneously the pressure of the water seeking to enter the ascus forces the poster (page 296) of the operculum inward, while the main part, or anter, of the operculum opens up, after the manner of a seesaw. These processes may be assisted by the divaricator muscles when present. The ascopore when present is not provided with any closing apparatus; hence water enters at once when the ascus expands. Retraction of the lophophore by the retractor muscles brings pressure to bear upon the ascus, causing it to eject water to the exterior.

Apparently the ascus may originate in two different ways. According to Harmer (1902, 1930), the ascus may arise as an invagination of the frontal membrane at the rear edge of the operculum. This process begins as a multiplication of nuclei at the site indicated (Fig. 120*D*); later a sac is seen advancing posteriorly beneath the calcified frontal wall (Fig. 120*E*). It results from this mode of formation that the roof of the ascus is continuous with the rear edge of the operculum as shown schematically in Fig.

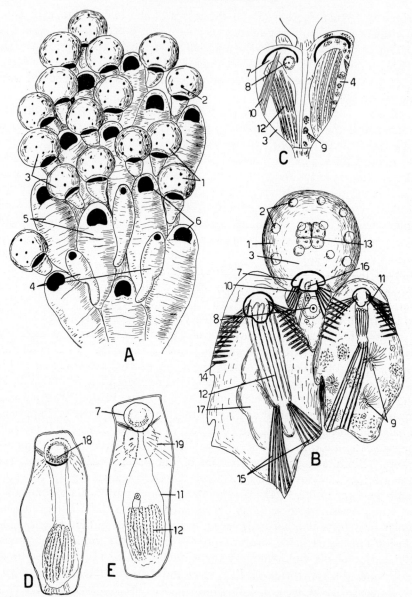

FIG. 120.—Sexual dimorphism, ascus. *A*, part of colony of *Hippothoa hyalina*, with male, female, and sterile zooids. *B*, three zooids of *A* enlarged. (*A, B, after Marcus, 1938a.*) *C*, pair of zooids, one male, one female, of *Synnotum aegyptiacum* (*after Marcus, 1941b*). *D*, beginning stage of ascus, *Watersipora*. *E*, later stage of *D*, ascus advancing. (*D, E, from slide, courtesy the Marcuses.*) 1, ovicell; 2, pseudopores; 3, female zooid; 4, male zooid; 5, sterile zooid; 6, orifice (opercula missing); 7, operculum; 8, ovary; 9, testes; 10, occlusor muscle; 11, tentacle sheath; 12, bunch of tentacles; 13, embryo; 14, parietal muscles; 15, retractor of lophophore; 16, remains of polypide; 17, digestive tract; 18, proliferation of nuclei; 19, advancing ascus.

107*J*. Another method of ascus formation is indicated by Harmer (1902) and Silén (1942a) by the fusion of a pair of calcareous folds extending from the lateral margins across the ventral side, thus enclosing the frontal membrane that then becomes the roof of the ascus, whereas the lining membrane of the fold becomes its floor. This process would be very similar to the formation of the calcareous frontal shield in cribriform cheilostomes, illustrated schematically in Fig. 107*G, H*. It explains better than the first method the attachment of the parietal muscles to the roof of the ascus.

In cyclostomes an internal mechanism for operating the lophophore is necessitated by the complete calcification of the zoecium. This mechanism was elucidated by Borg (1926a). The body wall extending across the orifice as a terminal membrane and turning in to line the long vestibule (Fig. 121*A*) closes the orifice, except for the small central opening into the vestibule. The diaphragm at the bottom of the vestibule is closable by a strong sphincter muscle. The coelom is completely divided into an inner and an outer sac by a cylindrical partition that extends from the diaphragm to the zooid base. Shortly posterior to the diaphragm this partition (membranous sac of Borg) is anchored to the zooidal wall by eight *fixator ligaments* (Fig. 121*A*), and at about the same level some filaments connect it to the tentacle sheath. Distal to the ligaments the outer sac is continuous with the coelom around the vestibule. Expansion of the vestibule by its dilator fibers compresses this part of the coelom, forcing coelomic fluid between the fixator ligaments into the outer coelomic sac below these ligaments. This act in turn compresses the inner coelomic sac, forcing the extrusion of the lophophore, by the usual eversion of the tentacle sheath; in cyclostomes there is no extrusion of a necklike region.

7. Polymorphism.—Polymorphism obtains in all groups of ectoprocts but reaches its most varied expression in cheilostomes. Typical zooids with fully developed feeding polypides are termed *autozooids* and were described above. Other types of zooids are termed collectively *heterozooids* and are characterized by the reduction of the polypide, which loses its nutritive and reproductive functions. The main types of heterozooids are avicularia, vibracula, and kenozooids. Specializations concerned with harboring the developing egg will be considered separately.

a. Avicularia.—Avicularia arise by the development of the operculum and its adjuncts at the expense of the rest of the zooid, and hence are limited to the order Cheilostomata, although not present in all members of this order. That avicularia are in fact altered autozooids is shown by their occurrence in some cases in place in the zooid rows as in *Flustra* (Fig. 121*B*). Such substitute, or *vicarious*, avicularia are usually smaller than the autozooids but may be of equal or larger size (Fig. 121*C, D*).

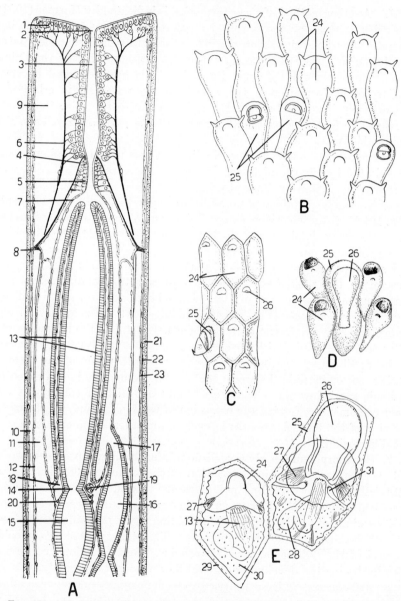

FIG. 121.—Mechanism of operating the lophophore, polymorphism. *A*, scheme of anterior end of a cyclostome (*after Borg*, 1926a). *B*, part of a colony of *Flustra* with autozooids and smaller avicularia (*after Marcus*, 1926a). *C*, part of a colony of *Cellaria* with autozooids and vicarious avicularium of equal size (*after Marcus*, 1937b). *D*, autozooids and much enlarged vicarious avicularium of *Adeonella* (*after Busk*, 1854). *E*, autozooid and enlarged avicularium with fully developed polypide, *Labioporella* (*after Marcus*, 1949). 1, terminal membrane; 2, orifice; 3, vestibule; 4, diaphragm; 5, sphincter muscle of 4; 6, dilator muscle of vestibule; 7, tentacle sheath; 8, fixator ligaments; 9, distal outer sac

They may differ from autozooids chiefly in the larger size, increased complexity, and augmented muscular supply of their opercula. Thus, it has long been known that some ectoprocts, notably some species of the genus *Steginoporella* (original spelling, later often spelled *Steganoporella*), have two sizes of zooids (Fig. 122*A*), known as A and B zooids, both with fully developed polypides. The larger or B zooids differ from the smaller A zooids primarily in the greater size, complexity, and muscular provision of their opercula (Fig. 123*A*). Despite the objections of Silén (1938), there is little doubt that the B zooids represent incipient avicularia (Harmer, 1900, 1902, 1926; Marcus, 1949). Vicarious avicularia with developed polypides are also known in *Cribrilina philomela* (Harmer, 1902), *Crepis decussata* (Harmer, 1926), species of *Acanthodesia* (Harmer, 1926; Hastings, 1929), *Crassimarginatella* (Marcus, 1939a; Fig. 122*D*), *Stylopoma schizostoma* (Hastings, 1932), and *Labioporella* (Marcus, 1949; Fig. 121*E*).

Vicarious avicularia, with or without a developed polypide, are, however, relatively uncommon. Usually avicularia are much decreased in size with a greatly reduced polypide and are found on the surface of the autozooids, being then termed *adventitious* or *dependent* avicularia. Such avicularia may occur almost anywhere on the autozooids but are more common around the orifice, either to its sides (Fig. 106*D, E*) or on the frontal surface below it (Fig. 122*F*). They may be *sessile*, adherent to the autozooid by their dorsal wall or even imbedded in its substance, or *pedunculate*, that is, mounted on a little stalk, then presenting the appearance of a miniature bird's head as in the familiar *Bugula* (Figs. 104*F*, 122*E*, 124*A*).

Avicularia have the same general structure as a cheilostome autozooid, consisting of a cystid, that is, a case of body wall, often calcified, enclosing a coelom (Figs. 123*D, E*, 124*A, B*). They differ essentially from autozooids in the stressing of the operculum and its adjuncts at the expense of the rest of the zooid. The operculum, now called *mandible*, may be absolutely larger than that of the autozooid (Figs. 121*C, D, E*, 122*D*) but usually is large only relative to the reduced zooid of which it forms a part. The mandible often differs in shape from the operculum of the autozooids and may be spatulate (Figs. 121*D, E*, 124*C*) or triangular and pointed (Fig. 106*D*), sometimes so much so as to project prominently (Fig. 106*F*). In the pedunculate type the mandible resembles the lower beak of a bird (Fig. 122*E*). The mandible is generally composed of two heavy layers of chitin with a space between (Fig. 124*A, B*) that communicates with the

of coelom; 10, proximal outer sac of coelom; 11, inner coelomic sac; 12, membranous sac; 13, crown of tentacles; 14, mouth; 15, pharynx; 16, intestine; 17, anus; 18, ring coelom; 19, ganglion; 20, coelomic septum; 21, calcareous layer of body wall; 22, epidermis; 23, peritoneum; 24, autozooid; 25, avicularium; 26, operculum; 27, occlusor muscles; 28, stomach; 29, gymnocyst; 30, cryptocyst; 31, knobs for attachment of divaricator muscles of mandible.

coelom. The part on which the mandible abuts on closure is termed the *rostrum* and is greatly thickened and strengthened, often by means of calcification; in the pedunculate type the rostrum resembles the upper beak of a bird (Figs. 122*E*, 124*A*). Behind the mandible is an area corresponding to the frontal membrane, sometimes underlain by a cryptocyst, even when this is wanting from the autozooids. The mandible is often bounded from the frontal membrane by a calcareous crossbar to which the mandible is hinged. In calcined specimens small sessile avicularia appear composed of a triangular depression that contained the mandible in life, a crossbar, and a round depression that was covered in life by the frontal membrane (Fig. 123*F*).

The coelom of the avicularium is mostly filled with muscle masses that operate the mandible. The occlusor muscles, now called adductors of the mandible, are greatly enlarged into muscle masses that originate on the dorsal and lateral walls of the avicularium and converge to a tendon that inserts on the inner surface of the mandible (Figs. 122*E*, 123*E*, 124*A*, *B*). There is usually present a pair of adductors, each with its own tendon, but sometimes the two tendons fuse to one or the muscle fibers form a single mass. Two pairs of adductor muscles occur in a few cases, notably in the B zooids of the Steginoporellidae (Fig. 123A), whereas the autozooids (A zooids) have but a single pair (Fig. 123*B*). The mandible is opened by a pair of abductor muscles or not infrequently by two pairs, a distal and a proximal (Figs. 122*E*, 123*A*), that presumably correspond to the divaricator and depressor muscles of the autozooid. The abductors originate on the dorsal wall of the avicularium and insert on the frontal membrane (Figs. 122*E*, 123*D*, *E*, 124*A*, *B*), sometimes on a special strengthening sclerite of the latter (Fig. 123*E*). The abductors act by pulling in the frontal membrane, and this causes the mandible to snap open, as can be seen by reference to the figures, especially Fig. 123*E*. The adductor fibers are cross-striated, whereas those of the abductors are smooth.

In the interior of the avicularium may be recognized in sections representatives of the main structures of the autozooid. The vestibule is commonly present bounded internally by the diaphragm (Fig. 123*D*), which, however, may lack an aperture (Fig. 123*E*). From the diaphragm a recognizable tentacle sheath leads inward, embracing the greatly aborted polypide, which usually takes the form of a protuberance or mass of cells bearing a tuft of long stiff bristles and underlain by a nucleated syncytial mass regarded by Marcus (1939a) as the ganglion (Figs. 122*E*, 124*A*). This aborted polypide, also called setiferous organ, would seem to be some sort of sense organ. That of *Bugula* is shown enlarged in Fig. 123*C*. It is usually attached to the wall or other parts of the avicularium by protoplasmic strands. In a number of cases, discussed by Marcus (1939a), the polypide is accompanied by a gland, often relatively large (Fig. 124*A*, *B*),

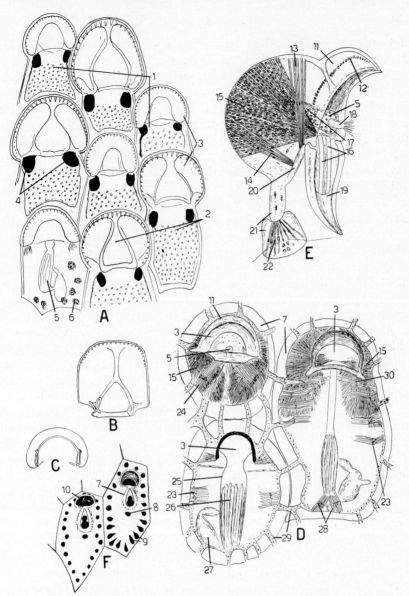

FIG. 122.—Polymorphism (continued). *A*, part of a colony of *Steginoporella*, showing A and B zooids (*after Marcus*, 1953). *B*, operculum of a B zooid of a species of *Steginoporella*. *C*, operculum of an A zooid of the same species as in *B*. (*B, C, after Harmer*, 1900.) *D, Crassimarginatella*, showing autozooid, ordinary avicularium, enlarged avicularium with polypide. *E*, pedunculate avicularium of *Bugula* with mandible opened. *F, Adeona*, with frontal sessile avicularia. (*D–F, after Marcus*, 1939a.) 1, A zooids; 2, B zooids; 3, operculum; 4, opesiules; 5, polypide; 6, testes; 7, avicularium; 8, ascopore; 9, areoles; 10, orifice exposed by loss of operculum; 11, rostrum; 12, wall of vestibule; 13, distal abductor (divaricator); 14, proximal abductor (depressor); 15, adductor muscle (occlusor); 16, tendons of adductors; 17, ganglion; 18, setiferous organ; 19, mandible (operculum); 20, frontal membrane; 21, peduncle; 22, muscles in peduncle; 23, parietal muscles; 24, abductor; 25, tentacle sheath; 26, bunch of tentacles; 27, digestive tract; 28, retractors of the lophophore; 29, interzooidal communications; 30, dilators of tentacle sheath.

that seems to correspond to the vestibular glands of autozooids as it is attached to or opens into the vestibule.

A given ectoproct may have more than one kind of avicularium (Fig. 124C); but all kinds of avicularia have the same essential construction. Figures 124A and B compare a pedunculate and a sessile avicularium from the same species; the former differs from the latter only in the extension of the rostrum into a beak and the presence of a peduncle. The peduncle may originate from the avicularium or from the autozooid or may combine outgrowths of both (Fig. 122E). When separated from both avicularium and autozooid by partitions (Fig. 122E) it constitutes a kenozooid (see below). The peduncle may contain muscle fibers (Fig. 122E) that accomplish bendings of the avicularium.

Probably to be classified as variants of avicularia are the peculiar heterozooids found in the anascan family Onychocellidae and in the ascophoran *Mastigophorella pesanseris*. In the former, the avicularia, called *onychocellaria*, have a conspicuous mandible winged along one or both sides (Fig. 141H, J). In M. *pesanseris* the mandible projects as a structure resembling the webbed foot of an aquatic bird (Fig. 124H).

Avicularia perform about the same functions as do the pedicellariae of echinoderms. They capture small organisms that may roam over the surface of the colony and prevent larvae from settling on the colony and overgrowing it. Especially the pedunculate type is in constant activity, bending about on its stalk and snapping its beak at small intruders.

An exhaustive study of avicularia was published by Silén (1938), and Marcus (1939a) has furnished valuable information and illustrations on the subject.

b. *Vibracula.*—Vibracula, also found only in cheilostomes, are heterozooids in which the operculum is altered into a long bristle, up to ten times the length of the autozooid, set into the reduced cystid in such a way as to be freely movable in all directions. Vibracula are of limited occurrence, found mostly in the anascan families Scrupocellariidae and Microporidae (old name, Selenariidae), further in a few unrelated species of other families. They may occur simultaneously with avicularia in definite relational positions (Fig. 124D). The bristle, also called *seta*, or, badly, flagellum, may be stiff or flexible and distally smooth or toothed along one or both sides (Fig. 124E). It is not merely an especially elongated mandible, for it differs from the latter basally, having basal projections that rotate on projections of the cystid (Fig. 124F, G) and being therefore movable in most or all directions, whereas the mandible of an avicularium can only open or close. The vibraculum is, however, otherwise similar to an avicularium, containing in its cystid remains of the polypide and adductor and abductor muscles to move the bristle (Fig. 124F). The function of vibracula is uncertain. Apparently their bristles sweep back and forth over the colony, preventing debris and larvae from settling.

c. Kenozooids.—Kenozooid is the name applied to heterozooids that lack zooidal differentiation and consist simply of body wall enclosing strands of tissue (Fig. 124*J*). Kenozooids are found in all groups of gymnolaemates. To this category belong stolons and stalks of all description, rhizoids and other root attachments, including their terminal hold-fasts and other expansions, the marginal zooids of some colonies, especially *Flustra*, the tubular zooids of the attachment disk of *Hornera*, and the chambers that in the family Reteporidae form the expanded base attached to the substrate and the layer or layers covering the outer surface of the upright fronds of the colony. Pore chambers and the resulting pore plates are kenozooids, as are also spines in some cases. As remarked by Silén (1942a): "A cavity enclosed by walls in Bryozoa must, generally seen, be a zooid."

d. Dwarf Zooids.—In the cyclostome genus *Diplosolen* small zooids, called *nannozooids* by their discoverer (Borg, 1926a), occur scattered irregularly among the autozooids (Fig. 148*E*), which they resemble in most details of structure; but they have only one tentacle, the digestive tract is reduced to a solid mass of cells, hence is functionless, and ring coelom, funiculus, and gonads are absent. Very dwarf zooids also occur in the cheilostome *Trypostega* (Marcus, 1937b; Fig. 143D). Dwarfism in relation to sexual differentiation was mentioned above (page 321).

8. Brood Chambers and Reproductive Habits.—Many ctenostomes shed their eggs, relatively few in number, mostly below 20, directly into the sea by way of the supraneural pore or intertentacular organ (Fig. 116*D*); but brooding obtains in the great majority of gymnolaemates. Brooding arrangements vary greatly, even within the same genus, and may be external or internal. A simple external device is seen in *Tendra* and some other Electridae in which a row of arched spines grows medially from the calcareous border (gymnocyst) on each side, covering over the frontal membrane and leaving a space between this and the spines that acts as a brood chamber (Paltschikowa-Ostroumova, 1925; Fig. 126*C*). Another device is seen in the boring ctenostome *Penetrantia*, in which an embryo begins development inside the maternal coelom and then somehow passes into the space between the two cuticles with which this genus is provided and completes development in a pronounced bulge of the outer cuticle on the anal (dorsal) side of the zooid (Silén, 1946, 1948; Fig. 125*G*). As the zooids with such bulges also differ in small details from nonbrooding autozooids, they classify as *gonozooids*, a type of heterozooid. *Tubucellaria* and other Tubucellariidae brood in the elongated tubular orificial collar (Waters, 1907; Marcus, 1937b) that thereupon swells and alters its shape (Fig. 126*B*); and brooding in the swollen base of the tubular orificial

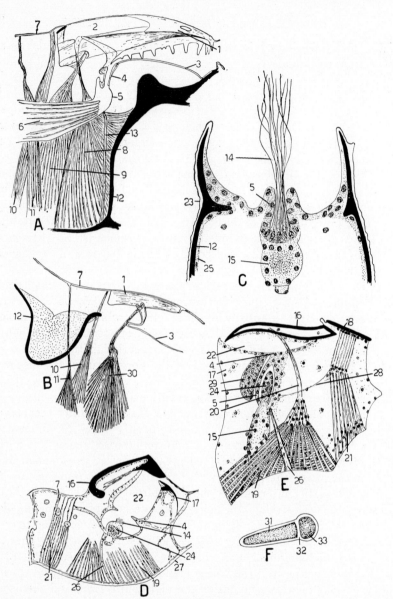

Fig. 123.—Polymorphism (continued). *A*, sagittal section through the opercular region of a B zooid of *Steginoporella*, showing muscle arrangement. *B*, similar for the A zooid of *Steginoporella*. (*A*, *B*, after Harmer, 1926.) *C*, section through the polypide of the avicularium of *Bugula*. *D*, median sagittal section of a sessile avicularium of *Flustra*. *E*, median sagittal section of a sessile avicularium of *Rhynchozoon*. (*C–E*, after Marcus, 1939a.) *F*, a calcined sessile avicularium. 1, operculum; 2, cavity of operculum; 3, vestibular membrane; 4, diaphragm; 5, tentacle sheath; 6, bunch of tentacles; 7, frontal membrane; 8, distal occlusor; 9, proximal occlusor; 10, divaricator muscle; 11, depressor musele; 12, calcareous wall of zooid; 13, dilator of tentacle sheath; 14, bundle of setae; 15, ganglion; 16, mandible; 17, rostrum; 18, thickening (sclerite) of frontal membrane; 19, mandibular adductor; 20, tendon of 19; 21, mandibular abductor; 22, vestibule; 23, cuticle; 24, remains of polypide; 25, epidermis; 26, retractor of lophophore; 27, wall of avicularium; 28, cytoplasmic strand; 29, vestibular gland; 30, occlusor of operculum; 31, depression for mandible; 32, crossbar; 33, depression covered in life by frontal membrane.

collar is also seen in *Turritigera* and other Lekythoporidae (Levinsen, 1909). Here also brooding zooids are so altered that they may be considered gonozooids. In the ctenostome *Alcyonidium duplex* the eggs after discharge to the exterior attach to the outer surface of the diaphragm and there develop to the larval stage (Prouho, 1892; Fig. 125*A*). In another ctenostome, *Bulbella abscondita*, up to six developing embryos may be found adherent to the outer surface of the body wall in the vestibular region (Braem, 1951; Fig. 125*B*). In the related *Victorella pavida* each egg as it emerges from the supraneural pore is caught in a depression of the adjacent dorsal body wall, and eventually passes into the coelom of the dorsal side of the vestibule where three or four developing embryos may be found (Braem, 1951; Fig. 125*C*, *D*); these escape by rupture through the body wall.

Brooding in the coelom is of common occurrence. In *Nolella dilatata* three or four eggs develop into larvae in the distal part of the coelom on the dorsal side, breaking out through the body wall when finished (Prouho, 1892; Fig. 125*F*). Apparently in this case the embryos are free in the coelom, but usually in coelomic brooding the embryos are enclosed in sacs probably formed of invaginated body wall. Development inside embryo sacs hanging from the zooid wall or opercular region into the distal part of the coelom is recorded for *Watersipora cucullata* (Waters, 1909; Mawatari, 1952a), *Beania magellanica* (Waters, 1912), *Diplodidymia* (Waters, 1913), various members of the family Adeonidae (Waters, 1912), *Zoobotryon pellucidum* (Waters, 1914), *Nolella papuensis* (Harmer, 1915; Silén, 1944c), also *Nolella gigantea* and *alba* (Marcus, 1938a), *Sundanella sibogae* (Braem, 1939; Silén, 1944c), and *Labiostomella* (Silén, 1944c). This condition was especially investigated by Silén (1944c) in the primitive cheilostome *Labiostomella gisleni* and some others of the species just mentioned. The sac consists of inturned body wall (epidermis, peritoneum, Fig. 125*J*, *K*), but the mode of entry into the sac remains unclear. The developing embryo eventually fills much or all of the cystid, and concomitantly the polypide usually degenerates. Generally, a single embryo sac with one contained embryo is present, but in some cases, for example, *Nolella gigantea*, several sacs each with an embryo may occur. In the family Adeonidae and a number of other forms mentioned by Waters (1912) the cystid containing such an embryonic sac is considerably enlarged (Fig. 125*H*) and may be regarded as a gonozooid. In some species these embryo sacs protrude to the exterior while developing. This seems to be the case in the curious genus *Aetea* where a sac containing an embryo hangs from the orifice during sexual reproduction (Osburn, 1912a; Waters, 1913; Fig. 141*F*). Also in *Carbasea indivisa* four or five such embryo sacs attached to the undersurface of the operculum protrude from the orifice while development proceeds (Stach, 1938a; Fig. 126*A*),

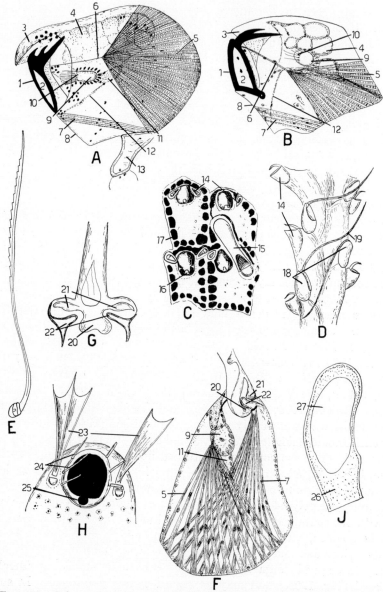

Fig. 124.—Polymorphism (concluded). *A*, pedunculate avicularium of *Synnotum*. *B*, sessile avicularium of *Synnotum;* compare with *A*. *C*, *Smittina* with two kinds of avicularia. *D*, *Scrupocellaria* with avicularia and vibracula in definite positional relations (*after Busk*, 1884). *E*, a vibracular bristle enlarged (*after Harmer*, 1926). *F*, structure of a vibraculum. *G*, base of same vibraculum as *F*, seen from in front, showing mechanism of rotation. *H*, two heterozooids of *Mastigophorella*, with duck's-foot mandible. (*A–C, F–H, after Marcus*, 1939.) *J*, a kenozooid, *Thalamoporella* (*after Silén*, 1938). 1, mandible; 2, cavity in mandible; 3, rostrum; 4, vestibular gland; 5, adductor muscle; 6, tendon of 5; 7, abductor muscle; 8, frontal membrane; 9, remains of polypide; 10, setiferous organ of

Through concomitant degeneration of the polypide, eggs may gain access into the vestibule or tentacular sheath that then serves as a brood chamber. The vestibule so serves for the single egg of *Bowerbankia caudata* (Braem, 1951; Fig. 125*E*). A variant of vestibular development is seen in *Cryptosula pallasiana*, where the egg develops in an invaginated pouch of vestibule above the diaphragm (Calvet, 1900). In *Walkeria uva* (Joliet, 1877) one egg and in *Pherusella tubulosa* (Prouho, 1892) and *Flustrellidra hispida* (Pace, 1906) four or five eggs are brooded inside the tentacle sheath. Brooding in the tentacle sheath following degeneration of the polypide was also noted by Prouho (1892) for *Alcyonidium variegatum* and *polyoum* and by Calvet (1900) for species of the ctenostome genera *Bowerbankia*, *Amathia*, and *Vesicularia*.

In most cheilostomes development takes place in a special external brood chamber, known as an *ovicell* or *oecium*, that typically perches like a helmet or hood on the anterior end of some or all of the autozooids of a breeding colony (Figs. 105*G*, *H*, 106*E*, *F*, 120*A*, *B*, 126*D*). The ovicell puts in an appearance only when an egg of some size is present in the ovary of the zooid concerned; hence its formation would seem to depend on some hormonal influence emanating from the maturing egg. Levinsen (1909) gave an extended consideration of ovicells that he classified into six categories: the *hyperstomial*, the *endozoecial*, the *endotoichal*, the *two-valved*, the *peristomial*, and the *acanthostegous*. The first three appear to be variants of the same structure, and for them the accounts of Silén (1944c, 1945) are here followed. The most common type, the hyperstomial, found in *Bugula* (Fig. 126*D*) and countless other cheilostomes, is free from the base of the succeeding zooid. It is formed of two body-wall evaginations, an outer one that encloses the inner one. The outer one begins as an outgrowth (usually bifid at first but soon fusing to one sac, Fig. 126*E*, *F*) of the body wall of the distal end of the zooid. The outgrowth continues to advance and curves into a hood shape (Fig. 126*G*, *H*). The hood is therefore double-walled (Fig. 127*A*), but each wall itself is composed of body wall; the outer wall is thick and heavily chitinized or usually calcified, often with pseudopores and surface sculpturing. The space between the two walls should be continuous with the coelom and is so represented by Silén (Fig. 126*J*); but the figures of Calvet (1900) and Correa (1948) show a partition here, presumably a secondary formation (Fig. 127*A*). The inner evagination is a simple sacciform outgrowth that comes to occupy the hollow of the hood (Fig. 126*J*); its cavity is continuous with the coelom of the zooid. The developing egg occupies the space

polypide; 11, ganglion; 12, cytoplasmic strands; 13, peduncle; 14, avicularia; 15, large spatulate avicularium; 16, lyrule; 17, areoles; 18, vibraculum; 19, vibracular bristle; 20, knoblike end of bristle; 21, projections of bristle base; 22, projections of vibraculum on which 21 rotates; 23, duck's-foot mandible; 24, spines; 25, opening into ascus; 26, cryptocyst; 27, opesium.

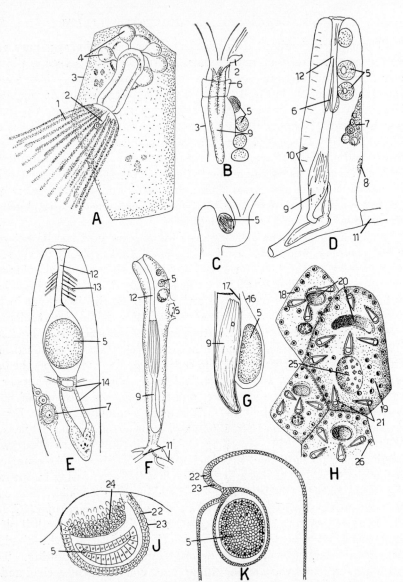

Fig. 125.—Brooding habits. *A, Alcyonidium duplex* with eggs fastened to the diaphragm. *B, Bulbella* with eggs stuck to the body wall. *C, Victorella*, with just emitted egg caught in a curve. *D, Victorella*, with three eggs in the distal coelom. *E, Bowerbankia*, with egg in vestibule. (*B–E, after Braem, 1951.*) *F, Nolella*, with eggs in distal coelom. (*A, F, after Prouho, 1892.*) *G, Penetrantia*, with embryo between the two cuticles (*after Silén, 1946*). *H, Adeonellopsis* with enlarged zooid acting as gonozooid (*after Levinsen, 1909*). *J*, embryo sac of *Labiostomella*. *K*, embryo sac of *Nolella*. (*J, K, after Silén, 1944c.*) 1, lophophore; 2, intertentacular organ; 3, wall of autozooid; 4, attached eggs; 5, egg or embryo; 6, pleated collar; 7, ovary; 8, testis; 9, polypide; 10, parietal muscles; 11, stolon; 12, vestibule; 13, vestibular dilators; 14, degenerated polypide; 15, places of exit of previous embryos; 16, outer cuticle; 17, inner cuticle; 18, autozooid; 19, gonozooid; 20, orifice; 21, sessile avicularia; 22, epidermis; 23, peritoneum; 24, epidermal cushion; 25, area of numerous ascopores; 26, areoles.

between the two evaginations, resting on the thickened epidermis of the inner one (Fig. 127A), which seems to have a nutritive function. The inner sac is provided with muscle fibers (Fig. 127A) by which the exit of the ovicell and the space between the hood and the inner sac can be widened.

The endozoecial ovicell differs from the hyperstomial one merely in being imbedded in the base of the succeeding zooid (Fig. 126J). Endotoichal ovicells, limited to the family Cellariidae (Fig. 127B, C), are excavations in the distal end of the same zooid above the orifice. According to a sagittal section furnished by Calvet (1900), the excavation is lined by inturned body wall and contains another sac of body wall housing the embryo.

The two-valved ovicell, although superficially resembling the hyperstomial type, appears of quite different origin and construction, consisting of two hemispherical valves that meet along a median suture often externally keeled. These valves apparently originate by the transformation of a pair of spines or tubercles, hence classify as kenozooids. Two-valved ovicells occur in *Thalamoporella* (Harmer, 1926; Fig. 142B), *Scruparia* (Hastings, 1941; Fig 141D), and *Alysidium parasiticum* (Levinsen, 1909; Fig. 127G, H). Related to the two-valved type is the external brood chamber of *Catenicula corbulifera*. Here an enlarged zooid, really a gonozooid, gives off two flat hollow plates, each of which in turn produces three larger flat hollow blades of circular outline (O'Donoghue, 1924; Fig. 128A); these six blades form a hollow basket in which eggs develop. Peristomial ovicell refers to the enlarged orificial collars ("peristome") that act as brood chambers in the Tubucellariidae and Lekythoporidae (page 331). The term acanthostegous ovicell applies to the external brood chambers found in the Electridae formed by the extension of spines over the frontal membrane (page 331). The last two types cannot properly be called ovicells.

The transfer of the egg into the ovicell was witnessed by Gerwerzhagen (1913) and Silén (1945). According to Silén, a single egg when ripe gains the distal end of the zooid where the supraneural pore is seen near the tentacle bases on the dorsal (anal) side. The extended zooid now retracts sufficiently to bring this pore opposite the entrance into the ovicell, and the egg squeezes out through the pore into the latter (Fig. 127D). Within the ovicell the egg develops into a ciliated larva that escapes into the sea. Silén (1945) found that young embryos removed from the ovicell into filtered sea water soon cease to develop and die; hence special conditions essential for development exist in the cavity of the ovicell.

Typically only one egg occupies the ovicell at a time, but exceptions occur. In *Thalamoporella rozieri* two or three eggs may occur simultaneously in the ovicell (Waters, 1909), four in *T. californica* (Hastings, 1929),

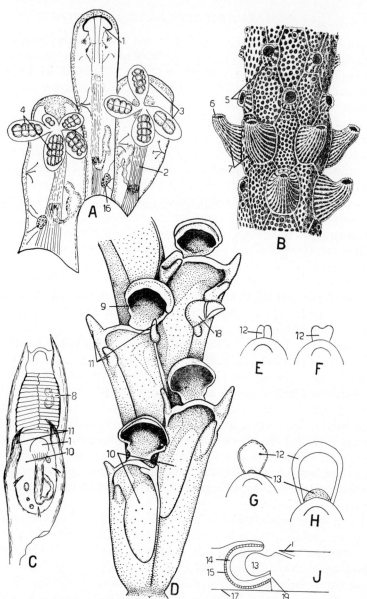

Fig. 126.—Brooding habits (continued). *A*, three zooids of *Carbasea indivisa*, two with external brood sacs attached to the operculum (*after Stach*, 1938b). *B*, *Tubucellaria*, with orificial collars used as brood chambers (*after Marcus*, 1937b). *C*, *Tendra*, with external brood chamber formed of spines crossed above frontal membrane (*after Palt-schikowa-Ostroumova*, 1925). *D*, *Bugula*, with ovicells (*after Rogick and Croasdale*, 1949). *E–H*, stages in the formation of a hyperstomial ovicell. *J*, scheme of an endozoecial ovicell. (*E–J*, *after Silén*, 1945.) 1, operculum; 2, polypide; 3, brood sacs; 4, embryo; 5, orificial collar; 6, secondary orifice; 7, orificial collars as brood chambers; 8, brood chamber of spines; 9, hyperstomial ovicell; 10, frontal membrane; 11, spines; 12, stages of outer sac of ovicell; 13, inner sac of ovicell; 14, outer sac developed into hood; 15, boundary between two zooids; 16, ovary; 17, wall of next zooid; 18, avicularium; 19, coelomic communication.

and up to six in *T. evelinae* (Marcus, 1941a); up to seven have been found in *Scruparia chelata* (Hastings, 1941). These, however, are among the genera listed above as having an ovicell of the two-valved type, hence differing from the ordinary ovicell of cheilostomes, and this fact may be related to the presence of more than one embryo in their ovicells, although apparently these two-valved ovicells do not have an internal partition.

From the foregoing it is evident that reproduction by the sexual method is not very prolific among brooding ctenostomes and cheilostomes. Silén (1944c) recorded that in *Labiostomella gisleni* each ovary contains about 100 ovocytes, about 10 attain the distal part of the zooid, but only one acquires an embryo sac and develops; hence this species produces only one larva per zooid in a breeding season. Similarly a female zooid of *Synnotum aegyptiacum* produces but a single larva during its life, then degenerating (Marcus, 1941b). In *Watersipora cucullata*, which broods in an internal embryo sac, 4 or 5 weeks elapse between successive incubations, to allow time for regeneration of the polypide, and only about three embryos are emitted by a given cystid during a breeding season (Mawatari, 1952a). Available data indicate that the same ovicell serves for only a very few successive eggs; thus in *Callopora dumerili* only three or four eggs develop successively in the same ovicell (Silén, 1945) and in *Bugula flabellata* about three (Correa, 1948). The number is limited by the regenerative powers of the polypide; this usually degenerates when an egg is developing in the embryo sac or ovicell, and as its presence is necessary for building another embryo sac or transference of another egg into the ovicell, sexual reproduction of a given zooid ceases if the polypide fails to regenerate. Even nonbrooding forms are not very prolific; thus about 10 eggs are emitted by *Farrella repens* and a maximum of 17 by *Electra pilosa* (Marcus, 1926b). On the other hand, in *Membranipora membranacea* an "almost numberless" lot of small eggs is rapidly emitted (Silén, 1945).

All cyclostomes brood in brood chambers, of which relatively few occur in a given colony. In all except two small groups the brood chambers are altered, enlarged zooids, that is, gonozooids. In the simplest cyclostomes, the Crisiidae, the gonozooids are conspicuous vaselike objects, definitely located with reference to the branching (Fig. 108D). The orifice, then called *oeciostome*, becomes the exit of the gonozooid and is usually tubular with an expanded rim. In more complicated types of cyclostomes as the tubuliporids and other fascicled forms (Figs. 100C, 109A) the gonozooid spreads by lobulations among the autozooids, often embracing them (Fig. 127E, F). The gonozooid is known to be a zooid by its containing a polypide, often only partially developed but sometimes attaining full development; it degenerates as the egg develops and furnishes nutritive material for it.

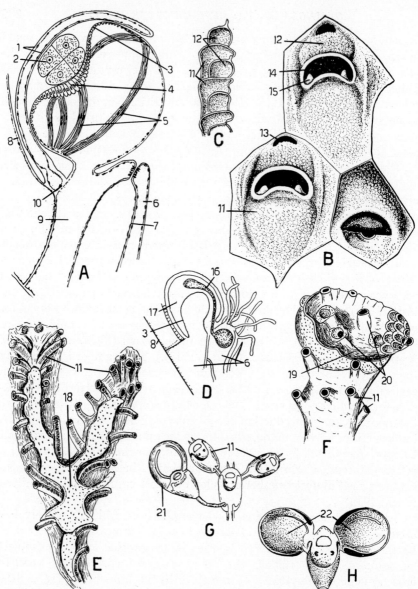

FIG. 127.—Brood chambers (continued). *A*, section through the hyperstomial ovicell of *Bugula* (*after Calvet*, 1900). *B*, endotoichal ovicells of a cellariid (*after Rogick*, 1956a). *C*, longitudinal section of a row of zooids of *Cellaria* with endotoichal ovicells (*after Levinsen*, 1909). *D*, egg passing from the supraneural pore of a zooid into the ovicell (*after Silén*, 1945). *E*, piece of *Tubulipora* with brood chamber (*after Osburn*, 1912a). *F*, brood chamber of a cyclostome *Filisparsa* cut open (*after Waters*, 1910). *G*, piece of *Alysidium parasiticum* with two-valved brood chamber. *H*, brood chamber of *G*, with valves opened. (*C, G, H, after Levinsen*, 1909.) 1, outer hoodlike evagination; 2, embryo; 3, inner evagination; 4, nutritive layer of 3; 5, muscles of 3; 6, zooid to which ovicell belongs; 7, tentacle sheath of 6; 8, next successive zooid; 9, coelom of 6; 10, partition between coeloms of outer evagination and zooid; 11, autozooid; 12, endotoichal ovicell; 13, opening of 12; 14, orifice of zooid; 15, condyles; 16, egg; 17, ovicell; 18, brood chamber; 19, cut-open brood chamber; 20, zooids passing through brood chamber; 21, gonozooid with two-valved ovicell; 22, valves of ovicell.

The brood chamber is compound in the two highest cyclostome suborders, Cerioporina and Rectangulata. In the former it is formed by the fusion of a fertile autozooid that produces the egg with a number of surrounding kenozooids and sterile autozooids. In the Rectangulata, comprising only the family Lichenoporidae, the brood chamber arises by the fusion of a number of alveoli (Harmer, 1896; Borg, 1926a). Each of the small circular colonies of this family has one or more brood chambers (Fig. 109*D*). When the colony is quite small, consisting of only a few zooids, the brood chamber begins as an alveolus, to which other alveoli are gradually added with breakdown of the intervening walls. As the alveoli are not zooids, being merely coelomic cavities, an ovigerous zooid must necessarily become associated with the growing brood chamber; this is typically one of the first few zooids of the colony. It fuses with the wall of the brood chamber, and an opening between the two is established.

It was discovered by Harmer (1890, 1893) and verified by all subsequent observers that polyembryony obtains in cyclostomes. Details were furnished for *Crisia* by Harmer (1893) and Robertson (1903), for *Tubulipora* by Harmer (1898), for *Lichenopora* by Harmer (1896), and for these and numerous other genera by Borg (1926a). Cyclostome colonies, usually monoecious or dioecious, may produce numerous eggs, but only those survive that attach to the polypide of an incipient gonozooid, whose zoecium enlarges as it grows by continuous calcareous deposition on a funnellike base. The gonozooid contains a female polypide whose degree of development differs in different cyclostomes. In each gonozooid of the colony a single egg (rarely more) develops after attaching itself to the proximal part of the polypide from whose tissues it acquires a follicle. This primary follicle usually disintegrates to furnish nutritive material and may be followed by a secondary follicle that likewise disintegrates. The embryo lies at the inner end of the membranous sac (Fig. 128*C*), and other parts of the polypide eventually disintegrate to supply nutritive material. In *Tubulipora* a column of nutritive tissue extends from the distal end of the membranous sac to the embryo (Fig. 129*B*). The embryo meantime has cleaved to a ball of cells that puts out lobulations. These cut off as secondary embryos (Fig. 129*A*), and in some genera probably some of these constrict again to produce tertiary embryos. The embryos lie in cavities in a nutritive mesh formed from the two follicles and the disintegrated polypide, with possible additions of fresh cells from the membranous sac. As many as 100 embryos or more are produced from one egg in this manner. These when mature escape from the oeciostome. Apparently the polypide of the gonozooid does not regenerate, and hence a given gonozooid produces only one brood of embryos.

In the Lichenoporidae development proceeds as above in the fertile

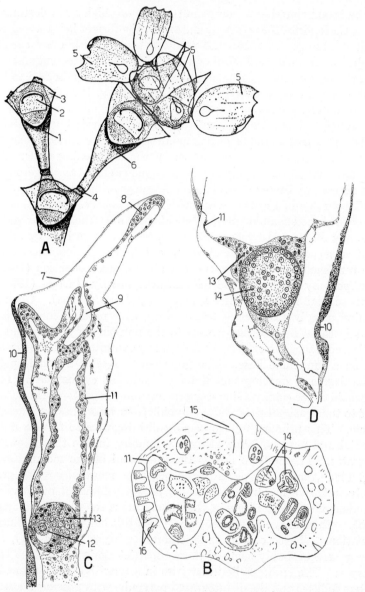

Fɪɢ. 128.—Brooding habits (continued). *A*, external brood chamber of *Catenicula corbulifera*, made of chitinous plates forming a basket (*after O'Donoghue*, 1924). *B*, cross section through the brood chamber of a tubuliporid, showing embryos (*after Waters*, 1914). *C*, longitudinal section of gonozooid of *Crisia*, showing relation of egg to zooid. *D*, later stage of development of *Crisia* embryo. (*C, D, after Harmer*, 1893.) 1, autozooid; 2, operculum; 3, triangular expansion bearing operculum; 4, joint; 5, plates (opened out flat) of basket; 6, gonozooid; 7, cuticle; 8, epidermis; 9, vestibule; 10, calcified wall; 11, membranous sac; 12, egg; 13, follicle; 14, embryo; 15, oeciostome; 16, pseudopores in cross section.

zooid associated with the brood chamber. The original polypide of this zooid usually degenerates, and the egg is furnished by a regenerated polypide. The egg is provided with two successive follicles and is further nourished by a very evident column of cells connecting it with the distal degenerated parts of the second polypide (Fig. 129C). Secondary and probably tertiary embryos are produced and nourished as above, and now the distended membranous sac in which they are contained works its way into the adjacent brood chamber, which it eventually fills. A brood chamber of a lichenoporid colony apparently produces but one brood of embryos (annually?), but Harmer (1896) is of the opinion that a second brood may arise, without explaining how this is possible.

Available data indicate that ectoprocts have an annual breeding season that extends over 2 or 3 up to 5 or 6 months. In the Northern Hemisphere the breeding season falls within the period from spring to autumn or even extends into early winter. A table given by Marcus (1926a) for over 60 species from the North and Baltic Seas, the British coasts, and the Mediterranean shows that the great majority breed within the months from April and May through October. On the New England coast colonies of *Bugula flabellata* are found with eggs or embryos in the ovicells from June into November (Grave, 1930), and off Santos, Brazil, the same species is recorded by Correa (1948) as found in the height of breeding in January (corresponding to the middle of the summer in the north). It is not known whether an individual zooid continues to produce eggs throughout the extensive breeding season, but from data given above it is evident that this is not the case in brooding species, which constitute the majority of ectoprocts.

The eggs of brooding species are generally relatively large and often colored red, orange, or yellow by their yolk supply, hence form conspicuous objects in their ovicells. The resulting embryos often retain these vivid colors. The small eggs and resulting embryos of nonbrooding species are likely to be more or less colorless.

It was shown for cyclostomes by Robertson (1903) and Borg (1926a) and for a ctenostome by Faulkner (1933), and no doubt the same applies to cheilostomes, that the germ cells originate from body-wall peritoneum at a very early stage of zooid budding, at a time when the zooid consists of nothing but body wall (Fig. 129D). The germ cells are recognizable at this time by their larger size and large round nuclei with a conspicuous nucleolus. As the polypide differentiates by invagination these primordial germ cells are carried inward with it, and only those that attain contact with the polypide develop into gonads, while the remainder die. Germinal lineage therefore definitely does not exist in ectoprocts.

The problem of fertilization has received the attention of numerous students of ectoprocts, most of whom report failure to observe the process.

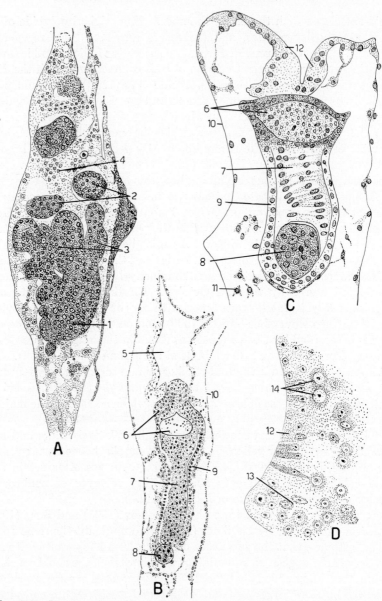

Fig. 129.—Brooding (concluded), embryology. *A*, longitudinal section of gonozooid
of *Crisia*, in process of polyembryony (*after Harmer*, 1893). *B*, longitudinal section of
brood chamber of *Tubulipora* with nutritive column (*after Harmer*, 1898). *C*, longitudinal
section of fertile zooid of *Lichenopora* with nutritive column (*after Harmer*, 1896). *D*, distal
body wall of incipient zooid of *Crisia*, showing origin of germ cells (*after Robertson*, 1903).
1, original embryo; 2, secondary embryos; 3, lobulations to produce secondary embryos;
4, nutritive mesh; 5, vestibule; 6, remains of polypide; 7, nutritive column; 8, embryo;
9, membranous sac; 10, body wall; 11, mesenchyme; 12, epidermis; 13, peritoneum; 14,
germ cells.

Calvet (1900) and Gerwerzhagen (1913) witnessed fertilization in living zooids of *Bugula;* here the eggs as they leave the ovary are at once fertilized by sperm of the same zooid. Most authors believe that such autogamous fertilization is the rule among ectoprocts. Self-fertilization in cases of extreme protandry could be explained by the finding of Marcus (1938a) that in many species a sperm has already entered the very immature ovocyte. Cross-fertilization must obtain in monoecious and dioecious species unless one assumes parthenogenesis, as was suggested by Robertson (1903) for *Crisia.* The difficulty of course is to explain how sperm from other zooids can gain entry into the coelom to fertilize the eggs. Sperm might conceivably enter by way of the supraneural pore or the intertentacular organ when these are present, but are not known to do so. Such openings are known for only a limited number of ctenostomes and cheilostomes. Marcus (1938a) listed the known cases of occurrence of a supraneural pore (20 species) or an intertentacular organ (13 species). These openings into the coelom are wanting in cyclostomes, a group in which monoecious and dioecious species are of common occurrence. Possibly sperm can penetrate the thin tenuous layers of the body wall or pass from one zooid to another by way of the interzooidal communications. Whatever may be the difficulties, it is clear that the eggs are fertilized in the coelom before emission to the exterior. In this connection the observation of Marcus (1926a) is of interest, that the sperm of *Electra* would not retain motility more than 10 minutes in sea water.

9. Embryology.—Main articles on ectoproct embryology are those of Barrois (1877, 1880, 1886), Vigelius (1886), Harmer (1887), Prouho (1890, 1892), Calvet (1900), Pace (1906), Marcus (1926b, 1938a), O'Donoghue (1927), and Correa (1948). Early development is similar in brooding and nonbrooding ctenostomes and cheilostomes. In these groups the egg undergoes holoblastic cleavage, generally equal or subequal, but sometimes with larger cells in the vegetal hemisphere. The cleavage pattern is usually of the radial type, with tiers of cells in line with each other (Fig. 130*A*, *B*), but is biradial in some species (Fig. 130*C*) with cells more or less alternating (Fig. 130*D*). A coeloblastula eventuates which gastrulates by primary delamination (I, page 260) at the vegetal pole. At a stage of about 64 to 128 blastomeres, four cells at the vegetal pole elongate into the blastocoel and their inner halves cut off as entoderm (Fig. 130*E*). The four cells so produced proliferate and fill the blastocoel with entoderm cells that also furnish mesenchyme, hence are in part entomesodermal.

There early becomes evident a horizontal ring of enlarged ectodermal cells near the equator of the embryo (Fig. 130*G*); these, which may be regarded as trochoblasts (II, page 13), acquire long cilia and constitute the *ciliary girdle* or *corona*, chief locomotory provision of the embryo. These coronal cells often continue to elongate for some time and in some

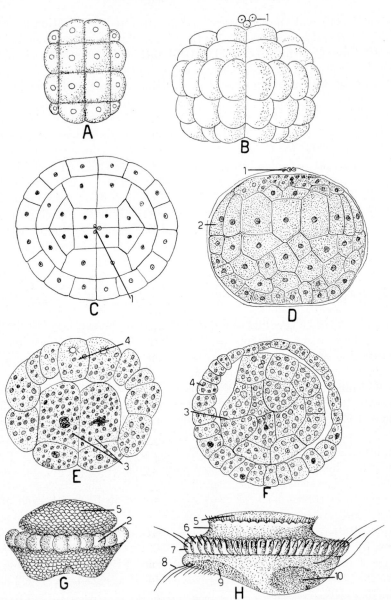

Fig. 130.—Embryology (continued). *A*, 32-cell stage. *B*, 64-cell stage of *Bugula*, seen from the side (*after Correa*, 1948). *C*, 72-cell stage of *Siniopelta*, seen from the animal pole, showing biradial arrangement. *D*, 160-cell stage of *Holoporella*, seen from the side, arrangement somewhat alternating. (*C*, *D*, *after Marcus*, 1938a.) *E*, *Flustrellidra*, beginning gastrulation by primary delamination at vegetal pole. *F*, later stage of entoderm formation. (*E*, *F*, *after Pace*, 1906.) *G*, *Alcyonidium mytili*, early larva with conspicuous *trochoblasts*. *H*, mature larva of *Alcyonidium mytili*, seen from the side. (*A*, *G*, *H*, *after Barrois*, 1877.) 1, polar bodies; 2, trochoblasts; 3, entoderm cells; 4, ectoderm; 5, apical organ; 6, groove; 7, ciliary girdle; 8, vibratile plume; 9, ciliated cleft; 10, adhesive sac.

larvae cover much of the surface (Fig. 131*D*, *F*). At the animal or aboral pole the ectoderm thickens and differentiates into the apical nervous organ found in many invertebrate larvae. This bears or is encircled by rigid cilia, presumably actually of the nature of sensory bristles. The apical organ is often delimited by a circular groove whose outer margin is frequently scalloped as in *Bugula* (Fig. 131*D*, *F*). Two epidermal invaginations become evident in the now concave oral surface, an anterior *pyriform organ* and a posterior *adhesive sac* (Fig. 131 *B*, *C*). The pyriform organ is a complex of gland cells associated with a ciliated depression, the *ciliary cleft;* the gland cells may form a single group but are often sub-divided into a median and paired lateral groups (Fig. 131*E*). The anterior end of the cleft often bears a tuft of especially long cilia, termed the *vibratile plume*. The apical nervous organ is connected to the pyri-form organ by a strand of combined nervous and muscular elements, and the nervous strand continues orally to supply the vibratile plume and ciliary cleft and to form a ring nerve for the ciliary girdle. The adhesive sac (also called internal sac, sucker, and originally mistaken for a stomach) is a large deep ectodermal invagination, often bilobed (Fig. 131*A*), whose cells take on a columnar form. Having arrived at about this stage of differentiation, the larva escapes from the egg membrane or from the zooid in brooding species and leads a free existence of variable duration.

The larvae of ctenostomes and cheilostomes present a varied appear-ance reducible to two main types. One of these called *cyphonautes* was correctly surmised by Prouho (1892) to develop only from nonbrooded eggs, those shed into the sea. The name cyphonautes was created by Ehrenberg (1834), who first saw the tiny creature on Nov. 25, 1832, in a sample of sea water from the Baltic and who classified it as a rotifer. The true nature of the larva was not elucidated until 1869 when Schneider observed the metamorphosis of Ehrenberg's cyphonautes into the cheilo-stome *Electra pilosa*. Cyphonautes larvae have been described for the ctenostomes *Alcyonidium albidum* and *Hypophorella expansa* by Prouho (1892) and *Farrella repens* by Marcus (1926b) and for species of the cheilostome genera *Membranipora* and *Electra* by Prouho (1892), Kupel-wieser (1905), O'Donoghue (1927), and Atkins (1955a); especially Kupelwieser has given an exhaustive account of the histological details. Figures and records of other, mostly unidentified cyphonautes larvae appear in Lohmann (1911), Marcus (1940), and Thorson (1946).

The cyphonautes larva has a triangular outline when viewed from the side (Fig. 133*A–C*) but is strongly compressed laterally. At the aboral pole, which is carried forward in swimming, is seen the knoblike apical nervous organ provided with bristles. The oral surface is encircled by the ciliary girdle, which forms a thickened edge here. The remainder of the body is enclosed in a bivalve shell secreted by and adherent to the under-

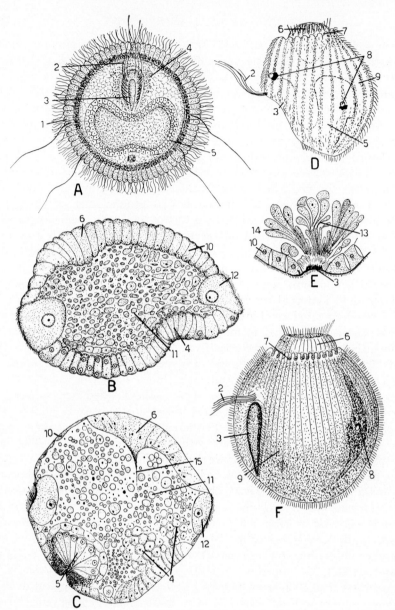

Fig. 131.—Embryology (continued). *A*, larva of *Alcyonidium mytili*, seen from the ventral side. *B*, vertical section through *Bugula* after entoderm formation. *C*, vertical section of later stage of *Bugula*. *D*, larva of *Bugula*, seen from the side. (*A, D, after Barrois*, 1877.) *E*, frontal section through the pyriform organ of *Bugula*. (*B, C, E, after Correa*, 1948.) *F*, larva of another species of *Bugula* (*after Calvet*, 1900). 1, ciliary girdle (corona); 2, vibratile plume; 3, ciliated cleft; 4, pyriform organ; 5, adhesive sac; 6, apical nervous organ; 7, groove; 8, pigmented spots; 9, very elongated coronal cells; 10, ectoderm; 11, entoderm; 12, coronal cell; 13, central mass of gland cells of pyriform organ; 14, lateral gland masses of pyriform organ; 15, neuromuscular strand from apical organ to pyriform organ.

lying flattened epidermis. The epidermis is exposed only along the anterior and posterior surfaces where the shell valves fail to meet and is here taller and flagellated. The interior of the larva contains a complete U-shaped digestive tract, formed as follows. The main mass of entoderm cells hollows out and arranges to a one-layered epithelium, thus becoming the stomach. Extensive stomodaeal and proctodaeal invaginations meet the stomach and break through, establishing a functional digestive tract of pharynx, stomach, and intestine. The ciliated pharynx is preceded by a spacious, mostly nonciliated cavity or vestibule, from which it is partly separated by a projecting mobile shelf (velum) limited to the posterior wall of the vestibule. The remaining organs of the cyphonautes are common to all ectoproct larvae. The pyriform organ as a glandular invagination associated with the ciliated cleft and vibratile plume is found in the anterior part of the oral surface, anterior to the vestibule. The adhesive sac as an extensive invagination of columnar cells is situated posteriorly between the vestibule and the anus (Fig. 133*B*) and in Kupelwieser's figure is shown producing a mass of secretion.

The cyphonautes has a good muscular and nervous provision. A main dorsal muscle, said to be striated, extends from beneath the apical organ, to which it sends a retractor strand, ventrally between the pharynx and the ectoderm to the pyriform organ around which it forks and sprays out, finally continuing to the adjacent corona with a median strand into the vibratile plume (Fig. 133*E*). The pyriform organ is also supplied with circular fibers accomplishing its protrusion. Two pairs of lateral muscles, also striated, originate on the inner surface of the valves at about their middle and extend anteriorly and posteriorly, respectively, to insert on the corona. From about the same point of origin a pair of smooth muscles supplies the adhesive sac. The valves are connected by an adductor muscle running transversely, located between the adhesive sac and the vestibule. A branch of the dorsal muscle extends from the apical region ventrally between the ectoderm and the intestine to supply the rear part of the corona, and the latter is further provided with a circular muscle. Most of the muscles mentioned serve primarily to retract various parts into the protection of the valves and to close the valves. Concerned with food ingestion are the circular muscles of the pharynx, causing peristalsis, and of the velum, narrowing the entrance into the pharynx.

The apical organ, shown in the available figures as a stratified, somewhat syncytial mass, is the nervous center of the cyphonautes. Nervous strands from it accompany the dorsal muscle anteriorly and posteriorly (Fig. 133*B*); the main anterior branch supplies the pyriform organ, ciliated cleft, and vibratile plume (Fig. 133*E*) and continues into the adjacent corona.   The posterior nervous strand also continues into the corona, where both join a circular strand.

The cyphonautes larva leads a somewhat extended free life, up to 2 months, and in some areas can be found during the entire year.   It feeds on minute organisms brought in by ciliary currents (Atkins, 1955b).   At length it seeks a suitable substrate and undergoes metamorphosis (see below), later shedding the valves.

A modified type of cyphonautes larva is seen in the brooding species, *Flustrellidra hispida* (Prouho, 1890; Pace, 1906).   This lacks a functional digestive tract but otherwise resembles a true cyphonautes (Fig. 132*D*). The entodermal mass may hollow out to form a stomach, and a stomodaeal invagination may appear, but intestine and anus are wanting and the parts formed eventually degenerate.   As the larva cannot feed, its free existence is brief and attachment soon ensues.

The eggs are brooded in the majority of ctenostomes and cheilostomes and give rise to a type of larva without special name and appearing externally quite unlike the cyphonautes.   These larvae, of which a number are figured in color by Barrois (1877), Calvet (1900), and Marcus (1938a), lack covering valves and are of rounded or oval shape (Fig. 131*D*, *F*), often anteroposteriorly elongated (Fig. 132*C*).   At the aboral pole, the apical organ forms a little turret set off by a groove often with a scalloped edge.   Below this groove the surface is formed largely or wholly by the coronal cells, often very elongated (Fig. 131*D*, *F*).   Red pigment spots, definitely located (Fig. 131*D*), are often present, each provided with a tuft of cilia (Calvet, 1900).   These spots are sometimes called eyespots in the literature, but their ocellar nature is uncertain.   Despite the difference in external appearance the internal structure of these larvae is much the same as that of the cyphonautes.   The oral half of the interior contains anteriorly the pyriform organ, denoted externally by the ciliated cleft with its vibratile plume, and posteriorly encloses the adhesive sac (Fig. 132*A*).   A digestive tract is wanting, and the remainder of the interior is filled with loose cells, derivatives of the four original entoderm cells.   Muscular and nervous systems are built along the same lines as in the cyphonautes but are less developed.   As larvae from brooded eggs have no digestive tract they cannot feed, and hence lead only a brief free existence, from less than an hour up to a day.

The development of cyclostomes differs throughout from that of other gymnolaemates.   The early blastomeres scatter throughout the follicle but later aggregate into a solid ball of cells (Fig. 128*D*) that constricts off secondary embryos as described above (Fig. 129*A*).   These are solid balls of blastomeres at first, but soon their cells arrange into two layers, ectoderm and mesoderm, around a central cavity (Fig. 132*F*).   One end now undergoes invagination to form the adhesive sac, and at the other end an

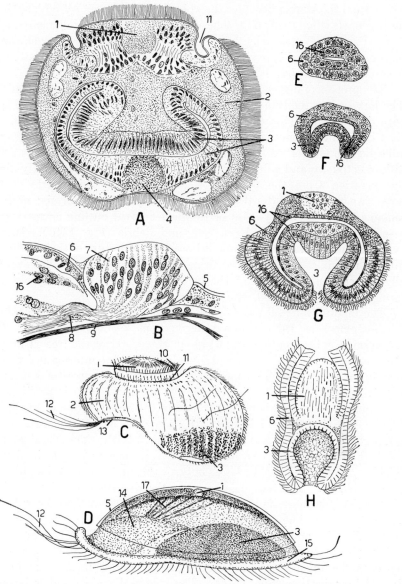

Fig. 132.—Embryology (continued). *A*, vertical section of late stage of *Bugula* (*after Vigelius*, 1886). *B*, section of apical nervous organ (*after Prouho*, 1890). *C*, larva of *Cellepora*. *D*, larva of *Flustrellidra hispida*. *E–G*, three stages in the development of a secondary embryo of a cyclostome (*after Calvet*, 1900). *H*, vertical section of late stage of a cyclostome. (*C, D, H, after Barrois*, 1877.) 1, apical nervous organ; 2, elongated coronal cells; 3, adhesive sac; 4, mass of glandular secretion; 5, shell; 6, ectoderm; 7, nervous center; 8, nerve strand; 9, muscular strand; 10, sensory bristles; 11, groove; 12, vibratile plume; 13, ciliated cleft; 14, pyriform organ; 15, ciliary girdle; 16, peritoneum; 17, muscle strands.

ectodermal thickening becomes the apical nervous organ set off later by a deep groove (Fig. 132F, G). The resulting larva has an elongated oval form (Fig. 132H) and lacks the other features common to gymnolaemate larvae as ciliary girdle, pyriform organ, ciliated cleft and plume, etc. As it cannot feed, its free life is also brief.

The process of metamorphosis is the same in all gymnolaemate larvae. The larva when ready hovers over the substrate seeking a suitable spot with the aid of the vibratile plume, which acts in a sensory capacity. It then by means of convulsive muscular contractions suddenly everts the adhesive sac (Fig. 134B), which spreads out over the substrate as a flat disk of ectoderm and adheres by means of its secretion, apparently aided by secretion from the pyriform organ. All projecting parts of the larva are retracted into the interior and undergo histolysis; nothing remains but a flattened mass of rounded or oval outline covered with ectoderm and containing loose cells and debris (Fig. 134C). In the cyphonautes, the two valves, opened out flat by rupture of their adductor muscle, remain for some time covering this mass (Fig. 134A), but eventually are cast off. Details of the metamorphosis of *Bugula* species are furnished by Grave (1930) and Lynch (1947).

The metamorphosed mass develops into the first zooid of the colony (cheilostomes) as follows (good account in Zschiesche, 1909). The ectoderm secretes a cuticle and at about the center of the free surface of the mass begins to proliferate and invaginate into the interior as a vesicle that becomes covered with mesenchyme, forming the peritoneum (Fig. 134C). According to Zschiesche, this mesenchyme also is proliferated from the ectoderm and is not a survival of the mesenchyme of the larva. The inner part of the vesicle now partly constricts as a second vesicle also composed of ectoderm and peritoneum (Fig. 134D). The distal part of the first vesicle thins to become the tentacle sheath; its proximal part thickens, gives off the tentacles as outgrowths, and becomes the pharynx (Fig. 134E, F). The tentacular outgrowths give evidence of an original bilaterality, for those on the anal side arise later than the others; hence the latter for a time form a horseshoe. The second vesicle elongates, curves distally, and becomes the remainder of the digestive tract (Fig. 134F). The two parts of the digestive tract do not communicate at first, but later the lumen breaks through. The ganglion is formed as an ectodermal invagination (Fig. 134F). The ring and main coeloms become defined by rearrangement of peritoneal cells. Muscle cells differentiate from mesenchyme cells. The tentacle sheath retains or reestablishes continuity with an ectodermal thickening (Fig. 134F) that eventually breaks through as the orifice. It will be noticed from Fig. 134F that the polypide lies parallel to the surface of the primary cystid, facing the future ventral wall. Before emergence it undergoes a rotation of 90°, thus

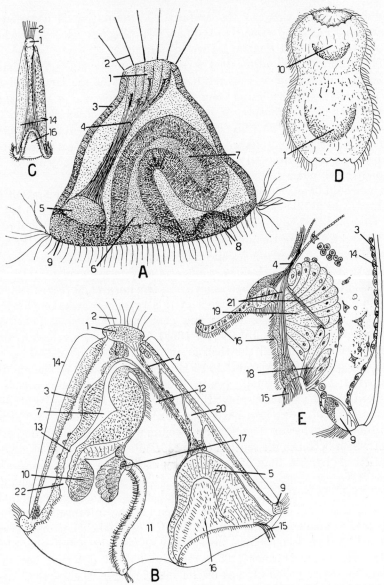

FIG. 133.—Embryology (continued). *A*, early *cyphonautes* of *Farrella*, shell not formed (*after Marcus*, 1926b). *B*, mature cyphonautes (*after Prouho*, 1892). *C*, end view of cyphonautes. *D*, mature cyclostome larva. (*C*, *D*, *after Barrois*, 1877.) *E*, sagittal section of the pyriform organ of the cyphonautes. (*B*, *E*, *after Prouho*, 1892.) 1, apical nervous organ; 2, sensory bristles; 3, ectoderm; 4, neuromuscular strand; 5, pyriform organ; 6, stomodaeum; 7, stomach; 8, proctodaeum; 9, ciliary girdle; 10, adhesive sac; 11, vestibule; 12, pharynx; 13, intestine; 14, shell; 15, vibratile plume; 16, ciliated cleft; 17, adductor muscle of valves; 18, median group of gland cells of pyriform organ; 19, lateral group of gland cells of pyriform organ; 20, cavity; 21, nervous strands; 22, anus.

becoming perpendicular to the surface.   This rotation is common in ctenostomes and cheilostomes but appears wanting in cyclostomes where the polypide forms at right angles to the surface.

The primary zooid, also called *ancestrula*, is now complete, consisting of the primary cystid or wall retained from that of the larva and the primary polypide regenerated from the larval ectoderm.   A single zooid arises from the metamorphosed larva except in *Membranipora* and the very closely related, possibly identical, *Acanthodesia* (Marcus, 1938a) where twin zooids are produced (Fig. 134*G, H*).   One or two up to five or six days usually elapse between attachment and the emergence of the completed polypide.

The cystid of the cheilostome ancestrula has received much attention, notably from Waters (1924, 1925, 1926).   It is usually a rounded or oval chamber that may resemble the ordinary autozooids of the species but often differs from them in shape and spination, as well as in the lack of avicularia, also often areoles and pseudopores.   In cheilostomes it very often is provided with a circle of spines around the orifice or frontal membrane when present and is then known as a *tata* ancestrula (Fig. 135*A, B*) because a *Membranipora* ancestrula of this type was mistaken by Van Beneden (1850) for an adult of a new genus that he named *Tata;* this name was then adopted by Smitt (1868) for these spiny ancestrulae. Harmer (1902) tabulated the then known tata ancestrulae, finding the number of spines to range from 5 to 15, being mostly 7 to 10.   The number of spines of the tata is usually greater than that of the ordinary zooids of the species when these are spiny; thus in a *Scrupocellaria* species studied by Lutaud (1953a) the tata has 9 spines, arranged in groups of 6 and 3 (Fig. 135*C, D*), whereas the ordinary zoecium retains only the group of 6, one of which becomes the scutum (Fig. 135*D*).   The same fact of greater spination of the tata than of the ordinary zoecia also appears in *Schizoporella* (Waters, 1924; Fig. 135*A, B*).   The ancestrula is generally believed by ectoproctologists to be of actual ancestral significance, but the nature of this significance is unclear.   Silén (1942a) interprets the spines of the tata as kenozooids and deduces that the original cheilostome colony consisted of a circle of zooids, hence later of a circle of branches (Fig. 141*B*).   However, Harmer (1902) already pointed out that the tata appears limited to cheilostomes of the flustrine type (i.e., with a large uncalcified frontal membrane) and is wanting in many cheilostomes. Lutaud (1953b) studied the calcification of the tata of *Scrupocellaria* and reported that the manner of formation and calcification of the spines indicates that they are not kenozooids.

The ancestrula quickly secretes a cuticle, and in calcareous species calcification very soon sets in by the deposition of minute crystals beneath the cuticle.   Details of the directions of spread of the calcification in the

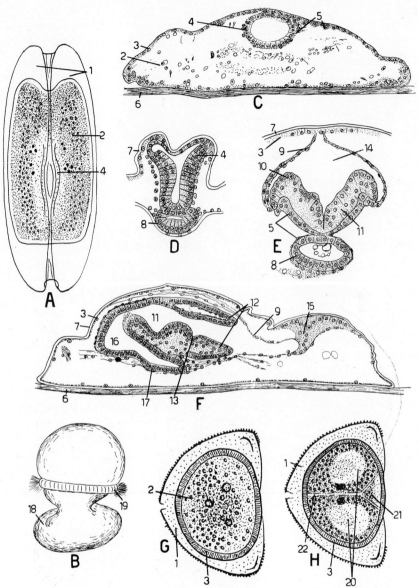

Fig. 134.—Embryology (concluded). *A*, *Flustrellidra hispida*, immediately after attachment, with opened valves (*after Prouho*, 1890). *B*, *Alcyonidium polyoum* in process of everting the adhesive sac. *C*, section through newly attached *Alcyonidium polyoum*, with primordium of the polypide. *D–F*, further development of the polypide. (*B–F*, *after Zschiesche*, 1909.) *G*, newly attached larva of *Membranipora*. *H*, later stage of *G*, twin zooids arising. (*G*, *H*, *after O'Donoghue*, 1927.) 1, bivalved shell; 2, disintegrating interior of larva; 3, surviving ectoderm of larva; 4, ectodermal vesicle (primordium of polypide); 5, peritoneum; 6, substrate; 7, cuticle; 8, second vesicle; 9, tentacle sheath; 10, beginning of tentacles; 11, pharynx; 12, tentacles; 13, ectodermal invagination to form ganglion; 14, vestibule; 15, site of future orifice; 16, stomach; 17, intestine; 18, everted adhesive sac; 19, ciliary girdle; 20, twin zooids; 21, beginning of third zooid; 22, wall between twin zooids.

355

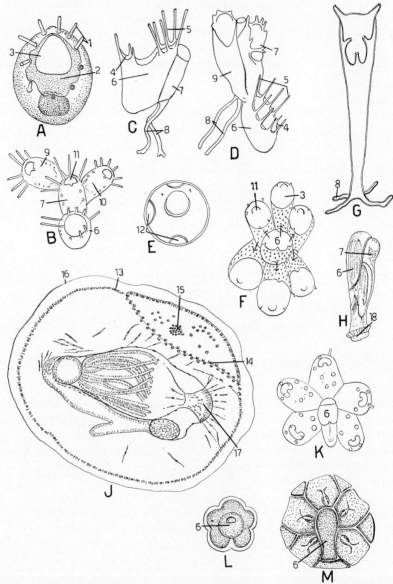

FIG. 135.—Colony formation. A, tata of *Schizoporella* (*after Harmer*, 1902). B, tata.
and first zooids of *Schizoporella* colony (*after Waters*, 1924). C, tata and first zooid with
rhizoids of *Scrupocellaria*. D, later stage of *Scrupocellaria*. (C, D, after Lutaud, 1953a.)
E, ancestrula of *Electra pilosa* partitioning off first zooids. F, young colony of *Electra
pilosa* with six zooids besides the ancestrula; arrows show origin of zooids. (E, F, after
Waters, 1924.) G, ancestrula of *Bugula* (*after Calvet*, 1900). H, ancestrula of *Bugula*
cutting off first zooid (*after Mawatari*, 1951). J, ancestrula of *Alcyonidium mytili* cutting
off first cystid (*after Zschiesche*, 1909). K, ancestrula of *Porella* with five zooids (*after
Waters*, 1925). L, ancestrula of *Smittina* with five protuberances to form zooids. M,

ancestrula of *Scrupocellaria* were given by Lutaud (1953b) and shown to differ greatly from the spread of calcification of the ordinary zoecia. Further, in the latter the frontal wall calcifies in two layers (olocyst, pleurocyst), whereas the ancestrula has but a single layer of calcification. Hence the calcification of the ancestrula appears in general more primitive than that of the ordinary zooids.

10. Colony Formation.—In the formation of a colony, the ancestrula buds off one to several zooids, each of these buds off one or more zooids in turn, these again bud, and by a continuation of these processes the colony expands and increases in number of zooids. Budding occurs by formation of a partition of body wall cutting off part of the parent cystid (Fig. 135*E*, *J*), preceded or not by a protrusion. The resulting chamber is a cystid and proceeds to produce a polypide in exactly the same way as the ancestrula produced its polypide, that is, by the invagination of an ectodermal thickening accompanied by peritoneum, and the subsequent differentiation of this invagination as already described. Main studies of budding in gymnolaemates are those of Seeliger (1890), Davenport (1891), Ladewig (1900), Römer (1906), Herwig (1913), Borg (1923, 1926a), and Soule (1954). These studies are in good agreement as to the main facts, but there is some divergence of opinion as to the origin of the peritoneum; the last four authors definitely find that the peritoneum is of epidermal origin in whole or in part.

The budding pattern of a colony of gymnolaemates is characteristic for each species and is already indicated by the budding pattern of the ancestrula. The latter may give off one bud that in turn buds in the same direction (Fig. 135*B*), and by continuing budding in the one direction a colony of monoserial, biserial, or multiserial branches results. Often the cheilostome ancestrula puts out three zooids on the same side, a median and two lateral (Waters, 1924), and these may continue budding in the same direction; or the ancestrula and the first two lateral buds may then bud on the opposite side (Fig. 135*F*), and the small rounded colony thus produced will by further budding in all directions produce a circular colony. An ancestrula of *Porella* giving rise to five zooids is shown in Fig. 135*K*. Similarly, the ancestrula of *Smittina* at once puts out five lobes, each of which becomes a zooid (Stach, 1938a; Fig. 135*L*); the next generation of zooids arises between the outer ends of the first five (Fig. 135*M*); and continued budding on this pattern results in a circular colony, with the ancestrula at the center. Similarly, the tata ancestrula of the Reteporidae gives off five or six buds in a circle around itself (Harmer,

later stage of *L*, first five zooids formed, second circle of five beginning. (*L*, *M*, *after Stach*, 1938a.) 1, spines; 2, cryptocyst; 3, frontal membrane; 4, group of three spines; 5, group of six spines; 6, ancestrula; 7, first zooid; 8, rhizoids; 9, second zooid; 10, third zooid; 11, operculum; 12, incipient zooids; 13, epidermis; 14, partition; 15, primordium of polypide; 16, cuticle; 17, site of future orifice; 18, remains of adhesive sac.

1934; Hass, 1948); all of these bud, giving another circle of zooids, and in this manner the colony expands into a general circular form with the ancestrula at the center. The ancestrula of *Labiostomella* is a rounded cystid without polypide that puts out a circle of 10 to 15 zooids, each of which originates an erect branch (Silén, 1942a; Fig. 141*A*, *B*). The fan-like budding from the twin ancestrulae of *Membranipora* is shown in Fig. 136*A*; later lateral zooids begin to bud backward, with eventual expansion of the colony in all directions. Expansion is caused by the production of two or more offspring by many of the zooids. In *Bugula* and some other forms with tata ancestrulae the first zooids of the colony may also have the tata morphology (Marcus, 1938a).

Cheilostome colonies soon develop avicularia, generally wanting from the ancestrula. An avicularium develops similarly to an autozooid for a time (Calvet, 1900; Ladewig, 1900), then diverges. It begins as a body-wall protuberance (Fig. 136*B*), of which the distal epidermis proliferates a vesicle into the interior; this vesicle becomes clothed with mesenchyme cells (Fig. 136*C*) and develops no further except for putting out a tuft of bristles, hence is the main part of the polypide of the avicularium. There is added to it a cell mass supposedly representing the ganglion, here apparently formed of mesenchyme cells. Further changes concern chiefly the differentiation of muscles from the mesenchyme (Fig. 136*D*, *E*) and the formation of mandible and rostrum. The latter structures begin as a horseshoe-shaped thickening of the distal epidermis (Fig. 136*D*, *E*) that secretes a very heavy cuticle and then subdivides into mandible and rostrum. Vibracula, which may be present on the ancestrula as in *Scrupocellaria* (Lutaud, 1953a), also begin as little body-wall protrusions.

Colony formation in cyclostomes was exhaustively studied by Borg (1926a). Here the ancestrula is a hemispherical cystid that quickly calcifies with pseudopores and puts out the first zoecium as an upright cylindrical protrusion (Fig. 136*G*). This lengthens and in the simplest cyclostome family, the Crisiidae, forms the second zooid by cutting off a small area by way of a calcareous partition (Fig. 136*H*). The second zooid lengthens and produces the third zooid by again secreting a cal-careous partition that cuts off a small portion of itself (Fig. 136*J*); and a continuation of the same process gives rise to a branching colony (Fig. 108*D*). The joints characteristic of the Crisiidae arise by absorption of the calcareous deposition and thickening of the cuticle. In more compli-cated types of cyclostome colonies, the colony expands distally by the simultaneous formation of a number of partitions cutting off new zooids. There is therefore present a peripheral growing zone, termed by Borg (unnecessarily) the *common bud*. This growing zone is usually terminal in the branches of the colony, which hence grow in a definite direction and expand by the increasing number of partitions that appear in the growing

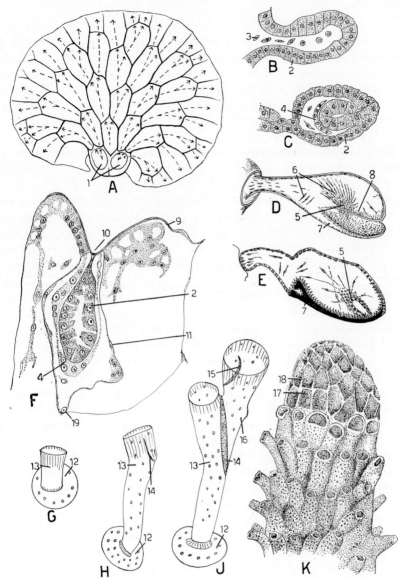

Fig. 136.—Colony formation (continued). *A*, young colony of *Membranipora villosa*, showing method of expansion (*after O'Donoghue*, 1927). *B*, *C*, young stages in formation of an avicularium (*after Ladewig*, 1900). *D*, *E*, later stages of avicularium formation (*after Calvet*, 1900). *F*, polypide formation in cyclostomes. *G*, *H*, *J*, three stages of budding from the ancestrula in the cyclostome *Crisia*. (*F–J*, *after Borg*, 1926a.) *K*, branch of higher cyclostome (*Pustulipora*) showing terminal growing zone with partitions for new zooids (*after Busk*, 1886). 1, twin ancestrulae; 2, epidermis; 3, mesenchyme; 4, peritoneum; 5, polypide; 6, muscle fibers; 7, mandible; 8, rostrum; 9, cuticle; 10, vestibule; 11, membranous sac; 12, ancestrula; 13, calcareous cylinder of first zoecium; 14, partition for second zoecium; 15, partition for third zoecium; 16, second zoecium; 17, growing zone with partitions for new zooids; 18, wall of zooid; 19, attachment of membranous sac to zooid wall.

zone (Fig. 136*K*).   The zone may, however, encircle the young colony that thus expands in a circular manner as in the Lichenoporidae.   In some genera the growing zone occupies a central position (Fig. 108*E*) in the branches and the new zooids form centrally, pushing the older ones peripherally, thus establishing fascicles.   Apparently, fascicles may also arise by calcification of intervening areas of zooids, with resulting death of the polypides.

Borg (1926a) also described the formation of the polypide in cyclostomes; this in general follows but differs in some details from the account given above for cheilostomes.   The polypide begins as in other gymnolaemates as a localized proliferation of body-wall epidermis; this invaginates as a vesicle that carries with it peritoneal cells, some of epidermal origin.   Other inwardly migrating epidermal and peritoneal cells combine to form the membranous sac, wanting in other ectoprocts, that encloses the developing polypide (Fig. 136*F*).   The epidermal vesicle remains connected with the body-wall cuticle and eventually pulls this inward to establish the vestibule (Fig. 136*F*).   As in other gymnolaemates, the vesicle constricts in two and the distal one becomes the tentacle sheath and pharynx whereas the proximal one furnishes the epithelium of the remainder of the digestive tract.   The ganglion originates as in cheilostomes (Fig. 134*F*), and muscles come from mesenchyme cells. As in cheilostomes, the tentacles originate as outgrowths of the pharyngeal epithelium at the base of the tentacle sheath, and later peritoneum invades these outgrowths.   The arrangement of the tentacles is distinctly bilateral at first and becomes circular later by appearance of tentacles at the anal end of the lophophore.   The tentacular coelomic lumina and the ring coelom are formed by the drawing apart of peritoneal cells.   In cyclostomes the tentacles at the time of their formation are directed toward the future orifice, and hence the rotation characteristic of other gymnolaemates is here wanting.   As the tentacles of the latter point at first toward the frontal membrane, Borg deduces that this membrane is homologous with the terminal membrane of cyclostomes.

Colony formation in carnose ctenostomes was especially studied by Soule (1953) in *Pherusella brevituba*.   Here the ancestrula, retaining for some time the bivalved shell of the cyphonautes and developing a perfect polypide, early cuts off at its periphery an outer circle of cystids with parietal muscles and an inner circle of cystids without muscles (Fig. 137*A*, *B*); the former eventually degenerate.   The ancestrula then buds off zooids laterally, first on one side, then on the other (Fig. 137*B*), and after about six zooids have filled up the central part of the colony, the peripheral cystids of the inner circle develop polypides, and thereafter the colony expands at the periphery in a circular manner.   Even more deviation from zooid formation in cheilostomes is seen in the stoloniferous

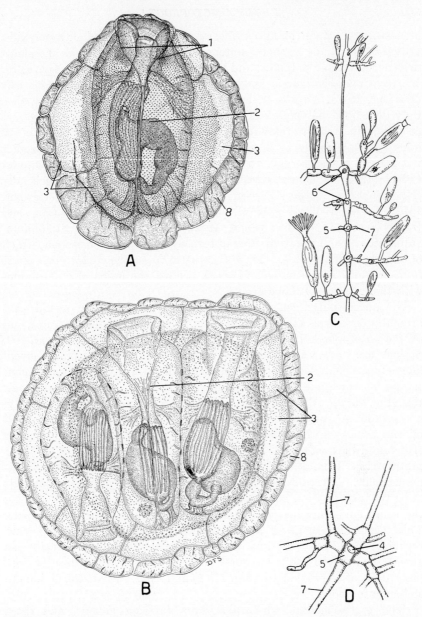

Fig. 137.—Colony formation (continued). *A*, ancestrula of *Pherusella*, carnose ctenostome, with polypide. *B*, later stage of *Pherusella*, with two additional zooids budded by ancestrula. (*A, B, drawings courtesy John and Dorothy Soule.*) *C*, beginning colony of stoloniferous ctenostome *Farrella*, produced by stolons from the ancestrula (*after Marcus, 1926b*). *D*, colony of *Mimosella* started by stolons from the ancestrula (*after Harmer, 1915*). 1, shells of cyphonautes; 2, polypide of ancestrula; 3, precociously formed cystids of future zooids; 4, pore plate of stem; 5, ancestrula; 6, pore plates where zooids have fallen off; 7, rhizoids; 8, outer circle of aborted cystids; these never form polypides.

ctenostomes. Here the ancestrula may or may not produce a polypide. Calvet (1900) made a general statement that the stoloniferous ancestrula does not develop a polypide, and this was confirmed by Silén (1942a) for *Walkeria* and *Vesicularia* and also appears to be the case in *Mimosella* (Harmer, 1915). However, an ancestrula of *Amathia lendigera* with a fully developed polypide is illustrated by Barrois (1877). In any case colony formation in stoloniferous ctenostomes differs from that of all other gymnolaemates in that the ancestrula does not bud off autozooids but instead gives rise only to stolons and rhizoids. This was stated by Calvet (1900) as generally true for the group and has been specifically established for *Farrella* (Marcus, 1926b; Fig. 137*C*), *Mimosella* (Harmer, 1915; Marcus, 1937b; Fig. 137*D*), *Zoobotryon* (Zirpolo, 1922b, 1923a), and *Walkeria* and *Vesicularia* (Silén, 1942a). In fact, in the Stolonifera, autozooids never arise from other autozooids but only from stolons, which of course are kenozooids. These facts seem to set the ctenostomes apart from other gymnolaemates and speak against the union of ctenostomes with cheilostomes into one group.

The ancestrula, then, of the Stolonifera is a rounded cystid that attaches by rhizoids and gives off one or more stolons that ramify and bud off the autozooids after varying patterns illustrated in Figs. 99 and 100. Stolons are body-wall protrusions composed peripherally of body-wall layers (cuticle, epidermis, peritoneum) and filled with a watery fluid containing mesenchyme, funicular cords, and the like. They grow at their tips (Fig. 138*A*), where the cells are more condensed, stain more deeply, and present an appearance of activity with mitotic figures. Stolons bud off the zooids of the stoloniferous colony after the following manner (Brien and Huysmans, 1937; Soule, 1954). The stolon puts out a slight protuberance (Fig. 138*A*) preceded by a localized proliferation of epidermal cells. The protuberance continues to elongate; the epidermal cells at its tip take on a low columnar form and proliferate rapidly, producing the usual epidermal ingrowth that is the primordium of the polypide. This ingrowth becomes a hollow vesicle around which a peritoneum organizes (Fig. 138*B*, *C*) and proceeds to develop into a polypide, as already described for other groups. Sooner or later a partition or pore plate arises at the zooid base (Fig. 113*A*) and similar partitions divide the stolons into nodes.

The gymnolaemate ancestrula never develops gonads, and these appear only after the colony has grown for some time by asexual methods. The differentiation of germ cells from the distal body wall of the zooid bud was already described (page 343).

The following data illustrate the rate of colony growth from the ancestrula under laboratory conditions. A diagram in Marcus (1926b) indicates the production of over 900 zooids by *Electra pilosa* in 10 weeks. *Membranipora villosa* produced about 20 zooids in 2 weeks (O'Donoghue, 1927). *Bugula neritina* had 6 to 8 zooids in 1 week, 50 in 3 weeks, about 600 in 1 month, and engaged in sexual reproduction at an age of 5 to 7 weeks (Mawatari, 1951). Similar data were given by Grave (1930) for *Bugula flabellata* in which the ancestrula buds a zooid about 4 days after attachment and the colony increases to 8 zooids in a week, 20 in 10 days, 100 to 170 in 2 weeks, and thousands in a month, reproducing sexually at that time. *Watersipora cucullata* propagated 4 to 6 zooids in 3 days, 20 in a week, 200 in a month, and reproduced sexually at a colony age of 4 or 5 weeks (Mawatari, 1952a). Friedl (1925) studied the settling and growth of colonies on boards suspended in the Adriatic off Rovogno. Growth occurred only from May through October. The best data were obtained on *Schizoporella sanguinea*, in which colonies started in June attained 25 zooids in 1 month, 400 to 500 in 2 months, and 30,000 in 5 months. Osburn (1944) recorded production of at least 10,000 zooids in 21 days by *Membranipora crustulenta* in Chesapeake Bay.

11. Degeneration and Regeneration.—An outstanding feature of gymnolaemate colonies is the constant process of degeneration and regeneration of polypides. Examination of colonies shows the presence in many of the zooids of a rounded brown mass termed the *brown body*. It was already known to some of the older observers (Nitsche, 1871; Joliet, 1877) that the brown body is a degenerated polypide. Such degeneration was repeatedly described in cheilostomes (Römer, 1906; Gerwerzhagen, 1913; Rey, 1927a). In general, the polypide retracts strongly, the tentacle sheath ruptures and collapses, muscles fragment, tentacles and foregut disintegrate, and the rest of the digestive tract, already of a reddish-brown color, balls up into a brown mass, usually enclosed in a membrane and suspended from the cystid walls by mesenchymal strands (Fig. 138*D*, *E*). Much of the disintegrating tissue is ingested by phagocytic mesenchymal or coelomic cells. In some species the brown body persists in the posterior part of the cystid; as many as three or four may accumulate there, testifying to repeated degeneration of the polypide of the same cystid. In other cheilostomes and some ctenostomes, the brown body is taken into the digestive tract of the regenerated polypide; the stomach caecum comes in contact with the brown body, cups around it (Fig. 138*E*), and closes together over it. The brown body may undergo some disintegration in the digestive tract and is eventually voided through the anus. In the formation of brown bodies in cyclostomes (Borg, 1923), the polypide retracts as fully as possible, the lophophoral retractors loosen and fall to pieces, the vestibule degenerates, and the fixator ligaments detach, with resulting collapse and degeneration

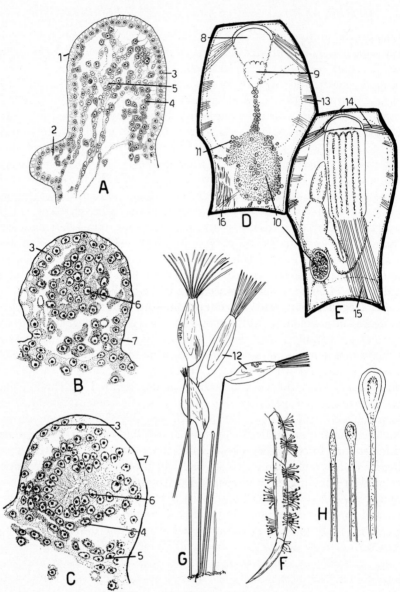

Fig. 138.—Colony formation (concluded), degeneration, regeneration. *A*, stolon end of *Bowerbankia*, showing histology. *B*, beginning stage zooid bud on stolon of *Bowerbankia*. *C*, later stage of zooid formation. (*A–C, after Brien and Huysmans*, 1937.) *D*, zooid of *Electra pilosa* with polypide degenerated to brown body and new polypide forming. *E*, *Electra pilosa*, brown body being taken in by stomach of new polypide. (*D, E, after Marcus*, 1926b.) *F*, colony of *Triticella* growing on crustacean leg. *G*, enlarged view of a few zooids of *Triticella*, showing long stalks. *H*, three stages in regeneration of a zooid from the stalk top. (*F–H, after Sars*, 1874.) 1, stolon tip; 2, beginning bud of zooid; 3, epidermis; 4, peritoneum; 5, mesenchyme; 6, epidermal proliferation for polypide; 7, cuticle; 8, operculum; 9, primordium of new polypide; 10, brown body; 11, coelomocytes; 12, zooids; 13, parietal muscles; 14, occlusor muscles; 15, retractor lophophore; 16, zoecium.

of the membranous sac. The brown bodies, up to two or three in number, here remain permanently in the cystid, well separated from the regenerated polypide by its membranous sac.

The new polypide regenerates from the distal cystid wall by the same process of polypide formation already described. Its regeneration is totally unrelated to the brown body resulting from the degeneration of the preceding polypide of the same cystid. Bronstein (1938c) showed that experimental destruction or excision of a polypide to prevent the formation of a brown body has no effect on the regeneration of a new polypide in the same cystid. He also proved experimentally that the site of origin of the primordium of the new polypide is not preformed but may be located at any point of the cystid and if the area where the polypide usually originates is cauterized, two polypides may be evoked, one distal and one proximal to the wound, but the former develops first and soon suppresses the latter. Contact of the developing polypide with the cystid wall determines the location of the orifice. The essential cause of the regeneration of a new polypide in a cystid is the absence of the old one whose presence then must exert some inhibitory effect on polypide regeneration.

In the stoloniferous ctenostomes after degeneration to a brown body, the remaining tissues of the polypide detach from the transverse septum at the zooid base and the entire zooid then falls off. This is reported for *Triticella* (Sars, 1874), *Walkeria* and *Bowerbankia* (Levinsen, 1907), *Farrella* (Marcus, 1926b), and *Zoobotryon* (Ries and Schoelsel, 1934) and is presumably general in this group. Usually there is no regeneration of a new polypide from the old transverse septum, although Levinsen (1907) stated that this may occur in *Walkeria* and *Bowerbankia* in actively growing regions. Where regeneration does not occur, the old septum remains visible for some time but eventually disappears. In *Triticella*, where the zooids are erected on long stalks (Fig. 138*G*), the top of the stalk may bud a new zooid when the old one falls off (Fig. 138*H*). Generally, however, loss of zooids in Stolonifera is compensated by the budding of new zooids from the stolons.

Natural senescence, exposure to unfavorable conditions, and sexual reproduction probably cover the various reasons assigned for polypide degeneration. Probably polypides are short-lived under the most favorable conditions. They degenerate in 1 to 2 weeks or at the most 3 to 4 (Rey, 1927a) in laboratory cultures and are very sensitive to unfavorable conditions, regressing rapidly under such circumstances as insufficient oxygen or food, alterations of salinity, presence of chemicals or dyes (Bronstein, 1938c; Ries and Schoelsel, 1934), and lowering of temperature or other changes associated with the onset of winter. Marcus (1926b) gave accumulation of excretory substances in the stomach epithelium as a

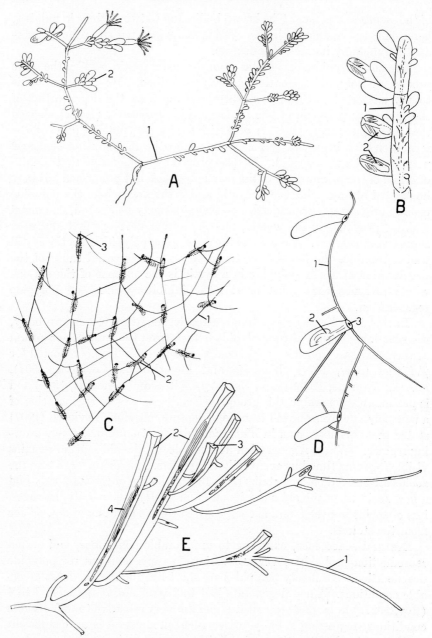

FIG. 139.—Ctenostomes. *A, Zoobotryon pellucidum,* from life, Brazil. *B,* small bit of *A,* enlarged. *C,* colony of *Terebripora,* removed from shell (*after Marcus,* 1938b). *D, Immergentia* (*after Silén,* 1948). *E, Victorella pavida* (*after Braem,* 1951). 1, stolon; 2, zooid; 3, orifice; 4, polypide.

main cause of polypide degeneration; this factor is no doubt operative but appears of less importance than others mentioned.   The onset of sexual reproduction constitutes an important cause of polypide degeneration. Production of eggs and sperm, internal brooding of embryos, development of an embryo in the ovicell are all accompanied or preceded by degeneration of the polypide, perhaps from mere want of space or possibly to furnish nutrition for the embryo.   Borg (1947) points out that in *Electra* old polypides are apparently incapable of producing intertentacular organs; hence prior to the annual spring period of sexual reproduction there is a wholesale degeneration of old polypides into brown bodies and regeneration of new polypides provided with intertentacular organs. Autumnal degeneration of colonies in temperate and colder waters followed by regeneration in spring is a common phenomenon discussed further under ecology.

Because of the processes just described the zooids of a colony are not in uniform condition but are usually more or less zoned.   At the periphery or at the tips of branches is found a growing zone with young active polypides; more proximally the older polypides show signs of degeneration; then follows a zone of cystids with brown bodies and without active polypides; and finally comes an area with active regenerated polypides as known by the presence of a brown body.   This zonation may be repeated two or three times, depending on the capacity of cystids to regenerate polypides.   Apparently polypides may not be regenerated by the same cystid more than three or four times; hence eventually the more basal cystids are empty and dead, except for containing brown bodies in species that do not eject these.   Zonation in *Bugula* colonies during the reproductive season was depicted schematically by Correa (1948).   From branch tips in the basal direction are found, successively: zone of new zooids without ovicells; zone of older zooids with newly formed, still empty ovicells; zone of zooids with degenerating polypides and developing embryos in the ovicells; zone of zooids with degenerated polypides, brown body, and mature larva in the ovicells; zone with empty ovicells (larvae having escaped) and regenerated polypides; and this zonation may be repeated along the branches two or three times until a proximal zone is reached where polypides no longer regenerate.   Stach (1938b) described a similar colony zonation in *Carbasea* belonging to the Flustridae: growing margin with young zooids, zone of reproductive zooids, zone of degenerating and regenerating polypides, and basal zone of kenozooids with attaching rhizoids.

It goes without saying that gymnolaemates have exceptional powers of regeneration, but the minute size of the zooids discourages exact experimentation.   Zirpolo (1922a) for the ctenostome *Zoobotryon* and Bronstein (1939) for membraniporids noted that the speed of wound repair, the rate of growth, and the power of regeneration are greater in the distal parts of colonies than proximally. Similar facts obtain for *Bugula* (Abeloos, 1951) where transverse pieces of the colony from below the growing zone usually do not regenerate but may do so. Some sort of gradient therefore exists in such colonies; Bronstein ascribes this gradient to properties of the coelomic fluid, which is richer in cells and more turbid because of greater protein content in the terminal parts of colonies. However, degenerated basal parts of colonies may grow out new branches as in *Bugula* (Abeloos, 1951), by outgrowth from the old orifice.

In cyclostomes (Harmer, 1891c) a broken zoecium secretes a calcareous diaphragm across the opening, and later a polypide bud can arise beneath this diaphragm, cause its absorption, and effect the completion of the broken zoecium into the regular tubular shape by calcareous deposition. In cheilostomes, however, zooids cut across do not complete themselves but produce a bud. An interesting study of regeneration in *Bugula neritina* was made by Abeloos (1951). This species has biserial branches showing right and left asymmetry. Any zooid cut across will bud out a single file of zooids having the same type of asymmetry as itself, but eventually two buds are produced, one of which develops the other type of asymmetry, and the biserial arrangement is thus resumed. The same result is obtained if one of the two terminal buds of a branch is removed; the other buds out a single zooid having the same asymmetry as itself; then two buds arise of opposite symmetry. Hence the two files of zooids seem to exert some inhibitory action on each other. Rectangular pieces of the incrusting *Membranipora* colony put out a growing zone from their distal edge (not any other edge) that divides up into cystids in which polypides appear; hence such pieces retain the polarization they had when part of the whole (Bronstein, 1938b).

There is great interchangeability between various zooid types. The formation of buds from stolons in stoloniferous ctenostomes may be regarded as a transformation of kenozooids into autozooids. In *Bugula* a stolon or branch may grow out of the orifice of an old zooid and give off new zooids (Abeloos, 1951; Aymes, 1956). The first zooids of regenerated branches of *Bugula* may resemble the tata ancestrula (Marcus, 1938a). Deteriorating laboratory cultures that have ceased normal growth may put out long stolons capable of budding zooids if conditions improve (*Bugula*, Aymes, 1956; *Zoobotryon*, Ries and Schoelsel, 1934). In *Zoobotryon* the surviving living material in old stolons migrates into new ones. Isolated fragments of *Bugula* rhizoids may emit stolons that bud, and isolated pieces of branches may develop stolons of attachment (Aymes, 1956). In cyclostomes (Harmer, 1891c) rhizoids are always capable of giving rise to stems that will bud out zooids and old zooids may send out a rhizoid that will originate a branch. It may be assumed that any gymnolaemate or piece of a gymnolaemate can put out stolons that, if conditions permit, can give rise to zooids and regenerate a colony. This, rather than replacement of lost parts, appears the typical mode of regeneration in the group.

Autozooids may be replaced by avicularia, and vice versa (Levinsen, 1907; Buchner, 1918). Entire zooids, necessarily of smaller size, may regenerate inside an old zoecium, utilizing the same orifice or opesium (Levinsen, 1907; Buchner, 1918). A new avicularium may regenerate inside an old one, and this may be repeated with the production of three avicularia inside each other (Levinsen, 1907). Whole zooids may be intercalated among zooids already present.

Seasonal cycles involving degeneration and regeneration of colonies are discussed under ecology.

12. Systematic Survey: Order Ctenostomata.—A simple classification, followed by Bassler (1953), divides the Gymnolaemata into three living and two extinct orders. Two of the living orders, Ctenostomata and Cheilostomata, are more closely related to each other than to the third living order and may eventually be reduced to suborders of one order (page 285; Marcus, 1938a; Silén, 1942a).

The ctenostomes are gymnolaemates with a simple, flexible, uncalcified zoecium composed of chitinous cuticle. The orifice lacks a closing apparatus, but the diaphragm usually bears a pleated collar which when folded blocks the vestibule. Heterozooids other than kenozooids in the form of stolons and rhizoids are lacking. The eggs are shed to the exterior or are brooded inside the ordinary zooids or while attached to their outer surface. It is not established that the simplicity of the ctenostomes is primitive. The group is often divided into four suborders, but Silén (1942a) and Soule (1954) have given grounds for reducing these to two, Stolonifera and Carnosa.

The stoloniferous colony consists of separate vaselike zooids springing from branching stolons divided up into internodes and separated from the zooid bases by transverse septa (Fig. 113A, C). The ancestrula originates the colony by putting out stolons that bud off the zooids. A distinctive feature of zooid development is the order of appearance of the musculature: vestibular and diaphragmatic dilators, lophophoral retractors, parietal muscles (Soule, 1954, 1957). The zooids may be borne singly or in pairs or in clusters (Fig. 99C–E). The orifice is terminal and often quadrangular from the pull of the four sets of dilator muscles.

Nolella (= *Cylindroecium*, family Nolellidae) is distinguished by the long, tubular zoecia that often incorporate foreign bodies (Fig. 104B) and are set directly upon a creeping stolon. Soule (1957) now places in the Nolellidae the genus *Victorella*, represented by the practically cosmopolitan species *Victorella pavida* (Fig. 139E). This species was discovered by Saville Kent (1870) on docks in the Thames River at London and has since been taken at numerous brackish localities along north European shores, also in the Black and Aegean Seas, Egypt, Japan, Australia, Chesapeake Bay (Osburn, 1944), Salton Sea, California (Soule, 1957), Brazil, and Uruguay (Brattström, 1954). According to Soule (1957), *Tanganella mülleri* (Fig. 140*G*), of which the brooding habits (Fig. 125*C*, *D*) were reported by Braem (1951), is identical with *Victorella pavida*. The indications are that *Tanganella symbiotica*, Lake Tanganyika, Africa (Rousselet, 1907), permeating fresh-water sponges but also found on stones and shells, is nothing but *V. pavida*. The relation of *V. pavida* to salinity is discussed later (page 406).

The stoloniferous family Vesiculariidae is characterized by the presence of a gizzard (page 310); here belong *Vesicularia* with zooids borne singly along the stolons (Fig. 99*C*); *Amathia* with double files of zooids spirally curved (Fig. 100*E*); *Bowerbankia* with clusters of zooids (Fig. 99*D*) and highly developed gizzard (Fig. 116*A*, *B*); *Cryptopolyzoon* with gizzard armature limited to two grinding plates (Fig. 115*F*); and *Zoobotryon* with irregularly arranged zooids on loosely branching erect colonies. *Zoobotryon pellucidum* (Fig. 139*A*, *B*) is one of the most common ectoprocts in warmer waters, forming conspicuous masses of loose branches resembling filamentous seaweeds. The Walkeriidae differ from the preceding family mainly in the absence of a vesicularian type of gizzard; in *Walkeria* (erroneously *Valkeria*) the zooids are clustered, and in *Aeverrillia* they occur in pairs (Fig. 99*E*) and are provided with an aberrant type of gizzard (Fig. 115*E*). In *Mimosella* (family Mimosellidae) the zooids, occurring singly or in pairs, are mounted on one to four very short internodes on which they are movable by way of a muscle arrangement in their base (page 398). The Buskiidae contain the single genus *Buskia*, in which the zooids are proximally adherent by lateral spinelike projections and are provided with a gizzard. *Buskia nitens* (Fig. 104*D*) is widely distributed, usually found growing on other ectoprocts or on hydroids. The family Triticellidae includes *Triticella*, epizoic on crustaceans, with zooids mounted on long stalks (Fig. 138*F*, *G*), and *Farrella* with aperture laterally elongated and altered into two chitinous lips (Fig. 104*E*).

The three families Terebriporidae, Penetrantiidae, and Immergentiidae live in the interior of live and dead shells of bivalves, snails, and barnacles, in cavities excavated by themselves (Marcus, 1938b; Silén, 1946, 1948, 1956; Soule, 1950a, b). Colonies of these families consist of slender stolons anastomosed into a network (except in the terebriporid genus *Spathipora*) that permeates the substance of the shells and bears the zooids singly at intervals (Fig. 139*C*). Holes on the outer surface of the shells reveal the presence of these colonies. The zooids are attached

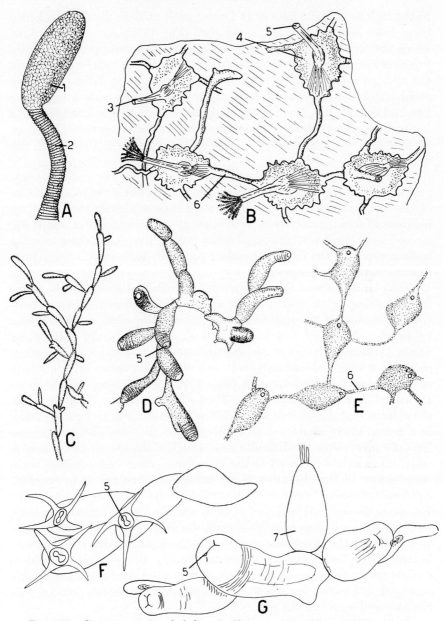

FIG. 140.—Ctenostomes (concluded). A, *Clavopora* (after Osburn, 1953). B, *Arachnoidea*, growing on a stone (after Rousselet, 1907). C, *Paludicella articulata* (after Davenport, 1891). D, *Sundanella sibogae* (after Harmer, 1915). E, *Arachnidium* (after Hincks, 1880). F, *Echinella* (after Korotneff, 1901). G, young colony of *Tanganella mülleri* (after Braem, 1951). 1, mass of autozooids; 2, stalk of rings of kenozooids; 3, distal erect part of zooid; 4, basal adherent expansion; 5, orifice; 6, tubular base of zooid; 7, ancestrula.

to the stolons at their sides or in *Immergentia* at their distal ends, hence hang down into the cavities in the shell (Fig. 139*C, D*). A gizzard, of which the structure has not been described, is generally present. *Penetrantia* is remarkable in that the zooid is incased in two cuticles and broods the embryo between these (Fig. 125*G*). According to Silén (1948) the zooid has two cuticles because it arises from two successive buds; the first bud degenerates, leaving its cuticle intact, and a second bud develops in the same site, producing the internal cuticle; the latter forms a sort of lid that can be closed down, shutting off the zooid from the hole to the exterior.

The carnose ctenostomes form typically gelatinous or leathery compact colonies of contiguous boxlike zooids, but some occur as loose colonies of vaselike zooids in single file. The ancestrula originates the colony by budding off zooids successively as in other gymnolaemates (Fig. 137*A, B*). According to the investigations of Soule (1953), the musculature in zooid buds appears in the following order: parietals, lophophoral retractors, dilators of the distal region.

The carnose type of colony construction with contiguous zooids, forming incrusting or upright growths and having subterminal, often protruding, orifices is exemplified by the genera *Alcyonidium, Flustrellidra* (= *Flustrella*), and *Pherusella* (= *Pherusa*), each in a family of the same name. Common species of *Alcyonidium* are *polyoum* and *mytili*, growing on shells, stones, and seaweeds and much used in European investigations of embryology; and *gelatinosum* (Fig. 101*C, D*), forming upright gelatinous cylinders or incrustations. Most modern ectoproctologists are of the opinion that *A. polyoum* and *mytili* are identical, but Le Brozec (1955) in a recent study of *Alcyonidium* insists that they are distinct species. This of course raises the difficulty as to which of the two species is meant when these names are used in the literature. *Flustrellidra* differs from *Alcyonidium* in the alteration of the orifice into two lips as in *Farrella*. *F. hispida*, forming brown spiny incrustations on seaweeds, is a common European species of which Hincks (1880) remarks: "In the size and beauty of its polypides it is unequalled among the Polyzoa." *Pherusella* is distinguished by the prominent multiporous pore plates with thick cuticularized rims (Soule, 1951). *Clavopora* (family Clavoporidae) forms a curious colony composed of a rounded or oval mass of crowded autozooids mounted and movable on a stalk of muscular kenozooids arranged in rings around a central tubular cavity (Fig. 140*A*).

The two remaining carnose families, Paludicellidae and Arachnidiidae, include a number of gymnolaemates that inhabit fresh or brackish water. They are easily distinguished from the ordinary fresh-water ectoprocts (phylactolaemates) by the circular shape of the lophophore. These forms lack the typical carnose structure, growing as files of tubular zooids,

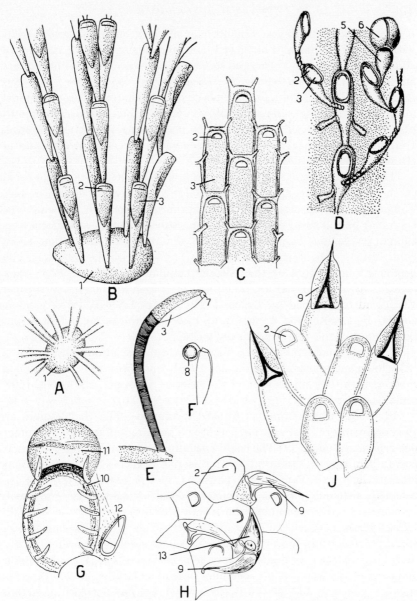

FIG. 141.—Anascan cheilostomes. *A*, ancestrula of *Labiostomella*, giving off a circle of zooids. *B*, scheme of the *Labiostomella* colony. (*A*, *B*, *after Silén*, 1942a.) *C*, *Membranipora membranacea* (*after Hincks*, 1880). *D*, *Scruparia* (*after Marcus*, 1940). *E*, *Aetea anguina*, zoecium proximally ringed. *F*, *Aetea* with external embryo sac. (*E*, *F*, *after Osburn*, 1912a.) *G*, *Callopora* (*after Osburn*, 1950). *H*, *Onychocella*, with mandible of onychocellarium winged on one side (*after Jullien*, 1881). *J*, *Smittipora*, mandible winged on both sides (*after Smitt*, 1872). 1, ancestrula; 2, operculum; 3, frontal membrane; 4, spine; 5, gonozooid; 6, two-valved ovicell; 7, orifice; 8, embryo sac; 9, mandible of onychocellarium; 10, autozooid; 11, ovicell; 12, avicularium; 13, cystid of opened onychocellarium.

branching at right angles (cruciform mode of growth, Rousselet, 1907) with terminal orifice and narrowed basal region suggesting a stolon; true stolons may, however, occur, and some genera are provided with a gizzard. In the Paludicellidae belong *Paludicella articulata* (Davenport, 1891; Rogick, 1935; Fig. 140*C*), probably cosmopolitan in fresh water in temperate climates, and *Pottsiella erecta* (Potts, 1884; Braem, 1940b), found in the eastern United States and sometimes permeating fresh-water sponges. Here possibly belongs *Bulbella abscondita* with interesting brooding habits (Braem, 1951; Fig. 125*B*).

The Arachnidiidae mostly form adherent networks with single zooids at the nodes of the net. In *Arachnoidea*, dredged on stones in Lake Tanganyika (Rousselet, 1907), the zooid is regionated into an erect columnar part, a basal toothed expansion adherent to the stone, and basal tubular extensions resembling stolons that connect with other zooids (Fig. 140*B*). In the marine genus *Arachnidium* also the zooids are connected into a network by their slender tubular bases (Fig. 140*E*). *Sundanella sibogae*, also marine, taken by the *Siboga* in Indonesia (Harmer, 1915) and redescribed by Braem (1939), forms typical files of creeping zooids (Fig. 140*D*) and broods in an internal embryo sac. It has since been found in the West Indian region.

The systematic position of the fresh-water genera *Hislopia*, India, with incipient gizzard (Annandale, 1916), and *Echinella*, Lake Baikal, Siberia, with four spines around the orifice (Korotneff, 1901; Fig. 140*F*) remains uncertain.

13. Order Cheilostomata : Suborder Anasca.—The cheilostomes are the dominant group of existing ectoprocts and are represented by numerous genera and species. The colony usually consists of boxlike contiguous zooids arranged in uniserial to multiserial branches or in continuous incrustations or as lamellate expansions, and is generally more or less calcified although sometimes membranous. Cheilostomes are easily recognized by the operculum (sometimes wanting) covering the ventrally located orifice, which may be extended by an orificial collar ("peristome"), resulting in a permanently open secondary orifice. Polymorphism reaches its highest expression in cheilostomes which, besides gonozooids and kenozooids, also may bear avicularia or vibracula. The eggs are generally brooded in ovicells which are not regarded as heterozooids but are usually outgrowths of the autozooids. The group is divisible into the Anasca without, and the Ascophora with, an ascus or compensatory sac operative in the extension and withdrawal of the polypide. In the following account only the more important families are mentioned.

The Anasca have a membranous ventral wall (frontal membrane) either exposed or covered over by a calcareous shield. The parietal muscles are attached to the frontal membrane and by their contraction pull the membrane in, thus bringing about the extrusion of the polypide. It is usual to classify the Anasca into seven divisions, following Harmer (1926) and Silén (1941).

The two lower divisions are completely uncalcified with a large oval frontal membrane ("aperture field") and without avicularia, vibracula, spines, or ovicells (except *Scruparia*). The general aspect is ctenostomatous, and two genera (*Aetea, Scruparia*) even have a circlet of little teeth apparently representing the pleated collar; but a typical operculum is present. The curious genus *Aetea* is the sole member of the division Inovicellata. The very simple colony consists of a succession of single zooids (Fig. 99*A*), each regionated into an adherent basal expansion and an erect tube distally expanded (Fig. 99*B*). The colony thus simulates a stoloniferous ctenostome. The embryo is brooded in an embryo sac that, according to Osburn (1912a) and Waters (1913), protrudes to the exterior through the orifice (Fig. 141*F*); but Hastings (1943) finds it attached to the frontal membrane below the orifice. The species *A. anguina* with ringed tubular region (Fig. 141*E*) is widely spread along the shores of warm and temperate regions. The second division, Scrupariina, comprises plantlike colonies with uniserial or biserial branches in which the tubular zooid base often springs from the frontal surface of the preceding zooid. *Scruparia* has two-valved ovicells that are borne on dwarf zooids (Fig. 141*D*). Bassler (1953) places here the curious genus *Labiostomella* regarded by Silén (1942a, 1944c) as a very primitive cheilostome, for which he created a new division Protocheilostomata. *Labiostomella* lacks a typical operculum, having instead an orifice biparted into two lips, and broods in an internal embryo sac (Fig. 125*J*). The ancestrula gives off a circle of 10 to 15 zooids, each of which originates an erect branch (Fig. 141*A*, *B*).

In the division Malacostega the boxlike zooids have calcified dorsal, lateral, and end walls, whereas the ventral wall is more or less occupied by a frontal membrane bearing near its distal end the orifice provided with a typical but membranous operculum. This group is generally regarded as occupying a central position among the cheilostomes (Silén, 1942a). The main families here are the Membraniporidae, Electridae, Flustridae, and Calloporidae. The first forms one-layered incrustations of rectangular zoecia without ovicells or avicularia and with the frontal membrane occupying the entire ventral surface. *Membranipora*, represented by the common species *M. membranacea* (Fig. 141*C*), has tubercles or spines at the corners of the zoecium (Fig. 106*A*). The very similar *Acanthodesia* (regarded by Osburn, 1950, as identical with *Membranipora*) is shown in Figs. 102*B*, *E*, and 106*B*; either may have a partial cryptocyst. *Conopeum* (Fig. 105*E*) is characterized by the proximal depressed areas of the gymnocyst. In the Electridae, also incrusting and also without

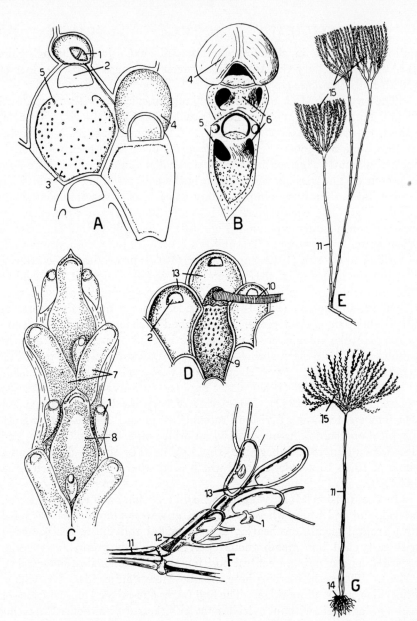

Fig. 142.—Anascan cheilostomes (continued). *A, Micropora (after Osburn*, 1950). *B, Thalamoporella* with ovicell *(after Marcus*, 1939a). *C*, piece of branch of *Himantozoum* with asymmetrical and symmetrical zooids *(after Busk*, 1884). *D, Selenaria*, with wall of cystid of vibraculum perforated with pseudopores *(after Busk*, 1854). *E*, branches of *Caulibugula (after Levinsen*, 1909). *F*, base of a branch of *Caulibugula*, showing tata form of lowest zooid *(after Marcus*, 1938a). *G*, entire colony of *Kinetoskias (after Marcus*, 1940). 1, avicularium; 2, operculum; 3, pseudopores; 4, ovicell; 5, opesiule; 6, polypide tube; 7, lateral sterile autozooids; 8, median fertile autozooid; 9, cystid of vibraculum; 10, base of seta of vibraculum; 11, stem of fused kenozooids; 12, basal zooid of branch, resembling tata; 13, autozooids; 14, rhizoids; 15, terminal tuft of branches.

376

ovicells or avicularia, the frontal membrane is reduced by the development of the gymnocyst to an oval area bordered with spines (*Electra*, Fig. 105*C*, *D*). To this family belongs *Tendra* with acanthostegous brood chamber (Fig. 126*C*). The Flustridae form erect, foliaceous colonies, typically with endozoecial ovicells and vicarious avicularia (Fig. 121*B*). In *Flustra* (Fig. 101*E*) the fronds are bilamellate, that is, with zooids on both surfaces, whereas in *Carbasea*, without avicularia or ovicells but with external embryo sacs (Fig. 126*A*), the fronds bear zooids on one surface only. The Calloporidae comprise Malacostega with hyperstomial ovicells and avicularia. In *Callopora* (Fig. 141*G*) there are spines along the opesial edge and small sessile avicularia between the zooids; larger vicarious avicularia are present in *Copidozoum* with, and in *Crassimarginatella* without, opesial spines. In the last a polypide may be present in the avicularium (Fig. 122*D*).

The division Coilostega comprises Anasca with fully developed cryptocyst extending to or around the orifice but leaving opesiular notches or holes for the passage of muscles to the overlying frontal membrane (page 296). The family Onychocellidae, mostly extinct, is characterized by the peculiar type of avicularium called onychocellarium with winged mandible (page 330); the ovicell is of the endozoecial type, and opesiular notches are present. Chief existing genera are *Onychocella* with mandible winged on one side only (Fig. 141*H*) and *Smittipora* with mandible winged symmetrically (Fig. 141*J*). The Microporidae (also called Selenariidae) have ordinary avicularia, also frequently vibracula; the ovicells are endozoecial, and open or closed opesiules are present, but there is no formation of a calcified polypide tube. In *Micropora* (Fig. 142*A*) there are small closed opesiules and small avicularia just in front of the operculum; the opesiules are open in *Selenaria*, in which the frontal wall of the cystid of the vibraculum is perforated with holes (Fig. 142*D*). In the Steginoporellidae, without ovicells or ordinary avicularia, the cryptocyst meets the dorsal wall between the opesiules, establishing a calcified polypide tube for the extrusion of the polypide. *Steginoporella* is notable for the differentiation of its autozooids into A and B types (Fig. 122*A*); the enlarged B zooids are incipient avicularia, being provided with large toothed opercula (Figs. 107*O*, *P*, 122*B*, *C*) and especially heavy opercular musculature (Fig. 123*A*, *B*). In *Labioporella* instead of B zooids there are large vicarious avicularia that may be provided with a developed polypide (Fig. 121*E*). The Thalamoporellidae, exemplified by *Thalamoporella* (Fig. 106*C*), also with calcified polypide tube and large vicarious avicularia, differ in the presence of free spicules in the coelom and large ovicells, which, however, are of the two-valved type (page 337), hence may contain several embryos. A valuable study of the anatomy and embryology of *Thalamoporella evelinae*, Brazil, was made by Marcus

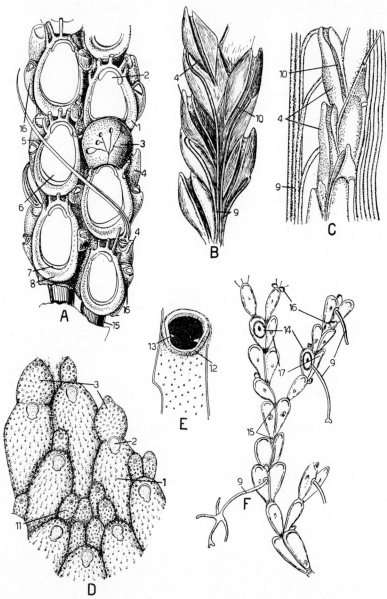

FIG. 143.—Anascan cheilostomes (concluded), ascophoran cheilostomes. *A, Scrupo-cellaria*, species without scutum, each autozooid accompanied by a vibraculum, most shown without seta (*after Marcus*, 1953). *B, Caberea*, back side, showing large cystids of vibracula (*after Marcus*, 1941a). *C, Amastigia*, back side, with marginal bundles of rhizoids (*after Busk*, 1884). *D, Trypostega* with dwarf zooids (*after Marcus*, 1937b). *E, Hippopodina* (*after Osburn*, 1952). *F*, branches of *Synnotum aegyptiacum*, with pairs of zooids (*after Marcus*, 1941b). 1, autozooid; 2, operculum; 3, ovicell; 4, cystid of vibraculum; 5, seta; 6, frontal membrane; 7, cryptocyst; 8, gymnocyst; 9, rhizoids; 10, groove for seta; 11, dwarf zooid; 12, orificial collar; 13, condyles; 14, female zooids; 15, joint; 16, avicularium; 17, male zooids.

(1941a). In the Cothurnicellidae, without ovicells or avicularia, the zooids are borne in uniserial branches (Fig. 100*A*) springing from a stolonate network. The Alysidiidae, without avicularia, are characterized by aberrant types of ovicells. In *Alysidium* the special gonozooid mounted on stalklike kenozooids bears a large two-valved ovicell (Fig. 127*G*, *H*) and in *Catenicula* there is a special brood chamber in the form of a basket made of several flat plates (Fig. 128*A*).

The division Pseudostega is a small group with complete cryptocyst, polypide tube, vicarious avicularia, and endotoichal ovicells buried in the base of the next succeeding zooid (Fig. 127*B*). The main family Cellariidae, discussed by Rogick (1956a), forms erect, branching, usually jointed colonies.

The division Cellularina (Harmer, 1923) comprises erect, branching colonies, attached by radicular fibers with uncalcified to moderately calcified zoecia, and typical avicularia and hyperstomial ovicells. The three families Bugulidae, Bicellariellidae, and Beaniidae, often united under the second name, include some of the most familiar Anasca. The Bugulidae form bushy, flexible colonies of uncalcified or slightly calcified zooids, all facing in one direction. In *Bugula* with mostly biserial branches and typical pedunculate avicularia an operculum is usually wanting (Figs. 101*A*, *B*, 118*C*, 126*D*). This is the most familiar gymnolaemate genus with many species, some of wide distribution as *neritina*, *flabellata*, and *turrita*. In the similar *Dendrobeania* an operculum is present and the colony consists of triserial to multiserial fronds. *Caulibugula* and *Himantozoum* are markedly polymorphic. In *Caulibugula* (= *Stirparia*, *Stirpariella*) the biserial branches of zooids are arranged in feathery tufts borne on long jointed stems composed of elongated kenozooids (Fig. 142*E*, *F*) and attached basally by other kenozooids in the form of rhizoids that also may occur in bunches on the stem (Marcus, 1925d). In addition the zooids are usually dimorphic, for the proximal zooid or zooids of each branch may differ from the more distal ones, sometimes resembling a tata (Harmer, 1926; Marcus, 1938a; Fig. 142*F*). *Himantozoum*, with almost sessile avicularia and biserial to multiserial branches borne on a stalk composed of fused kenozooids prolonged basally into attachment rhizoids, also has dimorphic autozooids. The zooids of biserial branches and the outer zooids of multiserial branches show right and left asymmetry; the median zooids are symmetrical (Fig. 142*C*) and brood the egg in the coelom. *Himantozoum* is an abyssal genus, known chiefly from the dredgings of the *Challenger* (Busk, 1884). In *Kinetoskias*, also abyssal, the colony consists of a tuft of biserial branches borne on the summit of a long erect stalk fastened in the bottom ooze by rhizoids (Fig. 142*G*). The zooids have a special muscle by which they can move (Silén, 1950; page 399). *Bicellariella*, main genus of the

Bicellariellidae, is characterized by the very long spines and reduced oval frontal membrane, carried in a tilted position on the cornucopia-like zooids (Fig. 105*B*). *Beania*, representing the Beaniidae, forms creeping colonies of separate zooids which consist of a recumbent tubular basal part adherent to the substrate and an erected oval distal part bearing the opesium bordered by spines (Fig. 103*G*, 105*A*); ovicells are generally wanting since brooding appears to be internal and the widely spread species *B. mirabilis* (Fig. 103*G*) also lacks avicularia.

The Scrupocellariidae form erect branching colonies attached by rhizoids and composed of biserial, often jointed branches. The zooids are typically provided with sessile avicularia, vibracula, and ovicells and are calcified, except for a more or less extensive frontal membrane over which there usually extends a bizarre branched spine (*scutum*) as a protective device. In the genus *Scrupocellaria* with spines and prominent hyper-stomial ovicells, each zooid, sometimes lacking a scutum, is provided with small sessile avicularia and a vibraculum located on its dorsal side near the posterior end and bearing a smooth seta (Fig. 143*A*). In *Amastigia*, characteristic of high southern latitudes, with multiserial unjointed branches, the rhizoids are grouped into a bundle on each side of the branches (Fig. 143*C*). *Caberea* forms biserial to multiserial, mostly unjointed branches and has very large vibracular cystids (Fig. 143*B*) from which the rhizoids spring and of which the seta is toothed along one side (Fig. 124*E*). In *Canda*, with small, strongly curved vibracular setae without teeth, adjacent branches are connected distally by transverse rhizoids and the ovicell is capped by an avicularium. *Menipea*, with jointed branches, lacks a scutum and has lateral bundles of rhizoids, as in *Amastigia*. *Tricellaria* is characterized by the short branch lengths between joints, comprising only two or three zooids.

The remaining small cellularine family, Epistomiidae, contains the genus *Synnotum*, with branches formed of zooids in pairs back to back connected by their tubular basal region. The common species, *S. aegyptiacum* (Fig. 143*F*), widely spread in warm waters, is sexually dimorphic with monoecious colonies (Marcus, 1941b; Fig. 120*C*).

The final division, Cribrimorpha, mostly extinct, comprises those families in which calcareous spines have fused across from the opesial edges forming a calcareous shield outside the frontal membrane, pierced with slits or holes. Practically all existing genera belong to the one family Cribrilinidae in which some genera are *Membraniporella* with long slits between the ribs of the shield (Fig. 105*F*), *Colletosia* with a row of holes between the ribs, prominent hyperstomial ovicells (Fig. 105*G*), and spines around the orifice, and *Cribrilina* (Fig. 105*H*) with less prominent ovicell, no spines around the orifice, and completely fused ribs leaving regular rows of small holes.

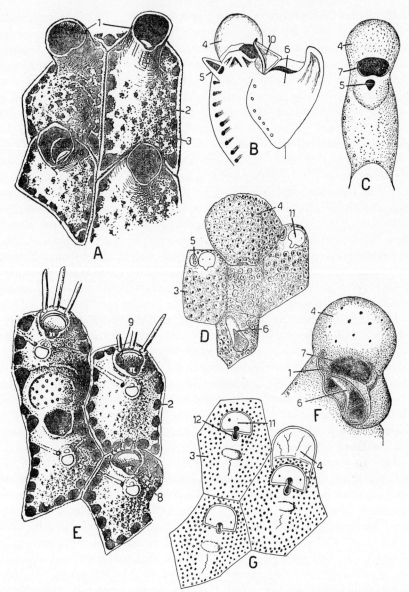

FIG. 144.—Ascophoran cheilostomes (continued). *A, Coleopora* with long orificial collars (*after Marcus, 1949*). *B, Escharoides* with small and large avicularia (*after Rogick, 1955b*). *C, Porella* with median avicularium. *D, Stylopoma. E, Smittina (after Marcus, 1949). F, Ramphostomella. (C, F, after Osburn, 1952.) G, Arthropoma. (D, G, after Marcus, 1937a.)* 1, orificial collar; 2, areoles; 3, pseudopores; 4, ovicell; 5, small avicularium; 6, large avicularium; 7, orifice; 8, lyrule; 9, condyle; 10, mandible; 11, operculum; 12, notch for ascus.

14. Order Cheilostomata : Suborder Ascophora.—This is an important group characterized by the possession of a compensation sac (ascus) for operating the lophophore.   Although this character appears very decisive, the Ascophora are not in fact sharply delimitable from the cribrimorph Anasca.   The colonies are usually incrusting with completely calcified zoecia (except for the operculum); the frontal wall is usually calcified in more than one layer.   Spines, avicularia, and hyperstomial ovicells are generally present.   The ascus is a sac located just beneath (dorsal to) the calcified frontal wall to which it is adherent.   It generally opens into the posterior wall of the orifice by a notch covered by a tab (poster) of the operculum (page 296).   The arrangement is such that as the main part (anter) of the operculum opens up to allow emission of the lophophore the poster sinks inward to permit the filling of the ascus with water, thus compensating for the reduction of space in the interior of the zooid. When the lophophore is retracted the water runs out of the ascus.   In some Ascophora the ascus opens separately to the exterior by an ascopore. The existence of the ascus was discovered by Jullien (1888a) in a preserved specimen of *Catenicella* in which the operculum happened to be open, permitting him to look inside.

The Hippothoidae are interesting as containing genera with polymorphic zooids.   *Hippothoa* may have male, female, and sterile zooids (Fig. 120*A*), and in *Trypostega* there are constantly present dwarf zooids (Fig. 143*D*) that possess polypides but lack gonads and are probably to be regarded as some sort of vicarious avicularium (Marcus, 1938a).   The Petraliidae have large zoecia with conspicuous pseudopores, hyperstomial ovicells, and a more or less developed orificial collar.   In *Petralia* the orifice has a smooth margin, and the orificial collar is but slightly developed, whereas in *Coleopora* there is a high, flaring orificial collar (Fig. 144*A*).   In *Hippopodina*, again, the orificial collar is but slightly developed, but the orifice shows a pair of condyles and may have an elongated avicularium to one or both sides (Fig. 143*E*).   The family Schizoporellidae is a large and important ascophoran group with conspicuous pseudopores, hyperstomial ovicells, and rigid operculum strengthened with sclerites and closing the ovicell, the orifice, and the notch that leads into the ascus.   In *Schizoporella*, the notch is rounded, and a pointed avicularium is often present to one or both sides of the orifice (Fig. 106*D*). *Schizoporella unicornis* (Fig. 102*D*) is one of the most common and widely spread incrusting cheilostomes.   Some other genera are *Stylopoma* with enlarged ovicell covering the orifice (Fig. 144*D*) and *Arthropoma* (Fig. 144*G*) without avicularia and with smooth central area of the frontal wall devoid of pseudopores.   In the families Hippoporinidae and Exochellidae pseudopores are less conspicuous or wanting except for the areoles and the orifice is not evidently notched posteriorly; in the former

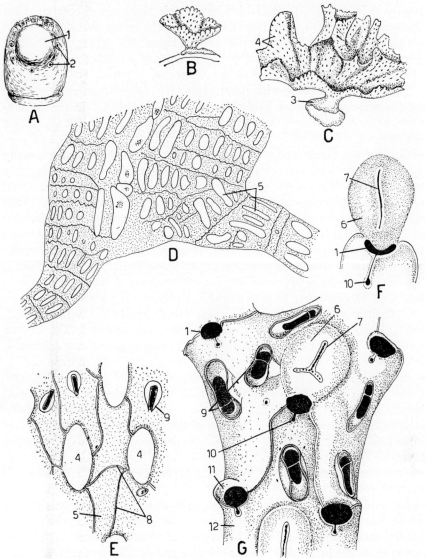

FIG. 145.—Ascophoran cheilostomes (continued). *A*, tata ancestrula with nine spines of the reteporid *Sertella* (*after Hass*, 1948). *B*, young colony of *Sertella*. *C*, mature colony of *Sertella*, natural size. (*B*, *C*, *after Hincks*, 1880.) *D*, basal attachment plate of a reteporid, made of kenozooids (*after Buchner*, 1924). *E*, back side of a reteporid, showing vibices (outlines of cystids of kenozooids). *F*, ovicell of *Sertella*. *G*, *Triphyllozoon*, with ovicell and avicularia. (*E–G*, *after Harmer*, 1934.) 1, orifice; 2, spines; 3, basal plate; 4, fenestrations; 5, kenozooids; 6, ovicell; 7, fissure of ovicell; 8, vibices; 9, avicularia; 10, spiramen; 11, orificial collar; 12, autozooid.

family it is somewhat subdivided by a projecting pair of condyles, but these are wanting in the latter family where the orifice therefore forms a simple round opening. In the Exochellidae the genus *Escharoides* (Rogick, 1955b) with orificial collar and often conspicuous avicularia (Fig. 144*B*) is mostly limited to the Antarctic.

The Microporellidae with main genus *Microporella* are characterized by the separate ascopore below the orifice (Fig. 106*F*). In the Mucronellidae (or Smittinidae) the ascus again opens in common with the orifice, which usually bears an orificial collar, has spines on the margin, and generally shows a lyrule and condyles prominently; pseudopores are usually wanting except for the areoles (Fig. 108*A*). Among the many genera may be mentioned *Mucronella*, with a prominent lyrule but no avicularia and often with a prominence (mucro) below the orifice; *Porella* (Fig. 144*C*) with lyrule and condyles small or wanting and with an avicularium; *Ramphostomella* (Fig. 108*A*) with large oblique asymmetrical avicularium below the orifice; and *Smittina* with pseudopores, well-developed lyrule, and median symmetrical avicularium beneath the orifice (Fig. 144*E*). The Tubucellariidae are notable for the alteration of the orificial collars into long curved tubes to act as brood chambers (Fig. 126*B*).

The important family Reteporidae (Buchner, 1924; Harmer, 1933, 1934; Hass, 1948) typically forms upright, strongly calcified, ruffled foliaceous colonies in the general shape of a cup or funnel, reticulated or fenestrated, that is, pierced by holes caused by the anastomosis of branches (Fig. 145*C*); but ordinary branching colonies without anastomoses also occur. The colony is highly polymorphic. It is fastened basally to objects by an expanded plate of kenozooids; the fronds of the cup- or funnel-shaped colonies consist of two or more layers of zooids, an inner layer facing the cavity composed of autozooids and an outer layer or layers of kenozooids (Fig. 146*A*, *B*) whose walls form obvious lines called *vibices* (Fig. 145*E*). Sessile avicularia of various shapes and sizes are present and may occur on both surfaces of the colony. The autozooids are usually more or less devoid of pseudopores, have an orificial collar whose dorsal wall is stiffened with a crenulated arch (vestibular arch, Fig. 146*D*), and are provided with hyperstomial ovicells, prominent at first but more or less imbedded in older colonies and peculiar in that their front wall is incompletely calcified, leaving what appears to be a fissure in calcined specimens (Fig. 145*F*). The development of a reteporid colony was described by Levinsen (1909), Harmer (1934) for *Iodictyum*, and especially by Hass (1948) for *Sertella*. The ancestrula, of the tata type (Fig. 145*A*), buds off a circle of zooids around itself, and as these multiply they elevate from the substrate in the form of a small funnel (Fig. 145*B*). The space between this and the substrate then becomes filled with kenozooids that are budded off from the autozooids and also themselves

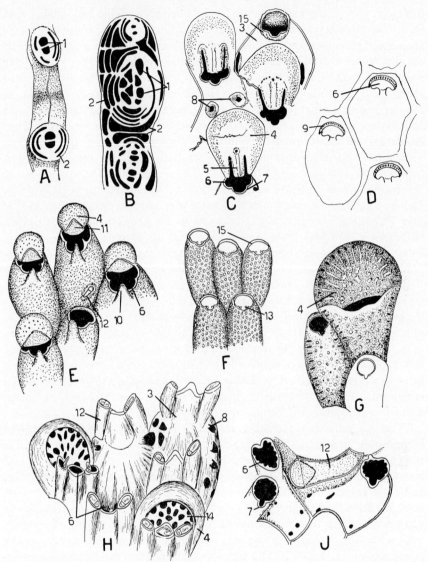

FIG. 146.—Ascophoran cheilostomes (continued). *A*, section of a young branch of *Retepora*. *B*, cross section of older branch of *Retepora*. *C*, *Iodictyum*, with tonguelike process on ovicells. *D*, *Rhynchozoon*, viewed from the back side, showing beaded vestibular arch. (*A, B, D, after Levinsen*, 1909.) *E*, *Rhynchozoon*, with ovicells (*after Hincks*, 1880). *F*, *Watersipora cucullata*, from life, Brazil. *G*, *Trigonopora* with ovicell (*after Osburn*, 1952). *H*, *Siniopelta* (*after Marcus*, 1938a). *J*, *Iodictyum* with large avicularium at fork. (*C, J, after Harmer*, 1934.) 1, cross sections of autozooids; 2, cross sections of kenozooids; 3, autozooid; 4, ovicell; 5, tonguelike process of ovicell above orifice; 6, orifice; 7, notch; 8, pseudopores; 9, vestibular arch; 10, protuberance; 11, lightly calcified part of ovicell; 12, avicularium; 13, condyle; 14, perforated front of ovicell; 15, orificial collar.

multiply.   Growing zooids at the funnel edge give off the kenozooids that form the outer layer of the colony.   According to Hass, the basal keno-zooids and the outer kenozooids are distinct as to mode of origin but both appear to be cystids without any polypide although they may bear avicularia.   As the funnellike colony expands, it may be thrown into ruffles, and these may fuse to tubes that may have the autozooid layer on the inside or the outside according to the way in which the folds fuse.   In reticulate species the growing edge separates into branches, and these later anastomose, forming the characteristic fenestrations.   A very large vicarious avicularium may occur at the branch fork (Fig. 146*J*).   Genera forming fenestrated colonies include *Iodictyum*, in which the upper edge of the ovicell opening bears a median keeled tonguelike projection (Fig. 146*C*); *Sertella*, in which the ovicell has a long median fissure (Fig. 145*F*); and *Triphyllozoon*, with a trifid fissure in the front wall of the ovicell (Fig. 145*G*).   In *Iodictyum* the autozooids are dimorphic since the orificial collar is complete in sterile individuals whereas the collar is deficient dorsally in fertile zooids to accommodate the ovicell.   Branching colonies with no or few anastomoses occur in *Retepora* and *Reteporella*, in both of which the ovicell has a simple median fissure.   *Rhynchozoon* forms incrust-ing colonies with areoles, with a prominence (*mucro*) just below the orifice, and with the lower part of the ovicell more lightly calcified than the rest (Fig. 146*E*).   Among the Reteporidae the posterior rim of the orificial collar often has a deep median indentation or groove (*rimule*) of which the end may separate off as a hole (*spiramen*) leading into the orifice to communicate with the ascus, hence corresponding in function to an ascopore, although of different origin and relations.

The Adeonidae are thickly calcified, incrusting to erect reticulate ascophorans in which the areoles are extended into tubes connected with the pore plates of the lateral zooidal walls; an orificial collar is present, and the embryos are usually brooded in sacs in enlarged gonozooids (Fig. 125*H*).   Of the genera may be mentioned *Adeona*, with erect fenestrated colony and separate ascopore (Fig. 122*F*); *Adeonellopsis*, with one to several ascopores in a median area of the zooid (Fig. 125*H*); *Adeonella*, with a spiramen; and *Trigonopora*, with very large ovicells borne on the gonozooids (Fig. 146*G*).   The Cheiloporinidae have conspicuous pseudo-pores, endozoecial ovicells or internal brood sacs, and simple orifices without a collar but with a pair of condyles.   *Cryptosula* with squarish and *Waterispora* with rounded orifice both form incrusting colonies and both brood internally.   *Cryptosula pallasiana* (Fig. 102*A, C*) and *Water-sipora cucullata* (Fig. 146*F*) are common, widely distributed species.   In the Phylactellidae, *Lagenipora* (Fig. 108*B*) is notable for the high spout-like orificial collar, and in the Crepidacanthidae with a pair of avicularia with very long mandibles at the sides of the orifice, *Mastigophorella*

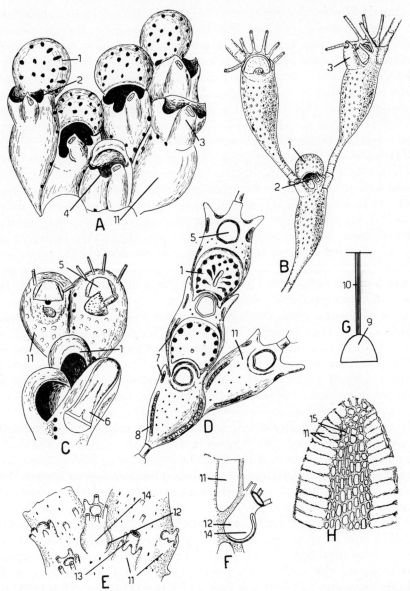

FIG. 147.—Ascophoran cheilostomes (concluded). *A, Cellepora. B, Savignyella. C, Holoporella.* (*B, C, after Marcus,* 1937a.) *D, Catenicella.* (*A, D, after Marcus,* 1938a.) *E, Turritigera. F,* section of a gonozooid of *Turritigera.* (*E, F, after Waters,* 1888.) *G,* colony of *Conescharellina* (*after Silén,* 1947b). *H,* longitudinal section of *G* (*after Canu and Bassler,* 1929). 1, ovicell; 2, orifice; 3, avicularium; 4, notch; 5, operculum; 6, large vicarious avicularium; 7, pore chambers; 8, vitta; 9, colony; 10, suspensory filaments; 11, autozooid; 12, gonozooid; 13, orificial collar; 14, brood chamber; 15, kenozooids.

(formerly *Mastigophora*) *pesanseris* has remarkable avicularian mandibles in the shape of a duck's foot (Fig. 124*H*). Irregularly piled up, erected zooids with orificial collar bearing a rimule, conspicuous porous hyperstomial ovicells, and one or two avicularia close to the orifice characterize the Celleporidae. Genera here include *Cellepora*, with median avicularium at the orificial collar (Fig. 147*A*), *Siniopelta*, with a pair of such avicularia (Fig. 146*H*), and *Holoporella*, with widely open nonporous ovicell (Fig. 147*C*). The Catenicellidae are a family of peculiar aspect, composed of delicate, jointed branches with one to three successive zooids, all facing in one direction, making up each internode between joints (Fig. 147*D*). As a main peculiarity there is present along each side of each zooid a longitudinal succession of chambers, mostly four in number, that seem to be kenozooids and communicate with each other and the autozooid by way of pore plates. The second chambers of the series may be altered into a pair of avicularia. In *Catenicella* (Fig. 147*D*) without and *Vittaticella* with a pair of avicularia the last chambers of the series are elongated into a tubular shape and are then called "vittae" (Fig. 147*D*). The Catenicellidae are mostly limited to the Southern Hemisphere. In the somewhat similar Savignyellidae, the internodes of the branches consist of a single zooid, an arrangement that produces a chainlike effect (Fig. 147*B*). The Conescharellinidae are a very peculiar family in which the small compact colonies hang from objects by delicate cuticularized tubes, therefore are usually brought up detached, hence formerly supposed to be free (Silén, 1947b). The colony in *Conescharellina*, in the shape of a beehive suspended by four tubes from the apex, consists of a peripheral layer of elongated autozooids enclosing a core of heterozooids (Fig. 147*G*, *H*). Another peculiarity of this family is that the opercula open toward the base of the zooid, the reverse of the usual situation. The final ascophoran family to be mentioned, the Lekythoporidae, with main genera *Lekythopora* and *Turritigera*, is characterized by the long tubular orificial collar, armed with small avicularia and brooding the eggs in a proximal expansion (Fig. 147*E*, *F*).

15. Order Cyclostomata or Stenostomata.—Although relatively small in number of species, this is a very distinctive group of ectoprocts, so much so that Borg (1926a, 1944), its chief student, proposes to raise the group to the rank of class coordinate with Gymnolaemata and Phylactolaemata. This view is favored by Buge (1952) and Silén (1954) but has not been generally accepted. The cyclostomes have tubular, fully calcified zoecia with a rounded terminal orifice closed in life by the terminal membrane with a central hole leading into a long vestibule provided at its inner end with a sphincter. The general structure of the zooid is shown in Figs. 121*A* and 148*A*. The cyclostome zooid differs from other gymnolaemate zooids primarily in the presence of a membranous sac extending from the distal part of the tentacle sheath to the rear end of the zooid (Fig. 148*A*) and dividing the main coelom into an inner sac that contains the digestive tract of the polypide and an outer one that extends to the terminal membrane, passing between the eight ligaments that attach the distal end of the membranous sac to the body wall. The membranous sac functions to operate the lophophore, as explained on page 325. Development by polyembryony in special gonozooids (page 341) also sets the cyclostomes apart from other gymnolaemates. Avicularia and vibracula are lacking, but heterozooids occur in the form of gonozooids, nannozooids (page 331), and kenozooids, mainly in the form of rhizoids. Colony formation (page 358) does not appear to differ fundamentally from that of cheilostomes.

It is usual to divide the existing cyclostomes into five suborders, for which Borg's names (1944) are to be rejected as corresponding to previously existing names. The suborder Articulata includes among existing cyclostomes only the family Crisiidae, which forms slender branching colonies with jointed attachment rhizoids, jointed branches, and vaselike gonozooids (Fig. 108*D*). The branch joints, which no doubt lend flexibility to the colony, consist of places where the calcification is lacking, the cuticle has ruptured, and a thick lamellated layer takes the place of the calcification (Borg, 1926a; Sawaya, 1943; Fig. 148*B*). The author's tests (Hyman, 1958) indicate that the joints are not chitinous. The several genera (*Crisia, Crisidia, Crisiella*, etc.) are distinguished by the number of zooids between the joints of branches without and those with a gonozooid. In *Crisidia* and *Bicrisia* a jointed filamentous process, apparently composed of kenozooids, springs from some of the zooids (Fig. 148*G*).

The colonies of all remaining suborders lack joints. The order Tubuliporina, which includes the majority of existing cyclostomes, forms branching to massive, adherent, or erect colonies without joints or rhizoids, with zoecia more or less fused, and with gonozooid generally spreading and lobulate. The central family, Tubuliporidae, comprises flabellate, lobulated, or branched colonies, adherent or somewhat erect, with elongated gonozooid and with zoecia protruding from the general mass and often arranged in transverse rows. The main genus *Tubulipora* with many species forms adherent or erect lobulate colonies (Fig. 148*C*) with zooids in clusters (Fig. 100*B, C*) and with flattened, spreading gonozooid (Fig. 127*E*). The Oncousoeciidae with gonozooid of simple contour are exemplified by *Stomatopora* with uniserial branches (Fig. 108*C*) except around the gonozooid (Fig. 148*D*). The Diastoporidae form incrusting or foliaceous growths with gonozooids again expanded and lobulate, embracing a number of autozooids, and autozooids forming a continuous series, not in clusters, and more or less imbedded in the general mass. Here may be mentioned *Diastopora* with erect, foliaceous colonies,

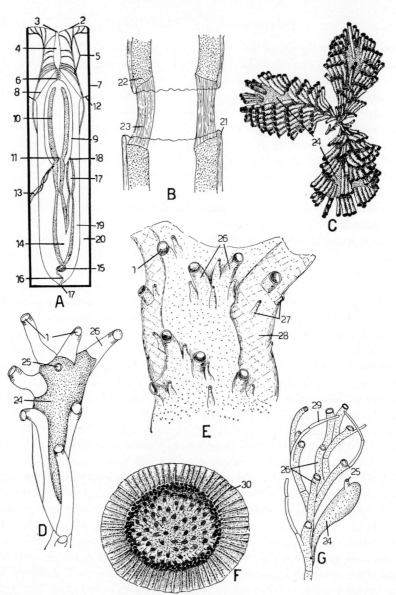

FIG. 148.—Cyclostomes. *A*, scheme of the structure of a cyclostome. *B*, structure of a crisid joint. *C*, colony of *Tubulipora* (actual length, 5 mm.). *D*, *Stomatopora* with gonozooid. (*B*, *D*, *after Borg*, 1926a.) *E*, *Diplosolen*, with nannozooids (*after Calvet*, 1931). *F*, colony of *Berenicea* (width, 4 mm.). (*A*, *C*, *F*, *after Marcus*, 1940.) *G*, some branches of *Bicrisia*, with jointed spines (*after Osburn*, 1953). 1, orifice; 2, terminal membrane; 3, entrance into vestibule; 4, vestibule; 5, dilator muscle of vestibule; 6, diaphragm with sphincter; 7, wall of cystid; 8, membranous sac; 9, tentacle sheath; 10, tentacles; 11, mouth; 12, fixator ligaments; 13, retractor of lophophore; 14, stomach; 15, ovary; 16, funiculus; 17, attachment of membranous sac to cystid; 17, intestine; 18, anus; 19, inner coelomic sac; 20, outer coelomic sac; 21, cuticle; 22, calcareous layer of body wall; 23, joint; 24, gonozooid; 25, oeciostome; 26, autozooids; 27, nannozooids; 28, secondary growth; 29, jointed spines; 30, growing zone.

Berenicea growing as a thin, incrusting circular sheet (Fig. 148*F*), and *Diplosolen* with nannozooids (Fig. 148*E*). The Entalophoridae are characterized by the erect cylindrical stems with zooids on all sides, whereas in the foregoing families the zooids open on one surface only. In this family the zone of formation of new zooids occupies the center of the stem and zooids are pushed out from the center in all directions (Fig. 108*E*). Of the many genera, mostly extinct, may be mentioned *Entalophora* (Fig. 108*E*) without kenozooids and with simple gonozooid not traversed by autozooids; and *Bientalophora* with the surface of the stems formed of a network of kenozooids through which the distal parts of the autozooids protrude (Fig. 149*E*). In the Frondiporidae the zoecia are arranged in cylindrical fascicles (Fig. 109*A*) that grow at the ends. Here belong *Frondipora* with short fascicles turned toward one surface and *Fasciculipora* with longer, more spreading fascicles.

In the remaining three suborders the zooidal wall is double, consisting of gymnocyst and cryptocyst with a narrow coelomic space between (page 301). The suborder Cancellata, mostly extinct, is represented by the existing family Horneridae with one existing genus *Hornera* (Fig. 109*B*, *C*) forming branching, treelike colonies (Fig. 149*A*) fastened by a basal disk composed of tubular kenozooids. On the stems the autozooids all face in one direction, whereas the brood chambers, which here also are expanded gonozooids, occur as conspicuous swellings on the other (dorsal) side of the stems (Fig. 149*B*). The structure of *Hornera* was explained on page 301; the spaces between the autozooids are filled with calcareous chambers opening on all sides of the stems by slits or pores. The interior of the gonozooid may also be subdivided into chambers by calcareous walls (Borg, 1926a). In the suborder Cerioporina, also mostly extinct, the compact colonies are composed solidly of elongated zooids whose orifices are flush with the surface and which consist of intermingled autozooids and kenozooids. The latter, for which fantastic names exist in the literature (mesopores, cancelli), differ from the usual kenozooid in being provided with an orifice; hence the colony surface in this suborder shows orifices of two sizes (Fig. 149*D*). The colony grows over the entire surface that thus constitutes a budding zone. The brood chamber is compounded of an autozooid that produces the egg and a number of surrounding kenozooids and sterile autozooids fused with it. In the main family Heteroporidae (Borg, 1933a) the zooids are not clustered and the kenozooids equal or surpass the autozooids in number. Main existing genera are *Heteropora* with smooth and *Borgiola* with warty surface, in both of which the kenozooids are much more numerous than the autozooids. The final suborder, Rectangulata, comprising only the family Lichenoporidae, forms warty or discoidal adherent colonies in which the tubular zooids with jagged projecting orifices radiate from the central region,

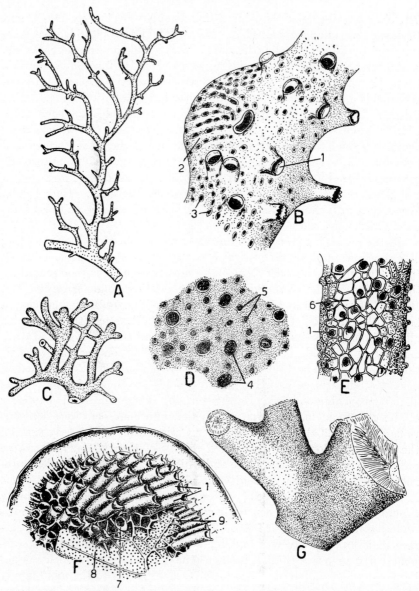

Fig. 149.—Cyclostomes (concluded), trepostomes. *A*, colony of *Hornera*. *B*, side view of branch of *Hornera*, showing brood chamber. (*A, B, after Calvet*, 1931.) *C*, colony of *Heteropora*, twice natural size. *D*, surface of *Heteropora*, showing two sizes of orifices. (*C, D, after Robertson*, 1910.) *E*, *Bientalophora* with kenozooids (*after Osburn*, 1953). *F*, *Lichenopora* with brood chamber opened (*after Marcus*, 1953). *G*, part of a colony of a trepostome (*after Ulrich*, 1890). 1, autozooids; 2, gonozooid; 3, openings of calcareous chambers; 4, orifices of autozooids; 5, orifices of kenozooids; 6, outlines of kenozooids; 7, oeciostome; 8, brood chamber; 9, alveoli of brood chamber.

with the areas between them occupied by coelomic cavities (alveoli, page 301; Fig. 109*E*). The brood chamber, or chambers, compounded by the union of a number of alveoli with an egg-producing zooid, occupy the central part of the colony in *Lichenopora* (Figs. 109*D*, 149*F*) with many ill-defined species, are radially located in *Disporella*.

16. Order Trepostomata.—This order, also called monticuliporoids, is wholly extinct, having flourished during the Palaeozoic era as heavily calcified massive, lamellate, or coarsely branching colonies, often of considerable size (Fig. 149*G*). The colony is solidly composed of long cylindrical or prismatic tubes paralleling the colony axis and opening at the surface by an orifice. These tubes are crossed at intervals by transverse partitions, sometimes imperfect, that seem to represent the end walls of zoecia, hence are erroneously called diaphragms. Therefore the long tubes of the colony consist of a linear succession of zoecia, although one is puzzled as to the location of their orifices; the central perforation in the end walls of some species might represent an orifice. It seems necessary to assume that each zooid dies after giving off its successor immediately distal to itself. The zoecia are longer with thinner walls in the proximal part of colonies, where growth was presumably rapid, shorter with heavier walls distally, presumably as a result of slowing down of growth processes as the colony ages (Fig. 150*A*). In many trepostomes the side walls of the zoecia are cut off by curved partitions (cystiphragms!) into small chambers that certainly seem to be pore chambers (Fig. 150*C, D*). Often zoecia contain a granular mass that suggests a brown body. In the distal part of colonies the zoecial tubes generally diverge, and between them are found types of heterozooids allied to kenozooids. A common type (mesopore!, better *mesozooid*) consists of a slender tube also crossed by transverse partitions and with a terminal orifice (Fig. 150*A*). In some genera there occurs another sort of heterozooid (acanthopore!, better *acanthozooid*), a small short tube with thick lamellated wall that continues above the colony surface as a spine (Fig. 150*F*). As a result of the presence of heterozooids the colony surface typically shows large and small pores intermingled (Fig. 150*E*). In some genera the colony surface bears regularly arranged tubercles (*monticules*) containing orifices that are larger or thicker-walled, or both, than the regular orifices. The areas (*maculae*) between the monticules generally bear the small orifices of mesozooids encircled by especially large autozooidal orifices. The purpose of such aggregations of zooids is unknown, although it has been suggested that the large orifices belong to gonozooids.

Stages of development of the trepostome colony are described by Cumings (1912). The ancestrula is a rounded chamber that as in cyclostomes gives off the first zooid (erroneously regarded as the ancestrula by Cumings) as a tubular upgrowth (Fig. 150*B*). This produces buds

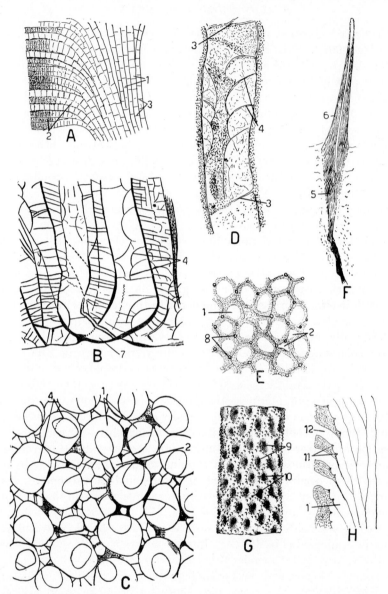

FIG. 150.—Trepostomes (concluded), cryptostomes. *A*, longitudinal section of a trepostome, showing rows of zoecia. *B*, longitudinal section of the base of the trepostome *Prasopora*, showing ancestrula. *C*, cross section of *Prasopora*, to show cystiphragms. (*B, C, after Cumings*, 1912.) *D*, a single zoecium of a trepostome, with cystiphragms. *E*, cross section of trepostome *Batostoma* with large and small zoecia. *F*, an acanthozooid in longitudinal section. (*D, F, after Cumings and Galloway*, 1915.) *G*, cryptostome *Rhombopora*, cylindrical with zoecia all around. *H*, longitudinal section of half of *Rhombopora*. (*A, E, G, H, after Ulrich*, 1890.) 1, autozooids; 2, mesozooids; 3, end walls; 4, cystiphragms; 5, part of acanthozooid below surface; 6, spine of acanthozooid above surface; 7, ancestrula; 8, acanthozooids; 9, orifices of autozooids; 10, acanthozooids on ridges; 11, hemisepta; 12, so-called vestibule.

distally and laterally, and these become the lowermost members of the linear successions of zooids that make up the colony (Fig. 150*B*).

17. Order Cryptostomata.—This order, also wholly extinct and limited to the Paleozoic period, does not appear to differ in any important respect from the preceding order. The colonies may form bifoliate expansions with zoecia on both surfaces back to back, or cylindrical branches with zoecia all around (Fig. 150*G*), or fenestrated, lacelike growths with zoecia on one surface only (Fig. 151*B*). As in trepostomes the zoecia occur in linear succession but are shorter with imperfect end walls (hemisepta). As also in trepostomes the proximal zoecia are thin-walled, the distal ones thick-walled. Mesozooids and acanthozooids (Fig. 151*A*), the latter often of two sizes, occur, as well as monticules and maculae. The main difference from trepostomes consists in the presence of a long tube between the external opening and the distal hemiseptum (Fig. 150*H*). This tube appears to be an orificial collar; hence the designation as vestibule in the literature is erroneous. The fenestrated type is exemplified in the family Fenestellidae, where the colony is formed of rigid upright branches, having two rows of zooids on one side only, joined by crossbars devoid of zooids (Fig. 151*B*).

18. Ecology: Habits and Behavior.—As already indicated, the gymnolaemates are, with few exceptions, sessile colonial marine animals that live permanently attached to rocks, shells, seaweeds, pilings, other animals, and in fact almost any kind of a stable substrate. A few live in peculiar situations. Notable among these are the ctenostome families Terebriporidae, Penetrantiidae, and Immergentiidae (page 370) that permeate live or dead mollusk and barnacle shells (Marcus, 1938b; Silén, 1946, 1948; Soule, 1950a, b). Openings to the surface occur on either the outer or the inner surface of the shell. The stolons do not merely take advantage of weak or corroded places in the shell but actively burrow. Silén's investigations indicate that burrowing is accomplished by the secretion of phosphoric acid that dissolves the calcareous matter of the shells. He found a much greater phosphorus content in shells containing colonies than in those without them. However, some other mechanism is required for the penetration of the outer layer of molluscan shells (periostracum) which is not calcareous. The stolons are able to pierce the periostracum, although colonies usually inhabit parts of shells from which this layer has been worn away. Another boring ctenostome, *Hypophorella expansa*, exists as a delicate stolonal network (Fig. 152*A*) between the layers of the tubes of the tubicolous polychaete annelids *Terebella* and *Chaetopterus*, with zooids projecting into the lumen of the tube, taking advantage of the water current maintained by the worms (Ehlers, 1876; Joyeux-Laffuie, 1888a, b; Prouho, 1892). The colony, originally started on the inner surface of the worm tube, becomes imbedded by additional layers of tube added by the worm, but the zooids are able to emerge into the lumen again by means of a boring apparatus in the form of a denticulate area just above the orifice (Fig. 152B).   This is operated by muscles and no doubt is capable of a rasping action.   The zooids of *Hypophorella* present a peculiar high-shouldered appearance because of the presence of a fluid-filled vesicle on each side of the distal end that seemingly acts as a cushion against bumping by the worm host.   Still another boring ctenostome, *Harmeriella terebrans*, was discovered by Borg (1940) in colonies of the ascophoran cheilostome *Tubiporella*, where its zooids occupy the cystids

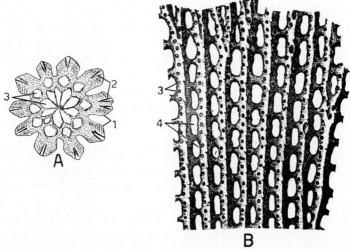

Fig. 151.—Cryptostomes (concluded).   *A*, cross section of *Rhombopora*.   *B*, a fenestrated cryptostome, *Fenestella*.   (*A, B, after Ulrich*, 1890.)   1, ridges with acanthozooids; 2, acanthozooids; 3, autozooids; 4, fenestrations.

after destroying the polypides.   Its own zooids protrude through the orificial collar or ascopore or areoles and appear able to bore through considerable thicknesses of calcareous wall.   The zooids of *Harmeriella* have a very long vestibular region which is armed with 16 to 22 longitudinal toothed cuticular ridges on its outer surface (Fig. 152C).   These could exercise a rasping action if the vestibular region is successively elongated and shortened.   According to Borg, the muscles of the area are much altered; the vestibular and diaphragmatic dilators are powerfully developed but limited to the ventral side and originate far proximally on the zooid wall, hence would exert considerable pull on the vestibular region. The zooid has three thickened roughened cuticular rings by which it adheres to the cystid wall of its host.   Mention may also be made here of the apparently nonboring *Watersiana paessleri* that lives in the tunic of a compound ascidian with its stolons submerged about 1.5 mm. below the surface and its zooids emerging through depressed openings on the

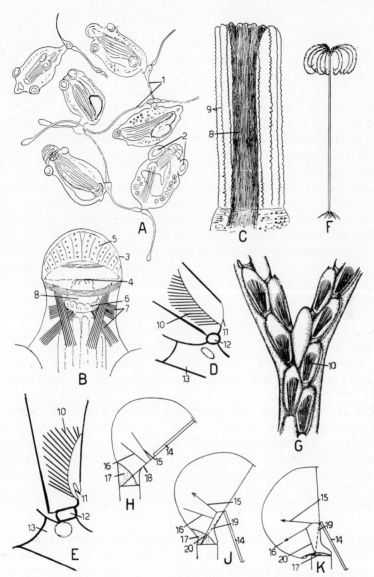

FIG. 152.—Boring gymnolaemates, motility. *A*, part of a colony of *Hypophorella*
expansa (*after Ehlers*, 1876). *B*, anterior end of *Hypophorella*, seen from in front, showing
file on upper lip (*after Prouho*, 1892). *C*, vestibular region of *Harmeriella*, showing toothed
ridges (*after Borg*, 1940). *D*, scheme of zooid of *Mimosella* in relaxed position close to
stem. *E*, scheme of zooid of *Mimosella* erected away from stem. *F*, *Kinetoskias* in relaxed
position with curled branches. *G*, part of branch of *Kinetoskias*, showing erector muscle in
each cystid (*after Marcus*, 1940). *H*, *J*, *K*, schemes to explain swaying of *Bugula* avicularium. *H*, down position, relaxed. *J*, distal abductor contracted, mandible opens. *K*,
proximal abductor contracted, back of peduncle bends in, avicularium jerks up. (*D–F*,
H–K, *after Silén*, 1950.) 1, stolon; 2, protective vesicle; 3, upper lip; 4, orifice; 5, rows of
teeth on upper lip; 6, diaphragm; 7, dilators of diaphragm; 8, vestibule; 9, toothed ridges;
10, erector muscle; 11, thin place of cystid wall; 12, kenozooid attaching zooid to stem;
13, stem; 14, mandible; 15, distal abductor; 16, proximal abductor; 17, thin place in
peduncle of avicularium; 18, frontal membrane; 19, dashed line indicates site of relaxed
frontal membrane; 20, frontal membrane when abductors are contracted.

external surface (Calvet, 1912). *Bulbella abscondita* appears regularly to burrow in pieces of wood and fallen twigs, especially those of coniferous trees, in brackish water (Braem, 1951).

The gymnolaemates are strictly benthonic, as must be expected of sessile animals. They are pelagic only in larval stages, for life upon the *Sargassum*, the floating seaweed of the North Atlantic, can hardly be regarded as pelagic, rather a variant of benthonic existence. Gymnolaemates of the genus *Membranipora*, which in general is addicted to incrusting seaweeds, regularly occur upon the *Sargassum*, and a few other gymnolaemates are sporadically found upon it (Hentschel, 1921; Timmermann, 1932). The *Membranipora* growing on the *Sargassum* belongs to several species that are not limited to this habitat, but by far the most common and typical species is *M. tuberculata* (includes *tehuelcha*). The colonies tend to grow on the main stems and leaf bases, not upon the distal parts of the leaves, and are part of a mixed community of sessile organisms, mainly hydroids, to a lesser degree barnacles, tunicates, and small tubicolous annelids.

Although gymnolaemates have been recorded as enduring exposure by recession of the tide, they in general do not withstand desiccation very well, and hence are rather limited to habitats that remain covered at low tide. The settling habits and reactions of larvae determine where colonies shall grow since the ancestrula, once attached, is incapable of changing its location.

With few exceptions the gymnolaemate colony and the individual zooid are incapable of locomotion. Movement is limited to the extrusion and retraction of the lophophore, of which the various mechanisms were already described, and to the bendings of the lophophore and its tentacles. The unattached *Monobryozoon*, consisting of an autozooid with basal kenozooids in the form of stolons (Fig. 103*A*), can move slowly by attaching the adhesive stolon tips to sand grains, for these stolons, contrary to the usual condition, contain muscle fibers (Remane, 1936). A few cases are known (review in Silén, 1950) in which whole autozooids are able to move upon their attachment; obviously only stoloniferous ctenostomes are so constructed that this would be possible. In *Farrella* (Marcus, 1926b) muscle fibers extend from the transverse septum at the zooid base into the proximal narrowed part of the zooid (Fig. 117*E*) and can move the zooid about 10°. The zooids of *Walkeria tremula* are said by Hincks (1880) to droop to the side when the polypide is retracted and to rise to an erect position when it extrudes; the mechanism here has not been described but is presumably similar to that of *Mimosella*. It has long been known that the zooids of all species of *Mimosella* can be moved upon the stolons, but a description of the behavior in living specimens was given only by Hincks (1880) for *M. gracilis*, a species with delicate branching stolons having a row of zooids on each side, each mounted on a short internode. Although the muscles in the zooid base responsible for the movement were seen by previous observers (Waters, 1914; Harmer, 1915; Marcus, 1937b), the mechanism of the movement was first elucidated by Silén (1950). In the zooid base is found a pair of fanlike erector muscles that originate on the proximal wall and insert on the lateral wall on the anal side of the zoecium. When the polypide retracts, the erector muscles relax and the zooids fold together above the stolon; when the polypide extrudes, the erector muscles contract and pull in a thin area of the zoecial wall near its base, thus causing the zooids to stand out on the branch again (Fig. 152D, E). These movements have been likened to the closing and opening of the leaflets of the leaves of the sensitive plant, whence the name *Mimosella*. The zooids of *Triticella*, mounted on long stalklike kenozooids (Fig. 138G), have been reported as movable on the top of the stalks, but Silén and others could not verify this on live material.

Among cheilostomes movement of branches is known for *Kinetoskias* and the closely related *Euoplozoum*. The former consists of a tuft of branches at the top of a long stalk (Fig. 142G). On the branches when erect the orifices and frontal membranes of the zooids face outward. As observed in life by Koren and Danielssen (1877), the branches may curl up bit by bit toward the stalk (Fig. 152F), in which position the frontal membranes face inward, the zoecia are curved, and the polypides are retracted. This, however, seems to be the resting position of the branches since the zoecia curve into this position if the erector muscle is extirpated (Silén, 1950). Each zooid contains a strong erector muscle (Fig. 152G) that originates in the proximal part of the zooid and diverges fanlike to its insertion on the frontal membrane. Contraction of this muscle pulls in the frontal membrane, pushes the polypide out, straightens the curve of the zoecia, and so erects the branches. As the zooids apparently act independently, straightening of a whole branch presumably results from the stimulating effect of erecting zooids on adjacent zooids.

The movements of avicularia and vibracula have constantly attracted the attention of naturalists, among them Darwin (1839). Only the pedunculate, or bird's-head, type of avicularium is movable as a whole, and this type is of limited distribution among cheilostomes. Even when present pedunculate avicularia are not necessarily movable; in fact, it is probable that movable avicularia are limited to the genera *Bugula* and *Bicellariella* (Rey, 1927b; Silén, 1950). In a living colony of *Bugula* the avicularia are seen incessantly swaying on their peduncles with mandible open. They move in their sagittal plane only, swaying up and down about once in 5 or 6 seconds (Harmer, 1910; Marcus, 1926b; Rey, 1927b). Forbes (1933) found that the avicularia of *Bugula* remained 2 to 10 seconds in the up position and 5 to 20 seconds in the down position, and

Marcus (1926b) recorded pauses of 1 to 19 seconds. At intervals of a minute or two, the mandible closes with a snap, remaining closed 1 to 5 seconds, during which the swaying ceases. Marcus (1939a) figured muscles in the autozoecial part of the peduncle of *Bugula ditrupae* that would seem capable of moving the avicularium in any direction (Fig. 122*E*), but Silén (1950) in *Bicellariella* and several species of *Bugula* failed to find any muscle fibers in the peduncle, and various observers attest that the avicularia are movable in one plane only. According to the analysis of Silén (1950), swaying is caused by the two abductors of the mandible in combination with an area of thin flexible membrane on the back side of the peduncle. The contraction of the abductors opens the mandible by pulling in the frontal membrane, and especially the pull of the proximal abductor on the lower part of the frontal membrane results in a deep indentation of the thin back wall of the peduncle, thus throwing the avicularium backward (Fig. 152*H–K*). With the mandible held open by the distal abductor, the proximal abductor regularly relaxes and contracts, evoking the swaying movement as the thin wall straightens out and bends in again. Obviously this movement must cease when the mandible closes.

The response of avicularia to stimuli of a type that would be met with in nature was best recorded by Harmer (1910). A fine hair was so firmly seized by the avicularia of a small colony of *Bugula* that the colony could be lifted out of the water. The avicularia of this same colony were observed to capture a small polychaete worm and two kinds of crustaceans and the latter were held at least 2 days. Forbes (1933) saw closure on the head of a small planarian that had made contact with the tuft of bristles of the polypide. Touching the interior of the avicularium with a fine point causes immediate closure of the mandible on the point (Darwin, 1839; Harmer, 1910; Marcus, 1926b; Rey, 1927b). An avicularium that has caught something remains closed and motionless for a varied length of time, up to days. Rey reported duration of closure for 5 seconds to a simple touch, for 5 to 10 minutes if the stimulating object was caught, and for 15 to 30 minutes if it was agitated. With repeated touches the duration of closure increased from 3 to 90 seconds at the twenty-second repetition, then decreased with further stimulation.

Various conditions affect the rate of avicularian movements. Shaking the colony or lifting it momentarily from the water excites the avicularia to rapid movements for a minute or two (Silén, 1950). Application of nutrients (bivalve juice, raw egg white) invokes acceleration of the swaying movements and increases the frequency of mandible closure to once in 8 to 20 seconds for several minutes; in general, particles in the water appear to act as mechanical stimuli, evoking closure (Forbes, 1933). Slight increase or decrease in the salinity of the sea water in Forbes's experiments evoked more frequent opening and closing of the mandibles, but stronger changes resulted in prolonged closure and cessation of swaying. Temperature changes and various salts and other chemicals also affect the rate of swaying and of mandible closure; details may be consulted in the articles of Rey and Forbes.

The activities of avicularia are independently effected; mechanical stimulation of the autozooid to which the avicularium belongs is without effect on the latter, and vice versa, nor does touching the cystid of the avicularium or the outer surface of the mandible evoke any response. Response follows only from contact with the bristle tuft of the polypide of the avicularium. Therefore it must be supposed that neuromuscular circuits occur within the avicularium itself. Darwin (1839) noted that a detached avicularium continued to open and close.

The behavior of vibracula, observed mainly in *Scrupocellaria* and *Caberea*, is similar to that of avicularia. Under normal conditions, the setae give a sweep every minute or two (Harmer, 1910), every 100 to 150 seconds (Marcus, 1926b). As described by Marcus for *Scrupocellaria*, the setae at rest are held in a transverse position; in giving a sweep they swing to an erect position, then return to the resting position again. The circuit occupies about 8 to 10 seconds, and a resting period then ensues, and this activity continues uninterruptedly throughout the life of the colony. The seta is capable of but this one motion, and mechanical stimulation only accelerates the motion and shortens the rest periods. According to Silén (1950), mechanical stimulation is effective only on the seta itself, not upon the cystid of the vibraculum. The activities of the setae of a colony are independent of each other and of the activities of the autozooids. However, it is claimed for *Caberea*, which has very large vibracular cystids on the back side of the colony (Fig. 143*B*) and long toothed setae, that the setae of a colony or branch move simultaneously (Darwin, 1839; Hincks, 1878). Hincks says: "After a short interval of quietude all the vibracula [i.e., the setae] on a shoot are seen, as if moved by one and the same impulse, to start into sudden activity, swinging themselves around to the front of the cells [i.e., the zoecia], and then sweeping backwards again and resuming their former position. After another interval the same synchronous and perfectly regular movement takes place, and so on continually." Busk (1854) suspected that colonies (presumably detached) of the Microporidae could be made to move by the synchronous action of the setae of their vibracula, and later informed Hincks that he had actually witnessed such movement (Hincks, 1878). Silén (1950) has confirmed that if a seta of *Caberea* is touched, even slightly, a large number respond and the response may spread to other branches. However, the setae are so densely placed that a moving seta inevitably touches others that thereupon respond, but if one selects a seta so placed that it does not touch others or if one cuts short the surrounding setae, then there

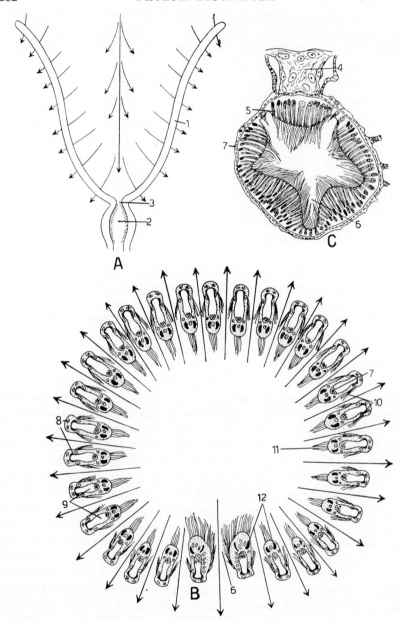

Fig. 153.—Food currents. *A*, lateral view of tentacular crown, schematic, showing ciliary currents (*after Borg,* 1926a). *B*, cross section near base of tentacular crown of *Flustrellidra,* showing direction of ciliary currents. *C*, cross section of pharynx of *Flustrellidra,* showing rejection groove. (*B, C, after Atkins,* 1932.) 1, tentacle; 2, pharynx; 3, mouth; 4, ganglion; 5, epithelial lining of pharynx; 6, rejection groove; 7, muscle fibers; 8, cross section of tentacle; 9, tentacular coelom; 10, lateral cilia; 11, frontal cilia; 12, nuclei of cells bearing sensory bristles.

is no transmission of the movement; hence the presumed synchrony is in reality a rapid metachrony.

The foregoing matters bring up the question of transmission of stimuli between zooids. Bronstein (1937) and Hiller (1939) reported nervous connections between zooids. Bronstein stated that mechanical stimulation of any part of the protruded polypide is not transmitted to other polypides, but if one touches, even lightly, the edge of the orifice of cheilostomes or the pleated collar of ctenostomes, not only the stimulated zooid retracts violently but adjacent polypides also retract. Stimulation of a cystid without polypide evoked no reaction from adjacent zooids with polypides. However, the gymnolaemate zooid is so minute that it is very difficult to confine a stimulus to a single zooid. Competent students of ectoprocts (Marcus, 1926b; Silén, 1950) have declared in the most positive manner that mechanical stimulation of a zooid does not evoke any response from adjacent zooids. Probably a violent retraction stimulates adjacent zooids directly.

Following retraction the polypide slowly emerges again. In undisturbed conditions all the polypides of a colony are fully extended, engaged in feeding. In most gymnolaemates not only the lophophore but a considerable extent of the necklike anterior end of the polypide is protrusible from the orifice (Fig. 111), exposing the anus to the exterior; but cyclostomes can protrude only far enough to bring the mouth on a level with the orifice. The expanded lophophore maintains a general funnel shape (Fig. 110B) and may be turned in any direction. Since the tentacles are provided with muscle fibers, they can move independently and are seen constantly flicking in and out. The tentacles may also spread out or close together, or their distal ends may bend together. Ectoprocts are ciliary feeders, apparently without the assistance of mucus. The lateral ciliary tracts of the tentacles maintain a strong beat that moves a current of water down the center of the tentacular funnel toward the mouth and out between the tentacles (Borg, 1926a; Atkins, 1932; Fig. 153A, B). Nutritive particles in the current are retained and swallowed. The food consists of microscopic organisms, mainly diatoms (Fig. 156). The ciliary beat can be stopped or reversed or its speed altered, perhaps a means of preventing the escape of food particles in the outgoing current. According to Borg (1926a), the addition of carbon or carmine suspension to the sea water results in partial or complete retraction of the tentacular crown, but Ries (1936), working on Zoobotryon, found that any small particles—carmine, carbon, sperm, blood corpuscles, starch grains, milk globules, thin emulsions of egg yolk and coagulated egg white—were swallowed indiscriminately unless offered in too dense suspension, whereupon retraction ensued. Rejection by means of ciliary reversal was seen only in case of overly large particles. Rejection can also be accomplished by the bending of the tentacle tips together, thus impeding the current, or by closure of the mouth.   Particles already taken into the pharynx may be ejected by reversal of the pharyngeal cilia, while the mouth is open. Atkins (1932) observed in *Flustrellidra hispida* (and the same had been seen in *Pherusella* by Prouho, 1892, and was later noticed by Marcus, 1941a, in various ctenostomes, further in *Watersipora cucullata*) a narrow ciliated groove in the ventral pharynx wall, continued onto the lophophoral base, whose cilia beat outward and carry unwanted particles away (rejection groove, Fig. 153*B*, *C*).   Rejected and ejected particles often gather near the mouth (Borg, 1926a) and are flushed away by a sudden widening followed by a sudden closure of the tentacular crown.   During feeding the mouth stands open most of the time, closing only now and then very briefly (Silén, 1944b) and constantly changing the size of its opening.   With the mouth open food may be swept into the pharynx by the action of the latter's cilia or by the expansion of the esophagus; and sudden contraction of the latter may cause the food to fly out of the open mouth.   Food generally accumulates in the esophagus and with closed mouth is swallowed into the stomach by a contraction wave passing along the pharynx.   Such swallowings occur at irregular intervals, perhaps two or three per minute.

Most of the available information about response to various factors is contained in the article of Marcus (1926b), who worked with *Farrella repens* and *Electra pilosa*.   Response to touch on the expanded lophophore ranges from bending of one tentacle to complete retraction.   After 10 to 20 repetitions of mechanical stimulation the polypide may fail to retract or may remain retracted.   The order of sensitivity to contact was cystid, mouth, inner surface of the tentacles, outer surface of the tentacles. Bronstein (1937) reported as very sensitive areas on which a touch would evoke violent retraction: margin of orifice, edge of operculum, pleated collar of ctenostomes.   No response follows mechanical stimulation of stolons.   Thigmotaxis must play an important role in the biology of gymnolaemates, but has been little studied.   If a piece of *Farrella* stolon with zooids is suspended from a vertical cord, the stolon will make contact with the cord and grow along it (Fig. 154*A*).   Pieces of *Electra* colonies detached from a substrate put out around the edge stolonlike outgrowths (Fig. 154*B*) that may show some zooidal differentiation.   They seek attachment, showing positive geotropic curvature, and on making contact differentiate into ordinary zooids.   In the absence of other contact these stolons may curve around and overgrow the piece of colony to which they belong.   Putting out of stolons is probably a general reaction of gymnolaemates to any factor that retards or suppresses normal growth. *Farrella* was found to exhibit positive rheotaxis.   Attached pieces of colonies placed in a current grow out stolons on the side facing the current

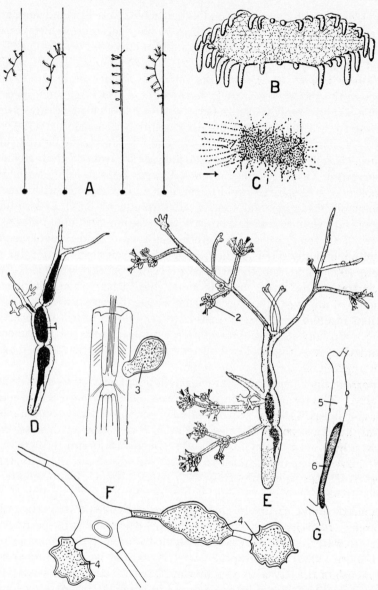

FIG. 154.—Ecology.   *A*, piece of *Farrella*, suspended from a cord, bending and growing
along the cord.   *B*, piece of *Electra* colony, detached from its substrate, putting out stolons
around the edge that show positive geotaxis.   *C*, *Farrella* colony growing against a current,
schematic.   (*A–C, after Marcus,* 1926b.)   *D*, piece of *Zoobotryon* remaining from disintegrating colony.   *E*, same piece as *D* regenerated 25 days later.   (*D, E, after Zirpolo,*
1923d.)   *F*, two pieces of *Victorella pavida* with winter buds (*after Braem,* 1951).   *G*,
winter bud of *Paludicella* (*after Harmer,* 1913).   1, living substance; 2, zooids; 3, type of
bud formed on free stems; 4, type of bud formed against substrate; 5, empty zoecium; 6,
winter bud.

(Fig. 154*C*), and the crowns of individual zooids were directed against the current. Colonies of *Farrella* and *Electra* showed no growth response to light, but the latter produced more zooids in darkened conditions, as also noted for this species by Issel (1912); but McDougall (1943) reported greater growth of *Bugula neritina* near the surface or in sunlit areas, although the zooids face away from the light. However, some species of *Bugula* exhibit positive phototaxis with zooids, rhizoids, and stolons growing toward the light in laboratory cultures (Schneider, 1955; Aymes, 1956). Colonies of *Tendra zostericola* tend to grow on the lighted side of aquaria (Bogolepov, 1907). *Farrella* and *Electra* react to gradually rising temperature by retraction, often followed by extension with slack tentacles, or by repeated rapid retractions and extensions, with eventual permanent retraction and loss of all response at 32°C. Lowering of temperature gave similar responses with cessation of response at 4°C. for *Electra*, 7°C. for *Farrella*. A lowering of even 3°C. may evoke sudden retraction of many zooids in the *Electra* colony, but normal extension soon follows. Thermal sensitivity appears vested in the tentacles. Weak concentrations of citric acid, quinine, and sugar, when eliciting any response at all, evoked a slack attitude of the tentacles; stronger concentrations resulted in lasting retraction, reversible on return to normal sea water. Both cystid and tentacular crown appear responsive to chemical stimulation, and the zooids detected quinine in concentrations weaker than appreciable to the human tongue.

Farrella and *Electra* showed considerable adaptivity to alterations of salinity. The former after initial reduced reactivity adjusted to normal behavior in sea water of 21 parts salinity per thousand (normal about 35 parts), but most zooids degenerated at 17.5 to 15 parts, although a few might adjust even to the latter figure. Zooids of *Electra* retracted at 31 parts but soon expanded; most zooids in time adjusted to 20 parts, but all were dead after some sojourn in 17.5 parts. Most gymnolaemates are probably able to adapt to some change of salinity. No decline of gymnolaemate fauna occurs in the Red Sea, with 38 to 40 parts salinity (Marcus, 1926a). Most species do not penetrate into permanently brackish waters. Of 18, mostly widely distributed, gymnolaemates taken by Osburn (1923) in Chesapeake Bay, 12 did not penetrate much above the mouth of the bay with a salinity of 32 parts. In a later study (1944) of the bay 12 of 22 species were found in areas of considerably lowered salinity, from 6 to 15 parts. Ctenostomes appear more adaptable to brackish water than cheilostomes, and cyclostomes apparently are rarely found in brackish locations. The outstanding example of a brackish-water gymnolaemate is the ctenostome *Victorella pavida* (Fig. 139*E*), whose distribution is thoroughly discussed by Braem (1951) and Brattström (1954). This species has been recorded from a variety of brackish canals, harbors, river mouths, bays, lakes, and ponds, but never from the open seashore, and is stated to endure a range of salinity from 1 to 27 parts, with an optimum at 2 to 3 parts. It occurs in many localities along the Baltic Sea, which is the largest brackish-water basin in the world, with salinity decreasing from 15 to 20 parts at its western end to 2 parts in its eastern bays. According to Borg (1947), very few gymnolaemates can endure conditions in the Baltic. Valkanov (1936, 1943) recorded *V. pavida* from river mouths opening into the Black Sea (also a very large body of brackish water), brackish lakes in Bulgaria, and three brackish localities on the Aegean Sea. In Chesapeake Bay the species was found at salinities varying from 3 to 27 parts, thriving best at 10 to 12 parts, where it would form a plushlike mat over boat bottoms, shells, and the like (Osburn, 1944). Among cheilostomes species of *Electra* and *Membranipora* show notable adaptability to decreased salinity, especially *M. crustulenta*, ranging from fresh water (two rivers in Tunis) to sea water of full strength and spread throughout the Baltic (Borg, 1931, 1947); it was found by Braem (1951) spreading rapidly up Baltic tributaries during summers of little rainfall, flourishing best at 4 to 5 parts salinity, and by Osburn (1944) throughout Chesapeake Bay at salinities of 6 to 32 parts. Other cheilostomes found by Osburn (1944) in the upper parts of Chesapeake Bay included *Membranipora membranacea*, *Electra pilosa*, and *Acanthodesia tenuis*. Species of the ctenostome *Bowerbankia*, notably *gracilis* and its variant *caudata*, tend to spread into brackish water, having been recorded from tributaries of the Baltic (Braem, 1951), the delta of the Ganges (Annandale, 1911b), and Chesapeake Bay (Osburn, 1932, 1944) well above the mouth at a salinity of 10 parts.

In warmer waters gymnolaemate colonies probably remain active throughout the year, but in temperate and cold zones seasonal cycles may obtain. Various species of *Bugula* are stated (Joliet, 1877; Grave, 1930; Mawatari, 1951) to fall to pieces in late autumn, surviving the winters only as small colonies produced by late larvae and resuming growth with temperature rise in spring. The polypides in these surviving colonies are, however, degenerate since the cystids contain brown bodies (Grave, 1930) and new polypides are regenerated in spring in the old cystids. At Naples colonies of *Zoobotryon pellucidum* disintegrate in autumn, but pieces of stem remain alive in a dormant state (Fig. 154*D*) throughout the winter and in spring put out stolons (Fig. 154*E*) into which their living tissue flows and which bud off zooids, reestablishing the colonies (Zirpolo, 1922a, b, 1923a, b, c). In Baltic areas *Membranipora crustulenta* ceases growth in autumn but the polypides survive the winter; with the onset of spring most of the old polypides degenerate and the newly regenerated polypides proceed to sexual reproduction from April to June, after which period asexual multiplication dominates (Borg, 1947). Harmer (1891b) noted that apparently dead stumps of *Crisia* colonies may bud out zooids in spring or send out rhizoids that give off branches with zooids; or old cystids may form a new orifice and regenerate a new polypide. Interesting facts have been furnished by Braem (1951) about winter survival in brackish tributaries of the Baltic of *Victorella pavida* and related ctenostomes characteristic of brackish or fresh habitats. These colonies die away at the onset of winter except for dormant winter buds that survive and in spring bud out a zooid and stolons, reestablishing the colonies. These winter buds are incipient zooids that secrete a thick crinkled cuticle about themselves and pass into a dormant state (Fig. 154F). They may form either on adherent stolons or erect branches. Colonies may begin making these winter buds in June, but most arise during the autumn months. Such buds are probably induced by falling temperature, but decline of food supply is also operative and will induce such buds in summer. With rise of temperature to 10 to 12°C., the heavy cuticle of the winter buds ruptures and the enclosed material resumes development into a polypide. A somewhat different type of winter bud, or *hibernaculum*, was described for *Paludicella articulata* by Harmer (1913). Here, too, the colonies die away in autumn, leaving alive only spindle-shaped winter buds that seem to represent the basal parts of zooids (Fig. 154G) and remain after the otherwise empty zoecium is cast off. These winter buds have a thick cuticle and yolklike inclusions and usually already show the primordium of a polypide that will develop in spring by the cracking open of the distal part of the winter bud into two valves. *Bulbella abscondita* seems to survive for long periods as stolons in submerged twigs and pieces of wood, putting out polypides under favorable conditions (Braem, 1951). Such pieces kept in aquaria in an unheated room survived through two winters and put out polypides in summer, despite receiving scarcely any food, probably drawing for nutrition on stolons concealed in the wood.

Larval behavior is of ecological importance in gymnolaemates since it determines the attachment sites of colonies. Larvae of *Bugula neritina*, *flabellata*, and *turrita* emerge from the ovicells only during daylight, beginning at dawn and continuing in increasing numbers during the early part of the day, decreasing later (Grave, 1930; McDougall, 1943; Lynch, 1947, 1949a, b; Mawatari, 1951). Hence larvae may be obtained by keeping the colonies in the dark and bringing them out into the light when larvae are wanted. These *Bugula* larvae are also strongly photopositive, a reaction that in nature may result in their moving away from the parent colonies, thus spreading the species. Positive response to light was also noted for larvae of *Bowerbankia imbricata* (Joliet, 1877) and *Watersipora cucullata* (Mawatari, 1952a), whereas Zschiesche (1909) found larvae of *Alcyonidium polyoum* indifferent to light. *Bugula* larvae generally rotate in a spiral path with the apical organ above or foremost. Before metamorphosis, *Bugula* larvae alter their positive reaction to light to a negative reaction and tend to settle in darker places and on the side of containers away from the light. In a series of horizontal chambers of varying illumination larvae of *B. neritina* tended to attach in the darker chambers (McDougall, 1943). During their photopositive phase *Bugula* larvae aggregated densely in yellow, orange, and red areas (Lynch, 1949b), but after becoming photonegative prior to attachment they select dark regions. At this time they also avoid surfaces painted with light colors or covered with glass plates of such colors and settle on dark colors (Visscher, 1927; Edmondson and Ingram, 1939). Avoidance of light probably also accounts for selection of the undersurface of horizontal or nearly horizontal plates or other objects and avoidance of surfaces much tilted from the horizontal (Grave, 1930; Miyazaki, 1938; McDougall, 1943). However, keeping larvae in darkness delays attachment and favors attachment to the surface film. McDougall (1943) noted selection of the slowest of water currents of varying speed.

The effect of altering environmental factors on the time of metamorphosis of *Bugula* larvae was studied by Lynch (1947, 1949a, b, 1952, 1955, 1956), but much of this work does not appear pertinent to the normal conditions of existence of the larvae. Raising the temperature to 30°C. accelerates attachment and metamorphosis, but temperatures of 32 to 35°C. are fatal. Mawatari (1951) reported an optimum temperature of 20 to 28°C. for larvae of *B. neritina*. Lowering the temperature prolongs the natatory period and delays attachment. The presence of a geotropic reaction appears uncertain. Lynch records that rise of temperature, keeping the larvae in darkness, and increasing the salinity of the sea water may result in attachment to the surface, but normally larvae tend to settle near the bottom in shallow water, probably as a combined result of the negative phototaxis developed prior to attachment and reduction of ciliary activity causing the larvae to sink rather than as a genuine geotropic response. Mechanical agitation also evokes descent of the larvae. Diluting the sea water delays the metamorphosis of *B. neritina* (but not of *B. flabellata* or *turrita*) and eventuates in descent after a long period of swimming at the surface. Increasing the salinity of the sea water by evaporation or addition of sodium chloride hastens the onset of metamorphosis, which may occur after a swimming period of 3 to 30 minutes in place of the usual 2 or more hours. This effect is not one of increased osmotic pressure since raising the pressure by means of sugar is ineffective. Raising the alkalinity of the sea water (up to pH 9.6 from the normal 8.0 to 8.2) had little effect on the length of the natatory period, but acidifying the sea water was deleterious, preventing normal metamorphosis even at pH 6; at pH 5.4 to 5.0 most larvae swam but briefly (not more than 15 minutes) and died in attempted metamorphosis or without attaching; in pH 4.6 ciliary action stopped within 3 minutes and the larvae sank to the bottom. Mawatari (1951) recorded pH 7.0 to 8.5 as optimum for larvae of *B. neritina.*

Lynch concludes that "heat, light, salinity, and the relative proportions of ions in the sea water can profoundly affect the natatory period of *Bugula* larvae and the subsequent growth of zooids." The reactions of *Bugula* larvae would seem to condition their attachment to the underside of horizontal substrates in somewhat darkened areas in water of good salinity not subject to agitation, hence somewhat below the surface.

19. Physiology.—As information about the occurrence of chitin in gymnolaemates is scanty and contradictory (Krukenberg, 1886; Ambronn, 1890; Wester, 1910), the author (1958) made extensive tests and found that the entire zoecium of ctenostomes, including the outer layer of the stolons, and of noncalcified cheilostomes, including avicularia, is composed of chitin; further, the cuticle of the zoecium and frontal membrane of calcified cheilostomes is chitinous. Contrary to the finding of Richards and Cutkomp (1946), the entire zoecium of *Bugula* is made of typical chitin.

The calcium carbonate of the zoecium of both recent and fossil gymnolaemates is in the form of calcite (Kelly, 1901; Meigen, 1901; Prenant, 1927; Stehli, 1956). Available data on the chemical composition of gymnolaemates, drawn mostly from the work of Loppens (1920) and Clarke and Wheeler (1922), are summarized by Vinogradov (1953). Loppens reported the ctenostome *Alcyonidium gelatinosum* to consist of 95 per cent water, 4.80 per cent organic matter, and 0.27 per cent salts, hence higher in water content than the cheilostomes *Flustra foliacea* with 80 to 84 per cent water and *Mem. membranacea* with 90 per cent. Following data are in terms of dry weight. Clarke and Wheeler gave the mineral constituents of a number of cheilostomes as 87 to 96 per cent calcium carbonate, 0.63 to 7 per cent of magnesium carbonate, 1.3 to 2.8 of calcium sulphate, a trace of calcium phosphate, and 0.2 to 5.5 of silicon (foreign sand grains?). Their analysis of *Bugula* was 63 to 64 per cent calcium carbonate, 10 to 11 per cent magnesium carbonate, 5 to 8 of calcium sulphate, and 1.6 to 2.7 of calcium phosphate. A high content of magnesium carbonate appears correlated with an increase in calcium phosphate and with less compact structure. Walther (1885) reported for two cheilostomes 84 to 90 per cent calcium carbonate and 2.5 to 4.7 per cent magnesium carbonate, together with silicon, iron, and aluminum. The study of Loppens (1920) attempted to correlate mineral constituents with ecological and growth factors, finding a variation in calcareous content from 33 to 98 per cent. The erect form of growth appears associated with higher calcareous content than the incrusting, thus: *Flustra foliacea*, erect 97 to 99 per cent, incrusting 60 to 65 per cent; *Electra pilosa*, erect

51.5 per cent, incrusting 33.4 per cent; and the same is true of *Mem. membranacea*. Loppens also claimed that the same species is more calcareous when growing in brackish than in sea water. Thus eight analyses of *Mem. membranacea* gave 44 to 68 per cent calcium carbonate in sea water, 75 to 91 in brackish water. Pieces from brackish water weighed twice as much as those of the same dimensions from sea water. Bouffandeau and Sandray (1955) analyzed dry *Mem. membranacea* and *Flustra foliacea*, finding 70 to 80 per cent minerals and 20 to 30 per cent organic materials. The minerals were said to consist of calcium carbonate and calcium phosphate in about equal quantities with a small amount of magnesium salts; the figure for phosphate here is certainly far higher than that obtained by previous workers. Phillips (1922) reported traces of copper, zinc, iron, and manganese in marine ectoprocts.

The scanty available information about pigments in gymnolaemates has been summarized by Karrer, Jucker, and Brande (1950) and Fox (1953). Carotenoids of the groups of carotenes and xanthophylls (IV, page 381) are known to occur in several species, and no doubt the yellow, orange, and red colors of larvae belong to this category. *Bugula neritina* and *flabellata* contain no carotenoids, but instead a purplish pigment vested in the coelomocytes and related to adenochrome, a red pigment previously known only from *Octopus* (Villela, 1948a, b). Carotenoids, mostly carotenes, were found to be responsible for the reddish color of *Schizoporella unicornis*, *Steginoporella magnilabris*, and a species of *Trigonopora* (Villela, 1948a).

The food was previously followed into the stomach (page 403), which shows an almost endless variety of movements and changes of shape (Silén, 1944b). Concomitant contraction of the cardia and expansion of the stomach caecum draws food into the latter, and the reverse actions can return particles to the cardia. No grinding action of the stomach was seen, but the caecal contents whirl constantly as a result of the action of the pyloric cilia. The food is thereby formed into a rotating cord extending from the caecum into the pylorus, and this cord rotates at a rate of 70 to 150 turns per minute. After remaining for some time in the stomach the food passes into the intestine but may be sucked back for further digestion by the sudden depression of the stomach roof. To pass the food remnants into the intestine the pylorus depresses into the stomach, and thereby its exit into the intestine, usually closed, is opened. In the intestine the food remnants are formed into fecal pellets that are sometimes pressed out by the retraction of the polypide but are usually voided by intestinal contractions while the polypide is extended.

Ries (1936) followed the fate of various particles offered (carbon, carmine, blood corpuscles, sperm, milk, yolk, coagulated egg white) in the transparent ctenostome *Zoobotryon pellucidum*. This species has a short

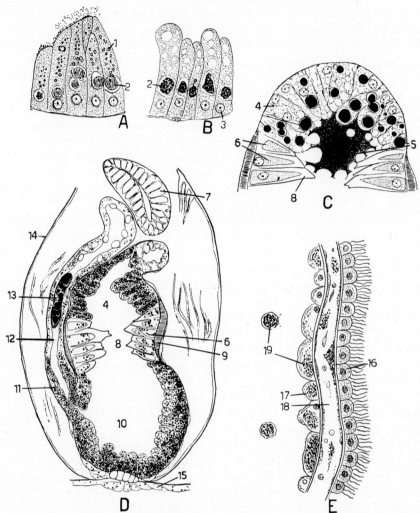

FIG. 155.—Physiology. *A*, caecal epithelium of *Zoobotryon*, 9 hours after feeding carbon particles. *B*, same as *A*, 24 hours after feeding carbon; carbon has attached to red-brown inclusions. *C*, phagocytosis of fat globules of milk by cardiac epithelium of *Zoobotryon*. *D*, horizontal section of a zooid of *Zoobotryon* after feeding egg yolk, showing fat spherules in cardia, gizzard, stomach caecum, and pylorus. (*A–D, after Ries*, 1936.) *E*, optical section of a tentacle of *Bugula*, after methyl green staining, showing emission of dye from the tentacle (*after Calvet*, 1900). 1, carbon particles; 2, red-brown inclusions; 3, nucleus; 4, cells of cardia; 5, fat; 6, cells of gizzard; 7, esophagus; 8, gizzard teeth; 9, muscles; 10, caecum; 11, pylorus; 12, intestine; 13, feces; 14, cystid; 15, stolon; 16, outer epithelium of tentacle; 17, inner epithelium of tentacle; 18, tentacular coelom; 19, dye.

ciliated pharynx, a long esophagus of vacuolated cells, and a long cardia altered proximally into a gizzard (Fig. 114E). Regrettably, Ries makes no statement as to the activity of the gizzard. Ingested carbon, carmine, and similar particles are whirled about in the stomach for some time, and then most are ejected in the fecal pellets beginning an hour or more after ingestion. Some, however, are taken into the epithelial cells of the stomach caecum and gradually accumulate in balls in the proximal part of these cells near the nucleus (Fig. 155A, B), attaching themselves to the red-brown inclusions already present in the caecal cells. Useless particles of this type are mostly retained only by the older polypides of the colony, rejected by the younger polypides that have not yet developed the red-brown inclusions. Fat spheres of milk and yolk are readily ingested and mostly fused into larger spheres that are moved about in the stomach and often defecated apparently unchanged. Part, however, within $\frac{1}{2}$ to 2 hours are phagocytized by the epithelium of the cardia and stomach caecum. The cardiac cells start bulging into the lumen, forming a syncytium with their tips, and thus taking in large fat globules (Fig. 155C). Within 2 to 5 hours fat ingestion occurs in the stomach and pylorus, and by 10 to 20 hours after feeding the epithelium of the entire digestive tract from the beginning of the cardia to the end of the pylorus is full of fat spheres (Fig. 155D). Within 2 to 3 days fat appears in all parts of the polypide, but the method of transport could not be ascertained. Blood corpuscles were haemolyzed in the digestive lumen but apparently not phagocytized by the epithelium. The latter engulfed sperm to some extent, and chromatin granules were later seen joining the red-brown inclusions. Grains of raw potato starch lay in the digestive lumen 2 or 3 days and then were voided unaltered; but starch grains swollen by heating were utilized. Some remained unaltered in the stomach lumen up to 20 to 26 hours, but thereafter the test for starch gradually disappeared and glycogen appeared throughout the stomach epithelium, including the gizzard. Apparently the starch is hydrolyzed in the lumen and absorbed as soluble split products, then re-formed into glycogen, eventually apparent throughout the entire zooid. After 40 hours glycogen disappeared from the digestive epithelium but could be followed along the funiculus through the pore plate at the zooid base and into the funicular cords and mesenchyme of the stolons. The fate of protein in the form of particles of coagulated egg white could not be followed satisfactorily, but protein seemed to be digested in the stomach lumen and the products absorbed by the stomach epithelium. Apparently fat, glycogen, and protein are stored in the stolons, which may survive adverse conditions and regenerate the colony from their food stores (page 408). Phagocytized non-nutritive particles are added to the red-brown inclusions of the caecal wall and become part of the brown bodies resulting from the degeneration of polypides. In stoloniferous ctenostomes, to which group *Zoobotryon* belongs, cystids containing brown bodies fall off and do not regenerate polypides.

Ries was unable to demonstrate the presence of formed enzymatic secretions, but the cardiac and caecal epithelia are generally believed to

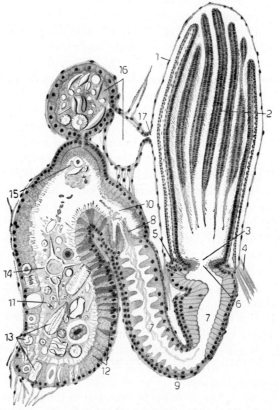

Fig. 156.—Physiology (concluded). Horizontal section of a polypide of *Thalamoporella evelinae*, showing diatoms in the caecal epithelium (*after Marcus, 1941a; original water color from this article, courtesy Eveline Marcus*). 1, tentacle sheath; 2, tentacular crown; 3, mouth; 4, retractor of the lophophore; 5, ganglion; 6, pharynx; 7, esophagus; 8, cardiac valve; 9, muscle layer; 10, cardia; 11, stomach caecum; 12, two types of enzymatic cells; 13, diatoms; 14, radiolarian; 15, pylorus; 16, intestine; 17, anus.

be glandular; they contain in at least some areas formed material probably of enzymatic nature (Figs. 115*C*, *D*, 156). Calvet (1900) saw vesicles discharging from the stomach epithelium into its lumen in several gymnolaemates and presumed the contents to be enzymatic. Roaf (1909) found peptic and starch-digesting enzymes but no trypsin or lipase in *Cellaria fistulosa*.

The reaction of the digestive tract of *Zoobotryon* was tested by Ries by means of particles of coagulated egg white stained with indicators. These showed the stomach contents to have a pH of 6.5 to 7.0, whereas the distal part of the intestine gave the same alkaline reaction as sea water, pH 8.2.

Based on Ries's work one may suppose that digestion in gymnolaemates is partly extracellular and partly intracellular. Intracellular digestion was also demonstrated for a cheilostome, *Thalamoporella evelinae*, by Marcus (1941a), whose sections showed diatoms in the cells of the caecal wall (Fig. 156). Both types of digestion take place primarily in the stomach caecum. Silén (1944b) observed the rotating cord in the caecum in a number of living gymnolaemates, including two carnose ctenostomes, and concluded that extracellular digestion occurs mainly while the food particles are involved in this rotation.

Gymnolaemates are devoid of an excretory system. Various workers, especially Harmer (1891a), Calvet (1900), Marcus (1926b), and Ries and Schoelsel (1934), have attempted to elucidate the mechanism of excretion by the usual method of exposing the animals to vital dyes added to the sea water. The results are unsatisfactory and difficult to summarize because different dyes affect various tissues differently, the same tissue reacts differently to different dyes, and different species take up dyes to very different extents. Some species are scarcely stainable at all. Harmer, applying mainly indigo carmine and bismarck brown to *Bugula* and *Flustra*, observed dye intake mainly by the coelomocytes, to a less extent by funicular tissue, young growing points, tentacles, and parts of the digestive tract, chiefly the caecum. Similar observations were made by Calvet, using the same dyes; they were taken up chiefly by the vesicular coelomocytes, tentacles, and wall of the digestive tract. *Bowerbankia* and *Amathia* scarcely stained at all. Marcus, employing methylene blue, noted intense staining of the intertentacular organ of *Electra pilosa*. The tentacles of *Bugula, Electra*, and *Farrella* accumulate the dye in vesicles that burst and discharge to the exterior. Dye also was gathered by the stomach epithelium, buds, stolon tips and other growing points, and funicular tissue and mesenchyme. In the experiments of Ries and Schoelsel on *Zoobotryon pellucidum*, basic dyes, especially toluidin blue, stained primarily the tentacles, to a lesser extent the tentacle sheath, coelomocytes, and growing tips of stolons. Acid dyes were taken up poorly and were generally deleterious, but might eventually accumulate in the tentacle sheath, digestive tract, stolon tips, and gizzard teeth. The last observation is interesting in that the gizzard teeth were already indicated as more alkaline than other parts. In general, any prolonged exposure to dyes is injurious and often results in degeneration of the colonies. The work with dyes seems to indicate tentacles, stomach epithelium, growing points, and mesenchymal tissue, including coelomocytes, as sites of excretion. Dyes are retained for long periods by coelomocytes, and this may be supposed to indicate that these cells store excretory matters. The colored inclusions that naturally accumulate in the caecal epithelium are generally regarded by students of ectoprocts as excretory matters, although there is some dispute that this accumulation is the direct cause of polypide degeneration. Besides the caecal epithelium the tentacles appear to be important sites of excretion. Calvet and Marcus have observed in living zooids the emission from the tentacles of granules and spherules containing dye (Fig. 155E), and the latter author also witnessed the passage of such particles without the use of dye. Harmer (1898) noted the presence of resistant brown vesicles in the tentacles and in or beneath the terminal membrane of cyclostome zooids and considered them to be of excretory nature, since they were very numerous in the tentacles of degenerating colonies and increased in number from spring through summer. Similar brown masses contained in vacuoles were noticed by Waters (1904) in the tentacle tips of *Smittina* and other cheilostome genera.

Respiratory and circulatory mechanisms are also wanting but are totally unnecessary in animals of such small size that also have a large expanse of surface by way of the tentacular crown. A circulation of the coelomic fluid is known only in the fresh-water gymnolaemate *Paludicella*, in which bunches of cilia occur on the coelomic wall in the proximal part of the zooid (Meyer, 1927). These produce a current running anteriorly on the dorsal side, posteriorly on the ventral side.

Luminescence has been claimed for several species of gymnolaemates, but all except the last record must be regarded as doubtful. Landsborough (1842, 1852) claimed to have seen luminescence in *Walkeria uva*, *Mem. membranacea*, and *Electra pilosa*. The second species was said to blaze like a sheet of fire when shaken, and the zooids of the last to light up like stars. Vélain (1877) stated of a species of *Bugula* growing on the wall of a cave on an island in the Indian Ocean that if agitated the branches became illuminated with bright colors passing from red to green or blue! It appears quite impossible that any species of *Bugula* is luminescent. Gadeau de Kerville (1890) claimed to have seen luminescence in *Scrupocellaria reptans*, and Molisch (1904) recorded luminescence again in *Electra pilosa*. Harvey (1952), however, failed to find any luminescence in *Electra pilosa* or *E. hastingsae*. The only record of luminescence in gymnolaemates to which one may give credence is that of Kato (1950) for *Acanthodesia serrata*, which when stimulated gives off a bluish light. He found a pair of luminescent areas on the frontal membrane, consisting of compact masses of spherical gland cells containing poorly staining granules. Each mass protrudes as a slight prominence with a pore, but no discharge of granules through the pore was observed.

20. Ecology : Geographic Distribution.—Gymnolaemates are found in all seas, in all latitudes, and at all depths to about 6000 m., although most abundant in the littoral zone, over the continental shelf, to a depth of 200 to 300 m. They are about equally abundant everywhere (Marcus, 1921a), except in brackish areas where their number is markedly diminished, as notably in the Baltic Sea. Hence, despite their delicate construction, they are obviously adaptable to a wide range of conditions, notably temperature, flourishing in both polar and tropical waters. This adaptability is attested by the considerable number of littoral cosmopolitan species, including in the term cosmopolitan both polar regions, and the larger number of widely spread species lacking only in polar areas. Among such littoral cosmopolitan and nearly cosmopolitan species that turn up in every collection may be mentioned the ctenostomes *Alcyonidium polyoum* and *mamillatum*, *Nolella dilatata* and *gigantea*, *Bowerbankia gracilis* (includes *caudata*), *Walkeria uva*, *Amathia distans* and *lendigera*, *Pherusella tubulosa*, and *Buskia nitens* (Fig. 104D); and the cheilostomes *Aetea anguina* (Fig. 141E), *truncata*, and *sica* (= *recta*), *Membranipora membranacea* and *tuberculata* (includes *tehuelca*), *Conopeum reticulum*, *Copidozoum tenuirostre*, *Beania mirabilis*, *Scrupocellaria scruposa*, *Caberea boryi*, *Colletosia radiata*, *Hippothoa hyalina* (Fig. 120A, B) and *divaricata*, *Tryptostega venusta* (Fig. 143D), *Hippodiplosia pertusa*, *Arthropoma cecili* (Fig. 144G), *Microporella ciliata* (Fig. 106F), *Parasmittina trispinosa*, and *Costazia* (= *Siniopelta*) *costazi*. There do not seem to be any cosmopolitan cyclostomes, and in general this group appears less adaptable than the other gymnolaemate groups. The wide distribution of many gymnolaemates may be attributed to dispersal on drifting seaweeds, floating pieces of wood, and ship bottoms. Thus Allen (1953) remarks that gymnolaemates never seen before on Australian coasts may suddenly become abundant, having been brought in on ships, evidently enduring passage through tropical waters.

Gymnolaemates other than these widely distributed species appear limited mainly by temperature, for there are a large number of species typical of polar and subpolar waters and another set characteristic of warmer waters. The gymnolaemates of arctic and subarctic waters have been extensively collected and described. Borg (1933b) reviewed the species found to that date and gave an extensive literature list, of which the more important articles on arctic gymnolaemates are those of Waters (1900), Bidenkap (1900, 1906), Kluge (1907a, b), Levinsen (1916), Nordgaard (1918, 1923, 1924, 1929), and Osburn (1919, 1923); and later Borg (1933c) summarized the findings from a zoogeographical standpoint. The literature to this time concerned primarily the Atlantic Arctic from the Kara Sea and Novaya Zemlya to Greenland. Lack of knowledge of the Pacific Arctic led the older workers to distinguish between an Atlantic arctic and a Pacific arctic gymnolaemate fauna. However, the later work of Osburn (1950, 1952, 1953, 1955) has shown that practically all true arctic gymnolaemates are circumpolar. A large number of species flourish in arctic waters at temperatures of about zero the year round. Because of difficult conditions at the surface most arctic species occur below 10 m. depth and the majority live between depths of 50 and 100 m., while few are found below 500 m. (Bidenkap, 1900). Therefore arctic gymnolaemates are primarily littoral. Of the common circumarctic species, apart from a number of cosmopolitan species in arctic waters, may be mentioned the ctenostome *Alcyonidium disciforme;* the anascan cheilostomes *Eucratea loricata, Carbasea carbasea, Terminoflustra* (= *Flustra*) *membranaceo-truncata, Membranipora serrulata, Hincksina* (= *Callopora*) *nigrans, Cauloramphus cymbaeformis, Callopora aurita, craticula, lineata, and whiteavesi, Bidenkapia* (= *Callopora*) *spitsbergensis, Tegella arctica and unicornis, Amphiblestrum trifolium, Doryporella* (= *Callopora*) *spathulifera, Microporina borealis, Tricellaria gracilis, Dendrobeania murrayana, Cribrilina annulata,* and *Reginella* (= *Cribrilina*) *spitsbergensis;* the ascophoran cheilostomes *Hippothoa expansa, Harmeria scutulata, Hincksipora* (= *Mucronella*) *spinulifera, Umbonula arctica, Stomachetosella* (= *Schizoporella*) *cruenta, Posterula* (= *Escharoides*) *sarsi, Ragionula* (= *Escharoides*) *rosacea, Schizomavella porifera, Hipplodiplosia reticulatopunctata, Stephanosella biaperta, Porella acutirostris, concinna,* and *minuta, Smittina arctica, bella,* and *minuscula, Parasmittina jeffreysi, Ramphostomella bilaminata, costata,* and *ovata, Cysticella saccata, Mucronella ventricosa, Costazia surcularis* and *ventricosa,* and *Myriozella plana* (= *Myriozoum crustaceum);* and the cyclostomes *Crisia eburnea, Proboscina incrassata, Diplosolen obelium, Tubulipora flabellaris,* and *Lichenopora verrucaria.* The scientific names used here follow Osburn (1955) and often differ much from the form of these names that appears in the literature of arctic gymnolaemates. In addition to strictly arctic species, the arctic gymnolaemate fauna also includes a number of arctic subspecies or varieties or close relatives of adjacent boreal forms or variants of widely spread species as pointed out by Borg (1933c).

Many of the arctic species spread south along the adjacent continental coast and participate in the boreal fauna. From the European Arctic they descend along the Scandinavian coast. Lofoten is regarded by Nordgaard (1918) as the southern limit of true arctic species and the northern limit of the northward spread of boreal species made possible by the warmer Atlantic currents along the Scandinavian coast. Main studies of the gymnolaemate fauna of European Atlantic coasts are those of Nordgaard (1906) and Silén (1935, 1943, 1951b, c) for Scandinavian coasts, Marcus (1926a, 1940, 1950) for the German and Danish North Sea, Echalier and Prenant (1951) for the channel coast of France, and

Hincks (1880) for the British Isles. Common species here, intermingled with arctic and cosmopolitan elements, are the ctenostomes *Farrella repens* (Figs. 117*E*, 137*C*), *Frustrellidra hispida,* and *Triticella koreni* (Fig. 138*F, G*); the anascan cheilostomes *Eucratea chelata, Electra pilosa, Membranipora crustulenta, Flustra barleei, foliacea,* and *securifrons, Callopora dumerili, Amphiblestrum flemingi, Caberea ellisi, Scrupocellaria reptans, scabra,* and *scrupea, Bicellariella ciliata, Bugula plumosa* and *flabellata, Kinetoskias smitti, Membraniporella nitida, Cribrilina punctata;* the ascophoran cheilostomes *Chorizopora brogniartii, Schizoporella unicornis, Cryptosula pallasiana, Hippodiplosia foliacea, Mucronella ventricosa, Palmicellaria skenei, Escharella immersa* (= *Mucronella peachii*), *Sertella beaniana,* and *Cellepora ramulosa, pumicosa, dichotoma,* and *avicularis;* and the cyclostomes *Crisidia cornuta, Filicrisia geniculata, Crisia eburnea, Tubulipora liliacea, Idmonea atlantica, Stomatopora major, Berenicea patina, Hornera lichenoides* and *violacea,* and *Lichenopora hispida.* These species are not necessarily limited to the area in question. Marcus (1950) listed a total of 148 species for the Denmark area, Hincks (1880) 229 for Great Britain.

From the European boreal there is the usual southward spread into the Mediterranean and along the eastern temperate Atlantic down the western African coast, the area often called boreo-lusitanian-mauritanian. Mediterranean gymnolaemates have been discussed by Waters (1896), Hincks (1886), Calvet (1902a, b, 1905, 1927a, b), Norman (1909), Friedl (1918), Marcus (1920), Canu and Bassler (1930a), and Gautier (1949, 1952, 1955b). There has been the usual collecting along these coasts to the Cape Verde Islands by the yachts of the oceanographic station of Monaco (Jullien and Calvet, 1903; Calvet, 1931), augmented by the collections of the *Travailleur* and the *Talisman* (Jullien, 1882; Calvet, 1906); other articles on the area are those of Norman (1909), Waters (1918), and Canu and Bassler (1925, 1928a). The gymnolaemate fauna of the Mediterranean and the adjacent coasts of the boreo-temperate Atlantic consists of a mixture of cosmopolitan and widely spread species, European boreal species, species widely spread in the temperate North Atlantic, and a limited number of species more or less characteristic of the region although often found sporadically elsewhere. In this last group may be mentioned the ctenostome *Mimosella gracilis;* the anascan cheilostomes *Flustra securifrons* and *papyracea, Cupuladria* (= *Membranipora*) *canariensis, Cellaria salicornioides, Bugula ditrupae,* and *Scrupocellaria bertholleti;* the ascophoran cheilostomes *Hippopodina kirchenpaueri, Umbonula verrucosa, Schizoporella sanguinea* and *linearis, Hippodiplosia ottomulleriana, Smittina* (or *Porella*) *cervicornis, Retepora couchii* and *mediterranea, Cellepora coronopus,* and *Myriozoum truncata;* and the cyclostome *Hornera frondiculosa.*

From arctic regions, there is the expected descent of species along the boreal and temperate Atlantic Coast of North America. Presumably many of the species arrive by way of Greenland, which has been well studied by a succession of expeditions. Osburn (1919) tabulated the gymnolaemate findings of 14 different collections from Greenland, comprising 182 species and varieties. Most of Greenland falls within the Arctic Circle, and its gymnolaemate fauna was included in the discussion of arctic gymnolaemates given above. Main articles on the gymnolaemates of eastern Canada from Labrador to the Bay of Fundy are those of Whiteaves (1901) and Osburn (1912b). The boreal fauna here consists for the most part of a mixture of cosmopolitan, arctic, and European boreal species already mentioned in the foregoing lists. Southward, articles on the gymnolaemates of the Massachusetts coast have been written by Osburn (1912a) and Rogick and Croasdale (1949). Here, too, there occur common cosmopolitan species such as *Walkeria uva, Alcyonidium polyoum, Bowerbankia gracilis, Aetea anguina* and *sica, Hippothoa hyalina, Microporina ciliata,* and *Parasmittina trispinosa;* and common arctic and European boreal species such as *Flustrellidra hispida, Eucratea loricata, Caberea ellisi, Scrupocellaria scabra, Bicellariella ciliata, Dendrobaenia murrayana, Bugula flabellata, Electra pilosa, Cribrilina annulata, Schizoporella unicornis, Cryptosula pallasiana, Crisia eburnea* and *denticulata, Tubulipora flabellaris* and *liliacea, Idmonea atlantica, Stomatopora diastoporoides,* and *Lichenopora verrucaria.* It follows from this that there are a large number of gymnolaemate species spread throughout the littoral zone of the temperate, boreal, and arctic Atlantic, hence occurring on both European and North American coasts. However, a few species appear limited to the North American side. Thus *Bugula cucullifera* has been found only from Labrador to Cape Cod. *Bugula turrita,* one of the most common species of the Cape Cod area, is also restricted to the western Atlantic, although ranging southward to Brazil. The ctenostome *Anguinella palmata* is a characteristic western Atlantic species, from Cape Cod to Brazil, but also occurs on western European coasts and in the Panamic region. Other ctenostomes that appear restricted to the western Atlantic are *Alcyonidium verrilli,* Cape Cod to Chesapeake Bay, *Aeverrillia armata,* Maine to Brazil, and *Triticella elongata,* Cape Cod to the Carolinas.

Arctic species apparently range no farther south than the Cape Cod area, but Atlantic boreal species may descend still farther southward. Osburn (1932, 1944) described the gymnolaemates of the Chesapeake Bay area, finding 18 species, including those just mentioned as restricted to the western Atlantic; most of the others are cosmopolitan or widely spread species except two, *Acanthodesia tenuis* and *Electra hastingsae* (= *monostachys*), which also occur in the European boreal area.

McDougall (1943) listed as the most common gymnolaemates of the Carolina area *Bugula neritina* and *avicularia, Schizoporella unicornis,* and *Anguinella palmata,* three of which have a fairly wide distribution, including the Atlantic boreal; the somewhat restricted distribution of the last was noted above but also includes the eastern boreal Atlantic. The gymnolaemates of the Carolina area have recently been extensively reported by Maturo (1957) and found to include many species typical of warmer waters, as this area lies on the edge of the subtropical zone; species descended from the north also appear off Carolina.

Available knowledge about the gymnolaemates of the Pacific Coast of North America, including the work of earlier investigators (Hincks, 1882–1884; Robertson, 1900, 1905, 1908, 1910; the O'Donoghues, 1923, 1925, 1927), together with his own work on the extensive collections of the Allan Hancock Expeditions, is presented by Osburn (1950, 1952, 1953) in a scholarly and comprehensive manner. The gymnolaemate fauna along the Pacific Coast of North America is zoned, although not very definitely, by temperature (Osburn, 1950). The arctic part of the coast, comprising Alaska and the islands of the Bering Sea, is known almost wholly from a collection made at Point Barrow, Alaska, well within the Arctic Circle. In this collection of 113 species, all but 11 were already known from the Atlantic part of the Arctic, hence are practically circumarctic (Osburn, 1955). Following the strictly arctic area comes a long stretch of coast from southern Alaska to Point Conception, California, along which the water is constantly cold the year round. Osburn notes some distinction here faunistically between the more northern and more southern parts of the coast with the boundary about at Vancouver Island but with much mixing of the two faunas in the Puget Sound and Vancouver areas. Collecting of gymnolaemates north of California has been most extensive in these two areas (Robertson, Hincks, the O'Donoghues). The gymnolaemates of the British Columbia–Puget Sound area are mainly a mixture of circumarctic, cosmopolitan, and general Pacific Coast species but include a few forms limited to the region, according to present information, such as the cheilostomes *Hincksina pallida, Callopora exilis, Dakaria dawsoni, Rhamphostomella cellata, Lepraliella bispina, Cheilopora praelonga,* and the cyclostome *Crisidia pugeti.* Circumarctic species usually do not descend below southern Alaska or British Columbia, but a few range as far as Southern California, as the cheilostomes *Callopora lineata, Tegella unicornis, Hippothoa expansa,* and *Porella acutirostris;* and the cyclostomes *Diplosolen obelium, Tubulipora flabellaris,* and *Lichenopora verrucaria.* These are also among the species that tend to range south on the western Atlantic Coast, hence are evidently adaptable to a wide range of temperature.

A large number of species appear limited to the Pacific Coast of North

America, extending from southern Alaska to Southern California, where they mingle with subtropical and tropical forms ascending from the Panamic region. Among these may be mentioned the anascan cheilostomes *Membranipora villosa, Copidozoum protectum, Tegella robertsonae, Chapperia patula, Tricellaria occidentalis, Scrupocellaria californica* and *diegensis, Bugula pacifica, Dendrobaenia curvirostris* and *laxa,* and *Reginella furcatus;* the ascophoran cheilostomes *Dakaria ordinata, Microporella umbonata* and *setiformis, Parasmittina collifera, Rhynchozoon tumulosum,* and *Lagenipora spinulosa;* and the cyclostomes *Tubulipora tuba* and *Filicrisia geniculata.* Some species, however, have a still wider range, extending from southern Alaska or British Columbia to Central America or the Galapagos Islands. *Hippodiplosia insculpta, Porella porifera,* and *Diaperoecia californica* are known to range to Costa Rica, and a considerable number of species reach the Galapagos Islands as the cheilostomes *Cauloramphus spiniferum, Callopora horrida, Cellaria diffusa, Bugula longirostris, Schizoporella cornuta, Mucronella major, Porella columbiana, Retepora pacifica,* and *Holoporella brunnea;* and the cyclostome *Crisia serrulata.*

Apart from circumarctic, cosmopolitan, and widely spread species there appear to be relatively few gymnolaemates in common between the temperate and boreal zones of the two sides of North America. The gymnolaemate faunas of these sides seem to be generally distinct, as concerns the cooler waters.

Although older works indicate a dearth of gymnolaemates in warmer waters, later work has shown such waters to be about as rich in species as colder ones (although the author found scarcely any gymnolaemates at Jamaica). Numerous studies cover the gymnolaemate fauna of tropical and subtropical waters: Hastings (1929), Canu and Bassler (1930b), and Osburn (1950, 1952, 1953) for the Panamic region; Smitt (1871, 1872), Osburn (1914, 1927, 1940, 1947, 1954) and Canu and Bassler (1928b) for the West Indian region; Marcus (1937a, 1938a, 1939a, 1941a, c, 1942a, 1949, 1953) for Brazil; Waters (1909, 1910, 1913, 1914) for the Red Sea and adjacent African coast; Canu and Bassler (1929) for the Philippines; Harmer (1915, 1926, 1934, 1957) for Indonesia from the collections of the *Siboga;* Hastings (1932) for the Great Barrier Reef; Kirkpatrick (1890a) for Torres Strait; and Canu and Bassler (1927a) for the Hawaiian Islands. In general, the tropical and subtropical Indo–West Pacific does not appear to have been thoroughly explored.

A considerable number of gymnolaemates occur around the world in tropical and subtropical waters and may be listed as tropicopolitan. These species are evidently limited by warmer temperatures, although the more adaptable ones may show some spread to the north and south of true subtropical waters. As tropicopolitan species may be mentioned the ctenostome *Zoobotryon pellucidum* (Fig. 139*A*), of which the author saw large masses off Brazil and which is also common in the Mediterranean; the anascan cheilostomes *Acanthodesia savarti, Electra bellula, Copidozoum tenuirostris, Parellisina curvirostris, Micropora coriacea, Discoporella umbellata, Nellia oculata, Scrupocellaria bertholetti, Bugula neritina, Synnotum aegyptiacum* (Fig. 143*F*), *Beania intermedia,* and *Holoporella albirostris;* the ascophoran cheilostomes *Hippothoa divaricata, Vittaticella elegans, Savignyella lafonti, Stylopoma informata, Hippoporina porcellana, Adeona violacea, Watersipora cucullata, Crepidacantha poissoni,* and *Mastigophorella pesanseris* (Fig. 124*H*); and the cyclostome *Crisia elongata.*

Areas of warmer waters usually have characteristic species of their own, besides cosmopolitan and tropicopolitan species. Thus the Panamic region, extending from Southern California to Peru and the Galapagos Islands, harbors some species not, to present knowledge, found elsewhere as the cheilostomes *Membranipora tenuis, Conopeum commensale, Antropora tincta* and *claustracrassa, Retevirgula tubulata, Onychocella alula, Chapperia condylata, Thalamoporella californica, Caulibugula californica, Hippoporella gorgonensis, Lagenipora hippocrepis* and *marginata, Coleopora gigantica,* and *Parasmittina crosslandi;* and the cyclostomes *Lichenopora buskiana* and *Disporella californica.* There are some gymnolaemates apparently limited to the Galapagos Islands, and according to Canu and Bassler (1930b), some of these are archaic forms previously known only as fossils, of which may be mentioned the cyclostomes *Proboscina lamellifera* and *Diaperoecia meandrina* and *subpapyracea.* Osburn (1954) noted that of the 170 species recorded for the Gulf of Mexico, 35 had not to that date been recorded elsewhere. He found no close relationship between species on the two sides of the Isthmus of Panama with only 16 species common to and limited to the Gulf of Mexico and the Panamic region and considered that most of the species had evolved since these waters were separated by the emergence of the Isthmus of Panama. The present Panama Canal furnishes a poor means of dispersal because much of it is fresh water.

In the West Indian region, by which is understood the central western Atlantic from the Carolinas to southern Brazil, including the Gulf of Mexico, the Caribbean and its islands, and the Bermudas, the gymnolaemate fauna consists of a mixture of cosmopolitan, tropicopolitan, and other widely spread species with a limited number of species restricted to the area. Of the last may be mentioned the anascan cheilostomes *Electra tenella, Crassimarginatella leucocypha, Velumella americana, Scrupocellaria regularis* and *cornigera, Canda carabiaca, Exechonella antillea,* and *Cribrilina floridana;* and the ascophoran cheilostomes *Schizoporella floridana, Rhynchozoon tuberculatum, Lagenipora verrucosa, Holoporella magnifica,* and *Pasythea tulipifera.* Osburn (1940) notes a considerable similarity between the gymnolaemate fauna of the West Indian region and that of the eastern tropical Atlantic and Mediterranean. There is the usual lateral spread in both directions, with some species ranging as far north as Cape Cod.

Much of the vast tropical and subtropical area termed Indo–West Pacific, extending from the east coast of Africa to Hawaii and Polynesia, has not been extensively explored for gymnolaemates. The latter here include many cosmopolitan, tropicopolitan, and other widely spread species, besides many that are typical of or limited to the region. The interesting ctenostome *Sundanella sibogae* (Fig. 140*D*) was one of the finds of the *Siboga* expedition to Indonesia (Harmer, 1915) but has since been found in the West Indian region; other ctenostomes of the area are *Nolella papuensis*, *Vesicularia papuensis*, and *Mimosella bigeminata*. Of cheilostomes, characteristic genera with 5 to 10 or more Indo–West Pacific species are *Steginoporella*, *Labioporella*, *Thalamoporella*, *Cellaria*, *Scrupocellaria*, *Beania*, *Bugula*, *Caulibugula*, *Gemellipora*, and *Holoporella*. Especially the anascan genus *Steginoporella*, notable for the differentiation of the autozooids into A and B types (page 327), centers in the Indo–West Pacific area, and an outstanding anatomical study of the genus was made by Harmer (1926) from *Siboga* material. The characteristic species here is *S. magnilabris*, also common in the West Indian region. Other characteristic cheilostomes are *Cupuladria guineensis*, *Retiflustra cornea* and *reticulum*, *Cellaria punctata*, *Setosellina coronata*, *Hiantopora radicifera* and *intermedia*, *Thalamoporella rozieri* (also in the eastern temperate Atlantic), *Cothurnicella cordieri* (Fig. 100*A*, also eastern Atlantic), *Cornucopina moluccensis*, *Scrupocellaria ferox*, *diadema*, and *spatulata*, *Canda retiformis*, *Caberea lata* and *transversa*, *Amastigia rudis*, *Hippopodina feegeensis*, *Stylopoma schizostoma* and *viride*, *Tubucellaria cereoides*, and *Holoporella mamillata*. Typical cyclostomes of the Indo–West Pacific area are *Tubulipora pulcherrima*, *Crisina radians*, *Diaperoecia intricaria*, and *Lichenopora novae-zelandiae*, the last of which extends from New Zealand through Indonesia to Ceylon and Japan and is also known from the Panamic region. The ascophoran family Reteporidae is especially characteristic of the tropical and subtropical West Pacific, being concentrated in the area from Torres Strait to Japan but also spreading into the Indian Ocean. Harmer (1934) reported 37 species of this family from Indonesia with 13 in the genus *Triphyllozoon;* and the genus *Iodictyum* appears limited to the warmer West Pacific, including Australia and Japan. *Reteporella graeffei* was stated to be the most common reteporid of Indonesia. The curious family Conescharellinidae (page 388) is also characteristic of the Indo–West Pacific area, extending to Japan (Silén, 1947b) and Australia. Canu and Bassler (1929) listed 32 species of this family from the Philippine area, with 13 species in the genus *Conescharellina* and 14 others known mostly from Australia and Tasmania and 14 species in the genus *Flabellopora* with 3 others known from Australia. The Petraliidae is another family mainly of Indo-Pacific distribution (Stach, 1936).

The Indo–West Pacific fauna extends well into Japan, where the two families just mentioned are well represented. Buchner (1924) listed 28 species of Reteporidae known to that date from Japan, and Silén (1947b) reported the occurrence in Japan of a number of conescharellinids. The study of the gymnolaemates of Japan was begun by Ortmann (1890), who already noted that Japan has species in common with almost every other region. Japanese gymnolaemates have since been studied by Okada (1917, 1920, 1921, 1923, 1933, 1934), Okada and Mawatari (1935–1938), Silén (1941, 1942c), and Mawatari (1952b, 1953, 1956). In general, the Japanese gymnolaemate fauna consists principally of cosmopolitan, tropicopolitan, and Indo–West Pacific species, with some admixture of endemic Japanese species, not as yet found elsewhere, and species descending from the north. Surprisingly few species characteristic of the Pacific Coast of North America have worked around to Japan. Confined to these two areas, according to present information, are *Dendrobaenia laxa*, *Caulibugula ciliata*, *Scrupocellaria californica*, *Filicrisia franciscana*, *Tubulipora pacifica*, and *Entalophora raripora;* two others, *Bugula californica* and *Membranipora serrilamella* (= *serrata*), are also found in the West Indian region. Farther north in the Kurile Islands (Okada, 1933; Mawatari, 1956), the Indo-Pacific elements have disappeared, although a few cosmopolitan species as *Aetea anguina* and *Hippothoa hyalina* remain, and there is a large admixture of circumarctic species. Mawatari (1956) has tabulated the known distribution of cheilostomes of the far northwest Pacific. The Hawaiian Islands form the eastern fringe of the central West Pacific area, but their gymnolaemate fauna does not appear to have been studied since the work of Canu and Bassler (1927a). Their 45 species plus 12 from the *Challenger* collections may be regarded as only a beginning of knowledge of the ectoprocts of these islands. They found some cosmopolitan and Pacific species but mainly undescribed forms.

In the southern Temperate Zone the main land masses are those of Australia, South Africa, and much of the Patagonian area of South America. Besides such older works as those of Busk, Hincks, MacGillivray, and others (listed by Borg, 1944), Australian gymnolaemates have been considered more recently by Marcus (1921b), Livingstone (1924–1926, 1928a), Hastings (1932), and Silén (1954). Northeastern Australia, especially the Great Barrier Reef, is on the fringe of the tropical West Pacific, and its gymnolaemates are practically identical with those of that area (Hastings, 1932). The remaining coasts of Australia are temperate, and apart from the usual widely spread and cosmopolitan species their gymnolaemates are mainly endemic, limited to Australia and New Zealand. Borg (1944) has commented on the richness of the gymnolaemate fauna of southern Australia, including adjacent islands. Characteristic of Australia are the family Catenicellidae and the genera *Adeona* and *Amathia;* of the latter genus MacGillivray already in 1895 listed 14 species. The cheilostomes of New Zealand are identical with or closely related to those of Australia (Livingstone, 1929). The available data on the gymnolaemates of South Africa to that date were assembled by O'Donoghue (1924), who, however, was unwilling to draw any zoogeographical conclusions, although a considerable endemic element is evident. O'Donoghue and de Watteville (1935, 1937, 1944) later added additional species, making a total of about 180 gymnolaemates recorded for South Africa. Marcus (1937b) reported on the adjacent island of St. Helena, which, however, is located in the subtropical zone. In fact, practically all the species found were already known from tropical and subtropical seas, but few are limited to them; and most of the species are more characteristic of temperate and subpolar areas. The Patagonian region of South America falling within the Temperate Zone has received scarcely any attention. Marcus (1921c) reported on a small collection from Juan Fernández islands off Chile and commented on a lack of endemism and a general relation to the subantarctic fauna.

In contrast to the foregoing there has been almost a superfluity of collecting in the subantarctic and antarctic regions, even prior to the reports of Busk on collections from Kerguelen (1876, 1879) and those made by the *Challenger* (1884, 1886; also Waters, 1888). Other collections are those of Ridley (1881) from the *Alert*, Jullien (1891) from the mission to Cape Horn, Kirkpatrick (1902) from the *Southern Cross*, Calvet (1904) from the Hamburg expedition to the Strait of Magellan, Waters (1904) from the Belgian expedition on the *Belgica*, Calvet (1909) from the French expedition, Kluge (1914) from the German south polar expedition on the *Gauss*, Thornely (1924) and Livingstone (1928b) from the Australasian expedition, Hastings (1943) from the *Discovery* report, Borg (1944) from the Swedish expedition, and Vigeland (1952) from that of Norway. The reports of Kluge and Hastings are limited to several families of anascan cheilostomes, but this deficiency is somewhat offset by Borg's report, dealing with cyclostomes. It appears, in fact, that systematic work on ascophoran cheilostomes was seriously handicapped by the lack of the *Siboga* report on this group; however, this report has finally appeared (Harmer, 1957). The Waters and Kluge reports concern mainly archibenthal and abyssal depths, whereas the foregoing and following discussions refer primarily to littoral species.

A valuable discussion of the gymnolaemates of high southern latitudes from the zoogeographical point of view was given by Hastings (1943), who pointed out that the gymnolaemates of subantarctic and antarctic zones are in general distinct. Characteristic anascan genera of these two zones, not much found elsewhere, are *Amastigia, Notoplites, Farciminellum, Cornucopina, Himantozoum,* and *Camptoplites.* The Subantarctic includes the Magellanic area (southern Patagonia, Strait of Magellan, Tierra del Fuego, Falkland Islands), the adjacent South Georgia and South Sandwich Islands, the islands of the Indian Ocean of corresponding latitude (Prince Edward, Crozet, Kerguelen Islands), and southern New Zealand and the subantarctic islands of New Zealand. Even in these frigid waters there are met familiar widely spread cheilostomes as *Aetea anguina, Hippothoa hyalina, Microporella ciliata,* and *Parasmittina trispinosa.* Common Magellanic cheilostomes are *Aetea curta, Chaperia galeata, Arachnopusia monoceros, Aspidosoma giganteum, Bugula hyadesi, Beania inermis, magellanica,* and *costata, Diachoris magellanica, Caberea darwini, Menipea patagonica, aculeata,* and *flagellifera, Tricellaria aculeata, Exochella longirostris, Amastigia nuda, crassimarginata,* and *benemunita,* and *Porella margaritifera.* Typical cyclostomes include *Crisia kerguelensis, Bicrisia organisans* and *edwardsiana, Nevianopora* (= *Idmonea*) *milneana, Diastopora dichotoma, Tubulipora stellata* and *fasiculifera,* or a variant thereof, *Filicea elegans, Disporella fimbriata,* and *Lichenopora canaliculata.* Ctenostomes appear wanting, except species of *Alcyonidium,* or perhaps they escape collecting through their small size and fragility. The gymnolaemates of Kerguelen were reported by Busk (1876, 1879), and this island was also visited by the *Challenger* and some later expeditions, but its gymnolaemates are in common with the Magellanic area or with South Africa, Australia, and New Zealand. Marcus (1922) found some gymnolaemates collected from subantarctic islands of New Zealand to be either widely spread species or in common with the Magellanic or Australian–New Zealand areas. There appears in fact to be a general identity or similarity between the subantarctic gymnolaemates and those of South Africa, Australia, and New Zealand. This may perhaps be attributed to a cold oceanic current known as the West Wind Drift that encircles the South Pole north of about latitude 65°, that is, does not quite reach the borders of the main antarctic land mass and "washes all temperate oceanic islands in the southern ocean, the southern part of South America, the south coasts of Africa and Australia, and branches off into currents flowing in a northerly direction near these continents" (Ekman, 1953). There is also an East Wind Drift, encircling the South Pole in the opposite direction close to the antarctic land mass.

The true, or high, Antarctic includes the main antarctic land mass and the Graham Archipelago with the adjacent South Shetland and South Orkney Islands. It is bounded from the Subantarctic by the Antarctic Convergence, an irregularly circular zone within the West Wind Drift where there is a sudden drop of temperature because the icy antarctic water with a temperature of zero degrees centigrade or below here sinks beneath the warmer subantarctic water, having a temperature of about 5°C. at the Convergence. As already indicated, antarctic gymnolaemates differ from subantarctic ones, but there are some species in common as *Caberea darwini* and some typically antarctic species extend into the Subantarctic as *Amastigia gaussi, Cornucopina pectogemma,* and *Lichenopora canuliculata*. Of the many cheilostomes taken in the Antarctic may be mentioned *Flustra flagellata, angusta,* and *antarctica, Ramphonotus inermis, Ogivalina lata, Cellaria mawsoni, Farciminellum antarcticum, Cornucopina polymorpha, Himantozoum antarcticum, Camptoplites bicornis* and its varieties, *tricornis, gigantus, angustus, retiformis, latus,* and *areolatus, Beania erecta, Amastigia antarctica, Notoplites antarcticus, tenuis, klugei, watersi,* and *drygalskii, Figularia spatulata, Emballotheca contortuplicata, Escharoides tridens, Smittina conspicua* and *antarctica, Retepora frigida, Inversiula nutrix,* and *Osthimosia eatonensis*. Evidently *Camptoplites,* closely related to *Bugula,* is the most characteristic cheilostome genus of the Antarctic, with 8 species and 6 varieties restricted to this region. There do not appear to be any typically antarctic cyclostomes. Borg (1944) described several new cyclostomes from antarctic localities. *Hornera antarctica* and *Lichenopora canaliculata* are typical cyclostomes of high southern latitudes that appear about equally common in both the Antarctic and Subantarctic. Hastings (1943) remarks that about half the species she studied occur on both sides of the antarctic land mass, hence are presumably circumpolar.

Cold currents from the West Wind Drift ascend north on both coasts of Patagonia, and consequently there is the expected spread of subantarctic gymnolaemates along these coasts to Peru and Brazil. Marcus (1938a) records two Magellanic cheilostomes, *Beania australis* and *Exochella longirostris,* in subtropical waters off Brazil. The Pacific Coast of Chile is one of the most poorly investigated faunal regions of the world, and nothing can be said of its gymnolaemate fauna. However, the adjacent island of Juan Fernández was reported by Marcus (1921c), who noted a subantarctic influence with three typical subantarctic species, *Caberea darwini, Nevianipora milneana,* and *Disporella fimbriata*. A remarkable distribution is shown by the Magellanic species *Beania magellanica,* which extends up the Pacific Coast of South America to Peru, is apparently lacking in the western Atlantic north of Patagonia, but reaches to the Mediterranean in the eastern Atlantic and to New Zealand, Australia, and Japan in the Indo–West Pacific.

The question whether there are any bipolar gymnolaemates is usually answered in the negative. However, the well-known circumarctic and circumboreal cyclostome, *Crisia eburnea,* descending in the Atlantic to the

Azores and Chesapeake Bay and in the Pacific only to Alaska, is recorded by Borg (1944) from Tierra del Fuego and appears definitely absent in the area between. Another cyclostome, *Lichenopora canaliculata*, mentioned above as common in antarctic and subantarctic waters, was found by Osburn (1953) at Point Barrow, Alaska.

The foregoing discussion is based primarily on latitude, that is, temperature, but other factors enter into the distribution of gymnolaemates of warmer and temperate waters. Thus many widely spread species found in the Atlantic and Indo–West Pacific are wanting from the eastern Pacific, that is, the Pacific Coast of the Americas, having failed to cross the deep waters of the eastern Pacific, called by Ekman (1953) the East Pacific Barrier. Here belong such familiar cheilostomes as *Schizoporella unicornis*, *Scrupocellaria scrupea*, and *Hippopodina feegeensis* and the ctenostome *Sundanella sibogae*. The first-named species has in recent years been introduced on the Pacific Coast of the United States with oysters. There are further many Indo–West Pacific species that also occur in the eastern Atlantic but are wanting from western Atlantic and eastern Pacific shores, being apparently unable to spread through boreal waters. Other species, as already noted, are limited to the two sides of the American continents and not found elsewhere as *Bugula californica*. The distribution of common species of *Bugula* illustrates varied ranges of occurrence. Thus *Bugula neritina* is tropicopolitan. *Bugula flabellata* is an Atlantic species ranging in the eastern Atlantic from Scandinavia to the Cape of Good Hope and in the western Atlantic from Maine to Brazil, but is also found sparingly in the Panamic region, and recorded from Australia by Silén (1954), probably brought in on ships. *Bugula avicularia* is typical of the European boreal but has sporadic records in the Indo–West Pacific regions. *Bugula turrita* appears limited to the western Atlantic from Massachusetts to Brazil.

Geographic variation is of wide occurrence in gymnolaemates and adds to the difficulties of identification. It was already noticed that there are numerous boreal variants of arctic species, and vice versa. Common antarctic species also show much variation. Thus Hastings (1943) describes two varieties of *Caberea darwini* and four of *Camptoplites bicornis*. The cosmopolitan species *Parasmittina trispinosa* seems to be the most variable of all gymnolaemates; thus Marcus (1937a) found two varieties on the coast of Brazil, Osburn (1940) mentioned four in the West Indies, and Canu and Bassler (1929) described five in the Philippine area and discussed eight others known in the literature.

Many gymnolaemates tolerate a wide range of depth, occurring from the intertidal zone or shallow water to archibenthal or even abyssal levels. A few examples may be given (data from Marcus, 1940, and Silén, 1951): *Eucratea loricata* to 1359 m., *Flustra barleei* to 1100 m., *Bugula avicularia* to 1324 m., *Bugula neritina* to 4060 m., *Colletosia radiata* to 1285 m., *Hippothoa hyalina* to 2018 m., *Canda simplex* to 3111 m., *Tessaradoma gracile* to 3700 m., *Cellepora dichotoma* to 2170 m., *Arachnopusa monoceros* to 5719 m. It is probably significant that these are also species with a wide horizontal range.

There are also a limited number of species that appear confined to deeper waters. Many of the records from deep water are still those of the *Challenger* (Busk, 1884) and the *Travailleur* and *Talisman* (Calvet, 1906). Later works that include gymnolaemates collected from deep water are those of Kluge (1914) for the German south polar expedition on the *Gauss*, Hasenbank (1932) for the German deep-sea expedition on the *Valdivia*, Hastings (1943) for the *Discovery* dredgings in the South Atlantic and South American Subantarctic and Antarctic, and Silén (1951a) for the Swedish deep-sea expedition. The last author has tabulated all records of gymnolaemates taken from depths greater than 3000 m. Of this list of 46 species and 2 varieties, 11 are also known for, or more typical of, littoral waters. The remainder are to present knowledge confined to archibenthal and abyssal depths. No ctenostomes are known from abyssal waters, and cyclostomes are not recorded below about 2000 m. Hence only cheilostomes have been taken in waters 3000 m. or more in depth. In this group "abyssal types are strikingly common in the families Scrupocellariidae, Bicellariellidae and Farciminariidae" (Silén, 1951a). In the last family the genus *Levinsenella* is notable as containing mostly abyssal species, and in the Bicellariellidae (used by these authors to include Bugulidae) the genera *Cornucopina*, *Himantozoum*, *Camptoplites*, and *Kinetoskias* contain two or three very abyssal species. The genus *Bifaxaria* in the family Bifaxariidae has three abyssal members. Most of the highly abyssal cheilostomes have been recorded only once, but three have been taken at different locations by different expeditions and may be supposed common in the ocean depths, namely, *Levinsenella magna*, *Cornucopina rotundata*, and *Himantozoum mirabile*. The deepest record to date at which gymnolaemates have been taken is 5719 m., dredged by the *Challenger* in the North Pacific, north of the Hawaiian Islands. Four species came up in this dredging, but only two could be exactly identified, namely, *Bifaxaria abyssicola* and *Arachnopusia monoceros*, not taken since.

21. Ecology: Biological Relations.—Gymnolaemates so habitually attach to other animals and to plants and so habitually live in crowded associations with other sessile animals that it is difficult to say when such relationships are other than accidental. However, some species are apparently prone to attach to seaweeds. Notable among these is *Membranipora tuberculatum*, habitually found on the floating *Sargassum*, although it may occur elsewhere. Gautier (1952) is of the opinion that there is some selection of particular kinds of algae or other seaweeds as a substrate by gymnolaemates.   In the area studied (French Mediterranean) *Microporella ciliata* was usually found on the alga *Peyssonellia*, and *Hippodiplosia ottomulleriana* nearly always on *Halimeda*.   In 1954 Gautier created a new species of *Electra*, *E. posidoniae*, said to occur only on the leaves of the seaweed *Posidonia*.

Various associations with other animals have been reported.   On the Great Barrier Reef, Hastings (1932) found that the hydroid *Zanclea protecta* regularly grows on gymnolaemate colonies, permeating the latter with its hydrorhiza.   The boring habits of certain families of ctenostomes that live only in mollusk and barnacle shells were noted above (page 370). Hincks (1880) described the species *Lepralia edax* that settles on small snail shells and eats away the shell substance, replacing this with its own calcareous formations.   Gautier (1955a) noted a tendency of certain gymnolaemates, especially of the genus *Hippopodinella*, to grow on the shells of small living snails or of similar shells occupied by hermit crabs. Kirkpatrick and Metzelaar (1922) regarded the growth of *Conopeum commensale* on snail shells occupied by the hermit crab *Petrochirus granulimanus* as a specific association.   Here the gymnolaemate, without destroying the snail shell, constantly increases in thickness, up to 56 layers, with the result that the shell becomes incased by a thick stony mass.   Numerous other cases of gymnolaemates growing on snail shells occupied by hermit crabs must be regarded as accidental associations. The association with other animals of the three ctenostomes described on page 396 is undoubtedly highly specific.   Species of the ctenostome genus *Triticella* (includes *Hippuraria*) habitually grow on the legs and other external parts of crabs (Fig. 138*G, F*), and Osburn (1912a, 1932) found *Triticella elongata* inside the gill chamber and on the gills of crabs on the Atlantic Coast of the United States.   The claim of Canu and Bassler (1928a) that *Costazia parvula* is parasitic on the coral *Porella cervicornis* in the Mediterranean appears unjustified since this gymnolaemate also grows elsewhere.

Gymnolaemates are constantly overgrown by other animals, but these relations also appear accidental in most cases.   It has been claimed that the Reteporidae are singularly free from other organisms, but Harmer (1934) noted the entoproct *Loxosoma* frequently growing on reteporids; further, a gymnoblastic hydroid occupying tunnels in the calcareous exoskeleton and emerging from holes below the fenestrations.   Silén (1954) also noted a great abundance of loxosomatids growing on reteporids and some other gymnolaemates in the Australian and Indo-Malay regions, but apparently not elsewhere.   Harmer (1915) reported a distinct species of *Loxosoma* dwelling in the ascus of *Lepralia celleporoides* in Indonesia and reaching the exterior by protruding through the unusually large ascopore of this cheilostome; this relationship seems to be of specific nature.

Gymnolaemates could hardly be called nourishing yet are eaten by a number of other animals. Hallez (1894) reported a polyclad flatworm *"Leptoplana" schizoporellae* (generic allocation uncertain) as definitely preying on *Schizoporella lineata* in the English Channel. Gymnolaemates are frequently eaten by echinoids (IV, page 554) and even by holothurians (IV, page 211). Presumably sufficiently small polychaete worms could invade the zoecia and eat out the contents, as seems the case with the family Syllidae (Malaquin, 1892). O'Donoghue (1927) noted that the snail *Corambe* is a pest on colonies of *Memb. villosa*, eating out all living matter from the zoecia, and no doubt other snails have similar habits. Osburn (1921) recorded that gymnolaemates, including calcified ones, are frequently eaten by fishes with the necessary type of gnawing jaws and the contents of the zoecia digested out; further, that remains of gymnolaemates were found in eider ducks.

Gymnolaemates must frequently cause the death of other sessile invertebrates by overgrowing them and suffocating them or preventing them from obtaining food. A tremendous struggle goes on among larvae of sessile invertebrates for suitable settling places. Osburn (1944) found that in Chesapeake Bay gymnolaemates, notably *Memb. crustalenta* and *Acanthodesia tenuis*, are serious enemies of oysters by covering over shells and other material and preventing the attachment of oyster larvae. On the other hand, gymnolaemate larvae are probably eaten in vast numbers by oysters and other filter-feeding invertebrates.

Besides their deleterious effect on oysters gymnolaemates are of economic importance as fouling organisms. The term fouling is applied to the accumulations of sessile organisms and other material on ship bottoms. Such accumulations slow the speed of boats and are otherwise expensive since they must be removed at intervals by dry-docking boats. Redfield (1952) listed gymnolaemates as among the principal fouling animals. Something over 130 species have been taken on ship bottoms, of which the most common are *Bugula neritina, flabellata,* and *avicularia, Schizoporella unicornis, Memb. membranacea, Watersipora cucullata,* and *Zoobotryon pellucidum.* Edmondson and Ingram (1939) listed *Bugula neritina* as the most common bushy species and *Schiz. unicornis* as the most common incrusting species involved in fouling at Hawaii, and the former is also the main fouling gymnolaemate at Japan (Mawatari, 1951). *W. cucullata* and *Acanthodesia tenella* were reported by Weiss (1948) as found in large quantities incrusting boat slips at Biscayne Bay, Florida. *Schiz. unicornis* might also in time grow over and smother barnacles and other fouling animals. Seasonal variations were noted by Weiss for these and *Bugula* species, and the appearance and disappearance of the latter were

FIG. 157.—Representative phylactolaemates. *A*, some branches of *Fredericella sultana*. with partially separated zoecia (*after Brien*, 1953). *B*, colony of *Plumatella repens*, growing on a water-lily leaf (*after Wesenberg-Lund*, 1896). *C*, bit of a *Plumatella* colony, showing relation of zooids to substrate (*after Kraepelin*, 1887). 1, main bud; 2, duplicate bud; 3, adventitious bud; 4, stomach caecum; 5, funiculus; 6, statoblast; 7, septum; 8, tentacular crown; 9, zoecium; 10, cellular part of body wall; 11, body wall; 12, intestine; 13, anus; 14, orifice.

found related to water temperature, with 29°C. as the upper limiting temperature. The responses of *Bugula* larvae to antifouling paints and other antifouling devices are considered in Redfield's book.

Fresh-water ectoprocts, including *Paludicella*, may pose another economic problem by blocking water pipes; this subject was reviewed by Harmer (1913). Such ectoprocts may form large masses, to which are added many other kinds of small fresh-water invertebrates, and may throw an entire water system out of gear. The death of *Paludicella* with the onset of winter taints the water and increases its bacterial content. More is said on this subject on page 495.

There are few reports of the occurrence of parasites in gymnolaemates. Hastings (1943) has reviewed the numerous reports of the presence of vermiform bodies in the coelom of various gymnolaemates, but the nature of these remains uncertain, although it is possible that in some cases they are parasitic protozoans. Marcus (1939b) made a study of a schizogregarine, *Sawayaella polyzoorum*, inhabiting the digestive tract of species of *Thalamoporella*, also occasionally found in *Watersipora cucullata*. The life cycle is typical, with the production of cysts filled with spores, each containing eight sporozoites. Such cysts emitted from the anus are ingested by other individuals.

V. CLASS PHYLACTOLAEMATA

1. Definition.—The Phylactolaemata are monomorphic fresh-water ectoprocts with a chitinous or gelatinous zoecium, horseshoe-shaped lophophore (tending to the circular in *Fredericella*), epistome, body-wall musculature, and open coelomic communications between zooids.

2. Colony Form.—The colony shows two general types of construction: the plumatellid and the lophopodid. In the former, exemplified by *Plumatella* and *Fredericella*, the colony ramifies over a substrate or is more or less erected from a substrate as branching tubes or bushy growths composed of a succession of more or less distinct zooids (Fig. 157). The zoecium varies from a thin hard cuticle, often incorporating foreign bodies, to a gelatinous encasement of some thickness. In the lophopodid type the colony is a compact gelatinous mass from which there protrude the tentacular crowns of the basally fused zooids. In *Lophopus* the colony consists of a small lobulate gelatinous mass of a few up to 50 or more zooids, all facing in one direction (Fig. 159*A*). *Cristatella* forms vermiform creeping colonies up to several inches long with a flat gelatinous undersurface, or sole, and a convex upper surface having two or three rows of zooids on each side facing outward and a central area free from zooids where statoblasts accumulate (Figs. 159*B*, 160). The remarkable *Pectinatella magnifica* consists of gelatinous masses of smooth contour that may increase to a very large size by autumn, up to several feet in diame-

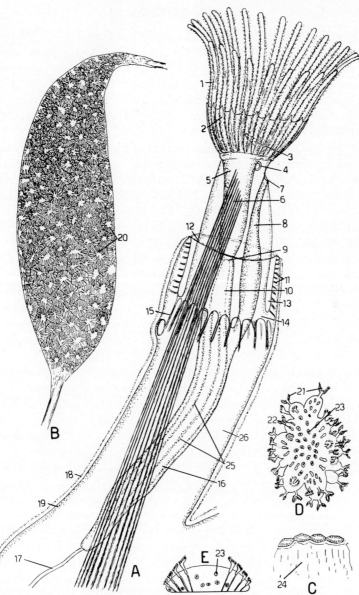

Fig. 158.—Representative phylactolaemates (continued). *A*, single zooid of *Frederic-ella*, showing structure (*after Allman*, 1856). *B*, *Pectinatella*, growing on a twig. *C*, profile view of bit of *Pectinatella*, showing relation of colonies to jelly. *D*, one colony of *Pectina-tella*, viewed *en face*. *E*, schematic section through a colony of *Pectinatella*, showing arrangement of zooids. (*D*, *E*, *after Hyatt*, 1866.) 1, tentacular crown; 2, intertentacular membrane; 3, epistome; 4, brain ganglion; 5, foregut; 6, retractor of lophophore; 7, anus; 8, intestine; 9, cardiac valve; 10, cardiac part of stomach; 11, dilators of vestibule; 12, orifice; 13, vestibule; 14, location of diaphragm; 15, duplicature bands; 16, stomach caecum; 17, funiculus; 18, cuticle; 19, cellular part of body wall; 20, one colony of the *Pectinatella* complex; 21, active zooids at periphery; 22, dead zooids; 23, statoblasts in center; 24, jelly; 25, colored stripes on stomach; 26, metacoel.

435

ter, according to Hyatt (1866), but usually less than 2 feet.   The surface of these masses is covered with a thin crust of small, polygonal, originally separate colonies (Fig. 158*B, C*) of 12 to 18 zooids that secrete basally a common jelly filling the interior of the mass.   In the individual colony living zooids are confined to the periphery and face outward (Fig. 158*E*), leaving a central area containing disintegrating zooids and statoblasts (Fig. 158*D*).

All phylactolaemate colonies except *Cristatella* live permanently attached to submersed objects such as rocks, aquatic plants, twigs, roots, and the like, in various types of fresh-water habitats.   *Cristatella* colonies creep about slowly on submersed objects, and young colonies of lophop- odids also move about for a time.   Colonies are founded either by the attachment of a sexually produced ciliated larva or by the germination of statoblasts, which are asexually produced reproductive bodies.

3. Structure of the Zooid.—As phylactolaemates lack polymorphism, all zooids are autozooids and have the typical ectoproct structure.   The anterior end is formed of the tentacular crown, or lophophore, which has the shape of a horseshoe (Figs. 157*C*, 160*A*), except in the genus *Fred- ericella* where it approaches a circular shape (Fig. 158*A*), more accurately oval or reniform.   As usual, the mouth is embraced by the lophophore and is overhung dorsally by a projecting flap (Fig. 162), the *epistome*, wanting in gymnolaemates, and supposed to represent the protosome, or anterior body region.   The lophophore is borne on the protrusible neck- like anterior part of the trunk, clothed with a thinned body wall, here also called tentacle sheath.   Around the proximal part of the necklike region the body wall is permanently invaginated to form a vestibule delimited at its inner end by a diaphragm (Fig. 158*A*).   At the inner end of the invaginated fold the tentacle sheath, or eversible part of body wall, is continuous with the cystid, or fixed part of the body wall.   Each zooid of a phylactolaemate colony has its own vestibular region, but otherwise the cystid walls are more or less wanting or reduced to strands, especially in the lophopodid type, where the colony is covered with a common cystid wall and a number of digestive tracts hang in a common coelom (Fig. 157*C*).   The digestive tract has the usual V-form, with the anus opening dorsally near the mouth.   The apex of the stomach caecum is attached to the body wall by a strong funiculus (Fig. 162); other funicular cords are wanting.   Because of its mode of formation (see later) the funiculus is always curved toward the ventral cystid wall, and hence has a concave and a convex side.   A main nervous mass, or ganglion, is located between mouth and anus at the base of the epistome.   Space between the digestive tract and cystid constitutes the main coelom (metacoel). All phylactolaemates are hermaphroditic, with gonads borne on the peritoneum.

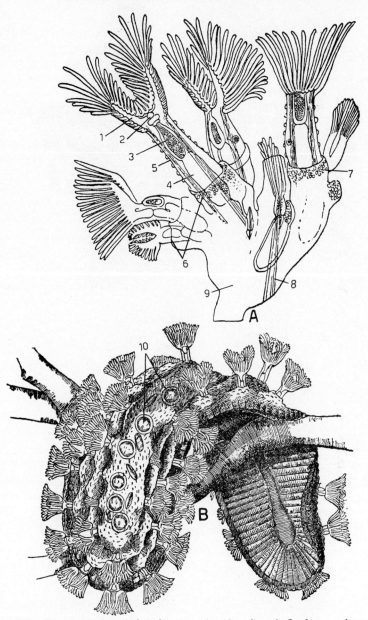

FIG. 159.—Representative phylactolaemates (continued). *A, Lophopus* colony, seen from the back side; all zooids face one way. *B,* colony of *Cristatella mucedo,* creeping on plant stems; zooids face outward on both sides. (*Both redrawn by Jullien,* 1885, *from Allman,* 1856.) 1, lophophore; 2, ganglion; 3, intestine; 4, stomach; 5, tentacle sheath; 6, orifice; 7, vestibule; 8, retractor of lophophore; 9, common coelom; 10, statoblast.

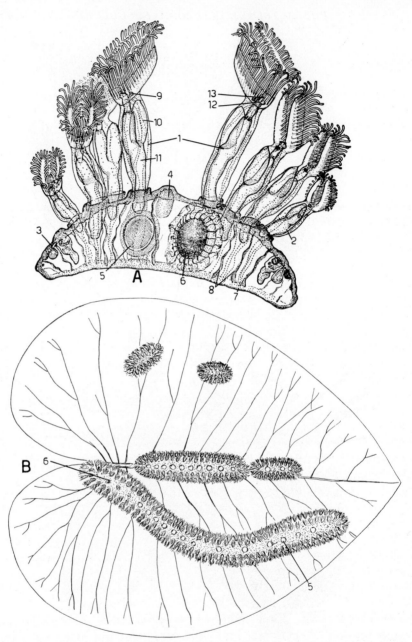

Fig. 160.—Representative phylactolaemates (concluded). *A*, section across *Cristatella* colony, showing zooid arrangement (*after Brien*, 1953). *B*, Colonies of *Cristatella mucedo* creeping on a water-lily pad (*after Wesenberg-Lund*, 1896); central colony has just divided. 1, innermost oldest zooids; 2, outermost youngest zooid; 3, marginal budding zone; 4, degenerating zooid; 5, young statoblast; 6, completed statoblast; 7, gelatinous creeping sole; 8, incomplete septa between zooids; 9, ganglion; 10, intestine; 11, caecum; 12, mouth; 13, epistome.

a. Lophophore.—The lophophore is crescentic, or shaped like a horseshoe (except in *Fredericella*); the two ends or arms of the horseshoe project freely (Fig. 159*A*), whereas the bend of the U passes below and above the mouth (Fig. 162). As in phoronids the convex side of the horseshoe passing ventral to the mouth may be termed outer and the concave side dorsal to the mouth inner. The horseshoe is fringed with a single row of ciliated tentacles. These are in general more numerous than in gymnolaemates, presumably because the crescentic shape allows room for more of them. In line with this supposition is the fact that *Fredericella*, with nearly circular lophophore, has the smallest tentacle number (20 to 30). In other genera with typical horseshoe-shaped lophophore the tentacle number ranges from 30 to over 100, being greatest in *Cristatella mucedo* with 80 to 100 tentacles and *Pectinatella gelatinosa* with 75 to 106. The number varies somewhat in different individuals of the same species and may increase with age. The first formed zooid of a colony often has fewer tentacles than subsequent members. The tentacles are hollow, containing a coelomic lumen continuous with the coelomic lumen (mesocoel) of the lophophore base. In cross section the tentacle is somewhat triangular (Marcus, 1934; Rogick, 1937b; Fig. 161*A*), composed mainly of a columnar epidermis, bearing a tract of cilia on each side and a third tract on the narrowed inner side related to a cell probably sensory (Fig. 161*A*). The epidermis of the outer, broader side contains one or two bladder cells, cells swollen with a large mass of secretion. The epidermis rests upon a definite basement membrane to the inner side of which is found the peritoneum lining the lumen. Between the peritoneum and the basement membrane on the inner and outer sides of the tentacle occur longitudinal muscle fibers (Fig. 161*A*); circular fibers are absent. There are also present tentacular nerves whose arrangement varies with species. In *Lophopus* (Marcus, 1934) there are present a pair of inner and outer lateral tentacular nerves and also a median inner nerve (Fig. 161*A*), whereas in *Cristatella* (Gerwerzhagen, 1913a) the tentacle contains one pair of lateral nerves and inner and outer bundles. The tip of the tentacle is pierced by a minute canal which may be closed by peritoneum on its inner end. Basally the tentacles are connected by a thin, transparent *intertentacular membrane* (Fig. 162), also called calyx, that is attached narrowly along the outer side of each tentacle and more or less descends in festoons between tentacles. This membrane consists of a thin epidermal extension of the wall of the lophophoral base that is carried along when the tentacles grow out. A slight groove marks the proximal boundary of the lophophore below the mouth.

b. Body Wall.—The cystid wall is much better developed histologically than in gymnolaemates. Its outermost layer, forming the zoecium, varies from a thin, firm cuticle, made of chitin, to a thick gelatinous deposit and

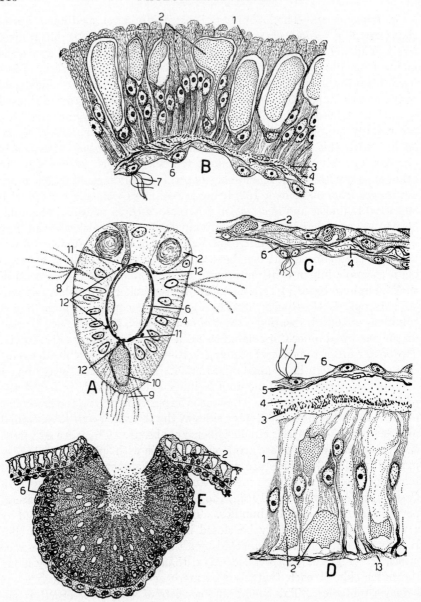

Fig. 161.—Structure of the body wall. *A*, cross section through a tentacle of *Lophopus* (*after Marcus*, 1934). *B*, section of the body wall of *Cristatella*. *C*, body wall of dorsal side of *Cristatella* colony. *D*, body wall of creeping sole of *Cristatella*. (*B–D*, after *Brien*, 1953.) *E*, epidermal gland of *Pectinatella* (*after Kraepelin*, 1887). 1, columnar cell; 2, vesicular cell; 3, circular muscle layer; 4, basement membrane; 5, longitudinal muscle layer; 6, peritoneum; 7, bunch of cilia; 8, lateral bunch of tentacular cilia; 9, median bunch of tentacular cilia; 10, sensory cell; 11, longitudinal muscle fibers; 12, tentacular nerves; 13, gelatinous cuticle.

may incorporate foreign bodies. Beneath it is found a tall epidermis composed in part of granular cylindrical cells, said by Brien (1953) to be secretory, and in part of bladder or vesicular cells (Fig. 161B), very abundant in some regions, especially at the orifice. These vesicular cells contain a large vacuole almost filled with a finely granular mass (Fig. 161B). One might suppose these granular masses to be forerunners of the zoecium, but this is denied by Marcus (1934), who finds them to be of fatty nature, hence serving as food reserve. Apparently, then, the zoecium must be secreted by the granular cells. In the base of the epidermis are found here and there clusters of indifferent cells that are concerned in reproduction. Beneath the epidermis occurs a layer of circular muscle fibers, then a basement membrane, then a layer of longitudinal muscle fibers, followed by the peritoneum (Fig. 161B). The occurrence of the basement membrane between the muscle layers indicates that the circular layer is of epidermal, the longitudinal layer of peritoneal, origin. It will be recalled that a muscle layer is lacking from the body wall of gymnolaemates. The peritoneum is well developed and bears bunches of cilia at intervals (Fig. 161B–D).

The body wall presents variations in different locations and in different species. In the inturned body wall that lines the vestibule the epidermis is much reduced in height, the vesicular cells, if present, bear reduced vacuoles, and the circular muscle layer gradually disappears. All layers, but especially the epidermis, of the tentacle sheath are greatly flattened, with small vesicular cells and only longitudinal muscle fibers. The dorsal wall of the *Cristatella* colony (Fig. 161C) is flattened, with scarcely any cuticle and with poorly developed muscle layers (Brien, 1953), whereas the creeping sole has an extremely tall epidermis covered with a gelatinous layer 3 mm. thick (Kraepelin, 1887), a strengthened basement membrane, and well-developed muscle fibers (Fig. 161D).

Kraepelin (1887) described and figured in *Pectinatella* large multicellular epidermal glands (Fig. 161E) near the orifice, about one to each zooid, that produce a milky, smeary secretion often seen clinging in lumps to the lophophore.

c. Digestive System.—This system quite resembles that of gymnolaemates. The rounded or oval mouth is located midventrally between the lophophoral ridges and is overhung dorsally but not closable by the epistome. The latter is a rounded to triangular hollow projection clothed with thin, sparsely ciliated body wall, of which the epidermis becomes taller and better ciliated toward the mouth. Its coelomic interior is crossed by peritoneal strands containing muscle fibers that accomplish alterations of shape and position of the epistome. The mouth leads into a short ciliated pharynx followed by a short to long nonciliated esophagus delimited from the stomach by a constriction marking the position of the

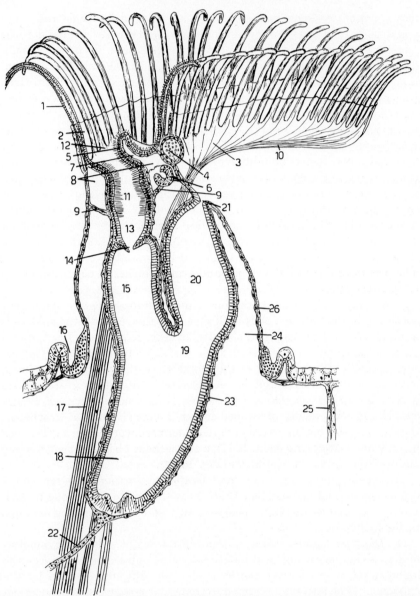

FIG. 162.—Structure of the zooid.   Median sagittal section of a polypide of *Cristatella* (*after Cori*, 1893).   1, tentacles; 2, intertentacular membrane; 3, ridge of lophophore; 4, sac of forked canal; 5, epistome; 6, ganglion; 7, protocoel; 8, mesocoel; 9, septum between mesocoel and metacoel; 10, branch of lophophoral retractor to lophophore; 11, pharynx; 12, mouth; 13, esophagus; 14, cardiac valve; 15, cardia; 16, invaginated fold of body wall; 17, retractor of lophophore; 18, stomach caecum; 19, pylorus; 20, intestine; 21, anus; 22, funiculus; 23, peritoneum; 24, metacoel; 25, septum between zooids; 26, tentacle sheath.

cardiac valve. The stomach is of elongated, cylindroid shape and composed as usual of cardia, caecum, and pylorus, not well delimited from each other, and is marked by longitudinal reddish-brown bands that indicate internal ridges. A dorsal widening of the distal end of the caecum forms the pylorus, separated from the intestine by a marked constriction, situated much posterior to the level of the cardiac constriction (Figs. 158*A*, 162); hence the pyloric limb of the stomach Y is much shorter than the cardiac limb. The intestine, wide at first, tapers to the anus, opening through the tentacle sheath, just below the lophophore on the dorsal side.

Apart from older works, the histology of the digestive tract was described by Müller (1914) for *Plumatella*, Marcus (1934) for *Lophopus*, Becker (1937) for *Plumatella* and *Cristatella*, and Rogick (1937b) for *Lophopodella*. The pharynx is lined with very tall, heavily ciliated, more or less granular epithelial cells, presumably secretory. The esophageal epithelium differs in the absence of cilia, the marked vacuolization of its basal half, and the pseudopodial protrusions of the distal ends of the cells (Fig. 163*A*). A conical valve protrudes into the cardia from the lower end of the esophagus (Fig. 162). Cardia, caecum, and pylorus are histologically similar, composed of two kinds of epithelial cells, very tall, bulging, vacuolated acidophilic cells typically forming longitudinal folds, and shorter, darker, granular basophilic cells located in the furrows between the folds (Fig. 163*B*). Cilia are wanting, and both types of cells have a striated border, wider on the acidophilic cells. The latter with age accumulate reddish-brown inclusions; hence the folds composed of them appear as the colored stripes already mentioned. The intestine has a smooth interior lined by cells similar to those of the stomach folds, of short columnar form, with a striated border and vacuolated interior (Fig. 163*C*). Both stomach and rectum secrete a peritrophic membrane around the food. The digestive epithelium is everywhere underlain by a basement membrane, especially thickened in the caecum, and outside of this occurs a layer of circular muscle fibers, wanting in the pharynx and sparsely present in the intestinal wall. Longitudinal fibers are lacking. The digestive tract is clothed externally with peritoneum.

d. Muscular System.—The muscles of the body wall, tentacles, and digestive tract were already considered; there remain for consideration the muscles that cross the coelom. The dilators of the vestibule are a number of short fibers that extend from the wall of the vestibule to the adjacent cystid wall and act to expand the vestibule. A conspicuous set of muscles, often called *duplicature bands*, arranged in a circle, originates distally on the cystid wall and inserts on the inner end of the invaginated fold ("duplicature fold") of the cystid (Fig. 158*A*). The inner end of this fold is usually at the level of the diaphragm; hence this circular set of muscles usually functions as diaphragmatic dilators. However, the

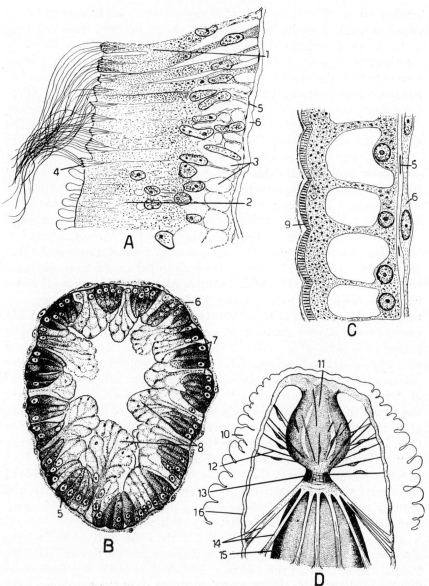

Fig. 163.—Histology of the digestive tract, muscular system. *A*, longitudinal section of junction of pharynx and esophagus (*after Müller*, 1914). *B*, cross section through the stomach of *Lophopodella*. *C*, longitudinal section of the intestinal wall of *Lophopus* (*after Marcus*, 1934). *D*, vestibular region of *Lophopodella* with retracted polypide. (*B*, *D*, *after Rogick*, 1937b.) 1, pharynx; 2, esophagus; 3, vacuolated bases; 4, ciliary attachments; 5, circular muscle layer; 6, peritoneum; 7, basophilic cells of furrows; 8, acidophilic cells of ridges; 9, striated border; 10, zoecium; 11, vestibule; 12, dilators of the vestibule; 13, sphincter of diaphragm; 14, duplicature bands; 15, tentacle sheath; 16, cellular part of body wall.

depth of the fold varies in different genera, and in *Stollela* the fold is very deep, occurring much proximal to the level of the diaphragm (Marcus, 1941; Fig. 164*A*, *B*), and the duplicature bands here insert on the tentacle sheath, as do also some of the vestibular dilators. The most prominent muscles of the polypide are the retractors of the lophophore, occurring in a strong band on each side of the digestive tract (Figs. 158*A*, 162). The retractor fibers originate posteriorly or laterally on the cystid wall and insert anteriorly at various levels from the esophagus to the base of the lophophore, with some fibers extending into the lophophore arms (Fig. 162). The retractor bundles may also be joined by fibers from the stomach wall. The muscles of the polypide appear continuous with the longitudinal fibers of the cystid wall; the duplicature bands are covered with peritoneum, but this does not seem to be the case with the other muscles. All the muscles are of the smooth type.

e. Protrusion and Retraction of the Polypide.—It will be noticed that parietal muscles are lacking, in correspondence with the presence of muscle layers in the cystid wall. The latter is flexible, not to say soft in some genera, and contraction of its circular muscle layer squeezes the interior and forces the polypide out. At the same time vestibule and diaphragm are expanded by contraction of their dilator muscles and the duplicature bands. Retraction is accomplished by the contraction of the retractors, pulling the polypide in, concomitant with the relaxation of the dilator sets of muscles, narrowing the vestibule and diaphragm. There is no closing apparatus, but circular muscles in the diaphragm contract and greatly narrow the passage (Fig. 163*D*). The duplicature bands appear to act partly as fixator ligaments, preventing protrusion of the diaphragmatic region. In *Stolella* where they insert on the tentacle sheath (Fig. 164*A*, *B*) they prevent complete eversion of this sheath; hence the polypide is not fully protrusible.

f. Coelom and Coelomocytes.—The coelom is divided into the usual three parts, all widely open into each other. The cavity of the epistome is considered the most anterior coelom or protocoel. It is crossed by muscular strands and opens widely into the second coelomic division, or mesocoel, that of the lophophore. The base, or ridge, of the lophophore is hollow, containing a coelomic cavity that has the shape of a U and that is continuous dorsally along one edge with the lumina of the outer tentacles, along the other edge with the lumina of the inner tentacles (Fig. 164*C*). The part of the lophophoral coelom passing ventral to the mouth would correspond to the ventral part of the ring coelom of gymnolaemates. The presence of the epistomial coelom at the concavity of the lophophore interferes here with the continuity of the lophophoral coelom with the lumina of the inner tentacles borne on the concavity. To overcome this difficulty the lophophoral coelom here sends a canal around each side of

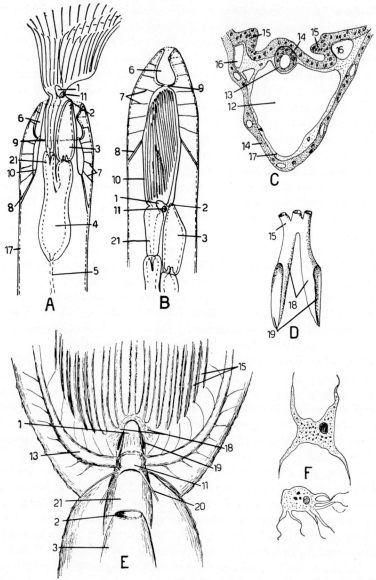

Fig. 164.—Musculature (concluded), coelom. *A, Stolella evelinae* with extended polypide. *B,* same with retracted polypide. (*A, B, after Marcus,* 1941.) *C,* section through a lophophore arm (*after Graupner,* 1930). *D,* forked canal of *Pectinatella* (*after Oka,* 1891). *E,* view from the dorsal side of *Lophophus,* showing forked canal in relation to tentacles (*after Marcus,* 1934). *F,* coelomocytes of *Cristatella* (*after Cori,* 1893). 1, epistome; 2, anus; 3, intestine; 4, stomach; 5, funiculus; 6, vestibule; 7, dilators of vestibule; 8, duplicature ligaments; 9, diaphragm; 10, tentacle sheath; 11, ganglion; 12, lumen of lophophore arm (mesocoel); 13, lophophoral nerve tract; 14, epidermis; 15, tentacle bases; 16, coelomic lumina of tentacles; 17, peritoneum; 18, the two arms of the forked canal; 19, coelomic openings of forked canal; 20, nerves of tentacle sheath; 21, foregut.

the ganglion and the epistomial coelom (Fig. 164D, E). These two canals converge and unite dorsally; from this union, which takes the form of a considerable sac in some genera, the canals into the tentacles at the concavity proceed (Fig. 164D). The two converging or diverging, according to the point of view, canals are called the *forked canal* (*Gabelkanal* in German) and have given rise to considerable controversy. They are considered nephridia by some workers, notably Cori (1893, 1941), who claimed the median sac opened by a definite pore to the exterior. This sac is wanting in *Lophopus* and *Pectinatella*, present in *Cristatella*, on which Cori worked. However, in no case is an opening to the exterior present (Braem, 1890). Marcus (1934) found in *Lophopus* and *Cristatella*, but not in *Pectinatella*, a weak spot in the basement membrane, completely covered, however, by epidermis on the outside and peritoneum on the inside. He admitted that material could work its way through this spot to the exterior. It appears that the forked canal cannot represent a pair of nephridia in the morphological sense but very likely has an excretory function (see later). The canals are lined by a cuboidal, heavily ciliated epithelium, quite different from the adjacent peritoneum (Fig. 165A, B).

The main coelom, or metacoel, is a spacious cavity surrounding the digestive tract and lined throughout by peritoneum. It is separated from the mesocoel by an imperfect septum that extends on the ventral side from the tentacle sheath to the pharynx and dorsally passes below the ganglion to the lophophoral base (Fig. 162). As already indicated, the metacoels of a colony are not definitely separated, especially in gelatinous types, although strands indicative of zooid boundaries may be present. Typically the digestive tracts of several to many zooids hang in a common coelom. There is better separation of zooids in branching types where, especially in *Fredericella*, an imperfect transverse partition may occur at the zooid base.

The metacoel lacks opening to the exterior except in three Brazilian species, *Stolella evelinae* and *agilis* and *Hyalinella carvalhoi*, where a pore is present in the inner side of the dorsal vestibular wall (Marcus, 1941, 1942; Fig. 165C). The emergence of statoblasts through this *vestibular pore* was witnessed.

The stomach caecum is attached to the ventral cystid wall by a strong funiculus in all phylactolaemates. This is always curved, hence has convex and concave surfaces. It is an outgrowth of the peritoneal part of the cystid wall, hence consists of a cylinder of basement membrane accompanied by longitudinal muscle fibers and covered externally by peritoneum (Fig. 165D). The funiculus is hollow, with a few free cells in its lumen.

The coelom is filled with a fluid circulated by the cilia of the peritoneum. It contains phagocytic amoeboid cells described by Cori (1893; Fig. 164F).

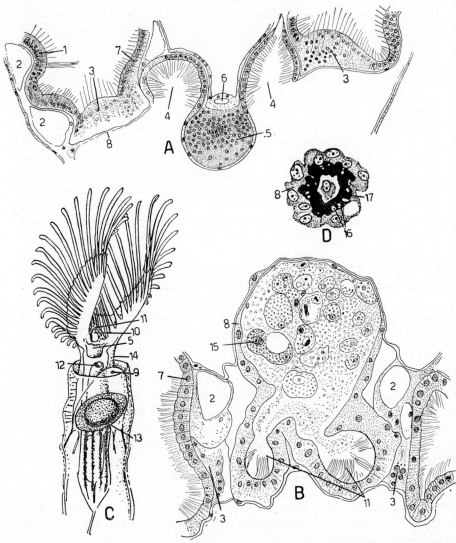

FIG. 165.—Coelom (concluded). *A*, section through the openings of the forked canal into the mesocoel, *Cristatella*. *B*, more dorsal section of the same series as *A*, showing opening of the forked canal into its sac. (*A, B, after Cori*, 1893.) *C, Stolella evelinae*, showing vestibular pore (*after Marcus*, 1941). *D*, cross section of the funiculus (*after Rogick*, 1937b). 1, tentacle base; 2, tentacular lumen; 3, nervous tract; 4, opening of forked canal into mesocoel; 5, ganglion; 6, protocoel; 7, epidermis; 8, peritoneum; 9, vestibular pore; 10, epistome; 11, forked canal; 12, anus; 13, statoblast; 14, tentacle sheath; 15, sac of forked canal filled with waste material; 16, longitudinal muscle fibers; 17, basement membrane.

g. Nervous System.—This system was best described by Gerwerzhagen (1913a) for *Cristatella* and Marcus (1934) for *Lophopus*. The nervous center, called ganglion or brain, is situated between pharynx and anus in the lophophoral coelom just above the septum separating this coelom from the metacoel (Fig. 162). The ganglion is a nervous mass applied against the dorsal wall of a closed vesicle composed of a delicate nucleated membrane, apparently of peritoneal nature (Fig. 166*A*). The nervous mass, which occupies about half of the vesicle, is oval in transverse view but has a characteristic crescentic or reniform shape in vertical sagittal section (Fig. 166*A*). The ganglion consists of a fibrillar interior covered peripherally with a layer of ganglion cells (Fig. 166*A*). From each side of the ganglion springs a large hollow ganglionated tract, usually called ganglionic horn, that passes into the lophophoral arm of that side and runs along the groove between the tentacular bases just beneath the epidermis (Fig. 164*C*). The lumina of the two lophophoral tracts are continuous with the lumen of the brain vesicle. In its course along the lophophoral arm each lophophoral tract gives off on each side a succession of branches badly called radial nerves (Fig. 166*B*). In *Cristatella* these emit several strands on each side on their way to the tentacle bases, where each forks, sending a branch into each of two adjacent tentacles (Figs. 167*B*, 168*A*). Thus in *Cristatella* each tentacle contains two branches, supposedly motor, arising from two adjacent radial nerves and located in the sides of the tentacle. The lateral strands given off before the fork unite to loose bundles, of sensory nature, that also ascend the tentacle (Fig. 168*A*), forming an inner and an outer nerve. Conditions in *Lophopus* differ somewhat in that each radial nerve forks twice, hence sending two nerves into each of two adjacent tentacles, and only an inner bundle is present. Hence the cross section of a *Lophopus* tentacle contains five nerves (Fig. 161*A*), all of which are sensory, according to Marcus, whereas in *Cristatella*, according to Gerwerzhagen, there are four, two lateral, an inner and an outer.

In any case the lophophoral tracts cannot supply directly the tentacles of the median part of the lophophore. On the dorsal side the epistome and its coelom are in the way, and ventrally the mouth and pharynx intervene. The radial nerves for the median tentacles of the concavity of the lophophore form a sort of ring, the *epistomial ring*, around the epistome before passing into these tentacles, and similarly the radial nerves for the median tentacles of the outer, or ventral, row of the lophophore form a *circumoral ring* before going off into the tentacles in question. These two rings in *Cristatella* are shown in Fig. 166*B*, and similar conditions exist in *Lophopus.*

Other parts are innervated directly from the ganglion. Delicate nerves pass from the ganglion into the epistome, which appears to be a

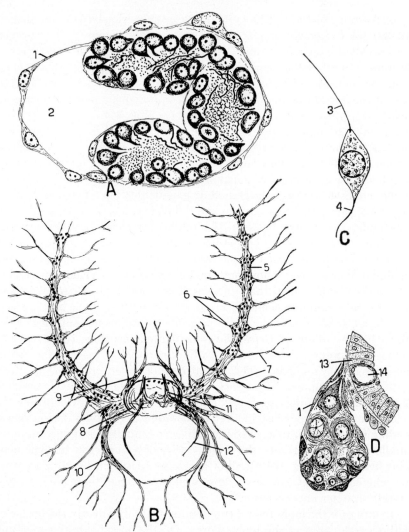

Fig. 166.—Nervous and reproductive systems.   *A*, median sagittal section of the ganglion of *Lophopus*.   *B*, general view of the main nervous system of *Cristatella*.   *C*, a sensory nerve cell of *Cristatella*.   (*B, C, after Gerwerzhagen*, 1913a.)   *D*, ovary of *Lophophus*. (*A, D, after Marcus*, 1934.)   1, peritoneal covering; 2, lumen of ganglion; 3, sensory bristle; 4, nerve fiber; 5, lophophoral tract; 6, nerves to inner tentacles; 7, nerves to outer tentacles; 8, ganglion; 9, epistomial ring for tentacles in lophophore concavity; 10, circumoral ring; 11, dorsal nerve of tentacle sheath; 12, ventral nerve of tentacle sheath; 13, epidermis; 14, vesicular cell.

sensory area of some importance. A dorsal and a ventral pair of nerves spring from the ganglion to innervate the tentacle sheath in which they branch extensively, lying between the epidermis and the muscle layer and forming a plexus (Fig. 167*A*). A number of fine nerves pass from the ganglion into the pharynx and continue along the entire digestive tract as a ganglionated plexus situated between the epithelium and the circular muscle layer and taking a ringlike form at the cardiac valve and at the anus.

In *Cristatella* there is present in the cystid wall to the inner side of the muscle layer a ganglionated plexus that has some anastomoses with the plexus of the tentacle sheath through the muscle layer and that is spread throughout the colony, thus explaining the coordinated creeping peculiar to this genus.

Sensory nerve cells of the usual type (Fig. 166*C*) are abundantly described for both *Cristatella* and *Lophopus* in the epistome, along the tentacles (Fig. 168*A*), in the intertentacular membrane, along the lophophore arm, and around the mouth (Fig. 167*A*). No special sense organs are present.

h. Reproductive System.—All phylactolaemates are hermaphroditic. The sex cells are of peritoneal origin, and the gonads are borne on the peritoneum. The ovary (Fig. 166*D*) is located on the ventral cystid wall near the vestibule, sometimes on the vestibular wall, and is closely associated with the adventitious asexual bud (Fig. 168*E*). The testis or testes occur on the funiculus (Fig. 168*B*, *C*) except in *Cristatella mucedo*, where they may also develop on the imperfect partitions between zooids; the funiculus may become almost completely covered with testes. In the Northern Hemisphere the sex cells ripen in summer, from May to July (Kraepelin, 1887; Braem, 1890), over a period of 3 to 4 weeks. The ciliated larvae may be found into September. Rogick (1943a) recorded larvae of *Plumatella casmiana* in Lake Erie in July and those of *Hyalinella punctata* (1939) in New York in August. All phylactolaemates are viviparous, brooding the embryos in an embryo sac attached to the cystid wall. The resulting ciliated larva, actually a young colony, escapes at the site of attachment of the embryo sac. The maternal polypide generally degenerates during the development of the embryo, and there is general degeneration of polypides throughout a colony engaged in sexual reproduction.

4. Embryology.—Main accounts of the embryology are those of Kraepelin (1892) for *Plumatella* and *Pectinatella*, Braem (1897) for *Plumatella* and (1908) for *Fredericella*, Marcus (1934) for *Lophopus*, and Brien (1953) for *Plumatella*. A good history of earlier accounts is given by Kraepelin. The egg develops in a body-wall invagination definitely located on the maternal cystid between the maternal polypide and the

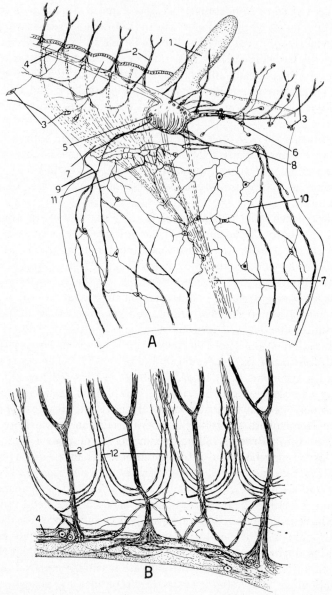

FIG. 167.—Nervous system (continued). *A*, innervation of the tentacle sheath, *Cristatella*. *B*, details of tentacular innervation. (*A, B, after Gerwerzhagen*, 1913a.) 1, epistome; 2, main nerves to tentacles; 3, sensory nerve cells; 4, lophophoral tract; 5, ganglion; 6, circumoral ring; 7, retractor lophophore; 8, ventral nerve to tentacle sheath; 9, dorsal nerve to tentacle sheath; 10, plexus; 11, plexus for lophophore retractor; 12, branches to form inner sensory nerve bundle of tentacles.

ovary (Fig. 168*E*), with the adventitious asexual bud on the other side of the ovary. The invagination in question will here be termed *embryo sac* to avoid the usual name oecium, already in use in gymnolaemates as an alternative name for ovicell. The embryo sac is usually regarded as an altered asexual polypide bud, but Brien rejects this interpretation as not consistent with the histological details of the sac as compared with those of beginning buds. The invagination consists of elongated epidermal cells covered by peritoneum (Fig. 168*E*). It develops no further but degenerates unless it acquires an egg. The passage of an egg into the embryo sac has not been witnessed. Braem believed that as the eggs enlarge in the closely adjacent ovary, the most advanced egg touches the embryo sac and is engulfed by it. Marcus reported that in *Lophopus*, ripe eggs are discharged into the coelom and circulated about; hence contact with the young embryo sac must be accidental. The formation of an embryo sac probably occurs under hormonal influence from the adjacent ovary, for embryo sacs arise only in the presence of ovaries but ovaries may occur in the absence of embryo sacs (Marcus). An egg that enters an embryo sac is already fertilized, generally while still in the ovary, possibly sometimes when free in the coelom. Fertilization presumably is accomplished by the sperm of the same zooid, or at least of the same colony, since there appears no means of entry of sperm from other colonies.

Having acquired an egg, the embryo sac proceeds to elongate rapidly, projecting into the coelom (Fig. 168*F*), and meantime the egg undergoes cleavage. Cleavage is holoblastic and results in a cluster of rounded blastomeres of equal to somewhat unequal size (Fig. 169*A*). The embryo is soon forced into an elongated shape by the elongation of the embryo sac and hollows out to become a coeloblastula (Fig. 169*B*). Braem thought the outer end of the elongated blastula, the end facing the attachment stalk of the embryo sac, is the vegetative pole, but convincing grounds for this opinion are wanting. Both Kraepelin and Braem believed entoderm formation occurs by inwandering at this pole of a few cells that quickly degenerate, but later authors have not verified this finding and it must be regarded with grave doubt. Braem also described mesoderm formation at this pole by a somewhat similar process, but here again verification is lacking. In a manner not clearly elucidated the embryo becomes two-layered, probably by rearrangement of cells (Fig. 169*B*). Its two layers are an outer ectoderm and an inner peritoneum; hence the embryo is now a cystid (Fig. 169*C*). In the meantime both embryo and embryo sac have continued to broaden and elongate and the epidermal lining of the embryo sac undergoes some degeneration (Fig. 169*C*). The outer end of the embryo is capped by a group of enlarged rounded cells, and in *Plumatella* these seem to participate in a ring of enlarged ectoderm cells at about the middle of the embryo that attach to

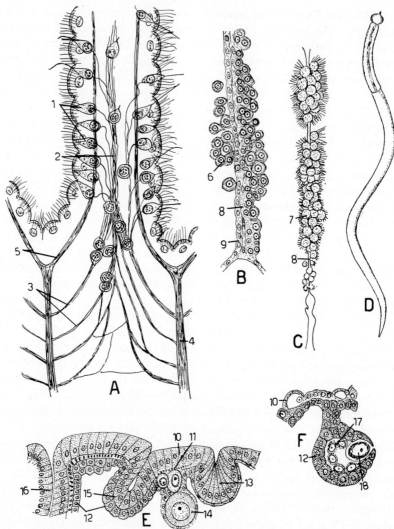

Fig. 168.—Nervous and reproductive systems (concluded), embryology. *A*, part of tentacle of *Cristatella* showing sensory innervation (*after Gerwerzhagen*, 1913a). *B*, funiculus, *Plumatella*, with early stage of testis formation. *C*, funiculus, *Plumatella*, testes matured (*after Braem*, 1890). *D*, sperm of *Plumatella* (*after Kraepelin*, 1892). *E*, ventral cystid wall of *Plumatella*, just below the polypide, showing arrangement of reproductive bodies. (*B, E, after Braem*, 1897.) *F*, embryo sac of *Lophopus*, just after engulfing an egg (*after Marcus*, 1934). 1, sensory nerve cells; 2, sensory bundle; 3, roots to form sensory bundle; 4, motor nerve; 5, fork of motor nerve at angle between two tentacles; 6, spermatogonia; 7, testes; 8, funiculus; 9, peritoneum of funiculus; 10, epidermis; 11, muscle layer; 12, peritoneum; 13, embryo sac; 14, ovary; 15, adventitious bud; 16, main, oldest bud; 17, epidermal lining of embryo sac; 18, egg.

the embryo sac forming the *placental ring* (Fig. 169D). This attachment may have a nutritive function but more probably acts to anchor the embryo in the sac. In *Fredericella* the attachment occurs at the upper pole (outer end) of the embryo in the form of a *placental disk* of irregularly arranged cells (Fig. 170A), in which the cap cells are incorporated.

The embryo, being a cystid, shortly behaves after the manner of cystids; that is, it buds one or more polypides on its outer end. These begin as the usual two-layered invaginations and proceed to differentiate into polypides exactly as in asexual budding (considered below). The number of primary polypide buds formed by the embryo differs in different genera; there is one (Fig. 170C) in *Fredericella*, one to four, generally two, in *Plumatella* (Fig. 170D), two in *Hyalinella* (Rogick, 1939), mostly four in *Cristatella* and *Pectinatella*. As additional buds soon arise, the number may appear indefinite and variable.

While the polypides are developing there arises around the middle of the embryo, below the polypidial region and below the placental ring (if present), a circular fold of body wall, the *mantle* fold (Fig. 169D). This advances forward (Fig. 170B), rupturing the placental ring and completely enclosing the polypidial area, but does not fuse, leaving a small opening. The embryo thus becomes an oval larva, about 0.5 to 2 mm. in length, depending on the species, and acquires a complete coat of cilia (Fig. 170C, D). It lies free in the embryo sac, whose wall has become reduced to a thin, stretched peritoneal layer, and shortly escapes by rupture of the site of attachment of the embryo sac to the maternal cystid. It swims about for a few minutes to not more than 24 hours, rotating with the pole opposite the polypides forward. At this pole Braem described a nervous accumulation, which he regarded as corresponding to the apical nervous plate of other invertebrate larvae; and a nervous concentration there with accompanying sensory nerve cells was also seen by Marcus (1926b) after methylene blue staining. Although usually called larva, the tiny creature is in effect a juvenile colony; the primary polypides are completely formed and histologically differentiated, and secondary polypide buds have started. The pole opposite the polypides soon seeks a suitable substrate, to which it attaches by glandular secretion. The polypides at once expand and extend through the mantle opening, concomitant with the shrinkage and recession of the mantle (Fig. 170E–G). The latter curls up into the base of the young colony, where it gradually degenerates.

It will be perceived that this embryonic history is just as unsatisfactory from the phylogenetic point of view as is the embryology of gymnolaemates. Entoderm formation is apparently completely suppressed; the mesoderm seemingly originates from the ectoderm, and coelom formation probably occurs by cell rearrangement.

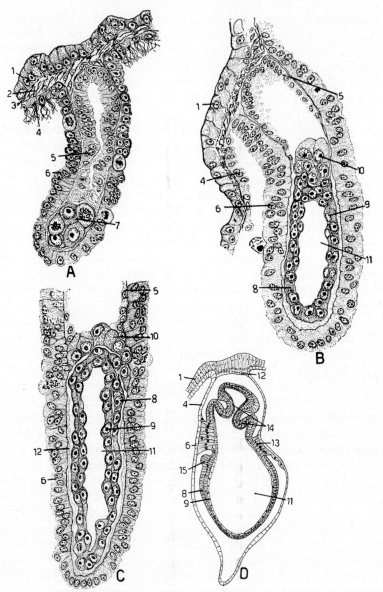

Fig. 169.—Embryonic development.　A, embryo sac with cleavage stage.　B, embryo as elongated blastula with peritoneum forming.　C, embryo has become a two-layered cystid.　(A–C, *Plumatella fungosa*, after Brien, 1953.)　D, *Plumatella fungosa*, placental ring formed, first buds beginning (*after Braem*, 1897).　1, epidermis; 2, basement membrane; 3, muscle fibers; 4, peritoneum; 5, epidermis of embryo sac; 6, peritoneum of embryo sac; 7, embryo in cleavage stage; 8, ectoderm of embryo; 9, peritoneum of embryo; 10, cap cells; 11, future coelom; 12, degenerated epidermis of embryo sac; 13, placental ring; 14, asexual buds; 15, beginning of mantle fold.

5. Asexual Budding.—The sexually produced juvenile colony after attachment continues the process of budding already begun while enclosed in the larval mantle, and thus the colony expands with an ever-increasing number of polypides. Asexual budding has been studied by a long succession of investigators but has been best elucidated by Brien (1936, 1953). In the simpler branching types as *Fredericella* and *Plumatella*, buds arise in a definite order on a definite area of the maternal cystid wall ventral to the vestibular region. Here there are regularly found three buds, a main bud *B*, already set off as an incipient zooid by a slight indentation, a duplicate bud *D*, budded from the ventral side of the attached end of *B*, and an adventitious bud *C* on the side of *B* toward the maternal polypide (Fig. 171*A*). Ovary and embryo sac when present are located between *C* and the vestibular region of the maternal polypide. When *B* grows out into a fully formed polypide, its duplicate bud *D* separates from it and becomes its main bud, developing at its base in turn a duplicate bud. Meanwhile the adventitious bud *C* becomes the main bud of the original polypide, producing at its base a duplicate bud, while the original polypide gives rise to a new adventitious bud. These processes continue, producing a branching colony. Any one polypide can give rise to only a limited number of successive adventitious buds; it then regresses and dies. Hence in branching colonies the basal parts are dead, and living active polypides are found only at the branch ends.

In gelatinous compact types of colonies budding follows a similar course with some variations. The zooids of a *Lophopus* colony all face in the ventral direction, with only their vestibular regions protruding from the general mass (Fig. 179*B*). On the ventral cystid wall at a definite distance below the vestibular region of each polypide buds appear in a bilateral arrangement with the main bud *B* accompanied by its duplicate bud *D* to the left of the median sagittal plane and the adventitious bud *C* to the right of this plane. Thus each zooid produces two daughters, not simultaneously but successively, and these repeat the process. Hence the colony expands in a fanlike manner, but in the ventral direction only. As the colony increases in size it develops lobulations, and these deepen, dividing up the colony into smaller colonies. As in plumatellid colonies, a zooid may produce a succession of adventitious buds but eventually degenerates. Hence there is a process of death of zooids along the dorsal side of the colony. The elongated, bilaterally symmetrical *Cristatella* colony grows only along the lateral edges where a budding zone occurs on each side below the outermost and youngest row of polypides (Fig. 160*A*). Here as in *Lophopus* two buds related to the plane of bilateral symmetry of the polypide form below each polypide, the *B-D* combination to one side and the adventitious bud *C* to the other side. Hence on the flanks of the colony each polypide originates two daughters and may form later

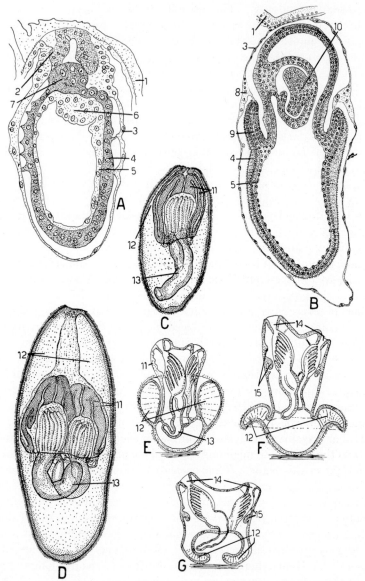

Fig. 170.—Embryology (concluded). *A*, embryo of *Fredericella* with cap placenta (*after Braem*, 1908). *B*, *Plumatella* embryo, with mantle fold developing (*after Kraepelin*, 1892). *C*, free larva of *Fredericella* with one polypide. *D*, free larva of *Plumatella*, with two polypides. (*C*, *D*, *after Brien*, 1953.) *E–G*, three stages in the attachment of *Pl. fungosa*, showing retraction and folding in of the mantle folds (*after Braem*, 1890). 1, maternal epidermis; 2, remains of epidermis of embryo sac; 3, peritoneum of embryo sac; 4, epidermis of embryo; 5, peritoneum of embryo; 6, beginning of polypide; 7, cap placenta; 8, remains of ring placenta; 9, mantle folds; 10, polypide bud; 11, wall of future cystid; 12, mantle; 13, digestive tract of polypide; 14, vestibule; 15, asexual buds.

adventitious buds. The older, more central polypides do not bud, but undergo a continual process of disintegration as new rows of polypides appear laterally. Hence the colony generally consists of about three rows of functional, active polypides on each side. As they increase in size, *Cristatella* colonies also divide up into smaller colonies (Fig. 160*B*). The individual colony of the compound colony of *Pectinatella* behaves like *Cristatella*, but being of circular rather than elongated form buds around the periphery. Here the outer youngest zooids produce the usual two buds on the ventral side, arranged bilaterally with respect to the median sagittal plane (Oka, 1891). Thus the colony undergoes dichotomous growth at the periphery.

A bud originates by the proliferation of the basal indifferent cells of the epidermis, following disappearance of the muscular layers and basement membrane of the body wall at the site of such proliferation. Braem (1890) believed that the basal epidermal cells constitute a store of embryonic reserve cells that are transmitted from generation to generation, and Marcus (1934) seems to support this view. Brien, however, asserts that these basal cells are simply dedifferentiated columnar epidermal cells that at the region of bud formation round up and migrate to a basal position, where they constitute a blastogenous zone giving rise to the main and adventitious buds (Fig. 171*B*). Brien therefore denies all possibility of a germinal line for asexual budding, and such is also definitely lacking in sexual reproduction. The epidermal proliferation invaginates, carrying with it the peritoneum, forming a two-layered primordium that continues to elongate and soon hollows to a two-layered vesicle (Fig. 171*C*, *D*). Conflicting accounts appear in the literature as to the manner of development of this vesicle into a polypide. The account of Oka (1891) for *Pectinatella* is similar to that of polypide development in gymnolaemates. The vesicle constricts at about its middle, the constriction represents the mouth region, the part of the vesicle distal to the constriction becomes the tentacle sheath, and the proximal part of the vesicle becomes the rest of the digestive tract, putting out the intestine as an outgrowth (Fig. 172*A–E*). A different story appears to obtain for *Plumatella*, *Cristatella*, and presumably other genera (Nitsche, 1875; Braem, 1890; Davenport, 1890; Kraepelin, 1892); subsequent authors have not concerned themselves with the later stages of bud development. The authors mentioned are in accord that following the stage of the simple two-layered vesicle, the lumen of the vesicle puts out two tubular outgrowths into the inner layer, which thus comes to bound two tubes (Fig. 172*F*). One of these tubes, on the future ventral side, is the primordium of the pharynx and esophagus; the other on the dorsal side furnishes the stomach and intestine. At first the inner ends of the two tubes are blind, but later they fuse to form a continuous digestive tract; the place of fusion is located at

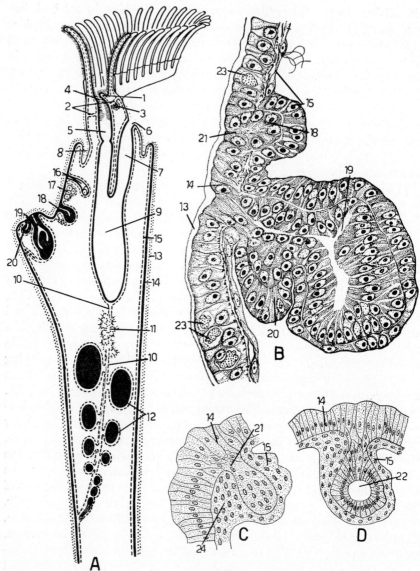

FIG. 171.—Asexual reproduction. *A*, scheme of a phylactolaemate, showing budding zone and site of statoblast formation. *B*, stages of asexual buds of *Pl. fungosa*. (*A*, *B*, *after Brien*, 1953.) *C*, beginning bud of *Pectinatella*. *D*, slightly later stage of *C*. (*C*, *D*, *after Oka*, 1891.) 1, epistome; 2, coelomic septum; 3, ganglion; 4, pharynx; 5, esophagus; 6, anus; 7, intestine; 8, vestibule; 9, stomach caecum; 10, funiculus; 11, testes; 12, statoblasts forming; 13, cuticle; 14, epidermis; 15, peritoneum; 16, embryo sac; 17, ovary; 18, adventitious bud; 19, main bud; 20, duplicate bud; 21, epidermal ingrowth; 22, epidermal vesicle; 23, vesicular cells; 24, peritoneal sheet to form funiculus.

the cardiac valve (Fig. 172*G*).   Thus the epidermal lining of the bud vesicle becomes the digestive epithelium.   As regards the development of parts other than the digestive tract, all accounts agree.   The ganglion is formed by an evagination of the dorsal wall of the future pharynx (Fig. 172*D, G*), and this soon cuts off as a sac (Fig. 172*E*).   Around the mouth on each side the coelom pushes inward as a pocket that raises a conical eminence, the primordium of the lophophore arm of that side (Fig. 172*C–E, G, H*).   These two coelomic pockets become connected below the mouth by a coelomic groove that closes over into a canal (Fig. 173*A*). This canal is the part of the lophophoric coelom that passes below the mouth, and the pockets just mentioned also close over, becoming the main lophophoral coelom.   The two lobes of the lophophore lie in the original distal part of the cavity of the bud vesicle; this cavity becomes the cavity of the tentacle sheath, which is formed by the thinning and expansion of its wall (Fig. 172*G*).   The two lobes of the lophophore are more or less fused at first, but later separate to form the arms of the typical horseshoe. They give rise to the tentacles from the ventral side in the dorsal direction by putting out hollow evaginations (Fig. 173*B*).   In the meantime there has been an invasion of peritoneum between the two limbs of the digestive tract, clothing them, and peritoneum also pushes in between the ganglion and the pharyngeal wall from which it constricted.   A tubular cavity, hence a coelomic canal, forming in the peritoneum here, becomes the epistomial canal leading from the epistome below the ganglion into the general coelom.   The epistome, an outgrowth from the dorsal rim of the mouth, incorporates a coelomic space as it pushes out.   The manner of formation of the forked canal was already indicated.   When the polypide is completed the original connection of the bud with the wall of the maternal cystid ruptures to become the orifice.

The development of the funiculus is of interest because of the role of this structure in the formation of statoblasts.   Two different accounts of the origin of the funiculus appear in the literature despite utilization of the same species as material.   Davenport (1890), Kraepelin (1892), and Buddenbrock (1910) ascribe the origin of the funiculus to a proliferation of peritoneal cells at the inner, or free, end of the young bud that grows toward and fuses with the maternal cystid wall just ventral to the neck or attached end of the bud.   According to Oka (1891), Braem (1890), and Brien (1953), a continuous sheet of peritoneum extends from the ventral wall of the very young bud to the adjacent maternal cystid wall (Fig. 171*C, D*), and as the bud elongates, the edge of this sheet separates off as the funiculus (Fig. 172*A*), which thus is from the start a continuous cord from the maternal cystid to the free end of the bud.   It seems probable this second view is the correct one.   The funiculus is at first composed solidly of peritoneum but later hollows, and the peritoneum secretes on the

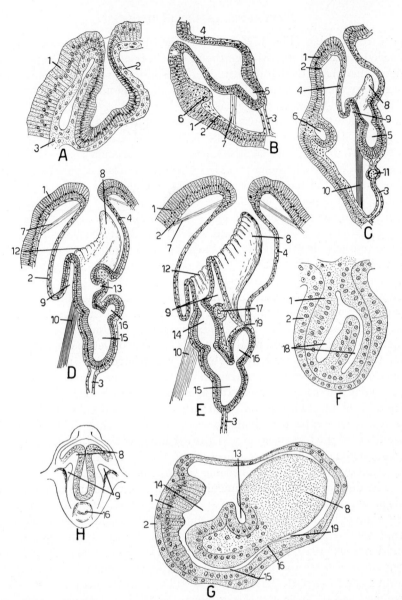

Fig. 172.—Budding (continued). *A–E*, further stages of bud development in *Pectinatella* (*after Oka*, 1891). *A*, invagination lengthened, funiculus separating off. *B*, invaginated vesicle subdividing, new bud starting. *C*, vesicle constricted into two vesicles, lophophore appearing. *D*, inner vesicle putting out intestine, ganglion evaginating from pharynx wall. *E*, digestive tract complete. *F*, bud of *Cristatella*, tubular outgrowths of lumen to form digestive tract. *G*, later stage of *F*, outgrowths have met and fused. (*F, G*, *after Davenport*, 1890.) *H*, bud of *Cristatella* of about stage of *G*, to show lophophore bulges, seen from behind (*after Nitsche*, 1875). 1, epidermis; 2, peritoneum; 3, funiculus; 4, future tentacle sheath; 5, inner vesicle; 6, beginning bud; 7, duplicature band; 8, lophophore; 9, coelomic invagination for lophophore; 10, retractor lophophore; 11, statoblast; 12, beginning of tentacles; 13, invagination to form ganglion; 14, pharynx; 15, stomach; 16, intestine; 17, ganglion; 18, tubular outgrowths of bud lumen; 19, location of future anus.

side toward the lumen a layer of longitudinal muscle fibers and the base-ment membrane. Hence the longitudinal fibers and its accompanying basement membrane are of peritoneal origin.

6. Statoblasts.—Phylactolaemates reproduce not only by the sexual method and by asexual budding but also by another asexual method, the production of statoblasts. A statoblast is a cell mass enclosed in a pro-tective shell that enables it to endure desiccation and severe temperatures. Statoblasts are produced on the funiculus throughout the growing season following sexual reproduction but most profusely toward autumn. It was discovered by Braem (1888), and since verified by all observers, that the cell mass of the statoblast is composed of two sorts of cells, epidermal and peritoneal. The peritoneal cells are those of the funiculus, but the epidermal cells migrate into the funiculus from the same store of basal epidermal or blastogenic cells that give rise to the epidermal layer of buds (Fig. 174*A*). In forming a statoblast several of these inwandered epi-dermal cells round up into a ball that soon hollows out, then resembling a blastula (Fig. 174*B*). Such vesicles cause a bulge of the peritoneal covering of the funiculus. Beneath this covering peritoneum the epi-dermal vesicle flattens to a disciform shape (Fig. 174*B*), and meantime peritoneal cells of the funiculus accumulate to its inner side and begin to store reserve food in the form of yolk spherules (Fig. 174*B*). The two-layered epidermal disk now grows around and encloses the mass of peritoneal yolk-containing cells in a double epidermal wall (Fig. 174*C*). The inner epidermal wall in contact with the yolk mass remains unaltered for the present and is destined to become the epidermis of the future zooid. The outer epidermal layer takes on a columnar form and begins the secretion of the shell of the statoblast. This secretion occurs on its inner surface next the inner epidermal layer and takes the form of a thick hard cuticle, known to be chitinous, that becomes a capsule enclosing the germinal mass, composed of the inner epidermal layer surrounding the yolk cells (Fig. 175*A*, *B*). The shell soon develops an equatorial suture that delimits two valves, a *dorsal*, or *cystigenic*, valve on the side where the epidermal disk was located, a *ventral*, or *deutoplasmic*, valve on the side where the yolk cells accumulated. Around the periphery the outer epidermis begins to project as a crest of very tall cells (Fig. 175*A*). The walls of these harden, the cell contents disappear, leaving a hollow interior that becomes filled with air, and there is thus formed around the capsule a more or less flattened ring of air cells, the *pneumatic ring*, or *annulus*, that acts as a float (Fig. 175*B*). In some genera similar but minor crests of the outer epidermis secrete between their two walls hooked spines. When these secreted parts have hardened and become dehydrated the statocyst is complete, consisting of the *capsule*, a central rounded or oval bulge containing the germinal mass, and the peripheral annulus provided or not with hooked spines (Figs. 175, 176). The deutoplasmic valve is generally more convex than the cystigenic valve, and further, the annulus typically extends farther over the capsule on the cystigenic side; consequently the statoblast floats with the cystigenic side up (Fig. 175C–E). Main articles on statocyst development are those of Braem (1890), Oka (1891), Kraepelin (1892), von Buddenbrock (1910), and Brien (1953).

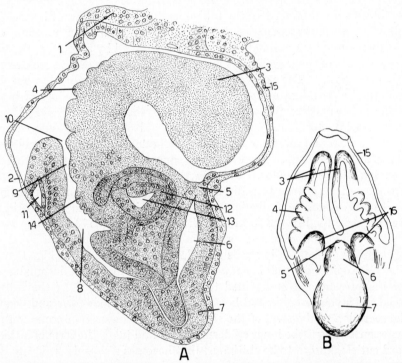

Fig. 173.—Budding (concluded). *A*, median sagittal section of later stage of *Cristatella* (*after Davenport*, 1890). *B*, stage similar to *A*, seen from behind (*after Nitsche*, 1875). 1, epidermis; 2, peritoneum; 3, lophophore; 4, beginning of tentacles; 5, future anus; 6, intestine; 7, stomach; 8, esophagus; 9, pharynx; 10, mouth; 11, ventral coelomic ring to complete mesocoel; 12, ganglion; 13, lumen of ganglion; 14, location of epistome; 15, tentacle sheath; 16, coelomic invaginations to form coelom (mesocoel) of lophophore.

The form of the statoblast differs in different genera and is more or less diagnostic, although the same species may produce more than one type. Rogick (1943b) proposed useful names for the three general kinds of statoblasts. Those without or with a reduced annulus that do not float but sink to the bottom or are cemented to the maternal tissues (Fig. 175J, K) are termed *sessoblasts;* floating types with a well-developed annulus of air cells but without spiny armature are called *floatoblasts;* and floatoblasts bordered with hooked spines are named *spinoblasts*. Sessoblasts, oval without an annulus, are the only type found in the genus

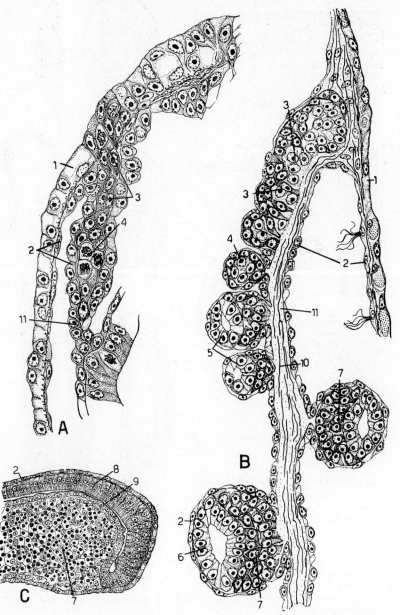

Fig. 174.—Formation of the statoblast. *A*, migration of basal epidermal cells into funiculus, *Lophopus*. *B*, funiculus with various stages of statoblast formation, *Cristatella*. *C*, epidermal disk growing around the yolk-containing peritoneal mass, *Cristatella*. (*All after Brien*, 1953.) 1, epidermis; 2, peritoneum; 3, migrating epidermal cells; 4, early stage of statoblast; 5, blastula-like stage of statoblast; 6, epidermal disk; 7, mass of peritoneal cells; 8, outer epithelium of statoblast; 9, inner epithelium of statoblast; 10, muscle fibers of funiculus; 11, funiculus.

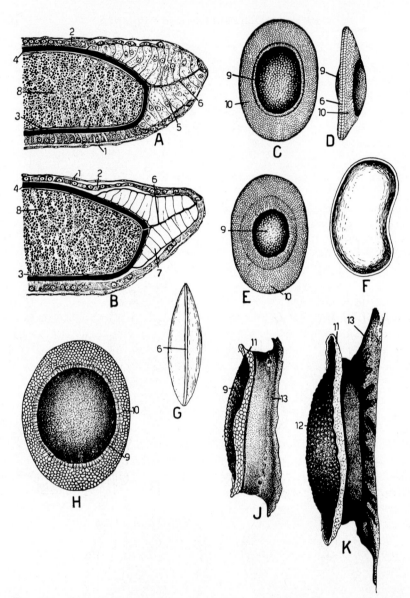

Fig. 175.—Formation of statoblast (concluded), statoblast types. *A*, formation of capsule and annulus, *Plumatella*. *B*, later stage of *A*, air cells of annulus completed. (*A*, *B*, after *Brien*, 1953.) *C–E*, floatoblast of *Hyalinella punctata* (after *Rogick*, 1940b). *C*, ventral, or deutoplasmic, view. *D*, side view. *E*, dorsal, or cystigenic, view; air cells partly cover capsule. *F*, sessoblast of *Fred. sultana*. *G*, side view of *F*. (*F*, *G*, after *Allman*, 1856.) *H*, floatoblast of *Pl. repens*, ventral view. *J*, sessile variant of *H*. (*H*, *J*, after *Rogick*, 1940b.) *K*, sessoblast of *Stolella* (after *Rogick*, 1943b). 1, peritoneum of funiculus; 2, outer epidermis; 3, inner epidermis; 4, capsule; 5, epidermal crest to form air cells; 6, valve line; 7, air cells; 8, enclosed yolk-containing peritoneal cells; 9, capsule; 10, annulus; 11, reduced annulus; 12, tuberculated capsule; 13, material to which sessoblast is cemented.

Fredericella (Fig. 175*F*, *G*) but may also occur in genera with floatoblasts as a variant. Eveline Marcus (1955) has suggested the name *piptoblasts* for sessoblasts not cemented to objects but lying free in the colonies. Floatoblasts of oval shape with a wide annulus of air cells are characteristic of *Plumatella* (Fig. 175*H*), *Hyalinella* (Fig. 175*C–E*), *Stolella*, and *Stephanella*. The floatoblast of *Lophopus* is fusiform in contour, with a very broad thin annulus (Fig. 176*A*), and in *Gelatinella* the entire surface of the floatoblast is covered with minute spines (Toriumi, 1955e; Fig. 176*C*). The spinoblasts are the best known and attract the most attention. Those of *Pectinatella magnifica* are rounded to squarish, edged with a single circlet of 11 to 22 long spines having anchorlike tips (Fig. 176*D*). In *Lophopodella carteri* short hooked spines are limited to each end of the oval spinoblast (Fig. 176*E*), shown in side view to be curved like a saddle (Fig. 176*F*). The most complicated type of spinoblast is that of *Cristatella mucedo*, in which each of the circular valves is armed with a circlet of spines having bifid to quadrifid extremities; but these are borne around the capsule and not on the edge of the annulus (Fig. 177). Further, the spines are shorter and fewer in number (10 to 34) on the cystigenic than on the deutoplasmic valve (20 to 50). Moreover, during the development of the *Cristatella* statoblast the secretion of a circular shelf directed from the cystigenic toward the deutoplasmic side separates the annulus from the deutoplasmic valve and lifts it away from the latter. Hence the annulus of the completed statoblast is borne entirely on the cystigenic valve (Fig. 177*C*, *D*), supported by upward curves of the spines of the deutoplasmic valve. It results that the shelf in question fits over the deutoplasmic valve after the manner of the cover of a pillbox (Fig. 177*C*, *D*). Details of these matters are admirably furnished by Brien (1953). In many statoblasts the capsule containing the germinal mass is mammillated, that is, covered with low tubercles (Fig. 175*K*). The length or diameter of statoblasts ranges from about 0.2 to 1.75 mm. Colored figures of statoblasts appear in Allman (1856) and Kraepelin (1887).

The number of statoblasts produced by a polypide varies with genus; usually the *Fredericella* polypide matures but one statoblast, and a single but large statoblast (Fig. 160*A*) is produced by each polypide in *Lophopus*, *Cristatella*, and *Pectinatella*. On the other hand, the funiculus of *Plumatella* develops a number of statoblasts in orderly succession from the oldest next to the stomach end of the funiculus to the youngest near its cystid attachment (Fig. 171*A*).

Statoblasts may be released and germinate during the same season (see later under ecology), but generally they accumulate throughout the growing season and are released by the disintegration of the colonies at the onset of winter. However, Marcus (1941, 1942) witnessed emission of statoblasts through the vestibular pore in the presence of active normal polypides in *Stolella evelinae* and *agilis* and in *Hyalinella carvalhoi*. Such statoblasts germinate in 1 to 2 weeks, and the young colonies eventuating soon again produce statoblasts. Wiebach (1952, 1953) also records the emission of statoblasts in species of *Plumatella* in the presence of a normal healthy polypide.

As already indicated, the capsule of the statoblast contains a germinal mass, composed of a flattened epithelium of epidermal origin enclosing a mass of yolk-filled cells or nucleated yolk of peritoneal origin (Fig. 175B). Under favorable conditions (discussed under ecology) statoblasts germinate. The two valves separate along the suture, the expanded germinal mass becomes visible, and soon a polypide projects from between the valves (Fig. 176A). Each statoblast gives rise to a single polypide, and this originates in the same way as in the case of asexual buds. At one, probably predetermined, site, the epidermal epithelium takes on a columnar form and proceeds to invaginate as a hollow vesicle around which some of the peritoneal cells of the yolk mass gather to form a peritoneum (Braem, 1890; Oka, 1891). There is thus produced a two-layered primordium that proceeds to develop into a polypide as described under asexual budding. The food supplies in the yolk mass are gradually utilized, lasting as long as 2 weeks in some cases, and the peritoneal cells thus reduced to normal appearance arrange themselves as a peritoneum beneath the epidermal epithelium not engaged in producing the polypide. In this way the cystid of the first polypide arises. A statoblast produces but a single polypide, but this soon starts to bud off other polypides and a small colony is soon established with the valves of the statoblast still clinging to its base (Fig. 179B). The epidermis of the germinal mass opposite the site of polypide formation thickens and becomes an adhesive pad, secreting adhesive material for attachment of the young colony.

7. Degeneration and Regeneration.—The polypides of phylactolaemates often degenerate from natural senescence, occurrence of sexual reproduction, lack of food, or exposure to unsuitable conditions. As described by Braem (1908), Marcus (1934), and Rogick (1938), degeneration usually begins by the prolonged retraction of the polypide; this is followed by disintegration of the tentacles from the tips basally, then by disintegration of interior tissues, finally by the disruption of the digestive tract, which remains seemingly intact for some time. In the meantime the polypide continues to shorten and condense and, having detached from the cystid wall, rounds up into a mass that circulates in the cystid and eventually breaks up into fragments that dissolve in the coelomic fluid and furnish nutrition for new polypides. In some cases (*Cristatella*, Marcus, 1926a; *Lophopus*, Marcus, 1934) the ball of disintegrated material finds its way into the vestibular region of the cystid, which is then constricted off. Although the degenerative processes in general resemble those occurring in gymnolaemates, a definite brown body is not formed. The cystid deprived of its polypide does not as a rule bud a new polypide, but new polypides arise elsewhere in the colony if conditions alter or improve.

Regeneration was studied mainly by Otto (1921) and Brien (1936). Tentacles cut off or bitten off by enemies (*Stolella*, Marcus, 1941) regenerate by simple growth and elongation. If the lophophore ends are cut off, the wound closes by contraction, some degree of dedifferentiation occurs in adjacent cells, a blastema forms and grows out, continuing the lophophore from the stump, although as a rule fewer tentacles arise than were removed. In *Lophopus* (Otto), no regeneration follows if both lophophore arms are cut off near their bases or if the distal part of the polypide is removed by section through the esophagus or the ganglion. Both parts die in such case. When the polypide is cut off below the stomach, the tentacle sheath closes across the cut and the polypide may survive and even feed for 2 days but then degenerates. Different results were obtained with *Fredericella* by Brien. An anterior end removed by a cut through the vestibular region (cut I in Fig. 178*B*) without including the budding zone dies, but the remaining part will regenerate a new anterior end if the digestive loop continues intact; if the digestive loop collapses and retrogresses, the main bud *B* develops and replaces the lost polypide. If the zooid is cut across at the level II in Fig. 178*B*, hence removing the anterior end with the three buds, the cut closes over, thus forming a small cystid, the lophophore degenerates, and the main bud *B* develops into a complete polypide while the adventitious bud degenerates. The basal half left by cut II regenerates a polypide if its digestive loop survives intact; if the digestive loop regresses and falls into the base of the cystid, the latter regenerates a polypide at the site of attachment of the old esophagus.

When colonies of *Fredericella* are cut across (Otto), the cellular layers of the body wall withdraw from the cut end, close together by contraction, and secrete cuticle to mend the cut. A new polypide may form from such a cystid end, usually after considerable elimination of degenerating and injured cells and reorganization of the remaining healthy cells into two definite epithelia. Such reformation of polypides at cuts is more likely to occur in young colonies early in the season and in cuts located apically in the colony, declining in the basal direction. If a polypide forms at a proximal cut surface, its polarity is reversed (such reversal wanting in *Plumatella*). If a number of distal growing ends of a colony are cut off simultaneously, polypide formation typically occurs on the main or the youngest twig; the cystids at other cut ends are often absorbed to contribute to the nutrition of the colony. Cutting colonies often causes the cellular part of the cystid wall to break up into short lengths inside the

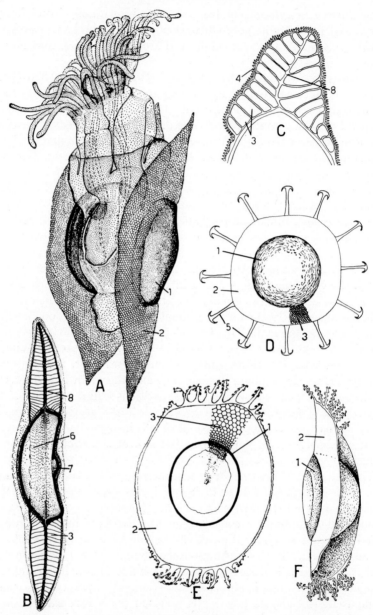

Fig. 176.—Statoblasts (continued). *A*, statoblast of *Lophopus crystallinus*, germinated, with young colony between the two valves. *B*, longitudinal section of statoblast of *Lophopus*. (*A, B, after Brien,* 1953.) *C*, part of longitudinal section of statoblast of *Gelatinella* (*after Toriumi,* 1955e). *D*, spinoblast of *Pectinatella magnifica* (*after Kraepelin,* 1887). *E*, spinoblast of *Lophopodella carteri* (*after Toriumi,* 1941). *F*, same as *E*, seen from the side (*after Rogick,* 1934). 1, capsule; 2, annulus; 3, air cells; 4, minute spines; 5, anchor spines; 6, cover, or cystigenous, valve; 7, ventral, or deutoplasmic, valve; 8, valve line.

cuticle, and these contribute to growth elsewhere. Similar fractionation of the cystid is quite common in *Fredericella* (Braem, 1908); it may be followed by degeneration, furnishing material for buds elsewhere, or by production of adventitious buds.

8. Systematic Survey.—The phylactolaemates are so similarly constructed that no systematic categories higher than family appear justified. The arrangement into four families proposed by Rogick (1935a) is acceptable (Marcus, 1942). The family Fredericellidae with the single genus *Fredericella* is the most primitive, forming colonies of tubular branches composed of fairly distinct zooids more or less separated by imperfect septa (Fig. 157*A*). The cuticle is here membranous, usually incorporating diatoms and other foreign particles. *Fredericella* is easily distinguished from all other phylactolaemates by the circular or nearly circular, more accurately oval or reniform, shape of the lophophore (Fig. 158*A*); the essential bilaterality of the lophophore is evident in young polypides developing from buds or statoblasts (Marcus, 1926a; Eveline Marcus, 1953). Statoblasts are either sessoblasts or piptoblasts, and the larva buds a single polypide (Fig. 170*C*). The most common species, *F. sultana*, is cosmopolitan and widely distributed in the United States. Another species or its variants, *F. australiensis*, differing in small details from *F. sultana*, especially in the absence of septa, has been taken in Australia, the Transcaucasus, Wyoming, and Lake Titicaca (Rogick, 1945b; Eveline Marcus, 1953, 1955).

In the other three phylactolaemate families the lophophore has an obvious horseshoe shape and statoblasts other than sessoblasts are produced, although the latter may also occur as a variant in the Plumatellidae. The family Plumatellidae, including the majority of phylactolaemate genera and species, forms ramifying, shrubby, fungoid, or somewhat gelatinous colonies, repent or erect with zooids distinct to varying degrees, usually only distally, and delimited or not internally by basal septa. Floatoblasts are typical of the family, but sessoblasts may occur. The main genus *Plumatella* (includes *Alcyonella*) is characterized by the tubular, relatively distinct zooids and the firm chitinous cuticle, usually pale to dark brown in color. The principal species, *Pl. repens* (Fig. 157*B*), with numerous named variants, is cosmopolitan in lakes, ponds, and streams everywhere. Some other widely spread species are *Pl. casmiana*, forming somewhat shrubby colonies (Fig. 179*A*); *Pl. fungosa* with a fungoid appearance caused by the squeezing of the zooids into parallel groups (Fig. 178*C*, *D*); *Pl. emarginata*, forming open to bushy growths, with notched cystid tip (Fig. 178*E*); and *Pl. fruticosa* with serrated branches. The serrations of the branches of *Pl. fruticosa* (Fig. 180*B*) represent the places from which zooids have dropped off. Such cast-off zooids are regarded by Wiebach (1954a, b) as reproductive bodies destined to found new colonies. However, after a month's observation of such castoff zooids in nature, he failed to see any colony formation from them, although indications of budding were noted. These zooids are produced early in the season before statoblast production has commenced. *Afrindella* (Annandale, 1912b), found in India and Africa, can be distinguished from *Plumatella* by its stiffer and more horny cuticle and the presence of a membranous extension of the orifice edge that folds over the retracted polypide (Fig. 178*F*). The four remaining plumatellid genera are characterized by the soft, transparent, gelatinous zoecium ("ectocyst"). This is especially soft in *Hyalinella* (includes *Australella*) with main species *H. punctata* of wide distribution (Fig. 180*D*). Another species, *H. vaihiriae*, originally described from Lake Vaihiria in Tahiti (Hastings, 1929b), has since been found in Utah (Rogick and Brown, 1942) and Brazil. Toriumi (1955e) separated *Gelatinella* from *Hyalinella* on the basis of the hardening of the gelatinous zoecium and the minute spination over the entire surface of the floatoblasts (Fig. 176*C*). *Stolella* is (perhaps insufficiently) distinguished from *Hyalinella* by the narrowed zooid bases resembling stolons ("pseudostolons"), connecting the single file of zooids (Fig. 180*A*). *Stolella indica* is known from India and the United States (Rogick, 1943b), and other species of *Stolella* occur in South America. *Stephanella*, with the single species *St. hina*, Japan (Oka, 1908; Toriumi, 1955c), is characterized by the very thick, soft, gelatinous zoecium, obscuring the branches (Fig. 180*C*).

The two remaining families form massive gelatinous colonies or aggregations in which the zooids are imbedded without definite boundaries. Statoblasts are spinoblasts except in *Lophopus*. In the Lophopodidae there is no organization of the colony into a vermiform creeping shape. *Lophophus* occurs as lobulate gelatinous colonies of up to 50 zooids, narrowing to a base attached to water weeds and other objects (Fig. 159*A*); the easily recognized statoblast (Fig. 176*A*) is fusiform, with a broad thin annulus narrowing at each end to a point said to represent an aborted spine. The main species, *Lophopus crystallinus*, widely spread, was made the subject of an excellent study by Marcus (1934). The somewhat similar *Lophopodella* is again best known by the characteristic spinoblast, oval or rectangular with a group of hooked spines at each end (Fig. 176*E, F*). The main species, *Loph. carteri*, known from Asia, Africa, and the eastern United States, was well studied by Rogick (1937b). Another species, *Loph. capensis*, appears limited to South Africa (Hastings, 1929a). *Pectinatella* occurs as small to huge gelatinous masses with characteristic spinoblasts bearing a single marginal circle of anchorlike spines (Fig. 176*D*). The best-known species, *Pect. magnifica*, is endemic to the eastern United States but has been introduced into central Europe. Its gelatinous mass is in reality compounded of a number of colonies pro-

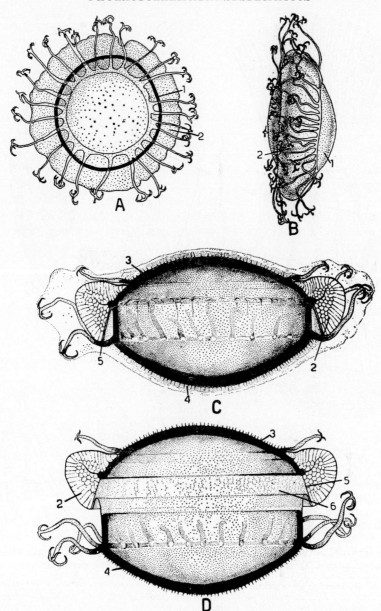

Fig. 177.—Statoblasts (continued). *A*, spinoblast of *Cristatella mucedo*, seen from the ventral side. *B*, side view of *A*. (*A, B, after Toriumi*, 1941.) *C*, *Cristatella mucedo*, section through the empty statoblast, showing shelf separating annulus from deutoplasmic valve. *D*, same as *C*, valves separating, showing pillbox effect. (*C, D, after Brien*, 1953.) 1, capsule; 2, annulus; 3, cystigenic valve; 4, deutoplasmic valve; 5, shelf; 6, part of cystigenic valve fitting over deutoplasmic valve.

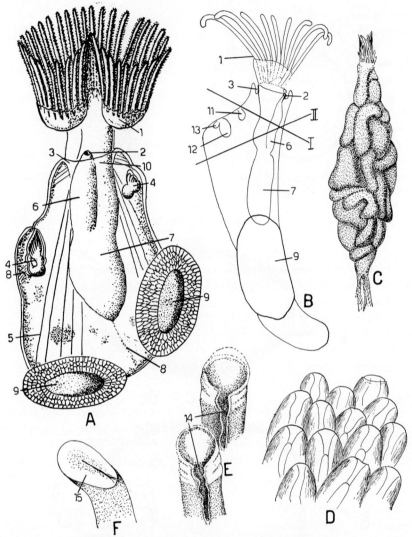

Fig. 178.—Statoblasts (concluded), regeneration, systematics. *A*, beginning *Pluma-tella* colony hatched from a statoblast, of which the valves are still present (*after Marcus*, 1925). *B*, scheme showing cuts in Brien's experiments (*after Brien*, 1936). *C*, *Pluma-tella fungosa*, growing on a twig. *D*, bit of *C*, showing zooid arrangement. (*C*, *D*, *after Allman*, 1856.) *E*, two zooids of *Pl. emarginata*, showing notch (*after Rogick*, 1935b). *F*, zooid end of *Afrindella*, showing closing apparatus (*after Annandale*, 1912b). 1, lopho-phore; 2, anus; 3, vestibule; 4, buds; 5, retractor lophophore; 6, intestine; 7, stomach; 8, funiculus; 9, valve of statoblast; 10, esophagus; 11, adventitious bud; 12, main bud; 13, duplicate bud; 14, notch; 15, closing apparatus. I, II, lines of cuts in Brien's experiments.

duced by the germination of an aggregation of statoblasts and also by the division of young colonies so germinated (Wilcox, 1906). These colonies, composed of 12 to 18 polypides, occur as a thin crust on the surface of the jelly secreted by their common bases (Fig. 158B, C). In each colony of the mass the active polypides occur around the periphery, facing outward, and the center contains degenerating polypides and statoblasts (Fig. 158D, E). Another species, *Pect. gelatinosa*, with the largest number of tentacles known in any phylactolaemate, up to 106, and with the hooks of the spinoblast reduced to a minute size, is known from Indo-Malaya and Japan (Toriumi, 1956a). The colony mass of this species appears to be produced by budding, not by the aggregation of originally separate colonies.

The family Cristatellidae is composed of the single genus *Cristatella* with the single cosmopolitan species *Cristatella mucedo*. This occurs as vermiform creeping colonies (Figs. 159B, 160B) up to 8 inches in length, having a convex dorsal surface and a ventral flat sole provided with a thick gelatinous cuticle. The polypides occur along the sides of the dorsal surface, facing outward (Fig. 160A). The distinctive spinoblast (Fig. 177) was described above.

There are about 50 species of phylactolaemates, of which 16 are known to occur in the United States at present writing. In addition, numerous varieties have been described, notably in the common species *Plumatella repens*, also in other species of *Plumatella*. It is not clear whether these variants are actually hereditarily distinct or result from environmental conditions.

9. Ecology: Habits and Behavior.—Phylactolaemates are found everywhere during the warmer months of the year in lakes, ponds, and slow rivers and streams, mostly in clear, well-oxygenated, quiet water containing an abundance of submersed vegetation. Generally not all the species known to occur in a region will be found in any one habitat, but as many as three or four species may flourish in close proximity (Brown, 1933). Generally phylactolaemates grow only in waters on the alkaline side and are absent from acid waters of the bog type, although sometimes present in acid lakes (Tanner, 1932). They mostly occur in shallow water of less than a meter in depth up to several meters, attached to submersed logs, twigs, rocks, shells, and vegetation, mostly on the under or shaded side, although light does not appear of importance in their distribution (Brown, 1933). Many species may be found in both well-lighted and shaded situations in shallow water; in deeper waters probably all occur on the upper surface of objects. Although most common in slight depths, some species, notably *Fredericella sultana*, have been found in large lakes at very considerable depths, from 20 to 170 m. Gelatinous types are somewhat limited to still waters, but plumatellids

Fig. 179.—Systematics (continued). *A*, colony of *Pl. casmiana* (*after Rogick*, 1941a). *B*, young colony of *Lophopus crystallinus*, still with statoblast valves (*after Brien*, 1953); note all lophophores facing in one direction, and budding zone also on that side. 1, budding zone; 2, statoblast valves; 3, funiculus; 4, statoblasts.

with resistant cuticle may occur in swift streams or along lake shores subject to wave action.

There appears to be some selection of substrate by at least certain species. The majority of phylactolaemate colonies are to be found on submersed vegetation, especially that extending out into clear water, away from bottom accumulations. However, the common pond plant *Chara* is rarely used as a substrate. The yellow water lily *Nymphaea* is preferred to the white one *Castalia* and is especially favored by *Cristatella*, which may be found in numbers on the undersurface of its leaves (Fig. 160*B*). Although Brown (1933) and Geiser (1937) found *Pectinatella magnifica* attached to water plants, this species generally occurs on dead material as submerged branches and twigs, walls, boat bottoms, and the like. Living plants could hardly support the great masses attained by this species.

Phylactolaemates in general are incapable of change of place after once attaching, but *Cristatella* moves about throughout life, and young colonies of *Lophopus, Lophopodella,* and *Pectinatella* may also move. Movement in these genera is often associated with lobulation and subsequent subdivision of the colonies with drawing apart of the daughter colonies. *Cristatella* moves either way in the direction of the long axis at a rate of 1 to 15 mm. per day (Marcus, 1926a); Harmer (1910) observed a small colony that moved 39 mm. in 3 days; Odell (1899) gave the rate as 1 inch (25 mm.) daily. Colonies, especially large ones, often remain quiescent in favorable locations. Small *Lophopus* colonies were observed by Wesenberg-Lund (1896) to move 5 to 6 cm. in 12 hours, later to cease movement and remain attached; by Harmer (1910) and Marcus (1934) to move about 6 to 8 mm. per day. *Lophopus* colonies on being detached can again attach by producing an adhesive secretion. They move in the direction to which the lophophores are oriented, that is, with the budding zone in advance. *Lophopodella carteri* may move as much as 3 to 4 inches (8 to 10 cm.) daily (Dahlgren, 1934). Young colonies of *Pectinatella*, newly derived from statoblasts, were observed by Brooks (1929) creeping along a secreted gelatinous cord at the rate of about an inch (25 mm.) in 3 days. Wilcox (1906) also records constant movement and subdivision of young *Pectinatella* colonies. The mechanism of locomotion is problematical. Older workers thought that the colony is somehow pulled along by the contractions of the lophophore retractors, and Wilcox (1906) supports this view, claiming that simultaneous retraction of all the polypides on one side of a young colony of *Pectinatella* moves the colony in that direction. With increasing size, loss of contractile vigor by the polypides, and stiffening of the jelly, colonies of *Pectinatella* cease movement. Another view, that the colony is wafted along by the combined currents of its lophophores, might be tenable for *Lophopus*, where all the

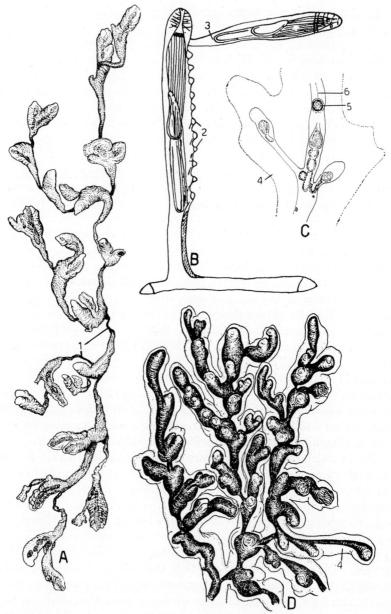

Fig. 180.—Systematics (concluded). *A*, colony of *Stolella indica* (*after Rogick*, 1943b). *B*, *Plumatella fruticosa*, showing a number of places where zooids have fallen off (*after Wiebach*, 1954a). *C*, small bit of *Stephanella hina* showing thick gelatinous zoecium (*after Toriumi*, 1955c). *D*, colony of *Hyalinella punctata*, preserved (*after Rogick*, 1940a). 1, pseudostolons; 2, places where side zooids have fallen off; 3, one remaining side zooid; 4, gelatinous zoecium; 5, statoblast; 6, funiculus.

lophophores point in one direction, that in which the colony moves; in fact, Wesenberg-Lund (1896) claims that small *Lophopus* colonies cannot creep if the lophophores are retracted. This explanation is also adopted by Brooks (1929), thus disagreeing with Wilcox, for small colonies of *Pectinatella*, said to move only in the direction faced by the lophophores and to be able to move against a water current. However, this explanation cannot apply to *Cristatella*, which has the best locomotory powers, since here the lophophores are directed laterally; further, Marcus (1926a) has shown in small colonies with one expanded polypide that the colony may move equally well in the direction faced by the lophophore or in the opposite direction. It may be assumed that *Cristatella* at least creeps by means of the body-wall musculature, which is particularly well developed in the creeping sole (Fig. 161*D*). Alternate contractions and expansions of the circular and longitudinal layers could easily accomplish locomotion.

When the polypide is expanded, the lophophore turns and bends in all directions, producing with its ciliary tract a current funneling into the mouth and detectable at least 2 mm. away (Brooks, 1929). As in gymnolaemates this current is the food-catching mechanism of phylactolaemates, which are thus ciliary feeders, or, as the process is often called, filter feeders. The current passes out between the tentacles, while the food particles are retained and directed into the mouth. The food consists of minute organisms, such as bacteria, diatoms, desmids, and other unicellular algae, protozoans, rotifers, and small crustaceans, but apparently not detritus. Rüsche (1938), studying the nutrition of *Plumatella fungosa*, noted nearly 40 minute planktonic organisms in its environment, mostly desmids, green flagellates, rotifers, and minute crustaceans, and found that most were indiscriminately ingested unless too large or too unwieldy in shape. Marcus (1934) figures the stomach caecum of *Cristatella* filled with diatoms and desmids. Various authors have commented on the voracity of phylactolaemates. Marcus (1926a) saw one *Plumatella repens* polypide ingest in 6 minutes 19 *Colpoda* and a large number of minute flagellates. Rüsche (1938) observed one *Plumatella fungosa* polypide swallow in 20 minutes 25 larger planktonic flagellates and an uncounted number of smaller plankters and in the presence of a rich culture of *Chlamydomonas* it would pass a continuous stream of this into the pharynx, which became stuffed full of them between swallows, occurring on the average every 20 to 25 seconds. The tentacles may be brought together to prevent escape of food organisms or widely spread to permit rejection of large or unwanted particles. Rejection is also accomplished by sudden retraction. Rotifers and crustaceans may escape by energetic movements and often cannot be swallowed anyway because of their shape. The tentacles are capable of independent movement.

Marcus and Rüsche attest that the cilia do not beat incessantly, as claimed by some authors, but can be arrested.

All observers have commented on the difficulty of maintaining phylactolaemate colonies in the laboratory. It is necessary to use natural or conditioned water, to eliminate enemies, to prevent accumulation of debris on the colonies, and to provide an abundance of food without adding enough to foul the water. Even at best, frequent changes of medium and diet or transfers to fresh cultures are necessary to prevent degeneration. Supplying suitable water and providing enough suitable food are the main difficulties. Marcus (1926a) recommended small aquaria thickly planted with water plants and regularly kept colonies healthy for 6 weeks, sometimes up to 10 to 12 weeks, whereas Rogick (1937c) and Brandwein (1938) employed finger bowls or other glass dishes. Apparently food successful with some species is rejected by others. Marcus (1926a) used very fine dried fish food, protozoan cultures (*Euglena* and *Colpoda* acceptable, *Chlamydomonas* unacceptable, contrary to Rüsche's finding), and scrapings from aquarium walls. Brooks (1929) tried to feed young colonies of *Pectinatella* on pure cultures of diatoms, monads, other protozoans, and bacteria, or on combinations of these, but obtained no growth although colonies might survive 6 weeks. Brown (1934) reported that colonies can be kept in the laboratory for some time by frequent changes of water and feeding of concentrated plankton, but did not succeed in continued culture. Rogick (1937c) found the following foods unsuitable for *Lophopodella carteri: Paramecium, Euglena,* green algae, malted-milk powder, dehydrated nutritive broth, fish food, but was successful with material from around the stems and bases of large plants being grown in greenhouse tanks; she also (1938, 1940b) often used aquarium water or aquarium scrapings containing an abundance of algae, protozoans, rotifers, and bacteria. *Hyalinella punctata* (Rogick, 1945a) accepted small ciliates and flagellates but rejected *Paramecium* and would not thrive on green algae alone. Bacterial scums evoked by adding cereals or, best, yeast to the cultures were then found satisfactory as food, and in this way one *Hyalinella* colony was maintained in continuous laboratory culture for over 6 months; this colony, however, was the sole survivor of 111 colonies germinated from statoblasts of which the others died at once or after producing 1 or 2 up to 20 polypides. Brandwein (1938) added minute protozoans (*Chilomonas, Colpidium*) to cultures of *Pectinatella magnifica* grown in finger bowls containing an agar layer with imbedded wheat grains overlain by a mixture of natural water and very dilute balanced salt solution; but frequent subculturing was necessary. Brandwein noted that *Pectinatella* would eat *Paramecium, Arcella, Blepharisma,* and rotifers.

Behavior toward environmental factors has been considered chiefly by

Marcus (1925, 1926a) and Brown (1933). The latter considers light as a relatively unimportant factor since the same species may be found in nature under varying conditions of illumination. However, most phylactolaemates show a preference for more or less shaded situations. *Fredericella sultana* is generally reported as addicted to shaded locations and may be found in water pipes in total darkness. Colonies of *Lophopus* and *Cristatella* tend to move from lighted into darkened areas. The latter thrives better in darkened than in lighted surroundings and tends to move about more and in straighter paths under lighted conditions (Marcus, 1926a). The sexually produced larvae of *Plumatella fungosa* (Marcus, 1926a) and *Pectinatella magnifica* (Williams, 1921) are negative to light, a reaction that would result in their settling and founding colonies in shaded locations.

Composition of the water is probably important, but little specific information is available. Brown (1933) found phylactolaemates most abundant in natural habitats rich in oxygen (6.3 to 7.4 cc. per liter), free from carbon dioxide, and on the alkaline side (pH 8.0 to 8.2). Rogick (1935b) took several species in abundance in Lake Erie at pH 7.2 to 8.0. *Plumatella* was collected in quite alkaline habitats in Utah (pH 8.8 to 8.9) by Brown (1933) and Tanner (1932) and *Lophopodella capensis* in a crater lake in central Africa at pH 8.3 to 9.1 (Jenkin, 1936). Although phylactolaemates are usually absent from acid waters, especially those of bogs, Tanner took *Plumatella* and *Fredericella* in rather acid lakes (pH 5.3 to 5.8) in Utah and Wyoming. Phylactolaemates probably never occur in brackish water. To be sure, Hyatt (1868) found *Fred. sultana* in a brook formerly running into a fresh-water lake but through drainage at the time subject to influx of sea water at high tide; but the reduction of these colonies to a few polypides indicates incipient disappearance. Phylactolaemates were killed in a fresh-water pond near the Massachusetts coast through influx of sea water in the 1938 hurricane (Rogick, 1940c, 1941c); at the latter report the pond had a salinity of 3.57 parts per thousand. Tentacles, epistome, and mouth region of phylactolaemates are sensitive to chemicals (Marcus, 1926a); perception is indicated by polypide retraction or assumption of a slack attitude by the tentacles. Sugar, quinine, common salt, citric acid, and saccharine were detected at about the same dilutions as perceived by the human tongue. The cystid appeared devoid of chemoreception.

Mechanical stimulation, jarring, vibrations, and the like, evoke polypide retraction, briefly in *Cristatella*, for longer periods in other genera. Repeated mechanical stimulation eventually fails to elicit any response. The tentacle tips seem insensitive to contact. The polypides of *Cristatella* and other lophopodid genera (Risley, 1940, for *Lophopodella*) are relatively unresponsive to contact and vibrations and emerge rapidly after retraction.   Stimulation of a cystid, but not of a polypide, is transmissible to other zooids, and the cystid in fact appears more sensitive to touch than are the tentacles.   Sufficient pressure on one cystid of a small *Cristatella* colony may evoke retraction of all the polypides of the colony.   Such transmission of cystid stimulation is probably wanting in *Fredericella* and other plumatellids with well-spaced zooids.

Phylactolaemates in general, including the ciliated larvae, are positively thigmotactic to a high degree, although the tendency of some species or variants to put out erect branches indicates a reversal of the thigmotactic response.   Tentacles are negatively thigmotactic, tending to avoid contact with each other and those of adjacent lophophores.

Negative geotaxis was noted by Marcus (1926b) for the larvae of *Plumatella fungosa;* this response would cause them to settle near the surface but is easily overcome by their negative phototaxis.   A weak positive geotaxis was indicated for *Cristatella.*

Plumatellids with hard cuticle can probably withstand some degree of desiccation for brief periods.   Kraepelin (1887) frequently found phylactolaemates growing in small brooks on flat stones and banks that would inevitably become more or less dry at the height of summer.   Allen (1882) reported that a colony of *Hyalinella punctata* recovered after 16 hours out of water.   Changes of water content of the gelatinous zoecium are probably prevalent in lophopodid types.   *Lophopus* or *Cristatella* colonies taken from water shrink and regain turgor when again submersed (Hyatt, 1868).   *Lophopus* colonies may be found with the gelatinous zoecium much swollen with water and well removed from the polypides (Fig. 159*A*) or much reduced in width and closely applied to the polypides (Fig. 179*B*). Apparently water can be emitted by contraction of the cystid wall or driven from one lobe of a colony into the coelom of another lobe.

Water temperature is undoubtedly the main environmental factor controlling growth and survival of phylactolaemate colonies.   Ordinarily in temperate and boreal zones the colonies die out at the onset of winter because of drop of temperature and survive only by way of their statoblasts.   Colonies derived from overwintered statoblasts hatched in spring when the temperature has risen sufficiently reach a maximum growth in summer or early autumn and die out when temperatures decline in late autumn.   Hence a regular annual cycle dependent on temperature obtains in the zones mentioned.   Such cycles are wanting in tropical areas, although statoblasts are produced in such areas also.   The ability to withstand temperature extremes varies with species.   *Fredericella sultana* withstands low temperature better than other species and is common in the depths of alpine and subalpine lakes in Europe where temperatures remain at 4 to 9°C. and where the species no doubt continues active throughout the year.   Brown (1933) found *F. sultana* at a maximum of colony size and abundance in Douglas Lake, northern Michigan, in November at a temperature of 5.5°C. and also took colonies in the Huron River in December and March when they had been subjected to 5°C. On the other hand, in another Michigan lake, colonies died at 8°C. *Fredericella sultana* also extends into farther northern latitudes (Greenland, 69°N) than any other phylactolaemate. *Plumatella repens* and *Cristatella mucedo* are also adjustable to low temperatures, being regularly found in alpine lakes at considerable depths, although not extending to such depths as does *F. sultana*. Rogick (1938) stated that colonies of *Lophopodella* and *Lophopus* may continue to survive during mild winters at 5 to 8°C. and may endure short exposures to zero degrees centigrade. Houghton (1860) indicated that in England, which has mild winters, *Fred. sultana* continues active throughout the year. Marcus (1934) reported finding active colonies of *Lophopus* under ice and capable of surviving for weeks at 5 to 8°C. *Plumatella repens* in Michigan localities mostly died at 6°C. (Brown, 1933). On the other hand, *Pectinatella magnifica* is a species adjusted to warmer temperatures. It flourishes only above 20°C. (Marcus, 1925; Brown, 1933), disintegrated in Michigan localities when the temperature fell to 12°C. (Brown, 1933), and can stand 10°C. for only a brief period (Brooks, 1929). In its endemic area, the eastern United States (Geiser, 1934), *P. magnifica* has not been taken north of about the level of the Canadian shore of Lake Huron and is absent from northern Michigan although abundant in the southern part of the state (Brown, 1933).

Perception of temperature change as indicated by retraction of the lophophore was studied by Marcus (1926a) in *F. sultana*, *Plum. fungosa*, and *Cristatella mucedo*. The last proved the most sensitive, detecting a rise of temperature of 12°C., whereas the two other species reacted first to rises of 15 to 17°C. Greater sensitivity was shown to lowered than to raised temperature. *Cristatella* perceived a drop of 3 to 5°C., *Pl. fungosa* one of 4 to 6°C., and *F. sultana* one of 8°C., from a starting temperature of 20 to 22°C.

In general, younger colonies and younger polypides are more reactive to all environmental factors than are older ones.

Much more attention has been devoted to the ecology of statoblasts than to that of the zooids. The old view that statoblasts germinate only after exposure to desiccation or freezing, or both, is erroneous, and already in 1896 Wesenberg-Lund declared that such treatment is unnecessary. Statoblasts produced in early summer will germinate without change of conditions during the same summer and produce another generation of statoblasts. Statoblasts arising later in the summer usually remain over winter and germinate in the following spring. Hence most species in temperate zones have two cycles annually of colonies germinated from statoblasts. This seems not to be the case with *Pectinatella magnifica*, partly because of late spring germination of this species, which starts to grow in spring only when temperatures have risen to 16 to 19°C., and partly because of the long dormant period, about 8 weeks, required by its statoblasts. All statoblasts must remain dormant for a period varying with species before they will germinate. Following this period they will often germinate in a few days when placed under favorable conditions of temperature and medium, but in any one batch of statoblasts collected at the same time there is generally observed a wide spread of germination time. Thus in Brown's experiments (1933) statoblasts of *Plumatella repens* collected August 14 and kept under water at room temperature hatched over a period from August 26 to October 7, mostly between August 31 and September 5; another lot collected September 5 germinated over a period from September 26 to the following March, mostly in October; statoblasts of *Pectinatella magnifica* collected September 5 and kept similarly hatched from November 8 to February 26, mostly from January 28 to February 19. Experiments of this type definitely prove that statoblasts germinate well without exposure to desiccation or freezing. However, outdoor exposure over winter shortens the germination time, although here probably the determining factor is the increased length of the dormant period. Brown (1933) reported that statoblasts of *Pl. repens* removed from living colonies in summer required 20 days on the average to germinate, whereas those collected outdoors from February to April hatched in 5 days on the average. Similarly, summer statoblasts of *Pectinatella* taken from the colonies required 60 days to germinate, while those collected outdoors in spring germinated in 3 to 6 days.

Freezing experiments conducted by Brown (1933) led him to conclude that freezing does not increase the *percentage* of germination. Statoblasts of *Pl. repens* frozen for 50 hours at −10°C. were not affected as compared with controls at room temperature. Statoblasts of *Pectinatella* collected outdoors in winter and kept at −12°C. from 2 to 175 days germinated slightly more rapidly and concluded germination in a shorter time the longer they were frozen. Freezing for 300 days greatly reduced the percentage of germination. *Pectinatella* statoblasts alternately frozen and thawed two to five times were not affected as to either rate or per cent of germination.

The effect of temperature on germination time was well shown by Brown (1933) for *Pectinatella* statoblasts. These germinated on the average in 19.5 days at 11°C., 10 days at 15°C., 6 days at 19°C., 5 days at 23°C., 4 days at 27°C., died after beginning germination at 31°C., and were killed by 35°C. The optimum germination temperature for this species lies between 19 and 27°C. Light was found without effect on percentage of germination, although statoblasts of *Pectinatella* kept in darkness germinated more rapidly than those in light. Oxygen content is of paramount importance since statoblasts of *Pectinatella* would not germinate in water low in or devoid of oxygen although retaining viability.

The effect of desiccation on statoblasts was tested by Brown (1933) and especially by Rogick (1938, 1940b, 1941b, 1945a). Brown found that summer statoblasts removed from living colonies would not withstand even one week of desiccation in open dishes. Statoblasts of *Pectinatella* collected outdoors in winter were killed by drying indoors at room temperature and if left outdoors in a sheltered position during winter and spring gradually lost germinative power after 10 days and were dead at 120 days. Similarly, Brooks (1929) reported adverse effects of desiccation at room temperature on *Pectinatella* statoblasts. Rogick also failed to obtain any germination of statoblasts of *Pl. repens* or *Pectinatella* dried 2 years or longer, but had better success with those of some other species, notably *Lophopodella carteri*, which germinated after being kept dry at room temperature or slightly below for periods up to 1543 days (4½ years), but not after 6 years of drying. The percentage of germination decreased with time of drying, but there was practically no change in germination time. Colonies developed from long-dried statoblasts appeared less viable than controls. Rogick also obtained germination of *Fredericella sultana* statoblasts dried 733 to 1103 days, although no polypides developed, and of *Hyalinella punctata* statoblasts dried 289 days in a refrigerator, but not of those dried at room temperature for this period. Later experiments (Rogick, 1945a) with the latter species confirmed the detrimental effect of drying at room temperature and the protective action of refrigeration. Statoblasts stored dry 9 months or more at room temperature failed to germinate whether dried at once or kept under water for a preliminary period of 327 days, whereas those stored dry in a refrigerator retained germinative power and gave good colonies after periods of 248 to 867 days. However, another lot stored dry in a refrigerator for 840 days failed to give any germination. One lot kept under water at room temperature for 327 days before storing dry under refrigeration had lost germinative power after 306 days of such drying, but a similar lot stored under water in a refrigerator gave good germination 540 days later, or after a total of 867 days since collection.

The available information indicates that statoblasts are adapted to withstand but do not require desiccation and freezing, that their ability to endure these conditions varies with species, and that in general desiccation is more detrimental than freezing. Apparent favorable influence of drying or freezing on germination time probably actually results from the lengthening of the dormant period.

The number of statoblasts produced is prodigious. Brown (1933) estimated that the *Pl. repens* colonies on plants in 1 sq. m. of the plant zone of Douglas Lake, Michigan, might release 800,000 statoblasts in the autumn disintegration.   Along the shores of this lake he found drifts of statoblasts 1 to 4 feet wide extending along half a mile of beach.   Such drifts mostly consist of dead statoblasts or valves left from germination.

As already indicated, colonies generally endure only for one summer, although sometimes continuing through the winter in mild climates or winters.   Zschokke (1900) put the length of life in lakes in high altitudes with short summers at 10 to 12 weeks, at sea level at 20 to 22 weeks.   In laboratory cultures, Rogick (1938) maintained colonies of *Lophopodella carteri* for 161 and 163 days and one colony of *Hyalinella punctata* for 181 days (Rogick, 1945a).   These colonies died out from accidental causes, and presumably colonies could be kept in the laboratory almost indefinitely if proper food and other conditions could be supplied, but these are very difficult of attainment.   The life of individual polypides is limited. In the articles cited, the first polypide from the statoblast lived 8 to 21 days in *Hyalinella*, 6 to 47 days in *Lophopodella*, later ones 13 to 33 days. Marcus (1925) considers that a single polypide lives hardly more than 6 weeks.   Colony growth from a statoblast is slow at first, as often 1 to 6 weeks elapse before the second polypide appears; later ones are produced at intervals of 1 to 8 days, and as the colony enlarges several polypides arise daily under good conditions.

In the normal annual cycle colonies hatched from overwintered statoblasts rapidly proceed to sexual reproduction, which occurs but once annually.   In laboratory cultures of *Hyalinella punctata* Rogick (1945a) observed sexual development 10 to 24 days after germination.   Wesenberg-Lund (1896, 1907) concluded from field observations that sexual reproduction is often altogether omitted in northern climates or in alpine lakes, possibly because of the shortness of the growing season.   Sexual reproduction usually lasts 3 to 4 weeks in nature (less than a week in Rogick's cultures), after which the gonads retrogress.   Asexual budding continues throughout the growing season in all colonies, whether produced from larvae or statoblasts, until stopped by temperature fall.   On attaining sufficient size gelatinous types of colonies usually subdivide as observed in *Cristatella, Lophopus, Lophopodella,* and *Hyalinella;* ramifying colonies may also fractionate (*Stolella,* Marcus, 1941).   Colonies proceed very rapidly to statoblast formation.   Marcus (1941, 1942) observed that in *Stolella* already the second or third polypide of a colony hatched from a statoblast might start forming statoblasts, and Rogick (1945a) observed them on the third or fourth polypide of her *Hyalinella* colonies, although in *Lophopodella* they first appeared on the fourteenth or fifteenth polypides.

Little is known about the annual cycle in tropical countries.   Annandale (1911) indicates greatest production of statoblasts in India at the approach of hot weather and statoblast germination at the onset of the rains or of cooler weather. Vorstman (1928a) noted common species in the ponds in the botanical garden at Buitenzorg, Java, flourishing throughout the year and constantly producing statoblasts. *Hyal. punctata* remained the same throughout a year of continuous observation and produced sexual larvae almost every month from August into June. Under such circumstances the value of statoblast production remains problematical.

10. Physiology.—As to the occurrence of chitin in phylactolaemates, contradictory reports exist. Zander (1897) obtained a negative result in *Plumatella*, Kunike (1925) a positive test in *Plumatella* and *Pectinatella*. The author's tests (1958) showed that the entire exoskeleton of *Fredericella* and *Plumatella* is composed of chitin. The jelly of *Pectinatella* (Kraepelin, 1887) consists of 99.7 per cent water; the mass left by pressing out as much water as possible was composed of 89.23 per cent water, 0.88 per cent ash (salts), 6 per cent protein, 1.25 per cent chitin, and 2.64 per cent other organic material. The presence of chitin was checked by crystallizing out glucosamine. Similar results were obtained by Morse (1930), who also crystallized glucosamine; he found that a mass of jelly weighing 1200 g. when fresh dried to 5 g. Lerner (1954) stated on the basis of insolubility in potassium hydroxide that the float of *Plumatella* and *Cristatella* statoblasts is chitinous but made no standard chemical tests. The author found that the float of *Pectinatella* statoblasts is made of chitin, but the hooks are only partially chitinous.

Material on digestion in phylactolaemates appears in the articles of Marcus (1925, 1926a, 1934), Becker (1937), and Rüsche (1938). The epistome apparently does not participate in food capture or swallowing but presumably acts in a chemoreceptive capacity, in which case it might regulate by nervous pathways acceptance or rejection of food; it is often stated to be very mobile, frequently raised or lowered, and may regulate the size of the mouth opening, although it definitely does not act as a cover to close the mouth. The mouth, in fact, appears to be held constantly open. Food is swept into the pharynx, where it is rotated into clumps by the action of the pharyngeal cilia. At very frequent intervals these clumps are passed into the stomach by a peristaltic wave along the esophagus. These intervals are given as 20 to 40 seconds in *Lophopus* (Marcus, 1934); 15 to 25 seconds in *Plumatella fungosa* (Becker, 1937); 20 to 75 seconds, mostly 20 to 25, in *Pl. fungosa* (Rüsche, 1938); and 16 seconds on the average in *Stolella* (Marcus, 1941). The intervals are longer if little food is available (40 to 60 seconds in *Pl. fungosa*, Rüsche). When food is abundant the animals feed continuously. Becker regards both pharynx and esophagus as secretory, and certainly the pseudopodial tips of the esophageal cells are indicative of digestive activity; but the food passes through the foregut so rapidly that no digestion could take place there, and Marcus using food stained with ammonia carmine failed to find any evidence of absorption in the foregut. However, foregut secretions could accompany the food into the stomach. In the stomach the food is driven back and forth by strong peristalses passing every 4 to 10 seconds according to species. These peristalses often cut off food into the stomach caecum, then drive it again toward the cardiac and pyloric regions. The caecal tip may be filled with digestive fluid. There is general agreement that digestive enzymes are secreted by the stomach epithelium; by the acidophilic cells of the ridges according to Marcus, who

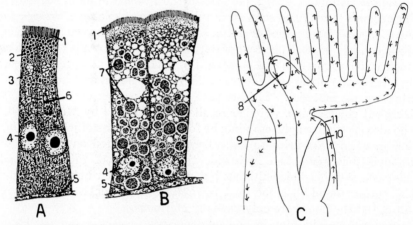

Fig. 181.—Physiology. *A*, basophilic cells of stomach caecum, *Pl. fungosa*, showing secretory granules. *B*, acidophilic cells of stomach caecum of *Cristatella*, showing food reserves. (*A*, *B*, *after Becker*, 1937.) *C*, scheme showing coelomic currents, *Pectinatella* (*after Oka*, 1891). 1, striated border; 2, secretion granules; 3, excretory granules; 4, nucleus; 5, peritoneum; 6, mitochondria; 7, protein reserve spheres; 8, epistome; 9, foregut; 10, intestine; 11, anus.

regards the basophilic cells of the furrows as replacement cells for the ridges; mainly by the basophilic cells according to Becker, who regards the acidophilic cells as absorptive (Fig. 181*B*). The occurrence of absorption in the stomach may be shown by the use of dyed food (Marcus). Food may pass from the stomach into the intestine in 5 to 15 minutes (Marcus), about every 90 minutes (Rüsche). The food noticeably diminishes in bulk in the intestine, which is therefore largely absorptive and shows little peristalsis. Food generally lingers in the intestine 30 minutes but remains longer, up to 24 hours, if only a small amount of food is present. Shortly before defecation, the anus opens widely, and in a few seconds the fecal balls are emitted while the lophophore is bent ventrally out of the way; in 2 or 3 minutes the intestine is again filled with food balls (Rüsche). The time required for food to pass the entire length of the digestive tract is given as 1 hour by Marcus, 2 to 3 hours by other workers, and no doubt varies with species. The time depends on the amount of food taken in and is lengthened when food is scarce, possibly because of weakening of the polypide. When food is abundant the time is relatively short, and digestion in fact seems rather inefficient as food often passes in an undigested state and organisms such as rotifers and nematodes have often been seen voided alive and uninjured. By examining fecal balls Rüsche estimated that one *Plumatella* polypide passed in 90 minutes 300 plankters of some size, not counting the minute plankters. Digestion seems to take place in an acid medium as Marcus (1926a) found the pharynx and esophagus alkaline, the stomach acid, and the intestine neutral to indicators. Digestion appears to be wholly extracellular.

According to Becker (1937), all parts of the digestive epithelium store food reserves, except the basophilic cells of the stomach, which are regarded as primarily secretory (Fig. 181*A*). The acidophilic cells of the stomach have chiefly an absorptive function and store fat, protein (Fig. 181*B*), and excretory granules, becoming stuffed with these products in senile polypides. Fat is the main food reserve, accumulated in pharynx, esophagus, the acidophilic cells of the stomach, and the intestine; further, in the tentacles, peritoneum, zoecium, and vesicular cells of the epidermis. Glycogen as small granules was found sparingly in all parts of the digestive epithelium except the pharynx and the basophilic cells, being especially present in the acidophilic cells; it also occurs in the stomach peritoneum, coelomocytes, and forming statoblasts, proceeding into the last from the stomach by way of the funiculus. In case of hunger fat disappears from the acidophilic cells that become even more vacuolated than usual but mostly is not lost from other sites.

The phylactolaemates are devoid of circulatory and respiratory mechanisms, but no doubt the circulation of the coelomic fluid in part compensates for the want of these systems. By means of the cilia on the peritoneum the coelomic fluid is kept in constant movement. As already noted by the older observers (Hyatt, 1868; Oka, 1891), the fluid follows a definite circuit, passing anteriorly along the dorsal side of the metacoel, ventrally along the mesocoel, and back along the ventral side of the metacoel (Fig. 181*C*). From the mesocoel the fluid passes into the lumina of the tentacles, up one side and down the other.

An excretory system is also lacking, for despite the claims of Cori (1893), the forked canal cannot be regarded as representing nephridia. The tentacles appear to be the chief site of excretion and refringent granules may be seen emitted from them normally (Marcus, 1934). When colonies are placed in solutions of neutral red or methylene blue the dyes accumulate in the tentacular epidermis and are eliminated to the exterior in 12 to 18 hours (Marcus, 1926a). Dyes taken in by mouth accumulate in the acidophilic ridges of the stomach and cause polypide degeneration. Dyes injected into the common coelom of *Lophopus* accumulate in the forked canal, tentacles, and general peritoneum but are ejected to the exterior only by way of the tentacles (Marcus, 1934). Similar observations were made by Gerwerzhagen (1913b) on *Cristatella*, where cells laden with carmine accumulate in the sac of the forked canal and are emitted by rupture of the sac. Normally, also, the forked canal and its sac (when present) may be seen filled with degenerating cells and waste materials (Fig. 165*B*). It seems to be generally admitted (Marcus, 1934; Becker, 1937) that the reddish-brown granules that accumulate in the acidophilic ridges of the stomach are of excretory nature. The filling of these cells with excretory granules no doubt contributes to the senescence and eventual disintegration of polypides. As to excretory products, Becker detected uric acid and guanin in the digestive lumen of *Plumatella* and *Cristatella*, Marcus ammonia in water in which *Lophopus* had remained for 70 hours.

11. Ecology: Geographic Distribution.—Phylactolaemates are found throughout the fresh waters of the world, except in polar regions, at a wide range of altitude from sea level to high mountain lakes and at depths varying from the extremely shallow waters of small streams and pools to the bottoms of large lakes.

Northern limits of the range have been summarized by Abricossoff (1933). Living colonies of *Fred. sultana*, showing structural variations similar to those of this species in the depths of alpine lakes (subspecies *duplessisi*), have been taken on stones in streams in Greenland at 69° north latitude (Wesenberg-Lund, 1907); and Abricossoff (1933) recorded a healthy colony of *Cristatella mucedo* from the Kola Peninsula (66°N). Statoblasts, but no living colonies, of *Pl. repens* are recorded from Spitsbergen (Richard, 1897) and Novaya Zemlya (Abricossoff, 1933), and statoblasts of *Pl. repens*, *Pl. fruticosa*, and *Cristatella mucedo* from the general area of Lappland and the Kola Peninsula, just north of the Arctic Circle (Levander, 1901, 1905, 1908). Living colonies of *Fred. sultana*, *Pl. repens*, *fruticosa*, and *fungosa*, and *Crist. mucedo* occur in Finland as far north as 63°, but *Hyal. punctata* is limited to the southernmost part of the country (Levander, 1908). *Crist. mucedo* was found in Swedish Lappland at 66°N, and *Fred. sultana* and *Pl. fruticosa*, *emarginata*, *repens*, and *fungosa* are distributed throughout Sweden south of Lappland (Borg, 1941). Active colonies of *Fred. sultana* are known from Iceland, but *Hyal. punctata* was taken only once there, and only statoblasts of *Crist. mucedo* have been collected there (Heding, 1938). *Fred. sultana*, *Pl. repens* and *emarginata*, and *Crist. mucedo* occur in Lake Baikal, Siberia, and the last is known from Kamchatka (Abricossoff, 1933). *Pl. repens* was recorded from Kodiak Island, Alaska, by Robertson (1900).

Reports from the Antarctic and Subantarctic are limited to the finding of flourishing colonies of *Fred. sultana* and *Hyal. punctata* on Tierra del

Fuego (Calvet, 1904).   Other records from the higher southern latitudes are those of *Fred. sultana* and *Pl. emarginata* from New Zealand (Dendy, 1906), the latter from Tasmania (Hickmann and Scott, 1932), *Lophopodella capensis* and *Pl. emarginata* in South Africa (Hastings, 1929a), and *Fred. australiensis, Pl. emarginata*, and *Lophopodella carteri* from southern Australia (Goddard, 1909).

Temperature conditions similar to those of high latitudes also exist in alpine and subalpine lakes.   Zschokke (1900) stated that three species, *Fred. sultana, Pl. repens*, and *Crist. mucedo*, are characteristic of alpine lakes, especially the first species.   *Fred. sultana* is in fact found throughout the lakes of Switzerland and northern Italy to altitudes of 2300 m. (Forel, 1884; Du Plessis-Gouret, 1884).   Despax (1926) recorded the three species mentioned plus *Lophopus* in lakes of the Pyrenees at heights of 2100 to over 2300 m.   *Pl. repens* was found by Richard (1896) in Caucasus lakes at an elevation of 1800 to 2000 m., and a form of *Fred. sultana* reported from a Brazilian lake at 1750 m. (Eveline Marcus, 1946).   Still higher records are those of Tanner (1932) for *Fred. sultana* in lakes of the Uintah Mountains, Utah, at heights of 3300 and 3400 m., and highest of all are the findings of forms of *Fred. australiensis* and *Stolella agilis* at altitudes of 3840 to 4150 m. in Lake Titicaca, Bolivia, highest large alpine lake in the world (Eveline Marcus, 1953, 1955). Although mostly growing in shallow water near the shore in mountain lakes, phylactolaemates may descend to deep water that remains perpetually cold; especially *Fred. sultana* lives in the depths of mountain lakes, having been taken in many Swiss and Italian lakes at depths of 25 to 100 m. (Forel, 1884), in Lake Lucerne at 30 to 170 m. (Zschokke, 1906).   It was found in abundance on the bottom of Lake Michigan at 23 to 36 m. (Ward, 1896).   The colonies are stuck loosely into the soft lake bottoms.

In the North Temperate Zone much the same species are found throughout the world.   The United States, well studied by Rogick in a series of articles (1934–1950), is especially rich in species, with records of *Fred. sultana* and *australiensis, Pl. repens, fungosa, fruticosa, emarginata, casmiana*, and *orbisperma* (rare), *Hyalinella punctata* and *vaihiriae, Stolella indica, Lophopodella carteri, Lophopus crystallinus, Pect. magnifica*, and *Crist. mucedo*.   The following are spread throughout Britain and temperate Europe: *Fred. sultana, Pl. repens, fungosa, emarginata*, and *fruticosa, Hyal. punctata, Lophopus crystallinus*, and *Crist. mucedo* (Allman, 1856, for Britain; Prenant and Bobin, 1956, for France; Borg, 1930, for Germany), with the addition of *Pect. magnifica* for Germany.   *Lophopus* is absent from Russia, and besides the other European species mentioned, Asiatic forms begin to appear there, as *Pl. casmiana, Stolella indica*, and *Afrindella tanganyikae* (Abricossoff, 1927, 1936).

Although the common European species are also encountered in the Orient, additional species and genera appear there. The phylactolae-mates of India were studied over a period of years by Annandale, who summarized the knowledge in 1911, recording *Fred. sultana*, *Pl. emargi-nata*, *fruticosa*, and *javanica*, *Afrindella tanganyikae*, *Hyal. punctata*, *Stolella indica*, *Lophopodella carteri*, and *Pectinatella gelatinosa*. It is diffi-cult to accept the absence of *Pl. repens;* and the validity of *Afrindella testudinicola*, found growing on the backs of large turtles in the Ganges, is questionable (Annandale, 1912b). The phylactolaemates of Japan were thoroughly and competently investigated by Toriumi (1951–1956), who also usefully evaluates many of the taxonomic confusions and synonyms. Common Occidental species also found in Japan include *Fred. sultana*, *Pl. repens*, *fruticosa*, *emarginata*, and *casmiana*, *Hyal. punctata*, *Lophopus crystallinus*, *Lophopodella carteri*, and *Cristatella mucedo*. Apparently limited to Japan are *Stephanella hina*, *Hyalinella minuta*, and *Gelatinella toanensis*. *Pectinatella gelatinosa* is also known from Korea, Formosa, India, and Java, *Pl. vorstmani* also from Java, and *Pl. osburni*, oddly enough, from Guatemala. There appears some similarity in the phy-lactolaemate fauna of Japan, India, and Malaya. Similarly in Java (Vorstman, 1928a, b) there is a mixture of common, widely spread species (*Pl. repens*, *emarginata*, *fruticosa*, and *casmiana*, *Hyal. punctata*, *Lophopo-della carteri*) with oriental species such as *Pl. javanica* and *vorstmani* and *Pectinatella gelatinosa*.

Knowledge of the phylactolaemates of Africa was summarized by Borg (1936a, b). Found there is the expected mixture of widely spread forms (*Fred. sultana*, *Pl. repens* and *emarginata*, *Hyal. punctata*, and *Lophopodella carteri*) with endemic and Asiatic species (*Afrindella tan-ganyikae* and *Lophopodella capensis*, *thomasi*, and *stuhlmanni*). Rogick (1945b) conjectures that some of Borg's *Fredericella* material was *Fred. australiensis*. Subsequently there was added *Pl. casmiana* (Lacourt, 1948).

The phylactolaemates of Brazil were discussed by Marcus (1941, 1942). The usual cosmopolitan species occur there (*Fred. sultana*, *Pl. repens*, *emarginata*, and *fruticosa*, and *Hyal. punctata*) plus species appar-ently endemic, at least not as yet found elsewhere, *Stolella evelinae* and *agilis*, *Hyal. carvalhoi*, and *Pectinatella jheringi*, of which the generic posi-tion remains uncertain (Hastings, 1929b). Other South American records are those from Tierra del Fuego and Lake Titicaca, already men-tioned. Undoubtedly this continent has been poorly explored with regard to fresh-water ectoprocts.

From the foregoing account it is evident that a number of phylacto-laemates are cosmopolitan or nearly so (exclusive of high polar regions) and will no doubt be found in the future in areas where they have not yet been recorded. Other species appear to be endemic, limited as yet to the region in which they were discovered. The distribution records of some others are little short of fantastic. There is *Hyal. vaihiriae*, for instance, known only from Tahiti and Utah, and *Pl. osburni*, found in Japan and Guatemala. *Stolella indica* was thought to be limited to India but suddenly turns up in Pennsylvania (Rogick, 1943b). *Pectinatella magnifica* was presumably endemic to the eastern United States and the adjacent border of Canada but about 1900 was found in the vicinity of Hamburg, Germany, apparently having been brought in on ships, and later spread into other central European localities. *Cristatella mucedo* is distinctly a circumboreal and North Temperate species, wanting altogether in warmer climates and in the Southern Hemisphere.

The foregoing discussion avoids the numerous subspecific names that have been proposed in the group. In so far as these are valid they may have a more restricted range than the nominal species and might contribute to a less haphazard picture of the distribution. As regards the numerous synonyms in the literature, the decisions of Toriumi as to their identity have been followed. According to him common species such as *Pl. repens*, *Pl. emarginata*, and *Fred. sultana* appear in the literature under at least eight other specific names.

The tendency of phylactolaemates to spread throughout the world is to be attributed to their statoblasts. In the dry state these could be blown long distances, and although experiments indicate that statoblasts of most species do not withstand drying very well, even a few days' survival would enable them to spread considerably. Statoblasts could also obviously be carried around in shipments of plants, fish, or other freshwater organisms and on boat bottoms in inland waterways. Presumably statoblasts cannot withstand sea water, and hence could not be carried overseas on the outside of ships but might be conveyed in certain types of cargoes. They could also be carried overland on the feet or other parts of the bodies of vertebrates. Brown (1933) determined that statoblasts ingested by salamanders, frogs, turtles, and ducks could pass in the feces in a viable state, in a considerable percentage in some cases. Of the vertebrates tried, ducks were the most destructive to the statoblasts, of which those recovered in the feces retained viability in only 4 per cent at the most. The time required for the statoblasts to pass through the digestive tract ranged from 14 hours to 2 weeks. The role of the hooks of spinoblasts in statoblast distribution remains uncertain. Brown (1933) is of the opinion that the hooks tend to limit dissemination of statoblasts rather than to facilitate it. According to his observations, the hooks of newly released spinoblasts are imbedded in jelly that prevents their functioning, but this jelly soon disintegrates, and then the spinoblasts aggregate in masses held together by the hooks. This behavior would seem to ensure perpetuation of the species in the same locality and, further, in *Pectinatella*, the availability of a number of contiguous young colonies necessary for building up the typical large jelly masses. Even floato-blasts, according to Brown, do not necessarily float, but the majority remain imbedded in the bottom debris. Perhaps this prevents too great exposure to severe winter conditions.

12. Ecology: Biological Relations.—Like other sessile animals, phy-lactolaemate colonies are inevitably sites of attachment and habitation of numerous other small animals, as protozoans, hydras, planarians, rotifers, gastrotrichs, nematodes, copepods, naid annelids, tardigrades, and insect larvae, and they may be intergrown with fresh-water sponges, but none of these associations appear of specific nature. Especially the fungoid masses of *Pl. fungosa* are inhabited by all sorts of animals such as those mentioned (Marcus, 1926a). Rogick (1935b), in a study of the phylactolaemates of Lake Erie, listed as the most frequent associates of the colonies sponges, sessile rotifers, leeches, ostracods, snails and their egg masses, and insect larvae, including chironomids, caddice worms, mayflies, and water pennies (larvae of the beetle family Psephenidae). The hollow interior of the jelly masses of *Pect. magnifica* harbors an assort-ment of roomers such as protozoans, planarians, snails, and crustaceans (Brooks, 1929), and Borodin (1928) noted that the jelly of *Pectinatella* is permeated with the burrows of chironomid larvae. The last, in fact, seem to be one of the most constant associates of phylactolaemate colonies.

It was already indicated that there may be some selection of substrate by phylactolaemates. Borg (1936b) suggests that *Pl. emarginata* is addicted to bivalve and snail shells, living or dead, but such a preference by this species does not appear in the accounts of other authors (Rogick, 1935b; Toriumi, 1952c), and in fact the photographs of the latter show the species attached to leaves and twigs. The claim of Annandale (1912b) that *Afrindella testudinicola* specifically grows on the backs of Gangetic turtles may be questioned, and it is even doubtful that this is a distinct species.

Many of the associates of phylactolaemates are also their enemies, feeding on polypides and statoblasts. The polypides are eaten by flat-worms, naid annelids, snails, oribatid mites, and insect larvae (Marcus, 1925, 1926a). The numerous planarians living in the hollow of *Pectinatella* jelly feed on the young polypides newly hatched from statoblasts (Brooks, 1929). Williams (1921) saw the rhabdocoel *Stenostomum* eat *Plumatella* polypides. Chironomid larvae are among the worst enemies, gathering on the colonies in hordes and eating not only the polypides but the germi-nal masses of the statoblasts, which they break into with their gnawing mouth parts. Marcus (1926a) observed a mass attack of the oribatid mite *Hydrozetes lacustris* on *Cristatella* polypides. Colonies are sometimes gnawed by fishes, and Rüsche (1938) surmises that water birds may devour colonies after tearing up the water plants on which they are growing.

In the past phylactolaemates often came into direct economic relation to man as troublemakers in city water systems; presumably with the installation in modern times of more efficient filtering systems at the intake such difficulties no longer arise. Not only did the pipes become clogged with ectoproct growths ("pipe moss") and the hordes of accompanying filter- and detritus-feeding animals, but fragments of disintegrated colonies blocked the water taps and water meters. A serious disruption of the water system of Hamburg was investigated by Kraepelin (1885), who found the greater part of the offending organisms to consist of mossy masses of *Fred. sultana*, species of *Plumatella*, the fresh-water gymnolaemate *Paludicella articulata*, and the fresh-water hydroid *Cordylophora*. Ectoprocts were also important constituents of the fauna that upset the water system of Rotterdam in 1877 (De Vries, 1890). *Fred. sultana*, with hordes of accompanying protozoans, sponges, and other small invertebrates, was found thickly coating the interior of the pipes of the Boston water system (Whipple, 1910). Harmer (1913) gives an extensive discussion of ectoprocts in water works with a review of literature. Troubles in water systems in England that he personally investigated were associated with growths of *Fred. sultana*, *Pl. emarginata* and *fungosa*, and *Paludicella*. Ectoprocts play a leading role in promoting accumulations of animals in water pipes because they furnish an excellent substrate and haven. Another sort of interference with water works was recorded by Geiser (1937). This involved *Pect. magnifica*, which in the summer of 1928 developed in vast numbers in a lake formed by damming a river near Independence, Iowa. In the late summer, especially after heavy rains, the jelly masses began floating down the river, clogging the grates at the water intake of a hydroelectric plant at the dam, and it was necessary to keep men constantly at the grates to clear them of the masses of *Pectinatella*. Geiser estimated that the total mass passed out of the lake during July and August must have amounted to scores of thousands of tons. Phylactolaemates may be of slight importance to man by clearing water of microorganisms and by participating in a food chain leading to fish; that is, they are eaten by chironomid larvae that in turn constitute an important food for fish.

The widely spread epizoic ciliate *Trichodina* (I, page 199) has been seen on the surface of *Cristatella*, and this phylactolaemate may also be infested with the parasitic larvae of the neuropterous insect *Sisyra* (Marcus, 1925). Two entoparasites are known to occur in phylactolaemates. One of these, *Nosema bryoides*, is a microsporidian (I, page 162). This parasite was found in *Pl. fungosa* by Korotneff (1892) and

Braem (1911), in both *Pl. fungosa* and *repens* by Schroeder (1914), and in *Lophopus crystallinus* and *Stolella evelinae* by Marcus (1934, 1941), hence presumably may attack any member of the group. The spermatogonia are the primary site of attack (Fig. 182*A*) of the parasite, but coelomocytes and peritoneum may also be invaded. The invaded cells hypertrophy, and infected spermatogonia soon fall from the funiculus, in long strands in *Stolella*, and fill the coelom, with the resulting degeneration of the polypide. The parasitic cycle starts with an amoeboid cell released from a spore; this rounds up, losing its amoeboid properties, and undergoes repeated simple or multiple fission. Finally, each of the fission products transforms into the usual microsporidian spore provided with a coiled thread (Fig. 182*A*). The other entoparasite, *Buddenbrockia plumatellae*, has been found in the coelom (Fig. 182*B*) of *Pl. fungosa* and *repens* and *Stolella evelinae* (Schroeder, 1910, 1912a, b; Braem, 1911; Marcus, 1941) as vermiform organisms resembling nematodes that may reach a length of 3.6 mm. Young stages, of oval or pyriform shape, are attached to the peritoneum of the host and consist of a covering cuboidal epithelium separated by a basement membrane from the interior filled with cells suggestive of gonocytes (Fig. 182*D*). As they mature, the parasites detach from the peritoneum, thereafter lying free in the coelom, elongate to a vermiform shape, and hollow out internally. The surface epithelium and basement membrane are retained, but internal to the latter there differentiates a muscle system of four longitudinal tracts that seem to occupy dorsolateral and ventrolateral positions. Between the four tracts occurs a single row of cells that thus occupy median and lateral positions (Fig. 182*E, F*). The interior cells thought to be gonocytes at first line the internal cavity, later become loose in this cavity as rounded cells, with large nuclei, apparently ovocytes (Fig. 182*C–F*). The muscle tracts enable the worms to undergo serpentine movements, similar to those of nematodes. Schroeder (1910) reported polar body formation by the ovocytes and figured early embryonic stages; in 1912 he figured small bodies thought to be sperm and believed the interior cells lining one end to be spermatogonia. The cleavage stages resemble those of mesozoans, also those of nematodes. The systematic position of *Buddenbrockia* is problematical. Schroeder subsequently withdrew his original suggestion that *Buddenbrockia* is a mesozoan, and certainly the possession of longitudinal muscle tracts as well as residence in a fresh-water host negatives this idea. Braem suggested that the parasite is the sporocyst stage of a trematode. The epithelial surface and interior germ cells accord with this surmise, but other features of *Buddenbrockia* do not fit with it. The four longitudinal muscle tracts and the serpentine movements recall nematodes, and Schroeder finally proposed that *Buddenbrockia* is a very degenerate nematode. But an epithelial epidermis and a body cavity

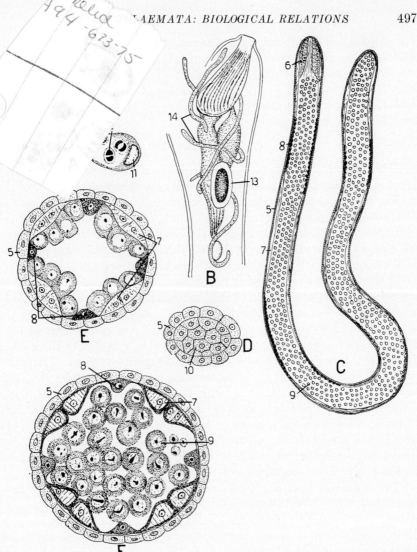

Fig. 182.—Parasites of phylactolaemates. *A, Nosema bryozoides (after Marcus, 1934).
B, Buddenbrockia plumatellae* in coelom of *Pl. repens (after Schroeder, 1910). C*, enlarged
view of *Buddenbrockia* from *Pl. fungosa. D*, section through a young *Buddenbrockia.*
(*C, D, after Schroeder*, 1912b.) *E*, section through the anterior end of a mature parasite.
F, section through the middle of a mature worm. (*E, F, from Stolella, after Marcus*, 1941.)
1, spermatogonia; 2, *Nosema;* 3, spore of *Nosema;* 4, filament of spore; 5, surface epithelium;
6, presumed spermatogonia; 7, longitudinal muscles; 8, cell rows; 9, free ovocytes; 10,
interior cells, future ovocytes; 11, nucleus of spermatogonium; 12, amoeboid infective
stage; 13, statoblast; 14, parasites in coelom.

full of germ cells are definitely not nematode characters, and further, the various systems characteristic of nematodes (nervous, excretory, reproductive) are totally wanting. Marcus (1941) has given the best discussion of the systematic position of *Buddenbrockia*, and one must concur with his opinion that present knowledge does not suffice to attach *Buddenbrockia* to any known group.

VI. RELATIONSHIPS

The phylactolaemates must be regarded as the most primitive existing ectoprocts because they preserve the fundamental cylindroid shape of the zooids, the regionation of the body into protosome (epistome), mesosome (lophophoral region), and metasome (trunk), the horseshoe form of the lophophore, and a muscular layer in the body wall that constitutes a simple mechanism for protrusion of the polypide. They are further primitive in the absence of polymorphism and the lack of elaborate devices for operating the lophophore and closing the orifice. The horseshoe form must be considered the original shape of the lophophore, not only by reference to phoronids but because bilaterality of the lophophore is evident in the ontogeny of all ectoprocts. On the other hand, the embryology of phylactolaemates is shortened and altered, but this is generally the case in fresh-water representatives of predominantly marine groups. Viviparity also, characteristic of all phylactolaemates, inevitably modifies the original course of development. Among the phylactolaemates, forms like *Fredericella* and *Plumatella* must be regarded as basic because the individuality of the zooids is more or less retained. Evolution within the group took the direction of development of a gelatinoid zoecium and increasing confluence of the zooids. No doubt *Cristatella* is the most highly evolved member of the class.

One supposes that phylactolaemates are derived from marine forebears, but it is impossible to relate them directly to any existing marine group. By common consent the cyclostomes appear nearer to the phylactolaemates than does any other group of ectoprocts. This is evidenced by the simple cylindrical form of at least the lower cyclostomes, the slight degree of polymorphism in the latter, and similarities of embryonic development. Already Harmer (1893) and Robertson (1903) noted similarities in the development of cyclostomes and phylactolaemates, and they were also emphasized by Borg (1926a). These similarities may be seen by comparing Figs. 128*C*, 129*B*, *C*, and 169*A*, *B*. On the other hand, the resemblances may result from the fact that development is viviparous in both groups, and there is certainly no resemblance at all between the resulting larvae. Much is made by Borg (1926a) of the fact that in both cyclostomes and phylactolaemates the polypide bud arises before the cystid in which it is to be housed is defined. However, cyclostomes are set apart from all other ectoprocts by several peculiarities, especially the mechanism of operating the lophophore by means of a coelomic sac that subdivides the metacoel, the formation of brood chambers from gonozooids, and polyembryony. It seems necessary to accept the conclusion of Buge (1952) that phylactolaemates and cyclostomes diverged from an ancestral ectoproct in pre-Cambrian times. It is generally thought by students of fossil ectoprocts that cyclostomes came from a common stem with the extinct trepostomes. This opinion is based on structural resemblances between trepostomes and certain extinct cyclostomes and on the studies of Cumings (1912) on developmental stages of monticuliporids. He has found that the monticuliporid ancestrula is a rounded chamber that gives off a tubular first zooid as in cyclostomes (Fig. 136G).

Ctenostomes and cheilostomes are obviously closely related, but neither is close to cyclostomes. The beginning of an operculum is already seen in certain ctenostomes such as *Farrella* with a movable lower lip (Fig. 104E). In both groups the lophophore is operated by the parietal muscles until cheilostomes become too calcified. There are other similarities in the muscular system. In both groups in budding the cystid wall is well defined before the polypide bud appears, and the young polypide undergoes a rotation of 90° to bring its tentacles in line with the orifice. A cyphonautes larva of identical structure is found in representatives of both groups. This larva is no doubt the most primitive of ectoproct larvae, as shown by its complete digestive tract and good muscular and nervous provision. However, its phylogenetic significance, especially the meaning of the two-valved shell, is unknown. These valves cannot relate to brachiopods since they are lateral, whereas the valves of brachiopods are dorsal and ventral. The embryonic and larval development of ctenostomes and cheilostomes is more primitive than that of cyclostomes and phylactolaemates, whereas both the latter are more primitive in some other respects.

It is generally accepted that the extinct group of cryptostomes is to be placed somewhere along the line of evolution of the cheilostomes. This opinion is based primarily on the researches of Cumings (1904), who has shown that the budding pattern of beginning colonies of cryptostomes is similar to that of cheilostomes.

From the foregoing discussion it is necessary to conclude that phylactolaemates, cyclostomes, and cteno-cheilostomes represent three different lines of evolution that have diverged from a common ectoproct ancestor in very early times, probably pre-Cambrian. According to Buge (1952) and Bassler (1953), cyclostomes reached the height of their evolution in Mesozoic times and are now in process of decline. They possibly became evident as fossils in the Cambrian, certainly in the lower Ordovician. Cheilostomes are the dominant ectoprocts at present, beginning in the Jurassic and still at the height of their differentiation, especially Ascophora. Ctenostomes have left a poor fossil record, but what are supposed to be the remains of stolons are recorded back to the Ordovician. Phylactolaemates cannot be expected to leave fossil remains; one fossil from the Cretaceous of Bohemia is doubtfully supposed to be a relative of *Plumatella*.

The relationship of ectoprocts to other phyla must be deduced from adult anatomy since the peculiarities of the embryology preclude assistance from this source. The cleavage pattern in the less modified cases is not of the spiral type. The author is unable to perceive the resemblance to the ctenophore cleavage pattern claimed by Barrois (1877). The manner of entoderm formation in gymnolaemates by primary delamination at the vegetal pole is not illuminating. The definitive entoderm and mesoderm appear to be of ectodermal origin, and the coelom is apparently formed by rearrangement of ectomesodermal cells. The resemblance of this process to coelom formation in phoronids is probably accidental since the mesoderm there is entomesodermal.

The cyphonautes larva may be regarded as some sort of trochophore, of which the lower part is missing as the metatroch encircles the ventral surface. Protonephridia are also wanting. The formation of trochoblasts is a definite allusion to the trochophore. The other types of ectoproct larva show even less resemblance to the trochophore. The pyriform organ and adhesive sac have no representatives in the trochophore. For those who refuse to accept the separation of entoprocts from ectoprocts, these glandular structures of ectoproct larvae may be considered as allusions to the glandular provision of the vestibule of entoproct larvae (III, Fig. 219A, B). If one accepts that ectoproct larvae belong to the category of trochophores, this places the Ectoprocta among the Protostomia.

As regards adult anatomy, the resemblance of phylactolaemates to phoronids is obvious. Both have the same body and coelomic regions, a definite septum between mesocoel and metacoel, a horseshoe-shaped lophophore as part of the mesosome and containing mesocoel, and a muscular body wall. The want of nephridia and circulatory system in ectoprocts may be attributed to their minute size. In both, the main nervous center is found in the mesocoel just anterior to the septum between mouth and anus, and ring connection around the pharynx is more or less developed. A general intraepidermal or subepidermal nervous plexus is present. Other details of anatomy and development differ so much as to preclude, in the author's opinion, uniting phoronids and ectoprocts in one phylum.

It thus appears that the Ectoprocta are to be placed among the Protostomia as having a trochophore type of larva, if rather considerably altered.   From want of good evidence the nature of their coelom cannot be stated, but definitely they are coelomate animals.   They appear to have their nearest affinity in the Phoronida, from which group they presumably are remotely derived.

Bibliography

HISTORICAL

Audouin, J., and **H. Milne Edwards.** 1828.   Résumé des recherches sur les animaux sans vertèbres. Ann. Sci. Natur., ser. 1, vol. 15. **Baker, H.** 1743.   *An attempt toward a natural history of the polypi.* 1753.   *Employment for the microscope,* pt. 2. **Baker, J.** 1952. *Abraham Trembley of Geneva.* **Blainville, H. M. de.** 1820. Flustre. In *Dictionnaire des sciences naturelles,* vol. 17. **Busk, G.** 1852.   On the priority of the term Polyzoa. Ann. Mag. Natur. Hist., ser. 2, vol. 10.   1859.   A monograph of the fossil Bryozoa of the Crag. Monogr. Palaeontogr. Soc. XI. **Cuvier, G.** 1798. *Tableau elémentaire d'histoire naturelle des animaux.* 1800. *Leçons d'anatomie comparée.* 1817. *Le règne animal distribué d'après son organisation.* **Dumortier, B.** 1835.   Recherches sur l'anatomie et la physiologie des polypiers composés d'eau douce. Bull. Acad. Roy. Sciences, Bruxelles, 2. **Edwards, H. Milne.** 1836.   Recherches anatomiques, physiologiques et zoologiques sur les eschares. Ann. Sci. Natur. Zool., ser. 2, vol. 6.   1837.   Recherches sur la classification naturelle des polypes. Bull. Soc. Philomatique Paris. 1841. *Cours élémentaire d'histoire naturelle.* 1843. *Elements de zoologie. Animaux sans vertèbres.* 2 ed. **Ehrenberg, C. G.** 1828. *Symbolae physicae seu icones et descriptiones animalium evertebratorum.* 1833.   Beiträge zur physiologischen Kenntniss der Corallenthiere. Abhandl. König. Akad. Wissensch. Berlin, pt. 1, Physik. Kl., read 1831.   1834.   Dritter Beitrag zur Erkenntniss grosser Organisation in der Richtung des kleinsten Raumes. Abhandl. König. Akad. Wissensch. Berlin, for 1833. **Ellis, J.** 1754.   Observations on a remarkable coralline. Philos. Trans. Roy. Soc. London 48, pt. 1.   1755a.   Concerning a particular species of corallines. Philos. Trans. Roy. Soc. London 48, pt. 2. 1755b.   Concerning the animal life of corallines. Philos. Trans. Roy. Soc. London 48, pt. 2.   1755c. *An essay towards a natural history of the corallines.* **Grant, R.** 1827. Observations on the structure and nature of Flustrae. Edinburgh New Philos. Jour. 3. **Harmer, S. F.** 1911.   The terms Polyzoa and Bryozoa. Proc. Linnaean Soc. London 123.   1947.   On the relative merits of the names Bryozoa and Polyzoa. Bull. Zool. Nomenclature 1. **Herdman, W.** 1911.   Notes on J. V. Thompson's use of the term Polyzoa. Proc. Linnaean Soc. London 123. **Huxley, T. H.** 1853. On the morphology of the cephalous Mollusca. Philos. Trans. Roy. Soc. London 143. **Imperato, F.** 1599. *Dell' historia naturale,* book 26, chap. 2. **Jussieu, B. de.** 1745. Examen de quelques productions marines. Mem. Acad. Roy. Sciences, Paris, for 1742. **Linnaeus, C.** 1758. *Systema naturae.* 10 ed. **Lister, J.** 1834.   Some observations on the structure and functions of tubular and cellular polypi. Philos. Trans. Roy. Soc. London 124, pt. 2. **Marsigli, Count de** (also spelled **Marsilli**). 1711.   Brieve ristretto del sagio fisico intorno all storia del mare. Suppl. Jour. Savans for 1707.   1725. *Histoire physique de la mer.* **Pallas, P.** 1766. *Elenchus zoophytorum.* **Peyssonel, S. de.** 1729.   Sur le corail. Hist. Acad. Roy. Sciences, Paris, for 1727.   1753.   Traité du corail. Philos. Trans. Roy. Soc. London 47. **Réaumur, R. de.** 1729.   Observations sur la formation du corail. Mem. Acad. Roy. Sciences Paris, for 1727.   1742. *Mémoires pour servir à l'histoire des insectes.* Vol. 6. **Rondelet, W.** 1558. *L'histoire entière des poissons.* Livre II, chap. 27, De la giroflade de mer. **Schneider, A.** 1869. Zur Entwicklungsgeschichte und systematische Stellung der Bryozoen und Gephyreen. Arch. Mikrosc. Anat. 5. **Stebbing, T.** 1911a. The terms Polyzoa and Bryozoa. Proc. Linnaean Soc. London 123. 1911b. On John Vaughan Thompson and his Polyzoa. Proc. Linnaean Soc. London 123. **Thompson, J. V.** 1830. *Zoological researches and illustrations.* V. On Polyzoa. **Trembley, A.** 1744. *Mémoires pour servir à l'histoire d'une genre de polypes d'eau à bras en forme de cornes.* **Van der Hoeven, J.** 1856. *Handbook of zoology.* Vol. I, *Invertebrate animals.* **Waters, W. A.** 1878. On Bryozoa. Proc. Manchester Literary Philos. Soc. 17. 1880. On the terms Bryozoa and Polyzoa. Ann. Mag. Natur. Hist., ser. 5, vol. 5. 1911. The terms Polyzoa and Bryozoa. Proc. Linnaean Soc. London 123.

GENERAL

Allman, G. 1856. *Monograph of the fresh-water Polyzoa.* Ray Society. **Annandale, N.** 1911. Freshwater Polyzoa. Fauna of British India. **Bassler, R. S.** 1922. The Bryozoa or moss animals. Smithson. Inst. Rept. for 1920, Publ. 2633. 1953. Bryozoa. *In* R. C. **Moore** (ed.), *Treatise on invertebrate paleontology,* pt. G. **Borg, F.** 1930. Moostierchen oder Bryozoa (Ectoprocta). *In* F. **Dahl** (ed.), *Die Tierwelt Deutschlands und der angrenzenden Meeresteile,* Teil 17. **Brien, P.,** and L. **Papyn.** 1954. Les Endoprocts et la classe des Bryozoaires. Ann. Soc. Roy. Zool. Belgique 85. **Buddenbrock, W.** 1932. Bryozoa Ectoprocta. *Handwörterbuch der Naturwissenschaften.* 2 ed., vol. 2. **Buge, E.** 1952. Classe des Bryozoaires. *In* J. **Piveteau** (ed.), *Traité de paléontologie,* vol. I. **Canu, F.,** and R. **Bassler.** 1923. North American late tertiary and quaternary Bryozoa. Bull. U.S. Nation. Mus. 125. **Cori, C.** 1941. Bryozoa. *In* W. **Kükenthal** and T. **Krumbach** (eds.), *Handbuch der Zoologie,* vol. 3, pt. 2, Lief. 15, 16. **Harmer, S.** 1910. Polyzoa. *Cambridge natural history,* vol. 2. 1913. The Polyzoa of waterworks. Proc. Zool. Soc. London. **Hyman, L.** 1958. Occurrence of chitin in lophophorates. Biol. Bull. 114. **Kraepelin, K.** 1887, 1892. Die deutschen Süsswasser-Bryozoen. 2 pts. Ahbandl. Gebiete Naturwissensch. Naturwiss. Vereins Hamburg, vols. 10, 12. **Marcus, Ernst.** 1940. Mosdyr (Bryozoa eller Polyzoa). Danmarks Fauna, vol. 46. **Nickles, J.,** and R. **Bassler.** 1900. Synopsis of American fossil Bryozoa. Bull. U.S. Geol. Survey, no. 173. **Prenant, M.,** and G. **Bobin.** 1956. Bryozoaires. Pt. I. Faune de France 60.

GYMNOLAEMATA

Abeloos, M. 1951. Morphogénèse des colonies du Bugula. C. R. Acad. Sci. Paris 232. **Alder, J.** 1857. Notice of several new species of Hydrozoa and Polyzoa. Quart. Jour. Microsc. Sci. 5. **Allen, F.** 1953. Distribution of marine invertebrates by ships. Australian Jour. Marine and Freshwater Research 4. **Ambronn, H.** 1890. Cellulose-reaction bei Arthropoden und Mollusken. Mitt. Zool. Stat. Neapel 9. **Annandale, N.** 1911a. Systematic notes on the ctenostomatous Polyzoa of fresh waters. Records Indian Mus. 6. 1911b. Freshwater sponges, hydroids, and Polyzoa. Freshwater Polyzoa. Fauna of British India, pt. III. 1916. Zoological results of a tour in the far east. Ctenostomata. Mem. Asiatic Soc. Bengal 6. **Atkins, Daphne.** 1932. The ciliary feeding mechanism of the entoproct Polyzoa and a comparison with that of the ectoproct Polyzoa. Quart. Jour. Microsc. Sci. 75. 1955a. The cyphonautes larvae of the Plymouth area. Jour. Marine Biol. Assoc. Unit. Kingd. 34. 1955b. The ciliary feeding mechanism of the cyphonautes larva. Jour. Marine Biol. Assoc. Unit. Kingd. 34. **Aymes, Y.** 1956. Croissance phototropique chez Bugula. C. R. Acad. Sci. Paris 242. **Barrois, G.** 1877. Mémoire

sur l'embryologie des Bryozoaires. Trav. Inst. Zool. Wimereux 1. 1880. Mémoire
sur le métamorphose des Bryozoaires. Ann. Sci. Natur., Zool., ser. 6, vol. 9. 1886.
Métamorphose de quelques Bryozoaires. Ann. Sci. Natur., Zool., ser. 7, vol. 1.
1925. Études complementaires sur la métamorphose des Bryozoaires. Ann. Sci.
Natur., Zool., ser. 10, vol. 8. **Bidenkap, O.** 1900. Die Bryozoen von Spitzbergen
und König-Karls-Land. Fauna Arctica 1. 1906. Fortegneke over de arktiske
Bryozoer. Bergens Mus. Aarbok, for 1905, no. 9. **Bobin, G.,** and **M. Prenant.**
1952. Structure et histogénèse du gésier des vesicularines. Arch. Zool. Exp. Gén. 89.
1954a. Sur un bryozoaire perforant. Arch. Zool. Exp. Gén. 91, Notes et Revue
no. 3. 1954b. Les Bowerbankia des côtes françaises. Arch. Zool. Exp. Gén. 91,
Notes et Revue no. 2. **Bogolepov, M.** 1907. Wachstum und Leben der Tendra.
Zool. Anz. 32. **Borg, F.** 1923. Structure of cyclostomatous Bryozoa. Arkiv
Zool. 15. 1926a. Studies on recent cyclostomatous Bryozoa. Zool. Bidrag 10.
1926b. Body wall in Bryozoa. Quart. Jour. Microsc. Sci. 70. 1931. Some species
of Membranipora. Arkiv Zool. 22A. 1932. Structure and development of Heteropora. Arkiv Zool. 24B. 1933a. A revision of the recent Heteroporidae. Zool.
Bidrag 14. 1933b. Die marinen Bryozoen des arktischen Gebietes. Fauna Arctica
6. 1933c. Die geographische Verbreitung der innerhalb des arktischen Gebietes
gefundenen marinen Bryozoen. Arch. Naturgesch., new ser. 2. 1940. On Tubiporella and a new boring bryozoan. Zool. Bidrag 18. 1941. On the structure and
relationship of Ciesura. Arkiv Zool. 33A. 1944. The stenolaematous Bryozoa.
Further Zool. Results Swedish Antarctic Exped. 1901–1903, vol. 3, no. 5. 1947.
Ökologie und Lebenszyklus von Elektra crustalenta. Zool. Bidrag 25. **Bouffandeau,
M.,** and **Y. Sandray.** 1955. Composition chimique du système tégumentaire de
deux bryozoaires. C. R. Soc. Biol. Paris 149. **Braem, F.** 1914. Die Knospung
von Paludicella. Arch. Hydrobiol. Planktonk. 9. 1939. Victorella sibogae.
Ztschr. Morphol. Ökol. Tiere 36. 1940a. Über die Querstreifung im Pharynx der
gymnolämen Bryozoen. Ztschr. Morphol. Ökol. Tiere 36. 1940b. Über Potsiella
erecta. Arch. Hydrobiol. Planktonk. 36. 1951. Über Victorella und einige ihre
nächsten Verwandten. Zoologica, Stuttgart, 37, Heft 102. **Brattström, H.** 1954.
Notes on Victorella pavida. Lunds Univ. Arsskrift 50, no. 9. **Brien, P.,** and **G.
Huysmans.** 1937. La croissance et la bourgeonnement du stolon chez les Stoloni-
fera. Ann. Soc. Malacol. Belgique 68. **Bronstein, G.** 1937. Étude du système
nerveux de quelques bryozoaires. Trav. Stat. Biol. Roscoff, fasc. 15. 1938a.
Présence de muscles striés chez les bryozoaires. Bull. Soc. Zool. France 63. 1938b.
Croissance résiduelle des fragments de zoarium chez Membranipora. C. R. Soc.
Biol. Paris 128. 1938c. Mecanisme de la formation du polypide chez Membranipora.
C. R. Acad. Sci. Paris 207. 1939. Gradients physiologiques dans une colonie de
bryozoaires. C. R. Acad. Sci. Paris 209. **Brown, D.** 1952. *The tertiary cheil-
ostomatous Bryozoa of New Zealand.* **Brozec, R.** 1955. Les Alcyonidium de Roscoff.
Buchner, P. 1918. Totale Regeneration bei cheilostomen Bryozoen. Biol. Cen-
tralbl. 38. 1924. Untersuchungen an japanischen Reteporiden. Zool. Jahrb. Abt.
System. 48. **Busk, G.** 1852. *Catalogue of marine Polyzoa in the collection of the
British Museum.* Vol. I, *Cheilostomata.* 1854. Vol. II, *Cheilostomata.* 1875.
Vol. III, *Cyclostomata.* 1874a. On Clavopora. Quart. Jour. Microsc. Sci. 14.
1874b. New polyzoon, Hippuraria. Proc. Zool. Soc. London. 1876. Polyzoa from
Kerguelen's Island. Ann. Mag. Natur. Hist., ser. 4, vol. 17. 1879. Zoology of
Kerguelen Island. Philos. Trans. Roy. Soc. London 168. 1884. Report on the
Polyzoa, the Cheilostomata. Rept. Scient. Results Voyage Challenger, Zool. 10.
1886. The Cyclostomata. Rept. Scient. Results Voyage Challenger, Zool. 17.
Calvet, L. 1900. Histoire naturelle des bryozoaires ectoproctes marins. Trav.
Inst. Zool. Montpellier, ser. 2, mém. 8. 1902a. Bryozoaires marins des côtes de

Cette. Trav. Inst. Zool. Univ. Montpellier, ser. 2, mém. 11. 1902b. Bryozoaires marins des côtes de Corse. Trav. Inst. Zool. Univ. Montpellier, ser. 2, mém. 12. 1904. Bryozoen. Ergebnisse der Hamburger Magalhaenischen Sammelreise 1892–1893, vol. 3. 1905. Bryozoaires de Cette. Trav. Inst. Zool. Univ. Montpellier, ser. 2, mém. 15. 1906. Bryozoaires. Exped. Scient. Travailleur et Talisman, vol. 8. 1909. Bryozoaires. Exped. Antarctique Française (1903–1905), Sci. Natur. 6. 1912a, b. Sur Watersia paissleri. C. R. Acad. Sci. Paris 154. 1927. Bryozoaires de Monaco et environs. Bull. Inst. Océanogr. Monaco, no. 503. 1931. Bryozoaires. Campagnes Scient. Monaco, fasc. 83. **Canu, F.,** and **R. Bassler.** 1925. Bryozoaires du Maroc et de Mauritanie. I. Mém. Soc. Sci. Natur. Maroc 10. 1926. Studies on the cyclostomatous Bryozoa. Proc. U.S. Nation. Mus. 67. 1927a. Bryozoaires des Iles Hawaii. Bull. Soc. Sci. Seine et Oise, fasc. 7, suppl. 1927b. Classification of the cheilostomatous Bryozoa. Proc. U.S. Nation. Mus. 69. 1928a. Bryozoaires du Maroc et de Mauritanie. II. Mem. Soc. Sci. Natur. Maroc 18. 1928b. Fossil and recent Bryozoa of the Gulf of Mexico region. Proc. U.S. Nation. Mus. 72. 1929. The Bryozoa of the Philippine region. Bull. U.S. Nation. Mus. 100, pt. 9. 1930a. Bryozoaires marins de Tunisie. Ann. Stat. Océanogr. Salammbo, no. 5. 1930b. The bryozoan fauna of the Galapagos Islands. Proc. U.S. Nation. Mus. 76. **Clarke, F. W.,** and **W. C. Wheeler.** 1922. The inorganic constituents of marine invertebrates. Profess. Papers U.S. Geol. Survey, no. 124. **Correa, Diva.** 1947. Note on Vittaticella. Communicaciones Zool. Mus. Hist. Natur. Montevideo 11, no. 43. 1948. A embriologia de Bugula flabellata. Zoologia, Univ. Sao Paulo, Brazil, no. 13. **Cumings, E.** 1904. Development of some paleozoic Bryozoa. Amer. Jour. Sci., ser. 4, vol. 17. 1905. Development of Fenestella. Amer. Jour. Sci., ser. 4, vol. 20. 1912. Development and systematic position of the Trepostomata. Bull. Geol. Soc. America 23. **Cumings, E.,** and **J. Gallaway.** 1915. Morphology and histology of the Trepostomata. Bull. Geol. Soc. America 26. **Danielsson, D.** 1868. Over 2 nye arter Bryozoer. Forhandl. Vidensk. Selskab. Christiania, for 1867. **Darwin, C.** 1839. *Journal of researches into the natural history and geology of the voyage of the Beagle.* **Davenport, C.** 1891. Budding in Paludicella. Bull. Mus. Comp. Zool. Harvard College 22. **Dawydoff, C.** 1948. Distribution géographique des genres Norodonia et Hislopia. C. R. Acad. Sci. Paris 226. **Dendy, A.** 1888. Anatomy of an arenaceous polyzoon. Proc. Roy. Soc. Victoria 1. **Devèze, L.** 1953. Utilisation possible du contenu bacterien des eaux par les larves cyphonautes. Recueil Trav. Stat. Maritime Endoume, fasc. 8. **Duncan, Helen.** 1939. Trepostomatous Bryozoa from the Traverse group of Michigan. Univ. Michigan Contribs. Mus. Paleontology 5. **Echalier, G.,** and **M. Prenant.** 1951. Inventaire de la faune marine de Roscoff. Bryozoaires. Trav. Stat. Biol. Roscoff, new ser. 2, suppl. 4. **Edmondson, C.,** and **W. Ingram.** 1939. Fouling organisms in Hawaii. Occasion. Papers Bernice P. Bishop Mus., Hawaii, 14. **Ehlers, E.** 1876. Hypophorella expansa. Abhandl. König. Gesellsch. Wissensch. Göttingen 21. **Ekman, S.** 1953. *Zoogeography of the sea.* **Faulkner, G.** 1933. The relation between somatic and germ cells in Alcyonidium. Ann. Mag. Natur. Hist., ser. 10, vol. 11. **Fischer, P.** 1866. Bryozoaires perforants de la famille des Térébriporides. Nouv. Arch. Mus. Nation. Hist. Natur. Paris 2. **Forbes, A.** 1933. Conditions affecting response of the avicularia of Bugula. Biol. Bull. 65. **Fox, D. L.** 1953. *Animal biochromes and structural colors.* **Friedl, H.** 1918. Bryozoen des Adria. Zool. Anz. 49. 1925. Koloniebildung, Besiedlung und Wachstum bei marinen Bryozoen. Arbeit. Zool. Inst. Univ. Innsbruck 2, Heft 3. **Fritz, M.** 1947. Cambiran Bryozoa. Jour. Paleontol. 21. **Gadeau de Kerville, H.** 1890. *Les vegetaux et les animaux lumineaux.* **Gautier, Y.** 1949. Bryozoaires des divers biotypes marins de la region de Marseille. Bull. Mus. Hist. Natur. Marseille 9, no. 4. 1952. Faune bryozoologique de la region de Villefranche. Bull. Inst. Oceanogr. Monaco, no. 1008. 1954a. Sur Clavopora. Recueil Trav. Stat. Marine Endoume, fasc. 13, bull. no. 8. 1954b. Electra pilosa des feuilles de Posidonies. Vie et Milieu 5. 1955a. Bryozoaires des gastéropodes de l'herbier de Posidonies. Vie et Milieu 6. 1955b. Bryozoaires de Castiglione. Bull. Stat. Aquiculture et Pêche Castiglione, new ser. 7. **Gerwerzhagen, A.** 1913. Untersuchungen an Bryozoen. Sitzungsber. Heidelberg Akad. Wissensch., Math. Naturwiss. Kl. 4, Abt. B, no. 9. **Graupner, H.** 1930. Zur Kenntnis der feineren Anatomie der Bryozoen. Ztschr. Wissensch. Zool. 136. **Grave, B. H.** 1930. Natural history of Bugula flabellata. Jour. Morphol. 49. 1933. Rate of growth, age at sexual maturity, and duration of life of certain sessile organisms. Biol. Bull. 65. **Haddon, A.** 1883. On budding of Polyzoa. Quart. Jour. Microsc. Sci. 23. **Hallez, P.** 1894. Catalogue des rhabdocoelides, triclades et polyclades du Nord de la France. 2 ed. Soc. Sciences Lille, Mém., ser. 4, vol. 19. **Harmer, S. F.** 1887. Sur l'embryogénie des bryozoaires ectoproctes. Arch. Zool. Exp. Gén., ser. 2, vol. 5. 1890. Origin of the embryos of cyclostomatous Polyzoa. Proc. Cambridge Philos. Soc. 7. 1891a. Nature of excretory processes in marine Polyzoa. Quart. Jour. Microsc. Sci. 33. 1891b. British species of Crisia. Quart. Jour. Microsc. Sci. 32. 1891c. Regeneration of lost parts in Polyzoa. Rept. British Assoc. Advanc. Sci. 60, for 1890. 1893. Embryonic fission in cyclostomatous Polyzoa. Quart. Jour. Microsc. Sci. 34. 1896. Development of Lichenopora. Quart. Jour. Microsc. Sci. 39. 1898. Development of Tubulipora. Quart. Jour. Microsc. Sci. 41. 1900. Review of Steganoporella. Quart. Jour. Microsc. Sci. 43. 1901. Structure and classification of the cheilostomatous Polyzoa. Proc. Cambridge Philos. Soc. 11. 1902. Morphology of the Cheilostomata. Quart. Jour. Microsc. Sci. 46. 1915. The Polyzoa of the Siboga Expedition. Pt. I. Entoprocta. Ctenostomata, and Cyclostomata. Siboga Exped. Monogr. 28a. 1923. Cellularines and other Polyzoa. Jour. Linnaean Soc. London 35. 1926. The Polyzoa of the Siboga Expedition. Pt. II. Cheilostomata Anasca. Siboga Exped. Monogr. 28b. 1930. Polyzoa. Proc. Linnaean Soc. London 141. 1931. Recent work on Polyzoa. Proc. Linnaean Soc. London 143. 1933. The genera of the Reteporidae. Proc. Zool. Soc. London. 1934. The Polyzoa of the Siboga Expedition. Pt. III. Cheilostomata Ascophora 1. Family Reteporidae. Siboga Exped. Monogr. 28c. 1957. Pt. IV. Cheilostomata Ascophora 2. Siboga Exped. Monogr. 28d. **Harvey, E.** 1952. *Bioluminescence.* **Hasenbank, W.** 1932. Bryozoa der deutschen Tiefsee-Expedition. Teil 1. Wissensch. Ergebn. Dtsch. Tiefsee-Exped. Valdivia 1898–1899, vol. 21, Heft 2. **Hass, H.** 1948. Reteporiden. Zoologia, Stuttgart, vol. 37, Heft 101. **Hastings, Anna.** 1929. Cheilostomatous Polyzoa from the vicinity of the Panama Canal. Proc. Zool. Soc. London. 1930. Association of a gymnoblastic hydroid with various cheilostomatous Polyzoa. Ann. Mag. Natur. Hist., ser. 10, vol. 5. 1932. Polyzoa. Scient. Repts. Great Barrier Reef Exped., vol. 4, no. 12. 1941. British species of Scuparia. Ann. Mag. Natur. Hist., ser. 11, vol. 7. 1943. Polyzoa. Discovery Repts. 22. **Hentschel, E.** 1921. Über den Bewuchs auf den treibenden Tangen der Sargassosee. Mitt. Zool. Mus. Hamburg, Beiheft zum Jahrb. Wissensch. Anstalt Hamburg 38. **Herwig, E.** 1913. Knospung bei den Bryozoen. Arch. Naturgesch. 79, Abt. A, Heft 12. 1915. Die Avicularien von Bugula. Arch. Naturgesch. 81, Abt. A, Heft 7. **Hiller, S.** 1939. The so-called colonial nervous system in Bryozoa. Nature, London, 143. **Hincks, T.** 1851. Notes on British zoophytes. Ann. Mag. Natur. Hist., ser. 2, vol. 8. 1862. Catalogue of the zoophytes of South Devon and South Cornwall. Ann. Mag. Natur. Hist., ser. 3, vol. 9. 1878. Notes on the movements of the vibracula in Caberea. Quart. Jour. Microsc. Sci. 18. 1880. *History of the British marine Polyzoa.* 2 vols. 1880–1885. History of the marine Polyzoa. Ann. Mag. Natur. Hist., ser. 5, vols. 6–9, 11, 13–15. 1882–

1884. Polyzoa of the Queen Charlotte Islands. Ann. Mag. Natur. Hist., ser. 5, vols. 10, 11, 13. 1886. Polyzoa of the Adriatic. Ann. Mag. Natur. Hist., ser. 5, vol. 17. 1888–1892. Polyzoa of the St. Lawrence. Ann. Mag. Natur. Hist., ser. 6, vols. 1, 3, 9. **Issel, R.** 1912. Il bentos animale delle foglie di Posidonia. Zool. Jahrb. Abt. System. 33. **Joliet, L.** 1877. Histoire naturelle des Bryozoaires des côtes de France. Arch. Zool. Exp. Gén., ser. 1, vol. 6. 1885. Bourgeonnement du polypide chez plusieurs ectoproctes marins. Arch. Zool. Exp. Gén., ser. 2, vol. 3, Notes et Revue. 1886. Recherches sur la blastogénèse. Arch. Zool. Exp. Gén., ser. 2, vol. 4. **Joyeux-Laffuie, J.** 1888a. Delagia chaeptopteri. C. R. Acad. Sci. Paris 106. 1888b. Delagia chaetopteri. Arch. Zool. Exp. Gén., ser. 2, vol. 6. **Jullien, J.** 1880. Nouvelle espèce de bryozoaires perforants. Bull. Soc. Zool. France 5. 1881. Nouvelle division des bryozoaires cheilostomiens. Bull. Soc. Zool. France 6. 1882. Bryozoaires. Dragages du Travailleur. Bull. Soc. Zool. France 7. 1888a. Sortie et rentrée du polypide chez les bryozoaires cheilostomiens. Bull. Soc. Zool. France 13. 1888b. Observations anatomiques sur les caténicelles. Mém. Soc. Zool. France 1. 1891. Bryozoaires. Mission Scient. Cap Horn (1882–1883), 6, Zool., pt. 3. **Jullien, J.,** and **L. Calvet.** 1903. Bryozoaires. Result. Campagnes Scient. Monaco, fasc. 23. **Karrer, P., E. Jucker,** and **C. Brande.** 1950. *Carotenoids.* **Kato, K.** 1950. On a luminous bryozoan. Dobuts. Zasshi (Zool. Mag.) 59. **Kelly, A.** 1901. Beiträge zur mineralogischen Kenntnis der Kalkausscheidungen im Tierreich. Jena. Ztschr. Naturwiss. 35. **Kent, W.** 1870. On Victorella pavida. Quart. Jour. Microsc. Sci. 10. **Kirkpatrick, R.** 1890a. Zoological collections made in Torres Strait. Scient. Proc. Roy. Dublin Soc. 6. 1890b. Hydrozoa and Polyzoa from the China Sea. Ann. Mag. Natur. Hist., ser. 6, vol. 5. 1902. Polyzoa. Rept. Collections Natur. Hist. Antarctic Region, Voyage Southern Cross. **Kirkpatrick, R.,** and **J. Metzelaar.** 1922. Commensalism between a hermit crab and a polyzoon. Proc. Zool. Soc. London. **Kluge, H.** 1907a. Sur Kenntnis der Bryozoen des Weissen Meeres. Annuaire Mus. Zool. Acad. Impér. Sci. St. Pétersbourg 12. 1907b. Zur Kenntnis der Bryozoen von West-Grönland. Annuaire Mus. Zool. Acad. Impér. Sci. St. Pétersbourg 12. 1914. Die Bryozoen der deutschen Südpolar-Expedition. Dtsch. Südpolar-Exped. 15, Zool. 7. **Koren, J.,** and **D. Danielssen.** 1877. Fauna littoralis Norvegiae III. **Korotneff, A.** 1901. Faunistic Studien am Baikalsee. Biol. Centralbl. 21. **Krukenberg, C.** 1886. *Vergleichend-physiologische Vorträge* I. **Kupelwieser, H.** 1905. Bau und Metamorphosis des Cyphonautes. Zoologica, Stuttgart, 19, Heft 47. **Ladewig, F.** 1900. Knospung der ektoprokten Bryozoen. Ztschr. Wissensch. Zool. 67. **Landsborough, D.** 1842. On the phosphorescence of zoophytes. Ann. Mag. Natur. Hist., ser. 1, vol. 8. 1852. *Popular history of British zoophytes.* **Le Brozec, R.** 1955. Les Alcyonidium de Roscoff et leurs caractères distinctifs. Arch. Zool. Exp. Gén. 93, Notes et Revue 1. **Levinsen, G.** 1907. Régénération totale des bryozoaires. Vorhandl. Kgl. Danske Vidensk. Selsk. Oversigt, no. 4. 1909. *Morphological and systematic studies on the cheilostomatous Bryozoa.* 1916. Danmark-Ekspeditionen til Grönlands Nordöstkyst 1906–1908. Meddel. om Grönland 43, no. 16. **Livingstone, A.** 1924–1926. Studies on Australian Bryozoa. Records Australian Mus. 14, 15. 1928a. Bryozoa from South Australia. Records South Australian Mus. 4. 1928b. The Bryozoa, suppl. rept. Australasian Antarctic Exped. 1911–1914, Scient. Repts., ser. C, Zool. and Bot., vol. 9, pt. 1. 1929. Bryozoa Cheilostomata from New Zealand. Vidensk. Meddel. Dansk Naturhist. Foren. 87. **Lohmann, H.** 1911. Die Cyphonautes der nordischen Meere. Nordisches Plankton, Abt. IX, Lief. 13. **Loppens, K.** 1920. Influence du milieu sur la composition chimique des zoécies des bryozoaires marins. Ann. Soc. Roy. Zool. Malacol. Belgique 51. **Lutaud, Geneviève.** 1953a. Premiers stades de la croissance zoariale chez le bryozoaire Scrupocellaria. Arch. Zool. Exp. Gén. 90, Notes et Revue

1. 1953b. Progression de la calcification chez Escharoides. Arch. Zool. Exp. Gén. 91, Notes et Revue 1. 1955. Sur la ciliature du tentacle chez les bryozoaires cheilostomes. Arch. Zool. Exp. Gén. 92, Notes et Revue 1. **Luther, A.** 1927. Vorkommen der Victorella pavida im finnischen Meerbusen. Mém. Soc. Fauna Flora Fennica 1. **Lynch, W.** 1947. Behavior and metamorphosis of the larva of Bugula. Biol. Bull. 92. 1949a. Acceleration and retardation of the onset of metamorphosis in Bugula. Jour. Expt. Zool. 111. 1949b. Modification of the response of Bugula larvae to light and gravity. Biol. Bull. 97. 1952. Factors influencing metamorphosis of Bugula larvae. Biol. Bull. 103. 1955. Synergism and antagonism in the induction of metamorphosis of Bugula larvae. Biol. Bull. 109. 1956. Effects of moderately low temperatures on the rate of metamorphosis of Bugula. Physiol. Zool. 29. **MacGillivray, P.** 1886. New or little known Polyzoa. Trans. Proc. Roy. Soc. Victoria 22. 1895a. Monograph of the Tertiary Polyzoa of Victoria. Trans. Roy. Soc. Victoria, new ser. 4. 1895b. Australian species of Amathia. Trans. Roy. Soc. Victoria, new ser. 7. **Malaquin, A.** 1892. Remarques sur l'absorption et l'excrétion chez les syllidiens. C. R. Assoc. Française Avanc. Sci. 21, pt. 2. **Marcus, E.** 1920. Mittelmeer Bryozoen. Sitzungsber. Gesellsch. Naturforsch. Freunde Berlin. 1921a. Verbreitung der Meeresbryozoen. Zool. Anz. 53. 1921b. Bryozoen. Results Dr. Mjöberg's Expedition to Australia 1910–1913, 24. Kong. Svenske Vetensk. Akad. Handl. 61, art. 5. 1921c. Bryozoa von der Juan Fernandez Inseln. *In* C. Skottsberg (ed.), Natural History Juan Fernandez and Easter Island 3. 1922. Bryozoen von den Auckland und Campbell Inseln. Vidensk. Meddel. Dansk Naturhist. Foren. 73. 1923. Hydrostatik bei Meeresbryozoa. Verhandl. Dtsch. Zool. Gesellsch. 28. 1924. Zur vergleichenden Embryologie der Bryozoen. Mitt. Zool. Mus. Berlin 11. 1925a. Zum Polymorphism der Bryozoen. Verhandl. Dtsch. Zool. Gesellsch. 30. 1925b. Bryozoa. *In* P. Schulze (ed.), Biologie der Tiere Deutschlands, Lief. 14. 1925c. Über Victorella symbiotica. Zool. Anz. 62. 1925d. Über Stirpariella. Vidensk. Meddel. Dansk Naturhist. Foren. 81. 1926a. Bryozoa. *In* G. Grimpe and E. Wagler (eds.), Die Tierwelt der Nord- und Ostsee, Teil VII, C1. 1926b. Beobachtungen und Versuche an lebenden Meeresbryozoen. Zool. Jahrb. Abt. System. 52. 1936a. Sobre o systema natural dos bryozoarios. Boletim Biologico 2, no. 4. 1936b. Sobre alguns phenomenos da vida dos bryozoarios marinhos. Archivos Inst. Biol. Sao Paulo 7, art. 16. 1937a. Bryozoarios marinhos brasileiros I. Zoologia, Univ. Sao Paulo, Brazil, no. 1. 1937b. Bryozoen von St. Helena. Vidensk. Meddel. Dansk Naturhist. Foren. 101. 1938a. Bryozoairos marinhos brasileiros II. Zoologia, Univ. Sao Paulo, Brazil, no. 2. 1938b. Bryozoarios perfuradores de conchas. Arquivos Inst. Biol. Sao Paulo, Brazil, 9. 1939a. Bryozoarios marinhos brasileiros III. Zoologia, Univ. Sao Paulo, Brazil, no. 3. 1939b. Sawayaella polyzoorum. Arquivos Inst. Biol. Sao Paulo, Brazil, 10. 1941a. Sobre Bryozoa do Brasil. Zoologia, Univ. Sao Paulo, Brazil, no. 5. 1941b. Sobre o desenvolvimento do Synnotum aegyptiacum. Arquivos Cirurgia Clinica Experim. 5. 1941c. Bryozoarios marinhos do litoral paranaense. Arquivos Mus. Paranaense 1. 1942a. Sobre Bryozoa do Brasil II. Zoologia, Univ. Sao Paulo, Brazil, no. 6. 1942b. Cryptopolyzoon evelinae. Proc. 8 Amer. Science Congr. Washington, vol. 3, Biol. Sci. 1949. Some Bryozoa from the Brazilian coast. Comun. Zool. Mus. Hist. Natur. Montevideo 3, no. 53. 1950. Systematical remarks on the bryozoan fauna of Denmark. Vidensk. Meddel. Dansk Naturhist. Foren. 112. 1953. Notas sobre briozoos marinhos brasileiros. Arquivos Mus. Nacion. Brazil 42. **Maturo, F.** 1957. Bryozoa of Beaufort, North Carolina. Jour. Elisha Mitchell Scient. Soc. 73. **Mawatari, S.** 1951. Natural history of Bugula neritina. Miscell. Repts. Research Inst. Natural Resources, nos. 19-21. 1952a. On Watersipora cucullata. I, II. Miscell. Repts. Research Inst. Natural Resources, nos. 25, 28. 1952b. Bryozoa of Kii Peninsula.

Publ. Seto Marine Lab. 2. 1953. Studies on Japanese ctenostomatous Bryozoa.
Publ. Seto Marine Lab. 3. 1956. Cheilostomatous Bryozoa from the Kurile Islands.
Pacific Science 10. **McDougall, K.** 1943. Sessile marine invertebrates at Beaufort,
North Carolina. Ecol. Monogr. 13. **Meigen, W.** 1901. Eine einfache Reaction
zur Untersuchungen von Aragonit und Kalkspath. Zentralbl. Minerol. Geol. Paläon-
tol. **Miyazaki, I.** 1938. Fouling organisms in the oyster farm. Japanese Soc.
Scient. Fisheries Bull. 6. **Molisch, H.** 1904. *Leuchtende Pflanzen.* **Moore, J.**
1903. *The Tanganyika problem.* **Nitsche, H.** 1869. Beiträge zur Kenntnis der
Bryozoen. Ztschr. Wissensch. Zool. 20. 1871. Über die Anatomie und Entwicklungsgeschichte von Flustra. Ztschr. Wissensch. Zool. 21. **Nordgaard, O.** 1906.
Die Bryozoen des westlichen Norwegens. *In* **A.** Appelöf, *Meeresfauna von Bergen.*
1912. Revision av norske Bryozoer. Kgl. Norske Vidensk. Selsk. Skrifter, for 1911,
no. 3. 1918. Bryozoa from the Arctic regions. Trömso Mus. Aarshefter 40. 1923.
Bryozoa. Rept. Scient. Results Norwegian Exped. to Novaya Zemlya 1921, no. 17.
1924. Bryozoa from Iceland. Kgl. Norske Vidensk. Selsk. Skrifter, art. 2. 1929.
Bryozoa. Norwegian North Polar Exped. Maud, Scient. Results, vol. 5, no. 10.
Nordmann, A. de. 1839. Anatomie et développement de Tendra. Ann. Sci.
Natur., ser. 2, vol. 11. **Norman, A.** 1909. The Polyzoa of Madeira. Jour. Lin-
naean Soc. London, Zool. 30. **O'Donoghue, C.** 1924. Bryozoa collected by the
Pickle. Union of South Africa, Fisheries and Marine Biology Survey, Rept. 3, for
1922, no. 10. 1927. Early development of Membranipora. Contribs. Canadian
Biol. Fisheries 3, no. 8. **O'Donoghue, C., and E. O'Donoghue.** 1923. Preliminary
list of Bryozoa from the Vancouver Island region. Contribs. Canadian Biol. Fisheries,
new ser. 1. 1925. List of Bryozoa from the vicinity of Puget Sound. Publ. Puget
Sound Biol. Stat. 5. 1927. Second list of Bryozoa from the Vancouver Island
region. Contribs. Canadian Biol. Fisheries, new ser. 3. **O'Donoghue, C., and
D. de Watteville.** 1935. Bryozoa from South Africa. Jour. Linnaean Soc. London
39. 1937. Notes on South African Bryozoa. Zool. Anz. 117. 1944. Additional
notes on Bryozoa of South Africa. Ann. Natal Mus. 10. **Okada, Y.** 1917. Cyclostomatous Bryozoa of Japan. Annot. Zool. Japonenses 9. 1920. Notes on Retepora
and Adeonella in Japan. Annot. Zool. Japonenses 9. 1921. Notes on some cheilostomatous Bryozoa. Annot. Zool. Japonenses 10. 1923. Bryozoa from the Straits
of Korea. Annot. Zool. Japonenses 10. 1928. Cyclostomatous Bryozoa of Mutsu
Bay. Sci. Repts. Tohoku Univ., ser. 4., Biol. 3. 1929. Cheilostomatous Bryozoa
of Mutsu Bay. Sci. Repts. Tohoku Univ., ser. 4, Biol. 4. 1933. Bryozoa from the
northern Kurile expedition. Bull. Biogeogr. Soc. Japan 4, no. 3. 1934. Bryozoan
fauna of the Shimoda marine biological station. Sci. Repts. Tokyo Bunrika Daigaku,
sec. B, vol. 2. **Okada, Y., and S. Mawatari.** 1935, 1936. Bryozoa around Izu
Peninsula. I, II. Sci. Repts. Tokyo Bunrika Daigaku, sec. B, vols. 2, 3. 1937.
Bryozoa along the coast of Onagawa Bay. Sci. Repts. Tohoku Univ., ser. 4, Biol. 11.
1938. Bryozoa along the middle part of Honshu, Japan. Annot. Zool. Japonenses 17.
Ortmann, W. 1890. Die Japanische Bryozoenfauna. Arch. Naturgesch. 56, pt. 1.
Osburn, R. C. 1912a. Bryozoa of the Woods Hole region. Bull. U.S. Bur. Fisheries
30. 1912b. Bryozoa from Labrador, Newfoundland, and Nova Scotia. Proc. U.S.
Nation. Mus. 43. 1914. Bryozoa of the Tortugas Islands. Publ. Carnegie Inst.
Washington, no. 182, Papers Tortugas Lab. 5. 1919. Bryozoa from the Crocker
Land Expedition. Bull. Amer. Mus. Natur. Hist. 41. 1921. Bryozoa as food for
animals. Science 53. 1923. Bryozoa. Rept. Canadian Arctic Exped. 1913–1918,
vol. 8, pt. D. 1927. Bryozoa of Curacao. Bijdr. Dierkunde 25. 1932. Bryozoa
from Chesapeake Bay. Ohio Jour. Science 32. 1940. Bryozoa of Porto Rico.
New York Acad. Sci., Scient. Survey Porto Rico and the Virgin Islands 16, pt. 3.
1944. Bryozoa of Chesapeake Bay. Chesapeake Biol. Lab. Publ. 63. 1947.

Bryozoa of the Allan Hancock Atlantic Expedition. Allan Hancock Atlantic Exped. Rept., no. 5. 1949. Genus Parellisina. Allan Hancock Foundation, Occas. Paper, no. 10. 1950, 1952, 1953. Bryozoa of the Pacific coast of North America. Allan Hancock Pacific Exped., vol. 14. 1954. Bryozoa of the Gulf of Mexico. U.S. Fish and Wildlife Service, Fishery Bull. 89. 1955. The circumpolar distribution of Arctic-Alaskan Bryozoa. In *Essays in the natural sciences in honor of Captain Allan Hancock*. **Osburn, R. C.,** and **R. Veth.** 1922. New type of bryozoan gizzard. Ohio Jour. Science 22. **Ostroumov, A.** 1887. Entwicklungsgeschichte der cyclostomen Seebryozoen. Mitt. Zool. Stat. Neapel 7. **Pace, R.** 1906. Early stages in the development of Flustra. Quart. Jour. Microsc. Sci. 50. **Paltschikowa-Ostroumova, N.** 1925. Ovidukt bei den Bryozoen. Zool. Anz. 65. **Peach, C.** 1878. Observations on British Polyzoa. Jour. Linnaean Soc. London, Zool. 13. **Pergens, E.** 1889. Untersuchungen an Seebryozoen. Zool. Anz. 12. **Phillips, A.** 1922. Search for metals in Tortugas marine organisms. Publ. Carnegie Inst. Washington, no. 312, Papers Tortugas Lab. 18. **Potts, E.** 1884. Paludicella erecta. Proc. Acad. Natur. Sci. Philadelphia 2. **Prenant, M.** 1927. Les formes minéralogiques du calcaire chez les êtres vivants. Biol. Reviews Cambridge Philos. Soc. 2. **Prouho, H.** 1890. Recherches sur la larve de Frustrella. Arch. Zool. Exp. Gén., ser. 2, vol. 8. 1892. Contribution à l'histoire des Bryozoaires. Arch. Zool. Exp. Gén., ser. 2, vol. 10. **Redfield, A., et al.** 1952. Marine fouling and its prevention. Woods Hole Oceanogr. Inst. Publ., no. 580. **Reichert, K.** 1870. Über Zoobotryon. Abhandl. Akad. Wissensch. Berlin, for 1869, pt. 2. **Remane, A.** 1936. Monobryozoon ambulans. Zool. Anz. 113. 1938. Ergänzende Mitteilungen über Monobryozoon. Kieler Meeresforsch. 2. **Rey, P.** 1927a. Le corps brun des bryozoaires ectoproctes. Bull. Soc. Zool. France 52. 1927b. Action de divers agents sur les mouvements des aviculaires de Bugula. Bull. Soc. Zool. France 52. **Richards, A.,** and **L. Cutkomp.** 1946. Correlation between chitinous cuticle and sensitivity to DDT. Biol. Bull. 90. **Ridley, S.** 1881. Polyzoa. Zoological collections in the Straits of Magellan and Patagonia. Proc. Zool. Soc. London. **Ries, E.** 1936. Futterungsversuche bei Zoobotryon. Ztschr. Vergl. Physiol. 23. **Ries, E.,** and **G. Schoelsel.** 1934. Vitalfärbung an Zoobotryon. Ztschr. Zellforsch. Mikro. Anat. 20. **Roaf, H.** 1909. The digestive enzymes of invertebrates. Rept. British Assoc. Advanc. Sci. 78. **Robertson, Alice.** 1900. Bryozoa. Papers from the Harriman Alaska Expedition VI. Proc. Washington Acad. Sci. 2. 1903. Embryology and embryonic fission in Crisia. Univ. California Publ. Zool. 1. 1905. Non-incrusting cheilostomatous Bryozoa of the west coast of North America. Univ. California Publ. Zool. 2. 1908. Incrusting cheilostomatous Bryozoa of the west coast of North America. Univ. California Publ. Zool. 4. 1910. The cyclostomatous Bryozoa of the west coast of North America. Univ. California Publ. Zool. 6. **Rogick, Mary.** 1935. Bryozoa of Lake Erie. Trans. Amer. Microsc. Soc. 54. 1945a. Studies on marine Bryozoa. I. Aeverrillia. Biol. Bull. 89. 1945b. Calcining specimens. Amer. Biol. Teacher 8. 1949. Studies on marine Bryozoa. IV. Nolella. Biol. Bull. 97. 1955a. Emballotheca. Trans. Amer. Microsc. Soc. 74. 1955b. Studies on marine Bryozoa. VI. Antarctic Escharoides. Biol. Bull. 109. 1956a. Bryozoa of the U.S. Navy Antarctic Expedition. I–IV. Proc. U.S. Nation. Mus. 105. 1956b. Studies on marine Bryozoa. VII. Hippothoa. Ohio Jour. Science 56. 1956c. Studies on marine Bryozoa. VIII. Exochella. Biol. Bull. 111. **Rogick, Mary,** and **Hannah Croasdale.** 1949. Bryozoa associated with algae. Biol. Bull. 96. **Römer, O.** 1906. Knospung, Degeneration, und Regeneration von einigen marinen ectoprocten Bryozoen. Ztschr. Wissensch. Zool. 84. **Rousselet, C.** 1907. Zoological results of the third Tanganyika expedition. Report on the Polyzoa. Proc. Zool. Soc. London. **Sars, G. O.** 1874. Om en hidtil lidet kjendt maerkelig slaegstype of Polyzoer.

Forhandl. Vidensk. Selsk. Christiania, for 1873. **Sawaya, M.** 1943. Sobre a articulacao em Crisiidae. Zoologia, Univ. Sao Paulo, Brazil, no. 7. **Schneider, D.** 1955. Phototropisches Wachstum von Bugula. Die Naturwissenschaften 42. **Seeliger, O.** 1890. Knospenentwicklung der Bryozoen. Ztschr. Wissensch. Zool. 50. 1906. Larven und Verwandtschaftbeziehungen der Bryozoen. Ztschr. Wissensch. Zool. 84. **Silbermann, S.** 1906. Über den feineren Bau von Alcyonidium. Arch. Naturgesch. 72, pt. 1. **Silén, L.** 1935. Bryozoa from the Skagerrack. Arkiv Zool. 28A. 1938. Zur Kenntnis der Polymorphism der Bryozoen. Zool. Bidrag 17. 1941. Cheilostomata Anasca collected by Sixten Bock's expedition to Japan and the Bonin Islands. Arkiv Zool. 33A. 1942a. Origin and development of the cheilo-ctenostomatous stem of Bryozoa. Zool. Bidrag 22. 1942b. Spiral growth of the zoaria of certain Bryozoa. Arkiv Zool. 34A. 1942c. Carnosa and Stolonifera collected by Sixten Bock's expedition to Japan and the Bonin Islands. Arkiv Zool. 34A. 1942d. Australian Bryozoa. Kungl. Fysiogr. Sällsk. Lund Forhandl. 12, no. 8. 1943. Notes on Swedish marine Bryozoa. Arkiv Zool. 35A. 1944a. Formation of the interzoidal communications of Bryozoa. Zool. Bidrag 22. 1944b. Division and movements of the alimentary canal of Bryozoa. Arkiv Zool. 35A. 1944c. Anatomy of Labiostomella. Kungl. Svenska Vetensk. Handl., ser. 3, vol. 21. 1945. Main features of development of the ovum, embryo, and oecium in the oeciferous Bryozoa Gymnolaemata. Arkiv Zool. 35A. 1946. Two new groups of Bryozoa living in the shells of molluscs. Arkiv Zool. 38B. 1947a. The spines of Flustra. Zool. Bidrag 25. 1947b. Conescharellidae. Arkiv Zool. 39. 1948. Anatomy and biology of Penetrantiidae and Immergentiidae. Arkiv Zool. 40A. 1950. Motility of certain zoids in Bryozoa. Acta Zoologica 31. 1951a. Bryozoa. Repts. Swedish Deep-Sea Exped., vol. II, Zool., no. 5. 1951b. Bryozoa collected by the Skagerak Expedition. Meddel. Göteborgs Mus. Zool. Avd. 122. 1951c. Swedish marine Bryozoa II. Arkiv Zool., ser. 2, vol. 2. 1954. Bryozoa and Entoprocta. Rept. Gislen's Exped. Australia. Lunds Univ. Arsskrift, Avd. 2, vol. 50, no. 17. 1956. On shell-burrowing Bryozoa from New Zealand. Trans. Roy. Soc. New Zealand III. **Smitt, F. A.** 1868. Kritisk förteckning öfver Skandinaviens Hafs-Bryozoer III. Öfversigt Vetensk. Akad. Förhandl. Sweden 24, for 1867, no 5. 1871, 1872. Floridan Bryozoa. Kongl. Svenska Vetensk. Akad. Handl. 10, no. 11; 11, no. 4. **Soule, J.** 1950a. Penetrantiidae and Immergentiidae from the Pacific. Trans. Amer. Microsc. Soc. 69. 1950b. A new species of Terebripora. Jour. Washington Acad. Sci. 40. 1951. Two new species of incrusting ctenostomatous Bryozoa. Jour. Washington Acad. Sci. 41. 1953. Post-larval zoarial development in Carnosa. Bull. South. California Acad. Sci. 52. 1954. Post-larval development in relation to the classification of the Ctenostomata. Bull. South. California Acad. Sci. 53. 1957. Two Ctenostomata from the Salton Sea. Bull. South. California Acad. Sci. 56. **Stach, L.** 1935. The genera of Catenicellidae. Proc. Roy. Soc. Victoria 47. 1936. Recent Petraliidae. Records Australian Mus. 19. 1938a. Colony formation in Smittina. Proc. Zool. Soc. London 108B. 1938b. Observations on Carbasea. Proc. Zool. Soc. London 108B. **Stehli, F.** 1956. Shell mineralogy in paleozoic invertebrates. Science 123. **Thornely, Laura.** 1924. Polyzoa. Scient. Repts. Australasian Antarctic Exped. 1911–1914, ser. C, Zool. and Bot., vol. 6, pt. 6. **Thorson, G.** 1946. Reproduction and larval development of Danish marine bottom invertebrates. Meddel. Komm. Danmarks Fiskeri-og Havundersögelser, ser. Plankton, 4, no. 1. **Timmermann, G.** 1932. Biographische Untersuchungen über die Lebensgemeinschaft des treibenden Golfkrautes. Ztschr. Morphol. Ökol. Tiere 25. **Toriumi, M.** 1952. Paludicella articulata. Sci. Repts. Tohoku Univ., ser. 4, Biol. 19. **Ulrich, B.** 1890. Paleozoic Bryozoa. Geol. Survey Illinois 8, pt. II, Paleontology. **Valkanov, A.** 1936. Notizen über die Brackwässer Bulgariens. Annuaire Univ. Sofia, pt. III,

livre 3. 1943. Victorella. Arbeit. Biol. Meeresstation Schwarzen Meer Varna 12.
Van Beneden, P. 1845a. Recherches sur l'organisation des Laguncula [Farrella].
Nouv. Mém. Acad. Roy. Sci. Belles Lett. Bruxelles 18. 1845b. L'anatomie, la
physiologie, et le développement des Bryozoaires. Nouv. Mém. Acad. Roy. Sci.
Belles Lett. Bruxelles 18. 1850. Sur les bryozoaires de la Mer du Nord. Bull.
Acad. Roy. Sci. Belgique, for 1849, 16. **Vélain, C.** 1877. La faune des deux Iles
St. Paul et Amsterdam. Arch. Zool. Exp. Gén. 6. **Vigeland, I.** 1952. Antarctic
Bryozoa. Scient. Results Norwegian Antarctic Exped. 1927–1928, no. 34. **Vigelius,
W.** 1884. Die Bryozoen gesammelt während der dritten und vierten Polarfahrt des
Willem Barents. Bijdragen Dierkunde, Deel III, art. IV, Afl. 11. 1886. Zur
Ontogenie der marinen Bryozoen. Mitt. Zool. Stat. Neapel 6. 1888. Zur Ontogenie
der marinen Bryozoen. Mitt. Zool. Stat. Neapel 8. **Villela, G.** 1948a. Biocromos
de invertebratos marinhos. Memorias Inst. Oswaldo Cruz 46. 1948b. Adeno-
chrome-like pigment of Bugula. Proc. Soc. Exptl. Biol. Med. 68. **Vinogradov, A.**
1953. Elementary chemical composition of marine organisms. Mem. Sears Foundation Marine Research, no. 2. **Visscher, J.** 1927. Nature and extent of fouling of
ships' bottoms. Bull. U.S. Bur. Fisheries 43. **Walther, J.** 1885. Die gestein-
bildenden Kalkalgen des Golfes von Neapel und die Entstehung structurloser Kalk.
Ztschr. Dtsch. Geol. Gesellsch. 37. **Waters, A. W.** 1878. Opercula in the determination of the cheilostomatous Bryozoa. Proc. Manchester Lit. Philos. Soc. 18.
1888. Supplementary report on the Polyzoa. Repts. Scient. Results Voyage
Challenger, Zool. 31. 1892. Gland-like bodies in the Bryozoa. Jour. Linnaean Soc.
London, Zool. 24. 1896. Bryozoa from Rapallo and other Mediterranean localities.
Jour. Linnaean Soc. London, Zool. 26. 1898. Observations on Membraniporidae.
Jour. Linnaean Soc. London, Zool. 26. 1900. Bryozoa from Franz Josef Land.
Jour. Linnaean Soc. London, Zool. 28. 1904. Bryozoa. Expedition Antarctique
Belge. Resultats Voyage Belgica, Rapp. Scient., Zool. 2. 1907. Tubucellaria.
Jour. Linnaean Soc. London, Zool. 30. 1909. Marine biology of the Sudanese Red
Sea. Bryozoa. Pt. I. Cheilostomata. Jour. Linnaean Soc. London, Zool. 31. 1910.
Pt. II. Cyclostomata, Ctenostomata. Jour. Linnaean Soc. London, Zool. 31. 1912.
Adeonella with remarks on the Adeonidae. Ann. Mag. Natur. Hist., ser. 8, vol. 9.
1913. Marine fauna of British East Africa and Zanzibar. Bryozoa Cheilostomata.
Proc. Zool. Soc. London. 1914. Bryozoa Cyclostomata, Ctenostomata and Endo-
procta. Proc. Zool. Soc. London. 1918. Marine Bryozoa of the Cape Verde
Islands. Jour. Linnaean Soc. London, Zool. 34. 1923. Mediterranean and other
Cribrilinidae. Ann. Mag. Natur. Hist., ser. 9, vol. 12. 1924. The ancestrula of
Membranipora and other cheilostomatous Bryozoa. Ann. Mag. Natur. Hist., ser. 9,
vol. 14. 1925, 1926. Ancestrulae of cheilostomatous Bryozoa. Ann. Mag. Natur.
Hist., ser. 9, vols. 15–18. **Weiss, C.** 1948. Seasonal occurrence of sedentary marine
organisms in Biscayne Bay, Florida. Ecology 29. **Wester, D.** 1910. Verbreitung
und Lokalisation des Chitins im Tierreich. Zool. Jahrb. Abt. System. 28. **Whiteaves,
J.** 1901. Catalogue of the marine Invertebrata of eastern Canada. Geol. Survey
Canada. **Yanagi, N.,** and **Y. Okada.** 1918. Japanese cheilostomatous Bryozoa.
Annot. Zool. Japonenses 9. **Zirpolo, G.** 1922a. Ricerche sulla rigenerazione del
Zoobotryon. Boll. Soc. Natural. Napoli, for 1920, 33. 1922b. Sullo sviluppo del
Zoobotryon. Monitore Zool. Ital., for 1921, 32. 1923a. Sulla biologia del Zoo-
botryon. Boll. Soc. Natural. Napoli, for 1921, 34, Comunicazioni verbali. 1923b.
Sul ringiovanimento die rami coloniali del Zoobotryon. Arch. Zool. Ital. 10. 1923c.
Sulla genesi della colonie primaverili del Zoobotryon. Boll. Soc. Natural. Napoli 4.
1923d. Ricerche sul rapporto fra sostanza blastogenica e sviluppo dei rami coloniali
nel Zoobotryon. Pubbl. Staz. Zool. Napoli 4. **Zschiesche, A.** 1909. Metamorphose von Alcyonidium. Zool. Jahrb. Abt., Anat. 28.

PHYLACTOLAEMATA

Abricossoff, G. 1927. Über die Süsswasserbryozoen der U.S.S.R. C. R. Acad. Sci. U.S.S.R. 1927A. 1933. Die Süsswasserbryozoen des arktischen Gebietes. Fauna Arctica 6. 1936. Über die geographische Verbreitung von Lophopus crystallinus. Arch. Mus. Zool. Univ. Moscow 3. **Allen, H.** 1882. Vitality of fresh-water polyps. Proc. Acad. Natur. Sci. Philadelphia 34. **Annandale, N.** 1909a. New genus of phylactolaematous Polyzoa. Records Indian Mus. 3. 1909b. New species of Fredericella. Records Indian Mus. 3. 1911. Fauna of British India. Freshwater sponges, hydroids, and Polyzoa. Pt. III. 1912a. Observations on the invertebrate fauna of the Kumaon Lakes. Records Indian Mus. 7. 1912b. Polyzoa associated with certain Gangetic tortoises. Records Indian Mus. 7. 1915. The genus Australella. Records Indian Mus. 11. 1921. Sponges, Hydrozoa and Polyzoa of Seistan. Records Indian Mus. 18. 1922. Polyzoa in the Colombo waterworks. Spolia Zeylanica 12. **Aplin, C.** 1860. Fresh-water Polyzoa in Australia. Ann. Mag. Natur. Hist., ser. 3, vol. 6. **Asper, G.** 1880. Beiträge zur Kenntnis der Tiefseefauna der Schweizerseen. Zool. Anz. 3. **Becker, G.** 1937. Untersuchungen über den Darm und die Verdauung von Bryozoen. Ztschr. Morphol. Ökol. Tiere 33. **Borg, F.** 1936a. Sur quelques bryozoaires d'eau douce nordafricaine. Bull. Soc. Hist. Natur. Afrique du Nord 27. 1936b. Über die Süsswasser Bryozoen Afrikas. Senckenbergiana 18. 1940. Freshwater bryozoan from North Africa. Bull. Soc. Hist. Natur. Afrique du Nord 31. 1941. Über die süsswasserbryozoen Schwedens. Zool. Bidrag 20. **Borodin, N.** 1928. Notes on Pectinatella. Zool. Jahrb. Abt. System. 54. **Braem, F.** 1888. Untersuchungen über die Bryozoan des süssen Wassers. Zool. Anz. 11. 1889a. Statoblastenbildung bei Plumatella. Zool. Anz. 12. 1889b. Die Entwicklung der Bryozoencolonie im keimenden Statoblasten. Zool. Anz. 12. 1890. Untersuchungen über die Bryozoen des süssen Wassers. Zoologica, Stuttgart, vol. 2, Heft 6. 1897. Die geschlechtliche Entwicklung von Plumatella fungosa. Zoologica, Stuttgart, vol. 10, Heft 23. 1908. Die geschlechtliche Entwicklung von Fredericella sultana. Zoologica, Stuttgart, vol. 20, Heft 52. 1911. Bryozoen und deren Parasiten. Trav. Soc. Impér. Natural. St. Pétersbourg, vol. 42, fasc. 2, sect. 1, Zool. 1912. Die Keimung der Statoblasten von Pectinatella und Cristatella. Zoologica, Stuttgart, vol. 26, Heft 67. **Brandwein, P.** 1938. Culture of Pectinatella. Amer. Natural. 72. **Brien, P.** 1936. Reproduction asexuée des phylactolémates. Mém. Mus. Hist. Natur. Belgique, ser. 2, fasc. 3. 1952. Fixation et métamorphose des larves de phylactolémates. C. R. Acad. Sci. Paris 235. 1953. Étude sur les phylactolémates. Ann. Soc. Roy. Zool. Belgique 84. 1955. À propos des bryozoaires phylactolemates. Bull. Soc. Zool. France 79. **Brooks, C.** 1929. Statoblasts and polypides of Pectinatella. Proc. Acad. Natur. Sci. Philadelphia 81. **Brown, C.** 1933. A limnological study of certain fresh-water Polyzoa. Trans. Amer. Microsc. Soc. 52. **Buddenbrock, W. von.** 1910. Beiträge zur Entwicklung der Statoblasten der Bryozoen. Ztschr. Wissensch. Zool. 96. **Calvet, L.** 1904. Bryozoen. Ergebnisse der Hamburger Magalhaenischen Sammelreise 1892–1893, vol. 3. **Colledge, W.** 1917. Lophopus brisbanensis. Proc. Roy. Soc. Queensland 29. **Cori, C.** 1893. Die Nephridien von Cristatella. Ztschr. Wissensch. Zool. 55. **Dahlgren, U.** 1934. Fresh-water bryozoon new to North America. Science 79. **Davenport, C.** 1890. Cristatella. Bull. Mus. Comp. Zool. Harvard College 20. 1904. Fresh-water Bryozoa of the United States. Proc. U.S. Nation. Mus. 27. **Dendy, A.** 1906. Occurrence of Fredericella sultana in New Zealand. Trans. Proc. New Zealand Inst. 39. **Despax, R.** 1926. Bryozoaires rencontrés dans quelques lacs pyrénéens. Bull. Soc. Hist. Natur. Toulouse 54. **De Vries, H.** 1890. Die Pflanzen und Tiere der Rotterdamer Wasserleitung. Bericht

Biol. Untersuch. Crenothrix Comm. zur Rotterdam 1887. **Du Plessis-Gouret, G.**
1884. Faune profonde des lacs de la Suisse. Neue Denkschr. Allg. Schweiz. Gesellsch.
Gesamt. Naturwissensch. 29. **Forel, F.** 1884. La faune profonde des lacs suisses.
Neue Denkschr. Allg. Schweiz. Gesellsch. Gesamt. Naturwissensch. 29. **Geiser, S.**
1934. Distribution of Pectinatella in the United States. Field and Laboratory 2.
1937. Pectinatella an occasional river pest in Iowa. Field and Laboratory 5.
Gerwerzhagen, A. 1913a. Das Nervensystem von Cristatella. Ztschr. Wissensch.
Zool. 107. 1913b. Untersuchungen an Bryozoen. Sitzungsber. Heidelberg Akad.
Wissensch., Math. Naturwiss. Kl. Abt. B. Biol. Wissensch. Abhandl. 9. **Goddard, E.**
1909. Australian freshwater Polyzoa. Proc. Linnaean Soc. New South Wales 34.
Graupner, H. 1929. Haltung und Aufzucht von Süsswasserbryozoen. *In* **E.**
Abderhalden (ed.), *Handbuch der biologischer Arbeitsmethoden*, Abt. 9, Teil 2. 1930.
Zur Kenntnis der feineren Anatomie der Bryozoen. Ztschr. Wissensch. Zool. 136.
Hartmeyer, R. 1909. Bryozoa. *In* **A. Brauer** (ed.), *Die Süsswasserfauna Deutsch-*
lands, Heft 19. **Hastings, Anna.** 1929a. Phylactolaematous Polyzoa from the
Transvaal. Ann. Mag. Natur. Hist., ser. 10, vol. 3. 1929b. Little known phylacto-
laematous Polyzoa. Ann. Mag. Natur. Hist., ser. 10, vol. 3. **Heding, S.** 1938.
Freshwater Bryozoa. Zoology of Iceland 4, pt. 66b. **Herwig, E.** 1913. Knospung
bei den Bryozoen. Arch. Naturgesch. 79, Abt. A, Heft 12. **Hickmann, V.,** and
E. Scott. 1932. Plumatella repens in Tasmania. Papers Proc. Roy. Soc. Tasmania.
Houghton, W. 1860. Fredericella sultana found in the winter. Ann. Mag. Natur.
Hist., ser. 3, vol. 6. **Hurrell, H.** 1927. Ecology of fresh-water Polyzoa in East
Anglia. Jour. Roy. Microsc. Soc., ser. 3, vol. 47. **Hyatt, A.** 1866, 1868. Observa-
tions on Phylactolaemata. Proc. Essex Inst. 4, 5. **Jenkin, P.** 1936. Alkaline
lakes of Kenya. Ann. Mag. Natur. Hist., ser. 10, vol. 18. **Judd, W.** 1950. Pec-
tinatella in Hamilton, Ontario. Canadian Field Natural. 64. **Jullien, J.** 1885.
Monographie des bryozoaires d'eau douce. Bull. Soc. Zool. France 10. **Kafka, J.**
1887. Die Süsswasserbryozoen Böhmens. Arch. Naturwiss. Landesdurchforsch.
Böhmen 6, no. 2. **Korotneff, A.** 1892. Myxosporidium bryozoides. Ztschr.
Wissensch. Zool. 53. **Kraepelin, K.** 1885. Die Fauna der Hamburger Wasser-
leitung. Abhandl. Naturwiss. Verein Hamburg 9. 1887. Die deutschen Süss-
wasserbryozoen I. Abhandl. Gebiete Naturwiss., Naturwiss. Verein Hamburg 10.
1892. II. Abhandl. Gebiet Naturwiss., Naturwiss. Verein Hamburg 12. 1893.
Über afrikanische und südamerikanische Süsswasserbryozoen. Verhandl. Naturwiss.
Vereins Hamburg, ser. 3, vol. 1, no. 6. 1906. Eine süssbryozoe aus Java. Mitt.
Natur. Hist. Mus. Hamburg 23. 1914. Land- und Süsswasserfauna Deutsch-
Südwestafrika. *In* **W. Michaelsen** (ed.), *Ergebnisse der Hamburger Deutsch-Südwest*
Afrikanischen Studienreise I. **Kunike, G.** 1925. Nachweis und Verbreitung
organischer Skeletsubstanzen bei Tieren. Ztschr. Vergl. Physiol. 2. **Lacourt, A.**
1948. Fresh-water Bryozoa from Belgian Congo. Revue Zool. Bot. Africaine 40.
Lerner, H. 1954. Zur Kenntnis des Feinbaues der Flottoblastenschalen von Pluma-
tella und Cristatella. Ber. Oberhess. Gesellsch. Natur- und Heilk. Giessen, Natur-
wiss. Abt. 27 (Festschrift W. J. Schmidt). **Levander, K.** 1901. Fauna- und Algen-
flora der süssen Gewasser an der Murmanküste. Acta Soc. Fauna Flora Fennica
20, no. 8. 1908. Verbreitung der Süsswasserbryozoen in Finnland. Meddel. Soc.
Fauna Flora Fennica 34. **Loppens, K.** 1902. Les bryozoaires d'eau douce. Ann.
Biol. Lacustre 3. **Marcus, E.** 1925. Bryozoa. *In* **P. Schulze** (ed.)., *Biologie der*
Tiere Deutschlands, Lief. 14. 1926a. Beobachtungen und Versuche an lebenden
Süsswasserbryozoen. Zool. Jahrb. Abt. System. 52. 1926b. Sinnesphysiologie und
Nervensystem der Larve von Plumatella. Verhandl. Dtsch. Zool. Gesellsch. 31.
1934. Über Lophopus crystallinus. Zool. Jahrb. Abt. Anat. 58. 1941. Sobre
Bryozoa do Brazil. Zoologia, Univ. Sao Paulo, Brazil, no. 5. 1942. Sobre Bryozoa

do Brasil II. Zoologia, Univ. Sao Paulo, Brazil, no. 6. **Marcus, Eveline.** 1946. New Brazilian form of Fredericella sultana. Communicaciones Zool. Mus. Hist. Natur. Montevideo 2, no. 31. 1953. Bryozoa from Lake Titicaca. Zoologia, Univ. Sao Paulo, Brazil, no. 18. 1955. Polyzoa. Percy Sladen Trust Expedition to Lake Titicaca. Trans. Linnaean Soc. London, ser. 3, vol. 1. **Meissner, M.** 1893. Neue Süsswasser Bryozoe aus Brasilien. Sitzungsber. Gesellsch. Naturforsch. Freunde Berlin. **Morse, W.** 1930. Chemical constitution of Pectinatella. Science 71. **Müller, A.** 1914. Histologie des Darmtraktes der Plumatella. Verhandl. Mitteil. Siebenbürg. Verein Naturwiss. Hermannstadt 65 (German text in Festschrift suppl.). **Nitsche, H.** 1868. Beiträge zum Anatomie und Entwicklungsgeschichte der Phylactolaematen. Arch. Anat. Phys. Wissensch. Med. 1874. Knospung der Süsswasserbryozoen. Sitzungsber. Naturforsch. Gesellsch. Leipzig. 1875. Knospung der Bryozoen. Ztschr. Wissensch. Zool. 25, suppl. **Odell, W.** 1899. Notes on fresh-water Polyzoa. Ottawa Naturalist 13. **Oka, A.** 1891. Observations on fresh-water Polyzoa. Jour. Coll. Sci. Univ. Tokyo 4. 1895. On the so-called excretory organ of fresh-water Polyzoa. Jour. Coll. Sci. Univ. Tokyo 8. 1907. Zur Kenntnis der Süsswasserbryozoenfauna von Japan. Annot. Zool. Japonenses 6. 1908. Eine neue Gattung von Süsswasserbryozoen. Annot. Zool. Japonenses 6. **Otto, F.** 1921. Regulationsvermögen einiger Süsswasserbryozoen. Arch. Entw'-mech. Organ. 47. **Prenant, M., and G. Bobin.** 1956. Bryozoaires I. Entoproctes, phylactolèmes, cténostomes. Faune de France 60. **Richard, J.** 1896. Sur la faune de quelques lacs éléves du Caucase. Bull. Soc. Zool. France 21. 1897. Entomonostracés recueillis à Jan Mayen et à Spitzberg. Bull. Soc. Zool. France 22. **Ridley, S.** 1887. Characters of Lophopus with a new species from Australia. Jour. Linnaean Soc. London, Zool. 20. **Risley, P.** 1940. Photographs of living Lophopodella carteri. Turtox News 18, no. 7. **Robertson, Alice.** 1900. Papers from the Harriman Alaska Expedition VI. Bryozoa. Proc. Washington Acad. Sci. 2. **Rogick, Mary.** 1934. Studies on fresh-water Bryozoa. I. The occurrence of Lophopodella carteri in North America. Trans. Amer. Microsc. Soc. 53. 1935a. Studies II. Bryozoa of Lake Erie. Trans. Amer. Microsc. Soc. 54. 1935b. Studies III. Development of Lophopodella carteri. Ohio Jour. Science 35. 1936. Studies IV. Variation of statoblasts of Lophopodella carteri. Trans. Amer. Microsc. Soc. 55. 1937a. Studies V. Some additions to Canadian fauna. Ohio Jour. Science 37. 1937b. Studies VI. Finer anatomy of Lophopodella carteri. Trans. Amer. Microsc. Soc. 56. 1937c. Culturing freshwater Bryozoa. *In* P. Galtsoff et al. (eds.), *Culture methods for invertebrate animals*. 1938. Studies VII. Viability of dried statoblasts of Lophopodella carteri. Trans. Amer. Microsc. Soc. 57. 1939. Studies VIII. Larvae of Hyalinella punctata. Trans. Amer. Microsc. Soc. 58. 1940a. Studies IX. Additions to New York Bryozoa. Trans. Amer. Microsc. Soc. 59. 1940b. Studies XI. The variability of dried statoblasts of several species. Growth 4. 1940c. An ecological effect of the New England hurricane. Ohio Jour. Science 40. 1941a. Studies X. Occurrence of Plumatella casmiana in North America. Trans. Amer. Microsc. Soc. 60. 1941b. Resistance of fresh-water Bryozoa to desiccation. Biodynamica 3. 1941c. Supplementary note on the effect of the 1938 hurricane. Ohio Jour. Science 41. 1943a. Studies XIII. Additional Plumatella casmiana data. Trans. Amer. Microsc. Soc. 62. 1943b. Studies XIV. Occurrence of Stolella indica in North America. Ann. New York Acad. Sci. 45. 1945a. Studies XV. Hyalinella punctata growth data. Ohio Jour. Science 45. 1945b. Studies XVI. Fredericella australiensis. Biol. Bull. 89. **Rogick, Mary, and C. Brown.** 1942. Studies XII. A collection from various sources. Ann. New York Acad. Sci. 43. **Rogick, Mary, and H. Van der Schalie.** 1950. Studies XVII. Michigan Bryozoa. Ohio Jour. Science 50. **Rousselet, C.** 1904. New fresh-water polyzoon from Rhodesia. Jour. Quekett Microsc. Club, ser. 2, vol. 9. **Rüsche, E.** 1938. Nahrungsaufnahme und Nahrungsauswertung bei Plumatella fungosa. Arch. Hydrobiol. 33. **Schölzel, G.** 1951. Statoblasten und Larven von Cristatella im Lichte der Vitalfärbung. Zool. Anz. 146. **Schroeder, O.** 1910. Buddenbrockia plumatellae. Ztschr. Wissensch. Zool. 96. 1912a. Weitere Mitteilungen zur Kenntnis der Buddenbrockia plumatellae. Verhandl. Naturhist. Mediz. Verein Heidelberg, new ser. 11, fasc. 3. 1912b. Zur Kenntnis der Buddenbrockia plumatellae. Ztschr. Wissensch. Zool. 102. 1914. Beiträge zur Kenntnis einiger Microsporidien. Zool. Anz. 43. **Schulze, P.** 1924. Die Nachweis und die Verbreitung des Chitins. Ztschr. Morphol. Ökol. Tiere 2. **Tanner, V.** 1932. Ecological and distributional notes on the Bryozoa of Utah. Proc. Utah Acad. Sci. 9. **Toriumi, M.** 1941–1943. Studies on fresh-water Bryozoa of Japan I-V. Sci. Repts. Tohoku Univ., ser. 4, Biol. 16, 17. 1951. Taxonomical study on fresh-water Bryozoa. I. Fredericella sultana. Sci. Repts. Tohoku Univ., ser. 4, Biol. 19. 1952a. Taxonomical study. III. Plumatella osburni. Sci. Repts. Tohoku Univ., ser. 4, Biol. 19. 1952b. Taxonomical study IV. Plumatella javanica. Sci. Repts. Tohoku Univ., ser. 4, Biol. 19. 1952c, 1954a. Taxonomical study VI, VII. Plumatella emarginata. Sci. Repts. Tohoku Univ., ser. 4, Biol. 19, 20. 1954b. Taxonomical study VIII. Plumatella fruticosa. Sci. Repts. Tohoku Univ., ser. 4, Biol. 20. 1955a. Toxonomical study IX. Plumatella repens. 1955b. X. Plumatella casmiana. 1955c. XI. Stephanella hina. 1955d. XIII. Hyalinella punctata. 1955e. XIV. Hyalinella toanensis. Sci. Repts. Tohoku Univ., ser. 4, Biol. 21. 1956a. XV. Pectinatella gelatinosa. 1956b. XVI. Lophopodella carteri. 1956c. XVII. General considerations. Sci. Repts. Tohoku Univ., ser. 4, Biol. 22. **Vorstman, Adrianna.** 1928a. Some fresh-water Bryozoa from West Java. Treubia 10. 1928b. Some fresh-water Bryozoa from East Java. Treubia 10. **Ward, H.** 1896. A biological examination of Lake Michigan. Bull. Michigan Fish Comm., no. 6. **Wesenberg-Lund, C.** 1896. Biologiske Studier over Ferskvandsbryozoer. Vidensk. Meddel. Dansk. Naturhist. Foren., ser. 5, vol. 8. 1907. Fredericella sultana and Paludicella ehrenbergi in Greenland. Meddel. om Grönland 34. **Whipple, G.** 1910. *Microscopy of drinking water.* 2 ed. **Wiebach, F.** 1952. Über den Ausstoss von Flottoblasten bei Plumatella. Zool. Anz. 149. 1953. Über den Ausstoss von Flottoblasten bei Plumatellen. Zool. Anz. 151. 1954a. Über Plumatella fruticosa. Arch. Hydrobiol. 49. 1954b. Proliferationsknospung bei Süsswasserbryozoen. Mikrokosmos 42. **Wilcox, Alice.** 1906. Locomotion in young colonies of Pectinatella. Biol. Bull. 11. **Williams, S.** 1921. Larval colonies of Pectinatella. Ohio Jour. Science 21. **Zander, E.** 1897. Untersuchungen zum Verständnisse der Iodreaktion des Chitins. Arch. Ges. Physiol. 66. **Zschokke, F.** 1900. Die Tierwelt in den Hochgebirgsseen. Neue Denkschr. Schweiz. Gesellsch. Ges. Naturwissensch. 37. 1906. Tiefenfauna des Vierwaldstättersee. Arch. Hydrobiol. 2. 1910. Die Tiefenfauna hochalpiner Wasserbecken. Verhandl. Naturforsch. Gesellsch. Basel 21. 1911. Die Tiefseefauna der Seen Mitteleuropas. Monogr. und Abhandl. Internation. Revue Ges. Hydrobiol. Hydrograph. 4.

CHAPTER XXI

THE LOPHOPHORATE COELOMATES—PHYLUM BRACHIOPODA

I. HISTORICAL

An exhaustive history of the phylum with bibliography was given by Muir-Wood (1955). According to this account fossil brachiopods were known in the early Middle Ages and were figured in the late sixteenth century. Drawings of brachiopod shells by Fabio Colonna (or Fabius Columna) in 1616 under the name of *conchae anomiae* are reproduced in Muir-Wood's book. Articles about and illustrations of brachiopods continued to be published throughout the eighteenth century. The shells were variously called anomites, conchites, terebratulites, and similar names. Linnaeus in 1758 placed the then known recent and fossil brachiopods under the name *Anomia* (actually the valid name of a bivalve) in his group Testacea under Vermes. It will be recalled that Linnaeus classified all invertebrates except insects as Vermes. Pallas (1766) seems to have been the first to figure the internal surface of the valves with their structures, and Gründler (1774) illustrated a valve of a "terebratule" with the lophophore in place. In 1797 Cuvier gave some preliminary notes on the anatomy of *Lingula* and suggested that it and other known brachiopods ought to be assembled into a special family of acephals. In 1798 Cuvier divided the mollusks into cephalopods, gastropods, and acephals, placing the three known brachiopod genera *Terebratula*, *Lingula*, and *Orbicula* under the last, which also included bivalves, tunicates, and barnacles. In 1802 Cuvier stated that brachiopods differ much from bivalves, lacking both head and foot, and suggested that they should constitute a fourth class of mollusks but failed to provide any name for such a class. His name brachiopodes in the French form for the group in question first appeared in 1805. The first use of the Latin form Brachiopoda is to be credited to Duméril (1806), who also separated brachiopods, including barnacles, as a distinct fifth order of mollusks; the other four were cephalopods, pteropods, gastropods, and acephals (including tunicates).

Brachiopods continued to be regarded as mollusks throughout the first part of the nineteenth century. In consequence of researches on the anatomy of brachiopods Owen (1835) placed them as a separate order of acephalous mollusks intermediate between these and tunicates, and later (1843) divided the acephalous mollusks into three classes, tunicates, brachiopods, and bivalves. It was also in 1843 that Milne Edwards created the name Molluscoides (later usually rendered Molluscoida or Molluscoidea) for the strange combination of Bryozoa and Tunicata, and Hancock (1850) as a result of a study of fresh-water bryozoans declared their relation to tunicates "too obvious to be questioned." In a later study of brachiopods, in which he corrected several previous misunderstandings as to their anatomy, Hancock announced (1857) the relationship of Bryozoa and Brachiopoda while still retaining the idea of a tunicate affinity. In 1853, T. H. Huxley, having learned of Hancock's view, suggested that brachiopods ought to be included with bryozoans and tunicates in the Molluscoides, and in 1854, having himself made some outstanding researches on brachiopod anatomy, concurred in Hancock's conclusion that brachiopods are allied to bryozoans. In 1869 Huxley rejected the idea of mollusk affinity of brachiopods and further supported the group Molluscoida, defined as constituted of the three classes Tunicata, Bryozoa, and Brachiopoda. He noted a "singular fundamental resemblance" between brachiopods and bryozoans. However, Gegenbauer (1859) and Haeckel (1874) continued to regard brachiopods as a group of mollusks.

Doubt that the brachiopods are mollusks had already been voiced by Steenstrup (1847–1849), who supported an annelid affinity, and this view was strongly urged by Morse (1870, 1873), who also effectively argued against a molluscan affinity. However, Dall (1870, 1871) rather demolished the idea of annelid affinity and upheld that of molluscan affinity, also supporting the relationship to tunicates, and hence the concept Molluscoidea as defined by Huxley. This mollusk-versus-annelid controversy continued for some time, and the idea of a tunicate affinity also persisted. Some sense was injected into the argument by Brooks (1877, 1879), who proved on good anatomical grounds that brachiopods cannot be closely related to either tunicates or annelids but that their nearest affinities are with bryozoans. However, he went on to relate bryozoans to mollusks by way of the veliger larva of the latter. In the meantime embryological studies on brachiopods had been made, and these led the brothers Hertwig in their famous article *Die Coelomtheorie* (1881) to point out the striking similarity in mode of enterocoel formation between brachiopods and chaetognaths. They rejected the supposition of mollusk affinity and accepted that of annelid affinity. Caldwell (1882) indicated, although rather vaguely, the affinity of phoronids, brachiopods, and bryozoans, but dragged in the sipunculoids as possible relatives. Blochmann (1892a) supported Caldwell's view and proposed the name Prosopygia for the assemblage of phoronids, bryozoans, brachiopods, and sipunculoids, and the idea of sipunculoid affinity had a brief acceptance about that time. Blochmann remarked that the idea of molluscan affinity had by then been abandoned, and the strange concept of tunicate affinity passed into oblivion after Kowalevsky (1866) proved the chordate nature of tunicate larvae.

Caldwell (1882) seems to have been the first to suggest affinity between Phoronida, Bryozoa, and Brachiopoda, but some of the points on which he based this conclusion are erroneous. He did not suggest any name for the assemblage of the three phyla with a lophophore. This remained for Hatschek, who in 1888 proposed the name Tentaculata to include the three groups Brachiopoda, Phoronida, and Ectoprocta. It is to the further merit of Hatschek that he omitted the Entoprocta from this assemblage. Although Hatschek's arrangement was not immediately accepted and various other arrangements continued to be proposed, even to the present time, there cannot be any doubt of the essential validity of Hatschek's concept. The same concept under the name Molluscoidea or Molluscoida appeared in some texts, notably Parker and Haswell's *Textbook of Zoology*, but this name should fall into oblivion as originally proposed for an impossible combination. The name Tentaculata, however, is rather unfortunate, as it had previously been used by Lankester in quite a different sense; further, tentacles occur in many other groups of animals. Lophophorata, or something of the kind, would have been a more appropriate term. A name Lophophora was in fact created by Schneider (1902) but was limited to *Phoronis* and Bryozoa, excluding Brachiopoda.

As already indicated, Brachiopoda is here regarded as a distinct phylum, allied to Phoronida and Ectoprocta.

II. CHARACTERS OF THE PHYLUM

1. Definition.—The Brachiopoda, or lamp shells, are coelomate Bilateria that are enclosed in a bilaterally symmetrical bivalve shell attached directly or by way of a stalk (pedicle) and composed of dorsal and ventral valves lined by a mantle lobe of the body wall, and that are provided with a lophophore, an open circulatory system with a dorsal contractile vesicle, and one or two pairs of metanephridia, also acting as gonoducts.

2. General Characters.—The most obvious part of a brachiopod is the shell, of which the two valves are dorsal and ventral in position, in contrast to the bivalved mollusks, in which they are lateral. The valves are bilaterally symmetrical but are more or less dissimilar. In one group of brachiopods, known as hinged, or *articulate*, brachiopods, the valves are hinged together posteriorly by a tooth-and-socket arrangement, whereas in the other group, the unhinged, or *inarticulate*, brachiopods, the valves are held together by muscles only. Most brachiopods are permanently attached to objects by a protruding fleshy stalk, the *pedicle*, or *peduncle*, of varying length; but in the family Lingulidae the very long pedicle is merely thrust into sand; hence members of this family may change location.

The body of the brachiopod occupies only about the posterior third of the interior space between the valves but sends a lobe of body wall, the *mantle*, to line each valve. The space between the mantle lobes, or *mantle cavity*, is largely occupied by the lophophore, which presents various degrees of complexity and varies in shape more than in other lophophorates. The nervous system is centered around the beginning of the digestive tract and includes a small supraenteric and a larger subenteric ganglion. There are well-developed muscles for operating the valves and pedicle as well as muscle fibers in the body wall. The mouth, located centrally in the lophophore, leads by an esophagus into a stomachic enlargement provided with one or more pairs of voluminous digestive glands. The intestine, continuing posteriorly from the stomach, ends blindly without an anus in articulates but opens by an anus into the mantle cavity in inarticulates, either in the median line posteriorly or on the right side after a forward curve. Hence the digestive tract is only exceptionally recurved as in other lophophorates. There is a well-developed coelom that, as typical of lophophorates, may be regarded as subdivided into an unpaired protocoel and paired mesocoels and metacoels. The coelom is crossed by mesenteries and sends tubular extensions into the mantle lobes. The circulatory system consists mainly of a middorsal vessel situated on the digestive tract and branching at both ends; as the blood apparently must return by tissue spaces the system must be regarded as an open one. The so-called heart consists of one or more contractile vesicles attached to the dorsal vessel. The excretory system is represented by one or two pairs of metanephridia, originally mistaken for hearts. Each begins with a funnellike nephrostome opening into the coelom and exits into the

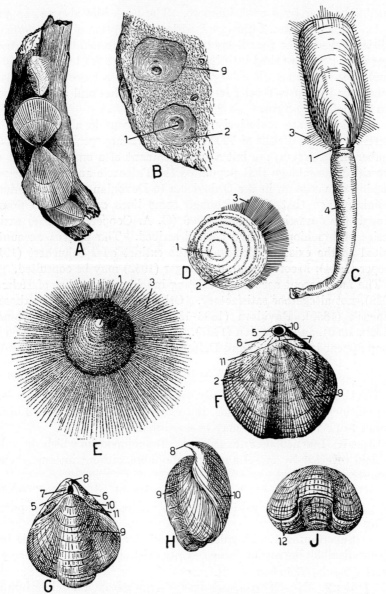

Fig. 183.—Types of brachiopods. *A, Terebratulina retusa* (= *caputserpentis*) on a piece of wood. *B, Crania anomala* on a stone. (*A, B, after Shipley, 1895.*) *C, Lingula. D, Discinisca* (*after Blochmann, 1900*). *E, Pelagodiscus atlanticus* (*after Davidson, 1888*). *F, Terebratella*, from the dorsal side. *G–J, Hemithyris psittacea. G*, dorsal view. *H*, side view. *J*, front view. (*C, F, G–J, after Blochmann, 1912a.*) 1, apex; 2, lines of growth; 3, setae; 4, pedicle; 5, foramen; 6, palintrope; 7, deltidial plates; 8, beak; 9, dorsal valve; 10, ventral valve; 11, hinge line; 12, marginal sinuosities.

mantle chamber by a nephridiopore. The nephridia also act as gonoducts. Brachiopods are dioecious, with the exception of a few hermaphroditic species. The gonads are borne on the peritoneum or mesenteries. Eggs and sperm are shed into the sea, or the eggs are brooded in brood pouches or in the mantle cavity. In either case a free-swimming larva eventuates that after a brief free existence attaches and metamorphoses into the definitive form.

Brachiopods are exclusively marine and occur in all seas from the intertidal zone to depths of 5000 m. The existing species, about 260 in number in 68 genera, are but a small remnant of a once abundant and diversified assemblage that populated the Paleozoic and Mesozoic seas, reaching a maximum in the Ordovician to Devonian eras and gradually declining since that time, although some lines continued to flourish through the Jurassic. About 30,000 (G. A. Cooper, in literis) extinct species of brachiopods have been described. The present account is limited to the existing species; for the extinct ones Schuchert (1913), Cooper (1944), Moore (1952), and Roger (1952) may be consulted.

The most recent account of existing brachiopods is that of Helmcke (1939), not altogether satisfactory. Other useful accounts are those of Hancock (1859), Davidson (1886–1888), Shipley (1895), Blochmann (1892b, 1900), and Thomson (1927). Bibliographies of literature on the group appear in Davidson and Dalton (1886) and Muir-Wood (1955).

III. CLASSIFICATION OF THE PHYLUM

The classification considers only existing forms. For complete classification, including extinct forms, the paleontological works cited above, further Muir-Wood (1955), may be consulted.

Class I. Inarticulata or Ecardines. Brachiopods in which the valves are held together by muscles only; lophophore without internal skeletal support; anus present.

Order 1. Atremata. Mineral constituent of the shell calcium phosphate; pedicle attached to the ventral valve, but both valves participating in its passage.

Superfamily 1. Lingulacea. Shell elongate, thin; pedicle long, tubular, flexible; burrowing forms. Only existing family Lingulidae with genera *Lingula*, *Glottidia*.

Order 2. Neotremata. Pedicle emerging from a notch or foramen confined to the ventral valve.

Superfamily 2. Discinacea. Mineral constituent of the shell calcium phosphate; apex of both valves more or less central, hence valves somewhat circular, with concentric growth lines. Only existing family Discinidae with genera *Discina*, *Discinisca*, and *Pelagodiscus*.

Superfamily 3. Craniacea. Mineral constituent of the shell

calcium carbonate; cemented when adult by the ventral valve, pedicle wanting. Only existing family Craniidae with genera *Crania, Craniscus.*

Class II. Articulata, or Testicardines. Valves locked together posteriorly by a tooth-and-socket arrangement; mineral constituent of the shell calcium carbonate; pedicle emitted through the ventral valve; lophophore with internal skeletal support; anus wanting.

In the past it was customary to divide the articulates into the orders Protremata and Telotremata after Beecher (1891), which were later prefaced by an order Palaeotremata for the Thecideidae by Thomson (1927). But in recent years these orders have met with so much criticism that they have fallen into disuse, and at present there is no agreement at all as to the orders of the Articulata. Muir-Wood (1955) recognized only suborders, and Williams (1956) would not commit himself to either orders or suborders but suggested that articulates should be grouped with reference to six genera: *Orthis, Pentamerus, Strophomena, Rhynchonella, Spirifer,* and *Terebratula.* All students of the group recognize superfamilies, reckoned at 24 by Williams (1956), 25 by Muir-Wood (1955), and there is considerable agreement as to the definitions of these superfamilies. The following superfamilies contain existing articulates.

Superfamily 4. Thecideacea. Lophophore schizolophous, with its lobes fitting into hollows of the dorsal valve. One existing family Thecideidae with existing genera *Lacazella* and *Thecidellina.*

Superfamily 5. Rhynchonellacea. Lophophore spirolophous without internal skeletal supports or with crura only; with two pairs of nephridia. With two existing families, Dimerellidae and Rhynchonellidae, with a number of genera.

Superfamily 6. Terebratulacea. Lophophore typically plectolophous with a short supporting loop. Existing family Terebratulidae, with many genera and species.

Superfamily 7. Terebratellacea. Lophophore mostly plectolophous with a long supporting loop recurved at its anterior end. Existing families, Terebratellidae, Megathyridae, Platidiidae, Kraussinidae, Zeilleriidae, Dallinidae.

IV. ANATOMY AND EMBRYOLOGY

It must be remarked, to begin with, that very few of the existing brachiopods have been well studied anatomically. Although these studies are now 50 to 100 years old, they still remain the chief sources of information and illustrations. Anatomical researches are available on *Lingula* (Hancock, 1859; Gratiolet, 1860; Davidson, 1886–1888; Blochmann, 1900), *Lacazella,* under the name *Thecideum* (Lacaze-Duthiers, 1861), *Crania* (Joubin, 1886; Blochmann, 1892b), *Discinisca,* under the name *Discina* (Joubin, 1886; Blochmann, 1900), *Hemithyris,* under the

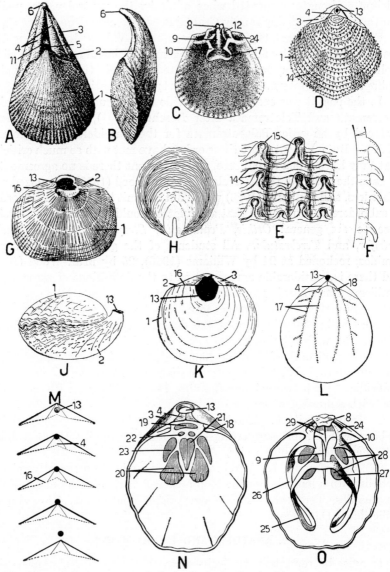

Fig. 184.—Shell characters. *A–C, Agulhasia davidsoni*, with triangular ventral valve. *A*, dorsal view. *B*, side view. *C*, interior of dorsal valve. *D, Tegulorhynchia döderleini*, from the dorsal side, showing spines (*after Davidson*, 1886a). *E*, small bit of *D*, showing spine structure (*after Leidhold*, 1922). *F*, profile view of spines of *Pantellaria echinata*. *G, Mühlfeldtia truncata*, with foramen moved into apex of dorsal valve. *H*, ventral valve of *Discinisca*, showing slot. *J*, side view of shell of *Magellania*. *K, Platidia*, from dorsal side, with foramen mostly in dorsal valve. (*F, G, K, after Fischer and Oehlert*, 1891.) *L*, interior of ventral valve of *Laqueus*, showing impressions of mantle canals. *M*, schemes, showing possible positions of the foramen relative to the ventral valve. (*A–C, M, after Thomson*, 1927.) *N, Magellania*, inside of ventral valve. *O, Magellania*, inside of dorsal valve. (*N, O, after Reed*, 1895, *original in Davidson*, 1886b.) 1, dorsal valve; 2, ventral

name *Rhynchonella* (Hancock, 1859; Davidson, 1886–1888), *Terebratulina* (Hancock, 1859; Davidson, 1886–1888), *Magellania*, under the name *Waldheimia* (Hancock, 1859; Davidson, 1886–1888); and *Argyrotheca*, under the name *Argiope* (Shipley, 1883; Schulgin, 1884). Especially the superb illustrations in Hancock (1859) and Blochmann (1892, 1900) have been repeatedly reproduced, for they are the best available figures of the internal anatomy. The articles of van Bemmelen (1883), Beyer (1886), Schaeffer (1926), and Senn (1934) are mainly histological.

1. Shell.—The brachiopod shell is composed of two separate valves that are bilaterally symmetrical but dissimilar. The valves are dorsal and ventral with reference to the enclosed body of the animal, although the ventral valve is usually uppermost in the normal orientation of the attached animal in life. The ventral valve, also called *pedicle valve*, from its relation to the pedicle, is generally larger than the dorsal valve, also called *brachial valve*, from its relation to the lophophore. The valves are usually of oval shape, somewhat elongated, with rounded anterior margin and tapering to the attached posterior end (Fig. 183*A*). They may also be transversely broadened (Fig. 184*G*) or triangular (Fig. 184*B*) or nearly circular as in discinids and craniids (Fig. 183*B*) or oblong as in lingulids (Fig. 183*C*). The valves are generally convexly curved, often greatly so (Fig. 183*H*); frequently the ventral valve is more convex than the dorsal one, and the latter may be flat or even concave (Fig. 190*D*); both valves are rather weakly convex in lingulids (Fig. 210*C*). The valve surface may be smooth or nearly so but commonly is marked with lines or ridges known as growth lines that parallel the margin, and also with radiating grooves, flutings, or plications. The latter throw the anterior margin into sinuous curves (Fig. 183*J*); the arrangement is such that usually a median projecting scallop of one valve fits into a median indentation of the other. Much attention is paid by brachiopod specialists to these sinuosities, and the usual series of names has been invented to cover the various types. Spination of the valves was not uncommon in extinct brachiopods but in existing forms is known in only two unrelated species, *Tegulorhynchia döderleini* (Fig. 184*D*), family Rhynchonellidae, dredged off Japan (Davidson, 1886; Leidhold, 1922), and *Pantellaria echinata*, family Kraussinidae, dredged off Africa (Fischer and Oehlert, 1891). In the former both valves are spinous, in the latter only the ventral valve. The spines are very small projections along the growth ridges where these

---

valve; 3, palintrope; 4, deltidial plates; 5, delthyrium; 6, beak; 7, short type of loop; 8, cardinal process; 9, medium septum; 10, crural process; 11, pedicle collar; 12, socket ridges; 13, foramen; 14, growth lines; 15, spine; 16, hinge line; 17, mantle canals; 18, hinge teeth; 19, impression of central connective-tissue bundle of pedicle; 20, diductor scars; 21, adductor scars; 22, scars of accessory diductors; 23, scars of ventral adjustor muscles of pedicle; 24, dental socket; 25, brachidium, long type of loop; 26, descending part of loop; 27, recurved part of loop; 28, scars of two heads of adductor muscles; 29, hinge plates.

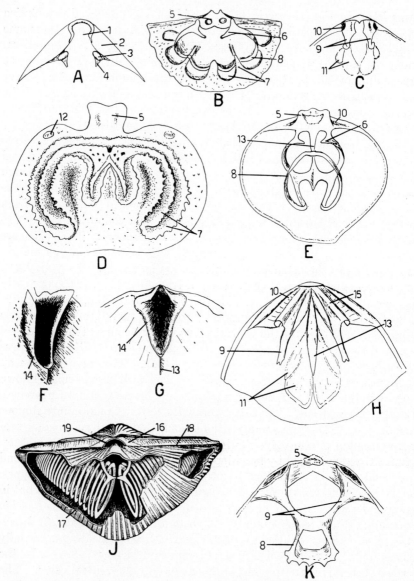

Fig. 185.—Shell characters (continued). *A*, posterior part of ventral valve of *Macandrevia cranium*, showing dental plates (*after Fischer and Oehlert*, 1891). *B*, dorsal valve of *Megathyris*, showing hollows and ridges supporting lobes of lophophore. *C*, *Hemithyris psittacea*, posterior end of dorsal valve, showing crura. *D*, dorsal valve of *Lacazella* with complex ridges supporting lophophore (*after Lacaze-Duthiers*, 1861). *E*, dorsal valve of *Terebratella* with long loop attached to medium septum. *F*, *G*, posterior end of dorsal valve of *Anastrophia* (extinct), showing spondylium (*after Cooper*, 1944). *F*, side view. *G*, front view. *H*, rhynchonellacean with crura and hinge plates. (*B*, *C*, *E*, *H*, *after Davidson*, 1887.) *J*, extinct spiriferacean from the Carboniferous, with spires (*after Reed*, 1895). *K*, *Terebratulina*, with short loop (*after Davidson*, 1886b). 1, delthyrium; 2,

intercept the radiating ridges of the plications. Leidhold (1922) has shown that the spines of *Tegulorhynchia* are simply upfolds of the growth ridges (Fig. 184*E*), but those of *Pantellaria* appear otherwise (Fig. 184*F*), although not satisfactorily described. Numerous figures of the shells of existing brachiopods appear in Davidson (1886–1888), and extinct shells are illustrated in Schuchert (1913), Cooper (1944), Roger (1952), and Moore (1952).

Existing shells range in size from 5 to about 80 mm., measured along the longer axis, but extinct brachiopods reached a width of around 375 mm., over a foot. Present shells are mostly of a yellowish-gray color, but some are almost transparent and glasslike and others show bright colors as orange, pink, or red, often as radiations.

It seems to be habitual with paleontologists to create a formidable terminology to cover every minute detail of extinct exoskeletons, and this state of affairs also exists with brachiopods. A long list of terms applied to the brachiopod shell appears in Moore (1952). It is a question how many of these terms are really necessary, and only a few will be explained here. The center of shell growth from which the growth lines and radial plications emanate, usually at or near the posterior end of the valves, is termed the *apex*. In some inarticulates, however, as discinids and craniids, the apex is more or less centrally located, and consequently the valves are more or less circular in contour with concentric growth lines and conical in profile, resembling a limpet (Fig. 183*B, D, E*). In discinids the ventral valve has a posterior notch or slot for the passage of the pedicle (Fig. 184*H*), but no such aperture is necessary in Craniidae since this family lacks a pedicle and the ventral valve is cemented to a substrate. In articulates the apex of the ventral valve is typically extended beyond that of the dorsal valve as a curved *beak* that usually bears a hole for the passage of the pedicle. When viewed in profile such an articulate shell as that of *Magellania* with its upturned beak perforated by a round hole (Fig. 184*J*) suggests a Roman lamp, whence the name of lamp shells applied to brachiopods.

The gap that would be left between the beak and the hinge line with the dorsal valve is filled in by a recurved part of the ventral valve termed the *palintrope* (Fig. 183*F, G*). The palintrope originally had a central triangular notch, the *delthyrium*, open to the hinge line, for the passage of the pedicle (Fig. 184*A*), but generally this notch is more or less closed off from the hinge line by a plate, the *deltidium*, or a pair of *deltidial plates*, leaving a rounded hole, the *foramen*, for the pedicle (Fig. 183*F, G*).

---

palintrope; 3, hinge teeth; 4, dental plates; 5, cardinal process; 6, crural process; 7, ridges and hollows of dorsal valve; 8, calcareous loop; 9, crura; 10, dental socket; 11, scars of two heads of adductor muscles; 12, scar of lateral adductor; 13, median septum; 14, spondylium; 15, hinge plate; 16, deltidial plates; 17, spire; 18, hinge line; 19, foramen.

Usually there is a pair of deltidial plates that advance across the basal part of the delthyrium (Fig. 184*N*). Concomitantly the foramen shifts its position toward the apex of the ventral valve and even beyond the apex (Fig. 184*M*). The cause of these changes seems to be increasing curvature of the beak that would make the pedicle less effective if it remained in the original position. In a small group of Terebratellacea, including the existing genera *Amphithyris*, *Platidia*, and *Pantellaria*, the foramen has migrated in the opposite direction, toward the dorsal valve, and the cardinal region of the latter has been absorbed, leaving a semicircular notch occupied by the pedicle (Fig. 184*K*). Names have been supplied by Buckman (1916, 1919) and Thomson (1927) to indicate the various positions that the foramen may assume.

The foregoing features are much less developed in the dorsal valve. The palintrope if present is small; its notch is called *notothyrium*, and the plate closing off the notch is the *chilidium*, or *chilidial plates* if more than one.

Varied structures are seen on the inner surface of the dried valves. Features common to both inarticulate and articulate valves are the muscle scars, that is, the impressions left by muscle attachments (Fig. 184*N*, *O*), and the impressions left by the coelomic channels of the mantle lobes (Fig. 184*L*). These channels are tubular, branching extensions from the main coelom into the mantle lobes. More conspicuous features of the inner surfaces of articulate valves are the articulation devices and the lophophoral supports. As inarticulate valves are held together by muscles only, they lack articulation devices and in a few cases may open widely (Fig. 191*C*). Articulate valves are locked together posteriorly by a tooth-and-socket device which is part of the valve structure and is to be seen only by taking the valves apart and inspecting the inner surface. This device permits the valves to open along their anterior margins by a limited gape only (Fig. 210*D*), mostly not more than an angle of 10°, and further, the valves can only open and close and are incapable of other movements. The external line of meeting of the dorsal and ventral valves on which the movement occurs is termed the *hinge line*.

The tooth part of the articulating device is found on the ventral valve in the form of a pair of small projections, the *hinge teeth*, situated along the free edge of the palintrope (Fig. 184*L*). These teeth may exist without support, or each may be buttressed by a vertical *dental plate* extending to the valve (Fig. 185*A*). In this latter case the space overhung by the palintrope is partitioned into a median and two lateral compartments, but the former may be subdivided by a vertical medium septum. Fusion of the distal ends of the dental plates produces a U-shaped ridge termed *spondylium* (Fig. 185*F*, *G*). The socket part of the valve articulation is borne at the posterior end of the dorsal valve. This consists of a deep

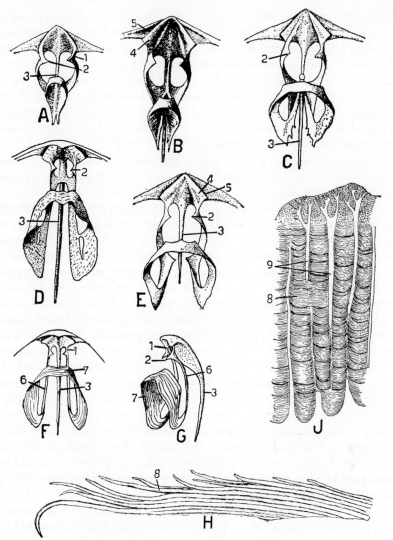

FIG. 186.—Shell characters (continued). *A–E*, stages of alteration of the brachidium during ontogeny of *Dallina septigera* (*assembled by Thomson*, 1927, *from various authors*). *F*, adult stage. *G*, adult stage, seen from the side. *H*, section of the ventral valve of *Discinisca*, showing lamellate structure; outer surface above (*after Blochmann*, 1900). *J*, section through the dorsal valve of *Crania*, showing mantle papillae (*after Blochmann*, 1892b). 1, crura; 2, crural process; 3, median septum; 4, hinge plates; 5, dental socket; 6, descending limb of loop; 7, recurved part of loop; 8, lamellae of shell; 9, mantle papillae.

indentation, or *dental socket,* under each edge of a median flat-topped elevation, the *cardinal process,* that fits between the teeth when the latter are locked into the dental sockets (Fig. 184O).   Supporting ridges, inner and outer, to either side of the dental sockets are variously known as *socket ridges, socket plates,* or *hinge plates;* they are confluent with the cardinal process.   A median septum may also be present.   *Cardinalia* is a convenient collective term for the skeletal structures of the beak region of the dorsal valve that serve in valve articulation and for attachment of muscles and the skeletal supports of the lophophore.

As already noted, it is the dorsal valve that is related to the lophophore.   The inner surface of this valve may be sculptured into ridges and hollows to accommodate the lobulations of the lophophore as in *Megathyris* (Fig. 185*B*); especially complicated sculpturings are seen in *Lacazella* (Fig. 185*D*) and other Thecideidae.   In most articulates, however, the lophophore is usually more or less supported by *internal* skeleton termed *brachial support,* or *brachidium,* absent in inarticulates.   In its simplest state, the brachidium consists of a pair of prongs, the *crura* (singular, *crus*), that project anteriorly into the lophophore base from the inner hinge plates (Fig. 185*C, H*); the crura may be free or attached to the dorsal valve by vertical *crural plates,* and when these are united distally the whole is termed *cruralium.*   The crura generally bear a medially directed sharp process, the *crural process* (Fig. 185*E*).   Crura obviously furnish support only to the lophophore base, yet, curiously enough, are typical of the Rhynchonellacea, which have spirolophous lophophores. Usually the crura are continued forward inside the lophophore by a calcareous ribbon that forms a loop.   This may be a simple short loop, as in the Terebratulacea, thence known as short-looped forms (Fig. 185*K*), or a long loop extended forward to the ends of the lophophore arms and then recurved backward as in the Terebratellacea, thence known as long-looped forms.   The long recurved loop has been rendered familiar by textbook figures of the dorsal valve of *Magellania* (Fig. 184*O*).   The loop may be free as in *Magellania* or attached to a medium septum of the valve as in *Terebratella* (Fig. 185*E*).   In the extinct group Spiriferacea that had spirolophous lophophores, the calcareous ribbon was also coiled into a *spire* in each arm, accompanying the coils of the arm (Fig. 185*J*).   Spires are wanting in present articulates that have spirolophous lophophores.

It was shown for a number of articulates by study of growth stages that the brachidium passes through extensive changes of form (Fig. 186*A–G*) during ontogeny (Friele, 1877; Douvillé, 1879; Fischer and Oehlert, 1892a; Beecher, 1895b), and these stages, to which the usual formidable names are applied, may resemble the end stages of other genera.   However, "no close agreement exists between the order of succession of patterns of loop as developmental stages in ontogeny and the succession of the same patterns in adult forms geologically during phylogeny" (Elliott, 1953a). Changes of brachidial pattern can be brought about only by resorption in some places and new formation elsewhere. Great importance is naturally placed by paleontologists on brachidial changes during geological time; some recent articles on this subject are those of Elliott (1953a), Stehli (1956a), and Williams (1956).

A puzzling matter is the frequent lack of relation between the shape of the lophophore and the extent of the brachidial support. The spirolophous type of lophophore is supported in Rhynchonellacea only by the crura. The Terebratulacea with a short loop and the Terebratellacea with a long loop have exactly the same type of lophophore in general (plectolophous), which therefore is poorly supported in the former superfamily. It appears, in fact, that the lophophore is mainly stiffened by the peculiar cartilagelike connective tissue of which it is largely composed and the discrete calcareous spicules abundantly found in many species in the connective tissue of mantle lobes and body wall, as well as in the lophophore.

The brachiopod shell is covered externally with a thin organic layer, the *periostracum*, and a varying amount of organic material, probably chitin, occurs throughout the shell. Otherwise, chemical analysis shows that the shell is of two types, phosphatic, characteristic of inarticulates (except Craniidae), in which the main inorganic constituent is calcium phosphate, and calcareous, characteristic of Craniidae and articulates, in which this constituent is calcium carbonate in the form of calcite. In phosphatic shells the organic material may be uniformly distributed throughout the mineral part as in discinids, where the shell is composed of lamellae diagonal to the surface (Blochmann, 1900; Fig. 186*H*), whereas in lingulids chitinous and phosphatic layers parallel to the surface alternate (Gratiolet, 1860; Chapman, 1914; Fig. 187*A*). Chapman has shown that the relative widths of the chitinous and phosphatic layers vary in different species of *Lingula*. Delicate tubules (which in life contain mantle papillae) at right angles to the surface may be present. The shell of *Crania* has a thick brown periostracum over calcareous lamellae crossed by vertical tubules (Fig. 186*J*) that branch in the periostracum. Articulate shells consist of a thin periostracum, said not to be a continuous sheet, below this an outer calcareous layer having a fine fibrous texture, and internal to this an inner calcareous layer made of long prismatic fibers of calcite that are slightly oblique to the shell surfaces (Fig. 187*B*). Each such fiber is secreted by one epidermal cell of the outer mantle epidermis (Williams, 1956; Fig. 187*B*). The calcareous layers may be crossed by vertical tubules, and such shells are then termed *punctate* because the inner ends of these tubules appear like dots on the inner surface of the dead shell (Fig. 187*F*). Shells devoid of tubules are termed

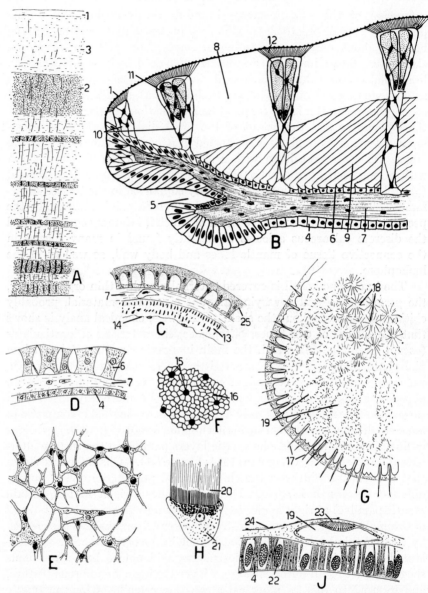

FIG. 187.—Shell characters (concluded), body wall. *A*, section through a valve of *Lingula*. *B*, scheme of a longitudinal section through the mantle edge and valve of an articulate (*after Williams*, 1956). *C*, section of anterior body wall of *Crania*. *D*, section of mantle lobe of *Crania*. (*C, D, after Blochmann*, 1892b.) *E*, connective tissue of an articulate (*after van Bemmelen*, 1883). *F*, inner surface of valve of articulate *Laqueus*, showing punctations and mosaic. *G*, mantle edge of *Terebratulina*, with setae and spicules (*after Hancock*, 1859). *H*, base of seta with large cell, *Discinisca*. *J*, mantle wall of *Lingula* to inner side of marginal sinus, with gland cells. (*A, H, J, after Blochmann*, 1900.) 1, periostracum; 2, calcareous layer; 3, chitinous layer; 4, inner mantle epidermis; 5, mantle

impunctate. There is also a category *pseudopunctate*, in which the calcareous layers contain calcitic rods that dissolve more readily than the rest of the valves; hence their inner ends also leave dots on the inner surface of the valves. The inner ends of the prisms of the inner calcareous layer form a pattern termed the *mosaic* on the inner surface of dead valves, seen only under magnification (Fig. 187*F*). The pattern of the mosaic has been considered of some value as a specific character. The tubules mentioned in the foregoing account are filled in life with papillae of the outer epidermis of the mantle. Skeletal formations such as the hinge mechanism are parts of the prismatic layer.

Each valve begins as a minute plate, the *protegulum*, presumably composed of periostracum, and enlarges by deposition along the edges of the protegulum, usually along its anterior and lateral margins; hence the protegulum remains at the posterior end of the valve, becoming the apex, and the valve elongates in the anteroposterior direction and widens laterally. Such growth is recorded by the characteristic lines or ridges on the valves that parallel the external contour. A slight posterior deposition produces the palintrope. In more or less circular shells as those of discinids and craniids deposition has occurred around the whole periphery of the protegulum; hence the apex remains in a more or less central position and the valves have a low conical shape in profile. The lines on the shell are here circular, concentric with the apex. Although called lines of growth, these markings probably represent periods of arrested or retarded growth. Obviously the periostracum and outer calcareous layer of articulate shells can be laid down only along the advancing mantle edge and hence cannot get later additions, whereas the prismatic layer is secreted over the entire outer epidermis of the mantle and therefore can be thickened later.

2. Body Wall.—The body of the animal occupies only the posterior part of the space between the valves. Its dorsal and ventral walls are adherent to the undersurface of the valves; its anterior, lateral, and to some extent posterior walls are free. The anterior wall is called in paleontological works diaphragm, but this bad term is here rejected. Anteriorly the body wall sends out a thin flat extension dorsally and ventrally to line those parts of the valves not occupied by the animal's body. These extensions are known as *mantle lobes*, or more simply, mantle, and the space between them, occupied mostly by the arms of the lophophore, is the *mantle cavity*.

---

groove; 6, outer mantle epidermis; 7, connective tissue; 8, fibrous calcareous layer; 9, prismatic layer; 10, mantle papillae; 11, secretory cells at end of papilla; 12, brush connecting to periostracum; 13, muscle layer of body wall; 14, peritoneum; 15, punctations; 16, mosaic; 17, setae; 18, spicules; 19, coelomic canal; 20, seta base; 21, large cell; 22, gland cell; 23, peritoneal thickening in wall of coelomic canal; 24, peritoneum of marginal sinus; 25, epidermis.

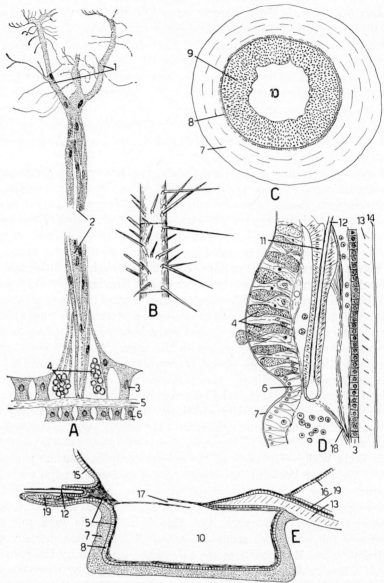

Fig. 188.—Body wall (concluded), pedicle. *A*, mantle papilla of *Discinisca*. *B*, part of a seta of *Discinisca*, showing thorns. *C*, cross section of pedicle of *Lingula* (*after Schaeffer*, 1926). *D*, section through the mantle near edge of *Lingula*, showing glandular zone (*after Beyer*, 1886). *E*, scheme of longitudinal section of the pedicle of *Discinisca*. (*A, B, E, after Blochmann*, 1900.) 1, arborescent tip of papilla; 2, elongated epidermal cells of papilla; 3, outer mantle epidermis; 4, gland cells; 5, connective tissue; 6, inner epidermis of mantle; 7, cuticle; 8, epidermis; 9, muscle layer; 10, coelomic lumen; 11, epidermal follicle of seta; 12, seta; 13, shell; 14, periostracum; 15, anterior body wall; 16, posterior body wall; 17, canal to main coelom; 18, retractor of the seta; 19, mantle.

The histology of brachiopods is imperfectly known. The best accounts are those of Blochmann (1892b, 1900), who unfortunately worked only with inarticulates; van Bemmelen (1883) and Prenant (1928) have given some information about articulates, whereas Schaeffer (1926) again worked with *Lingula*. The body is everywhere clothed with a one-layered epidermis, varying in height in different regions and becoming stratified over main nervous masses, according to van Bemmelen (Fig. 201*B*). Blochmann found that in inarticulates the epidermal cells are often separated basally by vacuoles (Fig. 187*C*, *D*), but Prenant reported the cells in complete contact in *Terebratulina*. The epidermal cells are interspersed, usually sparsely, but thickly in some regions, with gland cells containing large spheres of secretion (Fig. 187*J*). Beneath the epidermis is found a layer of connective tissue of varying thickness, usually composed of a homogeneous material containing stellate mesenchymal cells that may unite into loose networks (Fig. 187*E*). Fibrils are sometimes present in the connective tissue and are regarded by Blochmann as muscle fibers. The parts of the body wall adherent to the inner surfaces of the valves lack a muscle layer, but in the free parts of the body wall there are generally present beneath the connective-tissue layer one or more layers of muscle fibers (Fig. 187*C*) running in a general longitudinal direction and interspersed with connective tissue. Finally the body wall is lined by thin flat peritoneum, generally ciliated or flagellated.

The mantle lobes necessarily have the same histological construction as the body wall proper, since they are extensions of the latter. As such they are double with one layer of body wall in contact with the underside of the valve and the other layer facing the mantle cavity. The coelom one would expect between the outer and inner mantle walls is reduced by fusions of the connective-tissue layer to the coelomic channels already mentioned. There is, further, present in *Discinisca* and *Lingula* a *marginal sinus* that runs in the mantle near its edge and is not connected with any other body spaces.

The outer mantle epidermis is cuboidal to columnar and besides secreting much of the shell produces the *mantle papillae* that occupy the vertical tubules, or canals, in the valves of punctate shells. In *Crania* the papillae are peculiar in being arborescently branched at their outer ends (Fig. 186*J*) and are described by Blochmann as composed of very elongated epidermal cells (Fig. 188*A*). In articulate punctate shells the papillae begin at the mantle edge as little buds of the outer epidermis; as these move back with the forward advance of the mantle edge in growth, the epidermal cells stretch out to continue to fill the tubule as it elongates, and at the outer ends some become glandular and adhere to the periostracum by a brush of delicate processes (Prenant, 1928; Williams, 1956; Fig. 187*B*). The cells of the outer mantle epidermis in *Terebratulina* are

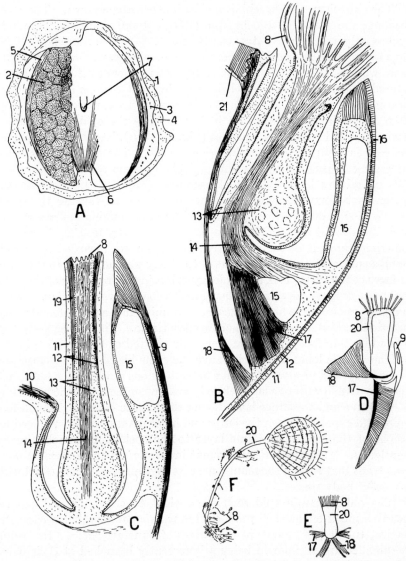

Fig. 189.—Pedicle (concluded). *A*, pedicle of *Discinisca*, seen from inside to show muscles filling lumen (*after Blochmann*, 1900). *B*, longitudinal section of pedicle of *Terebratulina*. *C*, longitudinal section of pedicle of *Hemithyris psittacea*. *D*, *E*, schemes of the peduncular muscles of articulates. *D*, side view. *E*, ventral view. (*B–E*, *after Ekman*, 1896.) *F*, *Chlidonophora chuni*, with long pedicle having lateral filaments (*after Chun*, 1903). 1, pedicle wall turned back; 2, rectus muscle (shown on one side only); 3, connective tissue of pedicle wall; 4, cuticle of pedicle; 5, external oblique muscles; 6, median oblique muscles; 7, inner end of coelomic canal to main coelom; 8, attachment filaments; 9, ventral valve; 10, dorsal valve; 11, cuticle; 12, epidermis; 13, loose connective tissue of pedicle; 14, central dense strand of connective tissue; 15, coelomic spaces; 16, ventral mantle; 17, ventral adjustor of the pedicle; 18, dorsal adjustor of the pedicle; 19, lamellate chitin; 20, pedicle; 21, dorsal mantle.

stiffened by firm fibrils (tonofibrils) that are extensively developed at sites of muscle attachment (Prenant); Blochmann found such fibrillar epidermal cells in inarticulates only at the latter sites (Fig. 191*D*).

The inner mantle epidermis is mostly cuboidal with each cell provided with a single cilium or well ciliated in *Terebratulina* (Prenant, 1928). The cells become more columnar toward the mantle edge, where a deep groove, the *mantle groove*, is the site of origin of the periostracum and also bears the setae. The periostracum thus begins to the inner side of the shell edge and curves over this edge to reach the free surface (Fig. 193*A*). In most existing brachiopods, the mantle edge is armed with setae or bristles (Fig. 187*G*) that may be very long, especially in discinids (Fig. 183*E*). They are produced in the mantle groove in deep tubular epidermal invaginations, or follicles, lined by a one-layered epidermis and having at the bottom a very large cell that presumably secretes the seta (Fig. 187*H*). A follicle may bear more than one seta. The setae are hard, yellowish bristles, usually spoken of as chitinous; they may be marked with rings and often bear lateral barbs or thorns (Fig. 188*B*). They are movable by muscles attached to the follicle base (Fig. 193*A*) and probably have a general sensory and protective function. The setae are borne by both mantle lobes and are generally longer anteriorly and decrease in length posteriorly. Just internal to the mantle groove there is frequently present a zone of tall, enlarged cells of the inner mantle epidermis that are filled with glandular secretion, said by Blochmann not to be of mucous nature. This glandular zone (Fig. 188*D*) is so well developed in *Discinisca* and *Lingula* that it is visible to the naked eye by its whitish color in the opened animal.

3. Pedicle.—Except for those species as *Crania* in which the ventral valve is directly cemented to a substrate, brachiopods are attached by way of a cylindrical stalk termed pedicle, or peduncle, that issues from the posterior end. In structure, development, and relation to the valves the pedicle differs in inarticulates and articulates. In lingulids the pedicle is long and flexible (Fig. 183*C*) and issues directly between the slightly notched posterior ends of the two valves, but is attached to the ventral valve only. It arises (Yatsu, 1902a; Ashworth, 1915) as an elevation of the posterior end of the ventral mantle lobe, including an evagination of the main coelom. As such it consists of the body-wall layers and encloses throughout life a coelomic lumen continuous with the main body coelom. In the mature state the leathery wall consists of a thick cuticle of concentric layers, a one-celled columnar epidermis, a thin layer of connective tissue, a thick muscle layer, and the lining peritoneum (Fig. 188*C*). The muscle layer is composed of spiral crisscrossed fibers attached at both ends to the connective-tissue layer (Blochmann, 1900).

In discinids the short pedicle issues from a notch or slot at the poste-

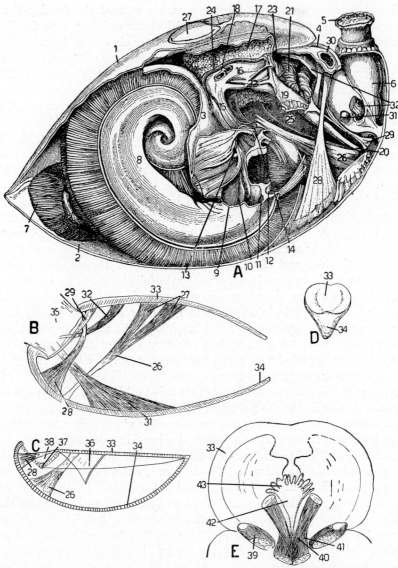

FIG. 190.—Muscular system. *A*, side view of *Magellania* with muscles and viscera in place (*redrawn by Huxley, 1877, from Hancock, 1859*). *B*, scheme of the valve muscles of articulates (*after Schulgin, 1884*). *C*, scheme of valve muscles of *Platidia* with foramen displaced into cardinal region (*after Fischer and Oehlert, 1891*). *D*, *Lacazella mediterranea*, twice natural size. *E*, muscles of *Lacazella*. (*D, E, after Lacaze-Duthiers, 1861.*) 1, dorsal mantle; 2, ventral mantle; 3, anterior body wall; 4, dorsal body wall; 5, attached end of pedicle; 6, pedicle exposed by cutting open surrounding body wall; 7, lateral arm of lophophore; 8, median spiral arm of lophophore; 9, place where other lateral lophophoral arm was cut off; 10, large arm canal; 11, small arm canal; 12, brachial gutter; 13, mouth; 14, subenteric ganglion; 15, esophagus; 16, stomach; 17, digestive glands of one side; 18, ducts of digestive gland of other side; 19, intestine; 20, blind end of intestine; 21, nephro-

rior end of the ventral valve (Fig. 184*H*), is also an outgrowth of the ventral mantle lobe (Ashworth, 1915), and consists of the usual layers (Blochmann, 1900): thick cuticle, epidermis, connective-tissue layer, thin layer of muscles, and peritoneum. Its coelom communicates with the general body coelom by only a narrow canal (Fig. 188*E*). Unlike *Lingula,* in which the coelomic lumen of the pedicle remains open throughout life, the originally large coelom of the discinid pedicle becomes filled up with muscles (Fig. 189*A*). There are three pairs of these muscles: a pair of large *rectus* muscles that fill most of the interior of the pedicle, extend from its distal end to insert on the valve adjacent to the slit, and evidently act to shorten the pedicle; a pair of thin *external oblique* muscles close to the wall of the pedicle with fibers slanting obliquely downward in a posteroanterior direction; and the *median oblique* pair, centrally located and converging obliquely in an anteroposterior direction toward the distal end of the pedicle (Fig. 189*A*).

In articulates the pedicle emerges from the beak of the ventral valve through the delthyrium or the foramen formed by the partial closure of the delthyrium by deltidial plates. The pedicle in articulates develops from a posterior lobe of the larva that becomes partly overgrown by the preceding part of the embryo, and thus its proximal end comes to occupy an invaginated position retained throughout life (Fig. 189*B, C*). Being thus largely embraced by the rear ends of the valves and mantle lobes, the pedicle of articulates is very restricted as to movements. It is still further restricted in such genera as *Hemithyris* and *Tegulorhynchia* (belonging to the superfamily Rhynchonellacea), in which the two deltidial plates, instead of meeting above the foramen, curve around the ventral half of the pedicle opening as secondary shell matter, forming then what is termed a *pedicle collar,* really only half a collar. In some cases the collar may complete itself, and the foramen is then of tubular shape.

The protruded part of the pedicle is usually short and thick in articulates and covered with a thick brown cuticle. Its histological construction was elucidated by Ekman (1896; Fig. 189*B, C*). Under the thick cuticle is found a one-layered epidermis, and the whole interior consists of connective tissue, being devoid of muscle fibers and coelom. A central band of denser connective tissue made of longitudinal fibrils (Fig. 189*B, C*) was previously mistaken for a muscle. The muscles that operate the pedicle are attached externally to it and are part of the body musculature,

---

stome; 22, gastroparietal band; 23, heart vesicle; 24, dorsal blood channel; 25, ventral mesentery; 26, adductor muscle; 27, dorsal ends of two heads of adductor muscle of one side; 28, diductor muscle; 29, accessory diductor; 30, attachment of diductor muscles on cardinal process; 31, ventral adjustor of pedicle; 32, dorsal adjustor of pedicle; 33, dorsal valve; 34, ventral valve; 35, pedicle; 36, median dorsal septum; 37, hinge tooth; 38, foramen; 39, lateral adductors; 40, median adductors; 41, diductors; 42, digestive tract; 43, digestive glands.

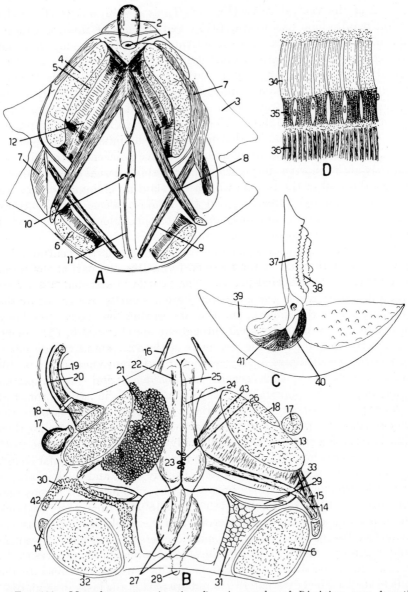

FIG. 191.—Muscular system (continued). *A*, muscles of *Discinisca*, seen from the
dorsal side (*after Blochmann*, 1900). *B*, muscles of *Crania*, seen from the dorsal side.
C, *Lacazella* with dorsal valve erected (*after Lacaze-Duthiers*, 1861). *D*, histology of muscle
attachment. (*B*, *D*, *after Blochmann*, 1892b.) 1, mouth; 2, esophagus; 3, opened body
wall; 4, anterior adductor, lateral part; 5, anterior adductor, median part; 6, posterior
adductor; 7, lateral oblique; 8, internal oblique; 9, posterior oblique; 10, entrance into
coelomic canal for pedicle; 11, nerve for pedicle; 12, connective-tissue partitions for nerve
entry; 13, anterior adductor; 14, superior oblique; 15, inferior oblique; 16, lophophore protractor; 17, lophophore retractor; 18, lophopore elevator; 19, brachial muscle; 20, brachial

considered below. Often the connective tissue forms a bulbous enlargement at the proximal end of the pedicle, as shown in Fig. 189B, C.

In both articulates and inarticulates the distal end of the pedicle, which
may be slightly expanded into an end bulb or ampulla, adheres to the
substrate by rootlike extensions or short papillae (Fig. 189B, C). Such
adhesion is usually so strong that the animal cannot be detached without
injury. *Chlidonophora chuni* (family Terebratulidae), dredged at
2253 m. in the Indian Ocean, is notable for the long slender pedicle bearing lateral and a terminal tuft of adhesive filaments that adhere to small
shells and the like (Fig. 189F). In *Lingula* without adhesive filaments
the distal part of the pedicle is especially glandular and is coated with a
sheath of agglutinated sand grains (Fig. 210C). *Lingula* and the similar
Glottidia are thus not permanently attached and can move about. In
both articulates and inarticulates there are examples of loss of pedicle
either ontogenetically or phylogenetically; such forms are permanently
cemented to the substrate by the ventral valve.

4. Muscular System.—As already indicated, the body wall frequently
contains a muscle layer to the inner side of the peritoneum and there are
further muscles in the mantle lobes and lophophore. Otherwise the
muscles take the form of definite bundles concerned with opening and
closing the valves and operating the pedicle. These bundles are located
in the main coelom, mostly posteriorly, and are revealed by opening the
body wall. They are fewer in number and simpler in arrangement in
articulates than in inarticulates since the former can only open and close
the valves as these are locked together posteriorly whereas inarticulates
can also move the valves upon each other. Varied names applied to the
muscle bundles are found in the literature. Those of Thomson (1927)
derived from Hancock (1859) are here adopted; a quite different set of
names appears in Helmcke (1939), and still others are found in very old
literature. For inarticulates the names of Blochmann (1892b, 1900)
appear most appropriate.

In articulates there are in general three sets of muscles, the *adductors*
or *occlusors* that close the valves, the *diductors* or *divaricators* that open
the valves along their anterior margins, and the *peduncular* muscles, or
muscles of the pedicle. The adductors originate by a pair of contiguous
scars medially near the posterior end of the ventral valve and proceed
almost vertically to the dorsal valve, each forking in two at about the

blood channel; 21, digestive gland, shown on one side only; 22, esophagus; 23, stomach;
24, dorsal mesentery; 25, main dorsal blood channel; 26, heart vesicles; 27, intestine; 28,
anus; 29, nephrostome; 30, gonad; 31, ilioparietal band containing blood plexus; 32,
peritoneal sheath of muscle; 33, nephridium; 34, prismatic layer shell; 35, modified epidermis
for muscle attachment; 36, muscle fibers; 37, dorsal valve; 38, ridges of dorsal valve; 39,
ventral valve; 40, diductor; 41, median adductor; 42, mantle blood channels; 43, duct
entrance of digestive gland.

middle of its course (Fig. 190*B*).   Hence there are four insertions on the dorsal valve (Fig. 184*O*).   The diductor muscles originate by a pair of scars on the ventral valve anterior to the adductor scars (Fig. 184*N*) and ascend obliquely backward to insert on the cardinal process (Fig. 190*A*). By pulling on this process they depress the posterior end of the dorsal valve, hence raise the anterior margin, but as the leverage is short the muscle needs to be stronger than the adductors.   There are also present two small accessory diductors which extend from the ventral valve behind the adductor scars to the cardinal process (Fig. 190*A*); in some species they are fused to the diductors.   In the small group mentioned above in which the cardinal area has been dissolved away and the foramen occupies its position, the main diductor pair is shifted to lie entirely behind the adductors and extends between the posterior ends of both valves (Fig. 190*C*).   The shell as a whole can be moved only by muscles extending between it and the pedicle.   Of these there are typically present in articulates two pairs of *adjustor* muscles, dorsal and ventral (Fig. 189*D*, *E*). The dorsal adjustors run from the ventrolateral sides of the pedicle to the hinge plates of the dorsal valve or to the valve itself, and the ventral adjustors from the dorsolateral sides of the pedicle to the ventral valve, where their scars are located to the outer side of the adductor scars.   In older works there is also mentioned a median unpaired peduncular muscle (sometimes paired), but this was shown by Ekman (1896) to consist of connective tissue.   It is the central bundle of denser fibrous connective tissue shown in the center of the pedicle in Fig. 189*B*, *C*.   At its attachment to the ventral valve it does in fact leave a transversely elongated scar behind all the other muscle scars (Fig. 184*N*).   The adjustor muscles can obviously be used to move the shell sidewise or up and down.   Further, the diductor and accessory diductor muscles pass close to the proximal end of the pedicle and have some attachment to its connective tissue.   Contraction of these muscles would force the pedicle out, that is, elongate it, hence erect the shell.   Therefore, according to Ekman (1896), any opening of the valves is necessarily accompanied by erection of the animal as a whole.

Lacazella, studied by Lacaze-Duthiers (1861), furnishes an example of an articulate devoid of a pedicle, hence with considerable modification of its muscular equipment.   The very convex ventral valve is fixed to a substrate and is covered as by a lid by the much smaller dorsal valve that can be opened to an erect position perpendicular to the ventral valve (Fig. 191*C*), much wider than is possible in other brachiopods.   The valves are operated by three pairs of muscles, two pairs of adductors and one pair of diductors (Fig. 190*E*).   The adductors that in other articulates are only partly subdivided are here completely divided into two pairs, lateral and median.   The median adductors correspond in their site of

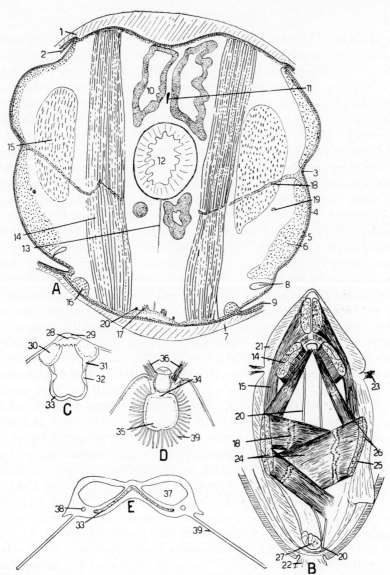

Fig. 192.—Muscular system (continued), lophophore. A, cross section through *Lingula* at the level of the anterior adductors. B, muscular system of *Lingula*, seen from the dorsal side. (*A, B, after Blochmann*, 1900.) C, brachidium of *Dyscolia*. D, disciform lophophore of *Dyscolia*. E, cross section of the lophophore of *Dyscolia*. (*C–E, after Fischer and Oehlert*, 1891.) 1, dorsal valve; 2, dorsal mantle lobe; 3, lateral body wall; 4, epidermis of body wall; 5, connective tissue of body wall; 6, muscle layer of body wall; 7, ventral valve; 8, nephrostome; 9, ventral mantle lobe; 10, digestive gland; 11, main dorsal blood channel; 12, intestine; 13, ventral mesentery; 14, anterior adductor muscle; 15, lateral muscle; 16, attachment external oblique; 17, attachment internal oblique; 18, connective-tissue partition; 19, nerve to muscles; 20, peduncular nerve; 21, opened body wall; 22, pedicle; 23, gastroparietal band; 24, median oblique; 25, external oblique; 26, internal oblique; 27, posterior adductor; 28, cardinal process; 29, site of diductor insertion; 30, site of attachment of dorsal pedicle adjustor; 31, crura; 32, crural process; 33, loop; 34, mouth; 35, lophophore; 36, dorsal pedicle adjustors; 37, large arm canal; 38, small arm canal; 39, tentacle.

541

origin to the adductors of other articulates but originate on small concave plates of the ventral valve; they diverge to their insertions on the dorsal valve.   The lateral adductors are short broad muscles located far later-ally, running between the two valves outside the hinge teeth.   The diductors originate on the ventral valve near the median adductors and insert on the cardinal process of the dorsal valve; pulling on this erects the dorsal valve.   The far lateral position of the lateral adductors is presumed to prevent any sidewise movements of the dorsal valve.

The most complicated muscle arrangements are those of inarticulates since here the muscles act to hold the valves together as well as to open and close them; further, the valves can be moved upon each other in various ways.   Excellent and well-illustrated accounts of the muscles of *Crania*, *Discinisca*, and *Lingula* have been furnished by Blochmann (1892b, 1900).   In *Crania* there are two quite separate pairs of conspicu-ous adductor muscles, anterior and posterior (Fig. 191*B*).   They extend almost vertically between the ventral and dorsal valves; the two members of each pair diverge slightly.   They close the valves, and presumably, if the anterior pair remains relaxed, the posterior pair could open the dorsal valve by pulling on its posterior end.   There are two pairs of long slender oblique muscles.   The superior obliques originate on a central knob of the ventral valve and curve dorsally, passing close behind the anterior adductors, to insert on the dorsal valve just to the outer side of the insertion of the posterior adductors (Fig. 191*B*).   These muscles could rotate the dorsal valve.   The inferior obliques originate on the ventral valve to the outer side of the posterior adductors and curve around near the body wall, passing ventral to the superior obliques, and to the outer side of the anterior adductors, to insert on the anterior body wall.   It will be noticed that there are no definite diductors.   Lifting of the dorsal valve is said to be caused by general contraction of the body wall, including presumably the inferior obliques.   Besides these four pairs of main muscles there are three pairs of minor muscles and an unpaired anal elevator in the median line posteriorly above the anus. The three small pairs are the lophophore protractors, lophophore retrac-tors, and lophophore elevators.   The protractors are a pair of small slim muscles originating at about the center of the dorsal valve and diverging to insert on the anterior body wall at the base of the lophophore arms. The retractors pass from the bases of the lophophore arms to insert on the dorsal valve to the outer side of the anterior adductors; Blochmann has shown that they are really muscle fibers in the wall of a coelomic diver-ticulum.   The elevators originate on the dorsal valve to the anterior side of the anterior adductors and extend into the arm bases up to the connective-tissue partition from which the muscle in the lophophore arm originates, hence appears as if continuous with the latter (Fig. 191*B*).

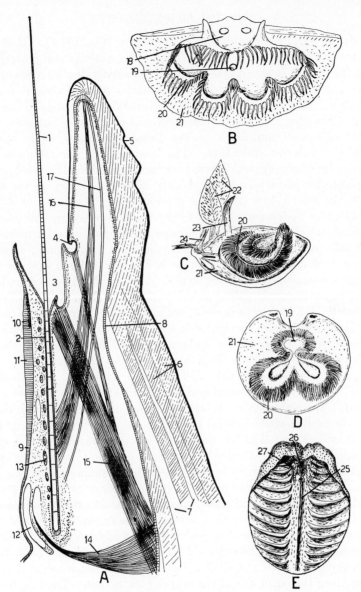

Fig. 193.—Muscular system (concluded), lophophore (continued). *A*, longitudinal section through the mantle edge of *Lingula* (*after Blochmann*, 1900). *B*, ptycholophous lophophore of *Megathyris* (*after Davidson*, 1887). *C*, zygolophous lophophore of *Magadina cumingi* (*after Davidson*, 1852). *D*, lophophore of *Platidia* (*after Davidson*, 1880). *E*, ventral valve of extinct oldhaminacean (*Oldhamina*) with ridges indicative of lophophoral lobulations (*after Pompeckj*, 1912). 1, seta; 2, setal follicle; 3, mantle groove; 4, starting point of periostracum; 5, periostracum; 6, chitinous layers of valve; 7, calcareous layers of valve; 8, outer mantle epidermis; 9, inner mantle epidermis; 10, marginal nerve; 11, thickened epidermis of glandular zone; 12, mantle canal; 13, marginal muscles; 14, levator of seta; 15, retractor of seta; 16, protractor of seta; 17, flexor of seta; 18, cardinal process; 19, mouth; 20, lophophore; 21, dorsal valve; 22, diductor muscles; 23, adductor muscle; 24, pedicle adjustors; 25, median septum; 26, adductor scar; 27, diductor scar.

A similar arrangement obtains in *Discinisca* (Fig. 191*A*). Here, too, there are two well-separated pairs of adductors, anterior and posterior, of which the former is much the larger and is subdivided into lateral and median parts. Lateral, internal, and posterior pairs of oblique muscles are present. The lateral obliques are flat muscles that proceed from the ventral valve along the body sides, pass along the outer surfaces of the anterior adductors, and insert on the dorsal valve close to the anterior part of the anterior adductors. The internal obliques originate on a median ridge of the ventral valve, pass backward along the inner surface of the anterior adductors, and, strongly diverging, insert on the dorsal valve to the outer side of the posterior adductors. The posterior obliques pass obliquely backward, ventral to the internal obliques, and insert on the dorsal valve, converging to the inner side of the posterior adductors.

Lingula and other lingulids have the most complicated muscular equipment of any existing brachiopods and are able to execute more vigorous movements than other types. In *Lingula* there is found near the esophagus the usual pair of anterior adductors (Fig. 192*B*), but only a single posterior adductor is present, not median, but somewhat to the left. There is separable from its right side a small flat bundle whose fibers run differently from those of the main muscle. The oblique muscles are especially well developed in *Lingula*, consisting of three pairs, termed by Blochmann median, internal, and external obliques. Of these the median[1] are the most powerful and conspicuous; they are further asymmetrical. The right one is a broad flat muscle that extends from the left side of the middle of the ventral valve obliquely upward to the right side of the dorsal valve. The left one occurs as two separate bundles on the right side of the ventral valve and extends obliquely to the left side of the dorsal valve, where its bundles meet to a common insertion (Fig. 192*B*). As both valves are movable, it is a question which is the origin and which the insertion of these muscles. The internal obliques are a pair of small thin muscles that attach medially on the ventral valve between the anterior adductors and pass obliquely laterally to attach to the dorsal valve along the outer side of the median obliques (Fig. 192*B*). The external obliques are similar but lateral to the internal obliques, passing along the outer side of the anterior adductors. There is, further, present a pair of lateral muscles that extend along the lateral walls from about the middle of the ventral valve forward to the outer side of the anterior adductors to converge to a median insertion on the median ridge of the dorsal valve.

The foregoing muscles course through the main coelom from which

---

[1] From discrepancies between the text and figures in Blochmann's account it appears that the median obliques are labeled internal, and vice versa, in all his figures; this was previously noticed only by Yatsu (1902a).

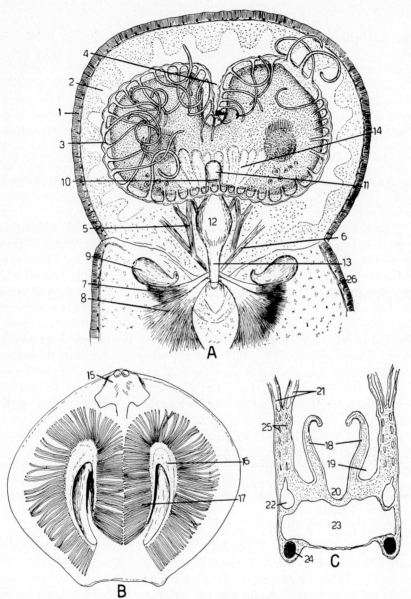

Fig. 194.—Lophophore (continued). *A*, schizolophous lophophore of *Argyrotheca* (*after Schulgin*, 1884). *B*, plectolophous lophophore of *Magellania* (*after Fischer and Oehlert*, 1891). *C*, section through arm of plectolophous lophophore of *Terebratalia*. 1, mantle edge; 2, mantle canals; 3, lophophore; 4, median indentation occupied by septum of valve; 5, adductor muscle; 6, diductor muscle; 7, dorsal adjustor pedicle; 8, ventral adjustor pedicle; 9, brood pouch; 10, mouth; 11, esophagus; 12, stomach; 13, intestine; 14, digestive glands; 15, cardinal process; 16, lateral arm of lophophore; 17, median arm of lophophore; 18, brachial fold; 19, brachial groove; 20, brachial gutter; 21, tentacles; 22, small arm canal; 23, large arm canal; 24, cross section of skeletal loop; 25, coelomic canals to tentacles; 26, marginal nerve.

they are bounded by a peritoneal sheath, clearly shown in Fig. 191*B*. In articulates, the muscles are tendinous toward their insertions (Fig. 190*B*) and sometimes elsewhere, but those of inarticulates appear to be fleshy throughout. In inarticulates the muscles often show transverse plates of connective tissue by which the nerve enters (Fig. 192*B*). The attachment of muscle fibers to the undersurface of the shell is by way of an altered epidermis of stiffened, striated cells containing tonofibrils (Blochmann, 1892b; Yatsu, 1902a; Prenant, 1928; Fig. 191*D*). The muscles in general are of the smooth type, but some (Hancock, 1857; van Bemmelen, 1883) claim that the posterior fork of the adductor muscle of articulates is cross-striated; but this is denied by others (e.g., Shipley, 1883) and seems improbable.

The mantle edge and the setae are provided with muscle fibers that seem to belong to the subperitoneal muscle layer of the body wall. They have been described in detail only by Blochmann (1900) for *Lingula*, in which they are better developed than in any other existing brachiopod. In the connective tissue of the mantle edge are found outer and inner bands of circular fibers that parallel the edge and diagonal fibers between these two bands. These presumably serve to retract the mantle margin. The muscles that operate the setae are located in the marginal mantle sinus. They comprise the retractors of the setae that run from the undersurface of the valve diagonally forward to the mantle groove inserting on the periostracal groove and the outer end of the setal follicles; the protractors of the setae that run diagonally backward from the underside of the shell edge to the inner end of the setal follicles; the flexors of the setae that parallel the protractors but lie nearer the shell; and the levators of the setae that originate on the inner surface of the shell opposite the inner end of the follicles and curve around these follicles to insert on the inner mantle wall, thus by their contraction raising the inner ends of the setae. These muscles are shown in Fig. 193*A*. The marginal sinus is further crossed by muscle fibers that would act to compress it and move the contained fluid.

5. Lophophore.—The lophophore is an outgrowth of the anterior body wall that projects into the mantle cavity and fills the greater part of this cavity, being usually quite voluminous relative to the size of the body of the animal. It presents far greater variations of shape in brachiopods than in the other lophophorate phyla but in general consists of lobulations edged with a row of tentacles (also called cirri and filaments). In the simplest type, known as *trocholophous*, the lophophore is a disciform area about the mouth; this type occurs in *Gwynia* (known specimens suspected, however, of being juveniles) and *Dyscolia* (Fig. 192*C–E*). The tentacle-bearing edge is here rather short, and subsequent evolution of the lophophore aims at increasing the length of this edge, hence the number of

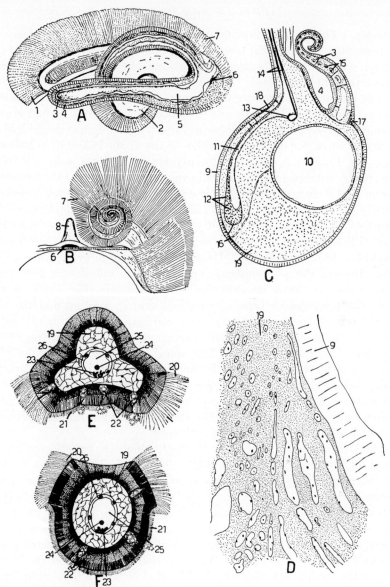

Fig. 195.—Lophophore (concluded). *A*, plectolophous lophophore of *Terebratulina*,
partly dissected to show structure (*after Hancock*, 1859). *B*, one arm of spirolophous
lophophore of *Discinisca*. *C*, cross section of arm of spirolophous lophophore of *Lingula*.
D, cartilaginous connective tissue of lophophore. (*B–D, after Blochmann*, 1900.) *E*, cross
section of outer tentacle of *Neothyris*. *F*, cross section of inner tentacle of *Neothyris*.
(*E*, *F*, *after Richards*, 1952.) 1, lateral arm of lophophore; 2, median arm of lophophore;
3, brachial fold; 4, brachial groove; 5, brachial gutter; 6, mouth; 7, tentacular fringe; 8,
esophagus; 9, epidermis; 10, large arm canal; 11, small arm canal; 12, brachial muscle; 13,
brachial blood channel; 14, branches of 13 to tentacles; 15, muscles of brachial fold; 16,
lower arm nerve; 17, main arm nerve; 18, accessory arm nerve; 19, connective tissue; 20,
lateral cilia; 21, frontal cilia; 22, gland cells; 23, longitudinal muscle fibers; 24, blood
channel; 25, coelomic lumen; 26, peritoneum.

tentacles.   This process first takes the form of simple lobulations.   In
the beginning stage of this, termed *schizolophous,* the anterior side of the
lophophoral disk indents medially, making the lophophore somewhat
bilobulate as in *Argyrotheca* (Fig. 194*A*), *Amphithyris,* and *Pelagodiscus.*
Further indentations produce up to four lobes in existing genera, *ptycholophous* type, seen in *Lacazella* and *Megathyris* (Fig. 193*B*); extinct genera
are said to have had up to 20 lobes as known by the supporting ridges on
the dorsal valve, for often such a ridge occurs at the indentation between
lobes (Fig. 193*E*).   A variant of the ptycholophous type, seen in *Platidia*
(Fig. 193*D*) with two lobes, differs in that these lobes are twisted on the
median part.   In a different line of evolution, the lophophore lengthens
laterally into a pair of arms.   This stage, called *zugolophous* (more
correctly, *zygolophous*), is frequently passed through ontogenetically but
is said (Elliott, 1953a) to occur in the adult state only in *Magadina cumingi*
(Davidson, 1852; Fig. 193*C*).   Usually this condition evolves along two
lines.   In one, the *plectolophous* type, a median coiled arm grows out
between the two simple lateral arms as in *Magellania* (Fig. 194*B*); in the
other, the *spirolophous* type, the median arm is wanting and the two
lateral arms elongate still further and coil into helicoidal spirals as in
inarticulates generally (Fig. 195*B*), further in existing articulates of the
superfamily Rhynchonellacea.   The spiral coils face dorsally in both
types.   The plectolophous type is the most common in existing brachiopods, being characteristic of the superfamilies Terebratulacea and
Terebratellacea, which contain most of present articulates.   The lophophore usually projects freely into the mantle cavity but in some species is
more or less fused to the dorsal mantle lobe.

The structure and histology of the lophophore are imperfectly known
except for Blochmann's studies (1892b, 1900) on the inarticulates *Crania,
Discinisca,* and *Lingula.*   Outlines of sections through lophophore arms
of some articulates appear in Hancock (1859), and nobody seems to have
bothered about the matter since until 1956, when Williams presented
some similar outline drawings of sections through the lophophore of
several articulates.   On inspecting a lophophore of the plectolophous
type as Fig. 194*B*, it is evident that a section through either the lateral
arms or the median arm must be double, that is, with a tentacular fringe
on each side.   Such a section (Fig. 194*C*) is convexly rounded on the side
away from the tentacular fringe.   To the inner side of each tentacular
row is found a deep groove, the *brachial groove,* bounded on its inner side
by a curved ridge, the *brachial fold,* or *brachial lip.*   As shown in Fig.
195*A*, the brachial groove is continuous medially with the mouth, and the
brachial fold passes above the mouth where it is considered an epistome.
Between the two folds is the broad median depression, or *brachial gutter,*
whose floor unites the two halves of the arm.   In the interior is seen a

large arm canal, probably formed by the union of two originally separate canals. To either side of or above the larger arm canal is a *smaller arm canal,* which gives off a coelomic canal into each tentacle of its side. Both large and small canals are extensions of the coelom, but in the adult the large arm canal has lost this connection and, further, has no connection with the smaller canals which open into the mesocoel that surrounds the esophagus. At each side of the large canal imbedded in the connective tissue is seen the cross section of the calcareous loop (Fig. 194C).

The relation of the loop to the lophophore in articulates is neglected in the literature, which usually limits itself to quoting Hancock (1859) that the whole of the calcareous support (in *Magellania*) is a "product of the inner lamina of the dorsal pallial lobe." This incomprehensible statement seems to mean that the calcareous support is secreted by the inner wall of the dorsal mantle lobe. But in that case it would be impossible to understand how the loop gets inside the lophophore; further, the skeleton-secreting layer is the epidermis of the *outer* wall of the mantle lobe. Thomson (1927), followed by Elliott (1953a), renders Hancock's statement "inner lamina of the dorsal brachial lobe," whether by mistake or intention is not evident. But this version is even less comprehensible than the original statement, for there is no structure in brachiopods termed "dorsal brachial lobe." Elliott (1956) indicates that all parts of the calcareous supports of the lophophore are secreted by the outer epidermis of the mantle lobes which is everywhere wrapped around the calcareous parts, but this author also fails to explain how this epidermis could get inside the lophophore. The author's sections of the plecto-lophous lophophore show that the calcareous loop is directly imbedded in the connective tissue. Elliott (1953a) also indicates that the loop is secreted *in situ* just beneath the surface of the lophophoral tissues. Morse (1871), studying the development of *Terebratulina,* which is a short-looped form, found that the loop is formed *in situ* by the fusion of calcareous spicules secreted in the tissues of the lophophore. In fact, discrete calcareous spicules are common in the connective tissue of mantle, body wall, and lophophore of articulates; they are wanting in inarticulates.

The calcareous support is therefore found in the connective tissue close to the epidermis on the side of the lophophore away from that bearing the tentacles. In the long-looped Terebratellacea the descending part of the loop is found inside the lateral arms of the plectolophous lophophore and the recurved part of the loop is inside the median spiral arm. In the short-looped Terebratulacea the loop is in the lophophoral base.

In spirolophous lophophores the arms are single, bearing a single fringe of tentacles. Sections of the spirolophous arm of inarticulates appear in Blochmann (1892b, 1900), and that of *Lingula* is reproduced here (Fig.

195*C*). The structure is the same as that of half of a plectolophous arm, but muscles of subperitoneal nature are more in evidence, found in the wall of the smaller arm canal and in the brachial fold, and of course internal skeletal support is lacking. The brachial muscle is prominent in the smaller canal and appears continuous with the lophophore elevator in *Crania* (Fig. 191*B*) but is actually separated from it by a connective-tissue partition.

The lophophore is clothed externally with a columnar epidermis containing gland cells, especially at the tentacle bases. In the base of the epidermis is found the nervous supply of the lophophore, described later. The arm canals are lined by peritoneum, as are also the lumina of the tentacles and the coelomic spaces that may occur in the brachial fold. The interior of the lophophore between epidermis and peritoneum is composed of firm connective tissue, resembling hyaline cartilage and like the latter made of a homogeneous ground substance containing cavities with cells (Fig. 195*D*). The lophophore is therefore rather stiff and not very motile, despite its containing muscle fibers.

The tentacles ("cirri") occur in a row along the entire edge of the lophophore. The row is generally double, that is, consists of closely placed tentacles that lean alternately outward and inward. The cross section of the tentacles is similar to that of other lophophorate phyla, but the outer and inner tentacles differ in shape and ciliary arrangement. The tentacle is clothed with a tall epidermis, of slender ciliated cells on the side toward the brachial groove, of shorter nonciliated cells on the opposite side (Fig. 195*E*, *F*), but is completely ciliated in some species. Gland cells are sparsely present in the epidermis. In the base of the epidermis of the ciliated side courses the tentacular nerve. Beneath the epidermis is a thick basement membrane, or perhaps more correctly, a layer of the stiff cartilagelike connective tissue. This is lined by peritoneum, and between it and the peritoneum occur longitudinal muscle fibers at one or both ends of the oval section of the lumen. The coelomic lumen contains a blood vessel. The cross section of the outer tentacles is somewhat triangular, with strong tufts of lateral cilia and short cilia on the frontal surface, that facing the groove (Fig. 195*E*). The cross section of the inner tentacles is more oval in shape with a more extensive area covered with the short frontal cilia; hence the lateral tufts are shoved more away from the groove and the nonciliated area is much shortened (Fig. 195*F*).

6. Digestive System.—The mouth is a transversely elongated slit found in the center of the lophophoral base between the brachial fold and the tentacular fringe (Fig. 195*A*). From the mouth the esophagus ascends forward and dorsally, then makes a posterior and downward bend to open into a stomachic enlargement, of varied length and delimitation.

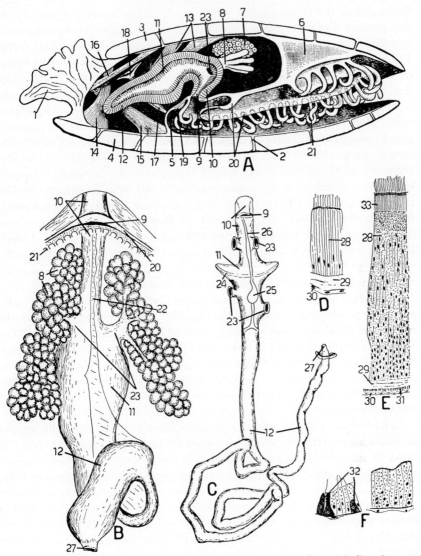

FIG. 196.—Digestive tract. *A*, schematic section of an articulate with digestive tract in place (*after Shipley*, 1895). *B*, digestive tract of *Crania* (*after Joubin*, 1886). *C*, digestive tract of *Lingula* (*after Hancock*, 1859). *D*, histology of stomach wall. *E*, histology of beginning of intestine. *F*, histology of digestive gland. (*D–F*, *Crania*, *after Blochmann*, 1892b.) 1, pedicle; 2, canals for mantle papillae; 3, dorsal valve; 4, ventral valve; 5, nephridiopore; 6, septum of dorsal valve; 7, gonad; 8, digestive gland; 9, mouth; 10, esophagus; 11, stomach; 12, intestine; 13, two heads of adductor muscle; 14, diductor muscle; 15, ventral adjustor of pedicle; 16, dorsal adjustor of pedicle; 17, nephridium; 18, nephrostome; 19, subenteric ganglion; 20, brachial fold; 21, tentacular fringe; 22, dorsal mesentery; 23, duct of digestive gland; 24, gastroparietal band; 25, heart vesicle; 26, main dorsal blood channel; 27, anus; 28, epithelium; 29, connective tissue; 30, peritoneum; 31, muscle layer; 32, gland cells; 33, rod border.

Surrounding the stomach and filling much of the interior space are the conspicuous digestive glands, often called liver. Typically these resemble bunches of grapes, being made up of numerous rounded acini (Figs. 191*B*, 196*B*). They open into the stomach by large ducts, usually one to three on each side. There is a pair of such ducts in *Crania* (Fig. 196*B*), four ducts in *Lingula* (Fig. 196*C*). In articulates the digestive gland usually is subdivided into a larger anterior and a smaller posterior lobe on each side. *Argyrotheca* and *Lacazella* differ from the usual in that the digestive gland consists of a cluster of fingerlike tubules, 6 to 8 on each side in the former genus (Fig. 194*A*), 10 to 16 in the latter (Fig. 190*E*). Those of each side open into the stomach by a common duct. From the stomach the narrowed intestine descends posteriorly and soon terminates blindly in articulates (Fig. 196*A*), mostly in a somewhat pointed end that hangs freely in the coelom. Exceptionally in *Hemithyris* the intestine turns dorsally again and presents a rounded expanded termination. Conditions supposedly nearer the original state of the intestine obtain in inarticulates. In *Crania* the intestine makes a forward loop, then expands into a rectum that proceeds posteriorly and opens in a median anus (Fig. 196*B*). In *Discinisca* the intestine turns forward, bearing to the right, and after presenting two enlargements (Fig. 197*A*) opens dorsally on the right side into the mantle cavity near the right nephridiopore. The longest intestine is found in *Lingula* (Fig. 196*C*), where after some convolutions the intestine without expansion opens as in *Discinisca* on the right side into the mantle cavity. It is impossible to say whether the recurved condition of the intestine in some inarticulates is reminiscent or not of the recurved digestive tract of other lophophorates.

The histology of the digestive tract is known chiefly from the studies of Blochmann (1892b, 1900) on inarticulates. The digestive tract is lined by an epithelium of extremely tall, slender cells, varying in height in different regions; they are mostly ciliated with a rod border (Fig. 196*D, E*). Gland cells, presumably secretory, are found here and there throughout the entire digestive system but are most abundant in the stomach epithelium, especially near the entrances of the ducts of the digestive gland. Beneath the epithelium is found a basement membrane or thin layer of connective tissue, followed by a scanty layer of muscle fibers, mostly circular in direction in the esophagus and anterior part of the stomach, longitudinal elsewhere. Finally, the digestive tract is covered externally with peritoneum. The digestive gland (Fig. 196*F*) consists of a columnar, scantily ciliated epithelium containing secretion droplets and sparsely interspersed with darkly staining gland cells; the epithelium is covered externally with very thin connective tissue and the peritoneum. Muscle cells are confined to the ducts.

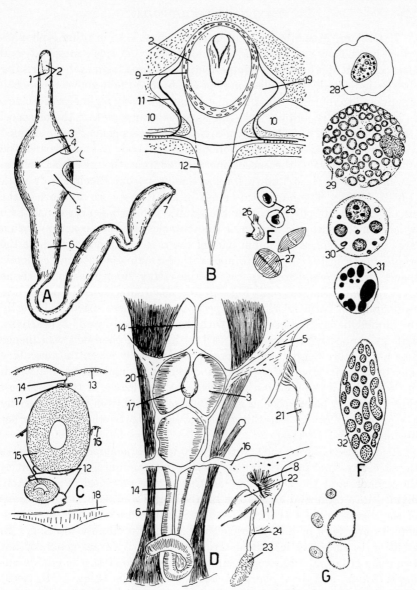

FIG. 197.—Digestive tract (concluded), coelom. *A*, digestive tract of *Discinisca* (*after Joubin*, 1886). *B*, mesocoel of *Crania*. *C*, cross section of *Crania*, showing mesentery. (*B, C, after Blochmann*, 1892b.) *D*, dissection of *Hemithyris*, showing mesenteries (*after Huxley*, 1854b). *E*, coelomocytes of *Lingula* (*after Yatsu*, 1902b). *F*, coelomocytes of *Terebratalia* (*after Ohuye*, 1936). *G*, coelomocytes of *Discinisca* (*after Morse*, 1902), 1, mouth; 2, esophagus; 3, stomach; 4, duct of digestive gland; 5, gastroparietal band; 6, intestine; 7, anus; 8, nephrostome; 9, periesophageal spaces; 10, proximal ends of large arm canals; 11, main blood channel to arm; 12, ventral mesentery; 13, dorsal body wall; 14, dorsal mesentery; 15, sections of intestine; 16, ileoparietal band; 17, heart vesicle; 18, ventral epidermis; 19, mesocoel; 20, adductor muscle; 21, anterior nephridium; 22, posterior nephridium; 23, gonad; 24, mesentery of gonad; 25, spherical coelomocyte; 26, phagocyte; 27, spindle bodies; 28, hyaline amoebocyte; 29, granulocyte with colorless spherules; 30, same with red spherules; 31, same with orange spherules; 32, same with brown spherules.

7. Coelom, Mesenteries, and Coelomocytes.—As in other lophophorates the coelom is theoretically divided into protocoel, mesocoel, and
metacoel, but these parts are imperfectly delimited from each other.   As
already indicated, the median part of the brachial fold above the mouth
is supposed to represent the epistome or anterior body region (protosome).
In inarticulates it contains coelomic spaces continuous with the mesocoel
(Blochmann, 1892b, 1900) but in articulates seems generally to be filled
with connective tissue.   The lophophore and body region around the
esophagus represent the mesosome and contain the mesocoel, whose
ramifications are best known for inarticulates from Blochmann's work
(1892b, 1900).   The large arm canals in the lophophore are part of the
mesocoel but cut off from it in the adult.   The small arm canals into
which run the coelomic lumina of the tentacles continue centrally into a
large coelomic space, the main part of the mesocoel, that surrounds the
esophagus (Fig. 197B).   Continuous with the main mesocoel are coelomic
spaces, the *periesophageal spaces*, in the rather thick connective-tissue
layer of the esophageal wall (Fig. 197B); the circular muscle fibers of the
esophagus are borne on the inner peritoneum of these spaces.   Dorsally
the esophagus is often in contact with the dorsal body wall, or nearly so,
with its connective-tissue layer fused with that of the body wall, hence
does not require mesenterial support here; ventrally a ventral mesentery
may be present (Fig. 197B), thus subdividing the main mesocoel, which
in *Crania* has insinuated itself between the two leaves of the mesentery
(Fig. 197B).   The mesocoel is completely separated from the metacoel by
a septum in *Crania*, but this does not seem to be the case in other
brachiopods.

The metacoel forms the main body cavity of brachiopods and encloses
the digestive tract posterior to the esophagus, the muscles of the valves,
the gonads, and the nephridia.   In *Crania* the metacoel is completely
divided into right and left halves by the dorsal and ventral mesenteries
of the digestive tract (Fig. 197C), but in other brachiopods these mesenteries are more or less imperfect and sometimes almost wanting.   In
addition to these vertical mesenteries, the digestive tract generally has
two pairs of lateral mesenterial supports, the *gastroparietal* bands (wanting in *Crania*) and the *ileoparietal bands*.   The former (Figs. 197D, 199B)
spring from the sides of the stomach, mostly in the vicinity of the ducts of
the digestive glands, and pass laterally in close association with the
adductor muscles or anterior adductors in inarticulates.   In Rhynchonellacea, which have two pairs of nephridia, the nephrostomes of the anterior
pair are embraced by the gastroparietal bands (Fig. 197D).   The
ileoparietal bands pass back along the sides of the digestive tract for some
distance before extending laterally as sheets that support the nephro-

stomes of the nephridia or of the posterior pair of nephridia in Rhyncho-nellacea. Besides these more or less regularly occurring mesenteries, irregular peritoneal strands connecting the intestine to the body wall may be present.

Special conditions obtain at the posterior end of the intestine in *Crania*, which is the only brachiopod with a median posterior anus. Shortly before reaching the anus the dorsal and ventral mesenteries of the intestine subdivide and pass to the lateral body wall, hence leaving an undivided coelomic cavity, the *anal chamber* of Blochmann (1892b), around the end of the intestine (Fig. 198*A*, *B*). Under the peritoneum of the anal chamber are found the circular fibers of the intestine, and just before the passage of the mesenteries to the lateral wall are found muscle fibers constituting an *anal protrusor*, according to Blochmann. The anal levator already mentioned occurs here in the dorsal body wall (Fig. 198*B*).

The mesenteries consist of connective tissue, sometimes containing muscle fibers, clothed on both sides by a flattened peritoneum sparsely provided with cilia (or flagella?) that keep the coelomic fluid in motion.

Posteriorly the metacoel in *Discinisca* and *Lingula*, presumably in other inarticulates also that are provided with a pedicle, is continuous with the lumen of the pedicle. In all brachiopods, the metacoels are continuous anteriorly with coelomic channels in the mantle lobes. These channels are usually called mantle (or pallial) sinuses, but this name dates from the time when these channels were erroneously supposed to be blood spaces. The term sinus is best reserved for a blood space; hence the structures in question will here be called *mantle canals*. As already indicated, these canals may leave impressions on the inner surfaces of the valves; hence their course is detectable even in fossil shells. Usually there are two or four main canals in each mantle lobe, and these branch richly to the periphery of the lobe. The pattern of the canals may be identical or similar in dorsal and ventral mantle lobes or differ. The patterns vary from genus to genus and are of some systematic value. A few patterns of common genera are shown in Fig. 198*C–F*. As in all coelomic cavities, the mantle canals are lined with peritoneum, and as this is ciliated, the contained fluid circulates.

The coelom is filled with a coagulable fluid that contains free cells. Blochmann (1900) noted two kinds of coelomocytes in *Discinisca*, a small somewhat spherical type and a larger type of irregular shape; similar findings were reported by Morse (1902; Fig. 197*G*). The coelomocytes of lingulids were also observed by Morse (1902), but more carefully by Yatsu (1902b) and Ohuye (1937). Yatsu described three sorts, a some-what spherical cell, an amoeboid, phagocytic type that put out blunt pseudopods, and spindle bodies (Fig. 197*E*). The last, very character-

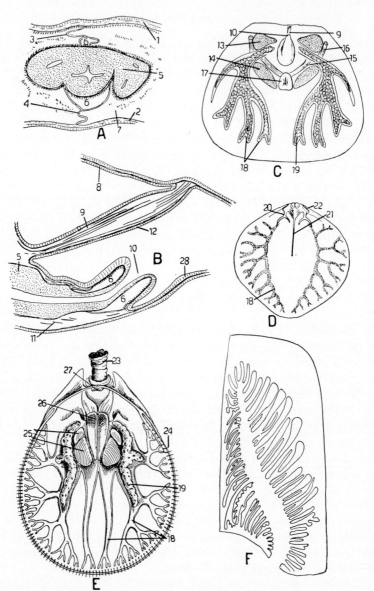

Fig. 198.—Coelom (continued). *A*, section through the rear part of the intestine of *Crania*, showing anal chamber. *B*, longitudinal section of posterior end of *Crania*, showing anal relations. *C*, ventral mantle of *Crania*, with mantle canals containing gonads. (*A–C*, after Blochmann, 1892b.) *D*, dorsal valve of *Magellania* with mantle canals; ventral valve same as *E* (after Fischer and Oehlert, 1892a). *E*, ventral valve of *Macandrevia*, showing mantle canals and gonads (after Blochmann, 1912a). *F*, half of the ventral valve of *Lingula* with mantle canals (after Blochmann, 1900). 1, dorsal body wall; 2, ventral body wall; 3, dorsal mesentery; 4, ventral mesentery; 5, intestine; 6, anal chamber; 7, metacoel; 8, dorsal mantle; 9, levator of the anus; 10, anus; 11, anal protractor; 12, posterior body wall; 13, posterior adductor; 14, anterior adductor; 15, superior oblique; 16, inferior oblique; 17, knob of ventral valve for muscle attachment; 18, mantle canals; 19, gonads; 20, crura; 21, median septum; 22, dental sockets; 23, pedicle; 24, setae; 25, attachment marks of two heads of adductor muscles; 26, scars of dorsal pedicle adjustors; 27, scar of diductor muscle; 28, ventral mantle.

istic of *Lingula* but rare in other brachiopods (Ohuye, 1937), are mostly fusiform but capable of assuming other shapes, without nuclei and with a fibrous interior. Yatsu gave evidence that the spindle bodies arise in definite sites by the transformation of the spherical cells. Ohuye (1937) identified in *Lingula* two additional types of coelomocytes not mentioned by Yatsu, eosinophilic and basophilic granulocytes. The coelomocytes of articulates were described for species of *Terebratulina* by Morse (1902) and Prenant (1928) and for *Terebratalia coreanica* and *Coptothyris grayi* by Ohuye (1936, 1937). *Terebratulina* contains amoeboid cells and colorless and colored granulocytes. In both articulates studied Ohuye noted a spherical type, several kinds of granulocytes, and, infrequently, a disciform type. The spherical, or hyaline, amoebocyte is phagocytic and agglutinable and appears a common type in the coelomic fluid of brachiopods, being often regarded as equivalent to a red blood corpuscle. The granulocytes contain colorless, red, orange, or brown spherules (Fig. 197*F*). The red globules are not lipochromes or any hemoglobin-like substance; the brown granules gave lipoid tests. Fat granules were also detected by Prenant in the hyaline amoeboid cells. Heller (1931) noted an amoeboid phagocytic type in *Hemithyris*.

8. Circulatory System.—This is generally present in brachiopods but imperfectly known. Early workers mistook coelomic channels for blood vessels and the nephridia for hearts. Although Huxley (1854) and Hancock (1859) identified the true heart, these false ideas continued for some time. Hancock, moreover, regarded the mantle canals as parts of the circulatory system and mistook branching networks of connective-tissue cells for blood plexi, hence gave a false complicated picture of the peripheral part of the circulatory system. However, Hancock's descriptions of the main vessels are accurate, according to Blochmann (1892b), and in fact remain the chief available accounts of the articulate circulatory system. This system in inarticulates was elucidated by Blochmann (1892b, 1900).

A contractile vesicle that may be called heart is found throughout brachiopods attached to the dorsal mesentery over the stomach region (Figs. 196*C*, 197*D*). *Crania* (Fig. 191*B*) appears exceptional in having several such vesicles instead of one, and a heart and much of the circulatory system are wanting in *Discinisca*, according to Blochmann (1900). Hancock stated that such a heart vesicle is present in all the brachiopods he examined, and Blochmann (1885) also found it generally present. The heart is a sort of appendage to a main middorsal blood channel that extends forward and backward from it supported by the dorsal mesentery where present. In the anterior direction this channel forks over the esophagus; each fork after communicating with sinuses in the walls of the digestive tract descends along the peritoneum of the mesocoel and enters the lophophoral arm of its side, running the length of the arm in the peritoneum of the smaller arm canal and giving off into each tentacle a branch that lies in the tentacular lumen (Fig. 199*B*).

Posterior to the heart the main dorsal channel is soon seen to be formed by the union of two mantle channels; each of these forks into a dorsal and a ventral mantle channel, which come from the dorsal and ventral mantle lobes, respectively, of that side. In the mantle lobes, these channels run in the mantle canals, dividing richly with the branching of the latter. They run on the inner side of the mantle canals, that is, the side next the mantle cavity, in a slight ridge there. The dorsal mantle channel pursues a direct course to the dorsal mantle lobe, running along the gastroparietal bands, but the ventral mantle channel follows a circuitous course, passing back in the ileoparietal bands and supplying the nephridia and (in inarticulates) gonads before swinging forward toward the mantle. Extensive systems of anastomosing sinuses exist in the ileoparietal bands, nephridia, and gonads.

The histology of the heart and main channels has been best studied by Schaeffer (1926), who used *Lingula*. The heart wall consists of an outer peritoneum underlain by a moderately thick layer of circular muscles (Fig. 199*C*). The main middorsal channel near the heart is similarly constructed except that the muscle fibers take a helicoidal course (Fig. 199*D*). Farther away from the heart, muscles are lacking and the wall of the channels consists of peritoneum resting on a thin layer of connective tissue (Fig. 199*E*). No definite lining layer was found anywhere. The whole circulatory system seems to consist of spaces in the mesenteries and under the peritoneum; hence the term channel rather than vessel has been applied in the foregoing account. Because there are no definite vessels and because the circuit must be completed through tissue spaces, the system must be regarded as an open one. It is not understandable why it is referred to as closed in the literature of brachiopods.

The circulatory system contains a colorless coagulable fluid that is generally reported as devoid of cells or nearly so. Presumably any cells found in the system would be coelomocytes.

9. Nervous System.—Knowledge of the nervous system is imperfect. Hancock (1859) gave some description of the nervous system of articulates, and this is substantially correct as far as it goes, according to van Bemmelen (1883); but Hancock failed to find the supraenteric ganglion and the nerves emanating from it. Hence the best account of the nervous system of articulates is that of van Bemmelen (1883), based primarily on *Gryphus vitreus*. Here the central nervous system encircles the beginning of the esophagus (Fig. 200*A*). Above the esophagus is the small, laterally elongated supraenteric ganglion, hardly worthy of the name of cerebral ganglion. It gives off on each side the main nerve to the arms; this nerve

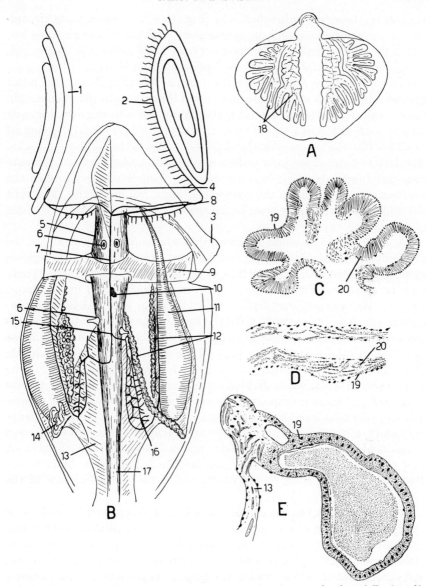

Fig. 199.—Coelom (concluded); circulatory system. *A*, ventral valve of *Terebratalia transversa* with mantle canals filled with gonads. *B*, viscera of *Lingula* with circulatory system. *C*, section through heart vesicle of *Lingula*. *D*, longitudinal section of main dorsal blood channel of *Lingula*, near heart. *E*, section of a genital sinus of *Lingula*. (*B–E*, *after Schaeffer*, 1926.) 1, coils of lophophore; 2, main blood channel to lophophore; 3, body wall cut open; 4, dorsal mesentery; 5, stomach; 6, ducts of digestive gland; 7, mid-dorsal blood channel; 8, anterior fork; 9, gastroparietal bands; 10, heart vesicle; 11, nephridium; 12, gonad; 13, ileoparietal bands; 14, nephrostome; 15, posterior fork into mantle channels; 16, blood plexus in gastroparietal bands; 17, intestine; 18, mantle canals; 19, peritoneum; 20, muscle layer.

runs in the base of the brachial fold (Fig. 195C).   One or more circumenteric connectives connect the supraenteric with the subenteric ganglion,
which is a large and conspicuous nervous mass below the esophagus.
From the circumenteric connectives spring additional nerves to the arms,
the accessory arm nerves and the lower arm nerves (Fig. 200A); the latter
give off a branch into each tentacle.   From the subenteric ganglion a main
lateral and several minor lateral nerves spray out into the dorsal mantle
lobe on each side, and a pair of thick trunks proceed posteriorly, giving off
branches into the ventral mantle lobes and nerves to the adductor muscles.
The latter continue into the pedicle as the peduncular nerves.   Delicate
branches innervate the dorsal mesentery.   Van Bemmelen locates the
nervous system mainly in the connective tissue, but his figures show that
the main ganglia are very close to the epidermis, if not actually in its base
(Fig. 201B).

A more detailed account is given by Blochmann (1892b, 1900) for the
inarticulates Crania, Discinisca, and Lingula.   In these forms the nervous
system is located mainly in the base of the epidermis (Fig. 202A).   There
may be some real difference here between articulates and inarticulates.
Further, the inarticulates studied by Blochmann lack a definite supraenteric ganglion (Figs. 200B, 201A).   Instead the circumenteric connectives continue above the esophagus, completing the circumenteric ring; as
in articulates these connectives give off the main arm nerve on each side
(Fig. 200B, C).   The subenteric ganglion forms a median mass in Discinisca and Lingula, but is divided into a pair of lateral masses in Crania
(Fig. 200C).   From it originate as in articulates the nerves for the mantle
lobes, for the muscles of the valves, and for the pedicle.   The accompanying figures, after Blochmann, show the arrangement of the nervous system
in inarticulates better than verbal descriptions (Figs. 200B, C, 201A).   A
ring nerve in the margin of each mantle lobe is present in Lingula and
Discinisca, being formed by the confluence of the peripheral ends of the
richly branching mantle nerves.

In inarticulates Blochmann has found a nervous plexus in the base of
the epithelial lining of the digestive tract.   Nervous plexi are probable in
the base of or just beneath the body-wall epidermis.   Van Bemmelen
(1883) noted such a plexus beneath the epidermis of the brachial groove
and throughout the entire wall of the arms.   As is usual in invertebrates,
ganglion cells occur everywhere throughout the nervous system.

No investigator has been able to demonstrate any sensory cells.
Blochmann (1892b, 1900) made a special effort to differentiate sensory
cells, using methylene blue and the Golgi method, but failed.   A pair of
statocysts is known to occur in larval or juvenile inarticulates and,
according to Yatsu (1902), is conspicuously present in adult Japanese
Lingula, although Blochmann (1900) positively denied their occurrence

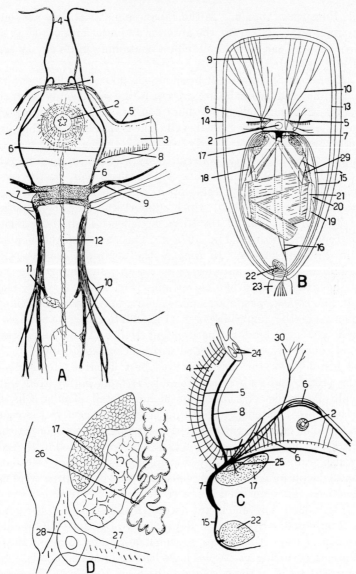

Fig. 200.—Nervous system. *A*, nervous system of *Gryphus* (*after van Bemmelen, 1883*). *B*, nervous system of *Lingula* (*after Blochmann, 1900*). *C*, nervous system of *Crania* (*after Blochmann, 1892b*). *D*, part of *Lingula*, showing statocyst (*after Yatsu, 1902b*). 1, supraenteric ganglion; 2, esophagus; 3, arm base; 4, accessory arm nerves; 5, main arm nerve; 6, circumenteric connectives; 7, subenteric ganglion; 8, lower arm nerve; 9, dorsal mantle nerves; 10, ventral mantle nerves; 11, nerve to adductor muscle; 12, dorsal mesentery; 13, marginal nerve of ventral mantle lobe; 14, marginal nerve of dorsal mantle lobe; 15, lateral nerves; 16, peduncular nerves; 17, anterior adductor; 18, lateral muscle; 19, external oblique; 20, internal oblique; 21, median oblique; 22, posterior adductor; 23, pedicle; 24, arm canals; 25, lophophore elevator; 26, digestive gland; 27, gastroparietal band; 28, statocyst; 29, nerves to oblique muscles; 30, mantle nerve.

in adult European *Lingula*. In the Japanese material they are found on the gastroparietal bands near the anterior adductor muscles (Fig. 200*D*). They consist of a sac of tall epithelium containing in its cavity some 30 statoliths (Fig. 201*C*).

10. Excretory System.—All brachiopods possess at least one pair of metanephridia, and two pairs are present in the superfamily Rhynchonellacea (Fig. 197*D*). Each nephridium consists of a large funnel-shaped nephrostome with greatly ruffled wall, and a tubular part that extends anteriorly along the lateral body wall and gradually narrows to the nephridiopore, located in the anterior body wall, hence opening into the mantle cavity. The nephrostomes of the single pair, or the posterior pair when two pairs are present, open into the metacoel through the ileoparietal bands (Fig. 197*D*) which support and more or less embrace them. The anterior pair of the Rhynchonellacea is similarly related to the gastroparietal bands (Fig. 197*D*). The shape of the nephridium varies in different genera. In *Lingula* the nephridia are exceptionally long and broad and much flattened (Fig. 199*B*). In other genera they are mostly short and shaped like cornucopia (Fig. 202*C*, *D*, *G*). Those of *Terebratulina caputserpentis* are curved like a horn, with fingerlike processes alongside the nephridiopores (Fig. 202*B*); these processes were supposed to be of glandular nature, but Heller (1931) found them to consist of connective tissue stiffened with calcareous spicules.

The histology of the nephridia was best described for *Lingula* by Schaeffer (1926) and for *Hemithyris* and *Terebratulina* by Heller (1931). The nephridia consist of a lining epithelium of tall, slender cells, flagellated (Heller) or ciliated (Schaeffer), a layer of connective tissue, thickened in the folds of the nephrostome, and an outer covering of peritoneum (Fig. 202*F*). The epithelium of the tube is filled with yellowish, reddish, or brownish granules, presumably of excretory nature, that often confer a color on the nephridium. Gland cells in the wall of the tube were figured by Schaeffer. The epithelial lining of the tube of *Hemithyris* is greatly folded (Fig. 202*E*), but this is not necessarily the case in other genera.

11. Reproductive System and Reproductive Habits.—All brachiopods are dioecious, except *Argyrotheca*, in which, according to Senn (1934), the three species occurring at Naples have hermaphroditic gonads. Earlier and persistent belief in the hermaphroditism of *Lingula* has been refuted by the findings of Schaeffer (1926) and Senn (1934). The sexes cannot be distinguished externally unless the color of the ripe gonads shows through the shell; the testes are pale, the ovaries often orange or red. Lacaze-Duthiers (1861) found a sex difference in the ventral valve of *Lacazella mediterranea*. This species broods its young in a median brood pouch that occupies a depression of the ventral valve (Fig. 202*H*), and this causes a corresponding external bulge (Fig. 202*K*).

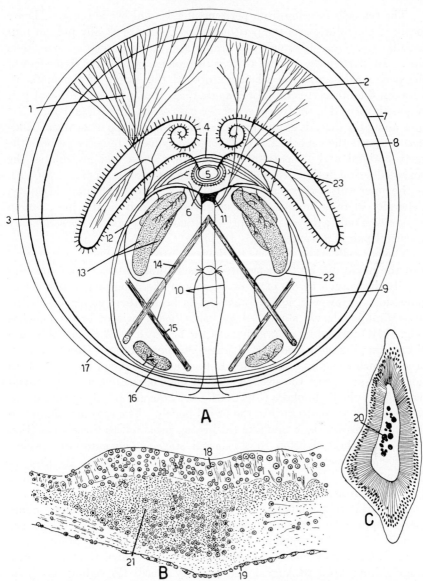

Fig. 201.—Nervous system (continued). *A*, scheme of the nervous system of *Discinisca* (*after Blochmann*, 1900). *B*, section through the body wall and subenteric ganglion of *Gryphus* (*after van Bemmelen*, 1883). *C*, statocyst of *Lingula* (*after Yatsu*, 1902b). 1, dorsal mantle nerves; 2, ventral mantle nerves; 3, main arm nerve; 4, circumenteric connectives; 5, esophagus; 6, plexus in wall of esophagus; 7, dorsal marginal nerve; 8, ventral marginal nerve; 9, lateral nerves; 10, peduncular nerves; 11, subenteric ganglion; 12, lateral muscle; 13, anterior adductor; 14, internal oblique muscle; 15, posterior oblique; 16, posterior adductor; 17, edge of mantle; 18, epidermis; 19, peritoneum; 20, statoliths; 21, ganglion; 22, nerve to oblique muscles; 23, nerve to lophophore.

The sex cells develop from peritoneal cells, and hence the gonads are localized convolutions of the peritoneum.   There are usually present four gonads that resemble bunches of grapes and are quite voluminous when ripe.   In inarticulates except *Crania* the gonads occupy the free edges of the peritoneal bands and when mature fill the spaces of the metacoel between the other viscera.   In *Lingula* (Fig. 199*B*) there is a dorsal pair of gonads formed in the free edges of the part of the ileoparietal bands that runs along the digestive tract and a ventral pair in the part of these bands that supports the nephridia.   In *Discinisca*, gonads are borne on both the gastroparietal and ileoparietal bands.   In *Crania* and articulates the gonads develop in the coelomic lining of the mantle canals (Fig. 198*C, E*), on the inner wall of these canals, that is, the wall facing the mantle cavity. Generally there is present a pair of gonads in each mantle lobe, but in *Argyrotheca* only a dorsal pair is present (Senn, 1934) and in *Lacazella* only a ventral pair (Lacaze-Duthiers, 1861).

The sex cells when ripe are discharged into the metacoel, are wafted into the nephridia by the currents of their lining interior, and thus are usually discharged to the exterior by way of the nephridia, which act as gonoducts.   However, a few brachiopods brood their young up to the free-swimming larval stage.   *Argyrotheca* has a pair of brood pouches (Fig. 194*A*) formed by enlargement of the nephridia.   A remarkable case of brooding is seen in *Lacazella* (Lacaze-Duthiers, 1861).   Here a median brood pouch occupies a depression in the ventral valve of females.   Into this pouch are thrust the swollen clublike ends of the two median ventral tentacles of the lophophore (Fig. 202*H*).   These are greatly enlarged and bent out of position to fit into the brood pouch.   The eggs attach, not to the club ends, but to a mufflike thickening proximal to these ends (Fig. 202*J*), and there develop to the larval stage.   The antarctic species, *Liothyrella antarctica*, broods its eggs in an area enclosed by the arms of the lophophore (Blochmann, 1906), and the New Zealand species, *Terebratella inconspicua*, broods in the mantle cavity (Percival, 1944).

Few data are available on the breeding season of brachiopods.   Some species appear to have an annual breeding season, whereas others are thought to breed throughout much of the year.   On the Maine coast *Terebratulina septentrionalis* has been observed to spawn at various times ranging from April to August and possibly breeds throughout the year there (Morse, 1873a).   McCrady (1860) recorded larvae of *Glottidia pyramidata* off the coast of South Carolina in June, and Brooks (1879) obtained them in Chesapeake Bay from the middle of July to the middle of August.   Among the early findings of larvae were those of Müller (1860, 1861) of *Pelagodiscus* off Brazil from February to April, late summer there.   Blochmann's (1900) specimens of *Discinisca lamellosa* came from Chile, and from the condition of their gonads July (winter) breeding

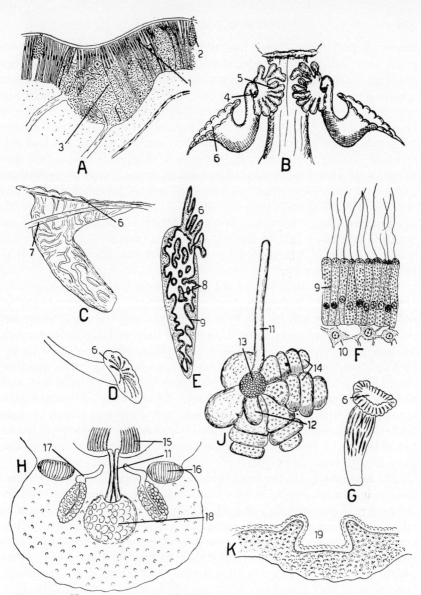

Fig. 202.—Nervous system (concluded), excretory system, reproduction. *A*, section through the base of the brachial fold of *Lingula*, showing main arm nerve (*after Blochmann*, 1900). *B*, pair of nephridia of *Terebratulina retusa*. *C*, nephridium of *Terebratulina septentrionalis*. *D*, nephridium of *Discinisca*. *E*, longitudinal section of nephridium of *Hemithyris psittacea*. *F*, lining epithelium of kidney of *E*. (*B, E, F, after Heller*, 1931.) *G*, nephridium of *Coptothyris grayi*. (*C, D, G, after Morse*, 1902.) *H*, opened *Lacazella*, showing two tentacles bent into brood pouch. *J*, one tentacle with adherent embryos. *K*, section of ventral valve of *Lacazella*, showing depression for the brood pouch. (*H–K, after Lacaze-Duthiers*, 1861.) 1, epidermis; 2, gland cell; 3, nerve; 4, nephridiopore; 5, glands at nephridiopore; 6, nephrostome; 7, mesentery; 8, folds of interior; 9, lining epithelium; 10, connective tissue; 11, tentacle; 12, swollen club end of tentacle; 13, ruff of tentacle; 14, embryos; 15, lophophore; 16, lateral adductor; 17, nephridium; 18, brood pouch; 19, depression of valve for brood pouch.

appeared probable. *Crania rostrata* from the French Mediterranean coast was thought by Joubin (1886) to breed throughout the year, although spawning was never observed in laboratory cultures; the gonads appeared most ripe from May to winter, declining in activity in the winter months. Lankester (1873) found *Gryphus vitreus* ripe at Naples in December but spent in spring. The larvae of *Lingula anatina* studied by Ashworth (1915) were collected in the southern part of the Red Sea, at times indicative of a May spawning and another in September; Ashworth postulated a succession of spawnings from March to September. Larvae of *Pelagodiscus atlanticus* were obtained by Ashworth near Ceylon in October. *Terebratella inconspicua* broods off New Zealand from early April to late May. According to Yatsu (1902a), Japanese *Lingula* breed from the middle of July to the end of August, probably spawning twice during this period. Sewall (1912) took larval *Lingula* off Burma from December to February.

Spawning has been witnessed in *Terebratulina septentrionalis* by Morse (1873a) and in *Lingula* by Yatsu (1902a). In the former the sex cells are discharged from the anterior margin and the eggs "drop just beyond the pallial membrane, hanging in clusters from the setae and covering the bottom of the dish in the immediate vicinity of the animal." In Yatsu's cultures both sexes of *Lingula* spawned in the early morning; clouds of eggs and sperm were forcibly discharged from the median funnel of setae (see behavior) like a jet of water. Mucus secreted by the mantle accompanied the spawning and enclosed the sex cells. Yatsu thought probably the females are stimulated to spawn by the discharge of sperm, but obtained no result by scattering sperm around females or injecting them into the mantle cavity.

12. Embryology.—As already indicated, the eggs are discharged into the sea, in which case fertilization must occur at discharge, or are brooded in brood sacs or in the mantle cavity, in which case fertilization must be internal. The eggs are rather yolky, as indicated by their usual yellow, orange, or red color. In *Lingula* the ovocytes are nourished during their growth in the ovaries by nutritive cells (Schaeffer, 1926; Senn, 1934), which, according to Senn, are altered ovocytes that become incorporated into the definitive ovocytes.

Accounts of the earlier and more important stages of the embryology have been given for *Lingula unguis* by Yatsu (1902a), *Terebratulina septentrionalis* by Conklin (1902), *Argyrotheca cordata* by Kowalevsky (1874, 1883), Shipley (1883), and Plenk (1913), *Lacazella mediterranea* by Lacaze-Duthiers (1861) and Kowalevsky (1874, 1883), and *Terebratella inconspicua* by Percival (1944). Additional information (see below) is available on larval stages of these and other forms. In all known cases cleavage is holoblastic, practically equal, and generally of the radial type,

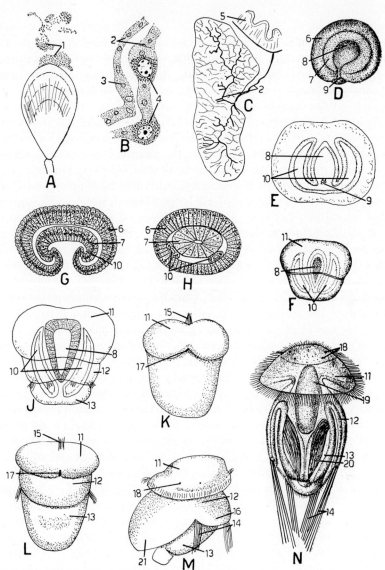

FIG. 203.—Reproduction (concluded), embryology. *A, T. septentrionalis* spawning (*after Morse*, 1902). *B*, ileoparietal band of *Lingula* with peritoneal cells transforming into ovocytes. *C*, section of mature gonad of *Lingula* borne on the ileoparietal band. (*B, C, after Schaeffer*, 1926.) *D–N*, development of *Argyrotheca*. *D*, gastrula. *E*, coelomic sacs forming. *F*, coelomic sacs separated. *G, H*, formation of coelomic sacs according to Plenk. *J*, embryo constricted into three regions. *K–M*, external changes of the embryo. (*G, H, K–M, after Plenk*, 1913.) *N*, larva completed. (*D–F, J, N, after Kowalevsky*, 1874, 1883.) 1, eggs; 2, ileoparietal band; 3, peritoneum; 4, ovocytes; 5, stomach wall; 6, ectoderm; 7, entoderm; 8, archenteron; 9, blastopore; 10, coelomic sacs; 11, anterior lobe embryo; 12, mantle lobe embryo; 13, peduncular lobe embryo; 14, larval setae; 15, apical tuft; 16, dorsal mantle lobe; 17, stomodaeum; 18, eyes; 19, enteron; 20, muscles; 21, ventral mantle lobe.

although variation in the pattern of the early blastomeres was noted by Conklin and Percival. A coeloblastula eventuates that gastrulates by the embolic method, except in *Lacazella*, in which the entoderm is formed by primary delamination or ingression, according to Kowalevsky. The formation of the mesoderm differs remarkably in the various accounts. In *Lingula* the mesoderm is proliferated from the sides of the archenteron as two cell masses (Fig. 204*D*) that hollow out to produce two coelomic sacs (Fig. 204*F*); these spread around the enteron but do not subdivide. In *Lingula*, therefore, the coelom is of the schizocoelous type. In *Argyrotheca*, according to Kowalevsky, confirmed by Shipley and Plenk, the archenteron forms the mesoderm by putting out near the blastopore a pair of lateral pouches (Fig. 203*E*), which cut off as sacs lying to either side of the archenteron that spread dorsally (Fig. 203*J*). Kowalevsky seems to indicate the same method of coelom formation in three other species that he studied, but gave no convincing details, and his figure for *Argyrotheca* differs somewhat from Plenk's (Fig. 203*G, H*). The coelomic sacs spread but do not subdivide. Conklin clearly demonstrates that in *Terebratulina* the mesoderm originates as a single sac that is cut off from the *anterior* end of the archenteron by a descending partition (Fig. 204*G*). This coelomic sac is about as large as the remaining enteron and later gets constricted into two sacs by the latter's expansion. The two sacs elongate but do not subdivide and later send extensions into the mantle lobes and pedicle (Fig. 205*C, D*). In *Terebratella* the mesoderm is similarly formed by the cutting off of a single sac from the archenteron by a descending partition, but here the sac comprises the *posterior* end of the archenteron (Fig. 206*A*). The sac advances anteriorly along the sides of the enteron as an upgrowth, solid at first, that later hollows and subdivides transversely, thus eventually forming an anterior and a posterior coelomic sac on each side of the enteron (Fig. 206*B, C*). Thus in brachiopods present evidence indicates that the coelom is a schizocoel in inarticulates, an enterocoel in articulates; but further studies are clearly desirable, especially in inarticulates.

In the meantime the blastopore has closed, generally by elongating first into a groove. The stomodaeum apparently originates from the anterior end of this groove. It joins the enteron that in *Terebratulina* puts out an outgrowth to meet it. In *Terebratella* the enteron has reduced to a solid rod prior to the formation of the stomodaeum. In so far as the data go, the stomodaeum forms the anterior part of the esophagus, the enteron the rest of the esophagus, stomach, and intestine. In *Lingula* the intestine elongates and comes in contact with the ectoderm, where a proliferation of cells helps establish the anus. The digestive glands arise as outpouchings of the stomach region.

The further development of inarticulates is known only for *Lingula*.

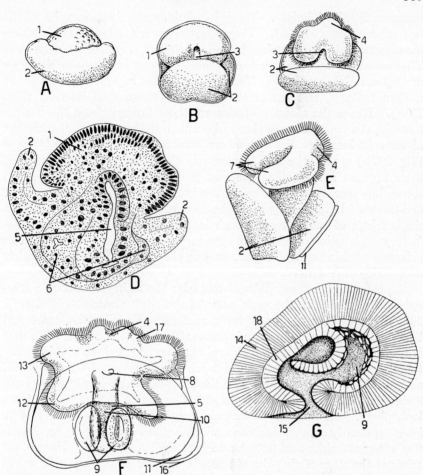

Fig. 204.—Embryology (continued). *A–F*, development of *Lingula* (after *Yatsu*, 1902a). *A*, mantle lobe forming. *B*, mantle lobe subdivided, stomodaeum invaginating. *C*, anterior lobe forming lophophore. *D*, section of about stage *B*, showing archenteron proliferating mesoderm. *E*, body projecting from mantle lobes. *F*, later stage with shell, lophophore, and coelomic sacs. *G*, formation of coelomic sac in *Terebratulina* (after *Conklin*, 1902). 1, anterior lobe; 2, mantle lobe; 3, stomodaeum; 4, median tentacle; 5, archenteron; 6, mesodermal proliferations; 7, lophophore; 8, mouth; 9, coelomic sac; 10, enteron; 11, shell; 12, first pair of tentacles; 13, second pair of tentacles; 14, epidermis; 15, blastopore; 16, vitelline membrane; 17, third tentacle; 18, entoderm.

The embryo becomes regionated into two parts by the bulging of its posterior half as an annular ridge, the mantle fold, that is thus marked off from the conical future body (Fig. 204*A*). The mantle fold continues to enlarge and subdivides into dorsal and ventral mantle lobes that grow forward, partly enclosing the future body (Fig. 204*B*). The latter also elongates, shows the stomodaeal invagination in its midventral region, and becomes distally lobulate. These lobulations are the primordia of the lophophore (Fig. 204C, E). They comprise a median bulge that becomes the median tentacle and paired lateral bulges that are additional tentacles. The median tentacle is a structure peculiar to larval inarticulates that may or may not disappear later. Tentacles are added in pairs adjacent to the median tentacle, and earlier tentacles are thus pushed laterally (Fig. 204F). Hence the oldest tentacles are those farthest from the median tentacle, the youngest ones those adjacent to the latter. As the number of tentacles increases, the lophophore takes a somewhat crescentic shape (Fig. 207D) around the now transversely elongated mouth, above which there appears a ridge that becomes the epistome (brachial fold). It seems, however, that the tentacles never completely encircle the mouth, and this would explain why the lophophore of adult inarticulates has but a single fringe of tentacles, although in fact the author found no satisfactory explanation of this in the literature. Meantime, the mantle lobes enlarge and thin out and begin secreting the shell, first as a thin cuticle over their entire surface.

At the stage of three pairs of tentacles the embryo becomes a free-swimming larva with the main parts of the adult already defined (Fig. 207D). The relatively small body containing the digestive tract and bearing distally the lophophore is enclosed between the mantle lobes that are covered externally by the larval shell or protegulum. This is distinguished by its angular posterolateral corners (Fig. 207D) and is still recognizable at the posterior end of the adult valves as a small white area. Swimming is accomplished by the cilia, limited to the tentacles of the lophophore. The number of tentacles continues to increase, the mantle lobes constantly expand, and concomitantly the valves enlarge by deposition along the sides and anterior edge of the protegulum. The pedicle arises at the stage of six pairs of tentacles as a bulge at the posterior end of the ventral mantle lobe, and into this bulge there extends an evagination of the coelom. The beginning pedicle thus consists of outer ectoderm and inner peritoneum, both of tall cells; later muscle is produced by the peritoneum between itself and the ectoderm. As the larva grows the pedicle elongates but remains coiled up in the posterior part of the mantle cavity until bottom life begins. At the stage of seven pairs of tentacles setae, probably secreted by ectodermal invaginations, appear around the edge of the mantle lobes. The larva develops directly into the adult *Lingula* without any very definite process of metamorphosis.

These characteristic inarticulate larvae with a bivalve shell enclosing a body bearing a bilateral lophophore with a limited number of ciliated tentacles are well-known objects in the plankton, where they may be taken with a net at suitable seasons. They were first seen and, remarkably enough, at once recognized as the larvae of an inarticulate brachio-

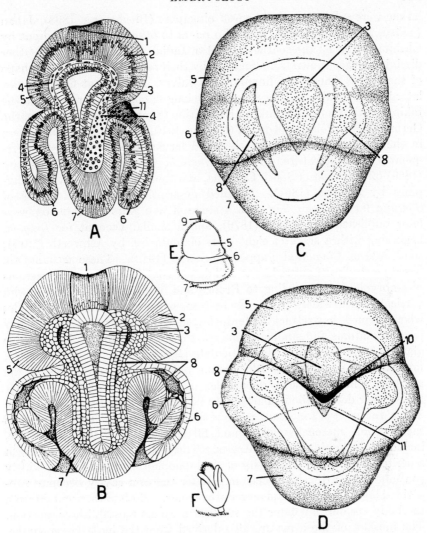

Fig. 205.—Embryology (continued). *A–D*, further stages of development of *Terebratulina* (*after Conklin, 1902*). *A*, longitudinal section, showing mesoderm, apical sensory plate, and mantle lobes enclosing peduncular lobe. *B*, latest stage available, showing spread of coelom. *C, D*, external views of similar stages. *E*, mature larva of *Terebratulina*. *F*, young *Terebratulina*, after mantle reversal. (*E, F, after Morse, 1873a.*) 1, apical sensory area; 2, ectoderm; 3, enteron; 4, mesoderm; 5, anterior lobe; 6, mantle lobe; 7, peduncular lobe; 8, coelomic sacs; 9, apical tuft; 10, stomodaeum; 11, ventral sense plate.

pod by Fritz Müller (1860, 1861), collecting off the coast of Brazil. Müller thought his larvae belonged to *Discinisca;* later workers assigned them to *Pelagodiscus atlanticus.* These larvae are recognized by the five pairs of principal setae, of which the fourth pair is larger and stouter than the others and armed with thorns (Fig. 207*C*). Identical or similar larvae were subsequently taken off Singapore (Blochmann, 1898), Japan (Yatsu, 1902a; Yamada, 1956, who refers to other Japanese findings by Ohshima), and off the southern point of India (Ashworth, 1915).   Other discinid larvae, known from lingulids by their retaining the circular shape of the valves whereas in lingulids the valves, although at first circular, later become oval or oblong, also by the long setae, are described from the takings of the German Plankton Expedition (Simroth, 1897) and from the German South Polar Expedition (Eichler, 1910); the latter collected them in the Antarctic at 3000 m.   Lingulid larvae also have appeared frequently in the literature.   Those of *Glottidia* were first seen by McCrady (1860) off the coast of South Carolina, and those of *Lingula* at the Philippines by Semper (1861).   Detailed descriptions and illustrations of *Glottidia* larvae, beginning with a stage of five pairs of tentacles, were later published by Brooks (1879), and a similar account for *Lingula*, beginning with a stage of eight pairs of tentacles, by Ashworth (1915); some data on *Lingula* also appear in Sewall (1912).   These accounts are based on studies of entire larvae and do not contribute to vexed questions of embryology.   According to Brooks and Yatsu, lingulid larvae swim vertically with widely gaping shells from which the tentacles protrude; when alarmed they retract the tentacles, close the valves, and sink.   They feed on diatoms and similar organisms that are digested in the digestive gland.   So far as known all inarticulate larvae have a pair of statocysts, mistaken for nephridia by Blochmann, but whether these persist in the adult state in all species is debatable.

Further details about inarticulate development are known only from Yatsu's account of *Lingula*.   Some of the mesodermal cells of the coelomic sacs become mesenchymatous and fill the cavity of the lophophore, including the lumina of the tentacles.   These cells later rearrange to form a peritoneal lining.   The cavity of the lophophoral arms is at first widely continuous with the body coelom.   Later the arm cavity becomes subdivided into the smaller and larger arm canals.   Both of these cut off from the body coelom, but later the small arm canals reestablish connection. The muscles of the arms are also derived from the loose mesenchyme. The body-wall musculature and the muscles that operate the valves come from cells proliferated by the body-wall peritoneum between itself and the ectoderm.   Hence the valve muscles when they assume their definitive positions are necessarily ensheathed with peritoneum.   The two coelomic sacs expand around the digestive tract, forming dorsal and ventral mesenteries by their contacts, but these are poorly retained in *Lingula*. The gastro- and ileoparietal ligaments arise as peritoneal folds.   There are no primary divisions of the coelom, which, as already related, is continuous from the start with the cavity of the lophophore.   Later the coelom puts out a pair of canals into each mantle lobe and an unpaired evagina-

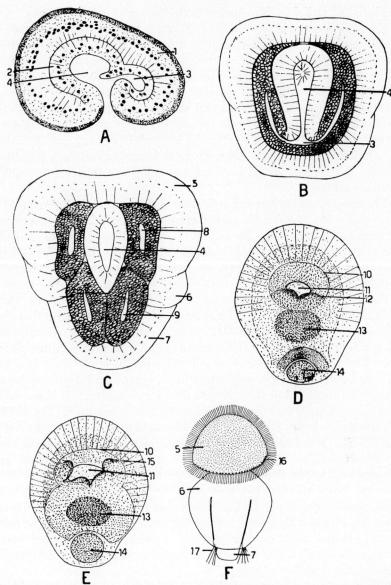

FIG. 206.—Embryology (continued). *A–F*, embryology of *Terebratella inconspicua* (*after Percival*, 1944). *A*, section of gastrula, showing cutting off of coelomic sac from posterior end of archenteron. *B*, view from front, showing spread of coelomic sac anteriorly. *C*, later stage, coelomic sacs cut off from enteron, divided transversely. *D*, beginning formation of tentacles of lophophore. *E*, second pair of tentacles forming. *F*, mature larva. 1, ectoderm; 2, entoderm; 3, coelomic sac; 4, enteron; 5, anterior lobe; 6, mantle lobe; 7, peduncular lobe; 8, anterior coelomic sac; 9, posterior coelomic sac; 10, edge of mouth; 11, stomodaeum; 12, first pair of tentacles; 13, definitive digestive tract; 14, pedicle; 15, second pair of tentacles; 16, pigment spots; 17, setae.

tion into the pedicle.   The coelomocytes are of peritoneal origin.   The canals of the nephridia are stated by Yatsu to grow in from the ectoderm as solid ectodermal rods that acquire a peritoneal covering as they push inward; later they hollow out.   The origin of the nephrostomes could not be ascertained.   The epistome extends to become the brachial fold of the entire lophophore.   Only one ganglion, the subenteric ganglion, develops, and this originates by thickening and proliferation of the ectoderm.   The statocysts are ectodermal invaginations.   At the stage of 10 to 15 pairs of tentacles the young *Lingula* protrudes its pedicle and takes to a bottom life.   Following protrusion the epithelium begins to secrete a gelatinous material that thickens and hardens, becoming the thick cuticle of the definitive pedicle.

The free-swimming larva of articulates differs superficially from that of inarticulates but is referable to the same general plan.   This larva was first seen and described by Lacaze-Duthiers (1861) for *Lacazella*, later by Morse (1871, 1873a) for *Terebratulina*.   The embryo, having formed the coelomic sacs as described above, becomes regionated into three parts by constrictions, an anterior lobe that develops into most of the body, a median lobe, the mantle, and a posterior lobe, the pedicle (Figs. 203*L*, 205*E*).   The mantle lobe rapidly grows backward as a circular fold that embraces the pedicle (Fig. 203*M*).   It soon shows evidence of bifurcation and grows more rapidly on the future ventral than on the future dorsal side.   The anterior lobe becomes ciliated, and the larva takes to a free life.   The anterior lobe in most cases has a central apical tuft underlain by a nervous center; but these structures are evanescent.   It also usually bears pigment spots that seem to represent pigment-cup ocelli (Fig. 207*B*); in *Lacazella* there are four such spots mounted on a headlike projection (Fig. 207*E*).   Bundles of long setae usually develop on the mantle fold; they seem to be absent in *Terebratulina*.   These setae are evanescent and later replaced by the definitive setae.   After a free life of up to 24 or 30 hours the larva attaches by the pedicle and undergoes metamorphosis, which consists primarily in the reversal of the mantle.   The mantle, previously directed backward around the pedicle, reverses so as to point forward around the body proper, its definitive position, and starts secreting the shell.   The young brachiopod now resembles comparable stages of inarticulates.

Information about internal changes is limited.   Conklin was able to follow the development of *Terebratulina* only to the stage shown in Fig. 205*B*.   The coelomic sacs spread throughout the three regions of the larva but never subdivide.   They are solid for a time but again develop a lumen.   Cells given off from the apical sense plate are thought to become the supraenteric ganglion, and a similar proliferation from a midventral sensory area (Fig. 205*A*) is thought to become the subenteric ganglion.

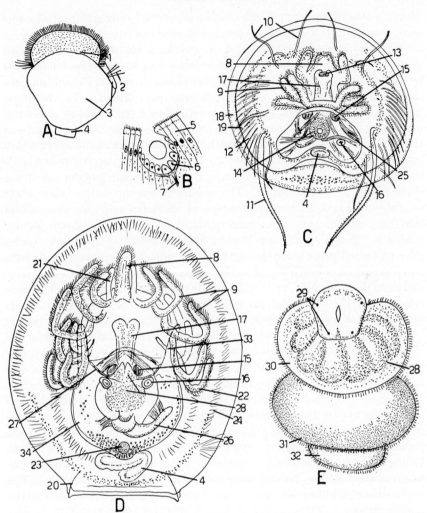

FIG. 207.—Embryology (concluded). *A, Terebratella inconspicua*, attached young animal after mantle reversal (*after Percival*, 1944). *B*, section of eye of *Argyrotheca* larva (*after Plenk*, 1913). *C*, larva of *Pelagodiscus atlanticus*. *D*, late stage of *Lingula*, with eight pairs of tentacles. (*C, D, after Yatsu*, 1902a.) *E*, mature larva of *Lacazella* (*after Lacaze-Duthiers*, 1861). 1, body of animal; 2, larval setae; 3, mantle lobes; 4, pedicle; 5, epidermis; 6, cup of ocellus; 7, nerve; 8, median tentacle; 9, other tentacles; 10, major setae; 11, fourth barbed seta; 12, minor setae; 13, mouth; 14, stomach; 15, anterior adductors; 16, statocyst; 17, esophagus; 18, dorsal shell; 19, ventral shell; 20, protegulum; 21, youngest tentacles; 22, oldest tentacles; 23, posterior adductor; 24, definitive setae; 25, muscles; 26, intestine; 27, gastroparietal bands; 28, lobes of digestive gland; 29, eyespots; 30, anterior lobe; 31, mantle lobe; 32, peduncular lobe; 33, mantle canals; 34, metacoel.

Morse's observations on *Terebratulina* concerned only external changes since the opacity of the larvae precluded study of internal changes.

Kowalevski's observations on *Argyrotheca* are unsatisfactory, and those of Plenk on the same species scarcely less so, as he had no stages beyond the early larva. The blastopore closes by slitlike elongation, and the stomodaeum probably arises from some part of this. The coelomic sacs spread along the enteron and meet below it to establish a ventral mesentery, but a dorsal mesentery is never formed (Fig. 203*J*). At times the coelomic sacs become filled with mesenchyme cells, at other times present definite lumina. Besides the apical sensory plate there is a midventral sensory plate as in *Terebratulina*, and both main ganglia arise from these plates as in the latter. The nephridia appear in the latest stage available to Plenk as nearly solid rods of epithelial cells; his assumption that they are of peritoneal origin cannot be credited without further evidence. Kowalevski, supported by Shipley, indicates that the tentacles arise as paired protuberances on the inner side of the dorsal mantle lobe and increase in number lateral to the preceding pair, until they eventually surround the mouth. It will be recalled that the lophophore of *Argyrotheca* is of the schizolophous type (Fig. 194*A*). A median tentacle is definitely lacking. The circle of tentacles becomes elevated on a ridge.

Some further details of articulate development are furnished by Percival (1944) for *Terebratella inconspicua*. Here the first tentacles arise as a pair of protrusions below the mouth, and subsequent ones are added lateral to the preceding pairs to form a crescent around the mouth (Fig. 206*D*, *E*). Relation of the site of stomodaeal invagination to the blastopore could not be demonstrated. The anterior pair of coelomic sacs lies in the anterior and mantle regions of the larva, the posterior pair in the pedicle. Nothing is said as to the ultimate fate of these sacs as such. Filling of the coelomic sacs with mesenchyme cells at times and subsequent reappearance of the lumina were noted as in other articulates. The nephridia are said to arise as coelomic diverticula extending forward to the mouth region.

Percival was unable to find suitable landmarks for orienting his larvae and, on the sole basis of the relations of a pair of muscles that he identified as the ventral adjustors of the pedicle, concluded that the valves of articulates are the reverse of the usual interpretation, that is, that the larger valve is dorsal. On this ground he concluded that articulates and inarticulates show little correspondence and should be placed in separate phyla. In 1953, however, as a result of the study of the development of *Tegulorhynchia nigricans* (of which, unfortunately, no details have been published), he withdrew this suggestion and acknowledged the correctness of the standard interpretation of the orientation of the valves. It turned out that what he had previously interpreted as one pair of muscles was in fact the primordium of a whole group of muscles and could not be used for orienting the valves. The *Tegulorhynchia* larva is provided with four bundles of long setae that serve as landmarks and could be followed through mantle reversal. It was then found that the orientation of the valves of the young *Tegulorhynchia* is the same as that of *Lingula*. The present author is of the opinion that the splitting of brachiopods into two phyla is wholly untenable.

Nevertheless there are some striking differences between the development of the two classes. The mantle fold in inarticulates develops in its definitive position and does not undergo reversal as in articulates. The pedicle of the latter is the whole posterior part of the body; in the former it is an outgrowth of the ventral mantle lobe. There is a puzzling discordance in the accounts of the origin of the lophophore, and knowledge of the origin of the nephridia is unsatisfactory. On the other hand, there are many similarities in the development of the two classes. The embryology furnishes poor support for the interpretation that the body and the coelom are fundamentally divided into three parts in brachiopods as in other lophophorates, and the interpretation of the epistome as the protosome appears without any basis whatever. Brachiopods, in fact, appear rather distinct from the other two lophophorate phyla, and that is a main reason why the author declines to acknowledge a phylum Tentaculata.

13. Systematic Account: Class Inarticulata.—This class is characterized by the lack of an interlocking mechanism for the valves, which are held together by tissues only, by the presence of an anus, by the lack of an internal skeletal support (brachidium) for the lophophore, and by the direct development of the mantle, without reversal, in embryology. The class has long been divided into the two orders Atremata and Neotremata. The former comprises the single existing superfamily Lingulacea, with the single existing family Lingulidae distinguished by the thin, elongated, partly chitinous valves, having calcium phosphate as their main inorganic constituent, and the long flexible pedicle containing a coelomic lumen. There are two existing lingulid genera, *Lingula* and *Glottidia;* the latter is distinguished from the former by having a median or bifurcated septum on the inner surface of the valves (Fig. 208*A*, *B*). There are about a dozen existing species of *Lingula*, mostly limited to the tropical and subtropical waters of the Indo–West Pacific area, and numerous extinct species. According to Thomson (1927), *L. unguis* is the correct name of the species usually called *L. anatina*. Although the genus *Lingula* is known since the Ordovician, reckoned at 350,000,000 years ago, no *existing species* of *Lingula* goes very far back, contrary to current belief. However, the differences between the valves of extinct and present species appear minor. Schuchert (1897) remarks that the only change observable during the long fossil history of the genus is the greater space occupied by the viscera and the smaller size of the lophophore in the ancient forms. There are no species of *Lingula* known to occur on the coasts of the Americas. *Glottidia*, which does not seem to be recorded as a fossil, is best known by the species *pyramidata* from the coast of the Carolinas and Florida; other species occur in the Panamic region.

The order Neotremata comprises two superfamilies, Discinacea and Craniacea. In the former the valves are also of the chitinophosphatic type but the apex is nearly central and the valves are therefore circular in outline, slightly conical in profile (Figs. 183*D*, 210*A*). A pedicle is present that in the only existing family Discinidae issues from a slot in the posterior part of the ventral valve (Fig. 184*H*). There are three existing genera, *Discinisca*, *Pelagodiscus*, and *Discina*. In the first the valves are about equal and the lophophore is spirolophous. The best-known species, *Discinisca* (= *Orbicula*) *lamellosa*, Panamic in distribution, was monographed by Blochmann (1900). In *Pelagodiscus* the ventral valve is smaller than the dorsal, the lophophore is said to be of the schizolophous type, and the mantle is beset with very long, barbed setae. The only existing species, *P. atlanticus* (Fig. 183*E*), is a cosmopolitan abyssal species whose larvae are sometimes taken in the tow (page 571). In the poorly known *Discina* the thick valves are equal and the reduced opening for the pedicle occurs near the apex.

In the Craniacea, with single existing family Craniidae, a pedicle is wanting and the calcareous shell is cemented ventrally to a substrate. A marginal sinus and marginal setae are wanting. The genus *Crania*, with the characters of the family, is also very ancient, dating from the Ordovician. It has a number of living species, of which the best known is *C. anomala* from north European coasts, monographed by Blochmann (1892b). The genus *Craniscus* differs in the presence of muscle ridges on the inner surface of the dorsal valve.

14. Class Articulata.—This class, in which the valves are locked together posteriorly, includes the majority of existing brachiopods. Other characters are the calcareous nature of the valves, the presence of a brachidium, the blindly terminating intestine without anus, the foramen in the ventral valve for the passage of the pedicle, and mantle reversal at metamorphosis. Muir-Wood (1955) lists 25 superfamilies in the class, of which 21 are wholly extinct.

The superfamily Thecideacea, with the single family Thecideidae, lacks a pedicle and is cemented to a substrate by the ventral valve. The interior of the dorsal valve bears high curved ridges that support the lophophore (Fig. 185*D*), and the mantle is devoid of setae and heavily spiculated. Of the two existing genera the better known is *Lacazella* (= *Thecideum*) with main species *mediterranea* (Figs. 190*D*, 191*C*), of which a good account was given by Lacaze-Duthiers (1861). In this

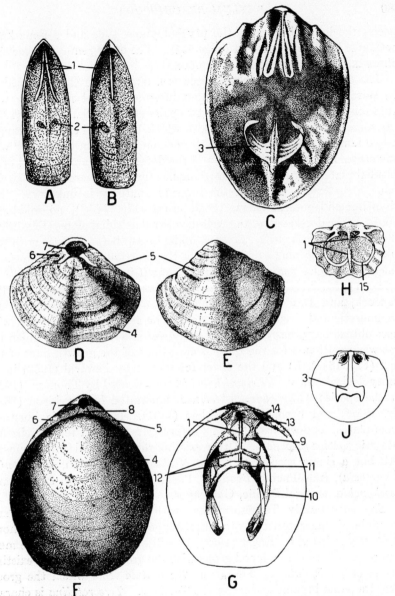

Fig. 208.—Brachiopods to illustrate systematic account. *A, B,* inner view of valves of *Glottidia pyramidata.* *A,* ventral valve. *B,* dorsal valve. *C,* interior of dorsal valve of *Bouchardia rosea,* showing reduced loop. *D, Terebratalia transversa,* dorsal view. *E,* same as *D,* ventral view. *F, Laqueus californianus,* dorsal view. *G,* same as *F,* inside view of dorsal valve, showing brachidium. *H,* interior of dorsal valve of *Argyrotheca cuneata,* showing brachidium. *J,* interior of dorsal valve of *Kraussina rubra,* showing reduced brachidium. (*All after Thomson, 1927, redrawn by him from Davidson.*) 1, septum; 2, impressions of anterior adductors; 3, remains of loop; 4, dorsal valve; 5, ventral valve; 6, palintrope; 7, foramen; 8, deltidial plates; 9, crural process; 10, descending part of loop; 11, recurved part of loop; 12, transverse bars; 13, hinge plates; 14, dental socket; 15, brachidium.

species the lophophore is of the ptycholophous type and a remarkable method of brooding is present (page 564). The other genus, *Thecidellina*, differs in the schizolophous lophophore.

The superfamily Rhynchonellacea is a large group characterized by the spirolophous lophophore, without internal skeletal support or with crura only, and by the presence of two pairs of nephridia. Roger (1952) lists some 135 genera in this group, of which 10 are still extant, arranged in two families, Dimerellidae and Rhynchonellidae. In the former with long crura, long middorsal septum in the dorsal valve, and reduced or no deltidial plates, hence with open triangular foramen, there is one existing genus, *Cryptopora*, of which the internal anatomy is unknown. The Rhynchonellidae have short, broad crura (Fig. 185C), no middorsal septum in the dorsal valve, and well-developed deltidial plates (Fig. 183G). The genus *Rhynchonella*, as now understood, became extinct in the Triassic. Of the nine existing genera the best known is *Hemithyris*, of which the species *psittacea* with prominent pointed beak (Fig. 183G–J) has been extensively treated in classical works on brachiopods by Huxley, Hancock, and Davidson. *Hemithyris* (= *Rhynchonella*) *psittacea* is a circumarctic and circumboreal species. The genus *Tegulorhynchia*, with short obtuse beak, has two species *döderleini* and *nigricans*, of which the first was mentioned for the spinous elevations of the growth lines of the shell (Fig. 184D, E) and the latter for its use by Percival (1953) in an embryological study. *Hispanirhynchia* was created by Thomson (1927) for the species "*Rhynchonella*" *cornea*, illustrated by Davidson (1887; Fig. 185H) and Fischer and Oehlert (1891). Its cardinalia illustrate hinge plates, as does also that of *Compsothyris*, created for the circumantarctic species *racovitzae*. Other existing rhynchonellid genera, mostly with but a single species each, are *Neohemithyris*, Japan, *Thomsonica* (= *Aetheia*), Indo-Pacific, *Basiliola*, Pacific, *Frieleia*, North Pacific, and *Neorhynchia*, Central Pacific, Galapagos.

The superfamily Terebratulacea, with one existing family Terebratulidae, is characterized by the short supporting loop in the lophophore. Of 64 genera listed by Roger (1952), 13 still exist, and of these the most important and the brachiopod genus with the greatest number of existing species is *Terebratulina*. The genus *Terebratula* from which the group takes its name became extinct in the Tertiary. *Terebratulina* is characterized by the transformation of the loop into a ring (Fig. 185K). Two of its species, *retusa* (= *caputserpentis*) and *septentrionalis*, have figured largely in morphological and embryological studies. *Dyscolia* (Fig. 192C–E) is notable for its trocholophous lophophore. In other genera the lophophore is plectolophous or nearly so. *Chlidonophora* was mentioned for the abyssal species *chuni* (Fig. 189F) with long pedicle bearing numerous attachment filaments. *Agulhasia* has a very triangular ventral valve with long beak bearing an open delthyrium provided with a pedicle collar (Fig. 184*A*, *B*). *Gryphus* (= *Liothyris*, *Liothyrina*), with short beak and well-developed pedicle collar, is best known by the species *vitreus*, Mediterranean, of which the valves were much figured by Davidson (1886b) and Fischer and Oehlert (1891) and which was used by van Bemmelen (1883) in his histological studies (Fig. 200*A*). The very similar *Liothyrella*, differing from *Gryphus* mostly in the angular shape of the loop, is known best by its main species *uva*, Panamic and Magellanic, also figured by Davidson. *Cancellothyris* for the Australian species *australis* (= *cancellata*) and *Abyssothyris* for the abyssal species *wyvillei* were both created by Thomson (1927) for species originally put in "*Terebratula*"; their valves also appear in Davidson's work. Other less known genera of the Terebratulidae are *Eucalathis*, *Cnismatocentrum*, *Murravia*, and *Surugathyris*.

The Terebratellacea are known by the long, recurved loop, usually associated with a plectolophous lophophore. The majority of existing brachiopods belong here, and it also was a great group in the past, comprising around 80 genera (Roger, 1952), of which 34 are still extant. Muir-Wood (1955) recognizes seven families, of which only one is wholly extinct. In the Megathyridae the loop is somewhat circular, lacking the recurved part, and the lophophore has not yet attained the plectolophous condition. Here belong *Gwynia* with trocholophous lophophore, *Argyrotheca* (= *Cistella*, *Argiope*) with bilobulate schizolophous lophophore (Fig. 194*A*), and *Megathyris* (= *Argiope*) with quadrilobulate, ptycholophous lophophore (Fig. 193*B*), supported by a scalloped loop that follows hollows of the dorsal valve (Fig. 185*B*). The Platidiidae, also lacking the typical terebratellacean loop but provided with a high median septum, include *Platidia*, notable for its sigmoid lophophore (Fig. 193*D*), and *Amphithyris* with schizolophous lophophore. In the Kraussinidae the brachidium is attached to a median septum and is imperfectly developed without recurved loop in *Kraussina* (Fig. 208*J*) and *Megerlina*, more typical in *Mühlfeldtia*, *Pantellaria*, and *Aldingia*. *Mühlfeldtia* (Fig. 184*G*) and *Pantellaria* are among the genera in which the foramen has usurped the cardinal area of the dorsal valve (page 526), and *Pantellaria echinata* was mentioned as having a spiny shell (Fig. 184*F*).

The three remaining terebratellacean families have the typical long loop, distally recurved. The Dallinidae with strong cardinalia have been much studied for the ontogenetic succession of stages of loop development (Fig. 186*A–G*). The best known of the 11 existing genera are *Dallina*, *Terebratalia*, *Dallinella*, and *Macandrevia* (correctly, *Macandrewia*) with dental plates (Fig. 185*A*) and *Frenulina* without them. *Dallina* with long middorsal septum and broad recurved part of the loop (Fig. 186*F*, *G*) has a common species *septigera* made familiar in classical works (David-

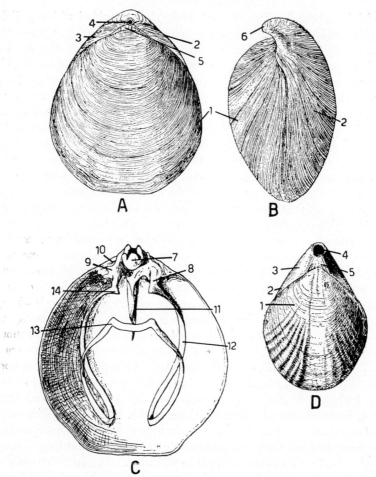

Fig. 209.—Systematic examples (concluded). *A*, dorsal view of *Neothyris lenticularis.* *B*, lateral view of *A*. *C*, interior of dorsal valve of *A*, showing brachidium. *D*, dorsal view of *Magellania australis.* (*All after Thomson*, 1927.)   1, dorsal valve; 2, ventral valve; 3, palintrope; 4, foramen; 5, deltidial plates; 6, beak; 7, cardinal process; 8, crura; 9, socket ridges; 10, dental sockets; 11, median septum; 12, descending part of loop; 13, recurved part of loop; 14, crural process.

son, 1886b). *Terebratalia* with shorter septum and narrow recurved part of the loop is familiar on the Pacific Coast of North America as the species *transversa* (Fig. 208*D*, *E*). *Dallinella*, distinguished from *Tere-bratalia* by the more plicated shell, has a species *occidentalis* (= *obsoleta*) off California. *Macandrevia* lacks a middorsal septum; the species *cranium*, North Atlantic, is well illustrated in classical works (Davidson, 1886a). In *Frenulina*, with main species *sanguinolenta*, western tropical Pacific, the middorsal septum reaches to the transverse band of the loop and is not united with the cardinalia.   Other genera of the Dallinidae are *Campages, Coptothyris, Diestothyris, Japanithyris, Jolonia,* and *Jaffaia*.

The family Laqueinidae, with dental plates, is characterized by the cross unions between the descending and recurved parts of the loop (Fig. 208*G*).   The genus *Laqueus*, with smooth, highly convex valves, is represented by the species *californianus* (Fig. 208*F*), found off the Pacific Coast of North America.   The only other existing genus of the family seems to be *Pictothyris*, Japan.

The last family, Terebratellidae, reaches the climax of the long-looped forms and, presumably, in all the loop passes through a complicated succession of ontogenetic stages as in the Dallinidae; however, the loop is imperfectly developed or retrogressed in the adults of some genera. There are no dental plates and no spicules in the body tissues.   Roger (1952) lists 11 existing genera, but some of these are unfamiliar or split off from others on minor grounds.   In *Bouchardia*, with single existing species *rosea*, Atlantic Coast of South America, the brachidium is reduced to a pair of curved processes from the middorsal septum (Fig. 208*C*). *Magadina*, with single existing species *cumingi*, Australia, is notable as the only brachiopod with a zugolophous lophophore in the adult state (Fig. 193*C*).   *Neothyris*, with typical terebratellid ("magellaniform") loop but reduced foramen, is best known by the species *lenticularis*, New Zealand, used by Richards (1952) in her study of ciliary feeding. *Magella*, New Zealand and Antarctic, with long septum and separated deltidial plates, is said by Thomson (1927) to be the direct ancestor of *Terebratella*.   *Terebratella*, with a number of species in the Southern Hemisphere, is characterized by the "terebratelliform" type of loop, in which the descending branches are connected to the septum by crossbars (Fig. 185*E*).   *Magellania* (= *Waldheimia*) reaches the climax of loop development in the family, with long, narrow loop entirely free from the septum (Fig. 184*O*).   The best-known species is *M. australis* (= *flavescens*), treated in the works of Hancock (1859) and Davidson (1886b).   Other existing genera are *Pirothyris, Stethothyris, Gyrothyris,* and *Victorithyris*.

V. ECOLOGY AND PHYSIOLOGY

1. Habits and Behavior.—Brachiopods are exclusively marine and benthonic, belonging for the most part to the shelf fauna, that is, the littoral zone from the lowest tide levels to the edges of the continental shelves; but some extend into abyssal waters.   Except the lingulids, they live permanently attached by the pedicle or, in the absence of a pedicle, directly by the ventral valve, to rocks, shells, and other firm objects. *Chlidonophora chuni* is especially adapted for life on the *Globigerina* ooze, having a long pedicle provided with delicate filaments that attach to

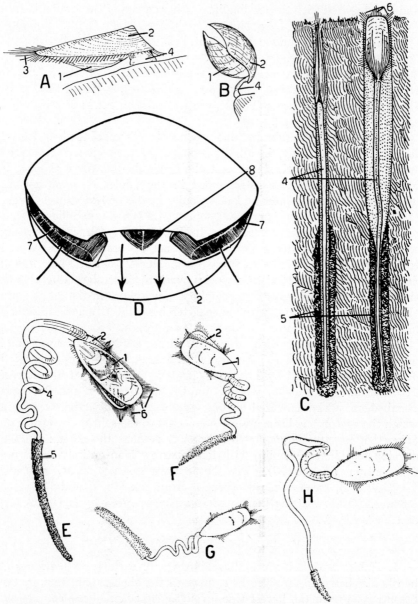

FIG. 210.—Ecology.   *A, Discinisca lamellosa* in natural position.   *B, Hemithyris psittacea*, erected (*after Heller*, 1931).   *C, Lingula* in its burrow, two views (*after François*, 1891). *D, Neothyris lenticularis* in feeding position (*after Richards*, 1952).   *E, Glottidia pyramidata* (*after Morse*, 1873b).   *F–H*, other attitudes of *Glottidia*.   (*A, F–H, after Morse*, 1902.) 1, dorsal valve; 2, ventral valve; 3, setae; 4, pedicle; 5, sand agglomeration around distal end of pedicle; 6, setae bundles that channel currents; 7, lateral arm lophophore; 8, median arm lophophore.

foraminiferan shells (Fig. 189*F*). Brachiopods, except lingulids, usually take a horizontal attitude, with the larger ventral valve uppermost (Figs. 183*A*, 210*A*), but may erect to a vertical position (Fig. 210*B*) by manipulating the adjustor muscles of the pedicle. However, some forms as *Lacazella* and *Crania* and other Craniidae are permanently cemented by the ventral valve with the dorsal valve uppermost (Fig. 190*D*). Movements of attached brachiopods are mostly limited to opening and closing the valves along their anterior margins. Typically, only a limited gape is possible (Fig. 210*D*), but *Lacazella* can erect its dorsal valve at right angles to the fixed ventral valve (Fig. 191*C*). Upon disturbance the valves close quickly. Some movement on the pedicle appears possible in most cases, such as various degrees of erection; *Terebratalia transversa* was observed to rotate considerably on its pedicle (Ricketts and Calvin, 1939), and such rotation is probably generally feasible.

Lingulids are more active than other brachiopods. Their habits have been described by François (1891), Morse (1873a, b), and Yatsu (1902c). They live in vertical burrows, flattened distally, cylindrical proximally, in sandy shores or in Japan on black, smelly mud flats. The animal has an erect position in the burrow (Fig. 210*C*) and when undisturbed partly protrudes the shell, with valves slightly opened. The burrow is lined with mucus, presumably secreted by the glandular zone of the mantle lobes, and the lower end of the long, flexible pedicle is encased with agglomerated sand grains stuck together with mucus. This encasement of the free end of the pedicle by agglomerated sand grains is a constant feature of lingulids, and the case is promptly reformed when lost. When put into a shallow dish of sand, lingulids are later found adherent to the bottom of the dish by this sand tube formed around the distal end of the pedicle. The opening of the natural burrow is slitlike, with three widenings maintained by the setae for the water currents (see below). The setae also may be bent across the mouth of the burrow to prevent sand from falling in. Upon disturbance the shell withdraws at once for a considerable distance into the burrow, whereupon the opening may be concealed by sand or mud falling into it. The setae are in general quite active, can swing back and forth in *Glottidia*, and can propel the animal over the sand by an oarlike action. In *Glottidia*, when removed from its burrow, the long slender pedicle is thrown into a succession of wormlike convolutions (Fig. 210*E–H*). Burrowing is accomplished by shoveling with the dorsal valve, moving it up and down, or by vermiform movements of the pedicle. The burrow may be later widened by lateral movements of the valves. The valves are evidently much more mobile in lingulids than in other brachiopods. The dorsal valve not only may be raised and lowered but can be slid sidewise on the ventral valve.

Both *Lingula* and *Glottidia* are stated by Morse (1902) to retreat into their burrows on the passing of a shadow.   He suggested that the brown pigment on the mantle edge might have some relation to phototactic response.   Lacaze-Duthiers (1861) recorded that *Lacazella* would snap down its raised dorsal valve at the passing of even a small shadow.

The brachiopods, like other lophophorates, are ciliary feeders, and the lophophore is their food-catching mechanism.   When the animal is feeding, the valves gape to the extent shown in Fig. 210*D* (a wider gape is possible in *Lacazella*, as already mentioned).   The tentacles usually extend only to the valve edges or slightly beyond, although Orton (1914) found the tentacles considerably protruded in feeding *Crania*.   Protrusion of the arm is mechanically impossible in most brachiopods, but *Hemithyris psittacea* has been seen to protrude an unrolled arm tip (Joubin, 1886; Morse, 1902).   All observers are agreed that a feeding brachiopod maintains two ingoing water currents, one on each side, and a median outgoing current (Fig. 210*D*).   In lingulids the setae incline to outline channels for these currents, being, further, longer at the sites of the currents and shorter on adjacent regions (Fig. 211*D*).   A detailed study of the feeding currents was made by Orton (1914) for *Crania*, Richards (1952) for *Neothyris lenticularis*, Chuang (1956) for *Lingula unguis*, and Atkins (1956) for *Terebratulina retusa*, *Gryphus vitreus*, and *Macandrevia cranium*.

Orton attributes the ingoing currents to the lateral tracts of tentacular cilia that beat across the tentacles in an inward direction and are somewhat assisted in producing the current by the cilia on the rest of the lophophore and on the mantle epidermis.   The tentacles are held close to the dorsal mantle; hence the larger particles fall onto the ventral mantle and are ejected by its currents.   It will be recalled that *Crania* is fastened to the substrate by its ventral valve; hence the dorsal valve is here uppermost.   The main current carrying the smaller food particles passes successively through the spiral turns of the lophophore, hence through tiers of tentacles whose cilia act as sieves to strain out the particles.   The frontal cilia are the main agents for catching and assembling these particles, which are finally passed into the brachial groove.   This is heavily ciliated with cilia that beat toward the mouth, into which suitable particles are conveyed.   Meantime the current, having reached the summit of the lophophore coil, proceeds centrally and exits.   Cilia on the lophophore arm adjacent to the brachial groove also beat toward this groove and aid in directing food particles into it; cilia on the lophophore arm opposite the groove beat away from the latter and carry particles to be expelled.   The secretion of mucus also plays an important role in the collection and transportation of food particles.   Mucus is secreted on the frontal side of the tentacles where glands may be seen in Fig. 195*E*, *F*.

Chuang's account for *Lingula unguis* agrees essentially with that of

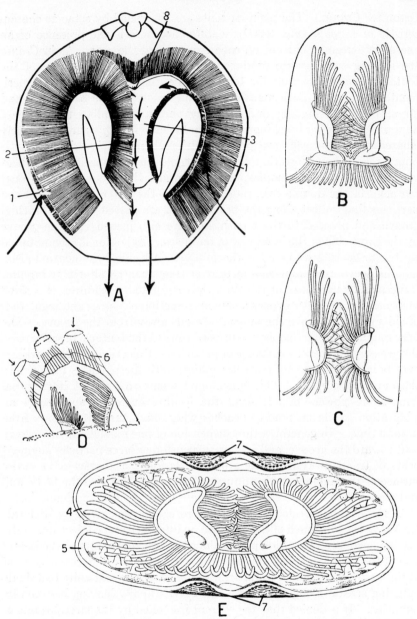

Fig. 211.—Ecology (concluded). *A*, interior of *Neothyris*, with one lateral arm partly cut away, showing course of the feeding current (*after Richards, 1952*). *B*, attitude of lophophore of *Glottidia*, ventral view from life. *C*, same as *B*, dorsal view. *D*, *Lingula* in feeding attitude with setae outlining water channels. *E*, *Glottidia*, feeding, seen from in front with lophophore in position. (*B–E, after Morse, 1902.*) 1, lateral arm of lophophore; 2, median arm of lophophore; 3, brachial gutter; 4, dorsal mantle lobe; 5, ventral mantle lobe; 6, setae; 7, mantle lobulations between currents; 8, mouth.

Orton for *Crania*. The main currents are channeled by setae as characteristic of *Lingula* (Fig. 211*D*); a difference here is the presence of an
accessory outgoing current on each side toward the rear. As in *Crania*
the ingoing currents are produced by the lateral tracts of cilia of the
tentacles that beat across the tentacles in an ingoing direction. Experimental removal of both mantle lobes did not affect the occurrence and
strength of the ingoing and outgoing currents. Unlike the state of
affairs in most other brachiopods, the tentacles of *L. unguis* are completely
ciliated. Mucous cells are present, although mucus is said to play a
minor role in transportation of food particles in this species. The beat
of the short cilia is complex, mostly toward the groove in the inner
tentacles of the double row, mostly away in the outer tentacles. Food
particles that collect along the brachial fold are passed into the brachial
groove and proceed to the mouth, and are also passed into the groove
by the short cilia of the inner row of tentacles. Rejection is accomplished
by tracts beating away from the groove. All cilia beat continuously,
but the speed and amplitude of beat of tracts can be altered to circumstances and acceptance or rejection thus regulated. Addition of a thick
suspension of particles evokes a copious secretion of mucus and regulation
of ciliary beat to move the mucous strands away from the groove. The
very mobile brachial fold can be pressed toward the tentacle bases to close
the groove and prevent entrance of particles. Rejection of large particles
may be accomplished by tentacle coilings until the particles fall off into
the outgoing current. This brachiopod seems to have at its disposal
remarkable powers of adjusting the feeding currents, apparently an
adaptation to life on muddy beaches where high turbidity occurs from
time to time. In general, a thin suspension of fine particles favors ciliary
beat toward the groove, and a thick suspension or large particles augment
beats of tracts away from the groove. Besides the tentacles the entire
surface of the lophophore is uniformly ciliated, as are also the body wall
and mantle lobes; these surfaces act mainly as rejection mechanisms.

A rather different account from the foregoing was given by Richards
for *Neothyris*, but much of it was based on inference and conjecture. The
ingoing current on each side passes along the brachial gutter of the lateral
arm of the plectolophous lophophore; these two currents necessarily meet
at the base of the median spiral arm, where they turn and unite to a single
outgoing stream along that arm (Fig. 211*A*), finally leaving between its
tentacles. It is denied that the current is evoked by the lateral tracts of
cilia. It is claimed that both lateral and frontal cilia of the tentacles beat
toward the tentacle tips and carry off heavier particles, dropping them
onto the mantle. Lighter particles remain in suspension, accumulate near
the brachial folds of the median arm, and are carried by the cilia on these
folds into the brachial grooves, whose cilia transport them to the mouth.

Some similar collection of suitable particles occurs in the lateral arms, but main food collection takes place in the spiral arm. Specimens dissected after being fed colored particles showed great concentration of such particles in the brachial groove of the median spiral arm along its length. As length in such a process is an important factor, the spiral coiling of the median arm of the plectolophous lophophore is thus explained. Mucus also plays an important role here. A thin sheet of mucus secreted by the epithelium of the brachial groove acts as a vehicle for ciliary transportation of the entrapped particles. The final entry of such mucous strings into the mouth appears to be aided by the ciliary beat of the esophagus. Mucus is also involved in the preliminary rejection of undesirable particles. Mucous strands containing such particles accumulate along the anterior edges of the mantle lobes and are finally ejected by a sudden closure of the valves. In the presence of a large amount of particulate matter in the water as silt or carmine powder, large quantities of mucus are secreted and all particles rejected, as Chuang also observed.

It may be said of Richards's work that she gives no satisfactory explanation of the origin of the current; the ingoing currents are said to be pulled in by the outgoing current, which is attributed to the cilia of the mantles and spiral arm. But there are said to be no cilia on the arms except those on the tentacles, brachial folds, and brachial grooves, and the cilia of the folds beat into the grooves, and those of the grooves into the mouth. It is difficult to believe that the mantle cilia are strong enough to evoke the current. As long as Richards's account was the only one for an articulate, one was forced to suppose articulates differ from inarticulates in this as well as other regards. But in 1956 Atkins studied the ciliary currents in three articulates and supported the accounts of Orton and Chuang that the main water current is evoked by the beat of the lateral tracts of tentacular cilia across the tentacles and in the direction from the inside to the outside of the lophophoral spaces. In young stages with simple trocholophous lophophore, the ingoing current is single and median and the water escapes through the tentacles all around the lophophore, exiting laterally and ventrally on each side. The frontal currents were found to be reversible, conveying small particles to the tentacle bases and so into the brachial groove, large particles to the tentacle tips for rejection. No change was observed in direction of beat of the lateral cilia. The tentacles appeared to be completely ciliated in the species observed by Atkins, and the short cilia on the side of the tentacles away from the groove beat toward the tentacular tips.

The food consists of minute organisms, especially diatoms. Hancock in 1859 already noted that diatoms are almost always present in the stomach and intestine of articulates. Lingulids are more general feeders; there have been seen in their digestive tracts (Hancock, 1859; Blochmann,

1900), besides diatoms, dinoflagellates, foraminiferans, radiolarians, mollusk larvae, small crustaceans, sponge spicules, annelid setae, calcareous rods of plutei, vegetable matter, and mud and sand.

Various authors have commented on the remarkable hardiness of brachiopods in laboratory cultures. Lacaze-Duthiers (1861) records that *Lacazella mediterranea* brought from the Mediterranean lived well for 6 weeks in the laboratory and displayed normal behavior. Joubin (1886) kept *Crania anomala* in the laboratory over 14 months, during which they were subjected to extremes of light and temperature and changes of salinity and were transported about two or three times. Blochmann (1892b) also noted that this species would live in a healthy condition for some time in aquaria. Morse (1902) kept *Glottidia pyramidata* for 6 months in a small dish of sand that also went on journeys, and reported similar survival for a species of *Lingula* that he brought from Japan to Massachusetts. Francois (1891) had good survival of *Lingula unguis* in the laboratory. Cloud (1948), however, could not keep *Terebratulina septentrionalis* even a few days and failed to transport them from Maine to Cape Cod.

Brachiopods do not reproduce asexually. They probably have good powers of regeneration, but definite experiments are wanting. It is known that the pedicle of lingulids regenerates promptly even when removed close to the valves (François, 1891; Yatsu, 1902c).

Morse (1902) surmises that lingulids live only about a year, since he found them in summer collecting all of one size without any small ones. However, Yatsu (1902c) observed that Japanese *Lingula* require a year to grow from the larval stage to a shell length of 5 mm.; and since the adults attain a shell length of 35 mm., the life span must be at least 7 years. Percival (1944) surmises that *Terebratella inconspicua* lives about 4 years.

2. Biological Relations.—Brachiopods tend to live in aggregations of the same or other species. This may result simply from the settling of larvae near or on adults in favorable sites. The dispersal power of larvae is generally judged as very limited. Blochmann (1892b) recorded getting 150 *Crania anomala* in one haul of the dredge off Norway near Bergen. Similarly 100 *Hemithyris psittacea* attached to each other or to pebbles were taken in one small dredge at Jan Mayen (Remy, 1928). Rein (1887) and Yatsu (1902c) have stated that *Lingula* is (or was) so common in certain Japanese localities as to be gatherable by the basketful. The MacGinities (1949) report that *Laqueus californianus* is sometimes dredged by the tubful off the Pacific Coast of North America and that the common lingulid of this region, *Glottidia albida*, may occur in spots in aggregations of about 20 to the square foot (also Mattox, 1955). Another common species of eastern Pacific shores, *Terebratalia transversa*, was found by Ricketts and Calvin (1939) in great numbers in a land-locked marine lake in British Columbia; the unusually large size and strong coloration of the individuals in this aggregation testified to highly favorable conditions. Mattox (1955) described an aggregation of brachiopods, including four species, along the northeastern coast of Santa Catalina Island, off Southern California. The most common member, *Laqueus californianus*, typically occurred in clusters of several up to 31 individuals attached to a rock or each other or a mollusk (Fig. 212). Another member, *Terebratalia transversa*, was more common off Santa Cruz Island, associated with still another brachiopod species.

As sessile animals brachiopods are necessarily associated with a long list of other sessile, sedentary, or burrowing animals, but none of these combinations has been shown to be specific. The MacGinities (1949) indicate a possible association of a sipunculoid, *Phascolosoma hesperum*, with *Glottidia albida* off California.

According to Blochmann (1908), brachiopods are often found in the stomach of fish. *Lingula* is eaten by man in Japan (Yatsu, 1902c), either whole or the pedicle only, and the pedicles are also eaten off

Fig. 212.—Cluster of *Laqueus californianus* growing on another brachiopod; note mantle canals. (*Photograph, courtesy Dr. Norman Mattox.*)

Queensland (Banfield, 1918). Blochmann (1892b) reported monocystid gregarines in the intestine of *Crania anomala*, and Shipley (1883) saw a lichomolgid copepod on the lophophore of *Argyrotheca*.

3. Physiology.—The shells generally consist of calcium carbonate in the form of calcite (Stehli, 1956b). Clarke and Wheeler (1915) analyzed the shells of four articulate species and found 1 to 5 per cent of organic matter. The inorganic matter consisted of about 98 per cent of calcium carbonate, with small amounts of silicon dioxide, aluminum ferrous oxide, magnesium carbonate, calcium sulphate, and traces of calcium phosphate. In the calcareous inarticulate, *Crania anomala*, the calcium carbonate was reduced to about 89 per cent and the magnesium carbonate increased to 8.63 per cent. In four species of phosphatic inarticulates (*Lingula, Glottidia, Discinisca*) the organic content of the valves ranged from 25 to 40 per cent, and of the inorganic constituents 75 to 92 per cent consisted of calcium phosphate, highest in *Lingula*. Other inorganic constituents were similar to those of articulates qualitatively, but magnesium carbonate was increased to 6.68 per cent in *Discinisca* and calcium sulphate to 3 to

8.37 per cent. *Discinisca lamellosa* is notable for the relatively large content of the last two salts. The author (1958) verified the old findings of Schmiedeberg (1882) and Krukenberg (1885) that the shells of inarticulates contain a large amount of chitin, except Craniidae, which are devoid of chitin. Articulate shells are devoid of chitin, but the thick cuticle of their pedicle, as also in lingulids, is made of chitin.

Food is passed along the digestive tract by peristalsis in the esophagus and stomach, witnessed in living brachiopods by Morse (1902). Nothing is known of the process of digestion, which seems to take place chiefly in the digestive gland, where diatoms and other food have been seen by Morse and other observers. The acini of the digestive gland constantly expand and contract (Morse, 1902) and continue this for hours in an opened animal. Hancock (1859) noted pellets of feces in the intestine of *Lingula* but never saw any feces in the intestine of articulates. However, Morse (1902) observed ejection of feces from the mouth in *T. septentrionalis*. According to Chuang (1956), fecal pellets in *Lingula* are moved into the outgoing current by cilia of the body wall anterior to the anus.

The small size of brachiopods and great expanse of surface of the lophophore obviate the necessity of a special respiratory mechanism in this group. Early observers regarded the lophophore as a respiratory structure comparable to the gills of mollusks, but it has long since been proved that the lophophore is primarily a food-catching device. However, the lophophore must inevitably be of respiratory service because of the great surface of exposure of the tentacles. The ciliary currents accomplish the dual function of feeding and of bringing in and carrying away respiratory gases. The tentacles contain blood channels, but probably the coelomic fluid circulating in the tentacular lumina and coelomic canals of the lophophore is more important in respiration than the circulatory system.

In the early days of investigation of brachiopod anatomy, there was much argument about the existence of a heart and a circulatory system. Some could not find the heart vesicle at all, and others that did find it never saw any contractions. Thus Morse (1902) never saw the heart contract in many specimens of articulates that were opened for this purpose and in which other activities continued for hours. Blochmann (1885, 1892a) is the only witness to contractions of the heart vesicle or vesicles and the middorsal blood channel. He saw the contractions in several living articulates as well as in *Crania* and records them as occurring every 30 to 40 seconds in timed cases. The presence of a conspicuous muscle layer in the wall of the heart and adjacent parts of the dorsal channel (Schaeffer, 1926; Fig. 199*C, D*) sufficiently indicates contractility of these parts.

All observers of living brachiopods have noticed the lively circulation, due to cilia (or flagella?), of the coelomic fluid in the mantle canals and coelomic canals of the lophophore and its tentacles; further, in the pedicle of lingulids. This circulation was naturally mistaken in early days for a blood circulation and even in 1941 Kawaguti designated the coelomic fluid as blood. This circulation is presumably of respiratory value. In all the canals the current runs in two opposed directions, out along one side, back along the other. This is made possible by the presence of a low ridge that divides the current. In the mantle canals the ridge is found in the wall nearest the shell.

The coelomic fluid is coagulable and often colored pink or violet, apparently from the presence of a respiratory pigment in its so-called corpuscles, the rounded type of coelomocyte already mentioned (page 555). Kawaguti (1941) investigated what he called the blood of *Lingula*, drawn from the mantle canals. This fluid turns reddish purple on contact with air, becomes colorless again in low oxygen. In the corpuscles is found a reddish-brown pigment, containing iron, but no copper, and determined by spectroscopic examination to be a haemerythrin, similar to that known for sipunculoids. This has a low ability to take up oxygen but is very easily reduced, readily giving up oxygen to the tissues. Nothing is known about the real blood, which presumably differs but little from the coelomic fluid with which it must be in communication by way of tissue spaces.

Heller (1931) attempted to investigate the function of the nephridia by the usual method of injection of dyes and carmine and carbon suspensions into the coelom. He used *Hemithyris psittacea*, in which the nephridial epithelium is greatly folded and highly glandular (Fig. 202*E*), and *Terebratulina retusa* with smooth, scarcely glandular lining (Fig. 202*B*). The former appeared much more active in excretory function. Particulate suspensions begin to be ingested in a few minutes by the amoeboid types of coelomocytes (also observed by Blochmann, 1892b, in *Crania*). Particles are also taken up by the peritoneal cells that then seem to detach and disintegrate. In the opened animal under magnification streams of particles could be seen moving toward the nephrostomes, and in removed nephridia rhythmic waves of flagellar beat toward the nephridiopores were observed. In *Hemithyris* some hours are required for injected material to pass through the complicated interior foldings of the nephridium. Mucus is secreted by the lining epithelium, and 4 to 5 hours after the injection mucous strands containing dyes, particles, coelomocytes, and disintegrated peritoneal cells are observed passing out of the nephridiopores. Material passed much more rapidly through the more simple nephridia of *Terebratulina*. Sections of nephridia removed and fixed at various times after the injection of carbon suspension showed absorption of particles by the nephridial epithelium, beginning 2 to 4 hours after the injection and continuing for 1 to 2 days, during which time the cells become filled with particles. Several days are required for the cells to rid themselves of the particles which are sometimes given off in vesicles. These processes are much more pronounced in *Hemithyris* than in *Terebratulina*. Injected dissolved dyes are taken in by coelomocytes, where they accumulate in colored vacuoles, and by the peritoneum; hence the whole interior becomes colored. This color rapidly fades, except in the nephridia, which tend to retain it for several days, up to 10. No distinction was noted between the effect of alkaline and acid dyes, and tests indicated that the interior of the brachiopod is neutral to litmus. The digestive tract appeared not to participate in the elimination of injected material.

Nothing is known of the functional activity of the nervous system, but the accounts of the ciliary feeding currents given by Chuang and Atkins indicate extensive nervous control of ciliary beat. The sudden closure of the valves on disturbance and the withdrawal of lingulids into their burrows by peduncular contraction must involve typical nervous circuits. Morse (1902) noticed that the statoliths in the statocysts of lingulids constantly vibrate. Yatsu (1902b) was of the opinion that the epithelium of the statocysts is ciliated, although the cilia in his preparations had been destroyed by fixation.

4. Geographic Distribution.—The brachiopods inhabit all seas at all latitudes and occur at all depths from the zone of low tide into the abyssal zone. They are very rarely found above low-tide levels, although Hertlein and Grant (1944) record one such finding of *Terebratalia transversa* in rock pools in Puget Sound above high-tide level. It is stated by Cori (1933) that brachiopods cannot endure water of less than 30 parts salinity per thousand, and hence are wanting from the Baltic and other brackish areas of north European coasts. However, Yatsu (1902c) found *Lingula* in normal and healthy condition after 20 days of heavy rain had flooded their mud flat with fresh water and muddy sediment, killing all the bivalves and other animals present. Schuchert (1911) estimated that 3 per cent of brachiopods live along the low-tide level, 81 per cent live on the continental shelves to depths of 200 to 300 m., and 3 per cent are permanent inhabitants of cold abyssal waters, with the remainder in the transitional or archibenthal zone. Valuable articles on distribution are those of Dall (1921) and Hatai (1936b).

At the present time brachiopods are most abundant around Japan, off southern Australia, and around New Zealand, and they occur in fair abundance in the North Atlantic, the Arctic, the Antarctic, and the Mediterranean (Cooper, 1954). This distribution seems to indicate a preference for cooler waters and an avoidance of fully tropical areas, where, however, brachiopods are by no means absent, although mostly confined to less shallow waters.

The characteristic brachiopod of the Arctic (Stephen, 1927; Grieg, 1928; Arndt and Grieg, 1933) is *Hemithyris psittacea* (Figs. 183*G*, *H*, 210*B*), which is practically circumarctic, also circumboreal. Remy (1928) found it so common at Jan Mayen at about 72° north latitude that 100 were taken in one haul of a small dredge. Elliott (1956) surmises that this species spread from the Pacific through the Arctic Ocean to the Atlantic in Pleistocene times. In the North Pacific it is spread south to Japan and Puget Sound and Oregon; in the western North Atlantic to Greenland, Labrador, and Maine; and in the eastern Atlantic along Norway to the Shetlands, Hebrides, Orkneys, and northern Britain. Other familiar North Atlantic species are *Macandrevia cranium*, Norway and Spitsbergen to Greenland and south to Spain and Cape Cod, *Terebratulina septentrionalis*, Norway, Scotland, Nova Scotia to Cape Cod and New York, *T. retusa* (= *caputserpentis*), Murman coast and Norway to the British Isles and into the Mediterranean, also Japan, *Terebratella* (generic name varies) *spitzbergensis*, Arctic Sea to Gulf of St. Lawrence, *Dallina septigera*, Norway to the Canary Islands, *Cryptopora gnomon*, North Atlantic to the West Indies, and *Crania anomala*, Norway to Portugal. It will be noticed that there is the usual southward spread from the arctic and boreal Atlantic along the coast of North America as far as Cape Cod and along northern European coasts to Spain or even Africa and into the Mediterranean. Some characteristic Mediterranean species not found north are *Lacazella mediterranea*, *Gryphus vitreus*, *Megathyris detruncata*, and species of *Argyrotheca*.

From the foregoing it is evident that the only brachiopod to be found in the shallow waters of New England is *Terebratulina septentrionalis*, extensively studied by Morse (1871, 1873a, b, 1902; Fig. 203*A*). A variant of *Macandrevia cranium* occurs in deeper water, below 250 m. Farther south the characteristic species is *Glottidia pyramidata* (Fig. 210*E–H*), not uncommon in very shallow water on sandy beaches from Carolina to the Gulf side of Mexico where it mingles with the West Indian fauna. West Indian brachiopods, as listed by Cooper (1954), include *Crania pourtalesii*, *Cryptopora gnomon*, *Terebratulina cailleti*, *Gryphus cubensis* and *bartlettii*, *Argyrotheca barrettiana*, *lutea*, and *schrammi*, and *Dallina floridana*, but most of these have not been found above depths of 100 m. The most common of these species appears to be *Ter. cailleti*, which has been recorded up to 30 m., and *Arg. schrammi* ascends to 45 m. *Cryptopora gnomon* is found throughout the North Atlantic, mostly at depths of 1800 to 4000 m., but in the West Indies ascends to about 200 m. It is interesting to note that another species of

Chlidonophora, incerta, occurs in the West Indian region but mostly in quite deep waters, 2000 to 3000 m., although there is a record of its occurrence at 540 m. near Havana. There are some species in common between the West Indies and the northeastern Atlantic as *Dyscolia wyvillei* (Fig. 192C–E) and *Platidia anomioides* (Fig. 193D), and a spread of species of deeper water across the Atlantic is understandable. Blochmann (1908) further called attention to the close resemblance between *Gryphus cubensis* and *G. sphenoideus,* from Portugal and the Bay of Biscay.

There is little knowledge of the brachiopods of the eastern coast of South America, north of the Magellanic area. Two West Indian species, *Argyrotheca lutea* and *barretiana,* are recorded as extending to Brazil, and *Bouchardia rosea* is known from Brazil only.

Hertlein and Grant (1944) have given an exhaustive account of the brachiopods of the Pacific Coast of North America and list 31 existing species from the Bering Sea to Panama, but few of these are common enough and accessible enough to be ordinarily seen. Some of the species are in common with Japan. The circumarctic *Hemithyris psittacea* descends into Puget Sound and onto the Oregon coast. The most common species limited to the Pacific Coast is *Terebratalia transversa* (Fig. 208D, E) found in shallow waters from Alaska to Mexico. These two species plus *Laqueus vancouveriensis* and *Terebratulina unguicula* were found by Du Bois (1916) to constitute the available brachiopod fauna of Puget Sound. All four have their maximum abundance in deeper waters, 54 to 160 m., but *Laqueus* and *Terebratalia* range to low-tide levels. The most common species in shallow water on the coast of California are *Glottidia albida,* burrowing in fine, clean sand and adaptable to changes of salinity and other conditions, and *Laqueus californianus* (Fig. 208F). These two species plus *Terebratalia transversa* and *occidentalis* constituted the aggregation already mentioned living along Santa Cruz Island (Mattox, 1955).

The Panamic region, from Southern California to Ecuador, Peru, and the Galapagos Islands, has a number of endemic brachiopods, especially members of the genus *Discinisca,* which seems to center there, with no less than four endemic species, including the well-known *D. lamellosa* (Fig. 210A). Another inarticulate of the area is *Glottidia audebarti.* Abyssal species of the Panamic region include *Gryphus clarkeana,* 2000 to 3600 m., *Macandrevia americana,* 220 to 3000 m., and other species of *Macandrevia,* and *Neorhynchia strebeli,* 3700 m.

Northward in the Pacific one passes to Japan, which has brachiopod elements in common with North America, northern Europe, and the tropical West Pacific as well as many endemic species. Japanese brachiopods have been thoroughly considered by Hatai (1936a, 1940). For its size Japan has the richest brachiopod fauna in the world, listed by Hatai in 1936 as 50 species in 23 genera, of which 34 species are limited to Japan. The common species of northern Europe, *Hemithyris psittacea* and *Terebratulina retusa*, extend to Japan and no doubt are of European provenance. About four species are found in common between Japan and the Pacific Coast of North America (*Frieleia halli*, *Terebratulina crossei* and *kiiensis*, and *Diestothyris frontalis*). About 10 species are also found in the tropical and subtropical West Pacific and may be regarded as having spread from there into southern Japan. The most common genera around Japan are *Lingula* with eight species, including *unguis*, of which five are limited to Japan; *Terebratulina* with nine species, four exclusively Japanese; and *Laqueus* with nine species limited to Japan. The following genera, mostly with one species each, are confined to Japan: *Neohemithyris*, *Coptothyris*, *Japanithyris*, *Pictothyris*, *Nipponithyris*, and *Surugathyris*.

The tropical and subtropical waters of the Indo–West Pacific area are relatively poor in brachiopods, except for the genus *Lingula*, which is spread through this area from the Philippines, Java, and Queensland to Japan and Hawaii and does not occur elsewhere. A wide distribution is shown by the most common species, *unguis* (= *anatina*). *Discinisca indica* is limited to the Indo-Pacific, although the genus in general is Panamic, and there are also some West Pacific species of *Crania*. Some other species characteristic of and mostly confined to the Indo–West Pacific are *Hispanirhynchia bartschi*, *Basiliola pompholyx*, *Terebratulina reevei* and *valdiviae*, *Gryphus borneoensis*, and *Frenulina sanguinolenta*. The genus *Jolonica*, with one species *hedleyi*, is known only from the Philippines.

Southern Australia, including Tasmania, lies outside the subtropical Pacific and shows the expected increase in brachiopod fauna with cooler waters, being about as rich in this group as Japan, with which country it about corresponds in latitude. About 20 species are confined to the southern Australia-Tasmania region, and the following genera with one species each are limited to this area: *Magadina*, *Pirothyris*, *Cancellothyris*, *Murravia*, *Jaffaia*, and *Aldingia*. *Lingula* is absent from southern Australia, although several species occur on the Queensland coast (Johnston and Hirschfeld, 1919), which may be regarded as on the fringe of the subtropical West Pacific. Some characteristic brachiopods of South Australia are *Cryptopora brazieri*, *Aetheia colurnus*, *Murravia exarata*, *Cancellothyris cancellata*, *Gryphus fulva*, *Argyrotheca australis*, *Kraussina atkinsoni*, *Megerlina lamarckiana*, *Aldingia willemoesi*, *Jaffaia jaffaensis*, *Magadina cumingi* (Fig. 193C), *Pyrothyris vercoi*, and *Magellania flavescens* (Fig. 209D).

The brachiopods of New Zealand are related to those of southern

Australia. *Terebratella inconspicua*, used by Percival (1944) in his embryological study, is common to the two regions. *Tegulorhynchia* is well represented in New Zealand, Tasmania, and southern Australia by fossil species (Chapman and Crespin, 1923), but only *T. nigricans* survives, limited to New Zealand. Other endemic brachiopods of New Zealand are *Crania huttoni*, *Morrisia* (or *Amphithyris*) *buckmani*, *Terebratella sanguinea*, and *Neothyris lenticularis* (Fig. 209*A–C*), used by Richards in her study of feeding (1952). As this is the only known species of *Neothyris*, the genus is endemic to New Zealand.

The brachiopods known from South Africa have not been found elsewhere, and the genus *Agulhasia* with the single species *davidsoni* (Fig. 184*A–C*) is limited to the region. The genus *Kraussina* appears centered around South Africa, having four of its seven species endemic to this region; the others are spread eastward into the Indian Ocean to Tasmania. Other species also not known elsewhere are *Terebratulina abyssicola* (not abyssal) and *Terebratella rubiginosa*.

The brachiopods of the Antarctic and Subantarctic have been collected by the usual succession of expeditions: the Mission to Cape Horn (Fischer and Oehlert, 1892a), the Belgian Expedition (Joubin, 1901), the National Antarctic Expedition (Smith, 1907), the German South Polar Expedition (Eichler, 1910), the Scottish Expedition (Jackson, 1912), the Swedish South Polar Expedition (Blochmann, 1912b), the Australasian Antarctic Expedition (Thomson, 1918), and the British Antarctic Expedition (Jackson, 1918). The species of the Subantarctic or Magellanic area are in general distinct from those of the true Antarctic. Typical Magellanic brachiopods are *Crania patagonica*, *Liothyrella uva*, *Terebratella dorsata* and *sowerbii*, and *Magellania venosa*. Fischer and Oehlert have commented on the large size of Magellanic articulates; thus *Magellania venosa* is the largest existing brachiopod, with an anteroposterior length of 82 mm., and other Magellanic species attain lengths of around 50 mm. Jackson (1918) remarks that the Magellanic brachiopods are mostly thick-shelled whereas the Antarctic ones are thin-shelled. *Liothyrella uva* has an interesting distribution, extending from the Magellanic region up the west coast of South America to Mexico, and further has a variant in the true Antarctic. The brachiopods of the subantarctic island of Kerguelen are related to but specifically distinct from those of the Magellanic region. Typical brachiopods of Kerguelen are *Liothyrella moseleyi*, *Terebratella enzenspergeri*, and *Magellania kerguelensis*, of which the first and third were already collected by the *Challenger* (Davidson, 1880), which collected at and around Kerguelen from December, 1873, to February, 1874. Some resemblance between the brachiopods of Kerguelen and New Zealand is indicated by the occurrence of *Tegulorhynchia nigricans* in both localities.

In the true Antarctic, collections have been made at several points on the edges of the land mass and some species have been repeatedly found, hence probably have a circumpolar distribution. The genera *Stethothyris* and *Compsothyris*, with one species each, are limited to the Antarctic. Characteristic antarctic species include *Crania lecointei*, *Liothyrella antarctica*, *Macandrevia lata*, *diamantina*, and *vanhöffeni*, *Stethothyris antarctica*, *Compsothyris racovitzae*, and *Magellania joubini* and *fragilis*. None of these is known to occur outside the Antarctic except *Macandrevia diamantina*, which is distributed from the Antarctic to the Gulf of Panama, but only in quite deep waters, 2100 to 4000 m.

A striking feature evident in the foregoing account is the limited distribution and high endemicity of many species and genera. It is not clear if this condition is real or the result of inadequate collecting. Again oversplitting of genera may account for the considerable number of genera with one species each, and that one very limited in distribution.

Most brachiopod species appear confined to waters of moderate depth and have a limited bathymetric range, usually not extending deeper than a few hundred meters. Some, however, range from shallow waters into the abyssal zone, for example, *Terebratulina retusa* to 3600 m., *Gryphus vitreus* to 2600 m., *Hemithyris psittacea* to 2200 m., and *Macandrevia cranium* to 4000 m. There are, however, genuine abyssal species that are never taken at moderate depths. The best known of these is *Pelagodiscus atlanticus* (Fig. 183*E*), said by Dall (1921) to be "the most cosmopolitan brachiopod known"; this has been taken at a number of locations, from 1500 to 5000 m., but sometimes occurs in archibenthal depths. Another widely spread abyssal species is *Abyssothyris wyvillei*, dredged from a variety of locations at 1800 to over 5500 m. This is the greatest depth at which brachiopods have been taken; they appear to be definitely absent from the abyssal trenches (IV, page 236). Both species of *Chlidonophora* are abyssal; *C. chuni* (Fig. 189*F*) is known only from the region of the Maldive Islands at 2300 m., and *C. incerta* occurs in the central Atlantic from Africa to the Gulf of Mexico to depths of 3300 m. *Dyscolia wyvillei*, originally discovered by the *Challenger* in the West Indies at 700 m., has since been taken in various locations in the eastern Atlantic from Spain to Africa at depths of 700 to 1900 m. and appears definitely limited to deeper waters.

Possible variation of shell form with environmental conditions augments the difficulty of species discrimination, hence also affects data on distribution. This matter was tested by Du Bois (1916) on Puget Sound brachiopods with the result that the valves of *Terebratalia transversa* were found to be shorter and more gibbous in rough water or strong currents.

VI. RELATIONSHIPS

1. Relations within the Phylum.—Brachiopods occur in the oldest fossiliferous rocks, those of Cambrian age, reckoned at about 500,000,000 years ago, and already were typically brachiopodan, with two rounded valves bearing muscle scars and impressions of coelomic canals. It is therefore evident that the origin of brachiopods occurred in pre-Cambrian times and is not traceable in the fossil record. The oldest brachiopods were inarticulates, belonging to the wholly extinct superfamily Obolacea, having a pair of simple rounded or oval valves of calcareophosphatic or corneous (chitinous?) composition with a groove on both or only the ventral valve for the passage of the pedicle. The lingulids seem to have been derived directly from the Obolacea. The genus *Lingula* goes back to Ordovician times, but *Glottidia* has no fossil record. The discinids and craniids seem to have had a common origin in another wholly extinct superfamily, Acrotretacea, that had circular valves with a subcentral apex and a simple orifice in the ventral valve for the pedicle. The genus *Crania* goes back to the Ordovician, but existing discinids are of relatively recent origin.

Articulates are evidently derived from inarticulates; there has taken place a process of evolution of the interlocking mechanism at the rear ends of the valves and of the skeletal support of the lophophore. Articulates have evolved from inarticulates along many different lines, and it would be impossible to follow these lines without a thorough exposition of the structure of extinct articulates, something that is outside the scope of this book and the capacities of the author. Of existing superfamilies the Rhynchonellacea have the longest fossil history, going back to the Ordovician. As both inarticulates and Rhynchonellacea have spirolophous lophophores, one suspects that this is the original type of brachiopodan lophophore, despite the generally accepted story (page 546) originating with Beecher that the lophophore began as a simple disk. This story is supported by embryology, and no doubt such a disciform stage is prevalent in ontogeny, but it is not clear that adult brachiopods ever generally had a disciform lophophore. The Terebratulacea with short brachidial loop are older (Silurian) than the Terebratellacea with long loop, and presumably there was a process of increasing complexity of brachidial support in the evolution of brachiopods. Here again it may be noted that the Rhynchonellacea have the least brachidial development.

2. Relation between the Lophophorate Phyla.—The common possession of a lophophore of similar anatomical and histological construction and similar positional relation to the body certainly proves an affinity between Phoronida, Ectoprocta, and Brachiopoda, but it is impossible to define this affinity in specific terms. All three phyla seem to be built on the same body plan; that is, there is an anterior region, or mesosome, bearing the lophophore and separated by a coelomic septum from the posterior trunk, or metasome. These two regions are not externally delimited. The usual supposition of a still more anterior region, or protosome, represented by the epistome, present except in gymnolaemates, does not appear to the author supported by either anatomical or embryological facts. The manner of formation of the epistome as a mere fold above the mouth, usually appearing rather late in development, does not support the concept that it represents the anteriormost body region. It may be acceptable that such a protosome existed in the remote ancestry of lophophorates, as seems to be indicated in the embryology of phoronids, but at the present time lophophorates seem to have but two body regions and two coelomic subdivisions. Even the septum between mesosome and metasome is poorly evidenced in brachiopods, being complete only in *Crania*. In all lophophorates the lophophore is supplied from the mesocoel, or part of the coelom anterior to the septum. If one insists that lophophorates originally had a protosome and protocoel, then it becomes necessary to suppose that they have lost their cephalization.

The nervous center is at present located in the mesocoel and also shows a poor degree of cephalization. It in general encircles the beginning of the digestive tract and has ganglionic enlargements either above or below the tract or in both locations. The center is mainly supraenteric in phoronids and ectoprocts, subenteric in brachiopods, wholly so in articulates. Common to lophophorates is the presence of a nervous plexus in the base of the epidermis. This is definitely a primitive character.

The secretion of an exoskeleton is common throughout the lophophorates but expressed differently in each group. It is impossible to relate the brachiopod shell to the exoskeleton of other lophophorates, especially as this shell was already present in its present form in the oldest fossiliferous rocks. There is no suggestion as to the significance of the bivalve shell of the cyphonautes larva of ectoprocts; this shell is lateral, whereas the brachiopod shell is dorsoventral. Chitinous secretion is common throughout lophophorates, and calcareous secretion is seen in ectoprocts and brachiopods. The chitinous setae of larval and adult brachiopods seem to have no counterparts in other lophophorates, unless the bristle of the cheilostome vibracula is to be so regarded. The setae of brachiopods are quite comparable with those of annelids, but setae are of such general occurrence that they probably have no phylogenetic significance.

A very puzzling matter is the similarity of construction of the lophophore in adult lophophorates and the great variation in its manner of development. In phoronids there are two sets of tentacles, a larval and a definitive set, and both seem to be related to the metatroch of the trochophore-type larva. There are no larval tentacles in other lophophorates. In inarticulate brachiopods the definitive tentacles put in an appearance during late larval life and have no relation to the ciliation. In *Lingula* the tentacles arise middorsally and are pushed in the ventral direction; hence, as in adult phoronids, the youngest tentacles are in the middorsal part of the lophophore. In *Terebratella* the tentacles begin below the mouth and arise successively in the dorsal direction; this would seem to be the opposite mode of growth from that of *Lingula*, but again the youngest tentacles are at the dorsal ends of the lophophore. In some other articulates the tentacles are said to sprout on the undersurface of the dorsal mantle lobe. Because of the peculiar development of ectoprocts, in which all larval structure disintegrates except the ectoderm, little weight can be placed on the origin of any definitive structures; the tentacles in buds appear on the pharyngeal region also in a ventrodorsal direction. A ventrodorsal succession of tentacle formation seems to be common to all lophophorates.

A recurved digestive tract is common to phoronids and ectoprocts but may simply represent an adaptation to sedentary life without phylogenetic significance. Possibly the articulate brachiopods had a recurved digestive tract until they lost the terminal part. One must suppose they originally had an anus. There is some recurvature of the digestive tract with a somewhat anteriorly placed anus in present inarticulates except *Crania*. *Crania* is the only lophophorate with a median posterior anus. It is not clear if one is to suppose that *Crania* has retained the original condition, but this is possible, especially as *Crania* is a very ancient genus and, further, has other generalized characters, being the only brachiopod with a complete septum between mesocoel and metacoel and with complete dorsal and ventral mesenteries in the metacoel.

A circulatory system is present in phoronids and brachiopods, best developed in the former, where it follows the general vermiform plan of dorsal vessel conveying the blood anteriorly and ventral vessel conveying it posteriorly with connections in the anterior part of the body. The system appears closed in phoronids but open in brachiopods; these lack the ventral vessel, hence must have a very imperfect circulation.

Phoronids and brachiopods also have in common a pair of metanephridia that constitute the coelomoducts of the metacoel and also act as gonoducts. That larval phoronids have protonephridia with solenocytes, later replaced by metanephridia, is taken by the author as clear proof that protonephridia preceded metanephridia in invertebrate phylogenesis. There has been much argument as to whether the presence in Rhynchonellacea of two pairs of metanephridia is indicative of segmentation. This question is usually answered in the negative, especially as there is a bifurcation of the nephrostome in some phoronids (page 243).

It is usually supposed that the larvae of lophophorates are of the trochophore type. This is evident in phoronids, less evident in ectoprocts, where most resemblance is evidenced by the cyphonautes larva, and little evident in brachiopods. The regionation of the articulate larva into three parts is puzzling since these three regions do not correspond to the supposed three regions of lophophorates. About all that remains of the trochophore in brachiopod larvae is the apical tuft.

The trochophore type of larva places the lophophorates among the Protostomia. A direct origin of the mouth from the blastopore is evidenced in phoronids and brachiopods. The origin of the mesoderm and coelom is unpleasantly variable among the three groups. In phoronids the mesoderm is wholly entomesodermal and the coelom originates by rearrangement of mesenchyme cells of entomesodermal origin. In ectoprocts, also, the definitive coelom arises by rearrangement of mesenchymal cells that here are of the ectomesodermal category. However, no conclusions can be drawn from ectoprocts because of their peculiar embryology in which all parts of the larva except ectoderm degenerate and all definitive structures arise from the ectoderm or nearly so. In the primary ectoproct larva there is present entomesoderm, but this never arrives at coelom formation before degenerating in the metamorphic process. It appears stretching the facts pretty far to suppose that the two strands of entomesoderm noticed by Pace (1906) in the development of the ctenostome *Flustrellidra* represent enterocoels. However, in brachiopods the coelom is definitely of the enterocoelous category, formed as sacs cut off from the archenteron. Here, too, there is a puzzling variation in the available accounts. In some there are a pair of sacs from the sides of the archenteron, in *Terebratulina* one anterior sac is cut off, in *Terebratella*, one posterior sac. The cutting off of the coelomic sacs in the last two cases does have some resemblance to enterocoel formation in chaetognaths, as noticed by several authors, but in fact the resemblance is not very exact, as may be seen by reference to the account of the embryology of chaetognaths. A division of the coelom in the embryology of brachiopods is seen in *Terebratella*, but here the anterior and posterior coelomic sacs seem to have no relation to the tripartition of either the larva or the adult. All that can be said is that the definitive coelom of brachiopods is of the enterocoelous type, at least in articulates. In the only studied inarticulate, *Lingula*, the mesoderm originates as solid proliferations of the sides of the archenteron, and the coelom, strictly speaking, is schizocoelous, but this manner of formation probably does not differ significantly from the typical enterocoelous method.

Among the lophophorates the phoronids seem to come nearer to a presumed type plan than do the two other groups. They have a muscular vermiform body, crescentic lophophore, strong septum regionating the body into trunk and anterior lophophore-bearing part, closed circulatory system with main dorsal and ventral vessels, a pair of metanephridia constituting the coelomic outlets of the metasome, and trochophore type of larva with protonephridia. Supposedly these were characteristics of the common lophophorate ancestor. Of the other groups the phylacto-laematous ectoprocts come closest to this plan, although lacking circulatory system and nephridia, but any direct relationship of phoronids and ectoprocts appears out of the question. Brachiopods are the most divergent from the common plan, although they do possess a circulatory system and metanephridia, not preceded by protonephridia in larval stages. On the other hand, the brachiopod *Crania* has, as already noted, generalized characteristics, and it is possible that the original lophophorate had a posterior anus. As already indicated, the recurved digestive tract is probably a secondary adaptation.

In short, it is impossible to indicate in any specific way relationship among the three lophophorate groups, and therefore a union of them into one phylum is not supported here.

3. Relation of the Lophophorates to Other Phyla.—The lophophorates belong to the Protostomia despite the enterocoelous formation of the coelom in brachiopods, but cannot clearly be attached to any members of this category. There are indications of spiral cleavage in phoronids (page 253) but not in other lophophorates. The cleavage pattern of brachiopods is reported as very variable, and the occasional occurrence of alternate tiers of blastomeres in early cleavage (Conklin, 1902; Percival, 1944) cannot be regarded as indicative of spiral cleavage. The formation of trochoblasts (page 345) in ectoprocts is definitely reminiscent of typical Protostomia.

In fact, however, the nearest affinities of the lophophorates seem to be with the deuterostomes. Both groups have the same body regionation into three parts, of which the anterior part, or protosome, is suppressed, except in hemichordates and pogonophores. A preponderance of the left side in phoronids recalls conditions in echinoderms. However, the resemblance is mostly with hemichordates, which have the same strong septum dividing the metacoel from the mesocoel. The tentaculated arms of pterobranchs presumably have some relationship with a lophophore and like the latter belong to the mesosome and contain an extension of the mesocoel. Similarly, the water-vascular system of echinoderms was probably originally in the form of a pair of tentacle clusters, and these also contain coelomic spaces belonging to the mesocoel.

It thus appears that the lophophorates constitute a connecting link between the Protostomia and the Deuterostomia, but the details of this connection cannot be stated. A common ancestry of the two groups is indicated; yet it then becomes difficult to understand how it comes that the two groups have quite different types of larvae, the trochophore for the lophophorates, the dipleurula for the deuterostomes. There is, further, the matter of the differing fate of the blastopore, becoming the anus in deuterostomes, the mouth in lophophorates and other protostomes. It is usual to explain this away by assuming a subdivision of the blastopore into mouth and anus, as is in fact seen in the embryology of some protostomes. An enterocoelous mode of forming the coelom is seen in lophophorates only in brachiopods, but nowhere in lophophorates is the division of the coelom into three successive pairs of sacs clearly expressed as it is in echinoderms. It may thus appear that deuterostomes show a further development of characters beginning in an unclear way in lophophorates, and thus branch off from protostomes by way of the latter.

A curious feature of lophophorates and deuterostomes that has not been found mentioned in the literature except in an interesting article by Steiner (1956) is the lack of cephalization. The author finds it difficult to believe that this lack of cephalization is primary, not the result of degeneration caused by the assumption of a sedentary life with associated ciliary (filter) feeding. The loss of cephalization is expressed in most of these phyla by the poor development of the protosome and protocoel, already in embryology. Steiner takes the viewpoint that the deuterostomes never had a head and therefore that *Amphioxus* inherited its poor cephalization directly from hemichordate ancestors. As cephalization generally characterizes protostomes, it would seem that loss of the head began with lophophorates, which passed on this condition to deuterostomes.

Because of the variable mode of coelom formation among the lophophorates and the poor information furnished by the peculiar embryology of ectoprocts, the author considers it desirable to abandon the concept Schizocoela and replace this term with the expression protostomatous coelomates. The lophophorates then fall into this category.

Bibliography

HISTORICAL

Brooks, W. K. 1877. Affinity of Mollusca and Molluscoida. Proc. Boston Soc. Natur. Hist. 18. **Caldwell, W.** 1882. Preliminary notes on the structure, development and affinities of Phoronis. Proc. Roy. Soc. London 34. **Colonna, F.** 1616. *Purpura.* **Cuvier, G.** 1797. Mémoire sur l'animal des lingules. Bull. Soc. Philomathique Paris 1. 1798. *Tableau élémentaire de l'histoire naturelle des animaux.* 1802. Mémoire sur l'animal de la lingule. Ann. Mus. Hist. Natur. Paris 1. 1805. *Leçons d'anatomie comparée,* vols. 3–5. **Dall, W. K.** 1870. Revision of the Terebratulidae and Lingulidae. Amer. Jour. Conchology 6. **Davidson, T.** 1852. A few new Brachiopoda. Proc. Zool. Soc. London. **Duméril, A.** 1806. *Zoologie analytique ou méthode naturelle de classification des animaux.* **Edwards, H. Milne.** 1843. *Élements de zoologie. Animaux sans vertèbres.* 2 ed. **Gegenbaur, C.** 1859.

Grundzüge der vergleichenden Anatomie. **Gründler, G.** 1774. Beschreibung und Abbildung zweier natürlichen Terebratulen in welche ihre Einwohner oder Thiere befindlich sind. Naturforsch. Halle 2. **Haeckel, E.** 1874. The gastraea-theory. Quart. Jour. Microsc. Sci. 14. **Hancock, A.** 1850. The anatomy of the freshwater Bryozoa. Ann. Mag. Natur. Hist., ser. 2, vol. 5. 1857. On the organisation of the Brachiopoda. Ann. Mag. Natur. Hist., ser. 2, vol. 20. **Hertwig, O.,** and **R. Hertwig.** 1881. Die Coelomtheorie. Jena. Ztschr. Naturwiss. 15. **Huxley, T. H.** 1853. Morphology of the cephalous Mollusca. Philos. Trans. Roy. Soc. London 143. 1854a. Contributions to the anatomy of the Brachiopoda. Proc. Roy. Soc. London 7. 1854b. Contributions to the anatomy of the Brachiopoda. Ann. Mag. Natur. Hist., ser. 2, vol. 14. 1869. *An introduction to the classification of animals.* 1877. *A manual of the anatomy of invertebrated animals.* **Kowalevsky, A.** 1866. Entwicklungsgeschichte der einfachen Ascidien. Mém. Acad. St. Pétersbourg, ser. 7, vol. 10. **Linnaeus, C.** 1758. *Systema naturae.* 10 ed. **Morse, E.** 1870. The Brachiopoda, a division of Annelida. Amer. Jour. Sci., ser. 2, vol. 50. **Owen, R.** 1833. On the anatomy of the Brachiopoda of Cuvier. Proc. Zool. Soc. London. 1835. On the anatomy of the Brachiopoda. Trans. Zool. Soc. London, for 1833. 1843. *Lectures on comparative anatomy and physiology of the invertebrate animals.* **Pallas, P.** 1766. *Miscellanea zoologica.* **Schneider, K.** 1902. *Lehrbuch der vergleichenden Histologie.* **Steenstrup, J.** 1847, 1848. Om Anomia. Oversigt Kgl. Danske Vidensk. Selsk. Forhandl. 1849. Om Brachiopodenes stilling i systemet. Naturhist. Tidsskrift, ser. 2, vol. 2, Heft 6.

LITERATURE SINCE 1859

Allan, R. 1940. A revision of the classification of the terebratelloid Brachiopoda. Records Canterbury Mus. New Zealand 4. **Arndt, W.,** and **J. Grieg.** 1933. Die Brachiopoden des arktischen Gebietes. Fauna Arctica 6, pt. 5. **Ashworth, J.** 1915. Larvae of Lingula and Pelagodiscus. Trans. Roy. Soc. Edinburgh 51. **Atkins, Daphne.** 1956. Ciliary feeding mechanisms of brachiopods. Nature, London, 177. **Banfield, E.** 1918. *Tropic days.* **Beecher, C.** 1891, 1892. Development of the Brachiopoda. Amer. Jour. Sci., ser. 3, vols. 41, 44. 1895a. Revision of the families of loop-bearing Brachiopoda. Trans. Connecticut Acad. Sci. 9. 1897. Morphology of the brachia. Bull. U.S. Geol. Survey 87. **Bemmelen, J. van.** 1883. Über den anatomischen und histologischen Bau der Brachiopoda Testicardinia. Jena. Ztschr. Naturwiss. 16. **Beurlen, K.** 1952. Phylogenie und System der Brachiopoda Articulata. Neues Jahrb. Geol. Paläontol., Monatshefte. **Beyer, H.** 1886. Structure of Glottidia. Studies Biol. Lab. Johns Hopkins Univ. 3. **Blochmann, F.** 1885. Vorläufige Mittheilung über Brachiopoden. Zool. Anz. 8. 1892a. Über die Anatomie und die verwandtschaftlichen Beziehungen der Brachiopoden. Arch. Vereins Freunde Naturgesch. Mecklenburg 46. 1892b. *Untersuchungen über den Bau der Brachiopoden.* Pt. I. Die Anatomie von Crania anomala. 1898. Die Larve von Discinisca. Zool. Jahrb. Abt. Anat. 11. 1900. *Untersuchungen über den Bau der Brachiopoden.* Pt. II. Die Anatomie von Discinisca und Lingula. 1906. Neue Brachiopoden der Valdivia- und Gaussexpeditionen. Zool. Anz. 30. 1908. Zur Systematik und geographischen Verbreitung der Brachiopoden. Ztschr. Wissensch. Zool. 90. 1910. New brachiopods of South Australia. Trans. Roy. Soc. South Australia 34. 1912a. Brachiopoda. *Handwörterbuch der Naturwissenschaften,* 1 ed., vol. 2. 1912b. Die Brachiopoden der schwedischen Südpolar Expedition. Wissensch. Ergebn. Schwed. Südpolar Exped. 1901–1903, vol. 6, Zool. 2, pt. 7. **Brooks, W. K.** 1879. Development of Lingula. Chesapeake Zool. Lab., Scient. Results of the Session of 1878. **Buckman, S.** 1916. Terminology for foraminal development in terebratuloids. Trans. Proc. New Zealand Inst. 48. **Chapman, F.** 1914. Notes on shell structure in Lingula. Jour. Roy. Microsc. Soc. 34. **Chapman, F., and I. Crespin.** 1923. The austral Rhynchonellacea of the "nigricans" series. Proc. Roy. Soc. Victoria 35. **Chuang, S.** 1956. The ciliary feeding mechanisms of Lingula. Proc. Zool. Soc. London 127. **Chun, C.** 1903. *Aus den Tiefen des Weltmeeres.* 2 ed. **Clarke, F., and W. Wheeler.** 1915. Composition of brachiopod shells. Proc. Nation. Acad. Sci. U.S.A. 1. **Cloud, P.** 1942. Terebratuloid Brachiopoda of the Silurian and Devonian. Spec. Papers Geol. Soc. America, no. 38. 1948. Notes on recent brachiopods. Amer. Jour. Sci. 246. **Conklin, E. G.** 1902. Embryology of Terebratulina. Proc. Amer. Philos. Soc. 41. **Cooper, G.** 1934. New Brachiopoda. Smithson. Miscell. Collections 91, no. 10. 1944. Phylum Brachiopoda. *In* **H. Schimer** and **R. Shrock** (eds.), *Index fossils of North America.* 1952. Significance of the stratigraphic distribution of brachiopods. Jour. Paleontol. 26. 1954. Brachiopoda occurring in the Gulf of Mexico. U.S. Fish and Wildlife Service, Fishery Bull. 89. **Cori, C.** 1933. Brachiopoda. *In* **G. Grimpe** and **E. Wagler** (eds.), *Die Tierwelt der Nord- und Ostsee,* Teil VII, c3, Lief. 24. **Crane, A.** 1892. Recent observations on the anatomy and development of Brachiopoda. Natur. Science 1. **Dall, W. H.** 1877. Brachiopods of Alaska and the adjacent shores of northwest America. Scient. Results Explor. Alaska 1865–1874, art. 3. 1894. Mollusca and Brachiopoda dredged in deep waters, chiefly near the Hawaiian Islands. Proc. U.S. Nation. Mus. 17. 1910. Report on the Brachiopoda obtained from the Indian Ocean by the Sealark Expedition in 1905. Trans. Linnean Soc. London, Zool., ser. 2, vol. 13. 1921. Annotated list of the recent Brachiopoda in the collection of the United States National Museum. Proc. U.S. Nation. Mus. 57. **Davidson, T.** 1880. Report on the Brachiopoda dredged by the Challenger. Rept. Scient. Results Voyage Challenger, Zool. 1. 1886a. On a living spinose Rhynchonella from Japan. Ann. Mag. Natur. Hist., ser. 5, vol. 17. 1886b, 1887, 1888. A monograph of recent Brachiopoda, pts. I–III. Trans. Linnean Soc. London, Zool., ser. 2, vol. 4. **Davidson, T., and W. Dalton.** 1886. Bibliography of the Brachiopoda. Paleontograph. Soc. Monogr. 39, for 1885. **Douvillé, H.** 1879. Note sur quelques genres de brachiopodes. Bull. Soc. Geol. France, ser. 3, vol. 7. **Du Bois, H.** 1916. Variation induced in brachiopods by environmental conditions. Publ. Puget Sound Marine Sta. 1. **Eichler, P.** 1910. Die Brachiopoden der deutschen Südpolar-Expedition 1901–1903. Dtsch. Südpolar Exped., vol. 12, Zool. 4, Heft 4. **Ekman, T.** 1896. Zur Kenntnis des Stieles der Brachiopoden. Ztschr. Wissensch. Zool. 62. **Elliott, C.** 1948. Evolutionary significance of brachial development in terebratelloid brachiopods. Ann. Mag. Natur. Hist., ser. 12, vol. 1. 1949. The brachial development of Kraussina. Ann. Mag. Natur. Hist., ser. 12, vol. 2. 1951. Geographical distribution of terebratelloid Brachiopoda. Ann. Mag. Natur. Hist., ser. 12, vol. 4. 1953a. Brachial development and evolution in terebratelloid brachiopods. Biol. Reviews Cambridge Philos. Soc. 28. 1953b. Classification of the thecidean Brachiopoda. Ann. Mag. Natur. Hist., ser. 12, vol. 6. 1954. The early lophophore and subsequent loop. Ann. Mag. Natur. Hist., ser. 12, vol. 7. 1956. On Tertiary transarctic brachiopod migrations. Ann. Mag. Natur. Hist., ser. 12, vol. 9. **Fischer, P., and D. Oehlert.** 1891. Brachiopodes. Expéditions scientifiques du Travailleur et du Talisman pendant les années 1880–1883. 1892a. Brachiopodes. Mission scientifique du Cap Horn. Bull. Soc. Hist. Natur. Autun 5. 1892b. Brachiopodes de l'Atlantique Nord. Result. Campagnes Scient. Monaco, fasc. 3. 1892c. Sur l'évolution de l'appareil brachial de quelques brachiopodes. C. R. Acad. Sci. Paris 115. **François, P.** 1891. Observations biologiques sur les lingules. Arch. Zool. Exp. Gén., ser. 2, vol. 9. **Friele, H.** 1877. Development of the skeleton in Waldheimia. Arch. Math. Naturvid. 2. **Grant, R.** 1920. Note on Crania anomala. Glasgow Natural. 8. **Gratiolet, M.** 1860. Études anatomiques sur la lingule. Jour. Conchyliol., ser. 2, vol. 4. **Grieg, J.** 1928. Brachiopods from Novaya Zemlya. Rept. Scient. Results Norweg. Exped. Novaya Zemlya 1921, no. 26. **Hall, J.,** and **J. Clarke.** 1892, 1894. An introduction to the study of the Brachiopoda. New York State Museum Ann. Repts., no. 45, for 1891, no. 47, for 1893. **Hancock, A.** 1859. On the organisation of the Brachiopoda. Philos. Trans. Roy. Soc. London 148. **Hatai, K.** 1936a. Recent Brachiopoda of Japan. Bull. Biogeogr. Soc. Japan 6, no. 8. 1936b. Recent Brachiopoda of foreign countries. Bull. Biogeogr. Soc. Japan 6, no. 10. 1936c. Note on Tegulorhynchia döderleini. Venus 6. 1940. The cenozoic Brachiopoda of Japan. Sci. Repts. Tohoku Univ., ser. 2, Geol. 20. **Heller, M.** 1931. Exkretorische Tatigkeit der Brachiopoden. Ztschr. Morphol. Ökol. Tiere 24. **Helmcke, J.** 1939. Brachiopoda. *In* T. **Krumbach** (ed)., *Handbuch der Zoologie,* vol. 3, 2d half. 1940. Die Brachiopoden der deutschen Tiefsee-Expedition. Wissensch. Ergebn. Dtsch. Tiefsee-Exped. Valdivia 24. **Hertlein, L.,** and **U. S. Grant IV.** 1944. The cenozoic Brachiopoda of western North America. Publ. Univ. California Los Angeles, Math. Phys. Sci. 3. **Hyman, L.** 1958. Occurrence of chitin in lophophorates. Biol. Bull. 114. **Jackson, J.** 1912. Brachiopoda of Scottish National Antarctic Exped. Trans. Roy. Soc. Edinburgh 48. 1918. Brachiopoda. British Antarctic (Terra Nova) Exped. 1910, Natur. History Repts., Zool. 2, pt. 8. **Johnston, T.,** and **O. Hirschfeld.** 1919. The Lingulidae of the Queensland coast. Proc. Roy. Soc. Queensland 31. **Joubin, L.** 1886. Anatomie des brachiopodes inarticulés. Arch. Zool. Exp. Gén., ser. 2, vol. 4. 1887. Anatomie des brachiopodes articulés. Bull. Soc. Zool. France 12. 1901. Brachiopodes. Expédition Antarctique Belge. Result. Voyage Belgica, Rapports Scient., Zool. 2. **Kawaguti, S.** 1941. Hemerthyrin found in Lingula. Mem. Faculty Sci. Taihoku Univ. 23, Zool., no. 12. **Kowalevsky, A.** 1874. On the development of the Brachiopoda. (Russian.) Izviestiia Obshchestvo Liubitelei Estestvoznanita, Antropologii i Etnografii (Proc. Imper. Soc. Natural Science, Anthropol. Ethnol.) 14. 1883. Abstract in French by **Oehlert** and **Deniker,** Arch. Zool. Exp. Gén., ser. 2, vol. 1. **Krukenberg, C.** 1885. Über das Vorkommen des Chitins. Zool. Anz. 8. **Kunike, G.** 1925. Nachweis und Verbreitung organischer Skeletsubstanzen bei Tieren. Ztschr. Vergl. Physiol. 2. **Lacaze-Duthiers, H. de.** 1861. Historie de la thécidie. Ann. Sci. Natur., Zool., ser. 4, vol. 15. **Lankester, E. R.** 1873. Summary of zoological observations made at Naples. Ann. Mag. Natur. Hist., ser. 4, vol. 11. **Leidhold, C.** 1922. Rhynchonella döderleini. Neues Jahrb. Mineral. Geol. Paläontol. Beilage 45. **MacGinitie, G.,** and **N. MacGinitie.** 1949. *Natural history of marine animals.* **Mattox, N.** 1955. Observations on the brachiopod communities near Santa Catalina Island. *Essays in the natural sciences in honor of Captain Allan Hancock,* Los Angeles. **McCrady, J.** 1860. On Lingula pyramidata. Amer. Jour. Sci. Arts, ser. 2, vol. 30. **Moore, R. C.** 1952. Brachiopods. *In* R. C. **Moore, G. Lalicker,** and **A. Fischer,** *Invertebrate fossils.* **Morse, E.** 1871. Early stages of Terebratulina. Mem. Boston Soc. Natur. Hist. 2. 1873a. Embryology of Terebratulina. Mem. Boston Soc. Natur. Hist. 2. 1873b. Systematic position of the Brachiopoda. Proc. Boston Soc. Natur. Hist. 15. 1902. Observations on living Brachiopoda. Mem. Boston Soc. Natur. Hist. 5. **Muir-Wood, Helen.** 1955. *A history of the classification of the phylum Brachiopoda.* **Müller, F.** 1860. Beschreibung einer brachiopoden larva. Arch. Anat. Physiol. 1861. Die Brachiopodenlarva von Santa Catharina. Arch. Naturgesch. 27, pt. 1. (Eng. transl. Ann. Mag. Natur. Hist., ser. 3, vol. 8.) **Ohuye, T.** 1936. Formed elements in the coelomic fluid of a brachiopod. Sci. Repts. Tohoku Univ., ser. 4, Biol. 11. 1937. Supplementary note.

Sci. Repts. Tohoku Univ., ser. 4, Biol. 12. **Orton, J.** 1914. On ciliary mechanisms in brachiopods. Jour. Marine Biol. Assoc. 10. **Percival, E.** 1944. Life history of Terebratella inconspicua. Trans. Roy. Soc. New Zealand 74. 1953. Orientation of telotrematous Brachiopoda. Nature, London, 171. **Plenk, H.** 1913. Die Entwicklung von Cistella. Arbeit. Zool. Inst. Univ. Wien 20. **Pompeckj, J.** 1912. Brachiopod-Paläontologie. *Handwörterbuch der Naturwissenschaften,* 1 ed., vol. 2. **Posselt, H.** 1898. Grönlands Brachiopoder. Meddel. an Grönland 23. **Prenant, M.** 1928. Notes histologiques sur Terebratulina. Bull. Soc. Zool. France 53. **Reed, F.** 1895. Paleontology of the Brachiopoda. Cambridge Natural History, vol. 3. **Rein, J.** 1887. Über Lingula. Sitzungsber. Niederrhein. Gesellsch. Bonn. **Remy, P.** 1928. Matériaux zoologiques raccoltés dans les mers arctiques. Ann. Sci. Natur., Zool., ser. 10, vol. 11. **Richards, Joyce.** 1952. Ciliary feeding mechanism of Neothyris. Jour. Morphol. 90. **Ricketts, E.,** and **J. Calvin.** 1939. *Between Pacific tides.* **Roger, J.** 1952. Classe des brachiopodes. *In* **J. Piveteau** (ed.), *Traité de paléontologie,* vol. II. **Schaeffer, Cornelia.** 1926. Anatomie und Histologie der Lingula. Acta Zoologica 7. **Schmiedeberg, O.** 1882. Ueber das chemische Zusammensetzung der Wohnröhren. Mitt. Zool. Stat. Neapel 3. **Schuchert, C.** 1897. Synopsis of the American fossil brachiopods. Bull. U.S. Geol. Survey, no. 87. 1911. Paleographic and geologic significance of recent Brachiopoda. Bull. Geol. Soc. America 22. 1913. Brachiopoda. *In* **C. Eastman** (ed.), *Zittel's textbook of paleontology,* vol. I, 2 ed. **Schulgin, M.** 1884. Argiope. Ztschr. Wissensch. Zool. 41. **Semper, C.** 1861. Reiseberichte. Ztschr. Wissensch. Zool. 11. **Senn, E.** 1934. Die Geschlechtverhältnisse der Brachiopoden. Acta Zoologica 15. **Sewall, R.** 1912. Development of the larva of Lingula. Records Indian Mus. 7. **Shipley, A.** 1883. Structure and development of Argiope. Mitt. Zool. Stat. Neapel 4. 1895. Recent Brachiopoda. Cambridge Natural History, vol. 3. **Simroth, H.** 1897. Die Brachiopoden der Plankton-Expedition. Ergebnisse der Plankton-Expedition, vol. II, F, f. **Smith, E.** 1907. Brachiopoda. National Antarctic Expedition (Discovery), Zool. 2. **Stehli, F.** 1956a. Evolution of the loop and lophophore in terebratuloid brachiopods. Evolution 10. 1956b. Shell mineralogy in paleozoic invertebrates. Science 123. **Steiner, H.** 1956. Gedanke zur Initialgestaltung der Chordaten. Rev. Suisse Zool. 63. **Stephen, A.** 1927. Report on the brachiopods collected in the British Arctic Expedition in 1926. Proc. Roy. Physical Soc. Edinburgh 21. **Termier, H.,** and **G. Termier.** 1949. Sur la classification des brachiopodes. Bull. Soc. Hist. Natur. Afrique du Nord 40. **Thomson, J.** 1915. Brachiopod genera. Proc. New Zealand Inst. 47. 1916. Classification of the Terebratellidae. Geol. Mag. London, ser. 6, vol. 3. 1918. Brachiopoda. Australasian Antarctic Expedition 1911–1914. Scient. Reports, ser. C, vol. 4, pt. 3. 1927. Brachiopod morphology and genera. New Zealand Board of Science and Art, Manual no. 7. **Walcott, C.** 1912. Cambrian Brachiopoda. Monogr. U.S. Geol. Survey, no. 51, 2 pts. **Williams, A.** 1956. The calcareous shell of the Brachiopoda and its importance to their classification. Biol. Reviews Cambridge Philos. Soc. 31. **Yamada, M.** 1956. Notes on discinid larvae. Annot. Zool. Japonenses 29. **Yatsu, N.** 1902a. Development of Lingula. Jour. College Sci. Univ. Tokyo 17, art. 4. 1902b. Notes on the histology of Lingula. Jour. College Sci. Univ. Tokyo 17, art. 5. 1902c. On the habits of Japanese Lingula. Annot. Zool. Japonenses 4. 1905. Note on the young Disciniscus. Zool. Anz. 29.

CHAPTER XXII

THE PROTOSTOMATOUS COELOMATES— PHYLUM SIPUNCULIDA

I. HISTORICAL

As animals of some size, sipunculoids were presumably seen by the ancients, but the first recognizable publication is that of Rondelet (1555), who gave a description and figures (Fig. 213) of two sipunculoids that he called microrhynchoterous and macrorhynchoterous worms, respectively. The former is readily identified as *Sipunculus nudus* (Fig. 213*A*). Gesner (1558) reproduced Rondelet's woodcuts under the same names. Bohadsch (1761) gave a description and two original figures of *Sipunculus nudus* under the name *Syrinx*, considering it a new type of zoophyte. Linnaeus (1767) in the twelfth edition of *Systema naturae* created the name *Sipunculus* and called Rondelet's two species *Sipunculus nudus* and *saccatus*, respectively, placing them in the Vermes Intestina. Pallas (1774) gave an original figure of a *Sipunculus* that he

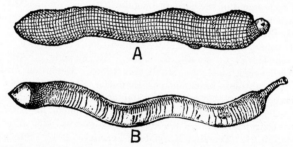

A

B

Fig. 213.—Earliest published figures of sipunculoids (*after Rondelet*, 1555). *A, Sipunculus nudus. B,* "Sipunculus saccatus."

called *Lumbricus phalloides*, although he knew of the names *Syrinx* and *Sipunculus*. Barbut (1783) also published original drawings from nature of sipunculoids that he classified as Vermes Intestina. Martin (1786) had specimens of *Sipunculus nudus*. Montagu (1804) discovered *Phascolion strombi* (which he called *Sipunculus strombus*) and described its mode of life in the empty shells of the snail *Strombus*. Pennant (1812) gave original figures of three sipunculoids that he called *Sipunculus nudus, saccatus,* and *strombus*. Lamarck (1816) considered sipunculoids to be closely related to holothurians, and hence placed them among the Radiaires Echinodermes; the same position was taken by Cuvier in the various editions of *Le Règne animal*. Neither author proposed a group name for sipunculoids. This seems to have been first done by Delle Chiaje (1823), who gave figures and a detailed description of *Sipunculus nudus* and proposed the group name Sifunculacei for sipunculoids, which he thought to be annelids. De Blainville (1828) used the group name Sipunculidia (including therein *Priapulus*) and supported a relationship to parasitic worms. In 1828 F. S. Leuckart created the generic name *Phascolosoma*, subsequently generally misapplied.

Following the period of Cuvier's dominance, the idea of a holothurian affinity lapsed and sipunculoids were generally regarded as worms allied to annelids or to parasitic worms. Quatrefages (1847) proposed a group Gephyrea to include Echiurea (*Echiurus* and *Sternaspis*) and Siponculea (*Sipunculus* and *Priapulus*). Quatrefages conceived the Gephyrea as intermediate between echinoderms and annelids and regarded sipunculoids as degenerate echiuroids. The concept Gephyrea (with the elimination of *Sternaspis* soon recognized as a polychaete annelid) won wide acceptance. Gegenbaur (1859) recognized Gephyrea as an order of Annulata, itself a class under Vermes, but in a later edition (1878) made Gephyrea coordinate with Annulata under Vermes. Hatschek (1881) did not accept Gephyrea altogether but recognized Sipunculacea (including Sipunculidae, Priapulidae, and Phoronidae) as a group under Annelida; subsequently (1888) he made Sipunculoidea an appendage to Annelida. Echiuridae were regarded as chaetopod annelids. Lang (1888) recognized a phylum Vermes with five classes, one of which, Prosopygii, included Sipunculacea (Sipunculidae, Priapulidae, Phoronidae), Bryozoa, and Brachiopoda, whereas Echiuridae were also considered to be annelids. The name and group Prosopygii was founded on the anterior position of the anus (not true of Priapulida!), but this cannot be regarded as a character of systematic importance. On somewhat similar grounds, the reduction of the dorsal surface and thereby of the oral-anal axis, Lankester (1885) assembled Sipunculida, Bryozoa, and Phoronida under the name Podaxonia. Sedgwick (1898) rejected Gephyrea and raised Sipunculoidea to phylum rank.

However, none of these ideas gained acceptance and Quatrefages' group Gephyrea for sipunculoids, priapuloids, and echiuroids gradually won practically universal acceptance in zoological books and faunal works. Even as late as 1955 this term was used in a faunal report. Pickford (1947) remarks on the remarkable tenacity with which the name Gephyrea has persisted in the literature. The reason seems to be that adopting the concept Gephyrea offers an easy way of disposing of three groups of very uncertain affinities. But as all modern students of these groups are agreed that there is no close relationship between them *the name and the concept Gephyrea must be obliterated from zoology.* Priapulida were already (III, pp. 183–197) discussed as a class of the phylum Aschelminthes with acknowledgment of the alternative view of considering them a separate phylum. Echiurida will be treated in the volume on Annelida, to which phylum they are undoubtedly related. Sipunculida is here treated as a distinct phylum. Of various renditions of the group name, Sipunculida appears most appropriate for the rank of phylum. Sipunculoid will be used as a common name, since sipunculid implies a family Sipunculidae, something that does not exist at present.

Main general works on sipunculoids are Selenka, de Man, and Bülow (1883), Selenka (1885), Théel (1905), Hérubel (1907), Shipley (1910), Spengel (1913a), Fischer (1925), Baltzer (1931), Harms (1934), and Pickford (1947). On individual species there are available the articles of Théel (1875) on *Phascolion strombi*, Andrews (1890b) on *Golfingia gouldi*, Cuénot (1900) on *Golfingia vulgaris*, Metalnikoff (1900) on *Sipunculus nudus*, Peebles and Fox (1933) on *Dendrostomum zostericolum*, Awati and Pradhan (1935, 1936) on *Dendrostomum signifer*, and Stehle (1953) on *Golfingia elongata*.

II. CHARACTERS OF THE PHYLUM

1. Definition.—The Sipunculida are unsegmented, vermiform coelomates, with body regionated into an anterior slender introvert and a posterior plump trunk, with terminal mouth generally encircled by tentacular outgrowths, with recurved digestive tract with highly coiled intestine opening dorsally at the anterior end of the trunk or on the introvert, with annelid type of nervous system, and with one or two metanephridia.

2. General Characters.—The sipunculoids are wormlike animals of sedentary habits of which the most striking feature by which they are easily identified is the introvert, which is habitually run in and out rapidly. The body is thus regionated into slender introvert and plumper trunk and consists of a muscular body wall enclosing a spacious undivided coelom containing the digestive tract, nephridia, and gonads. When the introvert is fully everted the mouth is seen at its tip surrounded by lobulations, usually more or less developed into tentacles. The mouth leads into an esophagus, followed by a long, recurved, spirally coiled intestine, hanging free in the coelom. The conspicuous anus is located in the middorsal line anteriorly, on the trunk or on the introvert. The nervous system consists of a dorsal brain, pair of circumenteric connectives, and a ventral nerve cord. A definite circulatory system appears wanting. A pair of metanephridia or only a single nephridium is present; they hang freely in the coelom. The nephridiopores are located ventrally on the anterior part of the trunk. All sipunculoids are dioecious. The sex cells are shed into the coelom, whence they exit through the nephridia. Development is of the spiral type, resulting in a trochophore type of larva that metamorphoses to the definitive state.

Sipunculoids are exclusively marine and are found in all seas at all latitudes from the intertidal zone to depths of about 5000 m. There are probably around 250 described valid species. These are assigned by Fisher (1952) to 13 genera. No systematic arrangement of the genera, even into families, has been proposed. Therefore the phylum consists of genera only.

III. ANATOMY AND EMBRYOLOGY

1. External Characters.—Sipunculoids are vermiform animals of cylindroid shape, with the body regionated into a slender anterior part, the *introvert*, and a plumper posterior *trunk*. The introvert can be completely invaginated into the trunk by means of strong retractor muscles. The relative lengths of introvert and trunk vary greatly in different genera and species. The introvert may be much shorter than the trunk as usually in the genus *Sipunculus* (Fig. 215A, C); or range from a fourth to a half to about the length of the trunk as in most species; or exceed the trunk in length as in species of *Phascolion* (Fig. 214E), *Aspidosiphon* (Fig. 214A), and *Onchnesoma* (Fig. 218D). The anterior end is sometimes globular, simulating a head, as in *Phascolion strombi* (Fig. 214E). The trunk usually terminates bluntly or in a point, but in the

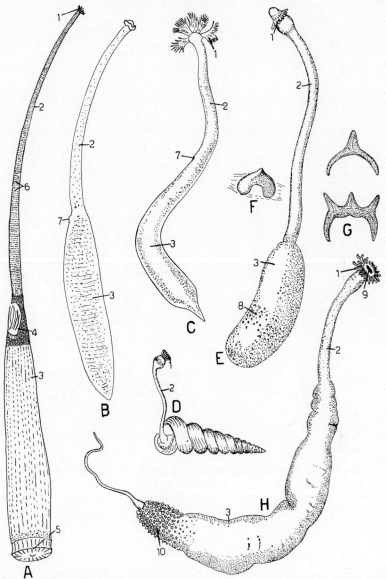

Fig. 214.—Types of sipunculoids. *A*, *Aspidosiphon speciosus*, from life, Bahamas. *B*, *Golfingia minuta*, from life, New England. *C*, *Dendrostomum*. *D*, *Phascolion strombi* ensconced in a snail shell (*after Théel*, 1875). *E*, *Phascolion strombi*. *F*, holdfast of *E*. (*E*, *F*, after Théel, 1905.) *G*, other types of *Phascolion* holdfasts. (*C*, *G*, after Selenka, de Man, and Bülow, 1883.) *H*, *Golfingia flagrifera* with tail (*after Selenka*, 1885). 1, tentacles; 2, introvert; 3, trunk; 4, anterior shield; 5, posterior shield; 6, circlets of spines; 7, anus; 8, holdfasts; 9, mouth; 10, papillae.

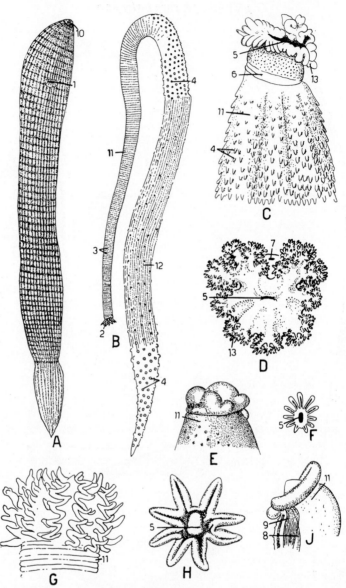

Fig. 215.—Types of sipunculoids (concluded), tentacles. *A, Sipunculus nudus*, preserved, trunk; introvert invaginated. *B, Phascolosoma nigrescens*, from life, Bahamas. *C*, introvert and tentacular crown of *Sipun. nudus (after Ward, 1891). D*, tentacular crown of *Sipun. galapagensis*, showing pore of cephalic tube *(after Fisher, 1947). E*, anterior end of *Golfingia minuta* with tentacles represented by bulges. *F*, tentacular crown of *Aspidosiphon (after Selenka, de Man, and Bülow, 1883). G*, anterior end of *Siphonosoma ingens (after Fisher, 1952). H*, tentacular crown of *Onchnesoma squamatum. J*, anterior end of *Onchnesoma steenstrupi. (E, H, J, after Théel, 1905.)* 1, anus; 2, tentacular crown; 3, circlets of spines; 4, papillae; 5, mouth; 6, smooth zone; 7, pore of cephalic tube; 8, esophagus; 9, retractor muscle; 10, site of retraction of introvert; 11, introvert; 12, trunk; 13, tentacular fold.

abyssal species, *Golfingia flagrifera* and *muricaudata,* is drawn out into a slender tail (Fig. 214*H*).

When the introvert is fully extended the mouth is seen in the center of the anterior tip, which may be termed *oral disk.* This is usually provided with body-wall extensions termed tentacles that range from mere bulges as in small species of *Golfingia* (Fig. 214*B*) to conical, digitiform, filiform, or branched projections of some length, and vary in number from less than 10 to numerous. Tentacles are completely wanting in some species, as the minute *Onchnesoma steenstrupi.*[1] In *Sipunculus* the tentacles take the form of a flat tentacular fold that completely surrounds the oral disk and has a scalloped or foliaceous margin (Fig. 215*C, D*). The tentacles occur in a single circlet around the mouth in *Phascolion* and some species of *Golfingia.* In the latter genus, however, complex conditions often occur, and the tentacles may be arranged in two or three cycles. In such case the inner, or primary, circlet has bulging ampullary bases around the mouth and the others form secondary or tertiary groups somewhat removed from the mouth (Fig. 217*B, C*); and the tentacles may be fused basally in pairs or clusters. In *Aspidosiphon* the single row of tentacles is incomplete ventrally to a greater or lesser extent (Fig. 215*F*). *Dendrostomum* is characterized by the bushy, palmately or dendritically branched tentacles that spring from four to eight main stems (Fig. 218*A, B*). In *Siphonostoma* there are numerous filiform or digitiform tentacles that in the species *S. ingens* are arranged in meridional rows (Fig. 215*G*), and in *Xenosiphon* the numerous small tentacles occur in tufts. *Phascolosoma* differs from other sipunculoids in that the tentacles, few to numerous, do not encircle the mouth but form a crescent, open dorsally, above the mouth (Fig. 216*B, C*). On the surface facing the mouth the tentacles bear a ciliated groove, that is, on their inner surface usually, outer surface in *Phascolosoma.* The tentacles increase in number with age, at least in some sipunculoids (Théel, 1905).

In *Golfingia* there is generally present on the middorsal region of the oral disk a bi- or quadrilobed ciliated cushion, the *nuchal organ* (Fig. 218*C*), which may cause some interruption or displacement of the dorsalmost tentacles. This organ is also present in *Siphonosoma, Siphonomecus,* and *Phascolosoma;* in the last it, together with the brain, lies just within the dorsal ends of the tentacular crescent (Fig. 217*A*). Peebles and Fox (1933) mention a conspicuous nuchal organ in *Dendrostomum zostericolum,* but regarding the occurrence of this organ in sipunculoids other than those mentioned, poor information is available in the literature. Just ventral to the nuchal organ or overhung by it or in the same general location in its absence (definitely absent in *Sipunculus*) is frequently found a median

---

[1] The oft repeated statement that the tentacles occur in two groups in *Onchnesoma* is erroneous, being based on a misunderstanding of Hérubel (1907).

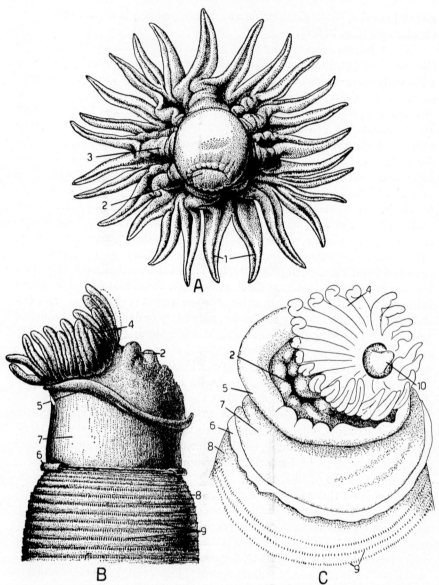

Fig. 216.—Tentacles (continued). *A*, tentacular crown of *Phascolion strombi*. *B*, side view, anterior end of *Phascolosoma*. (*A*, *B*, after *Théel*, 1905.) *C*, view looking down on tentacular crown of *Phascolosoma* (after *Selenka*, *de Man*, and *Bülow*, 1883). 1, furrow of tentacles; 2, mouth; 3, ampullary swelling at tentacle base; 4, tentacular crown; 5, cephalic collar; 6, cervical collar, broken in *B*; 7, smooth zone; 8, introvert; 9, circles of hooks; 10, eminence caused by brain.

unpaired or lateral paired openings of the *cephalic tube* or tubes leading toward the brain. In *Sipunculus* the middorsal pore of the single cephalic tube is evident just above the tentacular fold (Ward, 1891; Fig. 215D). The tube is represented by a large pit around the brain in *Phascolosoma* (Fig. 216C). In *Golfingia* two pores appear to be present, in front of or overhung by the nuchal organ.

Usually a short smooth zone, called collar by some, follows the oral disk. In *Phascolosoma* this zone is bounded on both sides by a projecting collar (Fig. 216B, C). The anterior, or *cephalic*, collar is a rounded ridge that is continuous dorsally with the ends of the tentacular crescent (Fig. 217A); the posterior, or *cervical*, collar is a thin fold or flange directed anteriorly. Apart from the smooth zone the entire body surface usually bears a variety of protuberances or thickenings such as tubercles, papillae, scales, spines, thorns, and the like, and these are frequently arranged regionally. In *Sipunculus* the introvert is covered with papillae (Fig. 215C), whereas the trunk is devoid of special structures and instead is marked off into small squarish or rectangular areas by the longitudinal and circular muscle layers of the body wall (Fig. 215A). Similar conditions obtain in *Xenosiphon*. Very often the introvert is provided in whole or in part with spines or thorns arranged or not in circlets. Circlets of spines are usually present on the introvert of *Phascolosoma* (Fig. 215B) and *Aspidosiphon* (Fig. 214A), and spines or hooks occur on the introvert of many of the numerous species of *Golfingia* (Fig. 217D), usually on the introvert of *Cloeosiphon* and *Lithacrosiphon*, further on the introvert of some species of *Dendrostomum*. The trunk of sipunculoids usually bears papillae of various sorts or glandular eminences or scalelike thickenings but is devoid of hooks or spines. Papillae also often occur on the introvert, even when this bears spines. In the genus *Phascolion*, which habitually dwells in the empty shells of gastropods and scaphopods (Fig. 214D), areas of the trunk are furnished with special hard thickenings, often called holdfasts (Fig. 214F, G), said to aid the animal in maintaining a grip on the shell. Extensive illustrations of surface structures of sipunculoids appear in Selenka, de Man, and Bülow (1883) and Théel (1905).

In the genera *Aspidosiphon*, *Cloeosiphon*, and *Lithacrosiphon* the anterior end of the trunk is armed with a shield. The shield in *Aspidosiphon* occupies the dorsal side of the anterior end of the trunk, hence displaces the introvert ventrally here, consists of irregular or polygonal hornlike or calcareous plates, and may be furrowed (Fig. 219G). In *Lithacrosiphon* the shield is a hard calcareous cone at the anterior end of the trunk (Fig. 217F), also displacing the introvert ventrally. The shield of *Cloeosiphon* surrounds the anterior end of the trunk, hence does not displace the introvert, and is composed of polygonal calcareous plates

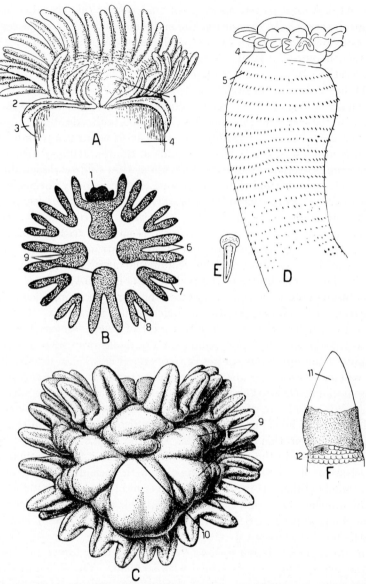

Fig. 217.—Tentacles (continued), general structure. *A*, anterior end of *Phascolosoma*, seen from the dorsal side, nuchal organ injured. *B*, scheme of tentacle arrangement obtaining in many species of *Golfingia* (*after Stehle*, 1953). *C*, tentacular crown of *Golfingia eremita*. *D*, anterior end of introvert of *Golfingia elongata*. *E*, spine of *D* enlarged. (*A*, *C–E, after Théel*, 1905.) *F*, anterior end of trunk of *Lithacrosiphon*, showing shield in form of a calcareous cone (*after Shipley*, 1902). 1, nuchal organ; 2, juncture of tentacular crown with cephalic collar; 3, cephalic collar; 4, smooth zone; 5, spines; 6, primary tentacles; 7, secondary tentacles; 8, tertiary tentacles; 9, expanded ampullary base of primary tentacles; 10, mouth; 11, calcareous conical shield; 12, anus.

(Fig. 239A). *Aspidosiphon*, but not the two other genera, also has a posterior shield covering symmetrically the posterior end of the trunk. It is usually a circular cap composed of radiating pieces (Fig. 214A). The presence of shields in sipunculoids seems to be associated with life in dead coral rock.

The anus is a conspicuous opening middorsally on the anterior end of the trunk, except in the genus *Onchnesoma*, where it occurs on the intro-vert, even near the mouth (Fig. 218D). The two nephridiopores on the ventral surface of the trunk at about the level of the anus are usually invisible to the naked eye. A terminal pore alleged to be present at the trunk tip in some species is probably a temporary invagination.

In size sipunculoids range from minute species 2 mm. or even less in length to quite elongated forms. The longest species seems to be *Sipunculus nudus*, of which Grube (1837) reported having had a specimen 60 cm. (about 2 feet) long. However, most sipunculoids are under half this length, and there are many small species. Colors are dull and uni-form, whitish, yellowish, buff, gray, grayish brown, or brown, and not infrequently the surface elevations may be dark brown.

2. Body Wall.—The body wall consists of the following layers: cuticle, epidermis, dermis, circular muscle layer, longitudinal muscle layer, and peritoneum (Fig. 219A, B). A thin layer of diagonal muscles may occur between the two mentioned layers but does not seem to be universally present. The cuticle, secreted by the epidermis, varies from a thin homogeneous layer, as mostly on the tentacles and introvert, to a thick lamellated stratum, as often on the posterior parts of the trunk. The cuticle is everywhere underlain by an epidermis of mostly cuboidal cells but columnar and heavily ciliated on the upper surface of the tentacles (presumably under surface in *Phascolosoma*) or both surfaces in some species. Cilia appear lacking elsewhere on the body surface than on the oral disk. Some authors report the epidermal cells as narrowed basally, hence not in contact there. Local epidermal activity produces special cuticular structures such as spines, scales, and the holdfasts of *Phascolion*. The spines or thorns, generally hollow, may be straight (Fig. 217E) but are usually curved hooks with single (Fig. 219C) or bifid (Fig. 219D) tips; rarely an accessory comb of spinelets occurs on the base (Fig. 219J). Spines seldom occur on the trunk but are common on the introvert, in whole or in part, arranged in circles (Fig. 217D) or irregularly disposed (Fig. 218C). Shipley (1890) stated that each hook is secreted by a raised epidermal papilla of connective tissue covered by large cuboidal epidermal cells. Stehle (1953) gave an unclear account and figure of the formation of a spine in a species of *Golfingia;* the epidermis proliferates to form a little cushion that secretes a homogeneous material capped by the spine which is continuous with the adjacent cuticle (Fig. 220A). Scalelike

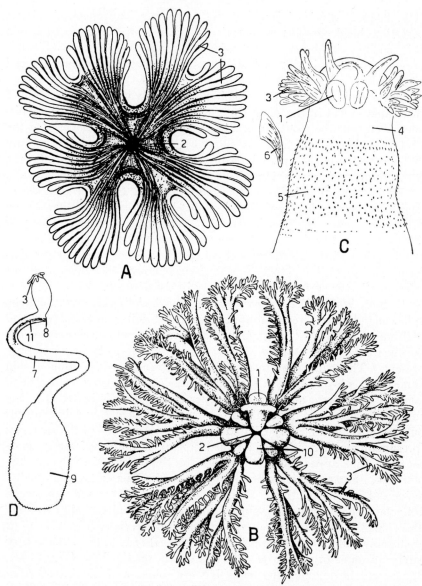

FIG. 218.—Tentacles (concluded), general structure (continued).   A, B, types of tentacles of Dendrostomum.   A, D. signifer (after Awati and Pradhan, 1935).   B, D. hexadactylum
(after Sato, 1930).   C, anterior end of the introvert of Golfingia vulgaris.   D, Onchnesoma
squamatum.   (C, D, after Théel, 1905.)   1, nuchal organ; 2, mouth; 3, tentacles; 4, smooth
zone; 5, hooks; 6, hook enlarged; 7, introvert; 8, anus; 9, trunk; 10, ampullary tentacle
bases; 11, rectum.

thickenings very common on papillae and forming the elements of the shields of *Aspidosiphon* are condensations in the cuticle (Fig. 219*H*). The holdfasts of *Phascolion* are elevations armed with an arch of thickened cuticle, of which some shapes are shown in Fig. 214*F*, *G*. The frequent brown color of the cuticle seems to be caused by pigment granules.

The epidermis is abundantly productive of glands that may be one-celled, two-celled, or many-celled. These glands often occur on papillae or other surface elevations, or themselves cause little elevations. The two-celled glands consist of two elongated cells, each with a vacuole, pressed closely together (Fig. 219*F*), and were thought by Metalnikoff (1900) to arise by the coming together of two originally separate unicellular glands. The most common type of multicellular gland consists of a number of elongated, curved, coarsely granular cells that are pressed together into a spherical body opening through the cuticle directly or by a short neck (Fig. 220*F*). The gland may be covered with only a thin membrane, as generally in *Sipunculus* and in *Golfingia gouldi*, or enclosed in a hull of flattened elongated epidermal cells, as reported by Shipley (1890, 1891) in species of *Phascolosoma* (Fig. 220*C*), also in *Golfingia elongata* (Jourdan, 1891; Stehle, 1953). Shipley, in fact, considered the gland to arise by a cuplike epidermal invagination. In another similar type described by Andrews (1890b) in *Golfingia gouldi* each cell contains a long vacuole (Fig. 220*B*); the same was seen in *G. elongata* by Jourdan (1891). Nickerson (1901) elaborated on this type of gland in *G. gouldi*, showing that each vacuole is an intracellular sac with a definite wall in early stages; each sac has a separate duct, and all the ducts unite to a main duct opening at the surface. Cuénot (1900) showed a similar condition in multicellular glands in *G. vulgaris* (Fig. 220*D*), but here the gland also contains ordinary gland cells as well as a sensory bud. Still another type appears composed of polygonal cells (Fig. 220*E*). What he designated as a mixed type of epidermal gland was found by Stehle (1953) in *Golfingia elongata;* this is an elongated body enclosed in a hull of flattened epidermal cells and composed of two sorts of cells, elongated, finely granular cells and shorter ones with coarse clumps of secretion (Fig. 221*A*). A nerve entering the base of multicellular glands has often been observed (Fig. 220*D*). Stehle (1953) showed the nerve spraying out over the gland cells (Fig. 221*A*).

The epidermis also contains an abundance of sensory organs, mostly in the form of sensory buds, discussed later. In some species these sensory buds occur only as part of a multicellular gland.

Glands and sensory buds may be located entirely in the cuticle or may project inwardly into the dermis, a layer of connective tissue beneath the epidermis and also permeating the muscle layers. It varies from a quite thick to a very thin stratum, and in the latter case the epidermis seems to

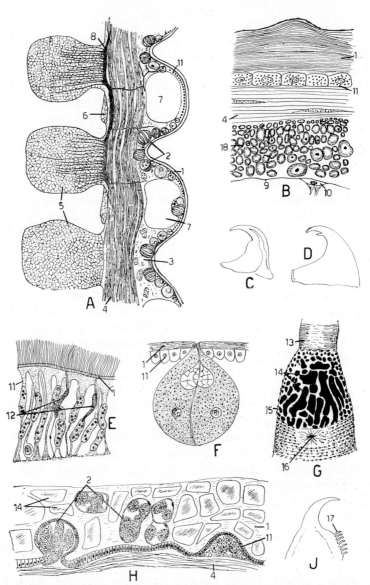

Fig. 219.—Body wall, glands. *A*, transverse section of the trunk wall of *Sipun. nudus.*
B, transverse section through the trunk wall of *Golfingia minuta* (*after Paul*, 1910). *C*, simple curved spine of *Phascolosoma*. *D*, spine with bifid tip from introvert of *Lithacrosiphon*
(*after Shipley*, 1902). *E*, epidermis of upper surface of the tentacular fold of *Sipun. nudus*
(*after Ward*, 1891). *F*, two-celled epidermal gland of *Sipun. nudus.* (*A, F, after Metalnikoff*, 1900.) *G*, shield of *Aspidosiphon mirabilis* (*after Théel*, 1905). *H*, section through
the shield of *Aspidosiphon* (*after Hérubel*, 1907). *J*, spine of *Golfingia hespera* with basal
comb of spinelets. (*C, J, after Fisher*, 1952.) 1, cuticle; 2, epidermal glands; 3, dermis; 4,
circular muscle layer; 5, longitudinal muscle bundles; 6, diagonal muscles; 7, longitudinal
coelomic canals; 8, nerve; 9, peritoneum; 10, ciliated peritoneal cell; 11, epidermis; 12,
sensory nerve cells; 13, introvert base; 14, cuticular thickenings of shield; 15, trunk; 16,
anus; 17, comb of spinelets; 18, longitudinal muscle layer.

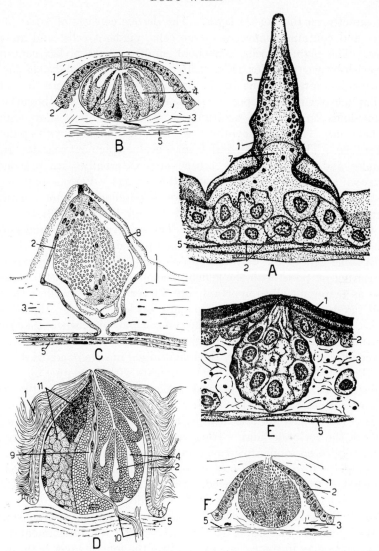

Fig. 220.—Glands of body wall (continued). *A*, spine of *G. elongata* in process of secretion. *B*, multicellular gland with long vacuoles, *Golfingia gouldi*. *C*, multicellular gland with epidermal sheath, *Phascolosoma* (*after Shipley*, 1890). *D*, complicated gland of trunk of *Golfingia vulgaris*, part secretory, part with long vacuoles, combined with sensory bud (*after Cuénot*, 1900). *E*, multicellular gland of polygonal cells. (*A, E, after Stehle*, 1953.) *F*, common type of multicellular gland, of long secretory cells, *Golfingia gouldi*. (*B, F, after Andrews*, 1890b.) 1, cuticle; 2, epidermis; 3, connective tissue; 4, vacuole; 5, circular muscle layer; 6, spine; 7, outflow of secretion; 8, epidermal sheath of gland; 9, sensory bud; 10, nerve; 11, secretory cells.

rest directly on the muscle layer. The dermis consists of a felt of fine fibers and contains connective-tissue cells, pigment cells, and amoebocytes. The pigment cells, amoeboid, multinucleate bodies containing yellowish-brown granules (Fig. 221*C*), are mostly responsible for the brown colors often present locally, as on papillae, scales, and the like.

Papillae of various shapes and sizes are widely present on the surface of sipunculoids on introvert or trunk, or both, and often show regional localization. They are elevations of the dermis covered with epidermis and cuticle. They are often dark from contained pigment cells or pigment granules and very frequently are covered externally with rounded or polygonal scales, formed of cuticular thickenings. Various papillae are illustrated in Fig. 221. Surface views of papillae are common in the literature (notably in Selenka, de Man, and Bülow, 1883), but very few figures of sections of them exist. The epidermal glands and sensory buds are usually located on papillae when present.

In some genera the dermis contains coelomic canals or spaces communicating by pores with the general coelom. Spengel (1912) regarded these as taxonomically important, but Fisher (1952) considers them of small taxonomic value. They are most evident in large, thick-walled species. They are best known in the genus *Sipunculus*, where they run as longitudinal canals under the longitudinal ridges of the trunk, that is, between the grooves caused by the longitudinal muscle bands of the body wall (Fig. 219*A*). These canals communicate with each other and also at regular intervals with the general coelom. The pores for the latter communications occur at the crossing of circular and longitudinal muscle bands. The canals are lined by peritoneum and contain the same elements as the coelomic fluid. The larger species of *Siphonosoma* are also provided with coelomic diverticula into the dermis (Spengel, 1912), but these take the form of blind sacs, often of irregular shape or branched and somewhat transversely arranged. In *Xenosiphon* there are "integumental coelomic spaces in the form of independent sacs of irregular outline" (Fisher, 1952). Coelomic spaces in the dermis appear wanting in other genera. According to Spengel (1912), the integumental coelomic spaces may in some cases extend into the muscle layer between the circular and longitudinal strata.

The muscle layer of the body wall is considered below. The peritoneum consists of a flattened epithelium provided here and there with tufts of cilia, also with urns and chloragogue cells.

3. Muscular System.—This consists of the body-wall musculature, the retractors of the introvert, and some small muscles concerned in anchoring the digestive tract. The body-wall musculature in general consists of outer circular and inner longitudinal layers. A thin diagonal layer exists between the other two in some sipunculoids but is infrequently

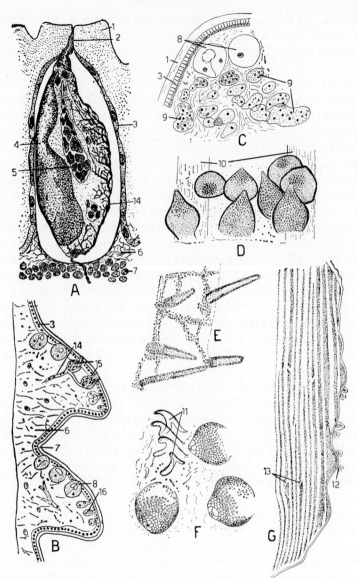

Fig. 221.—Glands (concluded), papillae, muscular system.   *A*, mixed epidermal gland of *Golfingia elongata* (*after Stehle*, 1953).   *B*, longitudinal section of the introvert of *Sipun. nudus*, showing two papillae (*after Metalnikoff*, 1900).   *C*, bit of cross section of the introvert of *Sipun. nudus*, showing pigment cells (*after Ward*, 1891).   *D*, pigmented papillae of the trunk of *Phascolosoma pacificum.*   *E*, long papillae from the trunk of *Phas. pellucidum.* *F*, scaly papillae and hooks from the introvert of *Phas. varians* (*after Shipley*, 1890).   *G*, inner side of part of the trunk wall of *Phascolosoma*, showing longitudinal muscle bundles. (*D, E, G, after Selenka, de Man, and Bülow*, 1883.)   1, cuticle; 2, neck of gland; 3, epidermis; 4, finely granular gland cell; 5, coarsely granular gland cell; 6, dermis; 7, circular muscle fibers; 8, two-celled gland; 9, pigment cells; 10, longitudinal muscle bands; 11, hooks; 12, papillae; 13, cross connections; 14, nerve; 15, sense buds; 16, young gland.

mentioned. In *Sipunculus* the diagonal layer is found on the inner side of the circular layer between the longitudinal bundles (Fig. 219*A*). The circular and longitudinal layers form continuous strata in some sipunculoids, that is, in *Golfingia* (except the species *G. gouldi*), *Dendrostomum*, *Phascolion*, *Onchnesoma*, *Cloeosiphon*, and *Aspidosiphon* in part. In *Golfingia gouldi*, some species of *Aspidosiphon*, and the genera *Sipunculus*, *Xenosiphon*, *Siphonosoma*, *Phascolosoma*, *Siphonomecus*, *Siphonides*, and *Lithacrosiphon*, the longitudinal layer of the trunk is divided into separate bundles (15 to 50) that project prominently into the coelom and give the interior surface of the body wall a striped appearance in the opened animal (Fig. 221*G*). This division of the longitudinal layer is wanting in the introvert and in *Sipunculus* at the posterior end of the trunk (Fig. 215*A*). The bundles are generally more or less anastomosed with each other by cross connections. In such genera as *Sipunculus* and *Xenosiphon*, there is an external longitudinal groove opposite each bundle (Fig. 219*A*). When the longitudinal layer is divided into bundles this is also usually the case with the circular layer, whose bundles also anastomose by cross connections. These circular bundles may also cause external circular grooves of the body wall. Consequently the external surface of the trunk may be formed into a regular pattern of square or rectangular cushions, as notably in *Sipunculus* (Fig. 215*A*).

The main muscles of the interior are the *retractors of the introvert*. These cross the coelom as free longitudinal bands extending from the beginning of the esophagus to various levels of the trunk wall. They are fused to the surface of the esophagus and then curve backward and become continuous with the longitudinal muscle stratum of the body wall. In many sipunculoids, as the genera *Sipunculus*, *Xenosiphon*, *Phascolosoma*, *Siphonosoma*, *Siphonides*, and *Golfingia* in part, there are four retractors, a ventral pair and a dorsal pair. They may be of equal length (Fig. 222*A*), or often the dorsal pair is shorter (Fig. 222*B*). The ventral pair originates on the ventral body wall to either side of the ventral nerve cord; the dorsal pair originates on the lateral walls. There is only one pair of retractors, the ventral pair, in *Dendrostomum*, *Aspidosiphon*, *Lithacrosiphon*, *Siphonomecus*, and *Golfingia* in part. A single retractor muscle originating in the posterior end of the trunk is characteristic of *Onchnesoma* (Fig. 223*B*). Variable conditions obtain in different species of *Phascolion;* this genus usually has a pair of ventral retractors, but these may be almost completely fused to form a single muscle and one dorsal retractor may be present in addition in some cases. More or less fusion of retractors anteriorly is of common occurrence. *Xenosiphon* differs from all other sipunculoids in possessing a pair of *protractors of the introvert*, short muscles extending from the brain region to the adjacent introvert wall (Fig. 225*A*). The contraction of the retractors obviously causes the

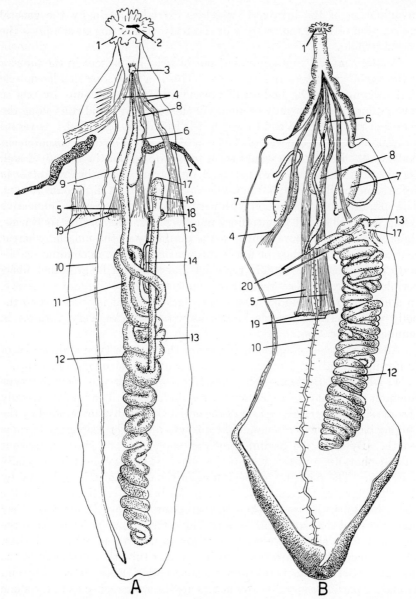

Fig. 222.—Muscular system (continued), internal anatomy. *A*, dissection of *Sipun.
nudus* with four equal retractors (*after Metalnikoff*, 1900).   *B*, dissection of *Golfingia vulgaris* with long ventral and short dorsal retractors (*after Théel*, 1905).   1, tentacles; 2,
mouth: 3, brain; 4, dorsal retractors; 5, ventral retractors; 6, esophagus; 7, nephridium; 8,
dorsal compensation sac; 9, ventral compensation sac; 10, ventral nerve cord; 11, loop at
beginning of intestine; 12, intestinal coil; 13, rectum; 14, rectal diverticulum; 15, spindle
muscle; 16, attachment strand of spindle muscle; 17, location of anus; 18, rectal glands; 19,
gonad; 20, fixing muscles.

invagination of the introvert, which is extruded again by the general contraction of the circular layer of the body wall acting to compress the coelomic fluid.

Another muscle commonly, but not invariably, present in the interior is the *spindle muscle* of the intestine. This is a very long slender muscle that originates in the body-wall musculature near the anus by one to several fine strands or may originate in the rectal wall and runs along the center of the intestinal coil to which it is frequently attached. It terminates posteriorly in the wall of the bend of the intestine or on the adjacent body wall. Its purpose would seem to be to shorten the intestinal coil. Its histological structure was studied by Harms (1920) in *Phascolosoma* species and by Stehle (1953) in *Golfingia elongata*, with discordant results. The spindle muscle is clothed with peritoneum and consists of connective tissue with imbedded longitudinal muscle fibers. According to Harms, these fibers take a spiral course in the periphery of the muscle, whereas centrally there is a mass of fibers thrown into waves, depending on the state of contraction. Stehle reported diagonal and longitudinal fibers peripherally around a central core of connective tissue containing a nerve. In addition to the spindle muscle the digestive tract is anchored to the body wall by short strands known as *fixing muscles*, very variable in number and location.

All the muscles of sipunculoids are of the smooth type and consist of fusiform fibers about 1 mm. long with a central nucleus (Olson, 1940).

4. Digestive System.—The digestive tract is of the recurved type common to animals of sedentary or sessile habits. The mouth, usually of some size, occupies the center of the oral disk, usually surrounded by the bulging bases of the tentacles, and leads into a straight esophagus of some length. By some the beginning of the esophagus for a short distance is termed pharynx, and this may be justifiable if the wall here is especially muscular. The pharynx, or beginning of the esophagus, is embraced by the retractor muscles as they turn here to become continuous with the body-wall musculature. When the retractors are fused anteriorly they may surround the esophagus for a considerable part of its length, and the esophagus then seems to emerge from among the retractors (Fig. 223A). The esophagus leads into the intestine, a long tube that descends to the posterior part of the trunk and then ascends. Both descending and ascending parts are spirally wound and are intermingled so as to form one coil (Figs. 222, 223). In a few species of *Golfingia* a short area at the end of the esophagus or at the beginning of the descending coil differs in bearing strong internal longitudinal ridges projecting into the lumen and externally visible (Fig. 224D). This area is termed stomach, although the name does not seem very appropriate. It has been noticed in *Golfingia gouldi*, where there are four reddish ridges (Andrews, 1890b),

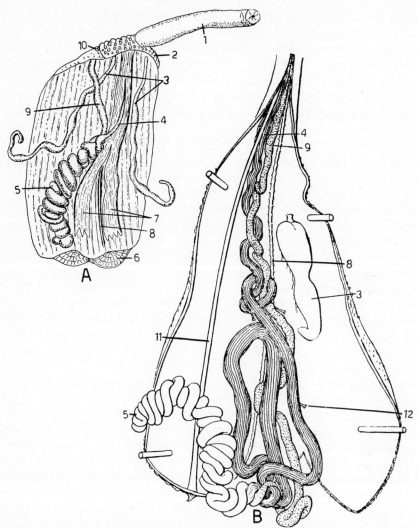

FIG. 223.—Muscular system (concluded), internal anatomy (continued). *A*, dissection of *Aspidosiphon*, with one pair of retractors (*after Selenka*, 1885). *B*, dissection of *Onchnesoma steenstrupi*, with one retractor and one nephridium (*after Théel*, 1905). 1, introvert; 2, anterior shield; 3, nephridium; 4, esophagus; 5, intestinal coil; 6, posterior shield; 7, ventral retractors; 8, nerve cord; 9, rectum; 10, anus; 11, retractor; 12, fixing muscle.

Golfingia minuta with several ridges (Paul, 1910), and *G. elongata* with four (Stehle, 1953). No doubt such a stomach region is present in other species of *Golfingia*, but no mention has been found of its occurrence in other genera. At the top of the coil the intestine straightens and as a straight tube, the rectum, runs to the anus, usually located middorsally near the anterior limit of the trunk but situated on the introvert in the

genus *Onchnesoma* (Fig. 218*D*).   Along its course the rectum often bears
a blind diverticulum, varying from a low projection to a tubular outgrowth.   By some only the part of the intestine distal to the diverticulum
is termed rectum.   Just prior to the anus the rectum may bear a pair of
bushy rectal glands or instead a number of fingerlike projections.   Before
opening into the anus the rectum may be attached to the adjacent body
wall by wing muscles, having no doubt a dilator function.   Some variants
may be mentioned.   In *Sipunculus* the descending intestine before entering the coil typically undergoes a loop (Fig. 222*A*), and a similar loop may
occur in *Xenosiphon*.   A typical intestinal coil is lacking in *Phascolion*, in
which instead the intestine makes several long loops (Fig. 224*A*).   The
eight divisions of the digestive tract declared by Stehle (1953) to exist in
Golfingia elongata are not of general applicability, and most of them are
based on slight constrictions or slight differences in wall structure.

The spindle and fixing muscles of the digestive tract were already
mentioned.   The mesenteries of the digestive tract will be considered
under coelom.

Available information about the histology of the digestive tract is
limited to the account of Metalnikoff (1900) for *Sipunculus nudus*, and
those of Andrews (1890b), Cuénot (1900), Paul (1910), and Stehle (1953)
for species of *Golfingia*.   In general, the latter genus shows more variation
along the tract than does *Sipunculus*.   In all cases the digestive tract is
lined throughout by a columnar ciliated epithelium generally thrown into
longitudinal folds, which are most marked in the so-called stomach of
species of *Golfingia*.   The epithelium is underlain by connective tissue
which forms the bulk of the folds when present and is in fact the main
constituent of the digestive wall.   It consists of a mesh of fibrils and
contains connective-tissue cells and a rich nerve plexus.   In some places,
notably the stomach region of *Golfingia*, the connective tissue is arranged
to form long cylinders (Fig. 224*C*) filled with a reddish gelatinous material
and oriented at right angles to the lumen.   Andrews records these
cylinders as continued along the ridges of the intestinal coil of *Golfingia
gouldi* but gradually disappearing along the ascending coil, and Cuénot,
who terms these cylinders cells of Leydig, found them along the descending coil of *G. vulgaris*.   In general, the sipunculoid digestive tract lacks
definite muscular layers.   Fine inner circular and outer longitudinal
fibrils believed to be of muscular nature are generally reported as present
in the connective-tissue layer.   In the pharynx of *G. elongata* Stehle
found the connective-tissue layer permeated with fine muscle fibers and
outside this a strong sphincter of circular fibers.   In general, however,
the connective-tissue layer of the pharynx, or beginning esophagus, is
simply continuous with the connective tissue of the retractor muscles that
are here fused to the surface of the digestive tract.   An inner circular and

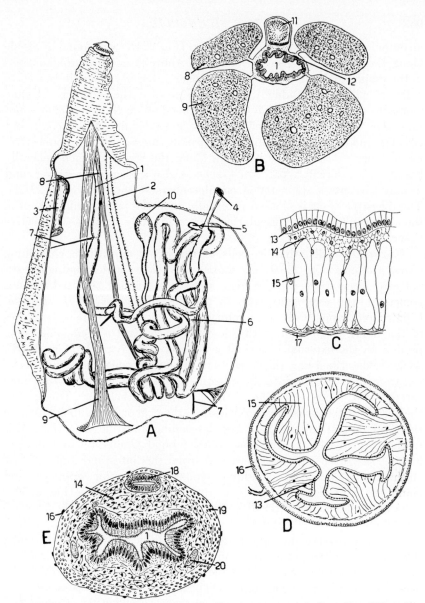

Fig. 224.—Internal anatomy (continued), digestive system. *A*, dissection of *Phascolion strombi* (*after Théel*, 1905). *B*, cross section through the esophagus of *Golfingia vulgaris*, surrounded by the four retractors (*after Cuénot*, 1900). *C*, section of the intestine of *Sipun. nudus*, showing long cylinders in the connective tissue (*after Metalnikoff*, 1900). *D*, transverse section through the stomach of *Golfingia gouldi* (*after Andrews*, 1890b). *E*, cross section of the esophagus of *Golfingia minuta* (*after Paul*, 1910). 1, esophagus; 2, ventral nerve cord; 3, end of rectum; 4, rectum cut across; 5, rectal diverticulum; 6, intestine; 7, fixing muscle; 8, dorsal retractor; 9, ventral retractor; 10, nephridium; 11, dorsal compensation sac; 12, nerves; 13, intestinal epithelium; 14, connective tissue; 15, cylinders; 16, peritoneum; 17, muscle fibers; 18, cephalic tube; 19, circular muscle layer; 20, circumenteric connective.

an outer longitudinal layer of muscle fibers (Fig. 224*E*) were found by Stehle along the esophagus, also by Paul, and Andrews noted a circular layer in the esophageal wall of *G. gouldi*, stronger anteriorly where it seemed to make a sphincter, gradually decreasing toward the stomach. Unlike stomachs in general, the wall of the so-called stomach of *Golfingia* is not muscular. The intestinal coil generally lacks definite muscle coats, but circular and longitudinal fibers are usually present in the connective-tissue layer. Muscularity increases along the rectum, which generally has at least a circular coat, in *Sipunculus* also a longitudinal layer, and usually presents a sphincter of circular fibers at the anus (Fig. 227*A*). The digestive tract is clothed externally with the peritoneum, which in the absence of definite muscular coats rests directly upon the connective tissue.

Enzymatic cells, that is, cells of the lining epithelium containing coarse granules (Fig. 225*D*), are mostly limited to the descending intestinal coil, where they may be very numerous. Stehle reported mucous goblets in the esophagus, also in the descending coil of *G. elongata*. Ciliated pits, apparently of secretory nature, appear common structures of the lining epithelium of the descending coil in *Golfingia*, and some project on the external intestinal wall as obvious papillae (Fig. 225*B*). Andrews described how the currents in these pits brought granular material from their bottom into the intestinal lumen. These pits often open through a papillary elevation of the intestinal epithelium. The cells at the bottom of the pit are generally less columnar, more of a cuboidal shape, than the general epithelium. The descending intestine of *G. elongata* is further provided with very long coiled tubular glands, up to 1 mm. in length, that also project externally from the intestinal wall. Their epithelium is decidedly glandular, containing secretion granules, and gland cells also occur around their outlet into the intestine (Fig. 225*C*).

A constant feature of the digestive tract of sipunculoids is the presence of a ciliated groove (Fig. 226). In *Sipunculus* this runs from the mouth to the rectal diverticulum and is externally visible as a reddish line along the tract. In *Golfingia* it runs from about the bend of the intestinal coil along the ascending coil to the rectal diverticulum. The lining cells decrease in height from a columnar shape at the opening of the groove to a cuboidal form at the bottom which lacks cilia (Fig. 226*B*). Cuénot and Andrews observed that a current directed toward the anus runs in the groove. The groove is reddish in *S. nudus* and *G. gouldi* because the connective tissue of its walls contains the same elongated radiating elements, possibly cells, as the stomach wall and these are reddish. They are not present in the groove wall in the other species studied. The groove always terminates in the rectal diverticulum, which in fact seems to exist for the purpose of receiving the end of the groove. In *Sipunculus*

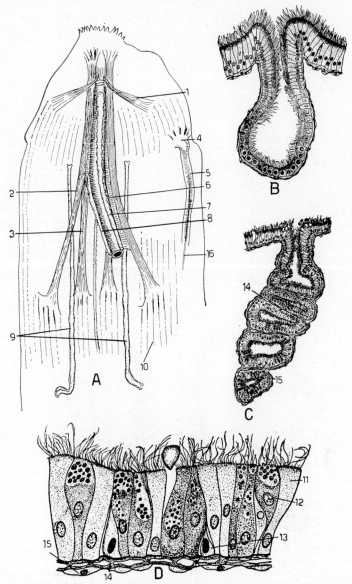

FIG. 225.—Internal anatomy (continued), digestive system (continued). *A*, dissection of *Xenosiphon branchiatum* (*after Fisher*, 1952). *B*, ciliated intestinal pit, *Golfingia elongata*. *C*, coiled tubular gland of intestine of *G. elongata*. *D*, longitudinal section of intestinal wall of *G. elongata*. (*B–D, after Stehle*, 1953.) 1, protractor muscles; 2, ventral retractors; 3, dorsal retractors; 4, location of anus; 5, rectum; 6, esophagus; 7, dorsal compensation sac; 8, ventral compensation sac; 9, nephridia; 10, longitudinal muscle bundles of body wall; 11, ordinary intestinal cell; 12, enzymatic cell; 13, replacement cells; 14, connective tissue; 15, peritoneum; 16, spindle muscle.

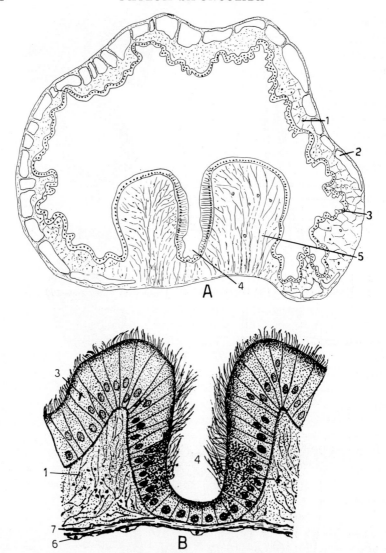

FIG. 226.—Digestive system (continued). *A*, cross section through the intestine of *Sipun. nudus*, showing ciliated groove (*after Metalnikoff*, 1900). *B*, ciliated groove of *Golfingia* (*after Stehle*, 1953). 1, connective-tissue layer; 2, sinus; 3, intestinal epithelium; 4, ciliated groove; 5, long spaces in connective tissue; 6, peritoneum; 7, muscle fibers.

nudus the diverticulum is seemingly of secretory nature, being lined by a flat epithelium of large cuboidal glandular cells containing vesicles. Metalnikoff is of the opinion that the diverticulum is normally developed in *Sipunculus* only in young animals, in which it may reach a length of 5 cm., and degenerates with age. In *Golfingia* the diverticulum has a scalloped epithelium and also appears secretory. Muscle fibers are usually present in the wall of the diverticulum.

In *Sipunculus*, but not so far as known in other genera, the connective-tissue layer of the intestinal wall contains a sinus crossed at frequent intervals by strands (Fig. 226*A*). This sinus does not communicate with any other body spaces.

5. Tentacular System.—The cavities of the tentacles are continuous with one or two tubular sacs adherent to the surface of the esophagus. In *Sipunculus* the tentacular fold contains a large flattened cavity broken up by cross connections; it is continuous with a circular cavity around the beginning of the digestive tract also crossed by columns of tissue. This ring cavity communicates with two long tubular blind sacs lying upon the esophagus, one on the dorsal side of the latter, the other along its ventral side. Each sac has about the same diameter as the esophagus, to which it is attached by a membrane. In *Golfingia* each tentacle contains three intercommunicating channels (Fig. 227*B*), and these join a ring space around the beginning of the digestive tract, from which one tubular sac extends along the dorsal side of the esophagus, without giving off any diverticula. *Siphonides, Phascolosoma*, and *Aspidosiphon* have one dorsal sac without diverticula, and *Xenosiphon*, like *Sipunculus*, possesses both dorsal and ventral sacs not diverticulated. In *Siphonosoma* only the dorsal sac is present, and this is covered with numerous short diverticula, also called villi (Fig. 228*A*). The most complicated conditions exist in *Dendrostomum*, where the single dorsal sac may give off a network of vessels over the esophagus (Fig. 229*B*) and also usually has several to many very long slender diverticula (Fig. 228*B*). In some cases channels are given off into the esophageal wall.

This system is lined by a flattened nucleated membrane resembling peritoneum and provided here and there with tufts of cilia. This is underlain by connective tissue containing muscle fibers, mostly circular, and this is covered externally by the peritoneum. The lumen contains the same elements as the coelom, and although there are no openings into the coelom the coelomocytes seem able to penetrate into the system. Metalnikoff (1900) records having stained coelomocytes by injecting dyes into the coelom and later finding such stained cells in the tentacular system.

The sacs of this system are contractile, and they act as compensation sacs for the tentacles, receiving the fluid from the latter when they contract and sending it into the tentacles when they expand. Therefore the term compensation sac appears preferable to the usual terms, polian vessel or contractile vessel. The expression vessel does not appear very suitable for a blind appendage. In older works this tentacular system was regarded as a circulatory system, evidently an error. Sipunculoids, in

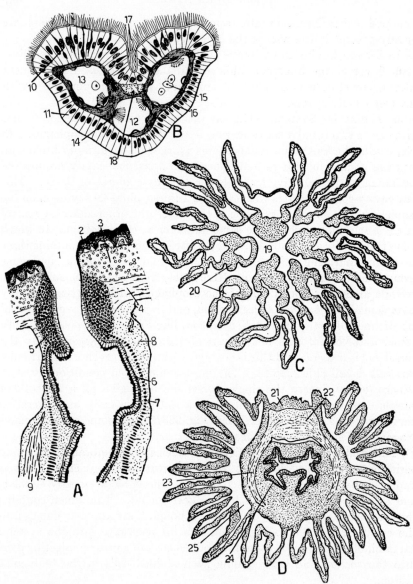

FIG. 227.—Digestive system (concluded), tentacular system. *A*, longitudinal section through terminal part of the rectum of *G. elongata*. *B*, cross section through a tentacle of *G. vulgaris (after Cuénot,* 1900). *C* cross section through tentacular crown of *G. elongata*, showing fusion of tentacles in pairs. *D*, more proximal section to *C*, showing tentacular canals entering circular canal. (*A, C, D, after Stehle,* 1953.) 1, anus; 2, cuticle; 3, circular muscle layer of body wall; 4, longitudinal muscle layer; 5, anal sphincter; 6, rectal epithelium; 7, muscle fibers of rectal wall; 8, connective tissue; 9, termination of spindle muscle; 10, ciliated epidermis of upper surface tentacles; 11, nonciliated epidermis of underside tentacles; 12, middle tentacular canal; 13, lateral tentacular canal; 14, ciliated cell of lining; 15, red coelomic corpuscles; 16, connective tissue with muscle fibers; 17, ciliated groove; 18, tentacular nerve; 19, mouth; 20, ampullary tentacular bases; 21, nuchal organ; 22, brain; 23, circumenteric connectives; 24, beginning of esophagus; 25, ring canal.

fact, lack a circulatory system. However, the fluid in the system does move, as several observers have attested, independently of retractions and expansions of the tentacles.

6. Coelom and Coelomic Elements.—The coelom extends without interruption from the beginning of the esophagus to the posterior end of the trunk. Only remnants of mesenteries are present. Where the anterior part of the esophagus lies between the anterior ends of the retractor muscles it is attached to them by a short mesentery on each side (Fig. 224*B*). The compensation sac or sacs are either directly in contact with the esophagus or attached to it by a mesentery (Fig. 229*D*). The spindle muscle is fastened to the midventral line of the ascending intestinal coil by a mesentery that presumably represents a remnant of a ventral mesentery; mesenterial strands containing muscle fibers extend at frequent intervals to the descending coil. The wing muscles of the rectum are in part mesenterial sheets, probably continuations of the mesentery of the spindle muscle. The strands attaching the spindle muscle to the body wall and also the fixing muscles are partly mesenterial in nature.

In several species of the genus *Siphonosoma* there is a succession of short transverse peritoneal folds on the inside of the trunk wall to either side of the nerve cord extending from about the level of the origins of the retractor muscles to the posterior end of the trunk. This condition was discovered by Keferstein (1866) in *Siphonosoma cumanense;* he gave a beautiful figure showing these folds, which is reproduced here (Fig. 230). Fisher (1950b) created the subgenus *Dasmosiphon* for the species (seven listed in 1952) of *Siphonosoma* possessing this peculiarity. Although the more or less regular repetition of these folds (there are about 70 pairs of them in *S. cumanense*) is certainly suggestive of the intersegmental septa of annelids, it is extremely improbable that the folds are indicative of segmentation. They are not in any way related to the intestinal coil.

The coelom is lined with a peritoneum of flattened cells, interspersed here and there with a granular cell bearing a tuft of cilia (Fig. 229*C*). Peritoneal cells may also be altered into chloragogue cells and fixed urns. The chloragogue cells, most often found on the esophagus, intestinal coil, and both surfaces of the compensation sacs, are bulging or clavate cells filled with yellow granules imbedded in a reticular cytoplasm (Fig. 229*A*). The fixed urns are curious structures found in some sipunculoids as *Sipunculus*, some *Golfingia*, *Phascolosoma granulatum*, *Aspidosiphon*. Their location varies with species; usual locations are the inner and outer peritoneum of the compensation sacs, peritoneum of mesenteries, peritoneal covering of the ascending intestinal coil. In *Sipunculus nudus* where they have been most studied they consist of a stalked vaselike elevation with vacuolated interior, sides covered with peritoneum, and top formed of a flattened disklike cell bearing several bunches of cilia (Fig.

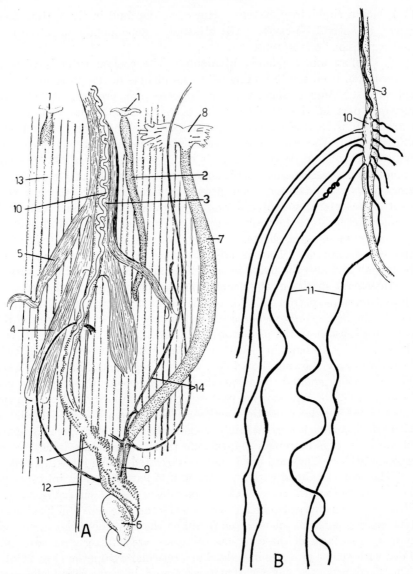

Fig. 228.—Tentacular system (continued). A, dissection of *Siphonosoma ingens* with long diverticulated compensation sac. B, compensation sac of *Dendrostomum zostericolum* with long diverticula. (*Both after Fisher*, 1952.) 1, nephrostome; 2, nephridium; 3, esophagus; 4, ventral retractors; 5, dorsal retractors; 6, beginning of intestinal coil; 7, rectum; 8, wing muscles; 9, spindle muscle; 10, compensation sac; 11, diverticula of 10; 12, nerve cord; 13, longitudinal muscle bundles of body wall; 14, attachment strands of spindle muscle.

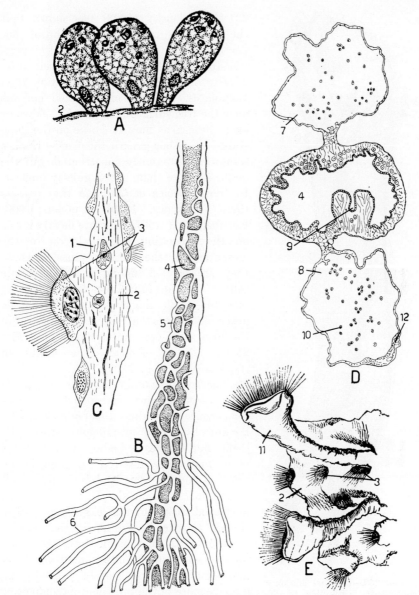

Fig. 229.—Tentacular system (concluded), coelom. *A*, chloragogue cells on the intestinal mesentery of *Golfingia elongata* (*after Stehle*, 1953). *B*, branching compensation sac with long diverticula (cut off) of *Dendrostomum pyroides* (*after Fisher*, 1952). *C*, section through the wall of the compensation sac of *Sipun. nudus* (*after Selensky*, 1908). *D*, section through the esophagus and the two compensation sacs of *Sipun. nudus* (*after Metalnikoff*, 1900). *E*, fixed urns of *Sipun. nudus* as seen in life (*after Lankester*, 1873). 1, lining compensation sac; 2, peritoneum; 3, ciliated cell; 4, esophagus; 5, network formed by compensation sac on esophagus; 6, diverticula of compensation sac; 7, dorsal compensation sac; 8, ventral compensation sac; 9, ciliated groove; 10, red corpuscles; 11, urn; 12, supposed site of formation of coelomic cells.

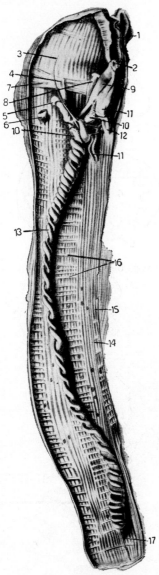

FIG. 230.—Internal anatomy (concluded). Dissection of *Siphonosoma cumanense* (*after Keferstein*, 1866). 1, invaginated introvert; 2, crown of tentacles; 3, attachment strand of spindle muscle; 4, location of anus; 5, rectum; 6, stump of right ventral retractor; 7, wing muscles of anal region; 8, nephridium; 9, esophagus; 10, compensation sac; 11, dorsal retractors; 12, left ventral retractor; 13, intestinal coil; 14, ventral nerve cord; 15, longitudinal muscle bundles; 16, peritoneal folds; 17, spindle muscle.

231*A*). Selensky (1908) has shown that the fixed urns arise as an elevation of connective tissue carrying with it the peritoneum, including one ciliated cell (Fig. 231*B*); the interior of the elevation then vacuolates, and the ciliated cell spreads over the free surface (Fig. 231*B*). Two or even three urns may be borne on the same stalk. In other genera the fixed urns are somewhat differently constructed, but the descriptions of them are singularly unclear. In those species of *Golfingia* that possess them (Andrews, 1890b; Cuénot, 1900; Hérubel, 1902, 1907) they are mostly borne on the ascending intestinal coil or the mesentery of the spindle muscle, where they are nestled among the chloragogue cells. They are funnellike, depressed along one side, while the protuberant lip of the other side is crowned by a ciliated cell in the form of a crescent or horseshoe (Fig. 231*C*, *D*). A similar type exists in *Aspidosiphon* (Fig. 231*C*).

The coelomic fluid contains an abundance of free elements that may be listed as red corpuscles, hyaline amoebocytes, granular amoebocytes or granulocytes, free urns, giant multinucleate bodies, and balls of waste material. The red corpuscle is the most abundant type and is found in all sipunculoids examined. It is a biconvex nucleated disk, but also can assume other shapes, ranging in size in different species from 6 to 32 microns in diameter. The interior contains granules, small vacuoles, and sometimes crystals and is judged to be fluid because of the brownian movement of the contents (Fig. 231*E–G*). Singly the corpuscles have a yellowish hue but en masse appear reddish and confer upon the coelomic fluid a pinkish or purplish tint.   This color is caused by an iron-containing substance, haemerythrin, permeating the fluid interior of the corpuscle. Andrews (1890b) estimated 90,000 red corpuscles and 3000 amoebocytes per cubic millimeter of the coelomic fluid of *Golfingia gouldi*, and Harms and Dragendorff (1933) gave a figure of 120,000 to 135,000 red corpuscles in *Phascolosoma lurco*.   Types of amoebocytes, not necessarily all present in the same species, include hyaline forms with fine or no granules and granulocytes with coarse granules that may be acidophilic, neutrophilic, or basophilic (Cuénot, 1900; Kollmann, 1908; Volkonsky, 1933; Ohuye, 1937, 1942; Fig. 231*H–K*).   Various types of multicellular bodies are reported in different species.   In *G. vulgaris* Cuénot (1900) noted large fluid-filled vesicles up to 540 microns in diameter with nucleated cytoplasmic accumulations on the wall (Fig. 232*A*).   Andrews (1890b) in *G. gouldi* found giant red corpuscles up to 123 microns in diameter, with several nuclei imbedded in a reticulate cytoplasm.   Similar giant multinucleate corpuscles occur in the coelomic fluid of *Dend. signifer* (Awati and Pradhan, 1935).   Especially large red corpuscles with lobulated nucleus were noticed by Metalnikoff (1900) in *Sipun. nudus*.   Giant lymphocytes (Fig. 231*L*), bodies of irregular contour containing gross inclusions, are recorded for *Phas. lanzarotae* (Harms, 1921) and *G. elongata* (Stehle, 1953). The same two authors, also Metalnikoff in *Sipun. nudus*, noted cell plates (Fig. 231*M*), flat plates of a number of cells, floating in the coelomic fluid.

The free urns constitute the most interesting element of the coelomic fluid.   These remarkable structures swim about in a lively fashion in the coelomic fluid of some sipunculoids, notably *Sipunculus*.   They were first seen in this genus in 1851 by Krohn, who mistook them for ciliate protozoans.   They occur only in species with fixed urns, obviously originating by the constricting of these from the peritoneum, but species with fixed urns do not necessarily produce free urns.   The free urns of *Sipunculus* consist of a transparent, globular, fluid-filled vesicle covered on one end with a disciform ciliated cell (Fig. 232*B*).   Some cytoplasmic strands course through the vesicle, and on its surface occur one or more stellate cells, obviously persistent peritoneal cells that covered the sides of the fixed urns (Fig. 231*A*).   The urn swims with the vesicle in advance, dragging behind it an accumulation of degenerating cells and other debris gathered by the ciliated cell (see under physiology).   The free urns of other genera differ from those of *Sipunculus*, just as do their fixed urns. The vesicle is covered over by the chloragogue cells among which the urn developed while fixed (Fig. 231*D*) and which come along with it when it becomes free (Fig. 232*C*).   At one side of the free end is a depression in which debris accumulates, and the projecting edge of this is topped by the ciliated cell in the form of a crescent or horseshoe (Fig. 231*D*).

It is probable that all types of elements in the coelomic fluid are derived from peritoneal cells or groups of peritoneal cells, including the lining of the compensation sacs (Kollmann, 1908; Ohuye, 1942).

7. Nervous System.—The central nervous system of sipunculoids is of the annelid type, not as yet met with in our survey of invertebrates. The brain is a bilobed mass situated dorsal to the beginning of the digestive tract, just above the dorsal compensation sac. From each side of the brain there issues a circumenteric connective that curves around the digestive tract and meets its fellow below the latter to form the ventral nerve cord. This continues along the midventral line of the coelom throughout the entire body length, giving off numerous lateral nerves along its course. Main descriptions and figures of the nervous system are those of Andreae (1881) and Metalnikoff (1900) for *Sipunculus nudus* (Fig. 232*D*), Andrews (1890b) for *Golfingia gouldi* (Fig. 232*E*), Cuénot (1900) for *G. vulgaris* (Fig. 233*A*), Awati and Pradhan (1936) for *Dend. signifer* (Fig. 233*B*), and Gerould (1938) for *G. verrilli*.

The anterior surface of the brain gives off nerves into the nuchal organ when present or the corresponding region and may bear papillary to leaf-like protrusions that constitute a sense organ, best developed in species of *Sipunculus* (Figs. 232*D*, 234*E*), also seen in *Xenosiphon* (Fig. 234*D*), and noted by Andrews in *G. gouldi* (Fig. 232*E*). In *Dendrostomum* the posterior surface of the brain gives off nerves into adjacent muscles (Fig. 233*B*), but usually most of the anterior nerves spring from the circumenteric connectives. Of these nerves, the main ones supply the tentacles in which they branch extensively with a main branch in each tentacular lobe situated to the inner side of the median of the three channels in the lobe (Fig. 227*B*). Close to the brain the connectives on each side give rise to a small pharyngeal nerve that enters the beginning of the digestive tract where it may form a ring and is the source of an extensive plexus in the wall of the digestive tract. From the connectives spring also the nerves to the retractor muscles of the introvert.

The ventral nerve cord runs midventrally to the posterior end without showing any evidence whatever of metamerism; neither is it in any way a paired structure. It gives off numerous lateral nerves oppositely or alternately or irregularly. In *Sipunculus* the first six or seven nerves from the cord are unpaired (Fig. 232*D*) with long roots; they supply the muscles of the introvert wall. The cord here is elevated a little above the body wall. The anterior part of the ventral nerve cord is accompanied by a pair of longitudinal muscles, the *paraneural* muscles (Fig. 233*C*). Typically each lateral nerve passes into the muscle layers of the body wall to the inner side of the circular layer, where it follows the curvature of the body wall, forming a complete ring with its fellow of the other side according to some authors, not anastomosed into a ring according to others. Where the circular muscle occurs in bands, each band has such

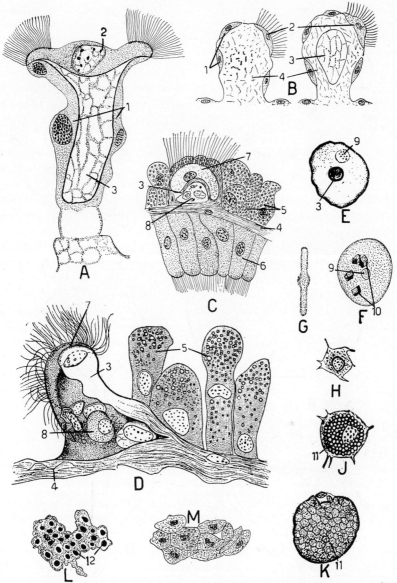

Fig. 231.—Coelomic elements. *A*, fixed urn of *Sipun. nudus*. *B*, two stages in the development of a fixed urn of *Sipun. nudus*. *C*, fixed urn of *Aspidosiphon*. (*A–C, after Selensky, 1908.*) *D*, fixed urn nestled among chloragogue cells, from ascending intestinal coil of *G. vulgaris*. *E*, red corpuscle of *G. vulgaris*. *F*, red corpuscle with crystals, *Phas. scolops*. *G*, side view of *F*. (*F, G, after Ohuye, 1937.*) *H*, hyaline amoebocyte. *J*, acidophilic granulocyte. *K*, neutrophilic granulocyte. (*E, H–K, G. vulgaris, after Cuénot, 1900.*) *L*, giant lymphocyte. *M*, cell plate. (*L, M, G. elongata, after Stehle, 1953.*) 1, peritoneal cells of stalk; 2, ciliated peritoneal cell at summit; 3, vacuole; 4, connective tissue; 5, chloragogue cells; 6, intestinal epithelium; 7, crescentic ciliated cell at top; 8, accumulated cell debris; 9, nucleus; 10, crystals; 11, coarse granules; 12, inclusions.

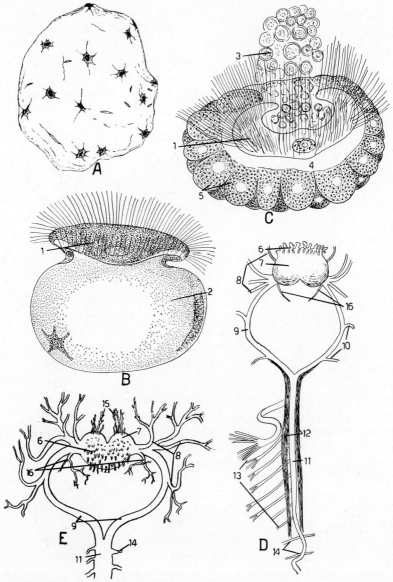

Fig. 232.—Coelomic elements (concluded), nervous system. *A*, vesicle of coelomic fluid of *G. vulgaris*, actual size about 0.1 mm. (*after Cuénot, 1900*). *B*, free urn of *Sipun. nudus*. *C*, free urn of *Phascolosoma*. (*B, C, after Selensky, 1908.*) *D*, central nervous system of *Sipun. nudus* (*combined after Andreae, 1881, and Metalnikoff, 1900*). *E*, central nervous system of *Golfingia gouldi* (*after Andrews, 1890b*). 1, ciliated cell; 2, vesicle; 3, debris accumulated by ciliated cell; 4, cavity; 5, chloragogue cells; 6, papilliform processes; 7, brain; 8, nerves to tentacles; 9, circumenteric connectives; 10, nerves to retractor muscles; 11, ventral nerve cord; 12, paraneural muscles; 13, nerves to introvert; 14, lateral nerves from cord; 15, nerves to nuchal organ; 16, pharyngeal nerves.

a more or less complete nerve ring. The most detail about the body-wall innervation has been furnished by Andrews for *G. gouldi*, where he reports a rich innervation in three concentric cylinders with radiating connections (Fig. 233*F*). Here each lateral nerve branches to form several circular nerves that tend to anastomose. From the circular nerves radiating branches pass internally to form a plexus just beneath the peritoneum. Similarly, radial branches pass externally from the circular nerves to originate a subepidermal plexus of mainly longitudinal fibers. This subepidermal plexus supplies nerves to the epidermal glands and sensory buds. The presence of a subepidermal plexus in the connective-tissue layer of the body wall was verified in *Sipunculus* by Metalnikoff, but he could not demonstrate a subperitoneal plexus. Cuénot also noted a peripheral plexus in *G. vulgaris*. At the posterior end of the body the nerve cord terminates by one or two nerves identical with the lateral nerves. In *Sipunculus* prior to this termination the nerve cord shows a fusiform enlargement considered by some to be a caudal ganglion; however, the swelling is caused mainly by an increase in the protective hull around the nervous part.

The nerve cord is covered by peritoneum; then comes a connective-tissue layer containing longitudinal muscle fibers that anteriorly concentrate into two bundles, the paraneural muscles already mentioned; there follows an inner sheath around the nervous part and permeating this with a supporting network. The nervous part consists of nerve cells ventrally, fiber tracts dorsally (Fig. 233*C*). In *Sipunculus* the tissue between the peritoneum and the inner sheath is especially thick and consists of neuroglia cells connected to each other by numerous fine filaments. An incredibly detailed account of the histology of the nerve cord of *Sipunculus* with special reference to the neuroglia was given by Mack (1902). This layer appears wanting in other genera. The brain has only thin covering layers, being sufficiently protected by surrounding structures. The brain is histologically similar to the ventral cord, but its fiber tracts tend to be more central, with the nerve cells surrounding them on all sides (Fig. 234*A*). Several types of nerve cells are described in brain and cord, including a large type definitely located. Neurosecretory cells have been identified in the brain of three species of sipunculoids (Gabe, 1953). The circumenteric connectives are entirely fibrillar, without nerve cells.

Andrews first described a rich nerve plexus of mainly longitudinal fibrils in the connective-tissue layer of the digestive wall; further, a similar plexus in the mesentery supporting the spindle muscle. Metalnikoff verified the presence of a nerve plexus in the gut wall by means of methylene blue injected into the coelom; the rather thin plexus was found to strengthen toward the rectum.

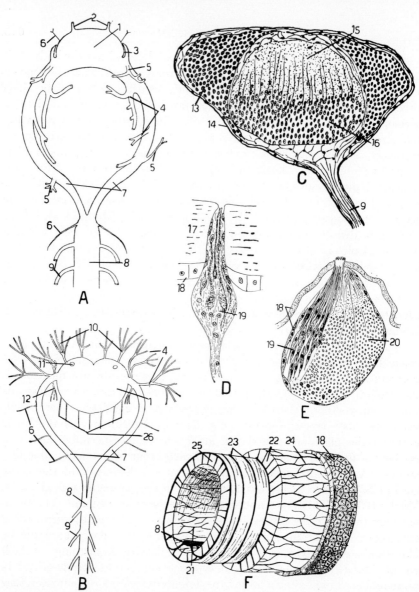

FIG. 233.—Nervous system (concluded), sense organs. *A*, central nervous system of
G. vulgaris (*after Cuénot*, 1900). *B*, central nervous system of *Dend. signifer* (*after Awati
and Pradhan*, 1936). *C*, cross section through the nerve cord in the introvert region,
Phascolosoma (*after Harms*, 1920). *D*, sensory bud from posterior end of *Sipun. nudus*
(*after Metalnikoff*, 1900). *E*, epidermal gland combined with sensory bud, *G. elongata*
(*after Jourdan*, 1891). *F*, schematic cross section of body wall, *G. gouldi*, to show nervous
arrangement and plexi (*after Andrews*, 1890b). 1, brain; 2, nuchal nerve; 3, ocular tube;
4, tentacular nerves; 5, nerves to retractor muscle; 6, nerves to body surface; 7, circumenteric connectives; 8, ventral nerve cord; 9, lateral branches of nerve cord; 10, anterior cerebral nerves; 11, ocellus; 12, pharyngeal nerve; 13, paraneural muscles; 14, peritoneum; 15,
fibrous part of cord; 16, part of cord with nerve cell bodies; 17, cuticle; 18, epidermis; 19,
sensory bud; 20, gland cells; 21, subperitoneal plexus; 22, circular muscle layer; 23, circular
nerves; 24, subepidermal plexus; 25, longitudinal muscle layer; 26, nerves to muscles.

8. Sense Organs.—The phylum appears well supplied with sense organs. Typical neurosensory cells with a terminal bristle were noted on the tentacular fold of *Sipun. nudus* by Ward (1891) and on the tentacles of *Siphonosoma cumanense* by Shitamori (1936) and are probably of general occurrence. A simple type of sense organ occurs on the tentacular fold and introvert of *Sipun. nudus* (Ward, 1891; Metalnikoff, 1900) in the form of a pit bordered by converging, elongated, heavily ciliated cells (Fig. 234*C*). According to Ward, the pit can be protruded as a papilla. The more usual type of sense organ, of common occurrence throughout the phylum, consists of fusiform buds of elongated epidermal cells entered basally by a nerve (Fig. 233*D*). The distal pointed ends of the epidermal cells, probably really neurosensory cells, of the bud pass through the cuticle to the surface or may be mounted on a cuticular papilla (Fig. 234*B*), as in *Golfingia vulgaris* (Cuénot, 1900) or *G. gouldi* (Nickerson, 1901). In some sipunculoids these sensory buds occur only in combination with multicellular glands (Fig. 233*E*), as claimed for *Golfingia elongata* (Jourdan, 1891) and *Siphonosoma cumanense* (Shitamori, 1936), but Stehle (1953) saw separate sensory buds in the former.

The brain is associated with curious sense organs, but knowledge of these is imperfect and confused, despite the effort of Gerould (1938) to clarify the situation. Mention was already made of the nuchal organ, a bi- or quadrilobed cushion of tall, ciliated epidermal cells situated at the middorsal edge of the oral disk (Fig. 218*C*). This is supplied by nerves, usually a pair of nuchal nerves, directly from the adjacent anterior surface of the brain. These nerves branch extensively to the underside of the epidermis of the nuchal organ, and the branches may have ganglionic swellings. The function of the nuchal organ is unknown, but presumably the organ is of chemoreceptive nature.

As already indicated, a single median cephalic tube or a pair of such tubes extends from the dorsal side of the oral disk inwardly toward the brain in some species; such are wanting in species in which the brain lies close to the surface. Gerould (1938) surmises that the presence of a long cephalic tube as in *Sipunculus*, removing the brain to an interior protected position, is associated with the habit of burrowing deeply. Inturned epidermis, probably ciliated, lines the cephalic tube or tubes and may be thrown into longitudinal ridges. At its inner end the cephalic tube expands into a saucerlike cavity, or the two tubes enter a common cavity that is cupped over a forward projection of the brain called by Ward (1891) the *cerebral organ*. Gerould's suggestion to replace this term with frontal organ is unfortunate as the latter expression is already in use in Turbellaria (II, page 91). In the absence of a cephalic tube or tubes the cerebral organ lies at the surface as in *Golfingia verrilli*, investigated by Gerould (1938). Although the cerebral organ appears to be continuous

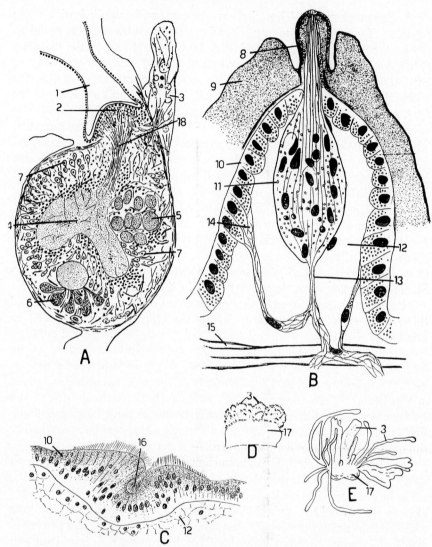

Fig. 234.—Sense organs (continued). *A*, longitudinal section of the brain of *Sipun. nudus* (*after Metalnikoff*, 1900). *B*, sensory bud of introvert of *G. vulgaris* (*after Cuénot*, 1900). *C*, sensory pit of introvert of *Sipun. nudus* (*after Ward*, 1891). *D*, papilliform processes from brain of *Xenosiphon branchiatum*. *E*, papilliform processes from brain of *Sipun. polynotus.* (*D, E, after Fisher*, 1947.) 1, cephalic tube; 2, cerebral organ; 3, papilliform process; 4, fibrous part of brain; 5, commissures; 6, large type of ganglion cell; 7, small type of ganglion cell; 8, papilla; 9, cuticle; 10, epidermis; 11, sensory bud; 12, dermis; 13, nerve of bud; 14, nervous terminations on epidermis; 15, circular muscle layer; 16, sensory pit; 17, brain; 18, tract for cerebral organ.

with the brain, its interior is more or less separated from the brain tissue by connective tissue (Fig. 234A). The cerebral organ is covered with a thick cuticle, and its interior contains tiers of nuclei without definite cell walls (Fig. 235A). These nuclei suggest nuclei of neurosensory cells and are associated with fibers that pass into the substance of the brain. It appears probable that the cerebral organ is of sensory nature, but there is no suggestion as to its function.

The claim of Awati and Pradhan (1936) that in *Dendrostomum signifer* the short cephalic tube opens at the beginning of the esophagus is incomprehensible. The same may be said of a similar claim by Hérubel (1907) for *Golfingia charcoti;* this author suggests that the cephalic tube is a kind of hypophysis!

In many sipunculoids there are evident a pair of brown or black pigment spots imbedded in the interior of the brain. These are suggestive of eyes, and histological investigation indicates that they are in fact pigment-cup ocelli. Each pigment spot is at the inner end of an *ocular tube* that descends into the brain tissue from the cavity at the inner end of the cephalic tube or tubes, or in the absence of such from the surface near the nuchal organ (Fig. 235B). The tubes composed of epithelial cells are dilated at their inner ends, which are formed of elongated cells containing pigment granules (Fig. 235C). Gerould (1938) noted photoreceptive cells associated with the pigment cells (Fig. 235C). The ocular tubes usually contain a transparent coagulated material in which there is imbedded in at least some cases a refringent body suggestive of a lens.

A still further structure associated with the brain is present in some sipunculoids, notably *Sipunculus*. This consists of a bundle of outgrowths of the anterior dorsal part of the brain above the cephalic tube and cerebral organ, from which structures it appears quite distinct although confused with the latter under the name frontal organ by Fisher (1947). These brain processes, for which no name seems to have been proposed, project into the coelom that lies between the brain and the dorsal wall of the introvert (Fig. 234A). In *S. nudus* the structure in question consists of a bunch of papillae, as also in *Xenosiphon branchiatum* (Fig. 234D). In some other species of *Sipunculus* described by Fisher (1947) the structure is more complicated, consisting of long filaments and leaflike projections (Fig. 234E). The histological structure of these cerebral outgrowths is mentioned only by Metalnikoff (1900), who failed to obtain satisfactory preparations. The outgrowths are covered with peritoneum, are partly separated at their bases from the brain tissue by connective tissue, and contain tracts of nerve fibers. They therefore appear to be of sensory nature, but as they have no connection with the exterior, seem to function with respect to the coelom and its contents.

Finally, there should be mentioned a pair of leaflike outgrowths into

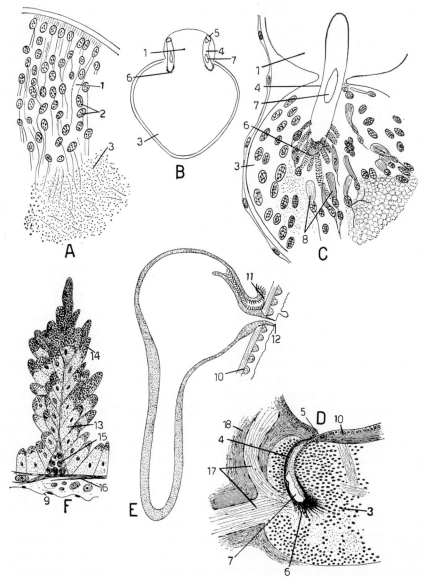

FIG. 235.—Sense organs (concluded), excretory system. *A*, histology of the cerebral organ of *Sipun. nudus* (*after Ward*, 1891). *B*, scheme of sense organs of brain of *G. gouldi.* *C*, ocular tube of *G. gouldi*, enlarged. (*B*, *C*, *after Gerould*, 1938.) *D*, section of one ocular tube of *G. vulgaris* (*after Cuénot*, 1900). *E*, longitudinal section of nephridium of *Phascolosoma* (*after Shipley*, 1890). *F*, one fold of the lining of the nephridium of *G. vulgaris*, showing histology (*after Hérubel*, 1907). 1, cerebral organ; 2, neurosensory cells; 3, brain; 4, ocular tube; 5, external opening of ocular tube; 6, pigment cells; 7, lenslike body in ocular tube; 8, retinal cells; 9, peritoneum; 10, body wall; 11, nephrostome; 12, nephridiopore; 13, lining epithelium; 14, secretory granules; 15, longitudinal muscle fibers; 16, circular muscle fibers; 17, nerve to retractors; 18, connective tissue.

the base of the cephalic tube in *Sipun. nudus* (Metalnikoff, 1900). Apparently these do not occur in any other sipunculoid.

9. Excretory System.—All sipunculoids are provided with metanephridia, typically in the form of a pair of elongated organs situated ventrally in the anterior part of the trunk. Only one nephridium, usually the right one, is present in the genera *Phascolion* and *Onchnesoma*. The left nephridiopore and canal leading to it may persist in *Phascolion strombi* (Moltschanov, 1909). One nephridium is wanting in some species of *Aspidosiphon*.

The nephridia are tubular sacs in the form of an elongated V (Fig. 235E), that is, consist essentially of a tube recurved upon itself and fused together except distally. The greater part of the sac therefore contains a single lumen, often somewhat expanded distally. At the distal end a narrowed terminal canal leads to the nephridiopore, and dorsal to this the nephrostome enters the common sac by way of a narrow ciliated canal. The nephrostome is usually a simple opening in contact on one side with the body wall, with a crescentic ciliated lip on the other side. In many species the nephridia are attached only by these openings and otherwise hang freely in the coelom. In others they are attached to the body wall for whole or part of their length by a mesentery or by strands.

The nephridial sac is clothed externally with peritoneum; this is followed by a connective-tissue layer containing strong circular and longitudinal muscle fibers; and finally the lumen is lined by an epithelium of rather large, bulging cells containing yellow to brown granules that lend these colors to the organ as a whole. In many species the epithelium is thrown into tall longitudinal folds supported by connective tissue, and the longitudinal muscle fibers are concentrated in the base of these folds (Fig. 235F). Between these folds may occur little pockets that cause external bulges of the nephridial wall (Harms, 1921; Kelley, 1953). Harms (1921) published a very curious article about *Phascolosoma lanzarotae*, in which he claimed the presence on these outpocketings between the epithelium and the peritoneum of cell clusters of the nature of the cortical cells of the vertebrate adrenal glands. He therefore ascribed an important hormonal function to the nephridia and declared that the removal of the proximal parts of the nephridia, where most of the cells in question are located, is fatal to the animal. These cells have not been seen by others, and it is impossible at present to evaluate the claims of Harms.

10. Reproductive System and Reproductive Habits.—The gonads form an inconspicuous fringe or ruffle borne on the coelomic wall at the origins of all or some of the retractor muscles (Fig. 222A, B). The sex cells are shed into the coelom at an immature stage and complete their maturation while floating in the coelomic fluid. They are then emitted through the nephridia, which act as gonoducts.   It is not clear by what means the ripe sex cells are directed to the nephrostomes.

So far as known, all sipunculoids are dioecious; the sexes are indistinguishable externally.   Paul (1910) thought that *Golfingia minuta* is hermaphroditic since he found both eggs and sperm in the coelom of living specimens; but this finding is inconclusive, as all gonads examined were female, and Gerould (1913) saw only unisexual individuals in hundreds of specimens of this species examined.   Harms (1921) reported two cases of hermaphroditism among hundreds of *Phascolosoma lanzarotae* but gave no details.   There is frequently a strange preponderance of females among sipunculoids.   Keferstein (1862) secured no males among 200 sipunculoids of the genus *Golfingia* (species *elongata, vulgaris*, and *minuta*) collected near The Hague.   Claparède (1863) found only one or two males among hundreds of females of *G. elongata*.   *Golfingia minuta* seems generally to occur only as females, although Gerould (1913) had males.   Awati and Pradhan (1936) reported a ratio of 1 male to 60 females in *Dendrostomum signifer*.

Few data are available on breeding habits.   Spawning generally occurs in summer.   Hatschek (1883) found that *Sipunculus nudus* spawns at night in July in the vicinity of Naples.   Cuénot (1900) noted that the sex cells of *Golfingia vulgaris*, after 6 months of ripening in the coelom, are shed during July and August on the channel coast of France, and Gerould (1906) gave the breeding period of this species in the same area as middle of June to middle of September.   The spawning season of *Golfingia gouldi* on the Massachusetts coast extends from the middle of June through August (Gerould, 1906); specimens brought into the laboratory would generally spawn on the same or the following night.   This author never observed spawning in nature.   On the California coast *Dendrostomum zostericolum* breeds during July and August (Peebles and Fox, 1933; Fisher, 1952), and the former authors saw quantities of white sperm emitted from the nephridiopores.   As the sex cells require months to ripen in the coelom, their presence there is not necessarily indicative of the imminence of spawning.

Gerould (1906) observed spawning in the laboratory in *Golfingia gouldi* and *vulgaris*.   Several hours prior to spawning the nephridia expand enormously through intake of fluid, presumably sea water through the nephridiopores, and ciliary currents are seen in the interior directed from the nephrostome to the proximal end.   The nephridia become filled with mature sex cells, whereas immature sex cells and coelomic elements are excluded in some unknown way.   During the hours between evening and dawn the sex cells are forcibly ejected through the nephridiopores in cloudlike jets.   The males precede, raising the anterior end from the bottom and swinging it about during the ejection of the sperm.   When the spermatic fluid touches the females they are stimulated to eject their eggs. The sperm become active only after ejection into the sea water, and fertilization promptly ensues.

11. Embryology.—Main accounts of the embryology are those of Hatschek (1883) for *Sipun. nudus* and Gerould (1906) for *Golfingia gouldi* and *vulgaris*. Cleavage (not seen by Hatschek) is clearly of the spiral type (II, page 10) and differs from the typical pattern only in that the micromeres are mostly larger than the macromeres. The usual four quartettes of micromeres are produced. The products of the first quartette cover the animal half or more of the embryo and form a typical annelid cross (Fig. 236*A*), at the 48-celled stage. At the animal pole four cells constitute the rosette, alternating with them are the four cells of the cross, and continuing them are two intermediate cells for each cell of the rosette. The remaining cells of the first quartette form a zone of about two circles of large cells just above the equator of the embryo; these cells are recognizable as trochoblasts and develop the cilia of the prototroch. As usual the fourth quartette and the macromeres furnish the entoderm and mesoderm. Gastrulation, best described for *Sipunculus* (Fig. 236*B*), occurs partly by epiboly, overgrowth by ectodermal cells of the second and third quartettes, partly by invagination. The entoderm remains a solid mass in *Golfingia* (Fig. 236*E*), contains a cavity in *Sipunculus* (Fig. 236*C*). The entomesoderm is the product of the cell 4d which furnishes typical pole cells, or teloblasts, that take up their positions at the sides of the entoderm (Fig. 236*B*) and proliferate a mesodermal band on each side. The blastopore, which has undergone considerable elongation, closes from behind forward, and at its anterior end, which temporarily closes, a group of ectodermal cells (stomatoblasts) proliferate and give rise to the stomodaeum that makes contact with the entoderm. The mouth is located in the trochoblast zone (Fig. 237*A*, *B*). The sipunculoids thus reveal themselves as Protostomia.

The embryo rapidly develops into a fairly typical trochophore (Fig. 237*A*). At the animal pole four cells, which appear to result from a single division of the original four cells of the rosette, develop long flagella and constitute an apical sensory area. This is followed by an area of small epidermal cells in which there appear a pair of red ocelli. Then comes the prototroch, a broad ciliated band borne on two circlets of large cells or trochoblasts. The stomodaeal invagination is in the midventral part of the prototroch. Passing below the stomodaeum there develops a strong band of cilia, the metatroch. The posterior half of the trochophore is covered by small ectodermal cells that become the definitive trunk epidermis. In the interior is found a solid mass of entoderm in contact with the stomodaeal invagination (Fig. 236*E*). Alongside the posterior part of the entoderm there is a mesodermal band on each side. The trocho-

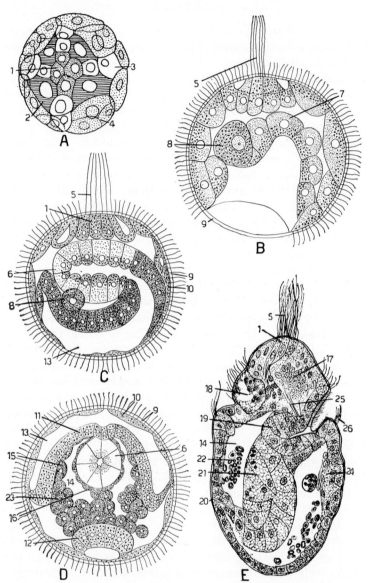

FIG. 236.—Embryology. *A*, late cleavage stage showing annelid cross, *Golfingia*. *B*, gastrula stage, *Sipun. nudus*. *C*, completed gastrulation, *Sipun. nudus*. *D*, transverse section through vegetal half of later stage than *C*, showing proliferation of entomesoderm, *Sipun. nudus*. (*B–D, after Hatschek*, 1883.) *E*, sagittal section of late larva, *Golfingia*. (*A, E, after Gerould*, 1906.) 1, rosette cells (stippled); 2, cells of cross (crosshatched); 3, intermediate cells; 4, other ectodermal cells; 5, apical tuft; 6, archenteron; 7, entoderm; 8, teloblast (primary mesoderm cell); 9, vitelline membrane; 10, ectodermal layer of nutritive membrane; 11, definitive dorsal ectoderm; 12, definitive ventral ectoderm of trunk; 13, space between embryo and nutritive membrane; 14, coelom; 15, somatic mesoderm; 16, splanchnic mesoderm; 17, brain; 18, prototroch; 19, stomodaeum; 20, anus; 21, digestive tube; 22, remains of yolk; 23, nephroblast; 24, ventral nerve cord; 25, beginning circumenteric connective; 26, metatroch.

phore swims about in a lively fashion and is strongly photopositive. In *Golfingia* the trochophore stage is reached on the second day, and by the end of that day begins to transform into a juvenile worm. In so doing it throws off the vitelline membrane in which it has continued to be enclosed.

The part of the larva posterior to the prototroch rapidly elongates, becoming the definitive trunk. The cells of the first quartette around the apical tuft (which soon degenerates) proliferate into the interior to form the brain. The larval ocelli thus become imbedded in the brain and persist as the adult ocelli. The ventral nerve cord arises independently of the brain by a midventral proliferation of trunk ectoderm. At its anterior end it grows out the two circumenteric connectives that extend to the brain and coalesce with it. The nerve cord is single in its inception, and there is no evidence in the embryology of a paired condition at any time. The entoderm, while still solid, sends an outgrowth toward the dorsal surface, and an anus is established there by a proctodaeal invagination. At a considerably later time, a lumen is finally established in the entoderm. The mesodermal bands split in typical schizocoelous fashion, forming the coelom and contributing a mesodermal layer to the inner side of the surface ectoderm and a mesodermal layer to the outer surface of the digestive tract (Fig. 236*D*). The trochoblasts disintegrate and pass into the interior to furnish food; adjacent ectodermal cells close over the place that they occupied. The nephridia of *Golfingia* arise after the appearance of the coelom as a pair of ingrowths, probably ectodermal, that become covered with peritoneum as they progress. The nephrostome and the ciliated tube that connects it with the main sac of the nephridium is said by Gerould to be of peritoneal origin. The four retractor muscles arise in the early trochophore from ectodermal cells of the first quartette that elongate and pass into the interior, differentiating into muscle fibers. These muscles are therefore of ectomesodermal origin, and the same seems to be true of the circular and longitudinal muscles of the trunk. The trochophore of *Golfingia* has an extra temporary pair of dorsal and ventral retractors for accomplishing larval movements.

As already indicated, the trochophore of *Golfingia* metamorphoses at the end of the second day by casting off the vitelline membrane, suddenly elongating into a vermiform shape (Fig. 238*A*), and exhibiting muscular activity, including introversion of the anterior part. The apical tuft and prototroch cells rapidly disappear. The larva continues to elongate into a cylindrical worm, only a fraction of a millimeter in length, that takes to the bottom and crawls after the manner of a geometrid caterpillar or may swim near the bottom by the metatroch, later lost. When the young worm is about a week old a pair of lateral projections appear at the anterior end (Fig. 238*B*). The tentacles develop from these and thus are of bilateral origin, although appearing radial in the adult. It would seem

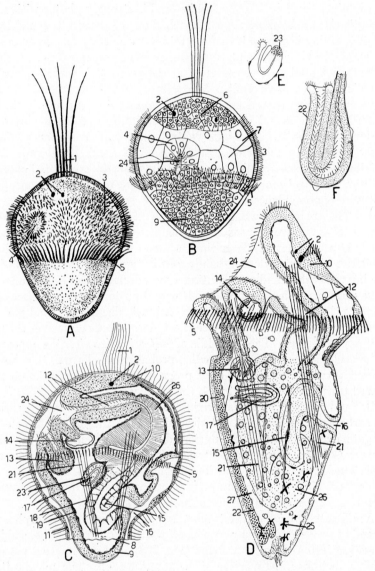

FIG. 237.—Embryology (continued). *A*, young trochophore of *Golfingia*. *B*, same, showing cells. (*A, B, after Gerould,* 1906.) *C*, trochophore of *Sipun. nudus,* throwing off the nutritive membrane. *D*, late trochophore of *Sipun. nudus. E, F,* stages in the development of the nephridium, *Sipun. nudus.* (*C–F, after Hatschek,* 1883.) 1, apical tuft; 2, ocelli; 3, prototroch; 4, stomodaeum; 5, metatroch; 6, ectoderm of introvert; 7, trochoblasts; 8, torn edge of nutritive membrane; 9, trunk ectoderm; 10, brain; 11, nutritive membrane; 12, esophagus; 13, first appendage of esophagus; 14, second appendage of esophagus; 15, intestine; 16, anus; 17, nephridium; 18, splanchnic mesoderm; 19, stomatic mesoderm; 20, body-wall muscles forming; 21, retractor muscle; 22, peritoneum; 23, site of nephroblast; 24, mouth; 25, pigment cell; 26, stomach; 27, coelom.

as if there must be a forward migration of the mouth to a terminal position, but this is not mentioned by Gerould. By the end of 2 weeks the juvenile worm has exhausted its nutritive supplies and must begin to feed. Sex cells become evident at the site of attachment of the ventral retractor muscles at an age of between 2 and 3 weeks. At the end of a month the young worms, still less than a millimeter in length, are approaching the adult morphology.

Gerould (1906) claimed evidence of metamerism in the nerve cord and mesoderm bands during the development of *Golfingia*, whereas Hatschek (1883) definitely denied any evidence for metamerism in the development of *Sipunculus*. Gerould never published any retraction of his statement, but in letters to W. K. Fisher and Grace Pickford, Gerould explained that appearances of metamerism were caused by contraction and buckling and positively denied any evidence of metamerism in *Golfingia*. This correction was incorporated by Pickford in later versions of her article on Sipunculida in the *Encyclopaedia Britannica*. Therefore on present knowledge there is no evidence whatever of the occurrence of metamerism in the embryology of sipunculoids.

The foregoing account is limited to Gerould's study of the development of *Golfingia*. This development is generally regarded as less modified than that of *Sipun. nudus*, described by Hatschek, although the latter, which will now be considered, appears more typical in some respects. For instance, the *Sipunculus* embryo has a small but definite blastocoel, wanting in *Golfingia*, and the embolic part of its gastrulation is more pronounced and results in a definite archenteron (Fig. 236*B, C*). A group of cells at the animal pole constitute an apical nervous center and produce an apical tuft of flagella. The mesoderm is formed as in *Golfingia* from a single mesentoderm cell that divides to a pair of pole cells, or teloblasts, each of which proliferates a mesodermal band. Also as in *Golfingia*, the blastopore closes from behind forward and the stomodaeum arises at its anterior end, making contact with the entoderm, which continues as a hollow sac. The main divergence from *Golfingia* consists in the formation in *Sipunculus* of a supposedly nutritive membrane ("serosa"). The embryo has meantime become completely ciliated, but a definite prototroch is wanting; instead the cells corresponding to the trochoblast cells migrate posteriorly over the vegetative half of the embryo, completely enclosing it in a one-layered membrane (Fig. 236*C, D*) that adheres to the underside of the vitelline membrane, here persistent as in *Golfingia*. A considerable space is left between this double membrane and the true definitive ectoderm of the vegetative part of the embryo (Fig. 236*D*); this space is continuous with small spaces between the vitelline membrane and the embryo in the animal half. In the interior the digestive tract continues to differentiate, establishing an anus as in *Golfingia*, and the mesoderm

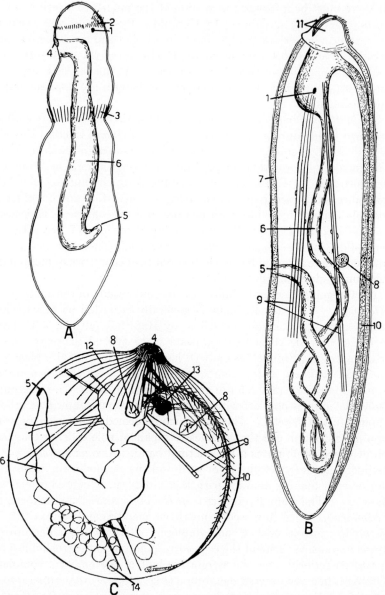

Fig. 238.—Embryology (concluded). A, larva of *Golfingia vulgaris* at 60 hours. B, juvenile of *Golfingia gouldi* at 9 days. (A, B, after Gerould, 1906.) C, *Pelagosphaera* (after *Mingazzini*, 1905). 1, eye; 2, prototroch; 3, metatroch; 4, mouth; 5, anus; 6, intestine; 7, muscle layer of body wall; 8, nephridium; 9, retractor muscles; 10, ventral nerve cord; 11, lobes to form tentacles; 12, muscle fibers; 13, glands attached to esophagus; 14, fat globules.

bands continue to proliferate, producing the coelom by the schizocoelous method (Fig. 236*D*). A pair of red ocelli appears in the apical nervous thickening. At about this stage the embryo ruptures the enclosing membrane (Fig. 237*C*) and becomes a free-swimming larva. Rupture begins at the vegetative end where the elongating trunk breaks through the membrane; the membrane is then gradually cast off in the anterior direction.

The resulting larva, slightly less than 1 mm. in length, swims around in the plankton for about a month. It was first put on record by Max Müller (1850), who recognized it as a sipunculoid, then described by Krohn (1851), who identified it correctly as the larva of *Sipunculus nudus*. The larva (Fig. 237*D*) resembles a very elongated trochophore. It has a strong metatroch that bounds a short ciliated anterior region, bearing the mouth and the dorsally displaced nervous thickening with ocelli, from a much longer conical posterior region. In the interior is seen the well-developed digestive tract, differentiated into esophagus, expanded stomach, and intestine opening by a dorsal, somewhat posteriorly located anus. At the beginning of the esophagus are two enigmatical ventral invaginations, of which the anterior one is glandular; these disappear at metamorphosis, and their role in larval life has not been ascertained. The nervous system develops as in *Golfingia*. The retractor muscles, accompanied in the larva by accessory retractors as in *Golfingia*, and the circular and longitudinal muscle layers of the body wall are said by Hatschek to develop from the somatic layer of the mesoderm, hence are of entomesodermal nature. No mention is made of any ectomesoderm, but it must be borne in mind that the details of spiral cleavage had not been worked out at the date of Hatschek's article and therefore he may have overlooked or misunderstood processes that would be sought by later investigators. A clear description is given of the origin of the nephridia, and this, too, differs from the story in *Golfingia*. In each mesodermal band a nephroblast becomes noticeable by its yellow inclusions (Fig. 236*D*). This cell proliferates a group of cells that arrange into a U-shaped nephridium (Fig. 237*E*, *F*); one cell retains the yellow inclusions, and this cell makes contact with the ectoderm to establish the nephridiopore. The entire nephridium therefore appears of entomesodermal origin.

After a month of free life the larva metamorphoses into a young worm by reduction of the anterior region, further elongation of the trunk, and gradual loss of the ciliary provision. It takes to the bottom, where it creeps about with the aid of in-and-out movements of the future introvert. The mouth is displaced to a terminal position, and the tentacles arise as in *Golfingia*. The continued elongation of the trunk brings the anus into a more and more anterior position. The stomach reduces to the same diameter as the rest of the digestive tract, and the intestine continues to

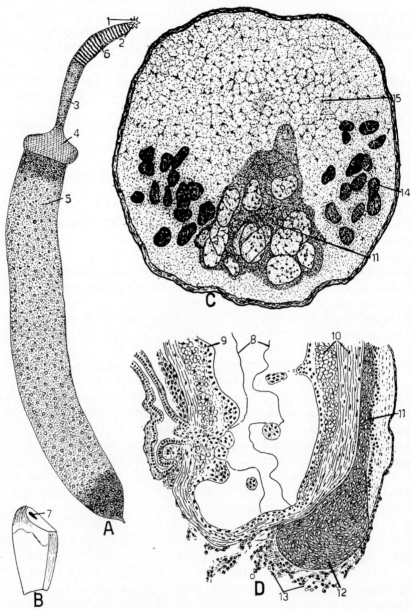

Fig. 239.—Systematics, regeneration. *A*, *Cloeosiphon aspergillum* (*after Sluiter*, 1884).
B, calcareous papilla from the shield. *C*, cross section of the nerve cord of *Aspidosiphon
mülleri*, showing the regeneration tract (*after Wegener*, 1938). *D*, early stage of regeneration
of *Phascolion strombi*, showing regeneration tract of nerve cord proliferating epidermis
(*after Schleip*, 1934a). 1, tentacles; 2, mouth; 3, introvert; 4, shield; 5, trunk; 6, circles of
hooks; 7, opening of gland contained in papilla; 8, cuticle; 9, epidermis; 10, muscle layers
of introvert; 11, regeneration strand of nerve cord; 12, ectodermal proliferation of strand; 13,
accumulating mesoderm for regeneration; 14, ganglion cells of cord; 15, fibrous part of cord.

elongate and coil.   Hatschek saw the dorsal compensation sac developing, but does not give its origin.   Hence it is impossible to know whether these sacs are of coelomic origin, as seems probable from their histology.

In 1905 Mingazzini described a pelagic larva that had been fished at a depth of about 500 m. in the South Pacific between New Caledonia and New Zealand on the planktonic expedition of the Italian ship *Liguria*. Mingazzini recognized this larva as a sipunculoid but considered it an adult form and named it *Pelagosphaera*.   It was a transparent spherical object 6 mm. in diameter with typical sipunculoid features: mouth at the anterior pole, recurved digestive tract with dorsal anus, ventral nerve cord, retractor muscles, and pair of nephridia (Fig. 238*C*).   Two objects borne on the esophagus were misidentified as gonads.   Senna (1906) found additional such larvae but of smaller size in the *Liguria* collections in Indonesian and Ceylonese waters and gave a detailed description.   He identified the alleged gonads as the two sacciform evaginations from the esophagus noted by Hatschek in larvae of *Sipun. nudus*, and hence reached the conclusion that *Pelagosphaera* is the larva of some species of *Sipunculus*.   The same conclusion was reached by Spengel (1907) from study of Mingazzini's description and figures.   Heath (1910) took two specimens, 2.5 and 3.2 mm. in diameter, in Monterey Bay, California, and confirmed the identification of the supposed gonads as sacs dependent from the esophagus.   Heath was unable after careful examination to find any nephrostomes on the nephridia.   Dawydoff (1930) collected many specimens alive on the coast of Annam.   These differed somewhat from preceding specimens, being papillate and having a metatroch.   Previous observers had failed to see any cilia on their specimens, probably because preservation had destroyed them.   Dawydoff also was unable to find any nephrostomes and declared positively that the nephridia of this larva are protonephridia.   He saw beginning metamorphosis; the larvae ceased activity, fell to the bottom, and began to elongate.   One specimen, 5 mm. in diameter, was taken by the *Discovery* off southeast Africa (Stephen, 1941).   Fisher (1947) recorded a considerable number of *Pelagosphaera* larvae, suspected to belong to *Sipunculus polymyotus*, taken in plankton tows in the West Indian region.   Some of these were about as large as the original specimen.   As in other preserved specimens, cilia were lacking; nothing is said about nephrostomes.   From the foregoing it is evident that *Pelagosphaera* cannot be maintained as a distinct genus of sipunculoids.

12. Regeneration.—Sipunculoids are devoid of any method of asexual reproduction but have considerable ability to regenerate.   When the tentacles of *Dendrostomum zostericolum* were cut off at their bases, no regeneration was observed within 2 to 3 weeks, although behavior and burrowing remained normal; but when the stumps of the branches were left, buds of new tentacular branches were seen developing on them (Peebles and Fox, 1933). Bülow (1883) cut off the distal ends of the introvert in *Golfingia vulgaris* and *Aspidosiphon mülleri* and noted complete regeneration in 3 to 5 weeks. A detailed study of introvert regeneration was made by Schleip (1934a, b) for *Phascolion strombi* and *Golfingia*

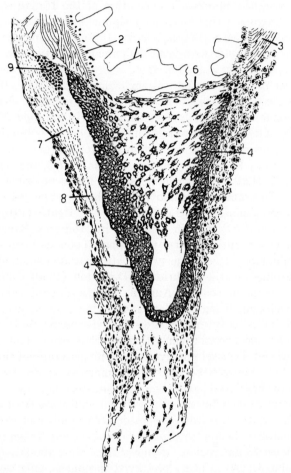

Fig. 240.—Regeneration (concluded). Later stage of regeneration of introvert of *Phascolion strombi* (*after Schleip*, 1934a). 1, cuticle; 2, epidermis; 3, muscle layers; 4, regenerated ectoderm to form epidermis; 5, mesodermal regenerate; 6, membrane closing cut surface; 7, fibrous part of nerve cord; 8, regenerating nerve cord; 9, ganglion cells.

minuta and by Wegener (1938) for *Aspidosiphon mülleri*, *Golfingia vulgaris*, *Golfingia* sp. unidentified, *Phascolosoma granulatum*, and *Sipunculus nudus*. All these species regenerate the oral end except *Sipun. nudus*, which, however, can replace portions of the introvert removed by cutting across the end of the partly introverted introvert, leaving the oral end inside. Although the articles of Schleip and Wegener are very detailed, they furnish no satisfactory account of the regeneration as a whole. Both authors claim the existence in the ventral nerve cord of a strand of regeneration cells below the layer of nerve cells (Fig. 239C). This strand is especially developed and obvious in *Phascolion strombi*, less evident in the other species. Following a cut across the introvert the wound contracts by muscular action and often the cut end introverts. The wound is closed by an aggregation of amoeboid coelomocytes that also differentiate into the mesodermal part of the regenerate (Fig. 240). The regeneration cells migrate to the cut area and proliferate a mass there that hollows out to a cylinder. This replaces the ectodermal parts of the intro-vert, that is, the epidermis and the nerve cord (Fig. 240). Nothing is said about the regeneration of the oral disk with its tentacles or the brain.

Andrews (1890b) saw regenerating posterior ends of *Golfingia gouldi*, and Spengel (1912) noted that the posterior part of the trunk can be regenerated in *Siphonosoma*. Schleip (1935) investigated the regenera-tion of the posterior end of *Phascolion strombi* and the very small *Golfingia minuta*. In the former species the intestinal coil herniates from the wound and the animal dies in 2 or 3 days. Following removal of the posterior end of *G. minuta* behind the intestinal coil, which is therefore not injured, the animals survive and regeneration ensues. At the cut surface the muscle layer separates from the cuticle, contracts, and invaginates slightly, thus partially closing the wound. Closure is com-pleted by the accumulation of coelomocytes, which are believed to regen-erate the mesodermal parts of the body wall. Regeneration of the ectodermal parts is ascribed to the regeneration cells of the nerve cord which migrate to the cut surface. In many cases the end of the intestinal coil gets strangled into the wound and usually degenerates, leaving two open intestinal ends, which in at least some of the observed cases even-tually grew together.

13. Systematic Account.—At present the sipunculoids are arranged into genera only; these have not been assembled into families, although presumably this will be eventually attempted. The most recent arrange-ment is that of Fisher (1952), who recognizes 13 genera, accepted by Edmonds (1955, 1956). The genus *Sipunculus* (includes *Pelagosphaera*) comprises large species in which the short, sharply demarcated introvert lacks spines and is covered with backwardly directed, scalelike papillae (Fig. 215C). The oral disk is edged with a flat tentacular fold incised peripherally into coarse to fine tentacles. In the middorsal line just out-side the tentacular fold a pore (Fig. 215D) leads into an unpaired cephalic tube into whose bottom projects a cerebral organ; the brain further bears above this organ a group of projections into the coelom (Fig. 232D). The longitudinal and circular muscles of the trunk wall are divided into distinct bundles, and these mark off the external trunk surface (except the extreme posterior end) into raised rectangular areas (Fig. 215*A*). The trunk wall further contains longitudinal coelomic canals overlying the intervals between the longitudinal muscle bundles (Fig. 219*A*). There are four retractor muscles, separate to their insertions around the esophagus, two nephridia, and simple dorsal and ventral compensation sacs on the esophagus (Fig. 222*A*). The beginning of the descending intestine forms a separate loop or coil before entering the main coil. The genus contains a number of species of which *S. nudus* (Fig. 215*A*), the most familiar and most studied sipunculoid, has a wide distribution. *Xenosiphon* (Fisher, 1954a) much resembles *Sipunculus*, from which it differs in having numerous small tentacles in tufts or pads, a pair of protractor muscles in the anterior part of the introvert (Fig. 225*A*), and a separate irregular coelomic sac in each rectangular elevation of the body wall. There are two species, *X. branchiatum* from the Panamic region and *X. mundanum* from Australia. *Siphonomecus* (Fisher, 1947), with the single species *multicinctus* from the Florida Keys, differs from *Sipunculus* in the absence of papillae and presence of spines on the introvert, presence of a prominent nuchal organ, reduction of the retractor muscles to two, separate coelomic space in each rectangle of the body wall, and provision with pinnate tentacles.

In the remaining genera the trunk surface is not marked off by grooves into rectangular cushions, although the longitudinal muscle layer is arranged in bundles in *Siphonosoma*, *Siphonides*, *Phascolosoma*, *Lithacrosiphon*, and some species of *Aspidosiphon*. *Siphonosoma*, with 24 species (in 1952), has numerous filiform tentacles (Fig. 215*G*), four retractors, separate coelomic sacs in the body wall of the larger species, and only a dorsal compensation sac, usually with numerous diverticula (Fig. 228*A*). In several species, notably *Siphonosoma cumanense*, there is a succession of short transverse peritoneal folds in the ventral part of the coelom to each side of the ventral nerve cord (Fig. 230). Some of the species have spines on the introvert, but most lack them. The genus *Siphonides* was created by Fisher (1952) for a single species *rickettsi* from the Gulf of California. This resembles *Siphonosoma* but is more simply organized, lacking coelomic sacs in the body wall and diverticula on the compensatory sac. It differs from all other sipunculoid genera in that the nephridia are strongly bilobed, with one lobe directed anteriorly.

In the next four genera the longitudinal muscle layer forms a continuous coat except in the single species *Golfingia gouldi*, where it is formed into bundles as in the preceding genera. It was shown by Fisher (1950a) that the name *Phascolosoma* had been misapplied for over a hundred years and that most of the species called by this name must be transferred elsewhere. He found that *Golfingia* (Lankester, 1885) is the first available name since others (*Homalosoma, Petalosoma, Stephanosoma*) are preempted. The genus *Golfingia* comprises sipunculoids of small to moderate size and slender shape with distinct tentacles arranged around the mouth in one or more circlets, except in very small species where the tentacles may form mere bulges (Fig. 214*B*). There is a prominent nuchal organ, and between it and the dorsalmost tentacles two cephalic tubes lead inward; there are, further, usually present a pair of ocular tubes sunk into the brain and having a pigmented ocellus at their inner end (Fig. 235*B, C*). The introvert is encircled with spines in many species (Fig. 217*D*), but these are lacking in others. Four or two retractor muscles and two nephridia are present. This is the largest sipunculoid genus; Fisher (1952) lists 75 species but indicates that the list is not complete. Some common northern species as *G. vulgaris* (Fig. 218*C*) and *margaritacea* have been called by six or seven additional names in the literature. *G. vulgaris* is the subject of Cuénot's account (1900). Other familiar species are *gouldi* (study by Andrews, 1890b), *verrilli, eremita, elongata* (study by Stehle, 1953), *minuta* (includes *sabellariae* and three other names, study by Paul, 1910; Fig. 214*B*), and *procera*. The genus *Dendrostomum* (erroneously *Dendrostoma*) is distinguished from all other sipunculoids by the four to eight tentacular stems branching palmately, dendritically, or pinnately (Figs. 214*C*, 218*A, B*). Members are mostly of considerable size with mostly two retractor muscles and single dorsal compensation sac provided with few to many, long or short diverticula (Fig. 228*B*). In 1952 there were 18 known species, of which the most familiar are *D. signifer* from the Indo–West Pacific region (study by Awati and Pradhan, 1935, 1936; Fig. 218*A*) and *D. zostericolum* (Peebles and Fox, 1933) from California. *Phascolion* comprises small species with a long slender introvert, globular "head" bearing a single circlet of tentacles (Fig. 216*A*), and plump trunk armed with holdfasts (Fig. 214*E–G*). Members of this genus habitually live in the empty shells of scaphopods and gastropods (Fig. 214*D*) or annelid tubes, and in correlation with the habit the body is often asymmetrical. There are one to three retractor muscles, a single (right) nephridium and intestinal loops instead of the usual coil (Fig. 224*A*). Of several species the best known is *P. strombi* (study by Théel, 1875; Fig. 214*D–G*), common in the North Atlantic. *Onchnesoma* is characterized by the location of the anus on the introvert, usually near the mouth (Fig. 218*D*). This is a genus of small species with long introvert, single nephridium, and single retractor muscle originating at the posterior end of the trunk (Fig. 223*B*). There are two species, *steenstrupi* and *squamatum* (Fig. 218*D*), both on north European coasts.

The genus *Phascolosoma* differs from all other sipunculoid genera in that the tentacles do not encircle the mouth but form a horseshoe dorsal to the mouth that embraces the nuchal organ (Fig. 216*B, C*); the anterior end of the introvert is further provided with two collars (Fig. 216*C*), one of which is continuous dorsally with the ends of the tentacular horseshoe (Fig. 217*A*).   The longitudinal muscle layer is arranged into bundles as in *Sipunculus;* there are two nephridia, mostly four retractors, and only a dorsal compensation sac mostly without diverticula.   In 1950a Fisher correctly pointed out that according to nomenclatorial rules the name *Phascolosoma* must be restricted to the species for which it was created, namely, *P. granulatum* (Leuckart, 1828) and other species having the same characters as *granulatum*.   It results from this that the great majority of the species that have been placed in *Phascolosoma* due to authors' mistakes must be transferred elsewhere.   *Physcosoma, Phymosoma,* and variants of these names are synonyms of *Phascolosoma*.   There are probably about 40 valid species of *Phascolosoma*, of which some common ones are *P. nigrescens* (Fig. 215*B*), widely spread in warmer waters, *P. agassizi*, Pacific Coast of North America, and *P. puntarenae*, Panamic region.

The three remaining genera are characterized by the possession of a horny or calcareous shield on the anterior end of the trunk.   In *Aspidosiphon*, with an additional shield covering the posterior end of the trunk (Fig. 214*A*), the base of the introvert lies ventral to the anterior shield.   The introvert is generally armed with circlets of hooks, and there is but one pair of retractor muscles more or less fused anteriorly (Fig. 223*A*).   There are around 25 species, mostly found in tropical and subtropical waters, chiefly in coral formations.   In *Cloeosiphon* the single shield forms a rounded cap surrounding symmetrically the base of the introvert; a single retractor muscle is present.   There appears to be but one valid species, *C. aspergillum*, recorded in coral formations throughout the Indo–West Pacific area (Fig. 239*A, B*).   *Lithacrosiphon* is characterized by the hard calcareous cone at the anterior end of the trunk (Fig. 217*F*) that displaces the introvert ventrally; both longitudinal and circular muscles of the trunk wall are arranged in bundles; there are two well-developed ocelli in the brain, one pair (ventral) of retractor muscles, and two nephridia.   The original species, *L. maldivense*, in coral rock from the Maldive Islands (Shipley, 1902), does not seem to have been refound, but Fischer (1922a) placed five other species in the genus, including *L. kükenthali* from Barbados.   Still two more species were described by Ten Broeke (1925) from corals at Curacao in the Caribbean.

14. Fossil Sipunculoids.—Certain fossils in the famous Burgess shales of British Columbia, of middle Cambrian age, were ascribed by Walcott (1911) to the "Gephyrea."   The specimens are pressed flat between the layers of shale and hence persist only as thin films, in which, however, much detail is discernible.   Walcott assigned the supposed "gephyrean" remains to four genera: *Ottoia, Banffia, Pikaia,* and *Oesia*.   *Ottoia* had a papillose introvert, very evident on one specimen, and *Ottoia, Banffia,* and

Oesia show hooks on one or both ends; but all are evidently segmented, *Ottoia* and *Pikaia* had a straight digestive tract, and the latter had parapodia and a pair of eyes and a pair of tentacles on the anterior end. It is obvious that these creatures cannot be sipunculoids, but presumably are annelids. Roger (1952) mentioned the finding of fossil madreporarian corals from the Miocene and Plio-Pleistocene of the Indo-Malay region and of tabulate corals (I, page 565) from the middle Devonian of Europe that have basal deformities similar to those produced at present by *Aspidosiphon* (see later) and plausibly ascribable to sipunculoids.

IV. ECOLOGY AND PHYSIOLOGY

1. Habits and Behavior.—Sipunculoids are exclusively marine, found from the intertidal zone to considerable depths and at all latitudes. They lead a sedentary existence, in burrows in sandy, muddy, mucky, gravelly, or shelly bottoms, in clefts and interstices of rocks, in porous lava, in the holdfast tangles of kelp, under beds of eelgrass and other vegetation, among coralline algae, under rocks, among corals, especially in cavities in rotting coral rocks or under slabs of decaying coral, in sponges, in empty shells and tubes of other animals, and in almost any protected situation. Definite tubes are never formed although the walls of burrows may be smoothed with secretion. The genera with shields are especially addicted to cavities in rotting coral rocks, and species of *Aspidosiphon* that inhabit northern waters may utilize instead shells and worm tubes or associate themselves with the northern coral *Lophohelia* (I, page 616). Probably the anterior shield of these genera acts to close the opening of the coral burrow when the animal retracts (Southern, 1913). Sluiter (1891) thinks these dwellers in calcareous rock hollow out their own burrows by means of epidermal secretions, but this seems improbable. He noted that such coral dwellers have a shorter, more muscular introvert and stronger introvert hooks than dwellers in sand or muck. Species of *Phascolosoma* also prefer hollows in coral rocks and when occurring in regions devoid of coral adopt related habitats. Thus the common species of the eastern North Atlantic, *P. granulatum*, is often found in cavities and crevices of limestone rocks and in beds of calcareous algae. The genus *Phascolion* generally lives in the empty shells of snails (Fig. 214*D*) and scaphopods or the tubes of annelids. *Phascolion strombi* fills the space between its body and the mouth of the shell or tube with mud, sand, and pebbles cemented together by its own secretions, leaving a hole for its emergence (Brumpt, 1897; Gerould, 1913). The extremely small *Golfingia minuta* may utilize small snail shells or shells of foraminiferans.

Each species probably has some habitat preference. When *Golfingia elongata* and *vulgaris*, *Sipun. nudus*, and *Phascolosoma granulatum* were placed together in a container with bottom partly covered with sand, partly with gravel, the last species burrowed into the gravel, the other three into the sand; but they would burrow into a substrate of gravel and rock fragments if no other was available.   When a mat of brown algae was provided, *P. elongata* selected this as a refuge in preference to gravel and rock fragments (Hérubel, 1907).   Southern (1913) also noted a preference of *G. elongata* for beds of vegetation and gave habitat preferences of various common European sipunculoids, as did also Cuénot (1922).   In general, sipunculoids avoid pure sand, no doubt because of its paucity of nutritive material.

Species of *Sipunculus* on the French coast are said by Hérubel (1907) to maintain a horizontal attitude in their burrows with the dorsal side up, parallel to the surface of the substrate.   They remain retracted into their burrows at low tide, thrust out the anterior end and expand their tentacles over the substrate at high tide.   *Golfingia* species observed by Hérubel burrowed at a right to an oblique angle with the surface.   *Golfingia gouldi* on the New England coast permeates muddy sand near low-tide level in all directions with irregular vertical and oblique burrows to a depth of half a meter (Andrews, 1890b; Gerould, 1913).   Similarly, *G. vulgaris* on the French coast occupies short irregular galleries (Cuénot, 1922).

When removed from their burrows or refuges sipunculoids usually show little movement beyond running the introvert in and out.   Most can crawl slowly by attaching the tentacular crown and then pulling the trunk forward.   Burrowing species burrow in again after removal from their burrows if placed on a suitable substrate.   Andrews (1890b) described the burrowing process in *Golfingia gouldi:* the introvert is run out, the tip applied to the surface exploringly until an unresistant spot is found, the introvert end is then expanded and pushed into the sand, the trunk then contracts, bringing the body forward, eventually to an erect position with the swollen introvert fixed in the sand, the introvert is then invaginated and everted again more deeply into the sand, and by repetition of these processes the animal buries itself vertically in a few minutes. After being covered the animal may proceed in any direction.   *Dendrostomum zostericolum* (Peebles and Fox, 1933) arches the fully extended introvert, applies its tip to the sand, drives it into the sand, swelling it behind the oral disk to obtain a purchase, and pulls the body into the sand by muscular contraction; it takes a curved path under the sand, coming to rest in its usual attitude with trunk curved under the sand and oral disk protruded above the sand.   Removal of the tentacles does not interfere with burrowing.   Similar burrowing behavior is shown by *Dend. signifer* (Awati and Pradhan, 1935).   The burrowing of *Sipun. nudus* is poorly described by von Uexküll (1903) and Zuckerkandl (1950).   It appears that the animal humps the middle part of the trunk upward, applies the oral disk to the sand, and drives the introvert into the sand by general contraction of the circular muscles. Swelling of the introvert just behind the oral disk acts as a holdfast while the trunk is brought forward through contraction of the longitudinal muscles. The introvert is then retracted and the cycle is repeated.

When undisturbed, the sipunculoid thrusts its anterior end out of the burrow or refuge and expands the tentacles for feeding and respiratory purposes. The tentacles are also employed for exploring the surrounding surface. On disturbance the animal instantly retracts the introvert, also contracts the trunk, and disappears from view.

A very remarkable habit and habitat are shown by *Phascolosoma lurco* in Indonesia (Harms and Dragendorff, 1933). This species lives there in earthen burrows that it constructs itself after the manner of earthworms, and may be kept in good condition for months in pots of soil. The burrows occupy a narrow zone to the inner side of mangrove growths just above the reach of high tides; they are simple vertical burrows filled with humid air and ending below at groundwater level. Their walls give evidence of having been plastered by secretions of the animals. The worms move actively in their burrows and readily turn around, although usually found with the anterior end up. When removed from their burrows the animals crawl actively by extending and attaching the introvert and then pulling the body forward. It is rather puzzling that numerous faunal records of *Phas. lurco* indicate an ordinary marine habit.

Besides burrowing and crawling some other movements are known for sipunculoids. It appears that members of the genus *Sipunculus* can swim by thrashing the body ends together, first to one side, then to the other. Hérubel (1907) saw a *Sipun. nudus* swim three times around a container, covering a continuous distance of over 6 m. Von Uexküll (1903) and Zuckerkandl (1950) also record swimming of this species, and the former says the regular body bendings occur, with all circular muscles contracted, by the alternate contraction and relaxation of the longitudinal muscles of the dorsal and ventral sides. This indicates that the animal swims on its side. Fisher (1954b) described as a new species *Sipun. natans*, a single specimen found swimming at night in the Gulf of California. On strong excitation, *Sipun. nudus* and *Golfingia gouldi* are said to assume a defense attitude (Zuckerkandl, 1950), an immobile, highly turgid state, with the longitudinal muscles maximally contracted. Still another type of movement is that of righting (von Uexküll, 1903). When placed dorsal side down, *Sipun. nudus* curves this side concavely by contraction of appropriate longitudinal muscles and falls over on one side; it then similarly curves this side and falls over into the correct position.

Experimental studies on behavior are limited to the work of Peebles and Fox (1933) on *Dend. zostericolum*. Behavior is dominated by a high degree of positive thigmotropism that induces the animal to burrow into other than natural substrates or to crawl under available objects.   When touched on the trunk the extended worm draws in the tentacles and invaginates the introvert; the same response results more rapidly to mechanical stimulation of the introvert, tentacles, or smooth zone, which last appears the most sensitive part of the animal.   Vibrations also evoked a response.   The species proved indifferent to other than bright light; it would not extend the tentacular crown into areas of direct sunlight and invaginated when a bright light was shone on the expanded tentacular crown but not when shone on other body areas.   Illumination of the dorsal side was more effective than that of the ventral side.   Von Uexküll (1903) observed that *Sipun. nudus* when illuminated from below would remain with its dorsal side down and does not right; however, it is found normally oriented when kept in darkness; hence its orientation is not directed by light.

Sipunculoids have a tough body wall and are probably resistant to temporary withdrawal of sea water as at low tide, being protected by secretions of the abundant epidermal glands.   One of three specimens of *Dend. zostericolum* survived and recovered normally after 12 days out of sea water in a moist chamber; this same species could endure loss of 38 to 43 per cent of its water content by air drying, but most were killed by loss of 45 per cent or more (Peebles and Fox, 1933), although rare individuals might recover after a loss of 48 to 50 per cent.   Wesenberg-Lund (1954a) mentions a species of *Phascolosoma* (*P. periannulata*) that inhabits channels in old coral blocks in the intertidal zone of coral islands and seems to require daily exposure out of sea water since it occurs only in blocks that are above the surf for a couple of hours daily.   Mention was made above of a species of this genus that actually lives in soil.

As may be expected from these findings, common littoral species survive well under laboratory conditions.   Hérubel (1907) remarked that species of *Golfingia* and *Sipunculus* would live in good condition for months in tanks at Roscoff; his own experiments indicated that different species vary in resistance and tend to die in other than natural substrates. *Dend. zostericolum*, utilized by Peebles and Fox (1933), appears remarkably resistant; four specimens in a small jar of sea water with sand were still living at the end of 103 days.   This same species would survive 2 or 3 weeks in stale sea water with or without sand, might live 5 to 6 weeks in a closed container of sea water and air if kept at 13°C., but died in a week or so at 23 to 26°C., and can endure sea water deprived of oxygen for at least a week but rapidly dies in sea water saturated with carbon dioxide.   Under adverse conditions the introvert usually remains invaginated, everts upon return to favorable conditions.   Edmonds (1957a) recorded survival of *Dend. cymodoceae* for 4 to 5 days under fluid devoid of oxygen. But *Sipun. nudus* is less resistant to absence of oxygen than these species of *Dendrostomum*. Placed in a closed cylinder completely filled with sea water deprived of oxygen, *Sipun.* was found after 24 hours fully extended with tentacles completely expanded and was dead in 48 hours (Baglioni, 1905).

As regards salinity Fischer (1925) remarks that sipunculoids are absent from the most brackish parts of the Baltic Sea and increase in number of species from the Skagerrak (salinity at least 30 parts per thousand) into the North Sea. In laboratory experiments sipunculoids recover from exposures to considerable changes of salinity. Adolph (1936) reported that *Golfingia gouldi* would survive indefinitely in sea water of 160 per cent and 55 per cent normal concentration.

Little is known of the feeding habits. From the presence of cilia and median ciliated grooves on the tentacular side facing the mouth one is inclined to assume a mucous-ciliary method of feeding on minute particles and organisms. Peebles and Fox (1933) and the MacGinities (1949) state that the tentacles of undisturbed animals are spread out over the substrate, and the former authors observed occasional introversion of the tentacular crown as if accumulated food were being removed. Sand dropped upon the expanded tentacles of *Dend. zostericolum* elicited no response, but after application of gelatin particles or meat extract to them the tentacles were temporarily infolded or sometimes introverted for a short time. Awati and Pradhan (1935) indicate that also *Dend. signifer* subsists on microscopic food collected by the tentacles by the mucous-ciliary method and ingested mainly by invagination of the introvert. Their examination of the intestinal contents showed ciliates, foraminiferans, small turbellarians, tiny crustaceans, polychaete larvae, and other small animals. However, a mucous-ciliary mode of feeding is difficult to reconcile with the general report (Fischer, 1925; Fisher, 1952) that sipunculoids habitually ingest large quantities of the substrate in which they live—sand, mud, and muck containing gross plant and animal remains such as fragments of corals and echinoderms, ectoprocts, annelids, crustaceans, and pieces of mollusk shells. Species of *Sipunculus* appear to ingest sand continuously as they burrow. In the intestine of *Onchnesoma steenstrupi* Shipley (1892) found vegetable debris, spicules, and much sand and mud. Peebles and Fox (1933) observed repeatedly that *Dend. zostericolum* had ingested considerable amounts of sand from their native habitat. They frequently emitted from the anus strands of feces containing sand particles, shell fragments, and other inorganic matter imbedded in a gelatinous matrix. This species would not ingest sand from which all organic matter had been removed by chemical treatment but would freely ingest such sand mixed with powdered serum albumin or powdered egg white. Chin and Wu (1950) found the intestine of *Phascolosoma scolops*, *Sipun. nudus*, and *Dend. minor* full of sand and mud with a slight admixture of diatoms, foraminiferans, radiolarians, bits of mollusk shells, crustacean appendages, annelid larvae, and algal fragments; but 95 per cent of the contained organisms were diatoms that thus constitute the main food of these sipunculoids, at least in the region concerned (Indochina).

2. Biological Relations.—As sedentary animals, sipunculoids are afflicted with the usual number of associates and parasites. The Protozoa are well represented. Metalnikoff (1900) sometimes saw a minute holotrichous ciliate in the coelomic fluid of *Sipun. nudus*, and Cuénot (1900) reported the holotrichous ciliate, *Cryptochilidium cuenoti*, as abundant in the esophagus of *Golfingia vulgaris*. Gregarines and other sporozoans are common in sipunculoids. In *Sipun. nudus* gregarines occur in the ascending coil of the intestine, and the eugregarine, *Urospora sipunculi*, is found in the coelom (Cuénot, 1902b). Dogiel (1907) investigated a schizogregarine, *Schizocystis sipunculi*, living in pockets in the ciliary groove of the intestine of *Sipun. nudus*, forming white spots visible to the naked eye; the adult schizonts in these pockets undergo schizogony, producing 150 to 200 progeny. Théel (1905) often saw sporozoans in the coelom of *Golfingia minuta* as well as vermiform protozoans, probably gregarines, in the intestine; this same sipunculoid is also the host of an interesting actinomyxid, *Tetractinomyxon intermedium* (Ikeda, 1912), and its red coelomic corpuscles are infested with an organism probably belonging to the blood coccidians (haemogregarines). This last undergoes schizogony in the red cells into two sizes of merozoites that infect new red cells and forms cysts in the granulocytes (Etherington, 1953). Other records of gregarines are the infestation of the rectum of *Phascolion strombi* with a eugregarine, *Lecudina franciana* (Arvy, 1952), and the presence of another eugregarine, *Extremocystis dendrostomi*, floating in couples in the coelomic fluid of *Dend. signifer* (Setna, 1931). Augener (1903) reported sporozoan cysts up to 2 mm. in diameter in the coelomic fluid of *Siphonosoma cumanensis;* when torn open these cysts spill out a multitude of rounded nucleated elements.

In the Indo-Malay region a remarkable association exists between members of the genus *Aspidosiphon* and solitary corals of the genera *Heteropsammia*, *Heterocyathus*, and *Stephanoceris* (Bouvier, 1894, 1895; Sluiter, 1902; Shipley, 1903). The coral attached to a snail shell occupied by an *Aspidosiphon* gradually overgrows the shell, which remains imbedded in its base, and probably lengthens by calcareous deposition the spiral cavity in which the sipunculoid lives. Subsidiary openings into the proximal parts of the spiral cavity are usually present (Fig. 241E) and originate, according to Sluiter, by separating off from the main opening. On retreating into its refuge the *Aspidosiphon* closes the opening by its

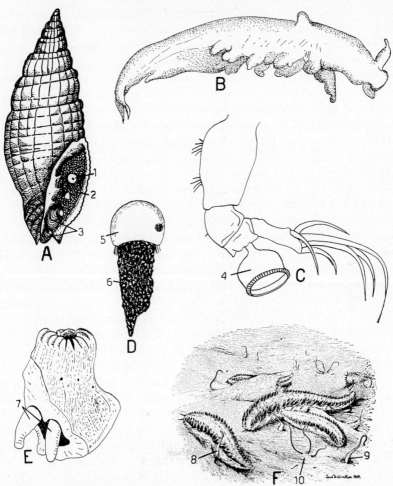

FIG. 241.—Biological relations, physiology. *A*, snail *Mitra* harboring an *Aspidosiphon* with two accompanying little bivalves (*after Knudsen, 1944*). *B*, peculiar parasitic copepod *Siphonobius gephyreicola* found in *Aspidosiphon brocki* (*after Augener, 1903*). *C*, copepod *Myzomolgus stupendus* with sucker on second antenna, taken from *Sipun. nudus* (*after Bocquet and Stock, 1957*). *D*, urn trailing a load of aggregated particles (*after Hérubel, 1907*). *E*, solitary coral *Heteropsammia* broken open to show sipunculoid in base (*after Shipley, 1903*). *F*, *Golfingia procera* attacking polychaete *Aphrodite* (*drawing by Poul Winther, courtesy Gunnar Thorson*). 1, anterior end of sipunculoid; 2, plug formed by sipunculoid in mouth of shell; 3, bivalves; 4, sucker; 5, urn; 6, mass of particles; 7, sipunculoid; 8, *Golfingia* with introvert inserted in annelid; 9, *Golfingia* in mud; 10, buried brittle star.

anterior shield. The association appears to be mutualistic since the coral gets moved around by the activities of the sipunculoid and the latter gains a secure refuge. The association begins at an early age of both participants, but it is not known whether the coral larva settles only on a shell occupied by an *Aspidosiphon* or whether the latter selects snail shells on which the coral is established. As Sluiter remarks: "It is certainly remarkable that three distinct genera of coral, each with but one species, should be inhabited by three distinct species of *Aspidosiphon*, and that neither commensal has hitherto been found apart from the other." There appears no specific relation between a given species of *Aspidosiphon* and a given species of coral.

The small and very slender *Golfingia hespera* frequents the burrows of other animals and has been found with the burrowing anemone *Edwardsiella* within the tubes of *Cerianthus*, in the burrows of the brachiopod *Glottidia albida*, and in the outer layers of the tubes of chaetopterid annelids (Ricketts and Calvin, 1939; the MacGinities, 1949; Fisher, 1952).

The intestine of sipunculoids is inhabited by umagillid rhabdocoels of the genus *Collastoma* (II, page 140), and this genus is not found in animals other than sipunculoids. It was discovered as the species *monorchis* in *Golfingia vulgaris* (Dörler, 1900). There have since been described *C. minutum* from *Phascolosoma granulatum* (Wahl, 1910), *C. eremitae* from *G. eremita* (Beklemischev, 1916), and *C. pacificum* from *Dend. pyroides* (Kozloff, 1953).

Trematode metacercariae are not infrequently found encysted in the tissues of sipunculoids. Cuénot (1900) refers to a metacercaria *leptosomum*, often encysted in the compensation sac of *G. vulgaris*, apparently an echinostome with adults in wading birds; and further mentions a metacercaria *capriciosa* with large suckers found encysted in the cephalic region, even the brain, of the same sipunculoid. This may be identical with the metacercariae reported by Stehle (1954) as encysted in the brain, also other tissues, of *G. elongata* and *vulgaris* and exercising a very destructive effect. Pérez (1924, 1925) noted larval stages of a trematode in the gonad of *Phascolion strombi;* they produced very spiny cercariae that he named *Cercaria rhodometropus*.

There is one report of the finding of an adult nematode in the coelom of *Cloeosiphon aspergillum*, fastened to the inner surface of the body wall by connective tissue (Augener, 1903).

Entoprocts of the family Loxosomatidae (III, page 535) are common and well-known commensals of sipunculoids. This occurrence was first noted by Vogt (1876), who named *Loxosoma phascolosomatum* (later transferred to the genus *Loxosomella*), found clustered chiefly on the posterior end of *G. elongata* and *margaritacea;* this same entoproct is also common on *G. vulgaris* (Cuénot, 1900, 1922) and further occurs on

Phascolion strombi (Bobin and Prenant, 1953a). Nilus (1909) reported *Loxosoma brumpti* and *Loxosomella murmanica* on *Phascolion strombi* in the Kola Fjord, and Osburn (1912) recorded *Loxosoma minuta* on *Phascolion strombi* and *G. eremita* on the New England coast. Harmer (1915) found *Loxosoma sluiteri* on *Phascolion convestitus* in the Malay region. *Phascolion strombi* appears a favorite roosting place for loxosomatids, although its habit of dwelling in shells and tubes would seem unfavorable for them. Besides the four entoprocts just mentioned as using this sipunculoid as host, there have been found on it in recent years six more species (Arvy and Prenant, 1952; Bobin and Prenant, 1953a, b), all belonging to the genus *Loxosomella* (page 747). Two or three different species of loxosomatids may be present on the same individual *Phascolion*. Still another *Loxosomella* species was reported by Bobin and Prenant (1953c) on *G. vulgaris* in the Mediterranean.

There is constant mention in the literature of a little syllid polychaete, *Syllis cornuta*, commensal with species of *Aspidosiphon* and *Phascolion* (Southern, 1913; Cuénot, 1922; Pérez, 1924, 1925; Knudsen, 1944). It appears that *Phascolion*, in addition to the main channel for its extension and retraction, maintains a secondary excretory channel through the cement mass with which it blocks the aperture of the inhabited shell or tube. In case the sipunculoid is lodged in a shell with a siphon, this subsidiary channel for the ejection of excreta is located in the siphon. The little syllid occupies this excretory channel where it benefits by outgoing currents and may find food particles in the ejecta of the host. It is probable that the commensal entoprocts also take advantage of this channel, although this is not mentioned by most authors.

Further commensals of *Aspidosiphon* and *Phascolion* are tiny bivalves of the family Montacutidae (Bouvier, 1895; Shipley, 1903; Cuénot, 1922; Pérez, 1924, 1925; Knudsen, 1944). These dwell in the channels maintained by the sipunculoid or at the surface of the cement plug (Fig. 241*A*) or even may be attached by byssal threads to the surface of the sipunculoid. They are also present with the sipunculoids that inhabit the base of solitary corals, as related above. As Pérez and Knudsen have emphasized, an *Aspidosiphon* or a *Phascolion*, especially *P. strombi*, may be the nucleus of an assemblage of animals, including parasites in the sipunculoid, the syllid, entoprocts, and bivalves on or with the sipunculoid, and barnacles, zoanthids, and sponges with contained associates attached to the snail shell inhabited by the sipunculoid.

Sipunculoids are infested by the inevitable parasitic copepods. Augener (1903) found a peculiar arthropod, probably a copepod, that he named *Siphonobius gephyreicola* (Fig. 241*B*), on a retractor muscle of *Aspidosiphon brocki;* the coelom contained numerous nauplius larvae presumably belonging to the parasite. Théel (1905) recorded a minute copepod with long egg sacs in the coelom of *Golfingia minuta*. Bocquet and Stock (1957) found two species of cyclopoid copepods, *Myzomolgus stupendus* and *Catinia plana*, adhering to the outside of *Sipun. nudus* by means of a stalked sucker on the third joint of the second antennae (Fig. 241*C*).

One would hardly suppose that sipunculoids are capable of preying on other animals, but Thorson (unpublished) reports that in the North Sea *Golfingia procera* attacks the annelid *Aphrodite aculeata*. The sipunculoid lives partly buried in the muddy bottom, waving its extended introvert about, and when this makes contact with a crawling *Aphrodite*, quickly introduces the introvert tip through the body wall of the polychaete and sucks out material while being dragged about by the victim (Fig. 241*F*).

Sipunculoids are often eaten by fish and are frequently found in their stomachs; further, by large anemones, crabs, and cephalopods (Fischer, 1925). Large sipunculoids of the genera *Sipunculus* and *Siphonosoma* are eaten by natives of the Palau Islands and Malay region and may be prepared like trepang (Sluiter, 1882; Sato, 1935).

Chaet (1955) claims that the coelomocytes of *Golfingia gouldi* when heated release a toxin containing protein and carbohydrate that is fatal to the sipunculoid as well as to other animals. It is not clear what relation possession of this toxin could have to the life of the sipunculoid in nature.

3. Physiology.—Andreae (1881) for *Sipun. nudus* and Andrews (1890b) for *Golfingia gouldi* showed that the cuticle dissolves in hot potassium hydroxide and therefore is not chitinous. The water content of *Dend. zostericolum* is 80 to 85 per cent of the wet weight (Peebles and Fox, 1933; Gross, 1954), but according to the latter, some of this is bound water. The water content is slightly lower in larger, hence older, specimens. Adolph (1936) reported 88 per cent water content in *Golfingia gouldi*. *Golfingia gouldi* contains 3.9 per cent by wet weight of lipoid substances, including cholesterol, fatty acid, and phospholipoids; after a month without food the content had fallen to 8.0 per cent, being lost mainly from the coelomic fluid, not the body wall (Wilber, 1947). Evidently the body-wall musculature is not a storehouse of lipoids in this species. Losses concerned mainly the fatty acids and phospholipoids, not the cholesterol. Analysis of the tissues of *Sipun. nudus* yielded 15 common amino acids, especially glycocoll, but also relatively high amounts of arginine and alanine (Duchateau *et al.*, 1952).

The body of sipunculoids may be regarded as a muscular bag filled with fluid; as such it invites investigation of osmotic changes and has been so utilized by a succession of workers (Quintin, 1900, on *Sipun. robustus;* Dekhuyzen, 1921, on *Sipun. nudus* and *G. vulgaris;* Harms and Dragendorff, 1933, on *Phascolosoma lurco;* Adolph, 1936, on *G. gouldi;* Koller, 1939, on *Phascolosoma japonicum;* and Gross, 1954, on *Dend. zostericolum*). In general, sipunculoids lack osmotic control, and as the coelomic fluid has about the same osmotic pressure as sea water, the intact animal when placed in diluted sea water takes in water and increases its weight, and loses water and decreases its weight in concentrated sea water. These changes continue until the coelomic fluid has become isotonic with the surrounding medium. On return to normal sea water the original weight is regained, or nearly so, if the salinity change to which the animal was subjected is not too drastic. It was found by both Adolph and Gross that the sipunculoid body gains water more rapidly in dilute media than it loses water in concentrated media and regains normal weight more slowly after exposure to dilute than to concentrated sea water. These facts suggest a differential permeability of the body wall to water. Gross, using bags of body wall tied off at the cut anterior end and immersed in varied concentrations of sea water in normal orientation and turned inside out, showed that the body wall is more permeable to water from the outside in than from the inside out. The body wall is generally regarded as impermeable to salts, although Gross found it slightly so. This author also indicated that some degree of osmotic control is possible in *Dend. zostericolum* by exchange of salts through the gut and nephridia and between the tissues and the coelomic fluid. Harms and Dragendorff also indicated an important role of the nephridia in osmoregulation in *Phas. lurco* but gave little proof. This animal lives in earthen burrows (page 669) and can endure submersion for only limited periods. The osmotic concentration of its coelomic fluid is constantly higher than that of the more or less brackish sea water permeating the ground immediately beneath the burrows. When placed in thoroughly washed sand permeated with distilled water the animal gave off considerable salts into the sand, and in sand with sea water maintained a higher osmotic pressure than that of sea water. This species seems to have better powers of osmoregulation than other sipunculoids. The best proof of an osmoregulatory function of the nephridia was furnished by Koller (1939) for *Phascolosoma japonicum*. He showed that animals operatively deprived of their nephridia gain much more weight in diluted sea water than normals and adjust imperfectly on return to normal sea water. Normal animals, further, have some ability, lost in operated individuals, to emit some of the absorbed water while still in the diluted medium.

Sipunculoids are obviously animals that operate by hydrostatic pressure. Body-wall contraction compressing the coelomic fluid obviously causes eversion of the introvert. Invagination of the introvert by its retractor muscles increases internal pressure because of the space occupied by the inrolled introvert and so prepares for the next evagination. The introvert cannot be operated in the absence of internal pressure as by a cut through the body wall. Zuckerkandl (1950) measured the internal pressure during varied activities of *Sipun. nudus* and *G. gouldi* by inserting glass capillaries into the coelom.

Because of the easy exposure of muscle and ventral nerve cord by a longitudinal cut through the dorsal body wall, sipunculoids furnish good material for a study of muscle-nerve physiology. The main study in this respect was made by von Uexküll (1896, 1903), using *Sipun. nudus*. The ventral nerve cord, susceptible to electrical but not mechanical stimulation, conducts equally well in both directions, at a slow rate (100 to 200 mm. per second) and with a strong decrement. Conduction in both directions was also proved by Baglioni (1905), who showed that stimulation of either of two pieces of body wall connected only by nerve cord laid bare results in contraction of both. Conduction is also transverse, presumably by way of the circular nerves of the body wall mentioned above, for stimulation of one side evokes contraction of both sides. The retractor muscles cannot be caused to contract by direct stimulation of the ventral cord and seem to be operated only reflexly by way of a nerve plexus. They contract on stimulation of the tentacles or the introvert, and if one is cut across its middle, both its halves continue to cooperate with the others. Stimulation of the introvert causes contraction of all four retractors even when the long nerves from the nerve cord (Fig. 232*D*) to the introvert are sectioned. Stimulation of the distal cut ends of these nerves evokes contraction of the muscle layers of the introvert wall. If the introvert is cut into rings, each retaining connection with the ventral cord, all contract on stimulation of one ring. The retractors contract from their posterior ends anteriorly and cooperate with the longitudinal muscles in the introvert wall. An eviscerated worm with body wall spread out but with brain and cord intact continues to go through burrowing movements for hours, that is, alternate shortening and lengthening of the body wall. According to von Uexküll, the main function of the brain is to inhibit contraction when a high state of tension already exists in the musculature, thus preventing rupture. In general, von Uexküll considered the muscles of *Sipunculus* to be more reactive than its nerves and more reactive than vertebrate muscle.

Some experiments on the role of the central nervous system in *Dend. zostericolum* were performed by Peebles and Fox (1933). After section of the nerve cord in the base of the introvert (without opening the animal) the sipunculoid lies inertly on the substrate and appears incapable of extending the tentacles and anterior region. After destruction of the brain with a needle the animals lived for a week or 10 days and were able to burrow in a slow, abnormal way but responded poorly to stimulation. Lack of muscle tone and slowing of reactions appeared the main results of brain ablation.

A large literature exists on the properties of the coelomic fluid of sipunculoids and its contained elements. The following data about the fluid (often called plasma), apart from the cellular elements, have been abstracted from the articles of Andrews (1890a), Enriques (1903), Botazzi (1908), Cantacuzene (1922), Damboviceanu (1926), Florkin (1933, 1937), Harms and Dragendorff (1933), Steinbach (1940), Florkin and Duchateau (1942), and Robertson (1953). The coelomic fluid constitutes about half the volume of the animal, and up to 15 cc. may be obtained from a large specimen of *Sipun. nudus*. It is slightly alkaline (only figure found was pH 7.6) and has about the same osmotic pressure as sea water, although generally slightly higher; but the ionic content differs quantitatively from that of sea water. Steinbach found more potassium and calcium but less sodium and chlorine in the coelomic fluid of *G. gouldi* than in sea water, whereas Robertson reported more potassium, calcium, and sodium and less magnesium, chlorine, and sulphate in *G. vulgaris* than in sea water. Especially the concentration of potassium exceeds that of sea water. The coelomic fluid contains protein, generally given as less than 1 mg. per cubic centimeter, and enzymes such as a protease and a lipase are occasionally reported as present. Florkin and associates found glucose in the coelomic fluid of *Sipun. nudus*, in concentrations up to 10 mg. per 100 cc., and state that such occurrence is characteristic of animals without a circulatory system. The coelomic fluid of many sipunculoids clots on removal from the animal, but this is not true of *Sipun. nudus* or of *G. elongata*. The clot consists of a loose jelly that is not formed by the fusion of coelomocytes but by the deposition of fibrils. It dissolves in acids and alkalies but not in water and probably contains protein. The coelomic fluid of *Sipun. nudus* coagulates when heated. Nitrogenous substances in the coelomic fluid are considered below under excretion.

The red corpuscles of the coelomic fluid have been extensively investigated. They contain a red respiratory pigment that is also found in the nerve cord and in the reddish areas of the wall of the digestive tract and gives the coelomic fluid a reddish or madder color. It was first proved by Lankester (1872) by the use of the spectroscope that this red pigment is not haemoglobin, and this finding has been verified by all subsequent investigators; further, the pigment does not contain the haeme radical at all. The pigment was named haemerythrin by Krukenberg (1880). Andrews (1890a) discovered that haemerythrin is a globulin containing iron and found that it dissolves in water, forming a madder pink solution that turns yellowish when deoxygenated. The iron content was given by Cuénot (1901) as 1.44 per cent by weight, about five times the iron present in vertebrate haemoglobin. Roche (1933a) found that haemerythrin crystallizes in the rhombic system and probably differs in different species;

thus the molecular weight of haemerythrin from *Sipun. nudus* is given as 66,000 (Roche and Roche, 1935), that of *G. gouldi* as 119,000 (Love, 1955). Marrian (1927) verified many preceding statements and found that the water solution of haemerythrin is unstable, except at pH 8 to 9, and dissociates readily. Florkin (1933) in an exhaustive article about haemerythrin verified previous findings but devoted himself mainly to oxygen absorption and dissociation. Haemerythrin takes up one molecule of oxygen to each three atoms of iron, and one molecule of oxyhaemerythrin transports the same quantity of oxygen as one molecule of oxyhaemoglobin. The oxygen capacity of sipunculoid red corpuscles is 21 per cent by volume, that of vertebrate red cells 25 to 68 volumes per cent. Carbon dioxide pressure is without effect on oxygen absorption as characteristic of respiratory pigments of animals without a circulatory system (Florkin, 1932). Further, haemerythrin, unlike haemoglobin, will not combine with carbon monoxide. Although sipunculoid red corpuscles have a rather low power to take up oxygen, the oxygen readily dissociates and is given up to the tissues at relatively low oxygen pressure. Florkin considers that in ordinary conditions of sipunculoid life, the haemerythrin is nearly completely saturated with oxygen, and hence is well adapted to the needs of the animal.

It might be mentioned that the red corpuscles are of some assistance in ridding the coelom of foreign particles. Injected dyes are taken into their vacuoles (Cuénot, 1902a, 1913), but only those of basic nature (Chapheau, 1928).

A great deal of attention has been paid to the properties of the other formed elements of the coelomic fluid and of the peritoneum. The phagocytic hyaline amoebocytes are generally considered to be young stages that after filling themselves with ingested particles lose their phagocytic abilities and become granulocytes. In their active phase they also ingest injected particles and dyes (Cuénot, 1891, 1900, 1913; Hérubel, 1907). The ordinary flattened peritoneal cells ingest to a slight extent foreign injected particles (Cuénot, 1902a; Hérubel, 1907), and the chloragogue cells which are altered peritoneum are highly active in this respect. They readily engulf carmine and carbon particles and some types of dyes injected into the coelom (Andrews, 1890b; Brumpt, 1897; Cuénot, 1900, 1913; Hérubel, 1902, 1907). Such particles add themselves to the yellow granules regularly present in the chloragogue cells. Hérubel claims these cells are acid, hence would show a selective action toward dyes.

Most observers are fascinated by the urns, both fixed and free, and their behavior and functions (Andrews, 1890b; Cuénot, 1900, 1902a, 1913; Metalnikoff, 1900; Hérubel, 1902, 1907; Selensky, 1908; Buytendyk, 1909; Harms, 1921). The urns, whether fixed or free, have the property of aggregating particles, such as disintegrating coelomocytes and injected carmine, carbon, bacteria, dyes, or mammalian red corpuscles (but not their own red corpuscles). Such particles brought to the urns by their ciliary action adhere to the ciliated cell apparently through the secretion of some viscous substance and soon accumulate to a considerable mass. Free urns swim with the ciliated cell behind, and hence trail this accumulated mass (Fig. 241*D*). These actions can be seen with living urns mounted on a slide with foreign particles. Urns are said to retain their vitality and activities 1 or 2 days after removal from the sipunculoid body. Some workers think the urns ingest and digest some of the accumulated particles, but it is more probable that the urns are devoid of phagocytic powers and are simply accumulators. Buytendyk found that injected bacteria accumulated by the urns failed to undergo any change in 24 hours. Selensky added litmus powder and phenolphthalein powder to urns in vitro; on accumulation by the urns these powders failed to undergo any color change. The urns are therefore neutral, a condition not favorable to digestive activities. Buytendyk could not detect any chemotactic response of urns to the types of bodies they accumulate. Cantacuzene (1922) and Cantacuzene and Vles (1922) suggest that the operation of the urns is governed by electric charges. They say the urns are positively charged, hence attract negatively charged material. The red corpuscles of their own coelomic fluid are also positively charged, hence do not adhere to the urns. Injected mammalian red corpuscles were found to be negatively charged and therefore are accumulated by the urns. The accumulated masses eventually break off and float in the coelomic fluid or collect in the posterior part of the coelom as "brown bodies" that may also include sporozoan spores and cysts. These bodies are of common occurrence in the coelom of sipunculoids. They seem eventually to be voided by way of the nephridia, for they have been seen inside the nephridia by some observers.

Sipunculoids are devoid of a circulatory and a respiratory system, but undoubtedly movements of the coelomic fluid through activities of the animal and circulation in the tentacular system accomplish the functions of circulation and respiration, at least in part. Semper (1864) saw motion in the tentacular system by ciliary action and by contractions but was confused on the anatomical relations. Andrews (1890b) first oberved a definite circulation in the tentacles (*G. gouldi*), proceeding peripherally in the lateral channels and back in the median channel of each tentacle. Andrews also noted that the compensation sac is contractile and will contract even when empty. Similar circulation in the tentacles has been seen by other authors in other species (Meyer, 1929; Peebles and Fox, 1933; Stehle, 1953). Although the compensation sac contains muscle fibers in its wall and is frequently referred to in the literature as contractile vessel (e.g., by Fisher, 1952) direct observations on its contractile activities appear scanty. Circulation in the tentacular system is usually ascribed to ciliary action and to body movements. The tentacles when fully spread are doubtless of considerable respiratory value. Meyer (1929) described definite ciliary currents in the coelom of species of *Golfingia*, ascribed to the activity of the ciliated peritoneal cells and fixed urns. In *G. elongata* the current runs anteriorly along the inner surface of the body wall; nothing is said about a return current. More complicated currents are described in *G. vulgaris*, in which there is a forwardly directed current along the dorsal body wall, a posteriorly directed current along the median ventral wall, and transverse currents from midventral to lateral regions on each side. Such coelomic streaming has not been seen by others, and Peebles and Fox definitely failed to find it in *Dend. zostericolum*. It would seem to be of little circulatory value compared with muscular activities.

Few data are available on the actual rate of oxygen consumption. Cohnheim (1911) gave the oxygen consumption of *Sipun. nudus* as 6 to 10 mg. of oxygen per hour per 100 g. fresh weight at 15°C. Edmonds (1957a) found a rate in *Dend. cymodoceae* of 0.0045 to 0.0055 cc. per gram fresh weight per hour in adults and 0.020 to 0.031 in juveniles, at 22°C. Chapheau (1928) stated that the coelomic fluid (including its cells) of *Sipun. nudus* at saturation contains 20 cc. of oxygen per liter (a similar figure was reached by Cuénot, 1901; Florkin, 1933; Edmonds, 1957a) as compared with 6 cc. in sea water and that the cells consume 4 cc. of oxygen per liter per hour. Henze (1910) showed that the oxygen uptake of *Sipun. nudus* varies with the oxygen content of the medium (also true of *Dend. cymodoceae* in Edmonds's experiments), but as the weight of the animals was not given, their rate of oxygen consumption cannot be calculated from his data. In Edmonds's experiments the average respiratory quotient of juveniles fasted for 4 days was 0.60, perhaps indicative of lipoid consumption. Under anaerobic conditions, lactic acid is produced.

The physiology of digestion is almost unknown. Enriques (1903) reported that the intestinal fluid of *Sipun. nudus* is colorless and alkaline and contains a protease digesting fibrin but no diastases. Similarly, a water extract of the intestinal wall was weakly proteolytic but devoid of diastases. The best study on digestion and absorption is that of Arvy and Gabe (1952), using *Phascolion strombi*. The esophageal epithelium contains some glycogen but no enzymes, hence is not digestive. The descending coil of the intestine was found to be the main seat of digestion and absorption. Its wall contained carbohydrates, of which only a small part was glycogen, osmiophilic lipoids, and especially ribonucleinic substance; these food stores declined during the period of ripening of the sex cells, but after their discharge in April and May increased again. The basal part of the descending coil was found rich in alkaline phosphatases, lipases, and glycogen stores. In contrast, the ascending intestinal coil contained practically no food stores except that the chloragogue cells on its outside were rich in glycogen.

The nephridia appear to be genuine organs of excretion, as well as agents of osmoregulation. Koller (1936, 1939) reported that removal of the nephridia is not fatal to *Phascolosoma japonicum* as claimed for *P. lanzarotae* by Harms (1921); further, Koller could not verify the claim of Harms that nephridia produce an adrenaline-like substance. As noted above, the nephridial wall contains muscle fibers, and Koller (1936, 1939) saw nephridia of *Phascolosoma japonicum* isolated in sea water contract rhythmically for hours at an initial rate of 5 to 10 per minute, gradually slowing with time. A number of nephridia in one vessel contract at a faster rate than isolated nephridia; Koller ascribed this to the secretion of a stimulating substance similar to histamine, also produced by the body wall and nerve cord.

Inert injected particles and some injected dyes as indigo carmine and acid fuchsin (but not ammoniated carmine) are eliminated by the nephridia as well as by the coelomic elements already indicated (Brumpt, 1897; Cuénot, 1900, 1913; Harms, 1921); these coelomic elements may be regarded as accessory excretory agents or athrocytes. The injected particles adsorb on the yellow granules already present in the nephridial epithelium (Fig. 235*F*). According to Cuénot, these granules are acid and probably consist of urates, but it has been impossible to demonstrate the excretion of uric acid by sipunculoids. In general, the nature of the yellow or brown granules in the chloragogue cells and the nephridial epithelium is unknown. Ladreyt (1903) considers that amoebocytes loaded with foreign particles pass through the nephridial wall and incorporate themselves into the nephridial cells, which then cut off and eject their tips. Metalnikoff (1900) also thinks that excretory materials pass through the nephridial walls into the epithelium and that the latter excretes them by breaking off small balls of its substance. However, entrance of foreign particles into the nephridia by way of the nephrostomes cannot be excluded, and ingoing currents at the nephrostomes were seen by Meyer (1929).

Data are available on nitrogen excretion. Harms and Dragendorff (1933) withdrew fluid from the lumina of the nephridia of *Phascolosoma lurco* by inserting a capillary tube. They reported this fluid as neutral, of about the same osmotic pressure as the coelomic fluid, devoid of protein, sugar, or urea but containing ammonium salts, and with a total solid content of 3.49 per cent. Delaunay (1926, 1927, 1931) analyzed the red corpuscles, coelomic fluid (including its cells), and various tissues of *Sipun. nudus* and arrived at the following figures in terms of parts per 100 of nonprotein nitrogen:

	Ammonium nitrogen	Amino nitrogen	Urea	Purine nitrogen
Red corpuscles..........	1.8	46.6	22.0	1.7
Coelomic fluid..........	11.6	14.3	5.3	4.2
Intestine...............	1.7	32.0	0.5	3.4
Muscles...............	1.8	65.6	0.5	1.5
Nephridia.............	3.6	37.2	1.7	5.6

The high urea content of the red corpuscles is very astonishing. It was verified at first by Florkin and Houet (1937) and Florkin and Duchateau (1942) also for other species, but after a more critical examination, the latter authors concluded that the nitrogenous substance in the red corpuscles is not urea, but allantoic acid or allantoin, which is hydrolyzed into urea and glyoxylic acid by the chemical procedures that were followed. The chain of enzymes necessary for the conversion of uric acid into ammonia by way of allantoin, allantoic acid, and urea was found present in the intestine and nephridia of sipunculoids, but not in the red cells. Hence sipunculoids belong to those animal phyla in which ammonia is the end product of nitrogen metabolism. The high amount of allantoic acid in the red corpuscles remains as an inexplicable chemical peculiarity of the Sipunculida.

An excellent study of nitrogen excretion was made by Edmonds (1957b) on *Dend. cymodoceae*. The sea water in which the animals were kept for 36 hours after 4 days without food to empty the gut was found to contain, in terms of milligrams per 100 g. wet weight per 24 hours, 1.18 to 1.32 mg. total nitrogen, of which 1.00 to 1.16 was ammonia nitrogen, 0.05 to 0.08 urea, and 0.00 to 0.05 amino nitrogen. Uric acid was entirely absent. Thus 83 to 90 per cent of the excreted nitrogen was in the form of ammonia, in confirmation of the view that sipunculoids are ammonotelic animals.

Sipunculoids belong to those groups of invertebrates that lack creatine phosphate and contain arginine phosphate or a very similar substance (Baldwin and Yudkin, 1950). The distribution of these two substances in invertebrates does not seem to have the phylogenetic importance formerly attributed to it (further, page 749).

4. Geographic Distribution.—Sipunculoids inhabit all seas except extremely brackish areas and are found at all latitudes. They are strictly benthonic, occurring mostly in the littoral zone, that is, from the intertidal region to the edge of the continental shelves, but also extend into abyssal waters, to a depth of 5000 m. They appear very adaptable to a range of temperature and depth and hence many have a wide distribution. The most notable of these is *Sipun. nudus*, which is practically cosmopolitan but is wanting in polar waters; it is to be understood as present in all other zones.

The group undoubtedly centers in warmer waters where the great majority of species are found, especially those of the genera *Aspidosiphon, Phascolosoma, Cloeosiphon, Lithacrosiphon, Dendrostomum,* and *Siphonosoma.* The home of numerous species of these genera is the great Indo–West Pacific region that extends from the Red Sea and the east coast of Africa through the Indian Ocean and the numerous Pacific islands to the borders of Polynesia. Many species are spread throughout this area. The sipunculoids of Indo–West Pacific waters have been treated in a long succession of articles (Sluiter, 1882, 1884, 1886, 1891, 1902; Selenka, de Man, and Bülow, 1883; Fischer, 1895, 1914b, 1922a, 1926a, b; Shipley, 1898a, b, 1903; Augener, 1903; Lanchester, 1905; Stephen, 1914, 1952; Monro, 1931; Sato, 1935; Leroy, 1942; Wesenberg-Lund, 1954b; Stephen and Robertson, 1952). Species widely spread throughout the area include *Sipunculus robustus, titubans,* and *discrepans, Siphonosoma cumanense, australe, edule, billitonensis,* and *vastum, Dendrostomum signifer, Aspidosiphon steenstrupi, mülleri, elegans, truncatus, klunzingeri, cumingi, gracilis,* and *corallifera, Cloeosiphon aspergillum,* only species of this genus, and *Phascolosoma nigrescens, scolops, lurco, dentigerum, asser, pelma, pacifica, albolineata,* and *nigritorquata.* There is a notable absence of species of *Golfingia,* although some, *pellucida* and *papillifera,* appear typical. Many of the foregoing species characteristically dwell in burrows and crevices of coral, living and dead, especially the latter, and are found by breaking open slabs of rotting coral.

The same species are found in other tropical and subtropical waters. From the western coast of central Africa are reported (Fischer, 1914a) a number of common Indo–West Pacific species: *Sipun. titubans, Siphonosoma cumanense, Phascolosoma scolops* and *nigrescens, Aspidosiphon mülleri, klunzingeri,* and *steenstrupi, Dend. signifer,* and *Golfingia papillifera.* In the corresponding area of the western tropical Atlantic or West Indian region (Keferstein, 1866; Shipley, 1890; Gerould, 1913; Fischer, 1914b, 1922a, b; Ten Broeke, 1925; Andrew and Andrew, 1953; Hedgpeth, 1954; Wesenberg-Lund, 1954b) occur some of the same species: *Sipun. robustus, Siphonosoma cumanense, Aspidosiphon elegans, cumingi,* and *steenstrupi, Phascolosoma nigrescens, scolops,* and *dentigerum,* and *Golfingia pellucida.* Such species may be regarded as nearly circumtropical, wanting only in the tropical eastern Pacific, having presumably like many other invertebrates failed to negotiate the East Pacific barrier. There are also characteristic West Indian species, of which may be mentioned *Phascolosoma varians* and *antillarum, Golfingia verrilli* and *catherinae, Aspidosiphon speciosus,* and apparently localized species of *Lithacrosiphon* (Fischer, 1922a; Ten Broecke, 1925) and *Aspidosiphon* (Cordero and

Mello-Leitao, 1952). The author, breaking open decaying coral rock in the Bahamas, found therein *Aspidosiphon speciosus* (Fig. 214*A*) and *Phascolosoma nigrescens* (Fig. 215*B*). Data on the remaining tropical area, the eastern Pacific or Panamic region, appear in Keferstein (1866), Fischer (1895, 1914b), Gerould (1913), and Fisher (1947, 1952). From these records it appears that *Sipun. titubans, Phascolosoma dentigerum,* and *Aspidosiphon truncatum* occur in the Panamic region; hence these three species complete the circle of the tropics. Some species, as *Golfingia pectinata* and *Phascolosoma antillarum,* are limited to the West Indian and Panamic regions, that is, occur on both sides of the Isthmus of Panama. Others are strictly Panamic, as *Sipunculus mundanus* and *galapagensis, Xenosiphon branchiatum, Siphonides rickettsi, Dendrostomum peruvianum,* and *Phascolosoma puntarenae.*[1]

Japan lies on the northern fringe of the tropical and subtropical western Pacific, and its marine fauna is generally a mixture of tropical and northern forms. Japanese sipunculoids have been treated by Ikeda (1904, 1924) and Sato (1930, 1934, 1937, 1939). Common tropical species found in Japanese waters include *Sipun. robustus, Siphonosoma cumanense, Phascolosoma scolops, nigrescens, pacificum, pelma,* and *albolineatum, Dendrostomum signifer, Aspidosiphon steenstrupi, elegans,* and *mülleri,* and *Cloeosiphon aspergillum.* Northern elements include *Golfingia vulgaris* and *margaritacea* and *Phascolosoma granulatum.* There are, further, many endemic species in the genera *Golfingia, Phascolosoma, Aspidosiphon, Phascolion,* and *Dendrostomum,* among which may be mentioned *Golfingia nigra, Phascolosoma japonicum,* and *Dendrostomum blandum* and *hexadactylum.*

Despite the predilection of sipunculoids for warm waters, arctic and boreal zones support many members of the group, with the usual southward spread along the continental coasts. Characteristic arctic sipunculoids (Théel, 1905; Chamberlin, 1920b; Fischer, 1928; Wesenberg-Lund, 1932, 1937) are *Golfingia margaritacea, eremita,* and *minuta* and *Phascolion strombi,* of which the first and last are circumpolar and circumboreal whereas the other two appear wanting in the Pacific Arctic. *Golfingia margaritacea* is one of the most widely spread sipunculoids in colder waters, reported under many names and subdivided into many subspecies. All four arctic species participate in an extensive sipunculoid fauna of the boreal North Atlantic, extending from Norway and Sweden along the north European coast, embracing the British Isles, and descending southward to varying extents along the continents bathed by the North Atlantic. Boreal Atlantic sipunculoids have been reported by Koren and

---

[1] It is to be noted that there is a Puntarenas on the west coast of Costa Rica and a Punta Arenas in the Strait of Magellan. The specific name here refers to the Costa Rica locality.

Danielssen (1877), Cuénot (1902b), Théel (1905), Gerould (1913), Southern (1913), Fischer (1925), Wesenberg-Lund (1930, 1933, 1939), Stephen (1934), and Lindroth (1941). Common species of northern and western European coasts, in addition to the four arctic species and the ubiquitous *Sipun. nudus*, are *Sipun. norvegicus* (= *priapuloides*), *Golfingia vulgaris, elongata, procera,* and *improvisa, Phascolosoma granulatum, Aspidosiphon mülleri* (= *mirabilis, radiata*), and *Onchnesoma steenstrupi* and *squamatum.* *Golfingia minuta* and *Onchnesoma steenstrupi* were found (Lindroth) to be the most common sipunculoids in the Skagerrak, and of the latter 800 might be dredged in a square meter of bottom. Southern reported that *Phascolosoma granulatum,* only member of this genus in colder waters, is the most characteristic littoral sipunculoid around Ireland, and *Golfingia minuta* and *vulgaris* and *Phascolion strombi* are also very common there. *Sipunculus norvegicus* extends south to the Azores and the Cape Verde Islands; *Golfingia minuta* and *margaritacea* also to the Azores; *G. elongata* spreads only into the Mediterranean, but *G. vulgaris* by way of the Mediterranean and Red Sea has spread itself through much of the Indo–West Pacific area. *Phascolosoma granulatum* has reached the Azores and Cape Verde Islands; in the former location it is the most common species, and 8000 small ones might be obtained per square meter from beds of coralline algae (Chapman, 1955). *Phascolion strombi* also extends to the Azores, and *Aspidosiphon mülleri,* also very common in the Azores, is spread down the west coast of Africa to the French Congo and also occurs on the east coast of Africa and in the Indian Ocean.

Some of these arctic and boreal sipunculoids descend along the northeastern coast of North America, although often only in deeper waters (Gerould, 1913). *Sipunculus norvegicus* is found to the Carolinas, and *Golfingia margaritacea, minuta, eremita,* and *procera* occur to varying points southward along the Atlantic Coast of the United States. *Phascolion strombi* has spread into the West Indian region and may be regarded as distributed throughout the Atlantic north of this region. The sipunculoid fauna of the Atlantic Coast of North America further includes a tropical element that ascends from the West Indian region as far as the Carolinas. There are further endemic elements, not known to occur elsewhere, notably *Golfingia gouldi* and *verrilli.*

Regarding the sipunculoid fauna of the Pacific Coast of North America Fisher (1952) has contributed an invaluable article. Boreal elements descending the coast include *Golfingia margaritacea* and *vulgaris* as far as Puget Sound, *G. procera* to California, and variants of *G. margaritacea* and *eremita* along California. A Japanese element is evident in the presence of *Dend. hexadactylum.* The sipunculoids of Southern California are mingled with Panamic species, already considered. There are, further, a number of sipunculoids that appear limited to the Pacific Coast of the

United States, mainly California: *Siphonosoma ingens, Golfingia hespera,* and *Dend. pyroides, zostericolum, perimeces,* and *dyscritum.* The most common intertidal sipunculoid of the Pacific Coast is *Phascolosoma agassizi,* recorded from Alaska to the Gulf of California, abundant in a variety of habitats. This species is also recorded from all parts of the Indo–West Pacific region as well as from the Mediterranean and Atlantic, but Fisher holds that these records refer to some closely related species, possibly *puntarenae,* which is Panamic, but might be present in other tropical waters.

As regards higher southern latitudes collections have been made from Australia, New Zealand, South Africa, and the Subantarctic and Antarctic. The sipunculoids of Australia are considered by Fischer (1919a, 1921, 1926b), Monro (1931), and Edmonds (1955, 1956). As might be expected, the sipunculoid fauna of Australia consists mainly of West Pacific elements, and this is especially true of the Great Barrier Reef area (Monro, 1931). Common species of the tropical West Pacific found on Australian coasts include *Sipun. robustus, Siphonosoma cumanense, australe,* and *vastum, Phascolosoma nigrescens, lurco, dentigerum, pacificum,* and *nigritorquatum, Golfingia pellucida, Dend. signifer, Aspidosiphon cumingi, steenstrupi,* and *klunzingeri,* and *Cloeosiphon aspergillum.* A Japanese element is seen in the presence of *G. misakiana.* There also occur variants of *G. margaritacea* and *G. vulgaris,* typical boreal species. There are also a number of endemic Australian species, not known to occur elsewhere, of which one, *Dend. cymodoceae,* was extensively used by Edmonds (1957a, b) in physiological experiments reported above.

The sipunculoids of New Zealand are apparently all endemic. Benham (1904, 1905) listed four species, of which *Phascolosoma annulata* and *Dend. huttoni* were said to be the most common.

South African sipunculoids (Stephen, 1942) are also mainly of Indo–West Pacific origin. The most common of the endemic species is *Golfingia capensis,* originally taken by the *Challenger* (Selenka, 1885) at the Cape of Good Hope.

Subantarctic and antarctic sipunculoids have been collected by a succession of expeditions (Selenka, 1885; Michaelsen, 1889; Fischer, 1896; Théel, 1911; Benham, 1922; Stephen, 1941, 1948; Wesenberg-Lund, 1955a). Only a limited number of species have been found, and nearly all of these belong to the genus *Golfingia.* Further, they are mostly species that we already met in northern waters; in short, sipunculoids exhibit to an astonishing degree the phenomenom of bipolarity (IV, page 401). Widely spread northern species as *Golfingia margaritacea, eremita, minuta,* and *improvisa* and *Phascolion strombi* are also the commonest sipunculoids of subantarctic regions. Théel (1911) was unable to find any difference between Swedish and antarctic specimens of *G. margaritacea* and *minuta* and *Phascolion strombi*. Other examples of bipolar sipunculoids are *G. intermedia*, previously known only from Ireland, taken in Commonwealth Bay, King George V Land, Antarctic (Stephen, 1948), and *G. muricaudata*, known from deeper waters off Ireland and in other Atlantic localities, found in the Antarctic by the German Deep Sea Expedition (Fischer, 1916, 1922c). Characteristic subantarctic and antarctic sipunculoids not known elsewhere are *G. anderssoni, nordenskjöldi, pudica, ohlini*, and *mawsoni*. *Golfingia pudica* is reported as very common at Kerguelen, *G. mawsoni* as the most abundant species at various stations in the true Antarctic (Stephen, 1948).

As common with marine invertebrates, many sipunculoids have a wide bathymetrical range, occurring from the littoral into archibenthal and even abyssal depths. To mention a few common species typically found at modest depths, *Sipun. nudus* may descend to 2275 m., *G. margaritacea* to 4600 m., *G. eremita* to 2000 m., *G. minuta* to 2300 m., *G. vulgaris* to 1900 m., *Phascolion strombi* to 1900 m., *Onchnesoma squamatum* to 1000 m., and *Aspidosiphon mülleri* to 1260 m. Data on deep-sea sipunculoids appear in the *Challenger* report (Selenka, 1885), reports of dredgings in the eastern temperate Atlantic (Sluiter, 1900; Roule, 1907), and from dredgings of the German (Fischer, 1916, 1922c) and Swedish (Wesenberg-Lund, 1955b) Deep Sea Expeditions; the last has tabulated the available data. There appears to be one widely spread abyssal sipunculoid, *G. flagrifera* (Fig. 214*H*), originally found by the *Challenger*, known only from depths of 3000 to 5000 m. *G. muricaudata*, another species with a little tail, is limited to archibenthal and abyssal waters to a depth of 3000 m. *Sipunculus norvegicus*, mostly an archibenthal species, has been dredged at 4400 m. in the eastern North Atlantic. Another archibenthal and abyssal species, *Phascolosoma abyssorum*, has been recorded to nearly 5000 m. Other abyssal species, seldom seen, are *Golfingia profunda*, 4255 m. in the eastern North Atlantic (Roule, 1907), and *Phascolion lutense*, 3600 m., collected by the *Challenger*. The *Galathea* expedition obtained sipunculoids at 8210 m. in the Kermadec Trench, but details had not been published at the time of writing.

V. RELATIONSHIPS

A close relationship of Sipunculida to Annelida is obvious. This is shown above all by the following features of development: typical spiral cleavage, annelidan cross, formation of entomesoderm from teloblast cells that proliferate mesodermal bands, formation of the coelom by schizocoely in the mesoderm bands, trochophore larva with apical tuft, prototroch, and metatroch. In the adult anatomy a strong point of resemblance is the annelid type of central nervous system.

The Sipunculida cannot, however, be placed in the phylum Annelida because of their total lack of segmentation, both in the adult and during development.

The Sipunculida are shown to be Protostomia because of the origination of the stomodaeum from or at the site of the anterior end of the blastopore.

The Sipunculida are therefore to be conceived as protostomatous coelomates placed along the main line of the Protostomia that leads to Annelida, Mollusca, and Arthropoda. They may be regarded as an intermediate stage in the evolution of segmented protostomatous coelomates.

Bibliography

HISTORICAL

Barbut, J. 1783. *The genera vermium in the orders of the Intestina and Mollusca Linnaei.* **Blainville, H. M. de.** 1828. Vers. *Dictionnaire des sciences naturelles,* vol. 57. **Bohadsch, J. B.** 1761. *De quibusdam animalibus marinis.* **Delle Chiaje, S.** 1823. *Memorie sulla storia e notomia degli animali sensa vertebre del regno di Napoli,* vol. I. **Gegenbaur, C.** 1859. *Grundzüge der vergleichenden Anatomie.* Later edition, 1878. **Gesner, C.** 1558. *Medicus Tigurinus. Historiae animalium, liber III, qui est de piscium et aquatilium animantium natura.* **Grube, E.** 1837. Versuch einer Anatomie des Sipunculus nudus. Müller's Arch. Anat. Physiol. **Hatschek, B.** 1881. Entwicklungsgeschichte von Echiurus und die systematische Stellung der Echiuridae. Arbeiten Zool. Inst. Univ. Wien 3. 1888. *Lehrbuch der Zoologie.* **Krohn, A.** 1851. Über die Larve des Sipunculus nudus. Muller's Arch. Anat. Physiol. **Lamarck, J. B.** 1816. *Histoire naturelle des animaux sans vertèbres,* vol. 3. **Lang, A.** 1888. *Lehrbuch der vergleichenden Anatomie.* **Lankester, E. R.** 1885. Polyzoa. *Encyclopaedia Britannica.* 9 ed., vol. 19. **Leuckart, F. S.** 1828. *Breves animalium quorundam maxima ex parte marinorum descriptiones.* **Linnaeus, C.** 1767. *Systema naturae.* 12 ed., vol. 3. **Martin, M.** 1786. *Observations on marine worms, insects, etc.* **Montagu, G.** 1804. Description of several marine animals found on the south coast of Devonshire. Trans. Linnaean Soc. London 7. **Müller, Max.** 1850. Über eine den Sipunculiden verwandte Wurmlarve. Müller's Arch. Anat. Physiol. **Pallas, P.** 1774. *Spicilegia zoologica,* fasc. 10. **Pennant, T.** 1812. *British zoology,* vol. IV. **Quatrefages, A. de.** 1847. Mémoire sur l'echine de Gaertner. Ann. Sci. Natur., Zool., ser. 3, vol. 7. **Rondelet, G.** 1555. *Libri de piscibus marinis. De insectes et zoophytes liber,* caput III. **Sedgwick, A.** 1898. *A student's textbook of zoology.* Vol. I.

LATER LITERATURE

Adolph, E. 1936. Differential permeability to water and osmotic changes in Phascolosoma. Jour. Cell. Comp. Physiol. 9. **Andreae, J.** 1881. Anatomie und Histologie des Sipunculus nudus. Ztschr. Wissensch. Zool. 36. **Andrew, W., and N. Andrew.** 1953. Some sipunculid worms of the Bimini region. Amer. Mus. Novitates, no. 1617. **Andrews, E.** 1889. Reproductive organs of Phascolosoma gouldi. Zool. Anz. 12. 1890a. Body-cavity fluid of Sipunculus gouldi. Johns Hopkins Univ. Circulars 9. 1890b. Anatomy of Sipunculus gouldi. Studies Biol. Lab. Johns Hopkins Univ. 4. **Arvy, L.** 1952. Sur deux parasites de Phascolion strombi. Bull. Lab. Maritime Dinard, fasc. 36. **Arvy, L., and M. Gabe.** 1952. Particularités histochimiques du tube digestif de Phascolion strombi. Bull. Lab.

Maritime Dinard, fasc. 36. **Arvy, L.,** and **M. Prenant.** 1952. Loxosoma nitschei sur les phascoliens de Dinard. Bull. Lab. Maritime Dinard, fasc. 36. **Augener, H.** 1903. Zur Kenntnis der Gephyreen. Arch. Naturgesch. 69, pt. 1. **Awati, P.,** and **L. Pradhan.** 1935, 1936. Anatomy of Dendrostoma signifer. Jour. Univ. Bombay 3, pt. V; 4, pt. V. **Baglioni, S.** 1905. Über das Sauerstoffbedürfnis des Zentralnervensystems bei Seetiere. Ztschr. Allg. Physiol. 5. **Baldwin, E.,** and **W. Yudkin.** 1950. The annelid phosphagen, with a note on phosphagen in Echinodermata and Protochordata. Proc. Roy. Soc. London 136B. **Baltzer, F.** 1931. Sipunculida. *In* **W. Kükenthal** and **T. Krumbach** (eds.), *Handbuch der Zoologie,* Bd. II. **Beklemischev, V.** 1916. Sur les turbellariés parasites de la côte Mourmanne. II. Rhabdocoela. Trav. Soc. Natural. Pétrograd, livr. 4, vol. 45. **Benham, W. B.** 1904, 1905. The sipunculids of New Zealand. Trans. Proc. New Zealand Inst. 36, 37. 1922. Gephyrea inermia. Austral. Antarct. Exped. 1911–1914, Scient. Repts., ser. C, vol. 6, pt. 5. **Bobin, G.,** and **M. Prenant.** 1953a, b. Les loxosomes du Phascolion strombi. Arch. Zool. Exp. Gén. 90, Notes et Revue, nos. 1, 3. 1953c. Sur trois loxosomes méditerranéens. Bull. Inst. Océanogr. Monaco, no. 1030. **Bocquet, C.,** and **J. Stock.** 1957. Copépodes parasites d'invertébrés des côtes de France. IV. Kon. Nederland. Akad. Wetensch. Proc., ser. C, Biol. Med. Sci. 60. **Botazzi, F.** 1908. Osmotischer Druck und elektrische Leitfähigkeit des Flussigkeiten der Organismen. Ergebn. Physiol. 7. **Bouvier, E.** 1894. Association de vers du genre Aspidosiphon avec les polypes madréporaires et un mollusque bivalve. C. R. Acad. Sci. Paris 119. 1895. Le commensalisme chez certains polypes madréporaires. Ann. Sci. Natur., Zool., ser. 7, vol. 20. **Brandt, A.** 1870. Anatomisch-histologische Untersuchungen über Sipunculus nudus. Mém. Acad. Sci. Pétersbourg, ser. 7, vol. 16, no. 8. **Brumpt, E.** 1897. L'histoire de Phascolion strombi. Arch. Zool. Exp. Gén., ser. 3, vol. 5. **Bülow, C.** 1883. Über Theilung mit nachfolgender Regeneration bei Würmer. Biol. Centralbl. 3. **Buytendyk, F.** 1909. Zur Physiologie der Urnen von Sipunculus. Biol. Centralbl. 29. **Cantacuzene, J.** 1922. Sur le rôle agglutinant des urnes chez Sipunculus. C. R. Soc. Biol. Paris 87. **Cantacuzene, J.,** and **F. Vles.** 1922. Sur le facteur électrique dans les réactions du sang chez Sipunculus. C. R. Soc. Biol. Paris 87. **Chaet, A.** 1955. Further studies on the toxic factor in Phascolosoma. Biol. Bull. 109. **Chamberlin, R.** 1920a. Notes on the sipunculids of Laguna Beach. Jour. Entomol. Zool. 12. 1920b. Gephyrea collected by the Canadian Arctic Expedition 1913–1918. Rept. Canadian Arctic Exped. 9, pt. D. **Chapheau, M.** 1928. Recherches sur la respiration de hématies du siponcle. Bull. Sta. Biol. Arcachon 25. **Chapman, G.** 1955. Fauna and flora of the Azores. III. Gephyrea. Ann. Mag. Natur. Hist., ser. 12, vol. 8. **Chin, T.,** and **C. Wu.** 1950. Diatoms in the intestine of Amoy Sipunculida. Lingnan Sci. Jour. 23. **Claparède, É.** 1863. *Anatomie und Entwicklungsgeschichte wirbelloser Thiere an der Küste von Normandie.* 1867. Sur le Loxosoma kersteini. Ann. Sci. Natur., Zool., ser. 5, vol. 8. **Cohnheim, O.** 1911. Über das Gaswechsel von Tieren mit glatter und quergestreifter Muskulatur. Ztschr. Physiol. Chem. 76. **Collin, A.** 1892. Gephyreen gesammelt während der Reise S.M.S. Prinz Adalbert. Arch. Naturgesch. 58, pt. 1. 1901. Die Gephyreen der deutschen Expedition S.M.S. Gazelle. Arch. Naturgesch. 67, Festschrift Ed. von Martens, Beiheft. **Cordero, E.,** and **A. de Mello-Leitao.** 1952. Duas novas especies do genero Aspidosiphon da Ilha da Trinidade. Mem. Inst. Oswaldo Cruz 50. **Cuénot, L.** 1891. Études sur le sang et les glandes lymphatiques, pt. 2. Arch. Zool. Exp. Gén., ser. 2, vol. 9. 1900. Le phascolosome. *In* **L. Boutan** (ed.), *Zoologie descriptive des invertebres,* vol. I. 1901. La valeur respiratoire du liquide cavitaire chez quelques invertébrés. Trav. Sta. Zool. Arcachon 5. 1902a. Organes agglutinants et organes cilio-phagocytaires.

Arch. Zool. Exp. Gén., ser. 3, vol. 10. 1902b. Contribution à la faune du Bassin d'Arcachon. II. Sipunculiens. Bull. Soc. Scient. Arcachon Stat. Biol. 6. 1913. Excrétion et phagocytosis chez les sipunculiens. C. R. Soc. Biol. Paris 74. 1922. Sipunculiens. Faune de France, no. 4. **Damboviceanu, A.** 1926. Détermination de certains constituants du plasma de Sipunculus. C. R. Soc. Biol. Paris 95. **Danielssen, D.,** and **J. Koren.** 1880. New northern Gephyrea. Ann. Mag. Natur. Hist., ser. 5, vol. 6. 1881. Gephyrea. Norweg. North Atlantic Exped. 1876–1878. **Dawydoff, C.** 1930. Quelques observations sur Pelagosphaera. Bull. Soc. Zool. France 55. **Dekhuyzen, M.** 1921. Les parois de certains animaux marins halisotoniques sont biologiquement semiperméables. Arch. Neérland. Physiol. 5. **Delaunay, H.** 1926. Sur l'excrétion azotée de vers. C. R. Soc. Biol. Paris 95. 1927. Recherches biochimiques sur l'excrétion azotée des invertébrés. Bull. Sta. Biol. Arcachon 24. 1931. L'excrétion azotée des invertébrés. Biol. Reviews Cambridge Philos. Soc. 6. **Dogiel, V.** 1907. Schizocystis sipunculi. Arch. Protistenk. 8. **Dörler, A.** 1900. Neue und wenig bekannte rhabdocöle Turbellarien. Ztschr. Wissensch. Zool. 68. **Duchateau, G.,** *et al.* 1952. Acides aminés non proteinques des tissus chez les vers. Arch. Internation. Physiol. 60. **Edmonds, S. J.** 1955, 1956. Australian Sipunculoidea I, II. Austral. Jour. Marine Freshwater Research 6, 7. 1957a. Respiratory metabolism of Dendrostomum cymodoceae. Austral. Jour. Marine Freshwater Research 8. 1957b. The metabolism of nitrogen compounds in Dendrostomum cymodoceae. Austral. Jour. Marine Freshwater Research 8. **Enriques, P.** 1903. I corpi pigmentati di Sipunculus nudus. Arch. Zool. Italiano 1. **Etherington, D.** 1953. On a sporozoan in the coelomic corpuscles of Phascolosoma. Parasitology 43. **Fischer, W.** 1895. Die Gephyreen des naturhistorischen Museums zu Hamburg. Abhandl. Gebiete Naturwissensch. Naturwiss. Verein Hamburg 13. 1896. Gephyreen. Ergebn. Hamburg. Magalhaens. Sammelreise 3. 1914a. Gephyrea. *In* **W. Michaelsen,** Beiträge zur Kenntnis der Meeresfauna Westafrikas 1. 1914b. Weitere Mitteilungen über die Gephyreen des naturhistorischen Museums zu Hamburg. Mitt. Naturhist. Mus. Hamburg 31. 1916. Die Gephyreenausbeute der deutschen Tiefsee-Expedition. Zool. Anz. 48. 1919a. Gephyreen der südwestküste Australiens. Zool. Anz. 50. 1919b. Über die Gattung Lithacrosiphon. Zool. Anz. 50. 1921. Gephyreen. Swedish Scientific Expeditions to Australia 1910–1913. Kong. Svenske Vetensk. Akad. Handl. 61. 1922a. Gephyreen des Reichmuseums zu Stockholm. Arkiv Zoologi 14, no. 19. 1922b. Westindische Gephyreen. Zool. Anz. 55. 1922c. Gephyreen der deutschen Tiefsee-Expedition. Wissensch. Ergebn. Dtsch. Tiefsee-Exped. 22, Heft 1. 1923. Gephyreen des Golfes von Siam. Vidensk. Meddel. Dansk Naturhist. Foren 76. 1925. Echiuridae, Sipunculidae, Priapulidae. Die Tierwelt der Nord- und Ostsee, Lief. 1, Teil VId. 1926a. Sipunculiden und Echiuriden der Hamburger Südsee-Expedition 1908–1909. Mitt. Zool. Staatsinst. Zool. Mus. Hamburg 42. 1926b. Sipunculoidea und Echiuroidea. *In* **W. Michaelsen** and **R. Hartmeyer** (eds.), Die Fauna Südwest-Australiens 5, pt. 3. 1928. Die Sipunculiden, Priapuliden und Echiuriden der Arktis. Fauna Arctica 5. **Fisher, W. K.** 1928. New Sipunculoidea from California. Ann. Mag. Natur. Hist., ser. 10, vol. 1. 1947. New genera and species of echiuroid and sipunculoid worms. Proc. U.S. Nation. Mus. 97. 1950a. The sipunculid genus Phascolosoma. Ann. Mag. Natur. Hist., ser. 12, vol. 3. 1950b. Two new subgenera and a new species of Siphonosoma. Ann. Mag. Natur. Hist., ser. 12, vol. 3. 1952. The sipunculid worms of California and Baja California. Proc. U.S. Nation. Mus. 102. 1954a. The genus Xenosiphon. Ann. Mag. Natur. Hist., ser. 12, vol. 7. 1954b. A swimming Sipunculus. Ann. Mag. Natur. Hist., ser. 12, vol. 7. **Florkin, M.** 1932. La courbe de dissociation de l'oxyhémérythrine. C. R. Acad. Sci. Paris 195. 1933.

Recherches sur les hémérythrines. Arch. Internation. Physiol. 36. 1937. Taux des substances réducteurs fermentescibles dans le milieu interieur des invertébrés. Bull. Soc. Chim. Biol. 19. **Florkin, M.**, and **G. Duchateau.** 1942. Sur le métabolisme de l'azote chez le siponcle. Arch. Internation. Physiol. 52. **Florkin, M.**, and **R. Houet.** 1937. Nouvelle démonstration de la surcharge en urée des hématies du siponcle. Arch. Internation. Physiol. 45. **Gabe, M.** 1953. Données histologiques sur la neurosécrétion chez quelques sipunculiens. Bull. Lab. Maritime Dinard, fasc. 38. **Gerould, J.** 1903. Studies on the embryology of the Sipunculidae. Mark Anniversary Vol. 1906. The development of Phascolosoma. Zool. Jahrb., Abt. Anat. 23. 1913. The sipunculids of the eastern coast of North America. Proc. U.S. Nation. Mus. 44. 1938. The eyes and nervous system of Phascolosoma verrilli and other sipunculids. Trav. Sta. Zool. Wimereux 13. **Gross, W.** 1954. Osmotic responses in Dendrostomum. Jour. Exptl. Biol. 31. **Grube, E.** 1868. Über Loxosiphon, Cloeosiphon und einige Phascolosomen. Jahresber. Schles. Gesellsch. Vaterland. Cultur, for 1867, 45. **Harmer, S. F.** 1915. The Polyzoa of the Siboga Expedition. Pt. I. Siboga Exped. Monogr. 28a. **Harms, W.** 1920. Bauchnervenstrang und Spindelmuskel von Physcosoma. Zool. Anz. 52. 1921. Morphologische und causalanalytische Untersuchungen über die Internephridialorgane von Physcosoma. Arch. Entw'mech. Organ. 47. 1934. Sipunculiden. *Handwörterbuch der Naturwissenschaften.* 2 ed., vol. 9. **Harms, W.**, and **O. Dragendorff.** 1933. Osmotische Untersuchungen an Physcosoma lurco. Ztschr. Wissensch. Zool. 143. **Hatschek, B.** 1883. Über Entwicklung von Sipunculus nudus. Arbeit. Zool. Inst. Univ. Wien 5. **Heath, H.** 1910. Pelagosphaera. Biol. Bull. 18. **Hedgpeth, J.** 1954. Miscellaneous Vermes, Gulf of Mexico. U.S. Fish and Wildlife Service, Fishery Bull. 89. **Henze, M.** 1910. Über den Einfluss des Sauerstoffdrucks auf den Gaswechsel einiger Meerestiere. Biochem. Ztschr. 26. **Hérubel, M.** 1902. Sur certains éléments peritonéaux du phascolosome. Bull. Soc. Zool. France 27. 1907. Recherches sur les sipunculides. Mém. Soc. Zool. France 20. 1908. Géphyriens. Exped. Antarctique Française 1903–1905, vol. 7. 1924. Quelques echiurides et sipunculides des côtes du Maroc et Mauritanie. Bull. Soc. Sci. Natur. Maroc 4. **Hilton, W.** 1917. The central nervous system of a sipunculid. Jour. Entomol. Zool. 9. **Ikeda, I.** 1904. The Gephyrea of Japan. Jour. College Sci. Univ. Tokyo 20, art. 4. 1912. Studies on some sporozoan parasites of sipunculoids. I. Arch. Protistenk. 25. 1924. Further notes on the Gephyrea of Japan. Japan. Jour. Zool. 1. **Jourdan, E.** 1891. Les corpuscles sensitifs et les glandes cutanées des géphyriens inermes. Ann. Sci. Natur. Zool., ser. 7, vol. 12. **Keferstein, W.** 1862. Beiträge zur Kenntnis der Gattung Phascolosoma. Ztschr. Wissensch. Zool. 12. 1865. Beiträge zur anatomischen und systematischen Kenntnis der Sipunculiden. Ztschr. Wissensch. Zool. 15. 1866. Über einige amerikanischen Sipunculiden. Ztschr. Wissensch. Zool. 17. **Keferstein, W.**, and **E. Ehlers.** 1861. Untersuchungen über die Anatomie des Sipunculus nudus. In *Zoologische Beiträge gesammelt in Winter 1859–1860 in Neapel und Messina.* **Kelley, Louise.** 1953. The histology of the nephridia of Golfingia gouldi. Thesis, Library, Fisk University, Nashville, Tenn. **Kesteven, H.** 1903. A new species of Dendrostoma. Records Austral. Mus. 5. **Knudsen, J.** 1944. A gephyrean, a polychaete, and a bivalve living together commensalistically in the Indo-Malayan seas. Vidensk. Meddel. Dansk Naturhist. Foren. 108. **Koller, G.** 1936. Beobachtungen an den Nephridien von Physcosoma japonicum. Die Naturwissenschaften 24. 1939. Über die Nephridien von Physcosoma japonicum. Verhandl. Dtsch. Zool. Gesellsch. 41, in Zool. Anz. Suppl. Bd. 12. **Kollmann, M.** 1908. Recherches sur les leucocytes et les tissus lymphoides des invertébrés. Ann. Sci. Natur., Zool., ser. 9, vol. 8. **Koren, J.**, and

D. Danielssen. 1875. Bidrag til norske Gephyrees Naturhistorie. Nyt Mag. Naturv. 21. 1877. Contribution to the natural history of the Norwegian Gephyreae. Fauna littoralis Norvegiae, pt. 3. **Kozloff, E.** 1953. Collastoma pacifica, a rhabdocoel from the gut of Dendrostoma. Jour. Parasitol. 39. **Krukenberg, C.** 1880. Blutfarbstoffe der Würmer. *Vergleichende physiologische Studien.* I. Reihe, 3 Abt. **Ladreyt, F.** 1903. Sur le rôle de certains éléments figurés chez Sipunculus. C. R. Acad. Sci. Paris 137. **Lanchester, W.** 1905. The sipunculids and echiuroids collected during the Skeet Expedition to the Malay Peninsula. Proc. Zool. Soc. London. **Lankester, E.** 1872. A contribution to the knowledge of haemoglobin. Proc. Roy. Soc. London 21. 1873. Summary of zoological observations made at Naples. Ann. Mag. Natur. Hist., ser. 4, vol. 11. 1885. Golfingia macintoshii, a new sipunculid. Trans. Linnaean Soc. London, ser. 2, vol. 2. **Leroy, P.** 1942. Sipunculiens d'Indochine. Note Inst. Océanogr. Indochinie 40. **Lindroth, Anne.** 1941. Echiuriden, Sipunculida, und Enteropneusta aus dem Skagerak 1933. Zool. Bidrag 20. **Love, W.** 1955. Molecular weight of hemerythrin of Phascolosoma gouldi. Biol. Bull. 109. **MacGinitie, G.,** and **N. MacGinitie.** 1949. *Natural history of marine animals.* **Mack, H.** 1902. Das Centralnervensystem des Sipunculus nudus. Arbeit. Zool. Inst. Univ. Wien 13. **Marrian, G.** 1927. A note on hemerythrin. Jour. Exptl. Biol. 4. **Metalnikoff, S.** 1900. Sipunculus nudus. Ztschr. Wissensch. Zool. 68. **Meyer, A.** 1929. Über Cölombewimperung und cölomatische Kreislaufsysteme bei Wirbellosen. II. Sipunculoiden. Ztschr. Wissensch. Zool. 135. **Michaelsen, W.** 1889. Die Gephyreen von Süd Georgia. Jahrb. Hamburg. Wissensch. Anstalten, Mitt. Naturhist. Mus. Hamburg, for 1888, 6, no. 3. **Mingazzini, P.** 1905. Un Gefireo pelagico: Pelagosphaera. Rendic. Accad. Lincei, Cl. Sci. Fis. Mat. Natur., ser. 5, vol. 14. **Moltschanov, L.** 1909. Nephridies de Phascolion. Bull. Acad. Sci. St. Pétersbourg, ser. 6, vol. 3. **Monro, C.** 1931. Polychaeta, Oligochaeta, Echiuroidea and Sipunculoidea. Great Barrier Reef Expedition 1928–1929, Scient. Repts. 4, pt. 1. **Murina, V.** 1957. Sipunculids collected on the first trip of the complex antarctic expedition of the Ob in 1956. Zool. Zhurnal 36. **Nickerson, Margaret.** 1899. Intracellular differentiation in gland cells of Phascolosoma. Science 9; Zool. Jahrb., Abt. Anat. 13. 1901. Sensory and glandular epidermal organs in Phascolosoma. Jour. Morphol. 17. **Nilus, G.** 1909. Notiz über Loxosoma murmanica und brumpti. Trav. Soc. Imper. Natural. St. Pétersbourgh, livr. 1, vol. 40. **Ohuye, T.** 1937. On the coelomic corpuscles in the body fluid of some invertebrates. VII. Sci. Repts. Tohoku Univ., ser. 4, Biol. 12. 1942. On the blood corpuscles and hemopoiesis of Dendrostoma minor. Sci. Repts. Tohoku Univ., ser. 4, Biol. 17. **Olson, M.** 1940. Histology of the retractor muscles of Phascolosoma gouldi. Biol. Bull. 78. **Osburn, R. C.** 1912. The Bryozoa of the Woods Hole region. Bull. U.S. Bur. Fisheries 30. **Paul, G.** 1910. Petalosoma minutum. Zool. Jahrb., Abt. Anat. 29. **Peebles, Florence,** and **D. Fox.** 1933. The structure, functions, and general reactions of Dendrostoma zostericola. Bull. Scripps Inst. Oceanogr. Tech. Ser. 3. **Pérez, C.** 1924, 1925. Le complexe ethologique du Phascolion strombi. Bull. Soc. Zool. France 49, 50. **Pickford, Grace.** 1947. Sipunculida. *Encyclopaedia Britannica,* vol. 20. **Przylecki, S.** 1926. La dégradation de l'acid urique chez les êtres vivants. 5. Arch. Internation. Physiol. 27. **Quintin, R.** 1900. Communication osmotique chez l'invertébré marin. C. R. Acad. Sci. Paris 131. **Ricketts, E.,** and **J. Calvin.** 1939. *Between Pacific tides.* **Robertson, J.** 1953. Further studies on ionic regulation in marine invertebrates. Jour. Exptl. Biol. 30. **Roche, J.** 1933a. Sur le pigment respiratoire des hématies du siponcle. C. R. Soc. Biol. Paris 112. 1933b. La composition de l'hémérythrine. Skand. Arch. Physiol. 69. **Roche, A.,** and **J. Roche.** 1935. Pression osmotique et poids moléculaires de l'hémérythrine du siponcle. Bull. Soc. Chim. Biol. 17. **Roger, J.** 1952. Classe du Gephyriens. *In* **J. Piveteau** (ed.), *Traité de paléontologie*, vol. II. **Roule, L.** 1907. Annélides et Gephyriens. *In* **A. Milne Edwards** and **E. Perrier** (eds.), *Expédition Scientifique Travailleur et Talisman*, vol. 8. **Sato, H.** 1930. Biological survey of Mutsu Bay. 15. Sipunculoidea. Sci. Repts. Tohoku Univ., ser. 4, Biol. 5. 1934. Sipunculoidea collected by the Soyo-Maru Expedition. Sci. Repts. Tohoku Univ., ser. 4, Biol. 9. 1935. Sipunculoidea of the West Caroline Islands. Sci. Repts. Tohoku Univ., ser. 4, Biol. 10. 1937. Sipunculoidea obtained in northeast Honshu, Japan. Saito Ho-on Kai Mus., Research Bull., no. 12, Zool., no. 4. 1939. Studies on the Sipunculoidea of Japan. Sci. Repts. Tohoku Univ., ser. 4, Biol. 14. **Schleip, W.** 1934a. Die Regeneration des Rüssels von Phascolion strombi. Ztschr. Wissensch. Zool. 145. 1934b. Der Regenerationsstrang bei Phascolosoma minutum. Ztschr. Wissensch. Zool. 146. 1935. Die Regenerationsvorgänge nach Amputation des Hinterendes von Phascolosoma minutum. Ztschr. Wissensch. Zool. 147. **Selenka, E.** 1875. Eifurchung und Larvenbildung von Phascolosoma elongatum. Ztschr. Wissensch. Zool. 25. 1885. Report on the Gephyrea collected by H.M.S. Challenger. Rept. Scient. Results Voyage Challenger, pt. 36, Zool. 13. **Selenka, E., G. de Man,** and **C. Bülow.** 1883. Die Sipunculiden. *In* **C. Semper,** Reisen im Archipel der Philippinen, Teil II, Bd. 4, Abt. 1. **Selensky, W.** 1908. Untersuchungen über die Urnen der Sipunculiden. Ztschr. Wissensch. Zool. 90. **Sellier, J.** 1900–1901. La lipase chez quelques groupes d'animaux inférieurs. Trav. Sta. Zool. Arcachon 5. **Semper, C.** 1864. Reisebericht. Ztschr. Wissensch. Zool. 14. **Senna, A.** 1906. Sulla strutura di alcune larve (Pelagosphaera). Raccolte planctoniche fatte della R. Nave Liguria nel viaggio di circumnavigazione 1903–1905, vol. 1, fasc. 1–2. **Setna, S.** 1931. On three new gregarines. Records Indian Mus. 33. **Shipley, A. E.** 1890. On Phymosoma varians. Quart. Jour. Microsc. Sci. 31. 1891. On a new species of Phymosoma. Quart. Jour. Microsc. Sci. 32. 1892. On Onchnesoma steenstrupi. Quart. Jour. Microsc. Sci. 33. 1898a. Sipunculoidea collected at the Loyalty Islands and in New Britain. Zool. Results A. Willey, pt. 2. 1898b. Gephyrean worms collected at Rotuma and Funafuti. Proc. Zool. Soc. London. 1902. Sipunculoidea with an account of Lithacrosiphon. *In* **J. S. Gardiner** (ed.), *Fauna and geography of the Maldive and Laccadive Archipelagoes*, vol. I. 1903. Report on the Gephyrea. *In* **W. A. Herdman** (ed.), *Report Pearl Oyster Fisheries of the Gulf of Manaar*, pt. 1, no. 3. 1910. Sipunculoidea. *Cambridge natural history*, vol. II. **Shitamori, K.** 1936. Histology of the integument of Siphonosoma. Jour. Sci. Hiroshima Univ., ser. B, Zool. 4. **Sluiter, C.** 1881. Ueber die Segmentalorgane und Geschlechtsdrüsen einiger Sipunculiden. Zool. Anz. 4. 1882. Beiträge zu der Kenntnis der Gephyreen aus dem malayisches Archipelago. I, II. Natuurk. Tijdschr. Nederland. Indie 41. 1884, 1886. Beiträge, etc. III, IV. Natuurk. Tijdschr. Nederland. Indie 43, 45. 1891. Die Evertebraten aus der Sammlung in Niederlandisch-Indien in Batavia. III. Die Gephyreen. Natuurk. Tijdschr. Nederland. Indie 50. 1900. Gephyriens provenant des campagnes de l'Hirondelle et de Princesse Alice. Resultats Campagnes Scient. Monaco, fasc. 15. 1902. Die Sipunculiden und Echiuriden der Siboga-Expedition. Siboga Exped., Monogr. 25. 1912. Géphyriens provenant des campagnes de la Princesse Alice. Resultats Campagnes Scient. Monaco, fasc. 36. **Southern, R.** 1913. Gephyrea of the coasts of Ireland. Dept. Agricult. Technical Instruction Ireland, Fisheries Branch, Scient. Investigations, no. 3. **Spengel, J. W.** 1907. Eine verkannte Sipunculus-Larve. Zool. Anz. 31. 1912. Einige Organisationsverhältnisse von Sipunculusarten. Verhandl. Dtsch. Zool. Gesellsch. 22. 1913a. Sipunculoidea. *Handbuch der Naturwissenschaften*, 1 ed., vol. 9. 1913b. Zur Organisation und

Systematik der Gattung Sipunculus. Verhandl. Dtsch. Zool. Gesellsch. 23. **Stehle, G.** 1952. Differenzieringen des Verdauungstraktus von Phascolosoma elongatum. Annales Univ. Saraviensis, Naturwiss. 1, no. 4. 1953. Anatomie und Histologie von Phascolosoma elongatum. Annales Univ. Saraviensis, Naturwiss. 2, no. 3. 1954. Die gewebezerstörende Wirkung von Cercarien in Rüssel und Gehirn verschiedener Sipunculiden. Ztschr. Parasitenk. 16. **Steinbach, H. B.** 1940. The distribution of electrolytes in Phascolosoma muscle. Biol. Bull. 78. **Stephen, A.** 1914. Sipunculids of the John Murray Expedition to the Red Sea and Indian Ocean. John Murray Exped., Scient. Repts. 7. 1934. The Sipunculidae of Scottish and adjacent waters. Proc. Roy. Physical Soc. Edinburgh 22. 1941. The Sipunculidae collected by the Discovery. Discovery Repts. 21. 1942. Notes on the intertidal sipunculids of the Cape Province and Natal. Annals Natal Mus. 10. 1948. Sipunculids. Brit. Austral. New Zealand Antarctic Exped. Repts., ser. B, vol. 5, pt. 4. 1952. Gephyrea. Manihine Exped. Gulf Aqaba. Bull. Brit. Mus. (Natur. Hist.), Zool. 1, no. 8. **Stephen, A., and J. Robertson.** 1952. A preliminary report on the Sipunculidae of Zanzibar. Proc. Roy. Soc. Edinburgh 64B. **Sulima, A.** 1914. Beiträge zur Kenntnis des Harnsäurestoffwechsels niederer Tiere. Ztschr. Biol. 63. **Ten Broeke, Ada.** 1925. Westindische Sipunculiden. Bijdragen tot de Dierkunde 24. **Teuscher, R.** 1874. Notiz über Sipunculus und Phascolosoma. Jena. Ztschr. Naturwiss. 8. **Théel, H.** 1875. Recherches sur le Phascolion strombi. Kungl. Svenska Vetensk. Akad. Handl. 14, no. 2. 1905. Northern and arctic invertebrates in the collection of the Swedish State Museum. I. Sipunculids. Kungl. Svenska Vetensk. Akad. Handl. 39, no. 1. 1911. Sipunculids of the Swedish Antarctic Expedition 1901–1903. Kungl. Svenska Vetensk. Akad. Handl. 47. **Uexküll, J. von.** 1896. Zur Muskel- und Nervenphysiologie von Sipunculus. Ztschr. Biol. 33. 1903. Die biologische Bauplan von Sipunculus. Ztschr. Biol. 44. **Vogt, C.** 1876. Sur le Loxosoma des phascolosomes. Arch. Zool. Exp. Gén. 5. **Volkonsky, K.** 1933. Étude cytologique des cellules sanguines des sipunculidés. Bull. Biol. France Belgique 67. **Wahl, B.** 1910. Das Genus Collastoma. Sitzungsber. Akad. Wissensch. Wien, Math. Naturwiss. Cl. 119, Abt. 1. **Walcott, C.** 1911. Middle Cambrian annelids. Smithson. Miscell. Collections 57, no. 5. **Ward, H.** 1891. On some points in the anatomy and physiology of Sipunculus nudus. Bull. Mus. Comp. Zool. Harvard 21. **Wegener, F.** 1938. Beitrag zur Kenntnis der Rüsselregeneration der Sipunculiden. Ztschr. Wissensch. Zool. 150. **Wesenberg-Lund, Elise.** 1930. Sipunculidae. Danish Ingolf Exped., vol. 4, pt. 7. 1932. The Godthaab Expedition 1928. Gephyrea. Meddel. om Grönland 79, no. 3. 1933. The collections of gephyreans in the Royal Museum of Natural History of Belgium. Bull. Mus. Roy. Hist. Natur. Belgique 9, no. 6. 1937. The zoology of East Greenland. Gephyreans. Meddel. om Grönland 121, no. 1. 1939. Gephyreans from Swedish waters. Göteborg Kungl. Vetensk. och Vitterhets Samhälles Handl., ser. B, vol. 6, no. 6. 1954a. Sipunculids collected in Oceania. Bull. Mus. Nation. Hist. Natur. Paris, ser. 2, vol. 26. 1954b. Sipunculoidea. Inst. Roy. Sci. Natur. Belgique, Bull. 30, no. 16. 1955a. Gephyrea from Chile. Repts. Lund Univ. Chile Exped. 19. Lunds Univ. Arsskrift, Avd. 2, vol. 51, no. 10. 1955b. Sipunculidae. Repts. Swedish Deep-Sea Exped. 1947–1948, vol. II, Zool., no. 15. **Wilber, C.** 1947. The effect of prolonged starvation on the lipids in Phascolosoma gouldi. Jour. Cell. Comp. Physiol. 29. **Zuckerkandl, E.** 1950. Coelomic pressures in Sipunculus nudus. Biol. Bull. 98.

CHAPTER XXIII

RETROSPECT

As there is no possibility of revising the earlier volumes, advantage is taken here of the availability of a small amount of space to recount some recent advances and comment on some viewpoints. Only brief accounts can be given, and in fact the main purpose is to furnish a bibliography of recent references.

1. Comments on Systematics.—The systematic arrangement of the animal kingdom, even of major groups, has not reached any stability and cannot be expected to do so within foreseeable time. A lack of decisive facts permits every zoologist to have his own opinion. However, many of the main differences concern the rank assigned to groups, and this matter of rank also determines how many phyla are recognized. Any acute observer cannot fail to notice the disease prevalent in zoological systematics today of raising the rank of groups and of assigning high ranks to groups that differ only in minor characters. This raising of ranks might be excused, but not justified, on the ground of providing room for more and more smaller and smaller subdivisions; but in fact it indicates a lack of a sense of judgment as to the worth of morphological differences and an exaggeration of the systematic value of small differences. The author deplores this constant raising of the ranks.

On some points in the systematic arrangement it is possible to take a firm stand. Hemichordata *must* be removed from Chordata and made an independent phylum of invertebrates (discussion, page 199). The concept Gephyrea must be obliterated from zoology (page 611), although no agreement has been reached as to the disposition of the three groups customarily united under this name. In 1946 Fisher proposed a phylum Poeobioidea for an aberrant worm *Poeobius* erroneously considered by its discoverer (Heath, 1930) to constitute a link between annelids and echiuroids. This phylum was unfortunately seized upon by some writers of elementary zoology books who took no notice of the fact that in 1947 Pickford reinvestigated the anatomy of *Poeobius* and found that this worm is simply an aberrant polychaetous annelid. Poeobioidea is therefore to be obliterated. Some zoologists persist in uniting Cnidaria and Ctenophora into one phylum Coelenterata and in including nemerteans in Platyhelminthes. The author considers both courses indefensible. Ctenophora are a sharply delimited group with definite characteristics that entitle them to separate phyletic rank.   It is even not at all settled that they have originated from Cnidaria (but see below).   Nemerteans are of so much higher a grade of structure than flatworms that they can be included with them only by greatly altering and weakening the definition of the latter.   It is further uncertain that nemerteans are descended from flatworms.

In recent years there has been much agitation for the adoption of uniform endings for the higher taxonomic categories, although this agitation has considerably subsided since the idea was rejected by the International Commission for Zoological Nomenclature.   The author is unable to perceive any sense to the idea, and its adoption would involve innumerable name changes, at least of spelling, often etymologically bad.   Certainly in the present state of instability of the zoological system and the lack of agreement about ranks and the prevalent constant changings of rank, the adoption of uniform endings would be futile.

2. Phylum Protozoa.—The Protozoa are the subject of very active research throughout the world, and an immense literature has appeared about them since 1940.   This research follows three main trends: morphological (including taxonomic descriptions), biochemical, and genetic.

a. Electron Microscope Studies.—As applied to Protozoa these have revealed as their main result that cilia (Jakus and Hall, 1946; Bradfield, 1953) and flagella (Brown, 1951; Brown and Cox, 1954; Pitelka and Schooley, 1955) have the same essential structure.   They consist of a bundle of fibers, generally 11, arranged as a pair of central fibers encircled by 9 peripheral fibers (reported by some as double), all enclosed in a sheath.   Pitelka and Schooley, investigating the flagella of 17 species belonging to 10 different groups of flagellates, found that all are structured after this pattern.   Flagella may bear on one or both sides delicate lateral filaments known as *mastigonemes*, or *flimmer*, wanting in cilia, and their sheath may contain longitudinal or spiral fibers, also wanting in cilia; but in general it is impossible to draw any definite distinction between cilia and flagella.   Electron microscope studies of discharged trichocysts of the *Paramecium* type (Jakus and Hall, 1946) show that these consist of an opaque head having the shape of an inverted tack and a long shaft regularly cross-striated.   The same structure was verified by Dragesco and Beyersdorfer (1953) for the discharged trichocysts of seven different species of *Paramecium*.   No light has been shed on the mechanism of elongation at discharge of this type of trichocyst nor of its function.   It is now stated that trichocysts are generated by the kinetosomes (basal bodies) of the cilia (A. Lwoff, 1950).

b. Cortical Structure and Infraciliary System.—Great importance is now placed in morphological and morphogenetic studies of ciliates on the *infraciliary system*, formerly called neuromotor system.   It is revealed by a silver-staining technique (Chatton and Lwoff, 1930; Corliss, 1953a), and the results so obtained have been confirmed by electron microscope photographs. In general the results accord with previous knowledge (I, pages 64–66). Each cilium springs from a basal body, now called *kinetosome;* some find an accessory body below this. The kinetosomes are connected in longitudinal rows by longitudinal fibers, formerly called infraciliary fibrils, now termed *kinetodesmas.* The kinetodesma is situated not below the row of kinetosomes to which it belongs but to its right. Apparently the kinetodesma is not a simple fibril but is compounded of short fibrils, one for each kinetosome, that point anteriorly (Metz, Pitelka, and Westfall, 1953; Metz and Westfall, 1954; Sedar and Porter, 1955). A longitudinal row of kinetosomes plus their kinetodesma constitute a *kinety.* Most ciliates therefore have this system of kineties in the cortex below the pellicle. The number of kineties varies in different ciliates but is more or less constant, within narrow limits, for each species. Apparently all ciliates have kinetosomes, although some as suctorians lack cilia and hence kinetodesmas in the adult state.

A valuable study of cortical structure in *Paramecium* by the electron microscope has been contributed by Sedar and Porter (1955). The pellicle is found to be a double membrane of which the outer component is continuous with the sheaths of the cilia, the inner component with the surface of the cortex; hence there are long spaces between the pellicle and the cortex. The peripheral circle of fibrils in the cilium is continuous internally with the surface of its kinetosome. The latter appears to have a tubular structure. The presence of a polygonal fibrillar system in the surface polygons appears doubtful according to Sedar and Porter, although verified by Metz, Pitelka, and Westfall (1953). Sedar and Porter confirm the presence of a lattice fibrillar net below the infraciliary system, first seen by Gelei (I, page 186), although Metz, Pitelka, and Westfall found no evidence of its existence.

The silver technique also reveals the buccal organelles, that is, the ciliary provision of the oral region and cytopharynx when present. The pattern of the buccal organelles is now considered of paramount importance in the systematics of ciliates. It appears that the much copied figure of the cytopharynx of *Paramecium* (I, Fig. 13A) is erroneous in that there is no lattice of kinetodesmas in the pharynx wall. This wall bears only the penniculus, the quadrulus (I, page 187), and a set of ridges (Ehret and Powers, 1957; Yusa, 1957). A motorium is nonexistent.

c. Morphogenetic Role of Kinetosomes.—The kinetosomes have genetic continuity; they reproduce by division, hence propagate indefinitely, but their activities are affected by cytoplasmic conditions. They play the dominant role in morphogenetic processes in ciliates as fission, regeneration, and various reorganizations (Lwoff, 1950; Corliss, 1953b; Weisz,

1954).   Morphogenesis in ciliates is vested in the kinetosomes; internal structures are of no importance except that a piece of macronucleus is necessary.   In many holotrichs the kineties are equivalent and all participate in morphogenetic processes.   From this condition there are gradations to ciliates in which one or a few of the midventral kineties are specialized as *stomatogenic kineties* that control polarity and development and maintenance of surface organelles.   In case of fission some of their kinetosomes propagate a group of kinetosomes occupying a small area (*anarchic field*).   These arrange in rows and reproduce the new mouth and buccal organelles for the posterior fission product (*opisthe*).   In the most specialized cases, the hypotrichous ciliates, all the old surface organelles dedifferentiate and disappear in fission and regenerations; an anarchic field of kinetosomes originates as above; these arrange into a pattern and migrate to the appropriate places where they generate the new organelles.

In flagellates the basal bodies or blepharoblasts of the flagella or centrioles when present play the same morphogenetic role as the kinetosomes of ciliates.   In fission they divide and the new granule generates the flagellum and related organelles (I, Fig. 22).   In the very complicated poly- and hypermastigote flagellates found in the intestine of termites and cockroaches (I, pages 113–118) the daughter centriole at fission generates the new flagellar bands, parabasals, axostyles, etc. (Cleveland, 1957b).

d. Mechanisms of Locomotion.—Little progress has been made toward an explanation of amoeboid movement and other forms of protoplasmic streaming.   The present status of the subject is reviewed by Noland (1957).   Some version of a gelation-solation theory (I, page 121) no doubt is basic to explanations of amoeboid movement.   Noland points out that mere gelation of the surface layer of the advancing pseudopod will not generate sufficient contractile force.   Folding and unfolding of long protein molecules with energy furnished by adenosine triphosphate as in muscle contraction may be involved.   Noland brings forward evidence that the surface of the amoeba may be covered with a thin layer of slime.

The manner in which a flagellum moves the flagellate seems to have been finally elucidated (Brown, 1945; Lowndes, 1945, 1947).   The spiral undulation passes along the flagellum from base to tip, never in the reverse direction, and has the same action as the inclined blade of a propeller.   Of course, there is no hint of how the spiral undulation is caused or the role of the basal body therein.

e. Cycles.—An important advance in the knowledge of protozoan life cycles is the demonstration of the occurrence of *pre-erythrocytic* stages in malarial parasites.   This was first indicated for species of bird malaria by Huff and Bloom (1935), Raffaele (1936), and James and Tate (1938), and more complete accounts appear in Huff and Coulston (1944, 1947) and Huff (1947). Following the demonstration of such stages in the life cycles of bird plasmodia, Shortt (1948) and Shortt and associates (1948, 1949, 1951, 1954) showed that these stages also occur in mammalian plasmodia. These findings prove that the classical story of the life cycle of malarial parasites contains a major error. The sporozoites injected into bird or mammal by the bite of an infected mosquito do *not* enter the red blood cells. Instead they pass into body tissues, mainly the liver in mammals, various blood-forming and endothelial tissues in birds, and there multiply by schizogony, producing one or more generations of merozoites that finally enter the red blood corpuscles. This finding explains the previously inexplicable fact that following infection some time elapses, usually several days, before infected red corpuscles can be found in the victim. Shortt and associates also pointed out the great difference in the course of the disease produced by the bite of an infected mosquito and that resulting from injection of infected blood.

In regard to cycles in ciliates, Sonneborn (1950a, 1954), verifying Diller (I, page 176), showed that the account of endomixis in *Paramecium* is erroneous and in fact there is no such process. Instead the rhythms in fission rate (I, page 177) are caused by a recurrent process of autogamy in which without conjugation the micronuclei behave as in conjugation but the products of the last micronuclear division fuse to produce a syncaryon. Sonneborn proved that autogamy in nonconjugating cultures is necessary for survival of clones, and in its absence the line dies out after a maximum of 350 generations. Therefore *Paramecium*, in the absence of some form of nuclear reorganization, is not immortal but has a definite limited life span resulting in senescence and death. On the other hand, many other genera of ciliates continue to propagate indefinitely by fission without the occurrence of any nuclear reorganization processes whatever (Fauré-Fremiet, 1953b). Sonneborn (1954) examined the famous clone of *Paramecium aurelia* maintained by Woodruff for many years (I, page 178) without conjugation (but constantly undergoing autogamy) and found that it belongs to one mating type and conjugates readily if mixed with the proper mating type (see under genetics).

Flagellates in general were believed to be devoid of sexual processes, but in recent years Cleveland (1949–1956a, summary in 1956b), in a series of remarkable articles, has demonstrated the occurrence of sexual stages in the complicated flagellates inhabiting the intestine of a woods roach, in correlation with the molting of the roach. Insects of course (except Collembola) do not molt in the adult stage; hence the flagellates undergo sexual processes only while in the intestine of nymphal stages. The onset of the sexual process in the flagellates is related to the onset of the molt of the nymphal host by a definite time interval that varies with each flagellate species from 50 days before to 3 days after the actual molt. When the proper time has arrived, the vegetative flagellate, which may be diploid or haploid according to species, alters physiologically into a gametocyte, generally without undergoing any morphological change. In some species the gametocyte with or without encystment divides into a male and a female gamete, of which the former is usually smaller. These fuse to form a zygote; in this fusion the organelles of the male gamete may be completely absorbed or the organelles of the two gametes may fuse to form a single set. The zygote undergoes two meiotic (maturation) divisions, giving rise to four vegetative flagellates. The zygote may encyst and undergo its divisions inside the cyst. In other species the maturation divisions may occur at the start of the cycle or the gametocyte may undergo two meiotic divisions, producing four haploid gametes as in animals in general. For further details and variants the original articles must be consulted. During its nymphal life the roach molts only once annually, in spring, and then only after a preceding exposure to winter cold. Hence the flagellates show sexual phenomena only once annually. Nymphal roaches kept at constant room temperature do not molt and neither do their flagellate symbionts undergo sexual cycles. Further proof of the absolute dependence of the sexual phenomena in the flagellates on the host molt, presumably by way of hormones, was given by Cleveland and Nutting (1956). If flagellates that have begun their sexual cycle in nymphs are transferred to adult roaches, they cannot complete the cycle and die. Further, if flagellates are transferred from adult roaches in which they never exhibit sexual phenomena to nymphs at the proper time before the latter molt, the sexual cycle is invoked.

Much work is in progress on the life cycle of the Foraminifera by growing them in cultures. Mention may be made of the articles of Le Calvez (1950, 1953), Arnold (1955a, b), and especially Grell, who has summarized his work in an outstanding article (1958) in which the life cycles of six different species are reviewed. In general, recent work verifies the classical account (I, page 133) of the life cycle as a succession of asexual and sexual phases, but there are many variations in detail. The agamonts and gamonts may differ in size, and gamonts may be sexually differentiated. According to Grell, association of the agamont with a microscleric shell and the gamont with a macroscleric shell applies only to a limited number of species. Some species produce amoeboid, others biflagellate gametes; gametes may be free-swimming or remain enclosed in the shell of the parent gamont. In some species gametes from the same gamont will fuse; in other species only cross-fusions occur.

The life cycle of the Radiolaria is still unknown. In Acantharia, Hollande and Enjumet (1957) have verified sporulation into biflagellate swarmers, presumably gametes.

f. Nature of Zooxanthellae.—Further proof of the dinoflagellate nature of zooxanthellae has been furnished by several authors. The zooxanthellae of corals may be of the *Gymnodinium* type (Kawaguchi, 1942) or belong to the armored type (Pringsheim, 1955). Zahl and McLaughlin (1957) and McLaughlin and Zahl (1957) cultivated zooxanthellae obtained from a scyphozoan medusa and an anemone in sea water enriched with nutrients and found that these after a time gave off typical dinoflagellate swarmers that would soon again revert to the motionless state. Hollande and Enjumet (1953) noted that the zooxanthellae of the radiolarians with which they worked are dinoflagellates belonging to the genus *Gymnodinium*.

g. Toxicity of Dinoflagellates.—It has long been known that bivalves that have fed on dinoflagellates of the genus *Gonyaulax* thereby become exceedingly poisonous and even fatal when eaten by man (Fowler, 1943). In recent years great concern has been aroused by mass mortality of fish and invertebrates, especially around Florida, in association with dis-colored water known as "red water" or the "red tide." This discoloration is caused by the appearance of hordes of dinoflagellates of the genus *Gymnodinium*, and it has been shown that the killing of fish and other animals is caused by the emanation of a toxin from the dinoflagellates, notably *G. breve*. To produce "red water" a concentration of 2 to 3 million dinoflagellates per liter is necessary; as many as 50 million per liter is not uncommon in "red water" (Ryther, 1955). The protozoan flour-ishes only in tropical and subtropical waters. A considerable literature is available on the subject (Gunter *et al.*, 1948; Davis, 1948; Graham, 1954; Lasker and Smith, 1954; Sater, 1954; Odum *et al.*, 1955; Hutton, 1956; Ballantine and Abbott, 1957; Ray and Wilson, 1957; Wilson and Ray, 1956). Abbott and Ballantine (1957) studied the toxin produced in cultures of *Gymnodinium* and obtained evidence that it acts upon the nervous system, but did not identify its chemical nature.

h. Nutrition of Phytoflagellates.—An extremely active field of pro-tozoan research is the study of their nutritional requirements and bio-chemistry by growing them in artificial media devoid of food organisms (*axenic* culture). These matters form the subject of two useful volumes (A. Lwoff, 1951; Hutner and Lwoff, 1955; see also Hutner and Trager, 1953). To date but one holozoic (phagotrophic) protozoan has been cultivated in a completely defined medium, that is, one composed entirely of constituents of known chemical composition. This is more easily possible with the free-living flagellates, whose nutritive requirements are reviewed by Hutner and Provasoli (1951, 1955). Only a limited number of green (photoautotrophic) flagellates will grow in the light in a medium of inorganic salts only (Hall, 1941; Schoenborn, 1942, 1950), although there is some suspicion that imperfections of technique may have accounted for this result.   Even in the light most require peptone or amino acids or particular vitamins or mixtures of these factors.   The discovery of the absolute requirement of vitamin B_{12} by certain flagellates has resulted in the use of these, especially strains of the small *Euglena gracilis*, as test organisms for this vitamin.   In the dark some photo-autotrophic flagellates may be cultured with only the addition of the organic salt sodium acetate as a source of carbon, but many require more complicated substances.   The ability of certain flagellates, both green and colorless, to grow in culture with only acetate as the organic source of carbon resulted in their designation as acetate flagellates.   It was later learned that they can also use other fatty acids (in place of carbohydrates), and acetate flagellates are now understood as flagellates "with exceptional ability to grow in the presence of high concentrations of free fatty acids" (Hutner and Provasoli, 1951) that are ordinarily fatal.   It should be added that the photoautotrophic flagellates require in the culture medium not only the usual inorganic salts but also apparently traces of the salts of metals.   The formula for the culture of *Euglena gracilis* (Hutner, Bach, and Ross, 1956) contains a mixture of salts of trace metals (iron, zinc, manganese, copper, cobalt, boron, molybdenum, and vanadium).

Besides green phytoflagellates, brown ones, mostly chrysomonads, have been grown in pure cultures (Hutner, Provasoli, and Filfus, 1953; Provasoli and Pintner, 1953).   Not only are these photoautotrophic but they ingest particulate food.   They can be grown in numbers in a medium of powdered skim milk, trypticase (pancreatic digest of casein), and sucrose.   Further analysis resulted in a medium of inorganic salts, salts of trace metals as above, a few amino acids, three vitamins (B_{12}, thiamin, biotin), a sugar or glycerol, and citrate.   This seems to be the simplest medium for any phagotrophic protozoan yet known.

i. Nutrition of Colorless Flagellates.—These are divisible into those that ingest food organisms or particles and those that do not.   The latter, also called chemoautotrophic flagellates, are believed to absorb nutrients from the medium.   Schoenborn (1946) grew a strain of the colorless euglenoid *Astasia longa* in a medium of inorganic salts including ferric chloride, but later (1952) found that this medium would not support growth of other strains of *Astasia longa* or of related species; nor was addition of acetate and various vitamins of any value.   It now appears that *Astasia longa* is only a strain of *Euglena gracilis* that has permanently lost its chlorophyll.   Apparently the problem of a defined medium for such colorless euglenoids has not been solved.

The little *Chilomonas paramecium* is a good example of a chemoauto-trophic flagellate.   Earlier reports of the cultivation of this flagellate in inorganic medium (I, page 59) appear erroneous.   Acetate and the vitamin thiamin are essential (Hutchens, 1948), and iron is necessary for maximal populations. Further studies (Cosgrove, 1950; Cosgrove and Swanson, 1952) have shown that only straight-chain, monovalent, even-numbered alcohols or fatty acids can be utilized as the sole carbon source.

Peranema trichophora exemplifies a phagotrophic (holozoic) colorless flagellate. Chen (1950), who gave a good account of its anatomy and biology, grew it in axenic culture on cow's milk, which is particulate. Storm and Hutner (1953) analyzed further the requirements in axenic culture and arrived at a complex medium composed of inorganic salts, salts of trace metals, citrate and acetate, nucleic acid derivatives, cholesterol, lecithin, 19 amino acids, 3 vitamins (B_{12}, thiamin, and riboflavin), and thioctic acid; but there were further necessary unidentified factors found in liver digests and cream.

j. Axenic Culture of Free-living Amoebae.—Such culture is naturally difficult since amoebae are highly phagotrophic organisms. Only complex media have succeeded. Reich (1935, 1948) grew a soil amoeba, *Mayorella palestinensis*, on a medium of salts, peptone, and glucose. *Acanthamoeba castellanii* was cultivated on peptone plus the usual salts (Cailleau, 1933); success was variable, depending on the source of the peptone. Neff (1957) cultivated axenically a species of *Acanthamoeba* on proteose-peptone or yeast extract enriched with glucose. Balamuth and Thompson (1955) give the medium of Storm and Hutner for the culture of *Acanth. castellanii* and *Hartmannella rhysodes*, containing inorganic salts, salts of trace metals, citrate and acetate, amino acids, nucleotides, vitamins, and an unknown crude factor from plant or animal materials. These small amoebae do not utilize carbohydrates.

k. Axenic Culture of Ciliates.—A completely defined medium in the culture of phagotrophic ciliates has been attained with the little ciliate *Tetrahymena* (formerly *Glaucoma*) *pyriformis*. This and related species, easily grown in proteose-peptone medium, have become important material in protozoological research. Under the leadership of Kidder, there has been worked out a defined medium (Kidder and Dewey, 1951) of 16 amino acids, 10 vitamins, 9 inorganic salts (calcium, magnesium, potassium, manganese, iron, zinc, copper), 4 nucleotides (derivatives of nucleic acid), glucose, sodium acetate, an oleic acid derivative known as Tween 80, and a tissue extract protogen, long of unknown nature but later shown to be thioctic acid (M. W. Bullock *et al.*, 1952). It is to be understood that all the named substances are *essential* nutritional requirements and the omission of any one of them results in decline of growth. Several species of *Paramecium*, a bacterial feeder, have now been grown axenically, but only on complicated substances of unknown chemical composition. Van Wagtendonk, Conner, Miller, and Rao (1953) grew *Par. aurelia* in a medium of 6 salts, yeast extract, proteose-peptone, 2 nucleotides, 10 vitamins, and a factor in lemon juice later identified (Conner, Van

Wagtendonk, and Miller, 1953) as a steroid substance, beta-sitosterol. Since 1942, W. H. Johnson has attempted the axenic culture of *Par. multimicronucleatum*, achieving success (Johnson and Miller, 1956) with a medium of 9 inorganic salts, 2 organic salts (sodium acetate and pyruvate), 6 vitamins, 17 amino acids, a steroid (stigmasterol), a chelating substance (ethylene diamine tetracetic acid), and an unknown factor from yeast extract, now under further analysis. *Par. trichium* has been grown by Jones, Keeshan, and Lilly (1957) on a similar medium, also containing yeast autolysate as the unknown factor. *Par. caudatum* has been attempted by Sato and Sato (1956) and Sterbenz (1956) on similar media. A general review of the axenic cultivation of bacterial-feeding ciliates other than *Tetrahymena* is given by Van Wagtendonk (1955). Carnivorous ciliates have not been grown in axenic medium (Lilly, 1953; Lilly and Cevallos, 1956) and when cultured in a sterile medium with one other protozoan as food, often require complicated supplements for successful growth.

1. Culture of Parasitic Flagellates.—The successful cultivation of parasitic protozoans in vitro is a necessary preliminary to study of their biochemistry, hence is a matter of importance. The culture of parasitic flagellates is reviewed by M. Lwoff (1951a). *Leishmania* and *Trypanosoma* have been maintained in vitro for over 50 years. Whole blood is essential in the medium. Further analysis has shown that the red cells can be replaced by haematin, the colored radical of haemoglobin, and vitamin C, but factors in serum, including B vitamins, are also essential. Citri and Grossowicz (1954, 1955) grew *Trypanosoma* (or *Schizotrypanum*) *cruzi* in a medium of casein hydrolysate, bovine albumin, haematin, salts, and filtered tomato juice, later replacing the last with 16 known growth factors. The human pathogenic trypanosomes, *Trypanosoma gambiense* and *rhodesiense*, require a complicated medium, including blood, not necessarily human. They have been grown (Tobie, von Brand, and Mehlman, 1950) on a solid medium of bacto-beef, bacto-peptone, bacto-agar, and whole rabbit blood overlain with the salts of Locke's solution. Good multiplication of trypanosomes in such media is obtainable, but in no case has anyone ever obtained in vitro the full trypanosomal stages such as occur in the blood of man. The only stages occurring in vitro are those found in the insect intermediate host. They are not infective. Von Brand, Weinbach, and Tobie (1955) found the metabolism of cultured trypanosomes widely different from that of trypanosomes taken from the blood of infected hosts.

The pathogenic trichomonads have also been under cultivation for years. Johnson and Trussell (1943, 1944) were the first to achieve the axenic culture of *Trichomonas vaginalis*, using a medium of bacto-agar, bacto-peptone, bacto-liver infusion, human serum, cysteine, maltose, and salts of Ringer's solution. Diamond (1957) cultivated various trichomonads of animals and man on trypticase (pancreatic digest of casein), yeast extract, maltose, cysteine, vitamin C, agar, and sheep serum. Anaerobic conditions, or at least low oxygen, are necessary.

m. Cultivation of Parasitic Amoebae.—*Entamoeba* (valid spelling) *histolytica* was first successfully cultivated outside the host by Boeck and Drbohlav (1925), using a medium of egg, serum, glucose, and Locke's salt solution; but the presence of bacteria was necessary. Reviews of the cultivation of this amoeba are given by M. Lwoff (1951b), Geiman and Becker (1953), Nakamura (1953), and Porter (1953). There has been a long struggle to culture this amoeba in the absence of bacteria or other food organisms, and in 1957 Nakamura admitted that indefinite growth without such food had not been attained. Reeves, Meleney, and Frye (1957) achieved multiplication through 20 transfers on an axenic medium of chick embryo juice (nearly cell-free), horse serum, trypticase, glucose, dipotassium phosphate, sodium chloride, yeast extract, and thiomalic acid; but growth was poorer than in the presence of bacteria and the medium failed if the embryo juice was too strongly centrifuged or heated, indications that actually the amoebae fed on suspended particles. For the cultivation of this amoeba low oxygen is essential and cholesterol and some form of carbohydrate are necessary growth factors.

A reptilian intestinal amoeba, *Entamoeba invadens*, very similar morphologically to *E. histolytica*, is under axenic cultivation (Stoll, 1957) on a complicated medium of liver infusion broth, acidified raw-liver extract, mucin, and peptone or trypticase.

n. Culture of Malarial Parasites.—Exoerythrocytic stages are readily cultivated in tissue cultures. This was first successfully accomplished by Hawking (1945), who grew chick tissues infected with exoerythrocytic stages of bird malaria in a medium of fowl serum, chick-embryo extract, and Tyrode's salt mixture. These stages of bird malaria were later also successfully grown on chick tissues in tissue culture by Dubin (1952, 1954) and Oliveira and Meyer (1955). The parasites continue to multiply by schizogony and remain infective to chicks, but erythrocytic stages do not appear. As regards erythrocytic stages, infected red blood corpuscles of birds and mammals can be maintained in vitro and will undergo schizogony although apparently gametocytes are not formed (review by McKee, 1951). The medium developed by a group of workers at Harvard, generally called the Harvard medium, contains the usual inorganic salts, sodium acetate, glucose and glycerol, amino acids, 11 vitamins, and 6 nucleotides. Spandorf and Manwell (1957) improved this medium by adding two more vitamins and liver coenzyme concentrate. Trager (1957) is courageously trying to grow in vitro the beginning uninucleate erythrocytic stage of a bird malaria, *Plasmodium lophurae*, freed from the red blood corpuscles.   The parasites are freed from the red cells by disrupting the latter with an antiserum.   The medium employed is highly complicated, consisting of an extract of red blood corpuscles mixed with nutrients.   Survival for 3 days with beginning schizogony has been achieved.

o. *Biochemistry of Protozoa.*—As soon as axenic culture of Protozoa in vitro is achieved, exact studies of their metabolism and general biochemistry become possible.   Great advances along these lines have been made, but because of the complex formulas and equations involved, the matter is unsuitable for review here.   General accounts of metabolism and biochemistry of Protozoa are given in Lwoff (1951), von Brand (1952), and Hutner and Lwoff (1955).

p. *Genetics of Paramecium.*—Under the leadership of T. M. Sonneborn of Indiana University, *Paramecium* has become almost as famous and as productive as genetic material as the fruit fly *Drosophila*.   The general results have been summarized in articles by Sonneborn (1950a, 1950b, 1957) and in the book by Beale (1954).   The excellent book by Wichterman (1953) is also to be commended for a general account of research results with *Paramecium*.   The genetics program began with the discovery by Sonneborn in 1937 of the existence of mating types in *Par. aurelia*.   An individual *Paramecium* will not conjugate with any other *Paramecium* of the same species but only with one of complementary mating type.   By study of natural populations of *Par. aurelia* Sonneborn (1938) reduced the many variants to eight varieties of two mating types each and one variety with a single mating type.   As these varieties also differ in size, rate of fission, relation of conjugation to temperature, and other matters, Sonneborn inclines to regard them as species and the mating types as sexes.   Typical conjugation occurs only between the two mating types within a variety, although weak reactions may be manifested by animals from different varieties.   Mating types and varieties also occur among other species of *Paramecium* (Sonneborn, 1938; Metz, 1954). In the green *Paramecium, Par. bursaria,* Jennings (1939) originally described three varieties with four, eight, and four mating types, respectively.   Subsequently three more varieties were discovered.   In case of several mating types within a variety all interbreed freely.   The occurrence of mating types has been established in a few other ciliates (Metz, 1954), as *Euplotes* and *Tetrahymena*.

Conjugation begins by the adhesion of paramecia of appropriate mating type, and this adhesion is a necessary preliminary to the nuclear changes that follow.   According to Metz (1954), adhesion occurs only on random contact and is not caused by any substance emitted into the medium.   The analysis of Metz (1954) indicates that adhesion is caused by specific mating-type substances produced on the surface of paramecia.

Thus living animals will adhere to dead ones of the proper type, and thereby become activated to go through the nuclear changes. Metz considers that the mating substances are located on the cilia. It has proved impossible to extract from paramecia any substance that affects the mating reaction.

The existence of mating types in *Paramecium* is obviously a direct invitation to genetic analysis, and during the years since the discovery of these types this analysis has expanded to cover a vast area. It was soon found that inheritance in *Paramecium* follows Mendelian laws, and over 20 single gene traits are now known (Sonneborn, 1955). In mixing races in genetic experiments it was soon noticed that some races give off into the medium a substance that kills other races. The former were then designated killers, the latter sensitives, and the toxic substance emitted is called paramecin. Further analysis showed that paramecin exists as refractile granules in definite cytoplasmic particles, then named kappa particles, and that these, like genes, consist of desoxyribonucleoprotein. Kappa particles multiply in the cytoplasm but can exist only in paramecia of suitable genetic constitution. They are transmitted cytoplasmically only. In case of conjugation between a killer and a sensitive, the killer exconjugant produces by fission only killer offspring, the sensitive exconjugant only sensitive offspring; unless, as occasionally happens, considerable cytoplasm is interchanged at conjugation, in which case both exconjugants produce killer cultures by fission. Kappa particles therefore behave like genes: they are self-propagating and control a hereditary trait. Hence they have been designated cytoplasmic genes, or, more briefly, plasmagenes. If such cytoplasmic inheritance could be firmly established, it would be a finding of first importance. But many believe the kappa particles are some sort of foreign organisms, something like viruses.

When a strain of *Paramecium* is suitably injected into a rabbit, the serum of the latter comes to contain an antibody or antibodies that will paralyze and kill members of the injected strain. Continued experiments of this type have shown that *Par. aurelia* is made up of an enormous number of antigenic types ("serotypes"). As immunological reactions are highly specific, an antiserum prepared from one serotype in general has no effect on members of another serotype. Serotypes seem to mutate readily. Analysis has shown that different clones of the same stock of one variety may contain different serotypes; that different varieties of *Par. aurelia* have on the whole different arrays of antigens; but similar serotypes may occur in the different varieties. On the whole there is more serological difference between different varieties than between stocks of the same variety. The antigenic substance of the *Paramecium* that invokes antibodies in rabbits seems to be borne on the cilia. Both genes and cytoplasmic factors are involved in the production of *Paramecium* antigens; hence serological analysis is being intensively pursued in the hope of establishing further proof of cytoplasmic inheritance.   As in the case of kappa particles, cytoplasmic factors are demonstrated when the exconjugants of two serotypes produce by fission only their own serotype unless considerable cytoplasm is passed during conjugation.   Autogamy in the exconjugant lines may or may not affect the serotype; when it does, micronuclear, that is, genic, influence is shown.   For further complicated details of the serological work on paramecia the book of Beale (1954) may be consulted.

q. The Protozoa as Acellular Animals.—The concept of the Protozoa as acellular organisms met with the usual resistance of inertia.   The extreme of a narrow, rigid view is expressed by Boyden (1957), and in fact this author appears unable to grasp the concept of organism.   The temperate, well-considered reply of Corliss (1957a) admits that some Protozoa conform to the definition of cell and others do not.   This is certainly not a satisfactory solution.   Nobody has any intention of denying some correspondence between protozoans and metazoan cells.   This correspondence is best seen between amoeboid protozoans and the various types of amoebocytes found in body fluids of Metazoa.   Yet it may be pointed out that the latter do not encyst and are often incapable of fission.   The claim of Boyden that there is "essential structural correspondence part for part" is simply untrue.   There are large numbers of structures in Protozoa that have no counterpart in metazoan cells.   Among them may be mentioned the nuclear dimorphism of ciliates (also seen in Foraminifera; Grell, 1956), the infraciliary system of ciliates, the complicated buccal organelles of ciliates, the complex organelles, including parabasal bodies and axostyles, of the hypermastigote flagellates, polyenergid nuclei, the tentacles of suctorians, attachment stalks.   Jones (1951) notes that *Dileptus anser* may have 16 or more micronuclei and over 100 macronuclei.   The macronuclei of ciliates are now known to be of the polyenergid type. Polyenergid nuclei are not equivalent to the polyploid nuclei of metazoans, for they play a definite role in complex life cycles, in which they at some point undergo multiple fission into monoenergid nuclei.   There are, further, numerous processes in protozoans not represented in metazoan cells as encystment and excystment, conjugation with exchange of micronuclei, multiple fissions and sporulations, complex cycles involving asexual and sexual reproduction, production of migratory forms showing ancestral reminiscence.   This last refers to the production of buds that become free-swimming migratory stages in suctorians and chonotrichs (Guilcher, 1951).   These stages, which might well be called larvae, have no resemblance to the parent form and are provided with a ciliary pattern that recapitulates the ancestral holotrichous ciliate.   These phenomena are referred to by Corliss (1953b) as "embryology at the protozoan level." Sonneborn (1950a) states that *Paramecium* is "far more complicated in morphology and physiology than any cell of the body of man." Lwoff (1950) says: "Protozoa are complete individuals, whole organisms, and behave as such." Obviously there is only one way of regarding Protozoa that will cover all facts about them, that is, as equivalent, not to a metazoan cell, but to an entire metazoan organism. The terms acellular and noncellular are probably unfortunate, and it is hoped better ones may be suggested. Because of familiarity one is apt to slip inadvertently into words like cellular and unicellular, and any such slips on the part of the author[1] when speaking of Protozoa should be discounted. It is unscientific to allow semantic difficulties to obstruct correct conceptions.

r. Classification of the Protozoa.—The classificatory arrangement of the Protozoa had reached considerable stability among protozoologists of the United States, as seen in the books of Jahn (1949), Hall (1953), and Kudo (1954), when many innovations were introduced in the two volumes on the Protozoa in the *Traité de zoologie* (Grassé, 1952, 1953). A projected third volume on ciliates has not yet appeared. These two volumes cover more completely the morphology and taxonomy of flagellates, rhizopods, and sporozoans than any previous works. On examining into the taxonomic arrangement in the volumes of the *Traité* one notices at once a high incidence of the disease of raising ranks. A useful history of taxonomic schemes for Protozoa appears in Hall (1953).

It is now customary to elevate the familiar four classes of Protozoa, originating with Bütschli, to the rank of subphylum. The author approves this as regards Ciliophora and possibly Sporozoa but cannot find it justifiable to separate flagellates and rhizopods by a gap as great as subphylum. Therefore either the union of flagellates and rhizopods into a subphylum Rhizoflagellata as in the *Traité* or the union of flagellates, rhizopods, and sporozoans into a subphylum Plasmodroma originating with Doflein is to be approved. Consequently the phylum will consist of two subphyla, Plasmodroma and Ciliophora, or of three subphyla, Rhizoflagellata, Sporozoa, and Ciliophora. Flagellata and Rhizopoda should then become stabilized as classes of either Plasmodroma or Rhizoflagellata; however, the author wonders whether flagellates and rhizopods should even be separated by a rank as great as class.

The Flagellata are divisible into plantlike phytoflagellates and animallike zooflagellates, and these terms are convenient, but the gradations between the two groups are such that expression of the groups as definite subclasses is of doubtful validity although generally adopted. It appears

---

[1] As regards the article "The Transition from the Unicellular to the Multicellular Individual," the title, the subject, and the publication thereof were forced upon the author.

better to divide the Flagellata directly into orders. As regards phyto-flagellates, these orders are raised to the rank of class in the *Traité*, which necessarily must then regard Flagellata as a superclass. Such elevations of rank appear unjustified. The orders of phytoflagellates appear to be quite well stabilized as in Vol. I (page 46); the *Traité* removes silico-flagellates and coccolithophorids (I, page 90) from the chrysomonads and raises them to the rank of class (!). No doubt these two interesting groups deserve a rank higher than that of family, but surely a rank of suborder of Chryosomadina as in Hall (1953) is adequate. As regards the zooflagellates the *Traité* increases the usual 4 or 5 orders to 14; this is done by raising subordinate groups to the rank of order. Thus Proto-monadina are divided into 5 orders with trypanosomes and choano-flagellates given ordinal rank; and Polymastigina and Hypermastigina are each broken up into 4 orders plus an order Diplozoa for the peculiar bilaterally organized polymastigotes (I, page 115). The very uncertain group Rhizomastigina (I, page 118) is absorbed by the *Traité* into the rhizopod order Lobosa, a good solution of the problem.

In the class Rhizopoda (which name has priority over Sarcodina) it is now usual and no doubt justifiable to draw a distinction between groups with flowing and those with stiff pseudopods. Hence the classification (I, page 46) is to be emended and Rhizopoda to be divided into two sub-classes, one of uncertain name, perhaps Sarcodina, for Lobosa and Foraminifera, and the other, named Actinopoda, for Heliozoa and Radiolaria. Whether, as in the *Traité*, Acantharia are to be separated from the other Radiolaria and elevated to the same rank with them remains uncertain. The very uncertain group Protomyxidea (I, page 127) is merged in the *Traité* into Heliozoa.

Whether Sporozoa are to be elevated to the rank of subphylum or even disrupted altogether into two groups, considered subphyla in the *Traité*, Telosporidia and Cnidosporidia, is indeterminate at present. The arrangement in Vol. I (page 47) may be retained except that Sarcosporidia is to be eliminated altogether. The work of Spindler and Zimmerman (1945) and Spindler (1947) has given good evidence that the Sarcosporidia are fungi. The union of Coccidia and Haemosporidia into one group Coccidiomorpha as in the *Traité* has much in its favor.

The classification of the subphylum Ciliophora is under revision by Corliss (1956, 1957b). A primary question is the retention of the stand-ard division of ciliates into the opalinids (subclass Protociliata) and typical ciliates (subclass Euciliata). Grassé (1952), following some earlier workers, insists that the opalinids are flagellates and places them in a superorder Opalinina among the zooflagellates. The flagellate view is also supported by Corliss (1955). Nonciliate characters of opalinids are the monomorphic nuclei, the absence of conjugation, the production of anisogametes, and the longitudinal direction of fission. On the other hand, a kinety system is present, with the kineties centered at the falx, an anteriorly located bar of aggregated kinetosomes; nuclear division occurs without any centriole, a body invariably present in flagellate mitoses; and fission may be transverse in asexual phases with a new falx produced by the kineties of the opisthe (Wessenberg, 1957). The flagellate nature of the opalinids must be regarded as unproved, and further research on the group is necessary to establish its systematic position.

The typical ciliates are arranged by Corliss (1956, 1957b), following Fauré-Fremiet (1950), into two subclasses: Holotricha and Spirotricha. Under the Holotricha are arranged the usual orders Gymnostomata, Trichostomata, Hymenostomata, Astomata, and Apostomea, but in addition Suctoria, Chonotricha, and Peritricha are moved into the Holotricha, plus a new order Thigmotrichida. The inclusion of Suctoria, called Suctorida, is justifiable on the grounds that their migratory buds develop a typical holotrichous pattern of ciliation (I, page 205). The inclusion of Chonotricha is based on the study of Guilcher (1951), who showed the holotrichous nature of the ciliature of the migratory phases ("larvae"). The order Thigmotrichida is a relatively new order established by the studies of Chatton and Lwoff (1949, 1950) for a group formerly considered hymenostomes that are parasitic in mollusks and are provided with a special area of thigmotactic cilia. The inclusion of Peritricha in Holotricha remains mysterious to the author despite the long argument about this in Corliss (1956). Corliss considers it necessary to remove *Paramecium* from the Trichostomata into the Hymenostomata on account of the pattern of its buccal organelles. Attention is called to the important monograph of Puytorac (1954) on the astomatous ciliates.

There then remain in the Spirotricha the three orders Heterotricha, Oligotricha, and Hypotricha, but the second is magnified into three by raising the tintinnids and entodiniomorphs (I, page 193) to the rank of orders. These two groups undoubtedly deserve at least subordinal rank. There has long been recognized (omitted from Vol. I) an additional order or suborder Ctenostomata (name requires alteration as identical with an order of ectoprocts) for a very small group of ciliates resembling hypotrichs.

3. Phylum Mesozoa.—The systematic position of this group remains enigmatical, and the life cycle of the dicyemids has still not been completed. Valuable contributions to the knowledge of the Mesozoa have been made by Nouvel (1947, 1948), McConnaughey (1949, 1951, 1954), and Stunkard (1954); the last has given an exhaustive review of the history of the group. This newer work has proved the reality of the stem nematogen as the earliest phase to be found in young cephalopods, which become infected shortly after hatching. It may also now be considered as established that the infusorigens are hermaphroditic individuals, or else they are the hermaphroditic gonads of the rhombogens. The infusoriform larva is therefore the product of a fertilized egg, and this increases its resemblance to a miracidium. It therefore appears that the sexual phase of the dicyemid cycle is passed in the cephalopod host and only asexual reproduction must occur in the presumed intermediate host. As infusoriform larvae are not directly infective to cephalopods, development in an intermediate host must be assumed. According to the analysis of Stunkard (1954), the infusiform larvae are probably swept into a benthonic, filter-feeding invertebrate in which only the urn persists and propagates asexually, with eventual production of stem nematogens that infect baby cephalopods. McConnaughey, opposing Gersh, has established the reality of the heterocyemids, which he has reduced to one genus, *Conocyema* (including *Microcyema*). He regards all known dicyemids as belonging to one family, Dicyemidae, including three genera, *Dicyemennea*, *Dicyema*, and *Conocyema*.

As regards the systematic position of the Mesozoa, most workers on the group continue to consider them as degenerate flatworms. Stunkard (1937) regards them as "degenerate or highly specialized flatworms, derived not from any existing group of the Turbellaria but from a very remote ancestor of all existing flatworms." This statement (and later ones; Stunkard, 1954) is obviously self-contradictory. Mesozoa cannot be at the same time degenerate flatworms and offshoots of a remote ancestor of flatworms. The author continues to reject the idea that the Mesozoa are degenerate flatworms, specifically trematodes. This appears utterly incompatible with their retention of a highly differentiated, phagocytic surface layer of cells. Neither is it understandable why the Mesozoa, occupying the same sort of habitat as countless trematodes, should have undergone so much greater degeneration than they. There is certainly some resemblance between the infusoriform larvae and miracidia; both are products of a fertilized egg and both have cell constancy, but the resemblance does not go much farther. Cell constancy is further seen in all known stages of dicyemids, but not in any stage of trematodes except the miracidium. Other good points against the concept of Mesozoa as degenerate flatworms appear in Dodson (1956). Stunkard destroys his own argument about mesozoans being degenerate flatworms when he says (1954): "From a hypothetical, generalized, planuloid progenitor it is possible to derive each of the existing groups of the phylum Platyhelminthes. Accordingly, it appears that the Turbellaria, Mesozoa, Cestoda, and Digenea have descended concomitantly from a common ancestral group of planula-like progenitors." Obviously this admits that the Mesozoa have remained close to the "generalized, planuloid ancestor." Hence a main supporter of the idea that mesozoans are degenerate flatworms tacitly admits that they have remained at the status of a planuloid.

The author continues to take the position that the Mesozoa as conceived at present are a well-defined group with definite and rather remarkable characteristics that entitle them to the status of a phylum. This phylum is placed between Protozoa and Porifera merely for want of exact knowledge where else to place it.[1]

4. Phylum Porifera.—In recent literature on sponges there is much consideration of the question whether sponges should continue to occupy the isolated position long assigned to them. On the chemical side the answer seems to be negative, whereas embryological studies support the old view.

a. Biochemistry of Sponges.—Bergmann (1949) has for years been studying the sterols of sponges. Sterols are alcohols of high molecular weight containing a benzene-ring complex (IV, page 382). In studies involving over 50 species of sponges, 10 different sterols were isolated, of which 8 were new. In a further study of lipoid substances in sponges, Bergmann and Swift (1951) obtained over 20 different fatty acids from each of two sponge species tried. These were high carbon acids, many with 26 or 28 carbon atoms, whereas in animals in general acids with no more than 24 carbon atoms are usual. Two acids were found not previously known in nature. Sponges are regarded by Bergmann as one of the best sources of unsaturated fatty acids of high molecular weight, and this author also subscribes to a generalization that the greatest diversity of lipids occurs in the lowest invertebrates and the number declines with rise of phyletic rank.

Whereas these studies on sponge lipoids indicate a divergence of sponges from other animals, other chemical studies support a contrary conclusion. Bergmann, Watkins, and Stempien (1957) isolated the nucleic acids from 16 different sponge species belonging to several groups and obtained from them the usual nucleosides; hence the nucleic acids of sponges do not differ significantly from those of other animals. Inskip and Cassidy (1955) determined that sponges yield the usual amino acids that thus are without phylogenetic value. Marks, Bear, and Blake (1949) obtained wide-angle X-ray diffraction patterns of spongin fibers of three genera of keratose sponges and found these patterns similar to those of vertebrate collagens. Using the same method, Gross, Sokal, and Rougvie (1956) verified this finding. They noted that spongin fibers contain hydroxyproline, glycine, and tyrosine in amounts comparable with the amounts in mammalian collagen,

---

[1] This seems the logical place to call attention to a slip in the labeling of Figs. 68 and 70 in Vol. I. The term "gonocyte" in the legends of these figures should have been "agamete."

and in general the amino acid pattern of spongin fibers is nearly identical with that of mammalian collagen. Low (1951) and Roche (1952) noted the occurrence of iodo- and bromtyrosine in spongin as in gorgonians (I, page 553). Roche and Robin (1954) found that both phosphoarginine and phosphocreatine occur in sponges and consider that the latter is less exceptional in invertebrates than often supposed. Chitin is wanting in sponges (Rudall, 1955); this author has developed the thesis that an abundance of collagen is paralleled by a want of chitin, and vice versa.

b. *The Question of Proterospongia.*—Tuzet (1945), experimenting with dissociated calcareous sponges, noted aggregations of choanocytes greatly resembling the original figure of *Proterospongia* (I, page 108) and considers that the latter was probably a sponge fragment. However, Gröntved (1956) described from the Danish plankton gelatinous masses containing 3 to 20 choanoflagellates that he ascribed to the genus *Proterospongia*. It appears probable that *Proterospongia* is a genuine colonial flagellate but without phylogenetic significance.

c. *New Morphological Findings.*—The occurrence of nerve cells in sponges is claimed by Tuzet, Loubatières, and Pavans de Ceccatty (1952), Tuzet and Pavans de Ceccatty (1953b), and Pavans de Ceccatty (1955). This claim is naturally based on histological appearance and staining reactions. The cells in question are bipolar or multipolar cells with long processes that stretch between structures and terminate on the latter by fine endings. Their nervous nature cannot be accepted without physiological evidence. A peculiar type of cell called lophocyte was discovered by Ankel and Wintermann-Kilian (1952) in a fresh-water sponge and later seen in various marine siliceous sponges by Tuzet and Pavans de Ceccatty (1953a), Tuzet and Paris (1957), and Pavans de Ceccatty (1957). This is an amoeboid cell bearing at one end, rarely both ends, a tuft of fibrils, either directly or on the end of a long filament.

The occurrence of porocytes in other than asconoid sponges has been doubted (I, 295), but Brien (1943a) pictures them in Spongillidae and considers them general in siliceous sponges. He states that they arise by the perforation of pinacocytes.

By scraping off the choanocyte layer of living pieces of *Leucosolenia*, Jones (1956) ascertained that the mesenchyme is a firm colloidal gel that holds the spicules in place. Jones believes that this gel is secreted by the choanocytes because it is softer adjacent to them.

d. *Embryology.*—The origin of spermatogonia or oogonia or both by the transformation of choanocytes is asserted by Leveaux (1942) for Spongillidae, by Duboscq and Tuzet (1944) for *Sycon*, and by Tuzet (1947) for *Leucosolenia* and *Reniera*. Duboscq and Tuzet (1941, 1942, 1944) and Tuzet (1947) also confirm for a number of calcareous sponges and for

Reniera fertilization by way of a sperm carried to the egg in an altered choanocyte (I, page 311). The occurrence of a stomoblastula stage that turns inside out to produce the definitive amphiblastula (I, page 322) is also verified for a number of calcareous sponges (Duboscq and Tuzet, 1941, 1942, 1944; Tuzet, 1948). These authors have also discovered in the flagellated half of the amphiblastula of calcareous sponges the presence of four altered cells arranged symmetrically in the pattern of a cross that they consider to be of phylogenetic significance. These four cells have lost their flagella and are further distinguished by the presence of a chromatic mass as a determinant. They eventually degenerate. Duboscq and Tuzet consider this cross as indicative of a primary tetra-radiate symmetry in sponges, comparable to that of many coelenterates, and further recalling the cross in spiral cleavage.

Valuable contributions on the subject of the embryology of sponges have been made by Meewis (1939, 1941), Levi (1952, 1953, 1956), and Ali (1956). These studies confirm the existence in sponges of two types of larvae, the amphiblastula characteristic of calcareous sponges (except *Clathrina*, referred to in I, page 322, as "some species of *Leucosolenia*"), and the parenchymula, characteristic of the Demospongiae. Levi (1956) contributes an outstanding study of the parenchymula. In both types of larvae what corresponds to the ectoderm of other Metazoa is relegated to the interior and becomes the layer of choanocytes, which probably is not to be regarded as entoderm. In the case of the amphiblastula the flagellated half invaginates into the interior to become the choanocytic lining (I, page 320); in the parenchymula the cells of the outer flagellated layer migrate into the interior and alter into choanocytes. There cannot be any doubt of the general truth of this migration (Levi, 1956) despite occasional denials (Brien, 1943b) and occasional exceptions (Meewis, 1939, for *Haliclonia*, in which the inwandered cells are said to degenerate and the definitive choanocytes to originate from archaeocytes). This peculi-arity of the embryology appears definitely to set the sponges apart from other Metazoa.

e. Classification.—Embryological studies (Tuzet, 1948) show that *Clathrina* should be separated from *Leucosolenia* and other Calcarea, for it lacks a stomoblastula and the cross cells and, further, has a parenchymula type of larva. Probably in the future the classification of the Calcarea will be organized along two lines, one based on *Leucosolenia* and the other on *Clathrina*.

The classification of the Demospongiae remains in a state of flux, but basic contributions toward stabilizing it have been made by Levi (1953, 1956). This author by an intensive study of its embryology has shown that *Halisarca* is unrelated to *Oscarella* (I, page 339) and instead is related to *Aplysilla* and the Dendroceratina (I, page 354). He regards *Halisarca* as a primitive demosponge, for its parenchymula larva develops into a primitive type of rhagon of asconoid structure. *Oscarella* and other Homosclerophora have an amphiblastula type of larva, but this is derived from a parenchymula by dissolution of the interior cells. Levi proposes to divide the Demospongiae into two subclasses: Ceractinomorpha, based on *Halisarca*, including the orders Dendroceratida, Dictyoceratida, Haplosclerida, and Poecilosclerida; and Tetractinomorpha based on *Oscarella*, including the orders Homosclerophora, Tetractinellida, Clavaxinellida, Epipolasida, Hadromerida, and Axinellida.

De Laubenfels (1948) monographed the Keratosa, recognizing four families: Spongiidae, Dysideidae, Aplysillidae (= Darwinellidae), and Halisarcidae; but at least the last two have been incorporated by Levi into his subclass Ceractinomorpha.

5. Phylum Archaeocyatha.—This is a group of extinct animals known by their calcareous skeletons preserved as fossils. They flourished extensively during the Cambrian, apparently forming dense aggregations on marine bottoms in a belt some distance from and paralleling the shore. Their systematic position has been very uncertain, and they have been allied to the usual procession of phyla (history in Okulitch, 1955). In 1943 Okulitch allied them to sponges under the name Pleospongia, but Vologdin (1940 and earlier) had already recognized them as a distinct type Archaeocyatha. This was raised to phylum rank by Okulitch and De Laubenfels (1953).

The skeleton of the Archaeocyatha typically consists of an outer calcareous cup enclosing an inner calcareous cup. Both cups are perforated and they are united to each other by vertical septa or otherwise. Further details of the structure will be found in Okulitch (1955). It is self-evident that these fossils cannot be calcareous sponges since, to mention the most obvious point, they lack spicules. They appear more of the nature of corals. It is claimed that they cannot be corals because a coelenteron was wanting and the living tissues were limited to the region between the cups. However, such statements must have a very uncertain basis, and especially the inclusion of the Archaeocyatha in the Parazoa (Okulitch and De Laubenfels, 1953) must be regarded with skepticism.

6. Phylum Cnidaria.—Research in this phylum concerns mainly nematocyst mechanism and chemistry and neuromuscular patterns.

a. Nematocyst Mechanism and Chemistry.—The factors that invoke the discharge of nematocysts have been brilliantly analyzed by Pantin (1942a, b); the analysis was verified by C. Jones (1947), although both investigators had been somewhat preceded by Wagner (1905). All three observers agree that nematocysts are independent effectors, not under the control of the nervous system, since response is never transmitted and discharge may be evoked on isolated tentacles. Many chemicals, but not food solutions, evoke discharge, but mechanical stimulation alone generally fails; however, it succeeds in animals or tentacles after addition of a little food solution to their medium. These and other facts show that nematocyst discharge is caused by mechanical stimulation, but this is effective only when its threshold has been lowered by chemical stimulation from the food object. This pattern assures that the nematocysts will not discharge to food emanations when the food object is still too far away to be reached by the nematocysts. Pantin indicates that the chemical substances in natural food that lower the threshold to mechanical stimulation are lipoids strongly adsorbed on proteins.

The mechanism of discharge appears to lie in a nervous circuit within the individual cnidoblast; for nematocysts will not discharge to natural stimuli in anaesthetized animals (Pantin; Jones; Glumac, 1953) but will still discharge when acted on directly by suitable chemicals. The cnidoblast contains within itself sensory, excitor, and effector elements; Pantin has shown that cnidocils are not a necessary part of the circuit, but no doubt they serve in most cnidarians. The mechanism of discharge is still uncertain. According to the analysis of Jones, who used hydra, the capsule wall is under tension, and when the contraction of the cnidoblast forces the operculum open, this tension causes the eversion of the tube. Jones dismisses the theory of discharge through swelling of the capsule contents by intake of water, finding that the capsule volume is diminished after discharge, and Yanagita (1943) and Yanagita and Wada (1954), using nematocysts of the anemone *Diadumene*, support this view. However, Picken (1953, 1957), using the extra-large nematocysts of the anemone *Corynactis*, supports the swelling theory, finding that the capsules are enlarged after discharge. This author found a constant process of swelling at the point of emergence of the everting tube, resulting in the lengthening of the tube. Robson (1953) confirmed these findings, indicating water absorption as important to the discharge, and supports the theory of Will (I, page 390).

Kepner and associates (1943, 1951), with reference to the stenoteles of hydra, claim that the tube is not attached to the summit of the butt in the undischarged state, that at the beginning of discharge, water enters and dissolves the tube into a "magma," that this is spun out into a filament by being squeezed through the summit of the discharged butt, and that there is no eversion of the tube in discharge. These preposterous claims have been devastated by the work of C. Jones (1947) and Semal-Van Gansen (1954a) on hydra and of Picken (1953, 1957) and Robson (1953) on the large holotrichous isorhizas of *Corynactis*. The last three workers used the electron microscope. That the tube in the undischarged state is continuous with the capsule wall at the summit of the nematocyst and that discharge occurs by the eversion of a preexisting and permanent tube

are not open to doubt.   Partially discharged nematocysts show the tube
in process of turning inside out.   They are especially illuminating in
Corynactis, where the armature of spines, perfectly visible in the undischarged state on the inside of the tube, can be seen turning out at the tip
of the partially discharged tube.

There is current interest in nematocyst poisons and the chemical
nature of the capsule wall.   Brown (1950), Picken (1953), and Yanagita
and Wada (1954) indicate that the capsule wall may be some form of
keratin.   Boisseau (1949, 1952), using microchemical tests on sections,
found evidence that the capsule contents consist of proteins, not nucleo-
proteins, but apparently albumins, mixed with phenols.   Hamon (1955a,
b) by similar methods also detected phenols in the nematocysts of a
siphonophore and an anemone, further indicated the presence of muco-
polysaccharides, as well as proteins.   The proteins and phenols are not
identical in different cnidarians, although the phenols are mostly ortho-
phenols.   Hamon found that the contents of spirocysts differ markedly
from those of regular nematocysts (anemone), consisting of simple muco-
protein or glycoprotein.   (It may be noted here that Pantin, 1942b,
reported discharge of spirocysts into food.)   Welsh (1955) tested the
effect of extracts of tentacles of *Physalia*, anemones, and other cnidarians
on crabs and was inclined to ascribe the toxic action to tetramine (I,
page 391) or similar quaternary ammonium bases and to 5-hydroxy-
tryptamine, a secondary derivative of the amino acid tryptophane.
However, these substances probably came from the tissues rather than
the nematocysts.   Now that Phillips (1956) has found a way of isolating
nematocysts (anemone), elucidation of the chemistry of the capsules and
the contents may be expected in the near future.   Preliminary results by
Phillips indicate that both capsule and contents are of protein nature.
Other compounds in the wall and tube suggest something similar to cartilage; in the contents were also found mucoproteins and hydroxyindoles.

b. Recent Findings on Hydra.—This animal remains of perennial
interest.   Mueller (1950) and Semal-Van Gansen (1952a) report that the
epidermal cells have two or three or more basal myonemes that branch
and anastomose, whereas the gastrodermal myonemes are single, delicate,
nonanastomosing fibers, best developed in the hypostome and tentacle
bases, often poorly evident elsewhere.   These authors, also Hess, Cohen,
and Robson (1957), regard the tonofibrils or supporting fibrils in the
epidermal cells (I, Fig. 107*D*) as myonemes.   Mueller also considers the
supporting rods of the cnidocils as of muscular nature.   Mueller found no
evidence of a continuous intraepidermal nerve net, but its presence was
verified by Semal-Van Gansen (1952b).   She found a nervous ring present
in the pedal disk but not in the hypostome; sensory nerve cells are most
abundant on the hypostome and pedal disk and appear associated with

gland cells. This author (1954b) published a detailed study of gastro-dermal structure and changes during intracellular digestion and storage of food reserves. She described the two kinds of gland cells in the gastro-dermis of the hypostome (I, Fig. 107*E*) and of the gastric region (I, Fig. 107*F*). It is the gastrodermis of the hypostome that is thrown into folds when at rest (I, page 437), not the mouth; the latter is circular, as pointed out by Mueller.

Ewer (1947) has clarified the role of the four types of nematocysts in the activities of hydras. The stenoteles and desmonemes discharge to food; the latter appear to have a higher threshold to mechanical stimula-tion than the former. The atrichous isorhizas appear not to respond to chemical stimulation but have a low threshold to mechanical stimulation, hence discharge when the tentacles touch the substrate and effect adher-ence of these during locomotion (hence the doubt expressed in I, page 390, is dispelled). Discharged isorhizas were found adhering to slides on which hydras had moved. Holotrichous isorhizas apparently discharge to disturbance by other than food objects. The pairs of spines seen on the coil of discharged volvents (I, Fig. 110*J*) are on the outside, not the inside, of the coil; but the inside of the coil is armed with transverse bars (Semal-Van Gansen, 1954a). This author (1951) and Brien (1951) deny the widely accepted story that nematocysts originate in regions distant from the site of utilization (I, page 387), finding depots of nematocyst forma-tion at the tentacle bases and displacement of such nematocysts along the tentacles by natural processes of tentacle growth. Nematocysts in the gastrodermis supposed to be in process of transportation are deteriorating specimens being digested, according to Semal-Van Gansen.

Brien and associates have contributed a valuable and beautifully illustrated series of articles on hydras, mainly with reference to the role of the interstitial cells in growth, regeneration, and reproduction. Brien (1951) regards hydras as immortal. An isolated *Hydra oligactis* gave off in 2½ years 476 buds and presumably could have continued to grow and propagate indefinitely under good conditions. (This species will not become sexual unless the temperature is markedly lowered, Brien and Reniers, 1949.) Hydras grow primarily in a zone at the anterior end of the column (Brien and Reniers-Decoen, 1950; Brien, 1951). If a colored graft is inserted here, the color is seen to spread gradually in the basal direction. Every part of the hydra occupies successively a more and more proximal position, until finally depleted cells are cast off at the aboral pore. The stalk constantly elongates at the expense of the gastric region but is also constantly shortened basally by elimination of material through the aboral pore. According to Brien, the cells of hydras are renewed about once in 45 days (from the interstitial cells). The interstitial cells are destroyed by X radiation (Brien and Reniers-Decoen, 1955). Such hydras may live for some days and feed, but eventually disintegrate. However if a piece from a nonradiated animal is grafted into a radiated one, interstitial cells from the graft migrate into the radiated part and ensure survival.

Ewer (1948) gave a useful summary of the described Hydridae of the world, listing 13 valid and 16 uncertain species. *Hydra vulgaris* and *attenuata* are recognized as distinct (European). *Hydra americana* is positively quite distinct from either. *Pelmatohydra* is to be merged into *Hydra*. Since Ewer's article a new species has been described for the United States (Hadley and Forrest, 1949) and five for Japan (Ito, 1947). However, the hydras of the world are still poorly known, and the matter is complicated by the existence of many bad descriptions.

c. Water Content of Medusae.—The water content of marine medusae is around 96 per cent (I, page 382; also Lowndes, 1942). The water content of the fresh-water medusa (*Craspedacusta sowerbyi*) is given by Dunham (1942) as 99 to 99.3 per cent, by Ookawa (1952) as averaging 98.2 per cent.

d. Chemistry of the Mesogloea.—Champetier and Fauré-Fremiet (1942) and Marks, Bear, and Blake (1949) found that the X-ray diffraction patterns of the axis of pennatulids and gorgonians belong to the collagen family. Chapman (1953a) concluded that the fibers in the mesogloea of hydro- and scyphomedusae are of collagenous nature, and Rudall (1955) determined the presence of abundant collagen in the mesogloea of *Alcyonium*. On the other hand, Bouillon and Vandermeersche (1956) declare that the fibers in the mesogloea of hydro- and scyphomedusae tested are of the nature of elastin. In either case the fibers of the mesogloea of medusae and anthozoans are comparable to the connective tissue of higher animals. This supports the author's contention (I, page 264) that the standard concept of the division of the Metazoa into diploblastic and triploblastic groups is false and that in fact all Metazoa except hydrozoan polyps are triploblastic. As regards hydrozoan polyps Rudall (1955) could obtain no evidence of collagen in the mesolamella (I, page 381), a suggestion that this thin layer does not correspond to the mesogloea of other cnidarians. The foregoing studies throw no light on the nature of the gelatinous part of the mesogloea of medusae.

e. Interesting Hydrozoans.—Hand (1955c) remarks that the Hydrozoa include a large number of peculiar animals. The curious *Protohydra* (I, page 440) appears common along northern European coasts and has also been found along the New England coast (Ruebush, 1939) and along South Africa (Omer-Cooper, 1957). Nyholm (1951a) found a specimen with a blastula in the coelenteron, an indication that perhaps direct development without a pelagic larva obtains. *Boreohydra*, common on the boreal coasts of Europe and also taken in the Subantarctic (Westblad,

1947, 1953), resembles *Protohydra* but has three or four very short tentacles. It reproduces by transverse fission and develops bulges thought at first to be gonophores; but these produce no germ cells, and Nyholm (1951b) found that germ cells arise directly in the epidermis of the polyp base. Rees (1957) places *Boreohydra* in the Corymorphidae. Very peculiar indeed is the minute solitary *Halammohydra*, of which three species have been found in European beaches (Remane, 1937; Swedmark and Teissier, 1950, 1957a, b). This is completely ciliated with an aboral adhesive sac of inturned epidermis, two circles of tentacles, and one circle of statocysts of the trachyline type (I, page 457) at the aboral pole, and a column with terminal mouth and no oral tentacles. It produces entodermal sex cells that develop along highly tetraradiate lines into an actinula (I, page 435); in fact, the creature seems to be a sort of permanent actinula, belonging to the Trachylina. The peculiar two-tentacled colonial hydroid *Lar*, which is the hydroid stage of the medusa *Proboscidactyla* (I, page 443), is commensal with sabellid worms, permeating the top of their tubes with a network of hydrorhizae (Hand and Hendrickson, 1950; Hand, 1957). Equally curious is the one-tentacled *Monobrachium*, addicted to bivalve shells (Hand, 1957). Also strange is the solitary *Eugymnanthea* (Crowell, 1957), with single oral circlet of tentacles and pedal disk, that inhabits the mantle cavity of bivalves, creeping slowly on their soft parts by its pedal disk and budding just above the latter. Another remarkable hydrozoan is the minute solitary *Psammohydra nanna*, from the Baltic, with three to five, mostly four, short tentacles at the base of the excessively long mobile manubrium (Schulz, 1950); it reproduces by transverse fission with the formation of a fission plane.

The enigmatical medusa *Tetraplatia* (I, page 467) has been taken in numbers off the Pacific Coast of the United States and thoroughly investigated by Hand (1955c), who, in agreement with Carlgren, gives decisive evidence that it is a trachyline medusa.

Records of the fresh-water medusa, *Craspedacusta sowerbyi* (I, page 461), continue to multiply. This medusa has now been found in the majority of states of the United States, also in Canada and on most other continents. Its occurrence is always sporadic; it may or may not recur in the same localities, and, strangely enough, the localities are usually man-made bodies of water. The life cycle of the similar African fresh-water medusa, *Limnocnida tanganyicae*, has now been elucidated (Bouillon, 1954, 1955). Here also the hydroid stage is a small colony without tentacles that reproduces by frustules (I, page 487) and buds off medusae.

Ankel (1951) declares that *Mnestra* (I, page 443) is not parasitic on the gastropod *Phyllirhoe* but the reverse. The gastropod when very small attaches by its pedal gland to the subumbrella of the *Mnestra*, which is possibly a siphonophore medusa, and inhibits its further development.

f. Nervous System and Neuromuscular Patterns.—The nervous system of cnidarians remains a subject of interest since cnidarians are the lowest animals that possess a nervous system (presumably the alleged nerve cells of sponges, if they exist, do not form a system). Arguments continue as to whether the system in cnidarians is synaptic or a continuous net. As regards hydras, present evidence (see above) supports the view of a continuous net with nerve cell bodies at the angles of the network. Komai (1942a), using the capricious rongalite white dye, reported a continuous net in the ephyra of scyphozoans. Using *Cerianthus* and several species of anemones, Leghissa (1949) supported the view of a continuous net, except as regards the neurosensory cells, which he found to make synaptic connections with the general net. He observed the greatest concentration of the nervous system in the oral disk, the presence of both intraepidermal and intragastrodermal nerve nets and their connection through the mesogloea, and the occurrence of nerve cell bodies in the mesogloea. On the other hand, Woollard and Harpman (1939) had found the system synaptic in two anemones and two scyphomedusae, although their illustrations are not very convincing. Pantin (1952) rejected Leghissa's results and found a well-developed synaptic lattice on the retractor face of the septa of *Metridium*. Meyer (1955) reported a synaptic system by methylene blue staining in the medusa *Rhizostoma*. Horridge (1953, 1954a, b, 1956a, b) made an intensive study of the nervous system of the adult and ephyra of *Aurelia*, finding it synaptic. The main nervous network can be seen in the living medusa under the phase-contrast microscope. The bulk of the evidence indicates that in anemones and scyphomedusae the nervous system is synaptic; however, the matter is of little importance because the main nerve plexus of these forms behaves like a continuous net.

Horridge's findings indicate the presence in *Aurelia* and other medusae of two nerve nets. The main subumbrellar net evokes the bell pulsation by causing one simultaneous contraction of circular and radial muscles. There is also present another more diffuse net with smaller cell bodies in both subumbrellar and exumbrellar epidermis that controls local reactions such as feeding and can inhibit the bell pulsations. The two systems intercommunicate at the rhopalial ganglia. Pantin (1950, 1952) supports the presence of two similar systems in anemones, a main obvious system that controls whole responses such as contraction of the column with accompanying closure of the sphincter over the disk and a more complex system (or systems) that operates localized responses and spontaneous behavior. Pantin terms the first a through conduction system because it conducts equally in all directions from the point of stimulation and evokes the same response regardless of the location of the stimulated point. The main nerve net of medusae is also a through conduction system. Pantin suggests that the second system is somewhat similar to the autonomic nervous system of vertebrates.

Pantin and associates have continued their illuminating studies of neuromuscular patterns in anemones (I, page 598). These will not be reviewed here, but reference is made to Ross and Pantin (1940), Batham and Pantin (1950a, b, c, 1951, 1954), Pantin and Dias (1952), and Passano and Pantin (1955) and to general articles of great interest by Pantin (1950, 1952, 1956).

In 1940 there was little evidence of transmission between polyps of alcyonarian colonies (I, page 564), but Horridge (1956c, d, 1957) has shown for various alcyonarians that such transmission may occur under proper conditions of stimulation. As in anemones, facilitation (I, page 598) obtains; that is, repeated stimuli at proper intervals are necessary to elicit spread of contraction over the colony. Gorgonians exhibit little transmission of stimuli, but spread of contraction over large areas of colony was observed in *Tubipora* and various madreporarians.

g. Siphonophora.—There are important recent articles on the Siphonophora by Garstang (1946), Totton (1954a), and Leloup (1954), but these are difficult to understand, especially that of Garstang. These articles, also that of Hadzi (1954), present evidence that the pneumatophore or float is not an altered medusoid but simply an aboral invagination. Hence the Physophorida with apical float are regarded as more primitive than the Calycophorida in which the aboral end of the planuloid larva atrophies and hence fails to produce a float. It further appears that the bracts are not altered medusoids, but apparently altered tentacles that gradually become gelatinous. Totton suggests that the swimming bells, which, it will be recalled, lack mouth, manubrium, and tentacles, are altered gonophores. There is general agreement that the Chondrophora diverge from the other siphonophores, so much so that Totton, but not the others, proposes to separate them as a distinct order coordinate with the other siphonophores. Garstang declares that the Chondrophora are the most primitive siphonophores because of their radial symmetry, simple tentacles, and general lack of polymorphism, whereas the other siphonophores (= Siphonantha, after Haeckel) exhibit bilaterality and are very polymorphic with branched tentacles. The evidence indicates that siphonophore ancestors were primitive trachylines with a floating or swimming actinuloid stage and an adult medusoid stage; later both phases amalgamated to form the siphonophoran colony, with its present polymorphism. The swimming or floating actinuloid stage was comparable to present forms such as *Pelagohydra* and *Margelopsis* (I, page 441). An actinuloid ancestry is favored by all the authors mentioned, at least for Chondrophora; Garstang relates the siphonanths to corynoid athecate hydroids.

It is clearly necessary to revise the classification of the Siphonophora, dividing it into Chondrophora (I, page 479) and the siphonophores proper, for which the name Siphonantha appears proper. Whether the divergence of these two groups justifies raising them to ordinal rank (in which case the name Siphonophora is retained for the second group) as done by Totton is still debatable. The Siphonantha are to be divided into the Physonectae with a float and a nectosome as in *Agalma* (I, page 475), the Calycophorae or Calycophora (I, page 473) without a float but with swimming bells (as in I, Figs. 150*B*, 151*B*), and the Cystonectae (= Rhizophysaliae) with a very large float and no swimming bells as in *Physalia* (I, page 479). It may be noticed in passing that Picard (1957) considers the divergence of chondrophorans from other siphonophores to be so great that he reduces them to an athecate family Velellidae under the superfamily Pteronematoidea, which also contains such medusae as *Zanclea* and *Gemmaria* (I, page 443).

Madsen (1956a) identifies *Eldonia*, one of Walcott's alleged fossil holothurians (IV, page 200), as a siphonophore. His restoration shows it with a float, a circle of bracts, and one large gastrozooid.

h. Metagenesis.—The Cnidaria are supposed to present the best examples of metagenesis, or alternation of generations. This expression was defined by Steenstrup (1842) as the production of offspring which at no time resembles its parent whereas the next generation, or the brood of the offspring, returns to the form of the original parent. Most zoologists, however, understand metagenesis to be an alternation of asexually reproducing and sexually reproducing generations. In a discussion of metagenesis in cnidarians Kramp (1943) points out that neither Steenstrup's definition nor the usual definition is generally applicable. As to the hydroid not resembling the medusa, every elementary zoology book has nice diagrams showing the very considerable resemblance. Kramp concludes that metagenesis is of very different nature in different animal groups, that it has arisen secondarily and independently within each group and in different ways, that it is not a well-defined principle of development, and fundamentally does not differ from an ordinary direct ontogeny. This last conclusion was also reached by Dawydoff (1928) from the facts of trachyline embryology.

The author regards alternation of generations as a nonsensical idea. It should be obvious that the life cycle of an animal must be a continuous process from the egg to the sexually mature adult. Cnidarian life cycles, instead of being set apart as something peculiar, should be fitted into the general pattern of animal life cycles. This is easily done by taking the trachyline life cycle—egg into actinula into medusa—as fundamental to the phylum Cnidaria. There is increasing evidence that this is the case. Totton (1954a, page 18) points out that actinuloid larvae occur in many groups of Hydrozoa (Trachymedusae, Narcomedusae, Chondrophora, possibly other siphonophores, Margelopsidae, Corymorphidae, Myriothelidae, Tubulariidae, Corynidae, and their allies) and concludes this must mean that the common ancestor of these groups had an actinuloid larva. Also Rees (1957), in an outstanding article on evolution in capitate hydroids, points out that the actinula larva persists in the more primitive families and is inclined to the view that the Hydrozoa are medusoid in origin and that the hydroid phase is a later development.

The author therefore adheres firmly to the view (I, page 635) that the ancestral cnidarian was a primitive medusa developed from an actinuloid larva. The latter took to budding off other actinuloids before completing its development, and in this way the hydroid phase arose. It is sufficiently evident that the hydroid is a juvenile stage by the fact that it is incapable of sexual development, except by default. Asexual reproduction during larval or juvenile stages is widely spread among invertebrates, and the cnidarian life cycle is merely one example of this. The life cycles of Protozoa that involve successive asexual and sexual phases may also be fitted into this pattern by regarding the asexual phase as juvenile. This is certainly the case in malarial parasites with successive schizogonic cycles before sexual differentiation occurs. Arnold (1955a, b) has shown that several asexual generations may occur in Foraminifera.

It follows from the foregoing argument that tetramerous radial symmetry as exhibited by hydroid medusae is fundamental to the phylum Cnidaria.

i. Coral Reefs.—The coral reef problem continues to excite interest and attention. Summarizing reviews appear in Stearns (1946), Ladd and Tracey (1949), and Hamilton (1957). Ladd and Tracey (1947) and Emery, Tracey, and Ladd (1954) reported on the borings into Bikini Atoll, and the latter give an exhaustive consideration of the features of a coral atoll as represented by Bikini. Of the five borings into Bikini, the deepest went to 2556 feet into probably Oligocene material. The cores consisted mostly of unconsolidated calcareous material and limestones, and the deepest ended in unconsolidated sand. There were present in the cores corals, coralline algae, mollusks, and foraminiferans. The evidence seemed to indicate deposition in shallow water, hence subsidence. Ladd *et al.* (1953) reported on two borings into Eniwetok Atoll that went to 4222 and 4630 feet, respectively. These borings ended in hard basement rock, of basaltic, that is, volcanic, nature. The borings indicate that the atoll is a thick calcareous cap on the summit of a volcano that rises 2 miles above the ocean floor. The findings confirm the belief that atolls developed on submerged mountaintops on which material was deposited as they subsided below sea level. There is now other conclusive evidence of subsidence in some coral areas of the Pacific (Hamilton, 1956, 1957).

There has been found between the Hawaiian and Mariana Islands a submerged mountain range having both sharp and flat summits. These summits were once a chain of islands on which corals grew as they subsided. Such facts support not only the idea of subsidence but also the theory of antecedent flat eroded platforms as a start for coral reefs. On the other hand, there is evidence in some areas of the Pacific of development of corals on rising foundations (Stearns, 1946). It is also probable that elements of the Daly glacial-control theory (I, page 619) are valid.

In a valuable article Yonge (1940) has summarized the research of the Great Barrier Reef Expedition on the biology of corals.

j. Deep-sea Cnidarians.—The Danish *Galathea* expedition to dredge the deep-sea trenches of the world has added to the depth records for cnidarians. Kramp (1956) summarized the knowledge of hydroids from depths greater than 6000 m., reporting five species, of which *Aglaophenia galatheae* came from the Java Trench at about 7000 m. depth and another new form from the Kermadec Trench at 8210 to 8300 m. The previous depth record for hydroids was 5300 m. Records of Scyphomedusae were increased only from the previous 5850 to 6660 m. Carlgren (1956) reported that anemones are not uncommon at great depths and may reproduce there, as shown by the presence of gonads and young. A new genus and species, *Galatheanthemum hadale*, was taken in the Philippine Trench at 10,190 m., and another member of this genus at 8300 m.

k. Classification.—The classification of the Scyphozoa and Anthozoa is fairly stabilized, but that of the Hydrozoa remains in a state of flux, primarily because of the difficulty of fusing hydroid and medusoid phases into one system. Knowledge of hydrozoan life cycles is still too imperfect to allow erection of one system, except in the capitate section of Anthomedusae, where Rees (1957) has achieved this goal. Rees regards solitary forms such as *Corymorpha* and some tubularians as the most primitive existing hydroids, as also testified by their possession of actinuloid larvae, and on this basis revises the classification of part of the Anthomedusae. The resemblance of the Olindiidae[1] to Leptomedusae has made the systematic position of this family problematical, and in 1938 Kramp erected for it and related families a new order Limnomedusae. This order has been generally accepted and in Russell (1953) contains three families—Olindiidae, Moerisiidae, and Proboscidactylidae, a rather heterogeneous assemblage. Russell (1953) raises Narcomedusae and Trachymedusae to the rank of order, whereupon the former order Trachylina lapses. Carlgren (1909) created the order Pteromedusae for the aberrant medusa *Tetraplatia*, an allocation accepted by Hand (1955c).

---

[1] The family Petasiidae in Vol. I, page 461, was a mistake and is to be obliterated. The fresh-water medusae belong to the Olindiidae, which is no longer divided on the basis of presence or absence of adhesive pads.

Trachymedusae, Narcomedusae, and Pteromedusae could be regarded as suborders of Trachylina. In accord with the present vogue of raising ranks, Russell (1953) recognizes Anthomedusae and Leptomedusae as orders; hence Hydroida lapses, except as a general name hydroid for polypoid phases. Thus Hydrozoa is conceived at present as composed of the orders Anthomedusae (or Athecata), Leptomedusae (or Thecaphora), Limnomedusae, Trachymedusae, Narcomedusae, Pteromedusae, Chondrophora, Siphonophora (or Siphonantha), Milleporina, and Stylasterina.

In Anthozoa the name Octocorallia seems to be preferred to Alcyonaria and Scleractinia to Madreporaria by students of these groups. It has long been recognized that certain anemones are closely allied to corals, and in 1944 Carlgren separated these off from Actiniaria as an order Corallimorpharia, including *Rhodactis*, *Ricordea*, and *Actinotryx* (I, page 586) (but not *Discosoma*) and *Corynactis*, noted for its very large atrichous isorhizas. Carlgren also recognizes a very small order Ptychodactiaria for two genera without basilar muscles or flagellated tracts on the septal filaments and with stalked gonads. Thus two orders are to be added to the subclass Zoantharia.

Mention may be made here of important systematic works on Cnidaria. Fraser (1944) monographed the hydroids of the Atlantic Coast of North America; Vaughan and Wells (1943) revised the families and genera of stony corals, and Wells (1956) gives complete classification of stony corals to genera; Smith (1943) published a manual of West Indian stony corals; Bayer (1956) has covered the Octocorallia (= Alcyonaria) to genera; Carlgren (1949) has monographed the anemones of the world, including keys to families and genera, and listing all known species; Hand (1954b, 1955a, b) has published valuable studies on the sea anemones of central California; Boschma (1957) lists the described species of Stylasterina; Russell (1953) published an authoritative and invaluable volume of general applicability on the hydromedusae of the British Isles, containing also much information about hydroids; Rees (1957) gives a revised classification of the capitate section of athecate hydroids; and Totton (1954a) has revised the classification of siphonophores. Attention is called to the volume on "Coelenterata" in R. C. Moore (ed.), *Treatise on Invertebrate Paleontology*, an outstanding achievement; especially notable in this volume is the account of extinct medusae.[1]

---

[1] Corrections for Chap. VII: Unaccountably Fig. 106*J* shows 10 tentacles, instead of the correct number 8, in the scheme of an alcyonarian polyp; a new corrected figure has been prepared. On Fig. 108*J* the two right-hand objects labeled 7 are epidermal nuclei, not nerve cell bodies. On page 366 the definition of Cnidaria was accidentally left out in doing some cutting and pasting here; this was remedied in later printings. On pages 409 and 447 information about *Hydractinia* was unaccountably mangled; this also has been rectified. According to Kramp (1949) both *Heterostephanus* and *Hypolytus* (page 411) are *Heteractis* (hydroid name) or *Euphysa* (medusoid name). *Acaulis*, not *Acaulus*, is the correct spelling of this name (pages 411, 412, 440).

7. Phylum Ctenophora.—It has been known for 100 years that there is a ctenophore, *Euchlora rubra*, provided with nematocysts. This ctenophore has been refound and studied by Komai (1942b) and Picard (1955). The natural supposition that the ctenophore obtains the nematocysts by eating medusae (Komai, 1951) appears untenable in the light of Picard's statements. He corroborates that the animal lacks colloblasts and side branches to the tentacles, that the nematocysts are limited to two longitudinal tracts along each tentacle, and that they are all of one kind, atrichous isorhizas, characteristic of Narcomedusae; he further finds that they are limited to the epidermis (contrary to Komai) and that there are large aggregations of them in the epidermis of the tentacle bases, which are depots for their formation. If the ctenophore obtained its nematocysts by eating some cnidarian, nematocysts must inevitably be found in the gastrodermis of the gastrovascular canals, and, according to Picard, this is never the case. The facts strongly support the origin of ctenophores from the trachyline stem. In any case, the fantastic theory of Hadzi (1923) of a degradation of ctenophores from polyclad larvae is to be utterly rejected. Hadzi gives no real grounds for this view, only theoretical vaporizings. Marcus (1958) claims that Ctenophora cannot be related to Hydrozoa because of their entodermal germ cells, aboral sensory center, and highly differentiated ectomesenchyme. Entodermal germ cells are not uncommon in Hydrozoa (I, page 431) and are definitely described in *Tubularia* (Lin and Berrill, 1948) and in Hydractiniidae (Berrill, 1953). An aboral sense organ occurs in the aberrant trachyline medusa *Hydroctena* (I, page 464). Origin of muscle fibers from inwandered ectoderm cells in ctenophores may be a genuine difference from Hydrozoa, but one wonders if this process is actually distinct from separation of basal epidermal myonemes as independent muscle fibers in many Cnidaria, including Trachylina (I, page 376). The biradial symmetry of ctenophores is obviously a derivative of tetramerous radial symmetry, as seen in hydrozoan medusae. However, Ctenophora cannot be included in the same phylum with Cnidaria because of their lack of nematocysts (with the exception noted above), occurrence of colloblasts, the presence of the comb rows, and especially the unique biradial type of determinate development.

In 1848 Leuckart created the name Coelenterata to distinguish radial animals with but one opening for the digestive tract from Echinodermata; Leuckart included ctenophores and cnidarians in his concept of Coelenterata. Later authors, for example, Hatschek (1888), inclined to add sponges to this assemblage. Coelenterata thus becomes an alternate name for Radiata and is thus employed by Marcus (1958). If Ctenophora is regarded as a distinct phylum, then Coelenterata lapses as a phylum name and is to be replaced with Cnidaria, originating with Hatschek (1888).

In recent years there have been described three new genera of platyctenid ctenophores: *Lyrocteis*, Japan (Komai, 1941, 1942c), *Savangia*, Indo-China (Dawydoff, 1950), and *Vallicula*, Jamaica (Rankin, 1956). New species of *Coeloplana* and *Ctenoplana* continue to be discovered, including a species of *Coeloplana* off Florida (Smith, 1945). The author knows of no new findings in embryology. Totton (1954b) has observed that the eggs, already fertilized, are extruded through the epidermis over the gastrovascular canals, not, as formerly thought (I, page 677), through the mouth.

8. Phylum Platyhelminthes.—The greatest activity in this phylum consists in the description of new species, including the elucidation of life cycles of parasitic forms. In all three platyhelminth classes there is no end to the finding of new species; hence the described species clearly represent but a fraction of the existing flatworms. There is also interest in the metabolism of parasitic platyhelminths.

a. Turbellaria.—Much new work has been done on the Acoela, especially by Westblad (1940–1948), Ivanov (1952), and Marcus (1952, 1954), with a multiplication of species, genera, and families.[1] Steinböck (1954) has demonstrated remarkable regenerative powers of a species of *Amphiscolops;* not only will any piece of this regenerate but pieces composed only of epidermis or of the interior syncytial mass also regenerate. Off South Africa occurs a species of *Convoluta* of which also any piece will regenerate and which in nature undergoes fission without preformed fission planes (Wager, 1913; Marcus and Macnae, 1954), rarely reproducing sexually. These facts support the concept of the very primitive nature of the Acoela among Bilateria. Additional acoels with intraepidermal nervous system (II, page 83) are now known (Westblad, 1948). The brain of acoels is often laterally extended with ganglionic enlargements (Westblad, 1948), as in Vol. II, Fig. 24*D*.

Jennings (1957) has contributed an outstanding account of ingestion, digestion, and food storage in representative Turbellaria. The acoel *Convoluta paradoxa* ingests smaller organisms by extruding the inner syncytium like a pseudopodium, larger ones by pressing them against the mouth; digestion takes place in vacuoles, and products are stored mainly as fat, slightly as glycogen. In the rhabdocoels *Macrostomum* and *Stenostomum* with pharynx simplex small animal prey is swallowed whole; *Mesostoma* with rosulate pharynx protrudes this against the prey, sucks in small ones whole, and the contents of larger ones after rupturing them. In all three digestion takes place in the lumen followed by phagocytosis by the intestinal epithelium. For the triclad *Polycelis*, the results of Willier, Hyman, and Rifenburgh (II, page 203) were verified, including a total absence of intraluminar digestion, and the storage of large amounts of

---

[1] *Ectocotyla* (II, pages 104, 129 132) is not an acoel, but an alloeocoel, of the family Monocelididae (II, page 150).

protein (granular clubs) and fat. The cotylean polyclad *Cycloporus* digests wholly in the lumen, the acotylean *Leptoplana* partly in the lumen followed by intracellular digestion. The former has peripheral anal pores (II, page 170), but no material was ever seen passing through them.

Jennings also contributes the first critical evidence of the nature of gland secretions and rhabdites in triclads. He attributes the slime trails left by the worms to the secretion of the marginal adhesive glands (II, page 74), although it appears to the author that the ventral cyanophilous glands (II, page 72) contribute substantially to the mucous trails in most triclads. The discharged rhabdites were seen to swell in water to form a gelatinous sheath around the body; this was basic, soluble in acids and alkalies, and apparently of pure protein nature. It appears to act as a protective layer for the worms.

According to evidence available to 1951, fresh-water triclads never fertilize themselves (II, page 125), but Anderson (1952) found that specimens of *Cura* (= *Curtisia*) *foremani* isolated from birth may lay fertile cocoons. *Dugesia gonocephala* in Japan exists in sexual and asexual races, and Okugawa (1957) has verified Kenk (II, page 159) that members of the asexual race may be induced to become sexual by grafting from a sexual race. When the anterior third of a sexual individual is grafted to the posterior two-thirds of a member of the asexual race, the latter develops testes and a copulatory apparatus. Ovaries and testes appear in an anterior third of an asexual worm grafted to the posterior two-thirds of a sexually mature worm. Okugawa attributes these results to hormonal influences rather than to cell migrations. New investigations on embryology include those of Seilern-Aspang on a marine triclad (1956) and on the rhabdocoel *Macrostomum* (1957). The former is the first study of the embryology of a marine triclad, which was found to develop much after the manner of a fresh-water triclad (II, page 176). The study of *Macrostomum* is of special interest as the first dealing with an entolecithal rhabdocoel. Cleavage follows the spiral plan but can be interpreted arbitrarily as of the duet type of acoels or the quartet type of polyclads. This seems to indicate a lack of fundamental difference between these two types and an imperfect beginning of spiral cleavage among the lower Turbellaria. At the stage of about 16 blastomeres, 4 yolky vegetative cells surround the others apparently as a nutritive envelope. The enclosed cells continue to cleave according to the spiral pattern. Along one side some that have been noticeable from the start for their lack of yolk begin to divide rapidly and establish two primordia, a more anterior one that produces the brain and pharynx and a more posterior one that gives rise to the ventral surface and gonads. The yolky cells of the other half of the embryo become the dorsal side and central region. Despite the spiral pattern of early cleavages the embryology is largely indeterminate since no particular blastomeres are associated with the primordia mentioned. There is no definite gastrulation or formation of germ layers.

For a number of years Benazzi and associates have been studying the caryology of planarians (summary in Benazzi, 1957). They have found that *Dugesia benazzii* and *lugubris* and to a lesser degree *Polycelis nigra* exist in a number of races as regards chromosome picture, as diploids and various kinds of polyploids. In crosses between polyploid races inheritance is maternal; the sperm is necessary to stimulate the egg to development but does not participate in cleavage. The same is true when the egg of a polyploid type is fertilized by a diploid type of sperm; but as the sperm of polyploids are generally haploid or nearly so, they participate in the development after fertilizing a diploid egg and the offspring are also mostly diploid, but are sometimes polyploid. Crosses between diploid eggs and tetraploid sperm, or vice versa, may yield a variety of chromosome pictures. Synapsis is often wanting in the ovocytes of polyploid races. Crosses between F_1 individuals are usually highly infertile.

Interest in the regeneration of planarians continues. Dubois (1949) has experimented extensively on the effect of X radiation on regeneration of fresh-water planarians. She has confirmed prior workers (II, page 189) that proper dosage destroys the free cells of the mesenchyme ("neoblasts") and prevents regeneration. These cells migrate to any cut surface, being apparently attracted by chemical emanations, undergo mitoses as they approach the wound, and aggregate to form the blastema, in which they differentiate to replace the missing tissues. Probably the view that these cells originate after cutting by dedifferentiation of body cells (II, page 189) is erroneous. Dubois has shown that if only part of a planarian is radiated, free mesenchyme cells migrate from the nonradiated part through the radiated part to a cut surface in the radiated part where they accomplish regeneration. Such regeneration is delayed over the normal time in direct proportion to the distance which the mesenchyme cells must travel. The attractive power of a cut surface ceases after the blastema has been formed, and mesenchyme cells will not pass one cut surface to reach a more distant one. Pieces of radiated worms grafted into nonradiated ones receive mesenchyme cells from the latter, and pieces of nonradiated worms grafted into radiated ones give them off into the latter but only if a cut is made. The migration of these cells is absolutely dependent on the presence of a cut surface.

In *Polycelis nigra*, which has a row of eyes along the margin of the anterior end (as in II, Fig. 32D), Lender (1950) and Wolff and Lender (1950) showed that the regeneration of these eyes is dependent on the presence of the brain and that this influence extends back to the copulatory region, beyond which implanted margins from which the eyes have been removed will not regenerate eyes unless a piece of brain is also implanted (Lender, 1951). Later work (Lender, 1956a, b) showed that an aqueous mince of brain to which planarians deprived of eyes and their own brain are exposed for 3 to 4 days is effective in inducing eye regeneration. Lender believes that both the inductive and inhibitory effects of the brain on regeneration are of chemical nature.

Chandebois has contributed a series of researches on the regeneration of the marine triclad *Procerodes lobata* (summarized in 1957).

Bröndsted (1955, 1956) has usefully summarized the subject of planarian regeneration. He has substantiated the findings and concepts of Child (II, page 182) but seems to imagine he has contributed something new by calling Child's physiological gradient by the name of "time-graded regeneration field."

The classification of the Turbellaria was stabilized by Bresslau in the *Handbuch der Zoologie*, who based it on the pioneering work of von Graff. Changes from the von Graff–Bresslau arrangement consist chiefly of juggling with ranks. In 1940 Karling, grossly exaggerating the value of yolk glands as a taxonomic character, threw the Acoela and the lower Rhabdocoela into one order Archoophora on the basis of a lack of yolk glands. Westblad (1948), abetting Karling, added Polycladida to this potpourri and designated all remaining Turbellaria as an order Neoophora having germovitellaria or separate yolk glands. Apart from the inadvisability of basing high systematic categories on a single character difference, yolk glands are a poor selection for this purpose since they occur in all gradations in the Turbellaria (II, page 119). A beginning of differentiation of yolk-supplying tissue is already seen in Acoela (II, page 119). It is impossible to categorize some turbellarians such as the Lecithoepitheliata (II, page 119) as to whether they have yolk glands or not. The author as a specialist on the Turbellaria considers the Karling-Westblad division of this class into orders Archoophora and Neoophora as unqualifiedly bad and rejects it altogether. Archoophora was further a bad name selection since it had already been used by Reisinger in an entirely different sense (II, page 149). One then returns to the standard division of the Turbellaria into several orders.

The Acoela offer some difficulties. It now appears usual to regard both *Nemertoderma* (II, page 132) and *Hofstenia* (II, page 150) as acoels, although both have a digestive lumen. However, the author does not regard the absence of a lumen in typical acoels as of any importance. Embryology shows that digestive lumina may come and go with the greatest of ease. Karling reduced Acoela to a suborder and created the suborders Hofsteniida and Nemertodermatida for the two genera in question. If these three suborders are to be recognized, they must be united into one order, for which a new name would then be necessary, such as Neoacoela.

It is desirable to avoid this, as can be done by regarding *Hofstenia* and *Nemertoderma* as worthy of family rank only.   Steinböck in his original description of *Nemertoderma* had given it only family rank.   Westblad (1949b) has added another genus *Meara* to the Nemertodermatidae. Hofsteniida was reduced to family rank by Papi (1957) in describing a new genus of the family Hofsteniidae, *Hofsteniola*.   Perhaps the curious genus *Xenoturbella*, for which Westblad (1949a) created a suborder Xenotur-bellida, can be disposed of as representing an acoel family Xenoturbellidae.

In 1924 Meixner proposed the division of the Rhabdocoela into three sections—Catenulida, Macrostomida, and Lecithophora—and in 1938 he raised these to the rank of order, renaming the last Neorhabodocoela (II, page 61).   The single protonephridium and the peculiarities of the reproductive system (II, page 137) seem to justify ordinal rank for the Catenulida, but there is less evident justification for ordinal rank for the Macrostomida (II, page 139), although these do differ from the remaining rhabdocoels in having a pharynx simplex.

The term Alloeocoela is anathema to Karling and Westblad, and the heterogeneous nature of this assemblage must be admitted.   The alter-native course of raising the suborders to the rank of orders was already proposed by Karling (1940) with some unnecessary alterations.   The four suborders (II, page 60) would then become orders.   The Archoophora in Reisinger's sense cannot be allied to acoels and lower rhabdocoels because of the plicate pharynx.   Meixner's inclusion of the Tricladida as a subgroup of Alloeocoela Seriata (II, page 61), also accepted by Karling, is to be altogether rejected.   Although the triclads appear to have evolved from this group of alloeocoels, their assemblage of distinctive character-istics entitles them to ordinal rank.

Ax (1956) considers an order Gnathostomulida necessary for two peculiar turbellarians with entolecithal eggs and intraepidermal nervous system but provided with a bulbous pharynx armed with two jaws.

At the present moment, then, the Turbellaria comprise the following orders: Acoela, Catenulida, Macrostomida, Neorhabdocoela, Gnathosto-mulida, Archoophora (original sense), Lecithoepitheliata, Holocoela, Seriata, Tricladida, and Polycladida.

b. Trematoda.—In this class great activity continues in the description of new species and the elucidation of life cycles.   In 1890 there were known slightly over 100 species of monogenetic trematodes; now this number has risen to around 700.   Similarly, the number of known species of digenetic trematodes has increased from 570 in 1890 to over 5000 today.

A few points appear worthy of mention.   Willey (1954) now declares that the lymphatic system (II, page 230) is simply a survival of the primary excretory system of the cercaria.   Pearson (1956) confirms the existence of an extra stage (mesocercaria) in the life cycle of *Alaria* (II, page 293).   In regard to the life cycle of the lancet fluke, *Dicrocoelium dendriticum*, Krull and Mapes (1952, 1953) have shown that the slime balls of cercariae (II, page 279) are not directly infective to the definitive host but require to be ingested by ants, in which they develop to encysted metacercariae.   Martin (1952) has found another polychaetous annelid serving as first intermediate host for a digenetic trematode (II, page 256); this is an antarctic terebellid in which rediae and fork-tailed cercariae were present.   Premvati (1955), studying schistosome sporocysts in the snail *Melanoides*, confirmed an earlier observation that first-generation sporocysts may produce miracidia.   These are typical schistosome miracidia, which apparently must arise by parthenogenesis; they do not get free but seem to develop into second-generation sporocysts in the snail host.   Buttner (1950–1951, 1955) has called attention to numerous cases of "progenesis" among digenetic trematodes, that is, the attainment of sexual maturity by metacercariae with production of viable eggs, hatching into infective larvae.   It would appear that many digenetic trematodes are in process of eliminating the definitive host.   The concept that the reproductive processes in the larval stages of digenetic trematodes are of the nature of polyembryony (II, page 265) has received further confirmation (Van der Woude, 1954; Ciordia, 1956).   The claims of Woodhead, extending over the years, of sexual processes in larval stages cannot be substantiated by anyone; Ciordia, in fact, using one of the same species in which Woodhead claimed sexual reproduction in the sporocysts, found no evidence thereof.   Dollfus *et al.* (1956) were able to rear a strigeid metacercaria removed from cysts in frogs to sexually mature adults by simply incubating them at 38°C. in Ringer's solution.   Probably the same can be done with other strigeid metacercariae that have warm-blooded vertebrates as definitive hosts.

La Rue (1957) has proposed a classification of the digenetic trematodes. He considers Digenea a subclass, which he divides into two superorders, based on a single character, the nature of the wall of the excretory bladder, a rather precarious basis.   Each superorder is then divided into orders and superfamilies, for details of which the original article must be consulted. La Rue correctly rejects the widely copied division of Digenea into Gasterostomata and Protostomata (II, page 266); the former includes only the family Bucephalidae, now known to be related to other families with fork-tailed cercariae (Stunkard, 1946).   Dubois (1953) has monographed the important group of strigeid trematodes (II, page 289). Skrjabin (1955–1956) is monographing (in Russian) the digenetic trematodes of the world, having produced at the present writing 12 volumes. A valuable contribution to the systematics of the Monogenea was made by Sproston (1946).

c. *Cestoda.*—Research is active in species descriptions, elucidations of life cycles, and metabolic and biochemical studies of worms in vitro. Wardle and McLeod (1952) have summarized knowledge of tapeworms in a useful volume.

Joyeaux and Baer (1950) find that *Gyrocotyloides* (II, page 350) is a valid genus. Riser (1956) has confirmed in another species the account of the trypanorhynchid life cycle given by Ruszowski (1934; overlooked in II). The operculated egg hatches into a ciliated coracidium containing an oncosphere with six hooks. When ingested by copepods this develops into a procercoid without typical tail. Plerocercoid stages in teleost fish and various invertebrates were already known (II, page 368), and other reports have since become available. Evidently the life cycle is very similar to that of pseudophyllids. Smyth (1949, 1954) has now obtained fertile eggs of both *Ligula intestinalis* and *Schistocephalus solidus* by cultivating the plerocercoids in vitro (II, page 409) in improved medium at a temperature corresponding to that of the definitive bird host. It will be recalled that the plerocercoids of these tapeworms reach an advanced stage in the intermediate fish host. Additional species of dioecious cestodes have been found in the family Acoleidae (II, page 398) by Coil (1955) and Cable and Myers (1956).

Studies on tapeworm embryology have been made by Ogren (1955, 1956, 1957a, b). In *Hymenolepis* and *Mesocestoides*, one of the first two blastomeres, recognizable by its greater yolk content, does not participate in the embryo but surrounds the other blastomeres as an embryophore or at least contributes to this. In *Oochoristica*, however, all blastomeres participate in the embryo, which becomes surrounded, under the original capsule, with a noncellular pseudoembryophore, apparently a secretion of the surface blastomeres of the embryo. In all cases the embryo is a ball of cells of about equal size in which there differentiate the onchoblasts that secrete the hooks, muscle fibers, and a pair of gland cells. These, the penetration glands of Reid (II, page 336), have now been demonstrated in the oncospheres of various cestodes. Their secretion appears to be of polysaccharide nature (Silverman and Maneely, 1955; Enigk and Sticinsky, 1957). Silverman (1954) enumerates the membranes of the oncospheres of *Taenia* as follows: outer thin chorionic membrane (capsule), thick, radially striated shell (embryophore), basement membrane of the shell, two-layered oncospheral membrane. The yolk is found between the capsule and the shell. Ogren (1957b) considers that there are seven known types of cestode development: mesocestoidid type in which the surface cells of the morula detach to form a cellular embryophore under the embryophore originated from one of the first two blastomeres; taeniid type with a thick, radially striated shell; anoplocephalid type with a pyriform apparatus (II, page 366); hymenolepid group, in which the entire embryo becomes the oncosphere and its surface cells secrete a noncellular pseudoembryophore; the linstowiid type, similar to the preceding, also with secreted pseudoembryophore; proteocephalid group in which surface cells detach to form a thin cellular embryophore, but all blastomeres participate in the embryo; and the diphyllobothriid type with a coracidium. In all cases the hooks occur at the end opposite that which develops the scolex; hence the latter is anterior.

Silverman and Maneely (1955) followed the penetration of taeniid oncospheres by enclosing these in short lengths of mouse intestine incubated in warm saline and fixed at intervals. The hooks seem to have only an anchoring action, and lysis of the intestinal wall is accomplished by the secretion of the penetration glands. The oncospheres penetrated the lining epithelium of the intestine in 10 minutes.

Wardle and McLeod (1952) present a complete classification of cestodes. This differs from that in Vol. II primarily in that *Spathebothrium* and related genera (II, page 375) and Caryophyllaeidae (II, page 375) are raised to the rank of orders. Euzet (1956) returns Lecanocephaloidea (II, page 358) to the Tetraphyllidea, proposing a new classification of the latter.

d. Capsule Formation.—There are numerous confirmations that the droplets in the yolk cells contain protein and a phenol and that the formation of the capsule in flatworms involves the quinone tanning of a protein (II, page 238). This has been shown for the triclad *Dendrocoelum lacteum* by Nurse (1950) and for polyclads by Valeurone (1953). Most trematodes also have quinone-tanned egg capsules (Smyth, 1951; Monné and Borg, 1954; Johri and Smyth, 1956). The function of the highly developed Mehlis's gland of trematodes then becomes problematical. Yosufzai (1953) in a detailed study of capsule formation in the liver fluke finds that Mehlis's gland secretes a hyaline fluid and concludes that this fluid forms the main part of the egg capsule. The capsule in pseudophyllid tapeworms is also found to be a quinone-tanned protein (Smyth, 1951, 1956), but this is not the case in taenioid cestodes (Johri and Smyth, 1956; Johri, 1957), which, however, have poorly developed yolk glands and a very thin, often evanescent capsule. The thick, cross-striated shell of Taeniidae is clearly not homologous with the capsule of trematode eggs.

e. Metabolism and Biochemistry of Parasitic Flatworms.—These topics constitute an increasingly active field of research. They have been reviewed by Bueding (1949, 1951), Moulder (1950), von Brand (1950, 1952), and Bueding and Most (1953). Current research on these subjects constantly appears in the journal *Experimental Parasitology*.

9. Phylum Rhynchocoela.—The occurrence of rhabdites in nemerteans was noted in Vol. II (page 465), but not sufficiently emphasized. Bürger (1890) described the presence of rhabdites in the surface epidermis of the everted proboscis of a number of nemerteans. His figures of these rhabdites are indistinguishable from turbellarian rhabdites. Gont-charoff (1957) presents electron-microscope photographs of rhabdites from the proboscis of *Lineus;* these show the rhabdites as composed of a solid core surrounded by a less dense sheath, but unfortunately no control study was made of turbellarian rhabdites. If true rhabdites occur in nemerteans, this would link them further with platyhelminths.

10. Phylum Acanthocephala.—Arguments continue as to whether the Acanthocephala are nearer the Platyhelminthes or the Aschelminthes. Haffner (1950), accepting the aschelminth view, makes a critical comparison of Acanthocephala with the various aschelminth classes. He rejects a priapuloid affinity partly on the ground that the anterior end of priapuloids is pentamerous (III, Fig. 88*C*), whereas that of acanthocephalans is hexamerous (III, Fig. 1*D*). However, it does not appear that hexamerous symmetry is fundamental to the Acanthocephala, nor is there the important difference in the development of the nephridia in the two groups claimed by Haffner. Minor grounds are given for rejection of relationship to other groups of Aschelminthes except Rotifera. Astonishingly, Haffner arrives at the conclusion that the Acanthocephala are closer to the Rotifera than to any other aschelminth group. The author finds the arguments for this strange conclusion very unconvincing.

On the other hand, Petrotchenko (1952) postulates a platyhelminth affinity, noting many differences from nematodes and resemblances in the nervous system between acanthocephalans and lower Turbellaria. He concludes that Aschelminthes and Acanthocephala are separate phyla that have arisen independently from a main acoel-polyclad stem leading to rhabdocoels, trematodes, and cestodes.

Ward (1951, 1952) has listed the species of Acanthocephala described since Meyer's 1933 monograph; the total is something over 500 species.

11. Phylum Aschelminthes.—This phylum met with less resistance than the author expected and bids fair to achieve wide acceptance. It must always be borne in mind that the ultimate contents of this phylum must await further knowledge of its present members.

a. Rotifera.—It was noted (III, page 105) that a study of the embryology of a less modified rotifer than *Asplanchna* was needed. This want has now been supplied by de Beauchamp (1956) for a pelagic rotifer *Ploesoma* (III, Fig. 27*A*). Cleavage is of the spiral type, and at the four-cell stage the embryo consists of three micromeres and a large macromere (as in III, Fig. 49*D*), which, as in *Asplanchna*, is the primordium of the female reproductive system, later dividing into two or four cells. The micromeres contain yolk globules, and as they continue to multiply these globules are relegated to their more posterior products that grow down over the macromere, and eventually form a vegetative cap, the future entoderm. By epiboly these entoderm cells, marked by the yolk globules, and the macromere get pushed into the interior and get covered over by the remaining products of the micromeres, which are ectodermal. The yolk-containing entoderm cells are displaced to a posterodorsal position in the interior and become the stomach. Hence the story of the formation of the stomach in *Asplanchna* from the dorsal embryonic wall (III, page 102) was an error of observation. There is a stomodaeal invagination at the middle of what is now recognizable as the ventral face of the embryo. This invagination occurs near the site of a mere gap that probably represents the blastopore. The stomodaeum probably gives rise to the mastax. Behind the stomodaeum a lobe grows out as the foot, and behind its base the anus arises by a proctodaeal invagination. The development generally conforms to the spiral type, but the entoderm originates from the cells *A*, *B*, and *C*, not from *D*. There is no marked bilaterality in the later stages.

Remane (1950a) considers that the trochal disks of the Bdelloidea are not developments of the circumapical band as supposed according to the views of de Beauchamp (III, page 72) but are lateral lobulations of the buccal field, corresponding to pseudotrochs. Remane further suggests that primitively the buccal field was three-lobed; the median lobe became the rostrum, and the lateral lobes developed into pseudotrochs or trochal disks with disappearance of the circumapical band.

Voigt (1956–1957) has provided a manual of identification of the rotifers of central Europe, generally applicable. Bartos (1951) has monographed the Bdelloidea, with special reference to the family Habrotrochidae.

b. Gastrotricha.—Sacks (1955) has worked out the embryology of the fresh-water chaetonotoid, *Lepidodermella squammata* (correct spelling, not *squamata*). Early cleavage suggests the spiral type, but the pattern is bilateral after the fourth cleavage. The four-cell stage consists of four equal blastomeres, *A* and *B* in the animal half, *C* and *D* in the vegetal half. However, the animal cells divide more rapidly; hence at the 24-cell stage there are 16 cells in the animal half, 8 in the vegetal half. A blastocoel arises, and at the 32-cell stage gastrulation occurs, consisting of the migration of two cells of the *A* series into the blastocoel, as in *Neogossea* (III, page 165). The blastopore is therefore at about the middle of the future ventral surface. The fate of the two invaginated cells is not stated, but presumably they produce the intestine. Just anterior to the blastopore, cells of the *A* and *B* series invaginate to form the stomodaeum, and near the posterior end on the ventral surface occurs a proctodaeal invagination. The stomodaeal invagination shifts anteriorly, and the digestive tract begins to be outlined. The embryo elongates and bends within the egg membrane after the manner of a nematode. By this time the embryo is recognizable as a young gastrotrich. The caudal forks and surface scales form, and the young animal hatches 22 to 31 hours after oviposition. The two conspicuous ventroposterior cells described for *Neogossea* (III, page 165) are absent in *Lepidodermella*. Swedmark (1955) briefly described the embryology of a macrodasyoid *Macrodasys affinis*. This lays three to six eggs, probably several times annually. Cleavage is of the spiral type, a blastocoel arises, and at gastrulation two cells are invaginated into the interior. Stomodaeum and proctodaeum complete the digestive tract, and at 10 days the young animals hatch. Similar observations were made on other marine species. The course of development may therefore be said to be similar throughout the class.

Brunson (1950) has given a useful, if unfortunately incomplete, account of fresh-water gastrotrichs in the United States. Many new species of marine gastrotrichs have been found in recent years on European coasts. The author failed to find them on North American coasts through looking in the wrong kind of habitat; it appears that they live only in sand. They were discovered on coasts of the United States by Sacks in the summer of 1951 in the vicinity of Woods Hole, Massachusetts; later he also found them in Long Island Sound and off Carolina. To the present time he has discovered seven macrodasyoid species and seven marine chaetonotoid species, of which only three are undescribed forms. Unfortunately Sacks has been unable to publish his findings. In the meantime Remane (1953) described a new species of *Turbanella* from El Salvador, Central America, and Wieser (1957) found six species, four of them new, in Puget Sound. Ruttner-Kolisko (1955) has discussed a new fresh-water macrodasyoid genus, *Marinellina*, that may be intermediate between fresh-water and marine gastrotrichs.

c. Kinorhyncha.—In this group there is nothing to report except the continued finding of new species. The group is still poorly known from North American coasts.

d. Priapulida.—The early development of *Priapulus caudatus* has been described by Zhinkin (1949) and Lang (1953); this later account by the latter differs considerably from his earlier story (III, page 193). Both authors agree that cleavage is of the radial type, with no hint of spirality. At the eight-cell stage there is a tier of four animal cells directly over four vegetal cells. The blastomeres are at first approximately equal, but later the vegetal ones are slightly larger than the animal ones. Cleavage results in a coeloblastula, which at the 64-cell stage undergoes a typical embolic gastrulation according to Lang, whereas Zhinkin regards the gastrulation as mainly epibolic. Lang noted strands of mesoderm arising around the archenteral base and filling the blastocoel, and observed hatching at this stage as a stereogastrula consisting of an ectodermal layer enclosing an inner syncytial mass. Neither author was able to carry the development beyond the gastrula stage.

Lang gives a lengthy discussion of the systematic position of the Priapulida. He accepts their placement among the Aschelminthes, declaring that the lining of their body cavity cannot be a peritoneum because it is devoid of nuclei. He proposes the subdivision of the Aschelminthes into one group (erroneously, subclass) comprising Rotifera, Gastrotricha, Nematoda, and Nematomorpha, and another group comprising Kinorhyncha, Priapulida, and Acanthocephala. Contrary to Haffner (1950), he supports a close affinity between Priapulida and Acanthocephala. This solution of the aschelminth problem is worthy of consideration; possibly each of his groups should constitute a phylum. Lang already proposed the name Rhynchohelminthes for the second group.

Fänge and Abesson (1952) have examined the body fluid of *Priapulus caudatus*. It is pink and milky, containing red cells in the form of biconvex disks to the number of 45,000 to 160,000 per cubic millimeter, also amoebocytes with petaloid pseudopods. The red cells contain haemerythrin, otherwise known only in *Lingula* (page 593) and sipunculoids (page 679). Similar findings obtain for *Halicryptus spinulosus*.

Lang (1951) and Wesenberg-Lund (1955) agree that the priapulids of high southern latitudes are not identical with the northern forms and constitute two distinct species, *Priapulus australis* and *P. tuberculatospinosus;* hence bipolarity (III, page 195) does not obtain for priapulids. The number of species in the class is thereby raised to five. It should have been mentioned that *Priapulus caudatus* occurs on the Pacific Coast of the United States.

e. Nematoda.—Here research is very active in taxonomy, accounts of life histories, and metabolic, biochemical, and physiological studies.

There is still uncertainty as to the identity of human and pig *Ascaris lumbricoides*. Takata (1951) reported that juvenile pig ascaris would mature in man but the infection disappears in a month or two. Sprent (1952) showed much better development of denticles on the lips in pig than in human ascaris. In discussing the histological peculiarities of nematodes (III, page 263) the author forgot to mention the well-known absence of cilia in the class; but probably the rod border of the intestine consists of degenerated cilia. Recent studies of cell constancy in nematodes indicate less perfect constancy than usually supposed. Wessing (1953), studying this question in *Rhabditis anomala,* found that mitoses cease at hatching in the tissues of anterior and posterior ends, which do not in fact lengthen much during ontogeny, but in the midgut, midventral nerve, trunk epidermis, and sex organs cell or nuclear multiplication continues throughout the juvenile stages, at first by mitosis, later by amitosis; hence there is cell inconstancy in these parts. Amitotic nuclear divisions were observed in the midgut epithelium of adult worms.

Frenzen (1955) found that specimens of *Ascaridia galli* from the Rhine area and from Indonesia differed considerably as to nuclear number. In this species also adults have many more nuclei than later juveniles, an indication of nuclear multiplication during juvenile growth. In *Heterakis gallinorum* there is also much multiplication of cells (or nuclei) in the midgut and reproductive system during ontogeny (Peng, 1957); the number of midgut cells increased from less than 500 in first-stage juveniles to about 4000 in adults, although no mitoses were observed. Wessing noted that the renette of *Rhabditis anomala* consists throughout ontogeny of a single H-shaped cell with the constantly elongating limbs of the H embedded in the lateral chords.

Axenic culture of nematodes proceeds apace. Stoll (1953) has continued the culture of *Neoaplectana glaseri* (III, page 404), using fresh sterile rabbit kidney on a dextrose-agar slant or a fluid medium of veal or heart broth plus raw-liver extract. Dougherty and Hansen (1956) have continued the axenic culture of a soil rhabditoid which they now call *Caenorhabditis briggsae*. Some success has been achieved with a defined medium containing 18 amino acids (of which 8 appear dispensable), 18 vitamins and related factors, 5 nucleic acid derivatives plus thymine, choline, and inositol, glucose, and a salt mixture including trace metals. On this medium juveniles slowly matured and laid eggs that hatched; but for really successful growth and maintenance a liver medium must be added. To the present, media containing protein extracts are essential for the axenic cultivation of saprophagous nematodes. The vinegar eel (*Turbatrix aceti*) was grown axenically in a medium of peptone, yeast extract, and ether extract of rat liver by Ells and Read (1952) and on liver homogenate plus chick embryo extract by Nicholas (1956). Weinstein (1953) grew the free-living stages of hookworms, which normally eat bacteria (III, page 413), axenically on chick embryo or rat liver extracts to the third infective stage; heating the extracts or passing them through a bacterial filter destroyed their ability to support growth. In 1956 Weinstein and Jones achieved the first successful cultivation in vitro of a parasitic nematode to sexual maturity, although there was no production of fertile eggs. They used the strongyloid *Nippostrongylus muris* on a medium of chick embryo extract, caseinate, yeast or liver extract, and mammalian serum. Similar results were obtained with another strongyloid, *Nematospiroides dubius* (Jones and Weinstein, 1957).

Rather surprising is the discovery in recent years of nematode-destroying fungi (reviews by Duddington, 1954, 1955). This author isolated 20 such kinds of fungi from English agricultural soils. Most capture nematodes by growing an adhesive network around them; others hold the nematode by sticky branches or knobs; still others produce sticky spores that adhere to the nematode and grow out hyphae into its body;

most astonishing is the throwing of a constricting loop around the worm. After capturing the nematode the fungus digests its interior.

New survival records for dried phytoparasitic nematodes are furnished by Fielding (1951), who found *Ditylenchus dipsaci* alive after 21 years and *Anguina tritici* after 28 years in the dry state (III, page 405).

The Danish *Galathea* expedition to the abyssal trenches increased the depth record for marine nematodes to 6620 m. in the Kermedec Trench (Bruun, 1956).

New research possibilities were opened by Dissanaike, Dissanaike, and Niles (1956, 1957), who found that microfilariae can be tagged with radioactive phosphorus. If mosquito larvae are reared in a medium containing phosphorus 32, they give rise to adult mosquitoes that contain P 32, and these in turn pass it on to the microfilariae they ingest when feeding on infected hosts. By this means it may be possible to follow the infective stages when injected by mosquitoes into man; their course in the human body is still unknown (III, page 377).

Much concern has been aroused in recent years by the discovery of the prevalence of trichinosis among the natives and mammals of the Arctic (general review by Rausch *et al.*, 1956). A high incidence of infection with juveniles was found in bears, especially polar bears, dogs, and other carnivores such as coyotes, wolves, foxes, ermine, weasels, wolverines, and lynx; little infection in whales, walrus, and seals. Thorshaug and Rosted (1956) reported infection in 59 per cent of 278 polar bears examined and in 10 per cent of the walruses. Probably the eating of insufficiently cooked meat of polar bears is a main cause of outbreaks of trichinosis among arctic natives.

Interest continues in the cuticle of nematodes, which reaches its greatest complexity in large ascaroids such as *Ascaris lumbricoides*. In a recent study of the cuticle of this worm, Bird and Deutsch (1957) verify the presence of nine layers: outer cortical layer covered by a thin osmiophilic, hence probably lipoid, film, inner cortical layer, fibrillar layer, homogeneous layer, actually containing radial striations, outer, middle, and inner fiber layers made of collagen, although this does not show the typical cross-banding in electron-microscope photographs, and the basal lamella, also with radial striations. Bird (1957) denied the presence of keratin but found instead that the external cortical layer is a quinone-tanned protein. Small amounts of carbohydrates are present in the cuticle (Bird, 1956). Bird (1954) and Bird and Rogers (1956) were able to isolate the cuticles of third-stage infective strongyloid juveniles; they consist of protein, yielding on acid hydrolysis only 9 amino acids, whereas adult cuticles yield 16 (Bird, 1956). Harris and Crofton (1957), measuring the internal turgor of the pig ascaris, attribute great importance to the fiber layers of the cuticle in maintaining shape and turgor, considering them an inextensible system that resists contraction of the longitudinal muscle layer of the body wall.

Monné and Hönig (1954a, b) and Monné (1956), investigating the egg membranes of various nematodes, find that an inner lipoid membrane is generally present and the outer protein coat is often a quinone-tanned protein. A chitinous shell (III, page 252) appears limited to ascaroids, where these authors find it made of thick chitinous layers alternating with thin protein layers. The end plugs of trichuroid eggs (III, Fig. 122G) are said to be composed of polysaccharide. The mammilated protein coat of ascaris eggs is reported as also containing mucopolysaccharide.

To the records of the occurrence of intrinsic haemoglobins in nematodes (III, page 425) should be added the oxyuroid *Heterakis gallinae* (Grembergen, 1954) and the spiruroid *Tetrameres confusa* (Ribeiro and Villela, 1956).

It is impossible to review here other findings in the chemistry and physiology of nematodes. An extensive review, with special reference to the large ascaroids, has been given by Fairbairn (1957). The article of Lazarus (1950) on respiratory metabolism of various helminths is valuable. Other main contributions to nematode biochemistry and physiology by Bueding, Cavier and Savel, Fairbairn and associates, Haskins and Weinstein, and Rogers are cited by Fairbairn.

Other works and articles on nematodes of general value and interest are the book by Goodey (1951), *Soil and Freshwater Nematodes;* the book by Mary Franklin (1952), *The Cyst-forming Species of Heterodera;* the articles by Chitwood (1951), Mai and Lear (1952), and Ellenby (1954) on the golden potato nematode, *Heterodera rostochiensis;* a review of cyst-forming plant parasitic nematodes by Steiner, Taylor, and Cobb (1951); a lengthy consideration of the genus *Rhabditis* by Osche (1952); a historical account of the American hookworm by Ackert (1952) and another on trichina by Reinhard (1958); and symposia on the filarioids *Loa* (Gordon, 1955) and *Onchocerca* (Adams, 1958), both of which may cause blindness in man.

In 1950 the Chitwoods presented a complete classification of nematodes, only slightly altered from their 1937 arrangement. They now regard Nematoda as a phylum, a view that probably cannot stand. They retain the primary division of Nematoda into Phasmidia and Aphasmidia. This arrangement was previously rejected by the author (III, page 216) but has been generally accepted. Examination of the definitions of Phasmidia and Aphasmidia given by the Chitwoods shows exceptions and qualifications to every item except the presence or absence of phasmids. Surely the presence or absence of these minute pouches (III, page 214) is hardly worthy of the rank of class or even subclass; perhaps superorder would be a suitable rank. In fact the whole classification of the group seems to be characterized by exaggeration of the worth of morphological differences. The present author supports the statement of Harris and Crofton (1957): "No one who has made even a casual study of the Nematoda can fail to have been struck by the extraordinary similarity in form and organization between the very large number of species, genera, orders and families which constitute the class." The following discussion limits itself to superfamilies.

The Aphasmidia include the free-living marine nematodes and two parasitic groups. The Chitwoods replace the Araeolaimoidea (III, page 285) by two groups, Plectoidea and Axonolaimoidea, separate the families Desmodoridae (III, page 279), Draconematidae (III, page 281), and Epsilonematidae (III, page 285) from the Chromadoroidea as Desmodoroidea, and raise certain enoploid families (III, page 270) to a superfamily Tripyloidea. Mermithoidea (III, page 272), Trichuroidea (III, page 380), and Dioctophymoidea (III, page 386) are also regarded as Aphasmidia.

The Phasmidia include the Rhabditoidea and the remaining parasitic groups. Tylenchoids and aphelenchoids (III, page 296) are now generally separated from rhabditoids as distinct orders (or superfamilies). The Chitwoods also erect Drilonematoidea for two families not mentioned in Vol. III. Rhabdiasoidea (III, page 304) is not recognized as distinct from Rhabditoidea but constituting two families, Rhabdiasidae and Strongyloididae, of the latter.

In the zooparasitic Phasmidia the Chitwoods still retain Trichostrongyloidea and Metastrongyloidea as distinct from Strongyloidea. The families placed under Oxyuroidea in Vol. III, pages 317–321, should be transferred to Ascaroidea, of which the correct form seems to be Ascaridoidea. Chabaud (1957) goes so far as to raise some of these families to the rank of superfamily (Cosmocercoidea, Subuluroidea, Heterakoidea); but Inglis (1957) retains the Heterakidae in the Ascaridoidea, including a good discussion of cordons (III, page 204), which he regards as extensions of the interlabial grooves. There is much discussion in the literature of the systematics of the Spiruroidea (Chabaud, 1954; Dollfus and Chabaud, 1957). These authors recognize the accuracy of the work of Chitwood and Wehr (III, page 353) and acknowledge the families Thelaziidae, Spiruridae, Tetrameridae, Acuariidae, and Gnathostomatidae but raise the Physalopteridae to a separate superfamily Physalopteroidea. The Chitwoods also raise the families Camallanidae and Cucullanidae (III, pages 365, 367) to the rank of Camallanoidea. In the Filarioidea the arrangement of Skrjabin and Schikhobalova (III, page 370) has been mostly rejected and the four families of Wehr and the Chitwoods (III, page 370) have been generally recognized as valid (Anderson, 1957), although Lopez-Neyra (1956) disagrees considerably. It will be noticed that the disease of raising ranks is rampant in the

Nematoda, where it is particularly offensive because of the slight differences between members of this class. Finally it should be mentioned that the indefatigable Skrjabin is monographing or editing the monographing of the zooparasitic nematodes of the world.

f. Nematomorpha.—In the account of this group the important article of Huus (1931) on *Nectonema* was unfortunately overlooked. This deficiency was remedied in later printings. Huus observed copulation in *Nectonema*, similar to that of gordioids (III, page 465), and the laying of spiny eggs, which, however, did not develop. Later early larvae of *Nectonema* were found in the crab *Munida*. These strongly resemble gordioid larvae, having an invaginable anterior end with a central armature encircled by two circles of hooks. The surface, however, lacks the superficial segmentation characteristic of the gordioid larva. These findings leave no doubt of the correctness of combining Gordioidea and Nectonematoidea into one class Nematomorpha.

12. Phylum Entoprocta.—As already discussed earlier in this volume (page 277), the Entoprocta are maintained as a phylum distinct from Ectoprocta. However, the author withdraws the idea of a relationship between Entoprocta and Rotifera (III, page 552), acknowledging that the cell constancy and lack of regenerative power in the latter make such relationship improbable. The idea of Brien and Papyn, also supported by Marcus (1958), that the entoprocts are an early offshoot of the line leading to ectoprocts is acceptable.

New species continue to be described, especially in the Loxosomatidae, where four genera are now recognized: *Loxosoma* without pedal gland at any stage, *Loxosomella* with pedal gland in the bud only, hence indistinguishable from *Loxosoma* in the adult state, *Loxocalyx* with pedal gland throughout life, and a recent genus *Loxomespilon* (Bobin and Prenant, 1953) without a stalk. The latter authors straightened out the confusion in the genera, pointing out that the type species of *Loxosoma* lacks a pedal gland at all stages.

13. Phylum Echinodermata.—A few articles of interest have appeared since the publication of Vol. IV.

a. Holothuroidea.—The toxic substance, named holothurin, of cucumbers (IV, page 237) has been investigated by Yamanouchi (1955), Nigrelli *et al.* (1955), and Chanley *et al.* (1955) and found to be a glucoside identical with or very similar to saponin. It is produced by the entire body, notably the body wall, and is not particularly related to the cuvierian tubules. As saponin and related substances are haemolytic, holothurin is especially toxic to vertebrates and, according to Yamanouchi, is not poisonous to crustaceans, mollusks, or anemones. He found the toxin present in most of 15 holothurian species investigated. It is harmless when eaten by man since species with the poison are eaten raw in Japan and are also used in making trepang. Yamanouchi confirms the native practice of mashing holothurians in fish pools to paralyze the fish.

Arnold (1957) has contributed an article on the behavior of the pearl fish toward its cucumber host (IV, page 243). The fish can live free indefinitely and after a time loses response to cucumbers. It will enter only aspidochirotes, cannot distinguish between species, tends to select larger individuals, and appears to recognize the host visually, also by emanations from it. Water coming from containers with holothurians had little effect, but a tube simulating a holothurian caused reactions in the fish if a current was passed through it and became very attractive if smeared with mucus from cucumbers. The cucumber's anus is located by contact or by the current coming from it.

Mosher (1956) has investigated evisceration and regeneration in the large West Indian aspidochirote *Actinopyga agassizi;* the digestive tract regenerates along the edge of the torn mesentery as in *Stichopus* (IV, page 205).

Madsen (1957) reexamined Walcott's supposed fossil holothurians of Cambrian age (IV, page 200) and agrees with H. L. Clark that they are not holothurians.

b. Asteroidea.—In 1955 to 1957 there was a sudden outburst of investigations on the feeding of sea stars on bivalves (Burnett, 1955; Feder, 1955; Lavoie, 1956; Christensen, 1957). These articles agree that sea stars do not excrete any toxic or paralyzing substance into the victim, that they can exert sufficient pull to open the valves (pulls of 3000 to 5500 g. were recorded), and that they can slither their stomach into a gap as small as 0.1 mm. The stomach could enter and digest bivalves whose valves were firmly bolted together or tightly bound with wire. It appears that most bivalves cannot close tightly enough to exclude the stomach and that the stomach is not damaged by the closure of valves upon it. The pull of the podia on valves is not continuous but intermittent.

c. Echinoidea.—In a study of the digestive tract of *Echinus esculentus* Stott (1955) found a subepithelial nervous layer present throughout in addition to the usual layers (IV, page 468). The pharynx epithelium contains mucous and enzymatic cells, that of the esophagus mainly mucous cells, that of the small intestine enzymatic cells. The acidity declines steadily from pH 5.9 at the mouth to 6.9 in the large intestine. Water circulates throughout the digestive tract, including the siphon, found to lack cilia, as does also the entire digestive epithelium. Iron saccharate fed was ingested by coelomocytes and transported by them through the intestinal wall into the adjacent haemal system, and thereby to the axial gland, gonads, and other parts. Stott concludes that the use of coelomocytes for intracellular digestion and for absorption and transport is associated with a poorly developed haemal system lacking a pumping mechanism.

In a study of calcification in the teeth of *Echinus esculentus*, Mac-Gregor, MacInnes, and Marsland (1956) note two kinds of calcification superficially resembling in texture and manner of formation the enamel and dentine of vertebrate teeth. The harder enamellike calcification covers the outer surface of the teeth and forms the chisellike cutting edge.

Durham and Melville (1957) have proposed a classification of the Echinoidea that differs greatly from that of Mortensen. They recognize *Bothriocidaris* (IV, page 507) as an echinoid. They reject the division of echinoids into Regularia and Irregularia, mainly on the ground that the latter have arisen polyphyletically from the former. Instead they divide the class into the subclasses Perischoechinoidea and Euechinoidea. The former includes *Bothriocidaris*, sole member of an order Bothriocidaroida, and Mortensen's groups Lepidocentroida, Melonechinoida, and Cidaroida (apparently spelling Cidaroidea is incorrect). The remaining echinoids, much rearranged, are placed in the Euechinoidea. For the details of the classification the original must be consulted. Durham (1955) has monographed the Clypeasteroida (claims the spelling Clypeastroida is incorrect), raising Mortensen's 5 families to 16 by rank elevations. This work contains good information about the test, but like other works on sand dollars fails to say anything about the distribution of the podial pores.

d. Phylogenetic Importance of Creatine.—It now appears that the phylogenetic significance of creatine in echinoderms (IV, page 700) has been exaggerated. Roche, Thoai, and Robin (1957) state that creatine is present in annelids, gephyreans, coelenterates, and sponges, as well as in echinoderms, and hence its occurrence cannot be used as a phylogenetic argument.

e. Deep-sea Records of Echinoderms.—The *Galathea* collections have added greatly to the depth records for echinoderms. A stalked crinoid, *Bathycrinus australis*, was taken at 8300 m. in the Kermedec Trench (Gislen, 1956). An asteroid of the abyssal family Porcellanasteridae (IV, page 403), *Eremicaster pacificus*, was secured from the Kermedec and Java Trenches at depths to 6620 m.; other asteroid records are a new species of *Hymenaster* at 6700 m. and a new species of *Freyella* at 6100 m., both in the Kermedec Trench (Madsen, 1956b). Other records are the abyssal echinoid *Pourtalesia* (IV, page 579) at 7250 m. in the Banda Trench and the ophiuroid *Ophiura loveni* (= *irrorata*) at 6700 m. in the Kermedec Trench (Madsen, 1956b). Especially noteworthy are the holothurians, which appear to be typical inhabitants of abyssal trenches (Hansen, 1956; Hansen and Madsen, 1956; Madsen, 1955) at depths exceeding 6000 m., especially members of the order Elasipoda (IV, page 235). The common abyssal elasipod *Elpidia glacialis* (IV, page 235) was found in abundance (5000 specimens) in depths to 8300 m. in various trenches; also taken were species of *Peniagone* (7000 m.), *Benthodytes*

(7300 m.), *Euphronides* (7300 m.), *Scotoplanes* (9790 m.). A new mopla-
donian was taken in the New Britain Trench at 8810 to 8940 m. The
depth record for echinoderms is still held by the *Myriotrochus* species
mentioned in Vol. IV (page 236), now named *bruuni*, inhabiting the
Philippine Trench at 10,210 m. (corrected figure). Both in number of
species and in number of individuals holothurians exceed all other echinoderms together as inhabitants of abyssal trenches.

There were also new findings of bathypelagic holothurians, that is,
cucumbers that float or swim above the bottom. One of these with a
floating brim similar to Fig. 50*B* in Vol. IV was a refinding of one of the
Challenger species, now transferred to a new genus, *Galatheathuria*. The
other, looking like a large medusa (25 cm. diameter), is a new species of
Enypiastes (= *Planktothuria*, IV, page 197).

14. The Enterocoel Theory and Other Phylogenetic Notions.—The
author hoped that the enterocoel theory was dead and buried, as it
deserves, but it is being kept alive by a group of zoologists, notably
Remane (1950b, 1951, 1954), Jägersten (1955), and Marcus (1958). The
enterocoel theory, it will be recalled (II, page 25), is to the effect that
the coelenteric pockets of Anthozoa pass directly into the coelomic sacs
of Bilateria. This bright idea is said to have originated with Leuckart
(1848; not available to the author) but was especially promulgated by
Sedgwick (1884). It follows as necessary corollaries of the enterocoel
theory that all Bilateria are coelomate, whether or not they have a
coelom, and that all coeloms are of the enterocoel variety, whether or not
they are seen to originate by this method.

The author regards the enterocoel theory as fantastic nonsense, for
which there does not exist a single scrap of genuine evidence. The theory
is a pure fabrication. It requires that the Anthozoa be regarded as the
basic cnidarians. This is in itself implausible since they are anatomically
the most complicated members of the phylum. The statement of
Alvarado (1956) that the Anthozoa are the most simple cnidarians is incomprehensible. If the Anthozoa are taken as the basic cnidarians, it
becomes very difficult to account for the origin of medusae. We are
asked to believe that Scyphozoa and Hydrozoa have evolved from
Anthozoa by some sort of retrogressive process, something that is highly
improbable since their polypoid phases lead the same kind of sessile
existence as do anthozoans and their medusoid phase is far more active
than any anthozoan. The coelenteric outpocketings of Anthozoa are
not formed by entodermal sacculations, but quite differently by the
ingrowth of septa from the body wall. They are obviously a device for
increasing the digestive and absorptive surface with increasing body
size and are without phylogenetic significance. Further, the gastric
pockets of Anthozoa occur *around* the main body axis, the coelomic sacs

of coelomates *along* the main body axis. The alteration of polarity required to pass from one to the other appears to the author to present an insuperable difficulty in the way of the enterocoel theory; but it is lightly passed over by Remane and Marcus, who simply assume an elongation in the axis of the mouth elongation. This seems to presuppose that the basic anthozoan took to moving on its oral surface.

Jägersten (1955) devotes considerable space to the matter of the bilaterality of the Anthozoa but does not explain how this proves that the Anthozoa are the basic group of the Cnidaria. His statement that "Anthozoa show in their organization the most primitive features" of the Cnidaria is the usual type of circular argument habitual with supporters of the enterocoel theory. Anthozoa are declared to be primitive, not from any real reasons, but because this is needed for the enterocoel theory. There can be no doubt that a tendency to bilaterality is deep-rooted in the Anthozoa, but it does not necessarily follow that this bilaterality requires a bilateral ancestor for the Cnidaria. The bilaterality of the Anthozoa when viewed with common sense appears to be a variant of radial symmetry. It is very difficult to conceive the complicated structure of the Anthozoa as evolved from a bilateral ancestor. Deviations of radial into bilateral symmetry are common. They are seen in Hydrozoa in the hydroid *Branchiocerianthus* (I, page 441) and in sertularian and plumularian colonies (I, Fig. 117*B*, *D*) and in echinoderms in holothurians, almost all of which exhibit some degree of bilateral symmetry, and in irregular urchins derived from regular, highly radial echinoids by the retreat of the aboral center along one radius. It is stretching matters rather far to suppose these bilateral deviations in echinoderms are directly referable to the original, very remote bilateral ancestor. Finally, it may be noted that medusae are by far the oldest fossils among the Cnidaria, extending back into pre-Cambrian times (Harrington and Moore, 1956), whereas the radiobilateral rugose and tabulate corals are first known from the middle Ordovician.

Sedgwick passes directly from an anthozoan to a segmented coelomate, in effect an annelid, but modern supporters of the enterocoel theory proceed to those coelomates in which the body and the coelom are regionated into three divisions, that is, the lophophorates and the deuterostomes. Remane and Marcus start with a cnidarian having four gastric pockets, a sort of scyphistoma larva, although both authors assert that they regard the anthozoans as the basic cnidarian group. These authors thereby tacitly admit that tetraradiate symmetry is fundamental to the Cnidaria. By assuming a tetraradiate ancestor, Marcus at least accounts for medusae by strobilation from this ancestor. However, the passage from the tetraradiate ancestor to the lophophorate-deuterostome condition with three pairs of coelomic pouches by biparti-

tion of the anterior and posterior pouch as imagined by Remane and
Marcus is not very convincing and has been justly criticized by Jägersten,
who in his turn invents the bilaterogastraea.   This is a nice little figment
of the imagination, a sort of junior dipleurula.   Jägersten declares that
to account for the bilaterality of the Anthozoa one must assume bilaterality already in the gastrula stage.   This bilateral gastrula conveniently
put out three pairs of gastral pockets along its axis.   This is absurd
because gastric pockets represent a response to a need for increase of
digestive surface, something totally unnecessary in such a minute
creature.   Jägersten's ideas are in fact a thinly disguised version of the
gonocoel theory, for his pockets are soon revealed as gonadal sacs.

Remane, Marcus, and Jägersten all imagine a protocoelomate or
archicoelomate type with three pairs of archenteral sacs at the bottom
of the Bilateria.   This archicoelomate idea was elaborated by Ulrich
(1949), who in fact proposes to separate the lophophorates and deuterostomes as a group Archicoelomata at the bottom of the Bilateria.   But
lophophorates and deuterostomes as seen today are all decephalized
animals of sedentary or sessile habits.   It is inconceivable that such
types should originate the Bilateria.   It appears self-evident that only
well-cephalized, active forms can originate definitive bilateral symmetry,
and only the Turbellaria fit these prerequisites.

The supporters of the enterocoel theory find it very difficult to account
for the Turbellaria.   They can explain them only as degenerate annelids,
and this view is totally unacceptable to the author.   We are asked to
believe that the Turbellaria have lost their coelom, lost their anus, lost
their nephrostomes.   This is asking too much of one's credulity.   Especially the protonephridial system appears definitely primitive, as shown
by its occurrence in the trochophore and in the phoronid larva.   It
further appears impossible to account for the nervous system of primitive
turbellarians by degradation from the annelid nervous system.   The
former gives clear evidence of a radial origin, as may be seen in Vol. II,
Figs. 23D, E, 24A, 25B.   Remane and Marcus both object to the passage
from a planuloid to an acoeloid type on the ground that this theory
necessitates two independent origins of the archenteron, or in the case
of the Acoela, transformation of a syncytium into an epithelium.   But
Remane (1951) defeats his own arguments by pointing out that some
planuloids have a digestive lumen and entodermal epithelium (in fact,
one such is figured in Vol. I, Fig. 131H) and that alteration of an entodermal epithelium into a syncytium is of common occurrence.   Hence
the mentioned difficulty is easily avoided by passing from a planuloid
type with entodermal epithelium and lumen to a primitive turbellarian
with the same.   The author has never considered the lack of a digestive
lumen in the Acoela as necessarily primitive or necessarily of phylo-

genetic significance. If *Hofstenia* and *Nemertoderma* are included in the Acoela (above, page 734), they are examples of Acoela with a definite intestine. The author, in placing primitive turbellarians at the root of the Bilateria, assigns most importance to their cephalization, active habits, and epidermal position and radial pattern of their nervous system.

The occurrence of spiral cleavage in entolecithal Turbellaria cannot be taken as evidence of retrogressive descent of these from annelids. Spiral cleavage has to begin somewhere, for it is inconceivable that it sprang full-fledged in the perfect form seen in annelids and mollusks. The imperfections and variations of spiral cleavage seen among the entolecithal Turbellaria indicate that it began among them.

Hadzi (1953) also reverses the order of evolution in the Cnidaria to read Anthozoa, Scyphozoa, Hydrozoa, but he does so on entirely different grounds, in fact rejecting the enterocoel theory. He wishes to pass directly (as also Steinböck, 1936) from some sort of multinucleate syncytial protozoan to the lower Turbellaria. He then can account for Cnidaria only by a backward retrogression from the Turbellaria. Hadzi has written many pages in three or four languages (1944, 1949a, 1951) on this peculiar "turbellarian theory of the Cnidaria." From all this verbiage it is possible to extract two arguments of some worth. One of them concerns the bilaterality of the Anthozoa. It was already considered above that this bilaterality does not necessarily indicate descent from a bilateral ancestor; in fact, it is very difficult to conceive the highly radial structure of anthozoans as derived from bilaterality. Hadzi's other argument is to the effect that a sessile mode of life leads to alteration in the radial direction. There is certainly some truth in this, but usually this radial alteration concerns only the anterior end, and even that usually does not become completely radial. Remane (1952) points out that radiality is not necessarily associated with a sessile mode of life. As nonsessile animals with radial anterior ends may be mentioned free-living nematodes, priapulids, kinorhynchs. Hadzi makes the precarious statement that there are no primarily radial Eumetazoa. It has already been indicated sufficiently that primary tetraradiate symmetry is fundamental to the phylum Cnidaria.

It is impossible to bypass the Cnidaria in the evolutionary story, first, because they are the animals in which ectoderm and entoderm were first clearly differentiated, and, second, because of the widespread evidence of tetraradiate symmetry, as for instance in the cross pattern in spiral cleavage, which is inexplicable except as an ancestral reminiscence. In a thoughtful and valuable article Saccarao (1952) has pointed out that the essence of gastrulation consists in the segregation of a loco-motive-protective-perceptive layer (ectoderm) from a nutritive layer (entoderm). This segregation first occurred in Cnidaria, which therefore cannot be ejected from their long-established position as direct ancestors of the remaining Eumetazoa. The manner in which this segregation occurs is of no importance. The author agrees heartily with Saccarao's concluding statement: "The gastrula considered a morphological unit is an idealistic concept with no real basis." The same is true of attempts to regard coelom formation as always enterocoelic. Nature is versatile and has various ways of reaching the same end.

The author regards such phylogenetic questions as the origin of the Metazoa from the Protozoa or the origin of the Bilateria from the Radiata as insoluble on present information. Also insoluble are such questions as to whether entoderm, mesoderm, and coelom have or have not some original mode of formation from which other modes are derived. Anything said on these questions lies in the realm of fantasy.

Bibliography

Abbott, B., and **D. Ballantine.** 1957. The toxin from Gymnodinium. Jour. Marine Biol. Assoc. 36. **Ackert, J.** 1952. Some influences of the American hookworm. Amer. Midland Natural. 47. **Adams, A.** (ed.). 1958. Symposium on onchocerciasis. Trans. Roy. Soc. Trop. Med. Hygiene 52. **Akabori, S., K. Satake,** and **A. Oono.** 1950. Amino acid components of spongin. Science (Japan) 20. **Ali, M.** 1956. Development of monaxonid sponge. Jour. Madras Univ. 26B. **Alvarado, R.** 1956. Origin and evolution of the coelomate Metazoa. Proc. 14 Internation. Congr. Zool. for 1953. **Anderson, J.** 1952. Sexual reproduction without cross-copulation in fresh-water triclad. Biol. Bull. 102. **Anderson, R.** 1957. Life cycles of dipetalonematid nematodes. Jour. Helminthol. 31. **Ankel, W.** 1951. Phyllirhoe, Mnestra. Verhandl. Dtsch. Zool. Gesellsch. for 1951. **Ankel, W.,** and **G. Wintermann-Kilian.** 1952. Eine neue gefundene hochdifferenzierte Zellart. Ztschr. Naturforsch. 7b. **Arnold, D.** 1957. Further studies on the behavior of Carapus. Pubbl. Staz. Zool. Napoli 30. **Arnold, J.** 1955a. An unusual feature of miliolid reproduction. Contrib. Cushman Found. Foraminifer. Research 6. 1955b. Life history and cytology of Allogromia. Univ. California Publ. Zool. 61. **Ax, P.** 1956. Die Gnathostomulida. Akad. Wissensch. Lit. Mainz, Abhandl. Math. Naturwiss. Kl., no. 8. **Baernstein, H.** 1953a. The enzyme system of the culture form of Trypanosoma cruzi. Annals New York Acad. Sci. 56. 1953b. Malic dehydrogenase and related enzymes in the culture form of Trypanosoma cruzi. Exptl. Parasitol. 2. **Balamuth, W.,** and **P. Thompson.** 1955. Comparative studies on amoeba. *In* S. Hutner and A. Lwoff (eds.), *Biochemistry and physiology of Protozoa,* vol. II. **Ballantine, D.,** and **B. Abbott.** 1957. Toxic marine flagellates. Jour. Gen. Microbiol. 16. **Bartos, E.** 1951. Rotatoria of the order Bdelloidea. Acta Soc. Zool. Bohemoslovenicae 15. **Batham, E.,** and **C. Pantin.** 1950a. Phases of activity of Metridium. Jour. Exptl. Biol. 27. 1950b. Muscular and hydrostatic action in Metridium. Jour. Exptl. Biol. 27. 1950c. Inherent activity in Metridium. Jour. Exptl. Biol. 27. 1951. Organization of the muscular system of Metridium. Quart. Jour. Microsc. Sci. 92. 1954. Slow contractions and spontaneous activity in Metridium. Jour. Exptl. Biol. 31. **Bayer, F.** 1956. Octocorallia. *In* R. C. Moore (ed.), *Treatise on invertebrate paleontology,* pt. F, Coelenterata. **Beale, G.** 1954. *The genetics of Paramecium* *aurelia*. **Beauchamp, P. de.** 1956. Le développement de Ploeosoma. Bull. Soc. Zool. France 81. **Benazzi, M.** 1957. Introduzione alla analasi genetica dei biotipi cariologici di tricladi. La Ricerca Scientifica, suppl. to 27, Convegno di Genetica. **Bergmann, W.** 1949. Comparative biochemical studies on the lipids of marine invertebrates. Jour. Marine Research 8. **Bergmann, W., and A. Swift.** 1951. Component acids of lipids of sponges. Jour. Organic Chem. 16. **Bergmann, W., J. Watkins,** and **M. Stempien.** 1957. Sponge nucleic acids. Jour. Organic Chem. 22. **Berrill, N.** 1953. Polymorphism within the Hydractiniidae. Jour. Morphol. 92. **Bird, A.** 1954. The cuticle of nematode larvae. Nature, London, 174. 1956, 1957. Chemical composition of the nematode cuticle. Exptl. Parasitol. 5, 6. **Bird, A.,** and **K. Deutsch.** 1957. Structure of the cuticle of Ascaris. Parasitology 47. **Bird, A.,** and **W. Rogers.** 1956. Chemical composition of the cuticle of third stage nematode larvae. Exptl. Parasitol. 5. **Bobin, G.,** and **M. Prenant.** 1953. Classification des loxosomes. Bull. Soc. Zool. France 78. **Boeck, W.,** and **J. Drbohlav.** 1925. Cultivation of Endamoeba histolytica. Amer. Jour. Hygiene 5. **Boisseau, J.** 1949. Données histochimiques sur le contenu capsulaire des nématocystes de Physalia. Bull. Sta. Biol. Arcachon, new ser., no. 1. 1952. Histochimie des cnidaires. Bull. Soc. Zool. France 77. **Boschma, H.** 1957. List of the described species of the order Stylasterina. Zool. Verhandl., no. 33. **Bouillon, J.** 1954, 1955. Hydropolyp of Limnocnida. Nature, London, 174; C. R. Acad. Sci. Paris 240. **Bouillon, J.,** and **G. Vandermeersche.** 1956. Structure et nature de la mesoglée des hydro- et scyphomedusae. Ann. Soc. Roy. Zool. Belgique 87. **Boyden, A.** 1957. Are there any "acellular" animals? Science 125. **Bradfield, J.** 1953. New features of protoplasmic structure. Quart. Jour. Microsc. Sci. 94. **Brien, P.** 1943a. La formation des orifices inhalants chez les Spongillidae. Bull. Mus. Roy. Hist. Natur. Belgique 19, no. 61. 1943b. L'embryologie des éponges. Bull. Mus. Roy. Hist. Natur. Belgique 19, no. 16. 1951. Contribution à l'étude des hydres d'eau douce. Bull. Soc. Zool. France 76. 1953. La perennité somatique. Biol. Reviews Cambridge 28. **Brien, P.,** and **M. Reniers.** 1949. Croissance et burgeonnement de Hydra fusca. C. R. Soc. Biol. Paris 143. **Brien, P.,** and **M. Reniers-Decoen.** 1950. La croissance, la blastogénèse, l'ovogénèse chez Hydra. Bull. Biol. France Belgique 83. 1955. La signification des cellules interstitielles des hydres. Bull. Biol. France Belgique 89. **Bröndsted, H.** 1955. Planarian regeneration. Biol. Reviews Cambridge 30. 1956. Experiments on the time-graded regeneration field in planarians. Biol. Meddel. Dansk Videns. Selsk. 23, no. 3. **Brown, C.** 1950. Keratins in invertebrates. Nature, London, 166. **Brown, H.** 1945. Structure and mechanics of the protozoan flagellum. Ohio Jour. Sci. 45. 1951. Structure of protozoan flagella. Proc. Oklahoma Acad. Sci. 31. **Brown, H.,** and **A. Cox.** 1954. An electron microscope study of protozoan flagella. Amer. Midland Natural. 52. **Brunson, R.** 1950. Introduction to the taxonomy of the Gastrotricha. Trans. Amer. Microsc. Soc. 69. **Bruun, A.** 1956. *The Galathea deep-sea expedition* 1950–1952. **Bueding, E.** 1949. Metabolism of parasitic helminths. Physiol. Reviews 29. 1951. Metabolism of helminths. *In* H. **Most** (ed.), Symposium no. 4, Section Microbiology, New York Acad. Medicine. **Bueding, E.,** and **H. Most.** 1953. Helminths: metabolism, nutrition and chemotherapy. Ann. Review Microbiol. 7. **Bullock, M., et al.** 1952. Nature of protogen. Jour. Amer. Chem. Soc. 74. **Bullock, W.** 1949. Histochemical studies on the Acanthocephala. Jour. Morphol. 84. **Bürger, O.** 1890. Anatomie und Histologie der Nemertinen. Ztschr. Wissensch. Zool. 50. **Burnett, A.** 1955. Efficiency of muscular force in the opening of clams by Asterias. Biol. Bull. 109. **Buttner, Alice.** 1950–1951. La progénèse chez les trématodes digénétiques. Ann. Parasitol. Humain Comp. 25, 26. 1955. Les distomes progénétiques sont-ils des préadultes ou des adultes véritables? C. R. Soc. Biol. Paris 149. **Cable, R.**, and **R. Myers.** 1956. A dioecious species of cestode. Jour. Parasitol. 42. **Cailleau, Relda.** 1933. Culture d'Acanthamoeba. C. R. Soc. Biol. Paris 114. **Calman, W. T.** 1949. *The classification of animals.* Methuen's Monogr. Biol. Subjects. **Canella, M.** 1957. Studi e ricerche sui Tentaculiferi. Ann. Univ. Ferrara, new ser., sec. III, Biol. Animali 1. **Carlgren, O.** 1909. Die Tetraplatien. Wissensch. Ergebn. Dtsch. Tiefsee Exped. Valdivia 19. 1944. Das System und die Entwicklungslinien der Anthozoen. Kungl. Fysiogr. Sallsk. Lund Förhandl. 14, no. 4. 1949. A survey of the Ptychodactiaria, Corallimorpharia and Actiniaria. Kungl. Svenska Vetensk. Handl., ser. 4, vol. 1, no. 1. 1956. Actiniaria from depths exceeding 6000 meters. Galathea Repts. 2. **Chabaud, A.** 1954. Sur le cycle évolutif des Spirurides. Ann. Parasitol. Humain Comp. 29. 1957. Sur la systematique des nematodes du sous-ordre Ascaridina. Bull. Soc. Zool. France 82. **Champetier, G.**, and **E. Fauré-Fremiet.** 1942. Étude roentgènographique de quelques corneines d'Anthozoaires. C. R. Acad. Sci. Paris 215. **Chandebois, Rosine.** 1957. Sur la régénération de la planaire marine Procerodes. Bull. Biol. France Belgique 91. **Chanley, J., S. Kohn, R. Nigrelli**, and **H. Sobotka.** 1955. Further chemical analysis of holothurin. Zoologica, New York, 40. **Chapman, G.** 1953a, b. Studies on the mesogloea of coelenterates. Quart. Jour. Microsc. Sci. 94; Jour. Exptl. Biol. 30. **Chatton, E.**, and **A. Lwoff.** 1930. Imprégnation par diffusion argentique de l'infraciliature des ciliés. C. R. Soc. Biol. Paris 104. 1949, 1950. Recherches sur les ciliés thigmotriches. Arch. Zool. Exp. Gén. 86. **Chen, Y.** 1950. Biology of Peranema. Quart. Jour. Microsc. Sci. 91. **Chitwood, B. G.** 1951. The golden nematode of potatoes. U.S. Dept. Agricult., Circular no. 875. **Chitwood, B. G.**, and **M. B. Chitwood.** 1950. *An introduction to nematology.* Sec. 1, revised. **Christensen, A.** 1957. The feeding behavior of Evasterias. Limnol. Oceanogr. 2. **Ciordia, H.** 1956. Cytological studies on the germ cell cycle of the Bucephalidae. Trans. Amer. Microsc. Soc. 75. **Citri, N.**, and **N. Grossowicz.** 1954, 1955. Medium for Trypanosoma cruzi. Nature, London, 173; Jour. Gen. Microbiol. 13. **Cleveland, L.** 1949–1956a. Hormone-induced sexual cycles of flagellates. I–XIV. Jour. Morphol. 85–88, 91, 93, 95, 97; Arch. Protistenk. 100. 1956b. Brief accounts of the sexual cycles of the flagellates of Cryptocercus. Jour. Protozool. 3. 1957a. Correlation between the molting period of Cryptocercus and sexuality in its Protozoa. Jour. Protozool. 4. 1957b. Types and life cycles of centrioles in flagellates. Jour. Protozool. 4. **Cleveland, L.**, and **W. Nutting.** 1956. Suppression of sexual cycles and deaths of the Protozoa of Cryptocercus resulting from change of hosts during the molting period. Jour. Exptl. Zool. 130. **Coil, W.** 1955. Dioecious cestode. Jour. Parasitol. 41. **Conner, R., W. J. van Wagtendonk**, and **C. Miller.** 1953. Isolation from lemon juice of a growth factor. Jour. Gen. Microbiol. 9. **Corliss, J.** 1953a. Silver impregnation of ciliated Protozoa. Stain Technology 28. 1953b. Protozoa and systematics. Yale Scient. Mag. 28. 1955. The opalinid infusorians. Jour. Protozool. 2. 1956. Evolution and systematics of ciliated Protozoa. System. Zool. 5. 1957a. Concerning the "cellularity" or acellularity of the Protozoa. Science 125. 1957b. Nomenclatural history of the Ciliophora. Arch. Protistenk. 102. **Cosgrove, W.** 1950. Chemoautrophy in Chilomonas. Physiol. Zool. 23. **Cosgrove, W.**, and **B. Swanson.** 1952. Growth of Chilomonas in simple organic media. Physiol. Zool. 25. **Crowell, S.** 1957. Eugymnanthea, a commensal hydroid. Pubbl. Staz. Zool. Napoli 30. **Davis, C.** 1948. Gymnodinium brevis, a cause of discolored water. Botan. Gazette 109. **Dawydoff, C.** 1928. *Traité d'embryologie comparée des invertébrés.* 1950. Nouveau ctenophore sessile. C. R. Acad. Sci. Paris 231. **De Laubenfels, M.** 1948. The order Keratosa. Allan

Hancock Found. Publ. Occas. Paper no. 3. **Diamond, L.** 1957. Trichomonads of animals and man in axenic cultures. Jour. Parasitol. 43. **Dissanaike, A., G. Dissanaike, and W. Niles.** 1956. Infective filarial larvae tagged with phosphorus-32. Trans. Roy. Soc. Trop. Med. Hygiene 50. 1957. Production of radioactive infective larvae of Wuchereria. Exptl. Parasitol. 6. **Dodson, E.** 1956. Systematic position of the Mesozoa. System. Zool. 5. **Dollfus, R., and A. Chabaud.** 1957. Phénomènes de convergence chez les Spirurides. Bull. Soc. Zool. France 82. **Dollfus, R., J. Timon-David, and J. Rebecq.** 1956. Maturité genitale provoquée expérimentalement chez Codonocephalus. C. R. Acad. Sci. Paris 242. **Dougherty, E., and E. Hansen.** 1956. Axenic cultivation of Caenorhabditis. Proc. Soc. Exptl. Biol. Med. 93. **Dragesco, J., and K. Beyersdorfer.** 1953. Étude comparative des trichocystes de sept espèces de Paramécies. C. R. 1 Congr. Internation. Micro. Electronique in 1950. **Dubin, I.** 1952, 1954. Cultivation of exo-erythrocytic forms of Plasmodium gallinaceum. Jour. Infectious Diseases 91; Exptl. Parasitol. 3. **Dubois, Françoise.** 1949. Migration des cellules de régénération chez les planaires. Bull. Biol. France Belgique 83. 1950. Potentialités histogénétiques des néoblasts chez Euplanaria. Année Biol., ser. 3, vol. 26. **Dubois, G.** 1953. Systematique des Strigeida. Mém. Soc. Neuchâtel. Sci. Natur. 8. **Duboscq, O., and O. Tuzet.** 1941. Sur les cellules en croix des Sycon. Arch. Zool. Exp. Gén. 81. Notes et revue no. 4. 1942. L'ovogénèse, la fécondation et les premiers stades du développement des éponges calcaires. Arch. Zool. Exp. Gén. 81. 1944. L'ovogénèse, la fécondation et les premiers stades du développement du Sycon. Arch. Zool. Exp. Gén. 83, suppl. **Duddington, C.** 1954. Nematode-destroying fungi. Nature, London, 173. 1955. Fungi that attack microscopic animals. Botan. Review 21. **Dunham, D.** 1942. The water content of Craspedacusta. Amer. Midland Natural. 28. **Durham, J.** 1955. Classification of clypeastroid echinoids. Univ. California Publ. Geol. Sci. 31. **Durham, J., and R. Melville.** 1957. A classification of the Echinoidea. Jour. Paleontol. 31. **Ehret, C., and E. Powers.** 1957. Organization of gullet organelles in Paramecium bursaria. Jour. Protozool. 4. **Ellenby, C.** 1954. The eelworm and the potato. Discovery 15. **Ells, H., and C. Read.** 1952. Cultivation of Turbatrix aceti. Jour. Parasitol. 38, sec. 2. **Emery, K., J. Tracey, and H. Ladd.** 1954. Geology of Bikini and nearby atolls. U.S. Geol. Survey, Profess. Paper 260-A. **Enigk, K., and E. Sticinsky.** 1957. Über die Bohrdrüsen der Onkosphäre von Davainea. Ztschr. Parasitenk. 18. **Euzet, L.** 1956. Nouvelle classification des tetraphyllides. Proc. 14 Internation. Congr. Zoology. **Ewer, R.** 1947. Functions and mode of action of the nematocysts of Hydra. Proc. Zool. Soc. London 117. 1948. Review of the Hydridae. Proc. Zool. Soc. London 118. **Fairbairn, D.** 1957. The biochemistry of Ascaris. Exptl. Parasitol. 6. **Fänge, R., and B. Abesson.** 1952. Cells of the coelomic fluid of priapulides. Arkiv Zool., ser. 2, vol. 3; Nature, London, 165. **Fauré-Fremiet, E.** 1950. Morphologie comparée et systématique des ciliés. Bull. Soc. Zool. France 75. 1953a. Morphology of Protozoa. Ann. Review Microbiol. 7. 1953b. L'hypothèse de la sénescence et les cycles de réorganization nucléaire chez les ciliés. Rev. Suisse Zool. 60. **Fauré-Fremiet, E., C. Rouiller, and M. Gauchery.** 1956. La structure fine des ciliés. Bull. Soc. Zool. France 81. **Feder, H.** 1955. Methods used by Pisaster in opening three types of bivalve. Ecology 36. **Fielding, M.** 1951. Observations on the length of dormancy in certain plant-infecting nematodes. Proc. Helminthol. Soc. Washington 18. **Fisher, W. K.** 1946. Echiuroid worms of the North Pacific ocean. Proc. U.S. Nation. Mus. 96. **Fowler, H.** 1943. Shellfish poison. Natural History 51. **Franklin, Mary.** 1952. *The cyst-forming species of Heterodera.* **Fraser, C.** 1944. *Hydroids of the Atlantic Coast of North America.* **Frenzen, K.** 1955. Studien der Zellkonstanz an Ascaridia galli.

Ztschr. Wissensch. Zool. 158. **Galtsoff, P.** 1949. The mystery of the red tide. Scient. Monthly 68. **Garstang, W.** 1946. The morphology and relations of the Siphonophora. Quart. Jour. Microsc. Sci. 87. **Geiman, Q.,** and **C. Becker.** 1953. In vitro growth and metabolism of Endamoeba histolytica. Ann. New York Acad. Sci. 56. **Gislen, T.** 1956. Crinoids from depths exceeding 6000 m. Galathea Rept. 2. **Glumac, S.** 1953. Fonctionnement des cellules à nématocysts chez l'hydre. Bull. Mus. Hist. Natur. Pays Serbe, ser. B, Sci. Biol., livre 5-6. **Gontcharoff, Maria.** 1957. Rhabdites of the proboscis of Lineus. C. R. Acad. Sci. Paris 244. **Goodey, T.** 1951. *Soil and freshwater nematodes.* **Gordon, R.** (ed.). 1955. Symposium on loiasis. Trans. Roy. Soc. Trop. Med. Hygiene 49. **Graham, H.** 1954. Dinoflagellates of the Gulf of Mexico. U.S. Fish and Wildlife Service, Bull. 89. **Grassé, P.** (ed.). *Traité de zoologie,* vol. I, fasc. 1, 2. **Grell, K.** 1950. Der Kerndualismus der Ciliaten und Suktorien. Naturwissenschaften 37. 1956. Der Kerndualismus der Foraminifere Glabratella sulcata. Ztschr. Naturforsch. 11b. 1958. Studien zum Differenzierungsproblem an Foraminiferen. Naturwissenschaften 45. **Grembergen, G. van.** 1954. Haemoglobin in Heterakis. Nature, London, 174. **Gröntved, J.** 1956. Taxonomical studies in some Danish coastal localities. Meddel. Danmarks Fiskeri- og Havundersögelse, new ser. 1, no. 12. **Gross, J., Z. Sokal,** and **M. Rougvie.** 1956. Structural and chemical studies on the connective tissue of marine sponges. Jour. Histochem. Cytochem. 4. **Guilcher, Yvette.** 1951. Contribution à l'étude des ciliés gemmipares, Chonotriches et Tentaculifères. Ann. Sci. Natur., Zool., ser. 11, vol. 13. **Gunter, G., et al.** 1948. Catastrophic mass mortality of marine animals and coincident phytoplankton bloom. Ecol. Monogr. 18. **Hadley, C.,** and **H. Forrest.** 1949. Taxonomic studies on the hydras of North America. 6. Amer. Mus. Novitates, no. 1423. **Hadzi, J.** 1923. Über den Ursprung, die Verwandtschaftsverhältnisse und das systematische Position der Ktenophoren. Rad Jugoslovenska Akad. Znanosti i Umjetnosti. 1944. Turbellarijska Teorija Knidarijev. Solvenska Akad. Znanosti in Umetnosti, Ljubljani, Matem. Prirod Razred, dela 3. 1949a. Die Ableitung der Knidarien von den Turbellarien und einige Folgerungen dieser Ableitung. C. R. 13 Congr. Internation. Zool. Paris, 1948. 1949b. Problems of mesoderm and coelom elucidated by the turbellarian theory of Cnidaria. Razprave Solvenska Akad. Znanosti in Umetnosti, Cl. IV, Hist. Natur. Med. 1951. Die Ableitung der Knidarien von den Turbellarien und einige Folgerung dieser Ableitung. Razprave Slovenska Akad. Znanosti in Umetnosti, Cl. IV, Hist. Natur. Med. 1953. A reconstruction of animal classification. Syst. Zool. 2. 1954. Die morphologische Bedeutung der Pneumatophore bei Siphonophoren. Razprave Slovenska Akad. Znanosti in Umetnosti, Cl. IV, Hist. Natur. Med. **Haffner, O. von.** 1950. Organisation und systematische Stellung der Acanthocephalen. Zool. Anz. Ergänz. Heft to 145. **Hall, R.** 1941. Food requirements and other factors influencing growth of Protozoa in pure culture. *In* G. Calkins and F. Summers (eds.), *Protozoa in biological research.* 1953. *Protozoology.* **Hamilton, E.** 1956. Sunken islands of the Mid-Pacific mountains. Geol. Soc. America Mem. 64. 1957. The last geographic frontier: the sea floor. Scient. Monthly 85. **Hamon, Maryvonne.** 1955a. Recherches histochimiques sur les nématocystes. Bull. Soc. Hist. Natur. Afrique du Nord 46. 1955b. Cytochemical research on coelenterate nematocysts. Nature, London, 176. **Hand, C.** 1954a. Three Pacific species of Lar. Pacific Science 8. 1954b, 1955a, b. The sea anemones of central California. Wasmann Jour. Biol. 12, 13. 1955c. Structure, affinities, and distribution of Tetraplatia. Pacific Science 9. 1957. Systematics, affinities, and hosts of Monobrachium. Jour. Washington Acad. Sci. 47. **Hand, C.,** and **J. Hendrickson.** 1950. A two-tentacled commensal hydroid from California. Biol. Bull. 99. **Hansen, B.** 1956. Holothuroidea from depths exceeding 6000 meters. Galathea Repts. 2. **Hansen, B.**, and **F. Madsen.** 1956. On two bathypelagic holothurians. Galathea Repts. 2. **Harrington, H.**, and **R. C. Moore.** 1956. Protomedusae. In **R. C. Moore** (ed.), *Treatise on inverte- brate paleontology*, pt. F. **Harris, J.**, and **H. Crofton.** 1957. Structure and function in nematodes. Jour. Exptl. Biol. 34. **Hartmann, M.** 1952. Polyenergide Kerne bei Protozoen. Arch. Protistenk. 98. **Hatschek, B.** 1888. *Lehrbuch der Zoologie.* **Hawking, F.** 1945. Growth of Protozoa in tissue culture. Trans. Roy. Soc. Trop. Med. Hygiene 39. **Heath, H.** 1930. A connecting link between the Annelida and the Echiuroidea. Jour. Morphol. 49. **Heider, K.** 1914. *Phylogenie der Wirbellosen.* In Die Kultur der Gegenwart, Teil 3, Abt. 4, Bd. 4. **Hess, A., A. Cohen,** and **E. Robson.** 1957. Observations on the structure of hydra as seen with the electron and light microscopes. Quart. Jour. Microsc. Sci. 98. **Hoffmeister, J.**, and **H. Ladd.** 1944. The antecedent-platform theory. Jour. Geol. 52. **Hollande, A.**, and **M. Enjumet.** 1953. Contribution à l'étude des Sphaercollides. Ann. Sci. Natur., Zool., ser. 11, vol. 15. 1957. Enkystement et reproduction isosporogénetique chez les Acanthaires. C. R. Acad. Sci. Paris 244. **Horridge, A.** 1953. An action potential from the motor nerves of Aurellia. Nature, London, 171. 1954a. Obser- vations on the nerve fibers of Aurellia. Quart. Jour. Microsc. Sci. 95. 1954b, 1955a, b, c, 1956a. The nerves and muscles of medusae. I–V. Jour. Exptl. Biol. 31, 32, 33. 1956b. The nervous system of the ephyra larva of Aurellia. Quart. Jour. Microsc. Sci. 97. 1956c. A through-conducting system coordinating the protective retraction of Alcyonium. Nature, London, 178. 1956d. Responses of Heteroxenia. Jour. Exptl. Biol. 33. 1957. Coordination of the protective retraction of coral polyps. Philos. Trans. Roy. Soc. London 240B. **Huff, C.** 1947. Life-cycle of malarial parasites. Ann. Review Microbiol. 1. 1957. Organ and tissue distribution of the exo-erythrocytic stages of various avian parasites. Exptl. Parasitol. 6. **Huff, C.**, and **W. Bloom.** 1935. A malarial parasite infecting all blood and blood-forming cells of birds. Jour. Infectious Diseases 57. **Huff, C.**, and **F. Coulston.** 1944, 1947. Preerythrocytic development of Plasmodium. Jour. Infectious Diseases 75, 81. **Hutchens, J.** 1948. Growth of Chilomonas paramecium in mass culture. Jour. Cell. Comp. Physiol. 32. **Hutner, S., M. Bach,** and **G. Ross.** 1956. A sugar-con- taining basal medium for vitamin B_{12}-assay with Euglena. Jour. Protozool. 3. **Hutner, S.**, and **A. Lwoff** (eds.). 1955. *Biochemistry and physiology of Protozoa*, vol. II. **Hutner, S.**, and **L. Provasoli.** 1951. The phytoflagellates. *In* **A. Lwoff** (ed.), *Biochemistry and physiology of Protozoa*, vol. I. 1955. Comparative bio- chemistry of flagellates. *In* **S. Hutner** and **A. Lwoff** (eds.), *Biochemistry and physiology of Protozoa*, vol. II. **Hutner, S., L. Provasoli,** and **J. Filfus.** 1953. Nutri- tion of some phagotrophic fresh-water chrysomonads. Ann. New York Acad. Sci. 56. **Hutner, S.**, and **W. Trager** (eds.). 1953. Growth of Protozoa. Ann. New York Acad. Sci. 56. **Hutton, R.** 1956. An annotated bibliography of red tides. Quart. Jour. Florida Acad. Sci. 19. **Huus, J.** 1931. Über die Begattung bei Nectonema und über den Fund der Larve. Zool. Anz. 97. **Inglis, W.** 1957. Comparative anatomy and systematic significance of the head in the Heterakidae. Proc. Zool. Soc. London 128. **Inskip, L.**, and **H. Cassidy.** 1955. Amino acids of sponges. Jour. Marine Research 14. **Ito, T.** 1947. New hydras of Japan. Sci. Repts. Tohoku Univ., ser. 4, Biol. 18. **Ivanov, A.** 1952. Acoela. Trudy Zool. Inst. Acad. Sci. U.S.S.R. 12. **Jägersten, G.** 1955. On the early phylogeny of the Metazoa. Zool. Bidrag 30. **Jahn, T.** 1946. The euglenoid flagellates. Quart. Review Biol. 21. 1949. *How to know the Protozoa.* **Jakus, M.**, and **C. Hall.** 1946. Electron microscope observations of the trichocysts and cilia of Paramecium. Biol. Bull. 91. **James, S.**, and **P. Tate.** 1938. Exo-erythrocytic schizogony in Plasmodium gallinaceum. Parasitology 30. **Jennings, H.** 1939. Paramecium bursaria, mating types. Amer. Natural. 73. **Jennings, J.** 1957. Studies of feeding, digestion, and food-storage in free-living flatworms. Biol. Bull. 112. **Johnson, G.,** and **R. Trussell.** 1943, 1944. Trichomonas vaginalis. Proc. Soc. Exptl. Biol. Med. 54, 57. **Johnson, W.,** and **C. Miller.** 1956. Nutrition of Paramecium. Jour. Protozool. 3. 1957. Nitrogen requirements of Paramecium. Physiol. Zool. 30. **Johri, L.** 1957. Egg formation in a cyclophyllidean cestode. Parasitology 47. **Johri, L.,** and **J. Smyth.** 1956. A histochemical approach to helminth morphology. Parasitology 46. **Jones, C.** 1947. Control and discharge of nematocysts. Jour. Exptl. Zool. 105. **Jones, E.** 1951. Encystment, excystment and the nuclear cycle in Dileptus anser. Jour. Elisha Mitchell Scient. Soc. 67. **Jones, Mary, C. Keeshan,** and **D. Lilly.** 1957. The axenic culture of Peranema. Jour. Protozool., suppl. to vol. 4. **Jones, Myrna,** and **P. Weinstein.** 1957. The axenic cultivation of Nematospiroides dubius. Jour. Parasitol., suppl. to vol. 43. **Jones, W.** 1956. Colloidal properties of the mesogloea in Leucosolenia. Quart. Jour. Microsc. Sci. 97. **Joyeaux, C.,** and **J. Baer.** 1950. Le genre Gyrocotyloides. Bull. Soc. Neuchâteloise Sci. Natur. 73. **Kawaguchi, S.** 1942. Investigations on reef corals. Science of the South Sea 5. **Kepner, W., et al.** 1943. The structure, development, and discharge of the penetrant of Pelmatohydra. Jour. Morphol. 72. 1951. The discharge of the nematocysts of hydra. Jour. Morphol. 88. **Kidder, G.,** and **V. Dewey.** 1951. The biochemistry of ciliates in pure culture. *In* A. Lwoff (ed.), *Biochemistry and physiology of Protozoa*, vol. I. **Komai, T.** 1941. A new remarkable sessile ctenophore. Proc. Imper. Acad. Tokyo 17. 1942a. The nervous system of some coelenterate types. Annot. Zool. Japonenses 21. 1942b. The nematocysts of the ctenophore Euchlora rubra. Proc. Imper. Acad. Tokyo 18. 1942c. Structure and development of the sessile ctenophore Lyrocteis. Mem. College Sci. Kyoto Univ., ser. B, vol. 17. 1951. The nematocysts in the ctenophore Euchlora rubra. Amer. Natural. 85. **Kramp, P.** 1938. Die systematische Stellung der Olindiiden. Zool. Anz. 122. 1943. On development through alternation of generations. Vidensk. Meddel. Dansk Naturhist. Foren. 107. 1949. Origin of the hydroid family Corymorphidae. Vidensk. Meddel. Dansk Naturhist. Foren. 111. 1956. Hydroids from depths exceeding 6000 meters. Galathea Repts. 2. **Krull, W.,** and **C. Mapes.** 1952, 1953. Studies on the biology of Dicrocoelium dendriticum. Cornell Veterinarian 42, 43. **Kudo, R.** 1954. *Protozoology.* **Ladd, H.,** and **J. Tracey.** 1947. Drilling on Bikini Atoll. Science 107. 1949. The problem of coral reefs. Scient. Monthly 69. **Ladd, H., et al.** 1953. Drilling on Eniwetok Atoll. Bull. Amer. Assoc. Petroleum Geol. 37. **Lang, K.** 1951. Species of Priapulus. Arkiv Zool., ser. 2, vol. 1. 1953. Die Entwicklung des Eies von Priapulus caudatus. Arkiv Zool., ser. 2, vol. 5. **La Rue, G.** 1957. The classification of digenetic Trematoda. Exptl. Parasitol. 6. **Lasker, R.,** and **F. Walton Smith.** 1954. Red tide. U.S. Fish and Wildlife Service, 55, Fishery Bull. 89. **Lavoie, M.** 1956. How sea stars open bivalves. Biol. Bull. 111. **Lazarus, Marian.** 1950. The respiratory metabolism of helminths. Austral. Jour. Scient. Research, ser. B, Biol. Sci. 3. **Le Calvez, J.** 1950. Recherches sur les Foraminifères. Arch. Zool. Exp. Gén. 87. 1953. Ordre des Foraminifères. *In* P. Grassé (ed.), *Traité de zoologie*, vol. I, fasc. 2. **Leghissa, S.** 1949a, b. Il tessuto nervoso delle attinie. Pubbl. Staz. Zool. Napoli 21; Rivista di Biologia, new ser. 41. **Leloup, E.** 1954. À propos des siphonophores. Vol. jubilaire V. von Straelen, pt. II. **Lender, T.** 1950, 1951, 1956a. Régénération des yeux de Polycelis nigra. C. R. Soc. Biol. Paris 144, 145; Jour. Embryol. Exptl. Morphol. 4. 1956b. Analyse des phénomènes d'induction et d'inhibition dans la régénération des planaires. Ann. Biol., ser. 3, vol. 32. **Leuckart, R.** 1848. *Über die Morphologie und die Verwandt-*

schaftsverhältnisse der wirbellosen Tiere. **Leveaux, M.** 1942. L'ovogénèse et la spermatogénèse des Spongillidae. Ann. Soc. Roy. Zool. Belgique 73. **Levi, C.** 1952. Structure de la larva et du rhagon de Halisarca. C. R. Acad. Sci. Paris 234. 1953. Sur une nouvelle classification des démosponges. C. R. Acad. Sci. Paris 236. 1956. Embryologie et systématique des démosponges. Arch. Zool. Exp. Gén. 93. **Lilly, D.** 1953. Nutrition of carnivorous Protozoa. Ann. New York Acad. Sci. 56. **Lilly, D.,** and **W. Cevallos.** 1956. Chemical supplements promoting growth in carnivorous ciliates. Trans. New York Acad. Sci., ser. 2, vol. 18. **Lin, C.,** and **N. Berrill.** 1948. Gonophore formation and germ cell origin in Tubularia. Jour. Morphol. 83. **Lopez-Neyra, C.** 1956. Revision de la superfamilia Filarioidea. Rev. Iberica Parasitol. 16. **Low, Eva.** 1951. Halogenated amino acids of the bath sponge. Jour. Marine Research 10. **Lowndes, A.** 1942, 1943. Percentage of water in jelly-fish. Nature, London, 150, 151. 1945, 1947. Flagellar movement. School Sci. Review, no. 100; Science Progress 35. **Lwoff, A.** 1950. *Problems of morphogenesis in ciliates.* 1951. *Biochemistry and physiology of Protozoa,* vol. I. **Lwoff, Marguerite.** 1951a. Nutrition of parasitic flagellates. *In* A. Lwoff (ed.), *Biochemistry and physiology of Protozoa,* vol. I. 1951b. Nutrition of parasitic amoebae. *In* A. Lwoff (ed.), *Biochemistry and physiology of Protozoa,* vol. I. **Mac-Gregor, A., D. MacInnes,** and **A. Marsland.** 1956. The teeth of the Echinoidea. Proc. Zool. Soc. London 127. **Madsen, F.** 1955. Holothurioidea. Repts. Swedish Deep-sea Exped. 1947–1948, vol. 2, Zool., no. 12. 1956a. Eldonia, a Cambrian siphonophore. Vidensk. Meddel. Dansk. Naturhist. Foren. 118. 1956b. Echinoidea, Asteroidea, and Ophiuroidea from depths exceeding 6000 meters. Galathea Repts. 2. 1957. On Walcott's supposed Cambrian holothurians. Jour. Paleontol. 31. **Mai, W.,** and **B. Lear.** 1952. The golden nematode. Cornell Extension Bull. 870. **Marcus, E.** 1952. Turbellaria Brasileiros (10). Zoologia, Sao Paulo, Brazil, no. 17. 1954. Turbellaria brasileiros (11). Papers Avulsos Dept. Zoologia, Sao Paulo, Brazil, vol. 11, no. 24. 1958. On the evolution of the animal phyla. Quart. Rev. Biol. 33. **Marcus, E.,** and **W. Macnae.** 1954. Architomy in a species of Convoluta. Nature, London, 173. **Marks, M., R. Bear,** and **C. Blake.** 1949. X-ray diffraction evidence of collagen-type protein fibers in the Echinodermata, Coelenterata, and Porifera. Jour. Exptl. Zool. 111. **Martin, W.** 1952. Another annelid first intermediate host of a digenetic trematode. Jour. Parasitol. 38. **McConnaughey, B.** 1949. Mesozoa of the family Dicyemidae from California. Univ. California Publ. Zool. 55. 1951. The life cycle of the dicyemid Mesozoa. Univ. California Publ. Zool. 55. 1954. Strange life of the dicyemid mesozoans. Scient. Monthly 79. **McKee, R.** 1951. Biochemistry of Plasmodium. *In* A. Lwoff (ed.), *Biochemistry and physiology of Protozoa,* vol. I. **McLaughlin, J.,** and **P. Zahl.** 1957. In vitro culture of zooxanthellae. Proc. Soc. Exptl. Biol. Med. 95. **Meewis, Henriette.** 1939. L'embryogénèse des Chalinidae. Ann. Soc. Roy. Zool. Belgique 70. 1941. L'embryogénèse des éponges siliceuses. Ann. Soc. Roy. Zool. Belgique 72. **Meixner, J.** 1924. Studien zum System der Turbellaria Rhabdocoela. Zool. Anz. 60. 1926. Beitrag zum System der Turbellarien Rhabdocoelen. II. Ztschr. Morphol. Ökol. Tiere 5. **Metz, C.** 1954. Mating substances and the physiology of fertilization in ciliates. In *Sex in microorganisms,* publ. by Amer. Assoc. Advanc. Science. **Metz, C., D. Pitelka,** and **J. Westfall.** 1953. The fibrillar systems of ciliates as revealed by the electron microscope. Biol. Bull. 104. **Metz, C.,** and **J. Westfall.** 1954. The fibrillar systems of ciliates. II. Biol. Bull. 107. **Meyer, G.** 1955. Vergleichende Untersuchungen mit der supravitalen Methylenblaufärbung am Nervensystems wirbelloser Tiere. Zool. Jahrb. Abt. Anat. 74. **Monné, L.** 1956. Histochemical properties of the egg envelopes and external cuticles of some parasitic nematodes. Arkiv Zool., new ser. 9. **Monné, K.,** and **K. Borg.** 1954. On the Gram staining of the egg envelopes of parasitic worms. Arkiv. Zool., new ser. 6. **Monné, L.,** and **G. Hönig.** 1954a, b. Properties of the egg envelopes of parasitic nematodes. Arkiv Zool., new ser. 6, 7. **Mosher, Carol.** 1956. Evisceration and visceral regeneration in Actinopyga. Zoologica, New York, 41. **Moulder, J.** 1950. Oxygen requirements of parasites. Jour. Parasitol. 36. **Mueller, J.** 1950. Some observations on the structure of hydra. Trans. Amer. Microsc. Soc. 69. **Nakamura, M.** 1953. Nutrition and physiology of Endamoeba histolytica. Bacteriol. Reviews 17. 1955, 1957. Growth factors for Endamoeba histolytica. Proc. Soc. Exptl. Biol. Med. 89; Biol. Bull. 112. **Neff, R.** 1957. Purification, axenic cultivation, and description of a soil amoeba. Jour. Protozool. 4. **Nicholas, W.** 1956. The axenic culture of Turbatrix aceti. Nematologica 1. **Nigrelli, R., J. Chanley, S. Kohn,** and **H. Sobotka.** 1955. Chemical nature of holothurin. Zoologica, New York, 40. **Noland, L.** 1957. Protoplasmic streaming. Jour. Protozool. 4. **Nouvel, H.** 1947, 1948. Les dicyémides. Arch. Biol. 58, 59. **Nurse, F.** 1950. Quinone tanning in the cocoon-shell of Dendrocoelum. Nature, London, 105. **Nyholm, K.** 1951a. Sexual phase of Protohydra. Arkiv Zool., new ser. 2. 1951b. Egg cells in the entoderm of Boreohydra. Arkiv Zool., new ser. 2. **Odum, H., et al.** 1955. Some red tide characteristics. Bull. Marine Sci. Gulf Caribbean 5. **Ogren, R.** 1955. Glandular regions in oncospheres of Hymenolepis. Proc. Pennsylvania Acad. Sci. 29. 1956. Development and morphology of the oncosphere of Mesocestoides. Jour. Parasitol. 42. 1957a, b. Development of Oochoristica. Proc. Pennsylvania Acad. Sci. 31; Jour. Parasitol. 43. **Okugawa, K.** 1957. Experimental study of sexual induction in Dugesia gonocephala. Bull. Kyoto Gakugei Univ., ser. B, no. 11. **Okulitch, V.** 1943. North American Pleospongia. Geol. Soc. America, Special Paper 48. 1955. Archaeocyatha. *In* **R. C. Moore** (ed.), *Treatise on invertebrate paleontology,* pt. E. **Okulitch, V.,** and **M. W. De Laubenfels.** 1953. Systematic position of Archaeocyatha. Jour. Paleontol. 27. **Ookawa, M.** 1952. Water content of fresh-water medusa. Dobutsugaku Zasshi (Zool. Mag.) 61. **Oliveira, M.,** and **H. Meyer.** 1955. Plasmodium gallinaceum in tissue culture. Parasitology 45. **Omer-Cooper, J.** 1957. Protohydra and Kinorhyncha in Africa. Nature, London, 179. **Osche, G.** 1952. Systematik und Phylogenie der Gattung Rhabditis. Zool. Jahrb. Abt. System. 81. **Pantin, C.** 1942a, b. Excitation of nematocysts. Nature, London, 149; Jour. Exptl. Biol. 19. 1950. Behavior patterns in lower invertebrates. Symposia Soc. Exptl. Biol. 4. 1952. The elementary nervous system. Proc. Roy. Soc. London 140B. 1956. Origin of the nervous system. Pubbl. Staz. Zool. Napoli 28. **Pantin, C.,** and **M. Dias.** 1952. Rhythm and afterdischarge in medusae. Anais Acad. Brasil. Ciencas 24. **Papi, F.** 1957. Sopra un nuovo turbellario della fam. Hofsteniidae. Pubbl. Staz. Zool. Napoli 30. **Passano, L.,** and **C. Pantin.** 1955. Mechanical stimulation in the seaanemone Calliactis. Proc. Roy. Soc. London 143B. **Pavans de Ceccatty, M.** 1955. Le système nerveux des éponges calcaires et siliceuses. Ann. Sci. Natur. Zool., ser. 11, vol. 17. 1957. La nature sécretaire des lophocytes. C. R. Acad. Sci. Paris 244. **Pearson, J.** 1956. Life cycles and morphology of the larval stages of Alaria. Canadian Jour. Zool. 34. **Peng, O.** 1957. Studien zu den Problem der Zellkonstanz. Zentralbl. Bakteriol. Parasitenk., Abt. II, vol. 110. **Petrotchenko, V.** 1952. On the position of the Acanthocephala in the zoological system. Zool. Zhurnal 31. **Phillips, J.** 1956. Isolation of active nematocysts of Metridium. Science 178. **Picard, J.** 1955. Les nématocysts du cténaire Euchlora rubra. Recueil Trav. Stat. Marine Endoume, Bull. no. 9, fasc. 15. 1957. Études sur les hydroides de la superfamilie Pteronematoidea. Bull. Inst. Oceanogr. Monaco, no. 1106.

Picken, L. 1953. Nematocysts of Corynactis. Quart. Jour. Microsc. Sci. 94. 1957. Stinging capsules and designing nature. New Biology, no. 22. **Pickford, Grace.** 1947. Histological and histochemical observations upon an aberrant annelid Poeobius. Jour. Morphol. 80. **Pitelka, D.,** and **C. Schooley.** 1955. Comparative morphology of some protistan flagella. Univ. California Publ. Zool. 61. **Porter, R.** 1953. Amebiasis. Ann. Review Microbiol. 7. **Premvati.** 1955. Cercaria multiplicata. Jour. Zool. Soc. India 7. **Pringsheim, E.** 1955. Die gelben Zellen der Koralle Cladocora. Pubbl. Staz. Zool. Napoli 27. **Provasoli, L.,** and **I. Pintner.** 1953. Ecological complications of in vitro nutritional requirements of algal flagellates. Ann. New York Acad. Sci. 56. **Puytorac, P. de.** 1954. Étude cytologique et taxonomique des infusoires astomes. Ann. Sci. Natur. Zool., ser. 11, vol. 16. **Raffaele, G.** 1936. Presumibili forme iniziale di evoluzione di Plasmodium relictum. Riv. Malariol. 15. **Rankin, Jessie.** 1956. Structure and biology of Vallicula. Jour. Linnaean Soc. London, Zool. 43. **Rausch, R., et al.** 1956. Occurrence of larvae of Trichinella spiralis in Alaskan mammals. Jour. Parasitol. 42. **Ray, S.,** and **W. Wilson.** 1957. Effects of unialgal and bacteria-free cultures of Gymnodinium brevis on fish. U.S. Fish and Wildlife Service, Fishery Bull. 57. **Rees, W.** 1957. Evolutionary trends in the classification of capitate hydroids and medusae. Bull. British Mus. (Natur. Hist.), Zool. 4, no. 19. **Reeves, R., H. Meleney,** and **W. Frye.** 1957. Bacteria-free cultures of Entamoeba histolytica. Ztschr. Tropenmed. Parasitol. 8. **Reich, K.** 1935. Cultivation of a sterile amoeba. Jour. Exptl. Zool. 69. 1948. Studies on the respiration of Mayorella. Physiol. Zool. 21. **Reinhard, E.** 1958. Demonstration of the life cycle and pathogenicity of the spiral threadworm. Exptl. Parasitol. 7. **Reisinger, E.** 1924. Die Gattung Rhynchoscolex. Ztschr. Morphol. Ökol. Tiere 1. **Remane, A.** 1937. Halammohydra. Ztschr. Morphol. Ökol. Tiere 7. 1950a. Die morphologische Ableitung des Räderorgans der Rotatoria Bdelloidea. Zool. Anz. Ergänz. Heft to 145. 1950b. Die Entstehung der Metamerie der Wirbellosen. Verhandl. Dtsch. Zoologen 1949 in Mainz. 1951. Die Bursa-Darmverbindung und das Problem des Enddarmes bei Turbellarien. Zool. Anz. 146. 1952. *Die Grundlagen des naturlichen Systems, der vergleichenden Anatomie und der Phylogenetik.* 1953. Ein neues Gastrotrich aus dem Pazifik. Zool. Anz. 151. 1954. Die Geschichte der Tiere. *In* G. Heberer (ed.), *Evolution der Organismen,* 2 ed., Lief. 2. **Ribeiro, L.,** and **G. Villela.** 1956. Paper electrophoretic studies of haemoglobins from Tetrameres. Revista Brasileira Biol. 16. **Riser, N.** 1956. Early larval stages of two cestodes from elasmobranch fishes. Proc. Helminthol. Soc. Washington 23. **Robbins, W., A. Hervey,** and **M. Stebbins.** 1953. Euglena and vitamin B_{12}. Ann. New York Acad. Sci. 56. **Robson, E.** 1953. Nematocysts of Corynactis. Quart. Jour. Microsc. Sci. 94. **Roche, J.** 1952. Biochimie comparée des scleroproteines iodées. Experientia 8. **Roche, J.,** and **Y. Robin.** 1954. Sur les phosphagènes des éponges. C. R. Soc. Biol. Paris 148. **Roche, J., N. Thoai,** and **Y. Robin.** 1957. Sur la presence de créatine chez les invertébrés. Biochim. et Biophys. Acta 24. **Ross, D.,** and **C. Pantin.** 1940. Factors influencing facilitation in Actinozoa. Jour. Exptl. Biol. 17. **Rudall, K.** 1955. Distribution of collagen and chitin. *In* Symposia Soc. Exptl. Biol., no. 9, Fibrous proteins. **Ruebush, T.** 1939. The occurrence of Protohydra on the east coast of North America. Science 90. **Russell, F.** 1953. *The medusae of the British Isles.* **Ruszowski, J.** 1934. Le cycle évolutif du tetrarhynque Grillotia. Mém. Acad. Polonaise Sci. Lettr., ser. B, Cl. Sci. Math. Natur., Sci. Natur., no. 6. **Ruttner-Kolisko, Agnes.** 1955. Marinellina flagellata. Österreich. Zool. Ztschr. 6. **Ryther, J.** 1955. Ecology of autotrophic marine dinoflagellates. *In* F. H. Johnson (ed.), *Luminescence of biological systems.* **Sac-**

carao, G. 1952. The meaning of gastrulation. Arquivos Museu Bocage 23. **Sacks, M.** 1955. Embryology of Lepidodermella. Jour. Morphol. 96. **Sater, Edna.** 1954. Florida's red tide problem. U.S. Dept. Interior, Fishery Leaflet 420. **Sato, H., and Y. Sato.** 1956. Studies on the sterile culture of Paramecium caudatum. Dobutsugaku Zasshi (Zool. Mag.) 65. **Schoenborn, H.** 1942. Nutritional requirements of Euglena gracilis in darkness. Physiol. Zool. 15. 1946. Growth of Astasia in an inorganic medium. Physiol. Zool. 19. 1950. Nutritional requirements of Euglena viridis. Trans. Amer. Microsc. Soc. 69. 1952. Nutrition of Astasia longa. Physiol. Zool. 25. **Schulz, E.** 1950. Psammohydra nanna. Kieler Meeresuntersuch. 7. **Sedar, A.** 1952. Electron microscope studies on the structure and morphogenesis of the cilia and silverline system of Paramecium. Proc. Amer. Soc. Protozool. 3. **Sedar, A., and K. Porter.** 1955. Fine structure of cortical components of Paramecium. Jour. Biophys. Biochem. Cytol. 1. **Sedgwick, A.** 1884. Origin of metameric segmentation. Quart. Jour. Microsc. Sci. 24. **Seilern-Aspang, F.** 1956. Frühentwicklung Procerodes. Arch. Entw'mech. Organ. 148. 1957. Die Entwicklung von Macrostomum. Zool. Jahrb., Abt. Anat. 76. **Semal-Van Gansen, Paulette.** 1951. Le cnidosome de l'hydre. Acad. Roy. Belgique, Bull. Cl. Sci., ser. 5, vol. 37. 1952a. Étude du système musculaire chez Hydra. Acad. Roy. Belgique, Bull. Cl. Sci., ser. 5, vol. 38. 1952b. Note sur le système nerveaux de l'hydre. Acad. Roy. Belgique, Bull. Cl. Sci., ser. 5, vol. 38. 1954a. La structure des nématocystes de l'hydre. Acad. Roy. Belgique, Bull. Cl. Sci., ser. 5, vol. 40. 1954b. L'histophysiologie de l'endoderme de l'hydre. Ann. Soc. Roy. Zool. Belgique 85. **Shortt, H.** 1948. Life cycle of Plasmodium cynomolgi. Trans. Roy. Soc. Trop. Med. Hygiene 42. **Shortt, H., et al.** 1948. The pre-erythrocytic stage of human malaria. British Med. Jour., no. 4550; Nature, London, 161. 1949, 1951. The pre-erythrocytic stage of Plasmodium falciparum. British Med. Jour., no. 4635; Trans. Roy. Soc. Trop. Med. Hygiene 44. **Shortt, H., R. Bray, and W. Cooper.** 1954. Further notes on the tissue stages of Plasmodium cynomolgi. Trans. Roy. Soc. Trop. Med. Hygiene 48. **Shortt, H., and P. Garnham.** 1948. The pre-erythrocytic development of Plasmodium cynomolgi and vivax. Trans. Roy. Soc. Trop. Med. Hygiene 41. **Silverman, P.** 1954. Morphology and development of the taeniid hexacanth. Ann. Trop. Med. Parasitol. 48. **Silverman, P., and R. Maneely.** 1955. Role of the secreting gland of the hexacanth. Ann. Trop. Med. Parasitol. 49. **Skrjabin, K.** 1955–1956. *Trematody zhivotnykh i cheloveka* (Trematodes of animals and man). 12 vols. **Smith, F.** 1943. Littoral fauna of the Miami area. I. The Madreporaria. Proc. Florida Acad. Sci. 6. 1945. The discovery of Coeloplana on American shores. Science 101. **Smyth, J.** 1949. Development of Ligula intestinalis. Jour. Exptl. Biol. 26. 1951. Egg-shell formation in trematodes and cestodes. Nature, London, 168. 1954. Fertilization of Schistocephalus solidus in vitro. Exptl. Parasitol. 3. 1956. A histochemical study of egg-shell formation in Schistocephalus. Exptl. Parasitol. 5. **Sonneborn, T. M.** 1937. Sex, sex inheritance, and sex determination in Paramecium. Proc. Nation. Acad. Sci. 23. 1938. Mating types in Paramecium aurelia. Proc. Amer. Philos. Soc. 79. 1941. Sexuality in unicellular organisms. *In* G. Calkins and F. Summers (eds.), *Protozoa in biological research.* 1950a. Paramecium in modern biology. Bios 21. 1950b. The cytoplasm in heredity. Heredity 4. 1954. The relation of autogamy to senescence and rejuvenescence in Paramecium. Jour. Protozool. 1. 1955. Heredity, development and evolution in Paramecium. Nature, London, 175. 1957. Breeding systems, reproductive methods, and species problems in Protozoa. In *The species problem,* publ. by Amer. Assoc. Advanc. Sci. **Spandorf, A., and R. Manwell.** 1957. In vitro cultivation of the avian plasmodia. Jour. Protozool., suppl. to vol. 4. **Sprent, J.** 1952. Anatomical distinction between human and pig strains of ascaris. Nature, London, 170. **Sproston, Nora.** 1946. Synopsis of the monogenetic trematodes. Trans. Zool. Soc. London 25. **Stary, Z., S. Tekman,** and **J. Öner.** 1956. Kohlenhydratgruppen des Spongins. Biochem. Ztschr. 328. **Stearns, H.** 1946. An integration of coral-reef hypotheses. Amer. Jour. Sci. 244. **Steenstrup, J.** 1842. *Uber die Generationswechsel.* Eng. transl. by Ray Soc., 1845. **Steinböck, O.** 1936. Eine Theorie über den plasmodialen Ursprung der Vielzeller (Metazoa). 4 Internation. Cong. Cytology. 1952. Keimblätterlehre und Gastraea-Theorie. Die Pyramide 1. 1954. Regeneration azöler Turbellarien. Verhandl. Dtsch. Zool. Gesellsch., Zool. Anz. Suppl. 18. **Steiner, G., A. Taylor,** and **G. Cobb.** 1951. Cyst-forming plant parasitic nematodes. Proc. Helminthol. Soc. Washington 18. **Sterbenz, F.** 1956. Axenic culture of Paramecium caudatum. Jour. Protozool. 3, suppl. **Stoll, N.** 1953. Axenic cultivation of Neoaplactana. Jour. Parasitol. 39. 1957. Axenic culture of Entamoeba invadens. Jour. Protozool. 4, suppl. **Storm, J.,** and **S. Hutner.** 1953. Nutrition of Peranema. Ann. New York Acad. Sci. 56. **Storm, J., S. Hutner,** and **J. Cowperthwaite.** 1951. Nutrition of two small amoebae in pure culture. Proc. 3 Ann. Meeting Amer. Soc. Protozool. 2, abstr. 5. **Stott, F.** 1955. Food canal of Echinus esculentus. Proc. Zool. Soc. London 125. **Stunkard, H.** 1937. Physiology, life cycles and phylogeny of the parasitic flatworms. Amer. Mus. Novitates, no. 908. 1946. Interrelationships and taxonomy of the digenetic trematodes. Biol. Reviews Cambridge 21. 1954. Life-history and systematic relations of the Mesozoa. Quart. Rev. Biol. 29. **Swedmark, B.** 1955. Développement d'un gastrotriche. C. R. Acad. Sci. Paris 240. **Swedmark, B.,** and **G. Teissier.** 1950. Développement d'Halammohydra. C. R. Acad. Sci. Paris 231. 1957a. Organization et développement des Halammohydra. C. R. Acad. Sci. Paris 244. 1957b. Halammohydra vermiformis et la famille des Halammohydridae. Bull. Soc. Zool. France 82. **Takata, I.** 1951. Experimental infection of man with ascaris of man and the pig. Kitasato Arch. Exptl. Med. 23. **Tartar, V.,** and **T. Chen.** 1941. Mating reactions of enucleate fragments of Paramecium. Biol. Bull. 80. **Thorshaug, K.,** and **A. Rosted.** 1956. Researches into the prevalence of trichinosis in Arctic and Antarctic waters. Nordsk Veterinaermedecin 8. **Tobie, E., T. von Brand,** and **B. Mehlman.** 1950. Cultural and physiological observations on Trypanosoma. Jour. Parasitol. 36. **Totton, A.** 1954a. Siphonophora of the Indian Ocean. Discovery Repts. 27. 1954b. Egglaying in ctenophores. Nature, London, 174. **Trager, W.** 1957. Nutrition of avian malaria. Acta Tropica 14. **Tuzet, Odette.** 1945. Sur la question de la Proterospongia. Arch. Zool. Exp. Gén. 84. 1947. L'ovogénèse et la fécondation de Leucosolenia et Reniera. Arch. Zool. Exp. Gén. 85. 1948. Les premiers stades du développement de Leucosolenia et Clathrina. Ann. Sci. Natur. Zool., ser. 11, vol. 10. **Tuzet, O., R. Loubatières,** and **M. Pavans de Ceccatty.** 1952. Les cellules nerveuses de Sycon. C. R. Acad. Sci. Paris 234. **Tuzet, O.,** and **J. Paris.** 1957. Les lophocytes de l'éponge Tethya. C. R. Acad. Sci. Paris 244. **Tuzet, O.,** and **M. Pavans de Ceccatty.** 1953a. Les lophocytes. C. R. Acad. Sci. Paris 237. 1953b. Les cellules nerveuses et neuromusculaires de Cliona. C. R. Acad. Sci. Paris 236. 1955. La mobilisation en amoebocytes des cellules des Halisarca. C. R. Soc. Biol. Paris 149. **Ulrich, W.** 1949. Über die systematische Stellung einer neuen Tierklasse (Pogonophora), den Begriff der Archicoelomaten und die Einteilung der Bilateria. Sitzungsber. Dtsch. Akad. Wissensch. Berlin, Math. Natur. Kl., no. 2. **Valeurone, Marialuisa.** 1953. Ricerche istochimiche sui granule vitellini dei policladi. Arch. Zool. Ital. Publ. Giubilare Pierantoni II. **Van der Woude, Anne.** 1954. Germ cell cycle of Megalodiscus. Amer. Midland Natural. 51. **Vaughan, T.,** and J. Wells. 1943. Revision of the Scleratina. Geol. Soc. America, Special Paper 44. Voigt, M. 1956–1957. *Die Rädertiere Mitteleuropas.* 2 vols. Vologdin, A. 1940. Subtype Archaeocyatha. Atlas of leading forms of the fossil faunas of the U.S.S.R. I. Cambrian. Von Brand, T. 1950. Carbohydrate metabolism of parasites. Jour. Parasitol. 36. 1952. *Chemical physiology of endoparasitic animals.* 1957. Recent trends in parasite physiology. Exptl. Parasitol. 6. Von Brand, T., E. Weinbach, and E. Tobie. 1955. Comparative studies of the metabolism of the culture form and bloodstream form of Trypanosoma gambiense. Jour. Cell. Comp. Physiol. 45. Wager, A. 1913. Some observations on Convoluta. Rept. 10 Ann. Meeting South African Assoc. Advanc. Sci. Wagner, G. 1905. Movements and reactions of hydra. Quart. Jour. Microsc. Sci. 48. Wagtendonk, W. van. 1955. Nutrition of ciliates. *In* S. Hutner and A. Lwoff (eds.), *Biochemistry and physiology of Protozoa,* vol. II. Wagtendonk, W. van, R. Conner, C. Miller, and M. Rao. 1953. Growth requirements of Paramecium aurelia in axenic medium. Ann. New York Acad. Sci. 56. Ward, Helen. 1951, 1952. The species of Acanthocephala described since 1933. Jour. Tennessee Acad. Sci. 26, 27. Wardle, R., and J. McLeod. 1952. *The zoology of tapeworms.* Weinstein, P. 1953. Cultivation of the free-living stages of hookworms in the absence of living bacteria. Amer. Jour. Hygiene 58. Weinstein, P., and M. Jones. 1956. The in vitro cultivation of Nippostrongylus muris to the adult stage. Jour. Parasitol. 42. Weisz, P. 1954. Morphogenesis in Protozoa. Quart. Rev. Biol. 29. Wells, J. 1956. Scleratinia. *In* R. C. Moore (ed.), *Treatise on invertebrate paleontology,* pt. F, Coelenterata. Welsh, J. 1955. Nature and action of coelenterate toxins. Deep Sea Research 3, suppl. 2. Wesenberg-Lund, Elise. 1955. Gephyrea from Chile. Repts. Lund Univ. Chile Exped. 1948–1949, no. 19. Lund Univ. Arsskrift Avd. 2, vol. 51, no. 10. Wessenberg, H. 1957. Life cycle and morphogenesis of Opalina. Jour. Protozool. 4, suppl. Wessing, A. 1953. Histologische Studien zu den Problemen der Zellkonstanz. Zool. Jahrb. Abt. Anat. 73. Westblad, E. 1940, 1942, 1945, 1946, 1948. Studien über skandinavischen Turbellaria Acoela I–V. Arkiv Zool. 32A, 33A, 36A, 38A, 41A. 1947. Notes on hydroids, Boreohydra. Arkiv Zool. 39A. 1949a. Xenoturbella bocki. Arkiv. Zool., new ser. 1, no. 3. 1949b. Meara stichopi. Arkiv Zool., new ser. 1, no. 5. 1953. Boreohydra simplex. Arkiv Zool., new ser. 4, no. 19. Wichterman, R. 1953. *The biology of Paramecium.* Wieser, W. 1957. Gastrotricha from the intertidal of Puget Sound. Trans. Amer. Microsc. Soc. 76. Willey, C. 1954. The relation of lymph and excretory system in Zygocotyle. Anat. Record 120. Wilson, W., and S. Ray. 1956. Occurrence of Gymnodinium brevis in the western Gulf of Mexico. Ecology 37. Wolff, E., and J. Lender. 1950. Sur le rôle organizateur du cerveau dans la régénération des yeux. C. R. Acad. Sci. Paris 230. Wolken, J., and G. Palade. 1953. Electron microscope study of two flagellates. Ann. New York Acad. Sci. 56. Woollard, H., and Harpman, J. 1939. Discontinuity in the nervous system of coelenterates. Jour. Anat. 73. Yamanouchi, T. 1955. Poisonous substance contained in holothurians. Publ. Seto Marine Biol. Lab. 4. Yanagita, T. 1943. Discharge of nematocysts. Jour. Fac. Sci. Tokyo Univ., sec. 4, Zool. 6. Yanagita, T., and T. Wada. 1954. Effects of trypsin and thioglycollate upon the nematocysts of the sea anemone. Nature, London, 173. Yonge, C. 1940. The biology of reef-building corals. Great Barrier Reef Exped., Sci. Repts. 1, pt. 13. Yosufzai, H. 1953. Shell gland and egg-shell formation in Fasciola. Parasitology 43. Yusa, A. 1957. Morphology and morphogenesis of the buccal organelles in Paramecium. Jour. Protozool. 4. Zahl, P., and J. McLaughlin. 1957. Isolation and cultivation of zooxanthellae. Nature, London, 180. Zhinkin, L. 1949. Early stages of development of Priapulus. Doklady Akad. Sci. U.S.S.R. 65.

ADDENDA TO THE BIBLIOGRAPHIES*

Beecher, C. 1895b. Development of Terebratalia. Trans. Conn. Acad. Sci. 9. **Benham, W.** 1899. Balanoglossus otagoensis. Quart. Jour. Microsc. Sci. 42. **Brown, C.** 1934. Laboratory study of fresh-water Polyzoa. Trans. Am. Microsc. Soc. 53. **Buckman, S.** 1919. Terminology for beak and foraminal development in terebratuloids. Trans. Proc. New Zealand Inst. 51. **Calvet, L.** 1927b. Faune des bryozoaires de la Méditerranie occidentale. Arch. Zool. Exp. Gén. 66, Notes et revue, no. 1. **Dall, W.** 1871. Supplement to the revision of Terebratulidae. Am. Jour. Conchol. 7. **Hatschek, B.** 1888. *Lehrbuch der Zoologie.* **Karling, T.** 1940. Zur Morphologie und Systematik der Alloeocoela und Rhabdocoela. Acta Zool. Fennica 26. **Lankester, E.** 1877. Notes on the embryology and classification of the animal kingdom. Quart. Jour. Microsc. Sci. 17. **Levander, K.** 1905. Zur Kenntnis des Planktons einiger Binnenseen. Festschrift Palmen, no. 11. **Meixner, J.** 1938. Turbellaria. *In* **G. Grimpe** and **E. Wagler** (eds.), Die Tierwelt der Nord- und Ostsee, Teil IVb, Lief. 33. **Metschnikoff, E.** 1870. Metamorphose einiger Seethiere. I. Über Tornaria. Ztschr. Wissensch. Zool. 20. **Meyer, A.** 1927. Über Cölombewimperung und cölomatische Kreislaufsystems bei Wirbellosen. Ztschr. Wissensch. Zool. 129. **Picard, J.** 1957. Études sur les hydroides de la superfamilie Pteronematoidea. Bull. Inst. Océanogr. Monaco, no. 1106. **Spindler, L.** 1947. A note on the fungoid nature of Sarcocystis. Proc. Helminthol. Soc. Washington 14. **Spindler, L., and H. Zimmerman.** 1945. The biological status of Sarcocystis. Jour. Parasitol. 31, suppl. **Zirpolo, G.** 1921. Ciclo biologico del Zoobotryon. Monitore Zool. Ital. 32.

* These titles were inadvertently omitted from the bibliographies for some of the chapters in this volume.

INDEX

Page numbers in **boldface** type refer to illustrations when not included in text references.